REVISE MATHEMATICS

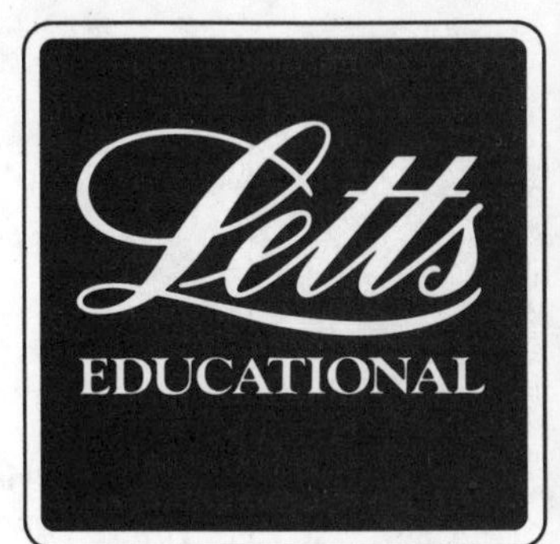

A REVISION COURSE FOR

GCSE

Duncan Graham, BSc, BSc(Hons), MSc
Senior Lecturer in Mathematical Education,
Polytechnic South West

Christine Graham, BEd(Hons)

BPP Letts Educational Ltd

First published 1979

Revised 1981,1984,1987, 1989
Reprinted with amendments 1988, 1989, 1989, 1992

British Library Cataloguing in Publication Data

Graham, Duncan
Revised mathematics: a complete revision course for GCSE.—4th ed.—(Letts study aids)
1. Mathematics—1961-
I. Title II. Graham, Christine
510 QA39.2

ISBN 1 85758 011 7

Printed and bound in Great Britain by
BPCC Wheatons Ltd, Exeter

PREFACE

This edition of *Revise Mathematics* has been written for the GCSE and SCE Standard Grade examinations. It has been produced after analysing the National Criteria for Mathematics, all the available syllabuses prepared by the various Examining Groups in the United Kingdom, specimen questions and actual GCSE and SCE examination papers published by the Examining Groups. Numerous other documents and research reports, not least the Cockcroft Report and the National Curriculum documents, which have appeared over the last few years, have been analysed and the findings incorporated into this book.

Most of the mathematics required by the new syllabuses has been listed in three broad categories. This has enabled the authors to specify precise syllabus requirements for each candidate entered for the examination. The material in this book covers the main syllabus requirements for candidates aiming for the Intermediate and Higher levels of GCSE and the General and Credit levels of SCE. It also provides a summary of the syllabus requirements for the Basic level of GCSE and the Foundation level of SCE. Candidates at all levels must have studied and understood these basic topics.

This book offers students a wide range of help and advice. The introduction gives a description of how to use the tables of analysis and guidance on the use of the book. Included in this is a section on studying and revising which encourages and assists students to develop and use good study skills. A guide to the GCSE examination helps to explain how this examination differs from its predecessors and gives its stated aims and objectives. One feature of the new examination is the widespread use of other forms of assessment which are supplementary to the traditional written examination papers. A chapter on these other forms of assessment includes a description of major coursework tasks such as investigations and problem-solving. Numerous questions are given in the latter part of this book. These are taken from the various Examining Groups specimen and actual GCSE and SCE examination papers and are as up to date as it is possible to be. Each question is keyed back into the relevant units in the core text of the book and answers are provided. Examples of the new Aural Tests are also contained in this section. Hints are given so that students can develop and improve their examination technique. An index has been included for quick and easy reference.

Since this book will be revised and updated regularly, comments on the content and presentation of this new edition would be most welcome write care of the publishers so they can be taken into account in the next edition.

Acknowledgements

We wish to thank the following people for their help in producing this book:

The editorial staff of Letts Educational; Mike Ashcroft and Mike Kenyon for their help and advice on various sections of the book Jim McAnally, our Scottish Consultant, who did such a thorough job on analysing the Scottish syllabus and keeping us fully informed of developments in the rapidly changing system in Scotland members of our families whose patience and understanding have been greatly appreciated and the numerous students and teachers who have written to us in the past and made helpful suggestions for future editions.

We are most grateful to the following Examining Groups and Boards for permission to use their specimen and actual GCSE and SCE questions included in this book: Northern Examination Association (NEA), Midland Examining Group (MEG), London East Anglian Group (LEAG), Southern Examining Group (SEG), Welsh Joint Education Committee (WJEC), Northern Ireland Schools Examinations Council (NISEC), Scottish Examinations Board (SEB).

None of the above can accept responsibility for the answers to the questions used and any mistakes in these must be solely our responsibility. The authors would be grateful to any readers who could inform us of any such mistakes they may encounter.

The authors and publishers wish to thank the controller of Her Majesty's Stationery Office for permission to use extracts from The National Criteria.

Duncan and Christine Graham 1992

CONTENTS

THE GCSE

What is GCSE?

GCSE stands for the General Certificate of Secondary Education. It is the single system of examinations which replaced GCE O-level, CSE and Joint 16+ examinations in England, Wales and Northern Ireland. In Scotland the examination which corresponds to GCSE is the Scottish Certificate of Education (SCE), Standard Grade. So whenever there is a reference to GCSE in this book, Scottish candidates should think about SCE, Standard Grade.

The first GCSE examinations were held in summer 1988.

Who is GCSE for?

GCSE is designed primarily for pupils in the fifth year of secondary education. But anyone, of any age, can take it. Candidates may study for it at school, college or privately.

Who administers GCSE?

GCSE is administered by groups of Examining Boards which have been formed from the original GCE and CSE Boards. There are four groups in England Northern, Midland, Southern, London East Anglia, one in Wales and one in Northern Ireland. In Scotland the SCE is administered by the Scottish Examination Board.

A list of all the groups, boards and their addresses is given on page xviii.

Who monitors GCSE?

GCSE is monitored by the Secondary Examinations Council.

The Council must ensure that:

(a) all the Examining Groups follow the National Criteria
(b) standards are comparable across different subjects, Examining Groups and over time.

What are the National Criteria?

The National Criteria are nationally agreed guidelines which all GCSE courses and examinations must follow. There are two parts to the criteria:

1 General criteria—which apply to all subjects and the general running of GCSE,
2 Subject criteria—which give the framework for GCSE in each of the 20 main subject areas.

The National Criteria will be reviewed regularly by the Secondary Examinations Council and changes will be made if necessary.

How were the National Criteria developed?

They were first drafted by the Joint Council of GCE and CSE Boards. Then they were revised in the light of comments from a wide range of interested groups: parents, schools and colleges, teachers associations, higher education, employers' organisations, local authorities, the Secondary Examinations Council, the Government,...

In mathematics the National Criteria were greatly influenced by the findings and recommendations of the Cockcroft Report 'Report of the Committee of Inquiry into the Teaching of Mathematics in Schools, 1982'. This report criticised many features of the old GCE O-level and CSE examinations. The aims and objectives from the National Criteria in mathematics are listed on page viii.

How does GCSE cope with candidates of different abilities in mathematics?

GCSE examinations demand more of able than less able candidates and award grades accordingly. Wherever possible mathematical ideas and questions use simple language. Problems are set in real life contexts and diagrams and pictures used to make questions clearer.

In mathematics the Examining Groups of suffer at least three levels of assessment. Some groups call these Foundation, Intermediate and Higher levels; others call them Levels 1, 2 and 3. A candidate should be entered at the level felt to be most appropriate to his or her mathematical abilities.

The content of each mathematics syllabus is divided into three lists (see Table 1, pages xii - xiii). In general, Level 1 (Foundation) candidates will be tested on topics in List 1 Level 2 (Intermediate) candidates on topics in Lists 1 and 2 Level 3 (Higher) candidates on topics in Lists 1, 2 and 3.

Most candidates in mathematics take two timed written examination papers. There is a choice of papers which will give candidates the chance to show what they know, understand and can do. Candidates may take two papers out of 'four-in-line' or they may take two papers out of 'three pairs' as shown in the diagrams below.

Four-in-line

Paper	Level of assessment
4, 3	Higher
3, 2	Intermediate
2, 1	Foundation

Three pairs

Papers	Level of assessment
5 and 6	Higher
3 and 4	Intermediate
1 and 2	Foundation

Are there only timed written GCSE examinations in mathematics?

All GCSE candidates, who are in full-time education, may be assessed on 'coursework tasks', aural tests, oral work and mental calculations as well as timed written examinations. Coursework tasks may be mathematical investigations, problem solving, practical work, extended pieces of project work,...

Alternative syllabuses should be available for external candidates but these are not for candidates in full-time attendance at schools or colleges.

SUMMARY

- The GCSE follows nationally agreed guidelines, called the National Criteria ...

  ...so courses throughout the country have more in common than under the old GCE O-level CSE 16+ systems.

- There is a choice of papers or questions at different levels differentiated assessment...

  ...so candidates, entered at the correct level, should meet questions within their reach.

- Examinations are designed to test more than just memory and skills ...

... so candidates have to show that they can apply what they have learnt.

- Different ways to assess candidates may be used...

  ... so as well as timed written examination papers, candidates may have to do coursework, oral tests, aural tests, practical work, projects, etc.

- Wherever possible questions are set in everyday situations ...

  ... so candidates are able to use what they learn in real life too.

National Criteria in mathematics: aims and objectives

The aims in the National Criteria in mathematics give the purposes for studying a GCSE mathematics course. The objectives describe what a GCSE candidate should be able to show they have achieved in mathematics when assessed.

The actual aims and objectives from the National Criteria are listed below. They are stated in brief 'educational language' which can look daunting and seem difficult to understand. These lists have been given so that you know what a GCSE mathematics course should be and what you should be able to do in mathematics. However, do not worry if you do not find them easy to follow. This book has been written with these aims and objectives in mind. So full use of this book will help you to cover the aims and achieve the objectives to the best of your ability.

AIMS

All courses should enable pupils to:

1 develop their mathematical knowledge and oral, written and practical skills in a manner which encourages confidence;

2 read about mathematics, and write and talk about the subject in a variety of ways;

3 develop a feel for number, carry out calculations and understand the significance of the results obtained;

4 apply mathematics in everyday situations and develop an understanding of the part which mathematics plays in the world around them,

5 solve problems, present the solutions clearly, check and interpret the results,

6 develop an understanding of mathematical principles;

7 recognise when and how a situation may be represented mathematically, identify and interpret relevant factors and, where necessary, select an appropriate mathematical method to solve the problem;

8 use mathematics as a means of communication with emphasis on the use of clear expression;

9 develop an ability to apply mathematics in other subjects, particularly science and technology;

10 develop the abilities to reason logically, to classify, to generalise and to prove;

11 appreciate patterns and relationships in mathematics;

12 produce and appreciate imaginative and creative work arising from mathematical ideas;

13 develop their mathematical abilities by considering problems and conducting individual and cooperative enquiry and experiment, including extended pieces of work of a practice and investigative kind;

14 appreciate the interdependence of different branches of mathematics;

15 acquire a foundation appropriate to their further study of mathematics and of other disciplines.

OBJECTIVES

Students should be able to:

1 recall, apply and interpret mathematical knowledge in the context of everyday situations;

2 set out mathematical work, including the solution of problems, in a logical and clear form using appropriate symbols and terminology;

3 organise, interpret and present information accurately

4 perform calculations by suitable methods; use an electronic calculator;

5 understand systems of measurement in everyday use and make use of them in the solution of problems;

6 estimate, approximate and work to degrees of accuracy appropriate to the context,

7 use mathematical and other instruments to measure and to draw to an acceptable degree of accuracy;

8 recognise patterns and structures in a variety of situations, and form generalisations; interpret, transform and make appropriate use of symbols;

9 recognise and use spatial relationships in two and three dimensions, particularly in solving problems; analyse a problem, select a suitable strategy and apply an appropriate technique to obtain its solution;

10 Interpret, transform and make appropriate use of mathematical statements expressed in words or symbols;

11 recognise and use spatial relationships in two and three dimensions, particularly in solving problems;

12 analyse a problem, select a suitable strategy and apply an appropriate technique to obtain its solution;

13 apply combinations of mathematical skills and techniques in problem solving;

14 make logical deductions from given mathematical data;

15 respond to a problem relating to a relatively unstructured situation by translating it into an appropriately structured form.

16 respond orally to questions about mathematics, discuss mathematical ideas and carry out mental calculations;

17 carry out practical and investigational work, and undertake extended pieces of work.

All GCSE candidates in mathematics in full-time education may be assessed on *all* these objectives.

INTRODUCTION AND GUIDE TO USING THIS BOOK

How this book can help you

This book was written to help you to study for a GCSE or SCE in Mathematics. Unlike a simple course textbook, it is a comprehensive, concise guide to your course, a study aid and a revision aid.

The main aim of this book is to help you gain the best grade that you can on your certificate.

It can help you to succeed because it:

- gives you detailed information about the examination you are taking,
- tells you which topics you need to study for your syllabus,
- gives you guidance on studying and revising,
- reminds you of important facts, mathematical words and their meanings,
- suggests ways for you to solve problems,
- gives you advice and hints for answering written, oral and aural examinations,
- shows you examples of mathematical investigations and problem solving,
- gives you a selection of actual and specimen examination questions to work through so that you can:
  - –practise your skills,
  - –apply your mathematics to real life situations,
  - –develop your problem solving ability,
  - –investigate situations mathematically.

Your syllabus

To use this book most effectively, you need to know exactly which syllabus you are studying. The answers to the following questions will help you to find out.

- Which certificate are you studying for: GCSE or SCE?
- What is the name of your Examining Group and Examination Board?
- What is the reference number or letter (if any) of your syllabus?
- Which Level are you working at: Intermediate or Higher?

Your topics

Most of the mathematics covered by the syllabuses in this book has been split into topics. These topics have titles which you will recognize easily, for example, Numbers, Circles, Formulae. To find out which are 'your topics', look at Table 1* on pages xii–xiii. You will see that the topics are in three lists. In the core text of the book the List 1 Summary notes briefly describe what you should be able to do for each topic in List 1, the List 2 and 3 Units contain detailed notes about each topic in Lists 2 and 3. However you may not have to study them all.

If you are working at the *Intermediate Level* (it may be called 2, *Q*, *I* or *General*), then you will have to study all the topics for your syllabus in *Lists 1 and 2*. Check *List 3* to see if any topics for your syllabus are marked *L2*. You will have to study these topics too.

If you are working at the *Higher Level* (it may be called 3, *R*, *H* or *Credit*), then you will have to study all the topics for your syllabus in *Lists 1, 2 and 3*. (Note: At least half the marks you can gain from the examination papers should come from questions on topics in Lists 1 and 2.)

To find 'your topics' in Table 1, look along the top row of the table and find your Examining Group. Then look down the column for your syllabus. Each of the boxes in the column relates to a topic in this book.

If a box has a dot ● in it, study that topic because it is on your syllabus. If a box has an L2 or L3 in it, that topic is needed at Level 2 (Intermediate) or Level 3 (Higher) for your syllabus.

If a box has a ^{T} in it, see your teacher to find out which part of the topic you need to study.

If a box has another symbol in it, look for the symbol in the table footnotes to find out what it means.

Your examination

Your GCSE or SCE examination may have several parts to it. Table 2* on pages xiv–xv lists some of the main details of the examinations for each of the syllabuses. From it you can find the answers to these questions for your syllabus.

- What are the target grades and grades available for my level?
- How many timed written examination papers will I take? How long will I have to answer each paper set? What percentage of the total marks will each paper carry?
- Will I have to do some 'coursework tasks' for my teacher(s) to assess? What percentage of the total marks will any coursework carry?
- Will I have to do any aural test? What percentage of the total marks will any aural test carry?

Table 2 also tells you whether you will take two papers out of 'four-in-line' or two out of 'three pairs' (see page vii).

If you know that your papers are 'four-in-line', you have extra information about the topics which will be tested in each paper:

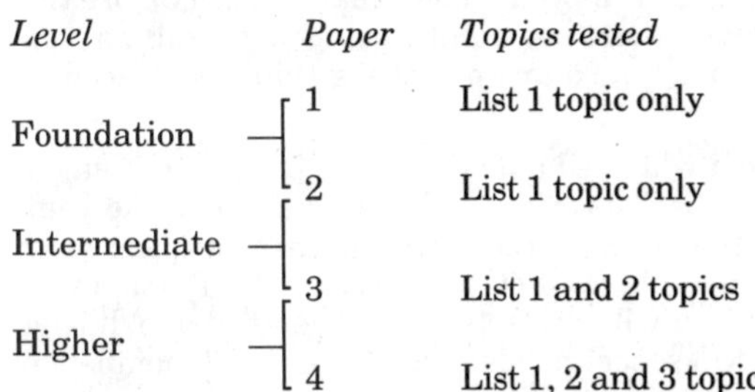

Level	*Paper*	*Topics tested*
Foundation	1	List 1 topic only
Foundation / Intermediate	2	List 1 topic only
Intermediate / Higher	3	List 1 and 2 topics
Higher	4	List 1, 2 and 3 topics

For example, if you are an intermediate level candidate, you know you can *only* be asked about List 1 topics on Paper 2 and that all the questions on List 2 topics (and some from List 1) must come on Paper 3.

Table 3* on pages xvi–xvii gives a brief description of the kind of coursework assessed by each Examining Group and when that coursework should be done.

*Tables 1, 2 and 3 have been prepared as thoroughly as possible from the new syllabuses. However, despite careful checking, omissions may have occurred. Whilst writing this book the authors found that some Examining Groups have not listed topics in their syllabuses at a given level but have included them in their questions. We have tried to take this into account when preparing these tables. A few topics are not in this book because they appear in the syllabus of only one Examining Group. If in doubt about any points in these tables, ask your teacher to check the information for your syllabus.

Guide to studying and revising

PLANNING YOUR TIME

Your time is important to you so you want to use it well. Planning your time can save you time. You are used to having a timetable at school. Your teachers made this for your school time. You can make one for your own study time and revision time. This helps you to organize your work sensibly, so you can have, and enjoy, your free time too! Your plan/timetable can remind you of deadlines for homework, coursework, etc., . . . and help you to keep them.

Your study plan/timetable

Psychologists have worked out the best way to use study time. They advise you to put your study time into fixed study sessions, say one or two hours long, and break these up into three or four short periods with planned breaks of about five minutes. In this way you will help yourself to keep concentrating. Follow each study session by a slightly longer break for recreation and relaxation.

Make your own study plan/timetable with this advice in mind. Be realistic! List the things you have to do and want to do. Put in deadlines if necessary. Remember to fit in free time for hobbies, sports, etc. Relaxation is an important part of your plan.

If you are working in the evening, begin as early as possible. You study best when you feel fresh. Leave yourself time to relax and do something different before going to bed.

Your revision plan/timetable

During your mathematics course you will study many topics. You cannot expect to remember them all without revising them. You may think that revision is something you do just before your final examinations. But, in fact, your revision really starts after the first lesson of your course. Research has shown that revising your topics regularly throughout your course will help you to understand and remember them more easily. If you revise a topic after the lesson, after a week, after a month, after a term, . . . then you will have revised it at least four times before you revise it again at the end of the year. Your final revision before the examination will then be mainly going over things you have already understood and practising things you need to be able to do.

Of course you will need a final revision plan/timetable for the few months before your actual examination. Make your revision plan/timetable in the same way as you made your study plan/timetable. But it will need to be much more concentrated! You will probably have time available during school hours and school holidays to revise in. Remember to include these times in your timetable too.

WHERE TO STUDY AND REVISE

If possible, work in a quiet room, away from distractions. Try to make somewhere your study place. This can have a good psychological effect on you. It can help you to settle down to work more easily. It can also help your friends and family to know that you are studying there. Hopefully they will not disturb you unnecessarily.

Your study place should be well ventilated and not too warm. A desk or table, on which you can spread your books, is best for working on. You need good lighting too: a reading lamp is ideal. Have a clock or watch handy so that you can plan your time. Keep all your books, paper, calculator and other essential equipment at hand in one place. This will save you time during your study periods.

HOW TO STUDY AND REVISE

You cannot study or revise mathematics by simply reading. You have to 'do mathematics' to understand and remember it. So when studying and revising, you need to have a pen or pencil and exercise book with you as well as this book.

Working through the notes and questions on 'your topics' in this book will remind you of the important facts, words, formulae, mathematical skills, etc., you need. You can do this just after you have studied each topic in class, at other times throughout your course and during your final revision programme.

Making notes

Making notes helps you to concentrate and understand what you are studying. Your notes will be helpful during your final revision programme. Here are some ideas about making notes.

As you work on each of 'your units' in this book, jot down notes and try to do the mathematics yourself. Make sure that your notes are organized and easy to read and understand. Use this book to help you.

Throughout this book key words and phrases are in bold type. You need to know the meaning of these for 'your units'. One way to learn them, and any other mathematical words you meet, is to make your own mathematical dictionary. Use a small notebook for this. Letter each page. Put them in alphabetical order. Write the words you meet on the correct page. Give their meaning. Use your own words if you can. Draw diagrams and pictures if it helps.

Make special 'mini' revision notes on cards for quick reference. You can keep them in your pocket or bag and use them in spare moments.

Make charts giving definitions, formulae, etc. Use colours, underlining, capital letters, etc., to make the information stand out. Hang the charts in your study place and/or bedroom.

Doing questions

In mathematics you have to be able to use and apply your mathematical knowledge and skills. One way to practise this is by doing questions.

In each unit in this book, there are worked examples. When you come to a 'Question', cover the given 'Answer' and try to answer the question yourself. Then compare your working with that given.

In the self-test units (pages 163 to 209) there are both GCSE and SCE questions. The GCSE questions are divided into sections of List 1, 2 and 3 questions. The List 1 questions are included so that you can check your understanding of the basic topics you are expected to have covered before studying the units in this book. You are told the main topic(s) relevant to each question. If you have difficulty answering any questions in List 1, then you need to revise these basic topics in greater detail. List 2 and 3 questions are based on the topics in Lists 2 and 3. The SCE questions are divided into sections of Foundation, General and Credit level questions. Try the questions on 'your topics' from both GCSE and SCE examinations. You are told the main unit(s) to look up if you need help. If you are unable to answer any of 'your questions', then work through the relevant unit(s) again. Then try the question again.

Testing yourself

Testing yourself regularly will help you to check your progress. You may think that you understand or remember something, this checks whether you really do. It helps you to pin-point the ideas, topics, etc., which you need to study or practise again. Test yourself on a topic immediately after revising that topic and again at regular intervals. Here are some ways to test yourself.

- Write out important definitions, formulae, etc., for 'your units'. Check them with the notes in the text.

- Re-do questions you have answered before, without looking at your previous working. Then check your answers.
- Try questions that you have not looked at before.
- Try questions in mock examination conditions. Allow yourself only the examination time for each question. Use only the equipment you are allowed in the examination room and any list of formulae provided by your Examining Group for the examination. If possible, do some complete examination papers to practise your examination technique. Do them against the clock and in examination conditions. Some hints for doing timed written examinations are given on page 215.
- Get a friend or relative to test you by asking you questions as in an aural test. More information on this is given on page 211. There are some questions for them to try on you on page 209. Practise both writing and saying your answers. Also practise working them out in your head and against the clock.

Talking about mathematics

Talking about your mathematics can help you to understand it better. It can show you where there are gaps in your knowledge and may help you to fill them. You have to sort out your own mathematical ideas to talk about them. The people you discuss your work with do not have to be experts to help. But experts are helpful too!

Talk about your mathematics with friends who are doing the same course. You can often help each other to sort out difficulties you are having. Your problem topic may be crystal clear to a friend.

Talk about your mathematics with your parents or other people you know who have not followed your course. They may have followed a different mathematics course or never have studied the subject at all. Try to explain something that you think you understand to them. Do they understand your explanation? Can you answer their questions? If not, then you need to think about the mathematics again.

To find 'your topics' in Table 1, look along the top row of the table and find your Examining Group. Then look down the column for your syllabus. Each of the boxes in the column relates to a topic in this book.

If a box has a dot ● in it, study that topic because it is on your syllabus. If a box has an L2 or L3 in it, that topic is needed at Level 2 (Intermediate) or Level 3 (Higher) for your syllabus.

If a box has a ^{T} in it, see your teacher to find out which part of the topic you need to study.

If a box has another symbol in it, look for the symbol in the table footnotes to find out what it means.

Table 1 – Analysis of examination syllabus

		LEAG				MEG			NEA			SEG			NISEC	WJEC	SEB
	Syllabus	A	B	S	11-16	1651	S	11-16	A	B	C	A	B	E			Stan. Grade
	List 1																
1.1	Calculator	•	•	•	•	•	•	•	•	•	•	•	•	•	•	•	•
1.2	Whole numbers	•	•	•	•	•	•	•	•	•	•	•	•	•	•	•	•
1.3	Four rules: whole numbers	•	•	•	•	•	•	•	•	•	•	•	•	•	•	•	•
1.4	Approximation and estimation	•	•	•	•	•	•	•	•	•	•	•	•	•	•	•	•
1.5	Factors and multiples	•	•	•	•	•	•	•	•	•	•	•	•	•	•	•	•
1.6	Number patterns	•	•	•	•	•	•	•	•	•	•	•	•	•	•	•	•
1.7	Squares and square roots	•	•	•	•	•	•	•	•	•	•	•	•	•	•	•	•
1.8	Directed numbers	•	•	•	•	•	•	•	•	•	•	•	•	•	•	•	•
1.9	Fractions	•	•	•	•	•	•	•	•	•	•	•	•	•	•	•	•
1.10	Fractions: + and –	•	•	•	•	•	•	•	•	•	•	•	•	•	•	•	•
1.11	Decimals	•	•	•	•	•	•	•	•	•	•	•	•	•	•	•	•
1.12	Four rules: decimals	•	•	•	•	•	•	•	•	•	•	•	•	•	•	•	•
1.13	Fractions to decimals	•	•	•	•	•	•	•	•	•	•	•	•	•	•	•	•
1.14	Percentages	•	•	•	•	•	•	•	•	•	•	•	•	•	•	•	•
1.15	Percentages of quantities	•	•	•	•	•	•	•	•	•	•	•	•	•	•	•	•
1.16	Money	•	•	•	•	•	•	•	•	•	•	•	•	•	•	•	•
1.17	Percentages of money	•	•	•	•	•	•	•	•	•	•	•	•	•	•	•	•
1.18	Wages and salaries	•	•	•	•	•	•	•	•	•	•	•	•	•	•	•	•
1.19	Taxes	•	•	•	•	•	•	•	•	•	•	•	•	•	•	•	•
1.20	Quarterly bills	•	•	•	•	•	•	•	•	•	•	•	•	•	•	•	•
1.21	Interest	•	•	•	•	•	•	•	•	•	•	•	•	•	•	•	•
1.22	Buy now, pay later	•	•	•	•	•	•	•	•	•	•	•	•	•	•	•	•
1.23	Profit and loss	•	•	•	•	•	•	•	•	•	•	•	•	•	•	•	•
1.24	Rates	•	•			•			•	•	•	•	•	•	•	•	•
1.25	Insurance	•	•	•	•	•	•	•	•	•	•	•	•	•	•	•	•
1.26	Tables	•	•	•	•	•	•	•	•	•	•	•	•	•	•	•	•
1.27	Points and lines	•	•	•	•	•	•	•	•	•	•	•	•	•	•	•	•
1.28	Angles	•	•	•	•	•	•	•	•	•	•	•	•	•	•	•	•
1.29	Related angles	•	•	•	•	•	•	•	•	•	•	•	•	•	•	•	•
1.30	Estimating angles	•	•	•	•	•	•	•	•	•	•	•	•	•	•	•	•
1.31	Measuring and drawing angles	•	•	•	•	•	•	•	•	•	•	•	•	•	•	•	•
1.32	Directions	•	•	•	•	•	•	•	•	•	•	•	•	•	•	•	•
1.33	Polygons	•	•	•	•	•	•	•	•	•	•	•	•	•	•	•	•
1.34	Triangles	•	•	•	•	•	•	•	•	•	•	•	•	•	•	•	•
1.35	Quandrilaterals	•	•	•	•	•	•	•	•	•	•	•	•	•	•	•	•
1.36	Circles	•	•	•	•	•	•	•	•	•	•	•	•	•	•	•	•
1.37	Drawing plane shapes	•	•	•	•	•	•	•	•	•	•	•	•	•	•	•	•
1.38	Tessellations				•	•	•	•				•	•	•	•	•	•
1.39	Symmetry	•	•	•	•	•	•	•	•	•	•	•	•	•	•	•	•
1.40	Moving shapes	•	•		•	•	•	•	•	•	•	•	•	•	L3	•	•
1.41	Similarity and enlargement	•	•		•	•	•	•	•	•	•	•	•	•	•	•	•
1.42	Scale models	•	•		•	•	•	•	•	•	•	•	•	•	•	•	•
1.43	Maps	•	•	•	•	•	•	•	•	•	•	•	•	•	•	•	•
1.44	Scale drawings	•	•	•	•	•	•	•	•	•	•	•	•	•	•	•	•
1.45	Simple solids	•	•	•	•	•	•	•	•	•	•	•	•	•	•	•	•
1.46	Nets	•	•	•	•	•	•	•	•	•	•	•	•	•	•	•	•
1.47	Length	•	•	•	•	•	•	•	•	•	•	•	•	•	•	•	•
1.48	Mass	•	•	•	•	•	•	•	•	•	•	•	•	•	•	•	•
1.49	Capacity	•	•	•	•	•	•	•	•	•	•	•	•	•	•	•	•
1.50	Time	•	•	•	•	•	•	•	•	•	•	•	•	•	•	•	•
1.51	Perimeter	•	•	•	•	•	•	•	•	•	•	•	•	•	•	•	•
1.52	Area	•	•	•	•	•	•	•	•	•	•	•	•	•	•	•	•
1.53	Surface area of a cuboid	•	•	•	•	•	•	•	•	•	•	•	•	•	•	•	•
1.54	Volume	•	•	•	•	•	•	•	•	•	•	•	•	•	•	•	•
1.55	Measures of rate	•	•	•	•	•	•	•	•	•	•	•	•	•	•	•	•
1.56	Average speed	•	•	•	•	•	•	•	•	•	•	•	•	•	•	•	•
1.57	Travel graphs	•	•	•	•	•	•	•	•	•	•	•	•	•	•	•	•
1.58	Change of units	•	•	•	•	•	•	•	•	•	•	•	•	•	•	•	•
1.59	Conversion graphs	•	•	•	•	•	•	•	•	•	•	•	•	•	•	•	•
1.60	Scales and dials	•	•	•	•	•	•	•	•	•	•	•	•	•	•	•	•
1.61	Ratio and proportion	•	•	•	•	•	•	•	•	•	•	•	•	•	•	•	•
1.62	Formulae	•	•	•	•	•	•	•	•	•	•	•	•	•	•	•	•
1.63	Flow diagrams			•	•		•	•		•		•	•	•	•		•
1.64	Flow charts			L3	•		•	•		•		•	•	•	•		•
1.65	Co-ordinates	•	•	•	•	•	•	•	•	•	•	•	•	•	•	•	•
1.66	Graphs	•	•	•	•	•	•	•	•	•	•	•	•	•	•	•	•
1.67	Collecting and displaying data	•	•	•	•	•	•	•	•	•	•	•	•	•	•	•	•
1.68	Averages	•	•	•	•	•	•	•	•	•	•	•	•	•	•	•	•
1.69	Simple probability	•	•	•	•	•	•	•	•	•	•	•	•	•	•	•	

Key: In syllabus row,
S means SMP
11 - 16 – SMP 11 - 16 syllabus
L2T – part of this needed at Level 2 - ask your teacher
L3T – part of this needed at Level 3 - ask your teacher

St – area under a straight line graph only
Br – brackets only
Qu – quadratics only for List 2

		LEAG				MEG			NEA			SEG			NISEC	WJEC	SEB
	Syllabus	A	B	S	11-16	1651	S	11-16	A	B	C	A	B	E			Stan. Grade
	List 2																
2.1	Numbers	•	•	•	•	•	•	•	•	•	•	•	•	•	•	•	•
2.2	Directed numbers: four rules	•	•		•	•	•	•	•	•	•	•	•	•	•	•	$L3^T$
2.3	Square and cube roots	•	•	•	•	•	•	•	•	•	•	L3	L3	L3	•	•	•
2.4	Number patterns	•	•	•	•		L3	•	•	•						•	$L3^T$
2.5	Fractions: four rules	•	•			•	•		•	•		•	•	•	•	•	$L3^T$
2.6	Fractions: decimals and percentages	•	•	•	•	•	•	•	•	•	•	•	•	•	•	•	•
2.7	Percentages 2	•	•	L1	L1	•	•	L1	•	•	•	•	•	•	•	•	•
2.8	Approximation	•	•	•	•	•	•	•	•	•	•	•	•	•	•	•	$L3^T$
2.9	Standard form	•	•	•	•	•	•	•	•	•	•	•	•	•	•	•	$L3^T$
2.10	Compound interest				L3	L3		L3	•	•					•	•	L3
2.11	Proportional division	•	•	•	•	•	•	•	•	•	•	•	•	•	•	•	•
2.12	Parallels and angles	•	•	•	•	•	•	•	•	•	•	•	•	•	•	•	•
2.13	Angles and polygons	•	•	•	•	•	•	•	•	•	•	•	•	•	•	•	•
2.14	Circles 2	•	•	•		•	•		•	•	•	•	•	•	•	•	•
2.15	Ruler and compasses constructions	•	•	•			•		•	•		•	•	•	•		
2.16	Simple loci	•	•	•	•	•	•	•		•	•	•	•	•	•	•	•
2.17	Congruence	•	•	•	•	•	•	•	•	•	•	•	•	•	•	•	•
2.18	Enlargement	•	•	•	•	•	•	•	•	•	•	•	•	•	•	•	•
2.19	Transformations	•	•	•	•	•	•	•	•	•	•	•	•	•	L3	•	•
2.20	Plane symmetry				•			•	•	•		L3	L3	L3			•
2.21	Area 2	•	•	•	$L3^T$	•	•	$L3^T$	•	•	•	•	•	•	•	•	•
2.22	Volume of prisms	•	•	•	•	•	•	•	•	•	•	•	•	•	•	•	•
2.23	Sets								•	•		L3	L3	L3		L3	•
2.24	Frequency distributions and averages	•	•	•	•	•	•	•	•	•	•	•	•	•	•	•	•
2.25	More statistical tables and diagrams	•	•	•	•	•	•	•	•	•	•	•	•	•	•	•	•
2.26	Probability	•	•	•	$L3^T$	•	•	$L3^T$	•	•	•	•	•	•	•	•	
2.27	Simple algebra	•	•	•	•	•	•	•	•	•	•	•	•	•	•	•	•
2.28	Simple indices	•	•	•	•	•	•	•	•	•	•	•	•	•	•	•	•
2.29	Brackets and common factors	•	•	•	•	•	•	•	•	•	•	•	•	•	•	•	Br
2.30	Simple linear equations	•	•	•	•	•	•	•	•	•	•	•	•	•	•	•	•
2.31	Formulae	•	•	•	•	•	•	•	•	•	•	•	•	•	•	•	$L3^T$
2.32	Gradient	•	•	•	•	•	•	•	•	•	•	•	•	•	•	•	•
2.33	Drawing algebraic graphs	•	•	•	•	•	•	•	•	•	•	•	•	•	•	•	Line only
2.34	Solving equations with graphs	•	•	L3	•	•	L3	•	•	•	•	L3	L3	L3	L3	L3	•
2.35	Simple inequalities				•	L3	L3	•	L3	L3	•	•	•	•	L3		•
2.36	Pythagoras' Theorem	•	•	•	•	•	•	•	•	•	•	•	•	•	•	•	•
2.37	Sine, cosine and tangent	•	•	•	•	•	•	•	•	•	•	•	•	•	•	•	•
	List 3																
3.1	Circle theorems	•	•	L2					•	•		•	•	•	•	•	•
3.2	Loci					•			•	•	•	•	•	•	L2		
3.3	Enlargement	•	•	L2	•	•	•	•	•	•		•	•	•	•		
3.4	Similar figures	•	•	L2	•	•	•	•	•	•	•	•	•	•	•	•	•
3.5	Combinations of transformations	•	•	•		•	•		•	•		•	•	•	•		
3.6	Circle measure	•	•		•	•		•	L2	L2		•	•	•	L2		•
3.7	Surface area and volume	•	•		$L2^T$	•	•	$L2^T$	•	•	•	•	•	•	•	•	•
3.8	Sets and symbols								•			•	•	•		•	
3.9	Measures of dispersion and cumulative frequency			L2	•	•	•	•	•	•	L2	$L2^T$	$L2^T$	$L2^T$	•		
3.10	Indices				•	•	•	•	•	•		•	•	•	•	•	•
3.11	Expansion of brackets	•	•	•	•	•	•	•	•	•	•	•	•	•	•	•	•
3.12	Factorization	•	•	•	•	•	•	•	•	•	•	•	•	•	•	•	•
3.13	Transformation of formulae	•	•		•	•		•				•	•	•	•		•
3.14	Linear equations	•	•		•	•	•	•	•	•		•	•	•	•	•	•
3.15	Simultaneous equations	•	•	•	•	•	•	•	•	•	•	•	•	•	•	•	Two linear
3.16	Quadratic equations	•	•	•	•	•	•	•	•	•	•	•	•	•	•	•	•
3.17	Algebraic fractions	•	•		•	•		•			•	•	•	•		•	•
3.18	Algebraic graphs	•	•	•	•	•	•	•	•	•	•	•	•	•	•	•	•
3.19	Graphical solution of equations	•	•	•	•	L2	•	•	•	•	•				•	•	Qu
3.20	Inequalities				•	•	•	•	•	•	•	•	•	•	•		•
3.21	Relations and functions	•	•	•	•		•	•	•	•	•	$L2^T$	$L2^T$	$L2^T$		•	•
3.22	Variation	•	•	•	$L2^T$		•	$L2^T$				•	•	•	•	•	•
3.23	Equation of a straight line	•	•		•	•	•	•	•	•		•	•	•	•	•	•
3.24	Gradient and area from graphs	•	•		$L2^T$	St	•	$L2^T$	•	•	•	•	•	•		•	
3.25	Trigonometry and problems	•	•	•	•	•	•	•	•	•	•	•	•	•	•	•	
3.26	Trigonometrical ratios and graphs				•	•	•	•							•		•
3.27	Sine and cosine rules					•										•	•
3.28	Vectors	•	•	•	•	•	•	•	$L2^T$	$L2^T$	•	•	•	•		•	
3.29	Matrices	•	•	•		•	•		•	•		•	•	•			
3.30	Vector and matrix transformations	•	•	•		•	•		•	•		•	•	•			

Table 2 – Schemes of assessment

Exam group	Syllabus	Level	Target grade(s)	Grades available	Written papers, time and weighting		Project/ coursework assessment	Mental and/or aural test(s)
LEAG	A	1(F)	F	E,F,G	P1 - 1½h (40%)	P2 - 1½h (40%)	15%	5%
		2(I)	D	C,D,E,F	P2 - 1½h (40%)	P3 - 2h (40%)	15%	5%
		3(H)	B	A,B,C,D	P3 - 2h (40%)	P4 - 2½h (40%)	15%	5%
	B	1(F)	F	E,F,G	P1 - 1h (25%)	P2 - 1h (25%)	45%	5%
		2(I)	D	C,D,E,F	P2 - 1h (25%)	P3 - 1½h (25%)	45%	5%
		3(H)	B	A,B,C,D	P3 - 1½h (25%)	P4 - 1¾h (25%)	45%	5%
	SMP	1(F)	F	E,F,G	P1 - 1½h (40%)	P2 - 1½h (40%)	15%	5%
		2(I)	D	C,D,E,F	P2 - 1½h (40%)	P3 - 1½h (40%)	15%	5%
		3(H)	B	A,B,C,D	P3 - 2h (40%)	P4 - 2½h (40%)	15%	5%
	SMP 11-16	1(F)	E,F,G	E,F,G	P1 - 1½h (33⅓%)	P2 - 2h (33⅓%)	28⅓%	5%
		2(I)	C,D,E	C,D,E,F	P2 - 2h (33⅓%)	P3 - 2h (33⅓%)	28⅓%	5%
		3(H)	A,B,C	A,B,C,D	P3 - 2h (33⅓%)	P4 - 2½h (33⅓%)	28⅓%	5%
MEG	1651	1 (Foundation)	E,F,G	E,F,G	P1 - 1½h (35%)	P4 - 1½h (35%)	24%	6%
		2 (Intermediate)	C,D,E	C,D,E,F	P2 - 2h (35%)	P5 - 2h (35%)	24%	6%
		3 (Higher)	A,B,C	A,B,C,D	P3 - 2h (35%)	P6 - 2h (35%)	24%	6%
	SMP	1 (Foundation)	E,F,G	E,F,G	P1 - 1½h (35%)	P2 - 1½h (35%)	24%	6%
		2 (Intermediate)	C,D,E	C,D,E,F	P2 - 1½h (35%)	P3 - 2h (35%)	24%	6%
		3 (Higher)	A,B,C	A,B,C,D	P3 - 2h (35%)	P4 - 2h (35%)	24%	6%
	SMP 11- 6	1 (Foundation)	E,F,G	E,F,G	P1 - 1½h (33⅓%)	P2 - 2h (33⅓%)	28⅓%	5%
		2 (Intermediate)	C,D,E	C,D,E,F	P2 - 2h (33⅓%)	P3 - 2h (33⅓%)	28⅓%	5%
		3 (Higher)	A,B,C	A,B,C,D	P3 - 2h (33⅓%)	P4 - 2½h (33⅓%)	28⅓%	5%

NEA	A and B	1(P)	E,F,G	E,F,G	P1 - $1\frac{1}{2}$h ($37\frac{1}{2}$%)	P2 - $1\frac{1}{2}$h ($37\frac{1}{2}$%)	25%	None
		2(Q)	C,D,E	C,D,E,(F)	P2 - $1\frac{1}{2}$h (34%)	P3 - 2h (41%)	25%	None
		3(R)	A,B,C	A,B,C,(D)	P3 - 2h (34%)	P4 - $2\frac{1}{2}$h (41%)	25%	None
	C	1(P)	E,F,G	E,F,G	P1 - $1\frac{1}{2}$h ($37\frac{1}{2}$%)	P2 - $1\frac{1}{2}$h ($37\frac{1}{2}$%)	25%	None
		2(Q)	C,D,E	C,D,E,(F)	P2 - $1\frac{1}{2}$h (34%)	P3 - 2h (41%)	25%	None
		3(R)	A,B,C	A,B,C,(D)	P3 - 2h (34%)	P4 - $2\frac{1}{2}$h (41%)	25%	None
SEG	A	1(F)	F	E,F,G	P1 - 1h (25%)	P2 - 1h (25%)	40%	10%
		2(I)	D	C,D,E,F	P2 - $1\frac{1}{2}$h(25%)	P3 - $1\frac{1}{2}$h (25%)	40%	10%
		3(H)	B	A,B,C,D	P3 - $1\frac{1}{2}$h(25%)	P4 - 2h (25%)	40%	10%
	B	1(F)	F	E,F,G	P1 - $1\frac{1}{2}$h (35%)	P2 - $1\frac{1}{2}$h (35%)	20%	10%
		2(I)	D	C,D,E,F	P2 - $1\frac{1}{2}$h (35%)	P3 - 2h (35%)	20%	10%
		3(H)	B	A,B,C,D	P3 - 2h (35%)	P4 - 2 h (35%)	20%	10%
	E	2(I)	D	C,D,E,F	P2 - $1\frac{1}{2}$h(35%)	P3 - 2h (35%)	20%	10%
		3(H)	B	A,B,C,D	P3 - 2h (35%)	P4 - 2 h (35%)	20%	10%
NISEC		1 (Foundation)	F	E,F,G	P1 - $1\frac{1}{2}$h (35%)	P2- $1\frac{1}{2}$h(35%)	20%	10%
		2 (Intermediate)	D	C,D,E,F	P3 - 2h (35%)	P4 - 2h (35%)	20%	10%
		3 (Higher)	B	A,B,C,D	P5 - $2\frac{1}{2}$h (35%)	P6 - $2\frac{1}{2}$h (35%)	20%	10%
WJEC		1	F	E,F,G	P1 - $1\frac{1}{2}$h (37%)	P2 - 2h (37%)	22%	4%
		2	D	C,D,E,F	P2 - 2h (37%)	P3 - 2h (37%)	22%	4%
		3	B	A,B,C,D	P3 - $2\frac{1}{2}$h (37%)	P4 - $2\frac{1}{2}$h (37%)	22%	4%
SEB	Standard Grade	Foundation ▲ LOW	5,6	5,6,7	F1 (K/U) - 40 minutes (40%) F2 (R/A) - 40 minutes (40%)		The element 'investigating' will be assessed internally and carries 20% of the overall marks available at each level.	F1 includes five questions which will be rad out to the candidates, but not printed in the paper.
		General	3,4	3,4,7	G1 (K/U) - 55 minutes (40%) G2 (R/A) - 55 minutes (40%)			
		Credit HIGH ▼	1,2	1,2,7	C1 (K/U - 1 h (40%)			

A candidate is graded (using Grades 1 to 7) on each of the three assessable elements (knowledge and understanding (K/U), reasoning and applications (R/A) and investigating (I)) and is also given an overall award (Grade 1 to 7) based on these elements in the ratio of 2 : 2 : 1 - the 1 being investigating. Grade 7 is for candidates who have completed the course but who have not achieved either of the target grades at each level.

Table 3 – Details of coursework

Exam Group	Syllabus	Level(s)	Coursework pattern
LEAG	A and SMP	All	• Candidates have to hand in two coursework tasks. • The coursework handed in must include tasks which contain practical, investigational and extended work; either separately or in combination. • Candidates may submit two tasks set by LEAG, two tasks set by the centre or one task set by LEAG with one task set by the centre. • Three tasks will be set by the LEAG. One task, which may be completed early in the course, will be suitable for candidates entered at any level; one of the two tasks for completion towards the end of the course will be suitable for candidates entered for Levels F and I; and the other for candidates entered for Levels I and H. • Candidates will be required to extend the work of two of the tasks submitted.
	B	All	• Candidates have to hand in five coursework tasks. • The coursework handed in must include tasks which contain practical, investigational and extended work; either ,separately or in combination. • Candidates may submit five tasks set by LEAG, five tasks set by the centre or a mixture of LEAG-set and centre-set tasks. • Seven tasks will be set by the LEAG. Three tasks, for completion earlier in the course, will be suitable for candidates entered at any level; two of the tasks for completion towards the end of the course will be suitable for candidates entered for Levels F and I; and two for candidates entered for Levels I and H. • Candidates will be required to extend the work of two of the tasks submitted.
	SMP 11-16	All	• Candidates may offer either Option A: 4 group-set tasks and 1 open-ended task, or Option B: 2 open-ended tasks (1 practical, 1 investigational). • Group-set tasks are developed by SMP and sent to schools as worksheets. Each task is either ST—to be done in school in one session, time limit one hour, or H—to be done in the candidate's own time over approximately two weeks. • Open-ended tasks are extended pieces of work taking approximately two weeks of classwork and homework time in mathmatics.
MEG	1651 and SMP	All	• Candidates have to hand in three assignments. • Candidates must hand in one assignment chosen from the category: investigational work. • The other two assignments must be chosen from two of the other categories: (a) practical geometry; (b) applications of mathematics; (c) statistics and/or probability.
	SMP 11-16	All	• Candidates may offer either Option A: 4 group-set tasks and 1 open-ended task or Option B: 2 open-ended tasks (1 practical, 1 investigational). • Group-set tasks are developed by SMP and sent to schools as worksheets. Each task is either ST—to be done in school in one session, time limit one hour, or H—to be done in the candidate's own time over approximately two weeks. • Open-ended tasks are extended pieces of work taking approximately two weeks of classwork and homework time in mathmatics.
NEA	A and B and C		• Examination centres are responsible for deciding what the coursework tasks should be. • Some activities must be extended pieces of work. • The coursework handed in must also contain some practical work and some investigational work. • A candidate's ability to talk about mathematics, using mathematical language, will be assessed.
SEG	A and B and E	All	• Candidates must hand in three units of work. • One of the units must be an extended piece of work. • The three units, taken together, should show that the candidate can carry out practical and investigational work. • It will be acceptable for some candidates to hand in a range of coursework which might be of a cross-curricular nature.

<table>
<tr><th>Exam Group</th><th>Syllabus</th><th>Level(s)</th><th>Coursework pattern</th></tr>
<tr><td>SEG /contd.</td><td>A and B and E</td><td>All</td><td>• It is the teacher's responsibility to provide suitable coursework activities, except for those candidates following syllabus E. For these candidates, the group will suggest some activities.
• Part of the assessment of a candidate's coursework will be conducted orally.
• Coursework may be done at any time during the five terms before the one in which the written papers are taken.</td></tr>
<tr><td>NISEC</td><td></td><td>All</td><td>• Candidates are normally required to hand in three assignments.
• The assignments must be chosen from these two areas:
1 (a) practical geometry; (b) measurement;
(c) everyday applications of mathematics; (d) statistics.
2 Pure mathematics investigations.
At least one assignment should be handed in from each area.
• It is the teacher's responsibility to set the assignments.
• Candidates will be expected to be able to discuss their work with their teacher.</td></tr>
<tr><td>WJEC</td><td></td><td>1

2 and 3</td><td>• Candidates at this level will have to:
(i) investigate a particular theme;
(ii) demonstrate and apply certain practical skills.
• Candidates will have to choose:
(a) one of two investigations set by the Board for (i);
(b) three out of four exercises set by the Board for (ii).
• Part of the assessment of the coursework will be done orally.
• Candidates at these levels will have to hand in two tasks. The two tasks will be:
(i) a practical investigation;
(ii) a problem-solving investigation.
• The topics for the tasks will be provided by the Board at the end of March in the year before the examination is taken.
• There will be choice of two topics for each task.
• Part of the assessment of the coursework will be done orally.
Note: Centres can choose their own topics for each investigation if they so wish.</td></tr>
<tr><td>SEB</td><td>Standard Grade</td><td>

Foundation

General

Credit</td><td>• The candidate has be demonstrate his or her ability to do the following at an appropriate level:
– Complete a range of investigations, set in familiar everyday or mathematical context, which require:
(a) use of measuring or drawing instruments,
(b) identification with guidance (except in a very familiar situation) of real data,
(c) use of real data either taken from available sources or from a survey,
(d) recognition of a simple pattern.
– Complete a range of investigations, set in every day or straightforward mathematical contexts, which require:
(a) identification and use of real data,
(b) use of measuring or drawing instruments,
(c) exploration of a pattern,
(d) formulation of a simple mathematical model.
– Complete a range of investigations, set in everyday or theoretical contexts, which require:
(a) recognition or exploration of a pattern,
(b) the making of a conjecture,
(c) the provision of a proof and/or extension of a problem by generalization
(d) formulation of a mathematical model,
(e) identification and use of real data,
(f) use of measuring or drawing instruments.
• At each level, the assessment grade for investigating will be based on:
(i) a range of activities,
(ii) three dissimilar investigations which represent the candidate's best work.</td></tr>
</table>

Examination Boards: Addresses

Northern Examination Association (NEA)

JMB — Joint Matriculation Board
Devas Street, Manchester M15 6EU

ALSEB — Associated Lancashire Schools Examining Board
12 Harter Street, Manchester M1 6HL

NREB — Northern Regional Examinational Board
Wheatfield Road, Westerhope, Newcastle upon Tyne NE5 5JZ

NWREB — North-West Regional Examinations Board
Orbit House, Albert Street, Eccles, Manchester M20 0WL

YHREB — Yorkshire and Humberside Regional Examinations Board
Harrogate Office – 31-33 Springfield Avenue, Harrogate HG1 2HW
Sheffield Office – Scarsdale House, 136 Derbyshire Lane, Sheffield S8 8SE

Midland Examining Group (MEG)

Cambridge — University of Cambridge Local Examinations Syndicate
Syndicate Buildings, 1 Hills Road, Cambridge CB1 2EU

O & C — Oxford and Cambridge Schools Examination Board
Purbeck House, Purbeck Road, Cambridge CB2 1PU and Elsfield Way, Oxford OX2 7BZ

WMEB — West Midlands Examinations Board
Mill Wharf, Mill Street, Birmingham B6 4BU

EMREB — East Midland Regional Examinations Board
Robins Wood House, Robins Wood Road, Aspley, Nottingham NG8 3NR

London East Anglian Group (LEAG)
(now known as University of London Examinations and Assessment Council)

London office — Stewart House, 32 Russell Square, London WC1B 5DN

Colchester office — The Lindens, Lexden Road, Colchester CO3 3RL

Southern Examining Group (SEG)

AEB — The Associated Examining Board
Stag Hill House, Guildford GU2 5XJ

OSEB — Oxford School Examinations Board
Ewert House, Ewert Place, Summertown, Oxford OX2 7BZ

SEG — Southern Regional Examinations Board
Unit 23, Monksbrook Industrial Park, Chandlers Ford, Eastleigh SO5 3RA

South-East Regional Examinations Board
Beloe House, 2-10 Mount Ephraim Road, Tunbridge Wells TN1 1EU

South-Western Examinations Board
23-29 Marsh Street, Bristol BS1 4BP

Wales

WJEC — Welsh Joint Education Committee
245 Western Avenue, Cardiff CF5 2YZ

Northern Ireland

NISEC — Northern Ireland Schools Examinations Council
(now known as Northern Ireland Schools Examinations and Assessment Council)
Beechill House, 42 Beechill Road, Belfast BT8 4RS

Scotland

SEB — Scottish Examination Board
Ironmills Road, Dalkeith, Midlothian EH22 1BR

LIST 1

List 1 contains the basic topics you are expected to have covered in your syllabus before studying the units in this book. Here are brief summaries describing what you should be able to do for each topic.

1.1 Calculator

You should be able to:

(a) use a calculator accurately and efficiently to do calculations and solve problems;
(b) check your calculator answers in various ways, e.g. by doing the calculation in a different way, by finding an approximate answer, by using your knowledge of numbers;
(c) write sensible answers based on the results on your calculator display.

1.2 Whole numbers

You should be able to:

(a) recognize and use whole numbers given in either figures or words;
(b) understand that our number system is based on ten (decimal) and place value, e.g. 52 means 5 tens 2 units and 25 means 2 tens 5 units;
(c) put whole numbers in order of size.

1.3 Four rules: whole numbers

You should be able to:

(a) add, subtract, multiply and divide whole numbers using a calculator;
(b) use your addition bonds to 20, e.g. $5+13=18$ and $18-13=5$;
(c) use your multiplication tables to 10×10, e.g. $9\times7=63$ and $63\div7=9$;
(d) do simple whole number calculations in your head and with pencil and paper;
(e) multiply and divide by 10, 100, 1000, ...;
(f) test whether a number can be divided exactly by 2, 3, 5 and 10, e.g. 340 ends in 0, so can be divided exactly by 2, 5 and 10.
(g) solve problems involving whole numbers.

1.4 Approximation and estimation

You should be able to:

(a) round off numbers to the nearest 10, 100, 1000, ..., e.g. 1375 is 1380 (to the nearest 10) or 1400 (to the nearest 100) or 1000 (to the nearest 1000);
(b) estimate the answer to a calculation, e.g. $53\times29\approx50\times30=1500$;
(c) use an estimate to check that an answer is sensible.

1.5 Factors and multiples

You should be able to:

(a) find the factors of a number, e.g. the factors of 10 are 1, 2, 5 and 10 because these are the numbers that divide exactly into 10;
(b) show that a number is a prime number, e.g. 17 is a prime number because its only factors are 1 and itself;
(c) find multiples of a number, e.g. the multiples of 3 are 3, 6, 9, 12, ...

1.6 Number patterns

You should be able to:

(a) recognize, name and make simple number patterns with special names, e.g.

even numbers: 2, 4, 6, 8, 10, ...
odd numbers: 1, 3, 5, 7, 9, ...
triangular numbers: 1, 3, 6, 10, 15, ...
rectangular numbers: 4, 6, 8, 9, 10, 12 ...
square numbers: 1, 4, 9, 16, 25, 36, ...
cube numbers: 1, 8, 27, 64, 125, 216, ...
Fibonacci numbers: 1, 1, 2, 3, 5, 8, ...

(b) find and continue a pattern in a set of numbers and describe it.

1.7 Squares and square roots

You should be able to:

recognize, find and use squares of whole numbers and square roots of perfect squares.

1.8 Directed numbers

You should be able to:

(a) recognize positive$^+$ and negative$^-$ numbers as directed numbers and relate them to real life situations, e.g. $^+20$°C is 20° above 0°C (freezing point) and $^-3$°C is 3° below 0°C;
(b) compare and order directed numbers using a number line, e.g. a thermometer scale;
(c) do simple calculations using directed numbers in a practical setting.

1.9 Fractions

You should be able to:

(a) understand the meaning of different types of vulgar fractions including proper fractions, e.g. $\frac{3}{4}$, improper fractions, e.g. $\frac{7}{3}$ and mixed numbers, e.g. $2\frac{1}{3}$;
(b) change improper fractions to mixed numbers and vice versa, e.g. $3\frac{1}{2}=\frac{7}{2}$;
(c) recognize and work out equivalent fractions, e.g. $\frac{1}{4}=\frac{2}{8}=\frac{3}{12}=\frac{4}{16}=\ldots$;
(d) cancel fractions and give a fraction in its simplest form, e.g. $\frac{3}{12}=\frac{1}{4}$;
(e) compare and order fractions;
(f) find a fraction of a number of things or a quantity.

1.10 Fractions: + and −

You should be able to:

(a) add and subtract fractions (with the same and different denominators) and mixed numbers;
(b) use fractions to solve problems.

1.11 Decimals

You should be able to:

(a) understand the meaning of decimal fractions such as tenths, hundredths, thousandths, ...;
(b) compare decimals and put them in order of size;
(c) give decimals as vulgar fractions, e.g. $0.7=\frac{7}{10}$, $0.03=\frac{3}{100}$, $0.123=\frac{123}{1000}$;
(d) state common decimals as simple fractions, e.g. $0.5=\frac{1}{2}$, $0.25=\frac{1}{4}$, $0.75=\frac{3}{4}$;

1.12 Four rules: decimals

You should be able to:
(a) add, subtract, multiply and divide decimals using a calculator;
(b) add and subtract decimals in your head and with pencil and paper;
(c) multiply and divide decimals by 10, 100, 1000, ...;
(d) do simple multiplication and division involving decimals in your head and with pencil and paper;
(e) solve problems involving decimals.

1.13 Fractions to decimals

You should be able to:
(a) give fractions in tenths, hundredths, thousandths, ... as decimals;
(b) use a calculator to change any fraction or mixed number to a decimal, e.g.
$\frac{18}{45} = 18 \div 45 = 0.4$;
(c) state the decimal equivalents of simple fractions, e.g.
$\frac{1}{2} = 0.5$, $\frac{1}{4} = 0.25$, $\frac{3}{5} = 0.6$

1.14 Percentages

You should be able to:
(a) understand the meaning of a percentage, e.g. 35% means '35 out of a 100';
(b) change a percentage to a fraction or decimal, e.g. 35% is $\frac{35}{100} = \frac{7}{20}$ and $\frac{35}{100} = 0.35$;
(c) state common percentages as fractions or decimals and vice versa, e.g. $5\% = \frac{1}{20} = 0.05$;
(d) change fractions, mixed numbers and decimals to percentages (using a calculator if necessary), e.g. $0.65 = 0.65 \times 100\% = 65\%$.

1.15 Percentages of quantities

You should be able to:
(a) use a calculator to find a percentage of a quantity such as a number or measurement e.g. 12% of 15 metres;
(b) calculate a simple percentage of a quantity without a calculator, e.g. 25% of 36 pupils;
(c) increase or decrease a quantity by a given percentage.

1.16 Money

You should be able to:
(a) use the coins and notes in our money system in practical situations;
(b) write amounts of money correctly, i.e. all in pence, e.g. 135p, or all in pounds, e.g. £1.35;
(c) change pounds to pence and vice versa;
(d) do simple money calculations without a calculator, e.g. working out a bill, giving change;
(e) use a calculator to do money calculations;
(f) round amounts of money to the nearest 1p, 10p, £1, ...;
(g) roughly check a money calculation by finding an approximate answer, e.g. to check a bill.

1.17 Percentages of money

You should be able to:
(a) find a percentage of an amount of money just like any other quantity (see Unit 1.15);
(b) use the 'penny in the pound' method to find a percentage of an amount of money, i.e. 1% of £(=100p) is 1p, so 1% is '1p in the pound';
(c) increase or decrease an amount of money by a percentage, e.g. 10% service charge, 5% discount.

1.18 Wages and salaries

You should be able to:
(a) understand and use words and terms such as–
wage, salary, hourly rate, overtime, piecework, bonus scheme, commission, gross, net, deductions;
(b) do calculations to solve 'wage and salary' problems involving these words.

1.19 Taxes

You should be able to:
(a) understand and use words and terms such as–
Income Tax, earned and unearned income, tax allowances, taxable income, tax rates, PAYE, VAT, inclusive and exclusive of VAT, zero rated;
(b) do calculations to solve simple 'tax' problems involving these words.

1.20 Quarterly bills

You should be able to:
(a) understand and extract information from quarterly bills such as electricity, gas and telephone bills;
(b) calculate or check the entries on these bills, e.g. number of units used, cost of units used, total cost.

1.21 Interest

You should be able to:
(a) understand and use words and terms such as–
interest, deposit, loan, rate of interest, per annum, net and gross rates, simple interest, principal, amount;
(b) calculate the simple interest and amount for a deposit or loan.

1.22 Buy now, pay later

You should be able to:
(a) understand and use words and terms such as–
credit, hire purchase, deposit, instalments, interest, mortgage;
(b) do calculations to solve problems involving these terms.

1.23 Profit and loss

You should be able to:
(a) find the profit, loss, cost price, selling price for an article;
(b) calculate the percentage profit (or loss) on the sale of an article using

$$\text{percentage profit (or loss)} = \frac{\text{profit (or loss)}}{\text{cost price}} \times 100\%.$$

1.24 Rates

You should be able to:
(a) understand and use words and terms such as–
rates, rateable value, rate in the £, water rate, standing charge;
(b) do calculations to solve 'rates problems' involving these terms.

1.25 Insurance

You should be able to:
(a) understand and use terms connected with insurance such as–
insurance policy, premium, third party, fully comprehensive, no claims bonus;
(b) calculate the premiums for different types of insurance, e.g. personal, accident, home, travel, vehicle.

1.26 Tables

You should be able to:
(a) read and extract information from tables and charts, e.g. timetables, ready reckoners, price lists, temperature charts, conversion tables;
(b) estimate values in between those given in a table;
(c) use tables and charts to help you to solve problems, e.g. planning a holiday from a holiday brochure.

1.27 Points and lines

You should be able to:
(a) identify, name and draw points and lines (straight, curved, intersecting);

(b) recognize and mark parallel, perpendicular and equal lines on diagrams;
(c) understand and use the idea of horizontal and vertical;
(d) draw parallel lines with a set square and ruler.

1.28 Angles

You should be able to:
(a) understand and use the terms – angle, clockwise, anticlockwise, vertex, ∠. ^;
(b) label and name angles with letters;
(c) recognize and mark equal angles on diagrams;
(d) use 'turns' or degrees (°) to describe the size of angles;
(e) recognize and identify special angles such as –
right angles (90°),
acute angles (between 0° and 90°),
obtuse angles (between 90° and 180°),
straight angles (180°),
reflex angles (between 180° and 360°),
full turn (360°).

1.29 Related angles

You should be able to:
identify and use the following angle facts –
Angles in a right angle add up to 90°.
Angles in a straight angle add up to 180°
Angles in a full turn add up to 360°.
Vertically opposite angles are equal.

1.30 Estimating angles

You should be able to:
estimate the size of an angle in degrees.

1.31 Measuring and drawing angles

You should be able to:
(a) use a protractor (either 180° or 360°) to measure an angle in degrees;
(b) draw an angle of a given size to a reasonable degree of accuracy;
(c) check whether the measurement or drawing of an angle is of the correct size.

1.32 Directions

You should be able to:
(a) recognize, describe and draw a direction given as either a compass direction, e.g. N30°E, or a bearing, e.g. 030°;
(b) change a compass direction to a bearing and vice versa;
(c) find the bearing of one point from another;
(d) fix the position of a point given its bearing from two other points or its bearing and distance from another point.

1.33 Polygons

You should be able to:
(a) recognize, identify and describe polygons including triangles, quadrilaterals, pentagons, hexagons, heptagons and octagons;
(b) recognize and draw the diagonals of a polygon;
(c) label and name polygons using letters;
(d) recognize, identify and describe a regular polygon, i.e. one with all angles equal and all sides equal;
(e) identify the symmetries of regular polygons.

1.34 Triangles

You should be able to:
(a) recognize different types of triangles, namely,
acute-angled triangle (all angles acute),
right-angled triangle (one angle a right angle),
obtuse-angled triangle (one angle obtuse),
equilateral triangle (3 equal sides, 3 equal angles),
isosceles triangle (2 equal sides opposite 2 equal angles),
scalene triangle (no equal sides, no equal angles);
(b) identify and describe the angle and side properties of these triangles;
(c) relate the properties of triangles to their symmetries;
(d) state and use the angle sum of a triangle (=180°).

1.35 Quadrilaterals

You should be able to:
(a) recognize different types of quadrilaterals, namely,
rectangle, square, parallelogram, rhombus, trapezium, kite;
(b) identify and describe angle, side and diagonal properties of these quadrilaterals;
(c) relate the properties of quadrilaterals to their symmetries;
(d) state and use the angle sum of a quadrilateral (=360°).

1.36 Circles

You should be able to:
(a) know the meaning of and use 'circle words' such as circle, centre, radius, radii, diameter, circumference, arc, semicircle;
(b) understand the meaning of π (the ratio of circumference to diameter) and its approximate values, e.g. 3, 3.14, $3\frac{1}{7}$, $\frac{22}{7}$ or from the [π] key on a calculator;
(c) find the circumference of a circle using the formula

$$\text{circumference} = 2 \times \pi \times \text{radius or } C = 2\pi r = \pi d;$$

(d) draw circles and arcs of a given radius using a pair of compasses.

1.37 Drawing plane shapes

You should be able to:
(a) use drawing instruments (ruler, protractor, pair of compasses, set square) to draw diagrams;
(b) construct a triangle given the size of the three sides or two sides and the included angle or one side and two angles;
(c) construct other plane shapes given the necessary measurements;
(d) use constructions to solve problems, e.g. by measuring lengths and angles.

1.38 Tessellations

You should be able to:
recognize, continue and draw tessellations (tiling patterns).

1.39 Symmetry

You should be able to:
(a) recognize, identify and draw any lines of symmetry of a plane shape;
(b) complete a shape given part of the shape and its lines of symmetry;
(c) find the order of rotational symmetry of a plane shape.

1.40 Moving shapes

You should be able to:
(a) describe the transformation (translation, rotation, reflection) used to produce a repeating pattern;
(b) use simple translations, rotations and reflections to produce patterns.

1.41 Similarity and enlargement

You should be able to:
(a) understand the idea of similar shapes and enlargements, i.e. the same shape but different sizes;
(b) recognize and identify similar shapes and enlargements;
(c) find the scale factor of a simple enlargement;
(d) enlarge a shape using a scale factor which is a positive integer.

1.42 Scale models

You should be able to:
(a) understand the meaning of a scale;
(b) give a scale in different ways, e.g. 1:20 or 1 to 20 or $\frac{1}{20}$ or 1 cm represents 20 cm;
(c) use the scale of a model to find a length on the real object or a length on the model;
(d) find the scale of a model from matching lengths on the model and real object.

1.43 Maps

You should be able to:
(a) understand the meaning of a map scale;
(b) use a map scale to calculate actual distances and distances on the map;
(c) find the scale of a map.

1.44 Scale drawings

You should be able to:
(a) understand, read and draw simple scale drawings;
(b) use scale drawings to solve problems, e.g. by measuring lengths and using the scale of the drawing.

1.45 Simple solids

You should be able to:
(a) recognize and name simple solids such as cube, cuboid, cylinder, sphere, cone, triangular prism and square-based pyramid;
(b) relate 'everyday' objects to mathematical solids, e.g. ordinary dice are cubes;
(c) identify any faces, edges and vertices of these solids;
(d) sketch simple diagrams of these solids.

1.46 Nets

You should be able to:
recognize, identify and draw the nets of simple solids.

1.47 Length

You should be able to:
(a) use metric units of length, e.g. millimetres (mm), centimetres (cm), metres (m), kilometres (km);
(b) use the commonly used Imperial units of length, e.g. inches (in. or ″), feet (ft. or ′), yards (yd.), miles;
(c) appreciate the approximate size of the main units of length, e.g. 1 km $\approx 2\frac{1}{2}$ times round a football pitch;
(d) choose the most suitable unit for a length to be measured;
(e) state and use the following relationships,

$$1 \text{ km} = 1000 \text{ m} \qquad 1 \text{ cm} = 10 \text{ mm}$$

$$1 \text{ cm} = \frac{1}{100} \text{ m} \qquad 1 \text{ mm} = \frac{1}{1000} \text{ m}$$

$$\text{or } 100 \text{ cm} = 1 \text{ m} \qquad \text{or } 1000 \text{ mm} = 1 \text{ m}$$

(f) do calculations involving lengths (in the same unit);
(g) measure lengths to the nearest mm, cm and m;
(h) estimate lengths, e.g. by using 'body measures', by 'eye'.

1.48 Mass

You should be able to:
(a) understand the idea of mass (an amount of matter);
(b) use metric units of mass, e.g. milligrams (mg), grams (g), kilograms (kg), tonnes (t);
(c) use the commonly used Imperial units of mass, e.g. ounces (oz.), pounds (lb.), stones (st.), tons;
(d) appreciate the approximate size of the main metric units of mass, e.g. 1 g $\approx$ mass of 4 paperclips;
(e) choose the most suitable unit for a mass to be measured;
(f) state and use the following relationships,

1 gram = 1000 milligrams	or	1 g = 1000 mg
1 kilogram = 1000 grams	or	1 kg = 1000 g
1 tonne = 1000 kilograms	or	1 t = 1000 kg

(g) do calculations involving masses (in the same unit);
(h) recognize the difference between gross and net mass;
(i) measure the mass of an object using a balance (and a set of masses) and a spring balance (with a scale);
(j) appreciate the difference between mass and weight.

1.49 Capacity

You should be able to:
(a) understand the basic idea of the capacity of a container (the amount of liquid it can hold);
(b) use metric units of capacity, e.g. litres (l), centilitres (cl), millilitres (ml);
(c) use the commonly used Imperial units of capacity, e.g. fluid ounces (fl. oz.), pints (pt.), gallons (gall.);
(d) assess the approximate capacities of commonly used containers, e.g. a teaspoon contains about 5 ml;
(e) choose the most suitable unit for the amount of liquid to be measured;
(f) state and use the following relationships,

1 centilitre = $\frac{1}{100}$ litre	or	1 cl = $\frac{1}{100}$ l
i.e. 100 centilitres = 1 litre	or	100 cl = 1 l
1 millilitre = $\frac{1}{1000}$ litre	or	1 ml = $\frac{1}{1000}$ l
i.e. 1000 millilitres = 1 litre	or	1000 ml = 1 l

(g) do calculations involving capacities (in the same unit);
(h) use measuring jugs, cylinders and measuring spoons to measure liquids, e.g. in science experiments or in the kitchen.

1.50 Time

You should be able to:
(a) understand and use the common time units and the relationships between them, e.g. year, leap year, month, week, day, hour, minute, second;
(b) read a calendar and use it to find time spans in days, weeks, ...;
(c) tell the time from a digital and 'dial' clockface;
(d) understand and use a.m. and p.m. times (12 hour times), e.g. 2.30 p.m. is 'half past two in the afternoon';
(e) understand and use 24 hour times, e.g. 16.30 hours is '16 hours 30 minutes after midnight';
(f) change 12 hour to 24 hour times and vice versa, e.g. 15.45 $\leftrightarrow$ 3.45 p.m.;
(g) add a period of time on to a 12 hour or 24 hour time, e.g. find the arrival time given the departure time and travelling time for a journey;
(h) find the difference between two times, e.g. to find how long a TV programme lasts.

1.51 Perimeter

You should be able to:
find the perimeter (total distance round) a plane shape.

1.52 Area

You should be able to:
(a) understand the basic idea of area (amount of surface covered);
(b) use tessellations to compare areas and square units to measure areas;
(c) use metric units of area, e.g. square millimetres (mm^2), square centimetres (cm^2), square metres (m^2), hectares (ha), square kilometres (km^2);
(d) use the commonly used Imperial units of area, e.g. square inches (sq. in.), square feet (sq. ft.), square yards (sq. yd.), acres, square miles;
(e) appreciate the approximate size of the main metric units of area, e.g. 1 m^2 is about the area of the roof of a Mini car;
(f) choose the most suitable unit for an area to be measured;
(g) find the approximate area of a shape by counting squares and estimating 'bits';

(h) calculate the area of a rectangle using the formula,

area of rectangle = length × width;

(i) work out and use the relationships between the metric units of area,

$1\ \text{cm}^2 = 100\ \text{mm}^2$ $\quad$ $1\ \text{ha} = 10\,000\ \text{m}^2$

$1\ \text{m}^2 = 10\,000\ \text{cm}^2 = 1\,000\,000\ \text{mm}^2$ $\quad$ $1\ \text{km}^2 = 1\,000\,000\ \text{m}^2 = 100\ \text{ha}$

(j) find the area of a triangle using the formula,

area of a triangle = $\frac{1}{2}$(base × height).

1.53 Surface area of a cuboid

You should be able to:
find the surface area of a cuboid (the total area of its faces).

1.54 Volume

You should be able to:
(a) understand the basic idea of volume (amount of space occupied by a solid);
(b) use cubes to measure volume;
(c) use metric units of volume, e.g. cubic millimetres (mm^3), cubic centimetres (cm^3), cubic metres (m^3);
(d) use the commonly used Imperial units of volume, e.g. cubic inches (cu. in.), cubic feet (cu. ft.), cubic yards (cu. yd.);
(e) appreciate the size of the main metric units of volume, e.g. a cube with edges 1 cm long has a volume of 1 cm^3;
(f) choose the most sensible unit for a volume to be measured;
(g) find the volume of a cuboid and use the formula,

volume of a cuboid = length × width × height;

(h) work out and use the relationships between the metric units of volume,

$1\ \text{cm}^3 = 1000\ \text{mm}^3$

$1\ \text{m}^3 = 1\,000\,000\ \text{cm}^3 = 1\,000\,000\,000\ \text{mm}^3$

(i) use the relationships between the units of volume and capacity,

$1\ \text{m}^3 = 1000\ \text{l}$ $\quad$ $1\ \text{l} = 1000\ \text{cm}^3$

$1\ \text{cm}^3 = 1\ \text{ml}$ $\quad$ $1\ \text{ml} = 1\ \text{cm}^3$

$1\ \text{mm}^3 = \frac{1}{1000}\ \text{ml}$ $\quad$ $1\ \text{ml} = 1000\ \text{mm}^3$

1.55 Measures of rate

You should be able to:
(a) understand, use and calculate common measures of rate, e.g. speed in kilometres per hour, prices in £ per metre, petrol consumption in miles per gallon;
(b) compare rates and use the comparison in decision making, e.g. to find the 'best buy'.

1.56 Average speed

You should be able to:
(a) understand and use the idea of average speed;
(b) calculate the average speed for a journey using

average speed = distance travelled ÷ time taken;

(c) do simple calculations involving distance, time and average speed.

1.57 Travel graphs

You should be able to:
(a) understand that a journey at constant speed can be shown by a straight line on a travel graph;
(b) read information from a travel graph describing a journey;
(c) use this information to find the average speed of a journey (or part of a journey);
(d) draw a simple travel graph from a description of a journey at steady speeds.

1.58 Change of units

You should be able to:
(a) change from one set of measurement units to another, e.g. m↔cm (in metric units), oz.↔lb. (in Imperial units), litres↔pints (between metric and Imperial units);
(b) change from one currency to another given the exchange rate, e.g. from £ sterling to $ dollars when £1 = $1.45.

1.59 Conversion graphs

You should be able to:
(a) use a straight line graph to convert one unit to another, e.g. °C↔°F, £ to francs;
(b) draw a straight line conversion graph from a given conversion table or exchange rate.

1.60 Scales and dials

You should be able to:
(a) read values from linear scales, e.g. on a ruler, thermometer, spring balance, measuring jug, graph, and from curved scales, e.g. on a clockface, protractor, speedometer, bathroom scales;
(b) estimate the value if the reading is between two marks on a scale;
(c) read dials on electricity and gas meters.

1.61 Ratio and proportion

You should be able to:
(a) understand the basic idea of ratio in practical situations;
(b) simplify a ratio, e.g. 20 to 12 ≡ 5 to 3;
(c) compare quantities using a ratio;
(d) use ratios to solve problems;
(e) understand and use the basic ideas of direct and indirect proportion;
(f) alter recipes and mixtures using direct proportion.

1.62 Formulae

You should be able to:
(a) understand the meaning of a formula given in words or in letters,

e.g. area of rectangle = length × width

or $\quad A = lw$

(b) use simple formulae to work out a result (by substituting numbers or values for the words or letters).

1.63 Flow diagrams

You should be able to:
(a) use and make flow diagrams and inverse flow diagrams to solve simple problems, e.g. 'think of a number' problems;
(b) use and write flow diagrams to make expressions in algebra.

1.64 Flow charts

You should be able to:
follow the steps given in a flow chart.

1.65 Coordinates

You should be able to:
(a) understand the use of coordinates to give the position of a point in relation to axes;
(b) give the coordinates of a point on a grid;
(c) plot points on a grid given their coordinates.

1.66 Graphs

You should be able to:
(a) read and interpret information given on a graph;
(b) draw a graph from data (information) which may be given in a table.

1.67 Collecting and displaying data

You should be able to:
(a) collect data by means of a simple survey;
(b) sort, classify and tabulate data, e.g. in a tally table;
(c) read, interpret and draw simple conclusions from statistical tables, pictograms, bar charts and pie charts;
(d) draw pictograms and bar charts from data.

1.68 Averages

You should be able to:
(a) find, for ungrouped data, the three main averages, namely,

mean (total of values ÷ number of values),

mode (the value which appears most often),

median (the middle value when the values are in order of size);

(b) understand the different uses of these averages and decide which is the 'best' average to use for some data;
(c) calculate the range of data.

1.69 Simple probability

You should be able to:
(a) understand the basic idea of probability (how likely something is to happen or not happen);
(b) give a measure of probability on a scale of 0 to 1;
(c) calculate simple probabilities (theoretical probability) for equally likely events,

probability of event happening =

$$\frac{\text{number of ways that event can happen}}{\text{total number of possibilities}}$$

e.g. probability of throwing a 2 with a dice is $\frac{1}{6}$;
(d) estimate simple probabilities from experimental results (experimental probability),

experimental probability =

$$\frac{\text{number of times the event happens during the experiment}}{\text{total number of times the experiment is done}},$$

(e) use probability to find an expected value in an experiment.

LIST 2

2.1 Numbers

REAL NUMBERS

There are many kinds of numbers. In mathematics we often classify them into sets and give them special names. Here are some examples.

counting numbers 1, 2, 3, 4, 5, ...
natural numbers 0, 1, 2, 3, 4, ...
integers ... −5, −4, −3, −2, −1, 0, 1, 2, 3, 4, 5, ...
positive integers 1, 2, 3, 4, 5, ...
negative integers −1, −2, −3, −4, −5, ...

Note Each of these sets of numbers is *infinite*, i.e. goes on for ever. However, the *counting numbers* and *natural numbers* each have a **smallest number** (1 and 0 respectively) but there is *no* largest or smallest *integer*. **Zero** (0) is an integer but is not a positive or negative integer.

All the numbers in this book belong to the set of **real numbers.** (There is also a set of *imaginary numbers* but they are not part of your GCSE course. If you go on to study more advanced mathematics, then you may study the set of imaginary numbers.) All real numbers are either **rational numbers** or **irrational numbers**.

real numbers
rational numbers   irrational numbers

A *rational number* can always be written as a **vulgar** or **common fraction**, i.e. as an integer divided by another integer (*not zero*). For example, $\frac{1}{2}$, $-\frac{7}{45}$, $\frac{21}{6}$, $-\frac{5}{3}$ are all rational numbers.

Here are some examples of sets of rational numbers.

proper fractions $\frac{1}{2}, \frac{2}{3}, \frac{5}{7}, \ldots$

improper fractions $\frac{10}{3}, \frac{5}{2}, \frac{129}{22}, \ldots$

mixed numbers $1\frac{2}{5}\ (=\frac{7}{5})$, $3\frac{1}{8}\ (=\frac{25}{8})$, $6\frac{2}{10}\ (=\frac{62}{10})$, ...

integers $0\ (=\frac{0}{1})$, $+1\ (=+\frac{1}{1})$, $-6\ (=-\frac{6}{1})$, ...

terminating decimals $0.5\ (=\frac{5}{10})$, $-0.731\ (=-\frac{731}{1000})$, $1.06\ (=\frac{106}{100})$, ...

recurring decimals $0.\dot{3}\ (=\frac{1}{3})$, $0.\dot{0}\dot{9}\ (=\frac{1}{11})$, $0.\dot{1}42\,85\dot{7}\ (=\frac{1}{7})$, ...

An *irrational number* is one that is *not* rational. So it cannot be written as a vulgar fraction.

For example, $\sqrt{2}$ is an irrational number. You cannot find a vulgar fraction which when multiplied by itself gives 2.

Another well-known irrational number is π. You cannot find an exact value for π.

$\pi = 3.141\,592\,653\,589\,793\,238\,462\,643\,383\,279\,5\ \ldots$

Remember Values you use such as $3\frac{1}{7}$ or 3.14 are only *approximations.*

When an irrational number is written as a decimal, the decimal is **infinite**, i.e. it goes on for ever.

Any real number can be represented by a point on a **real number line**. If all real numbers are put on a line in order of size, then there are no 'holes' or 'gaps' on the line. Here is part of the real number line with some numbers marked on it.

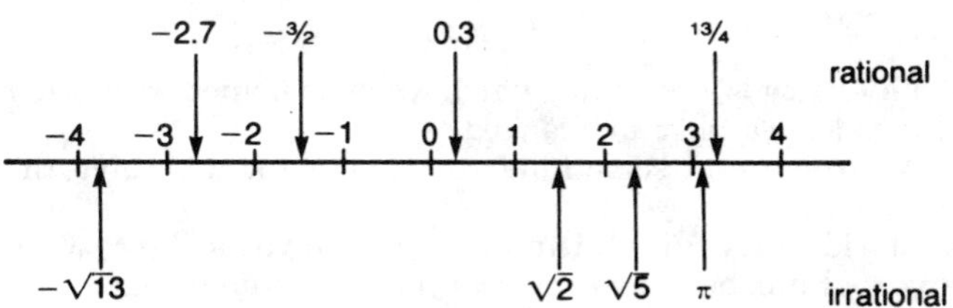

Question

Here are some real numbers.

$1, \sqrt{3}, 0, -5$

To which set(s) of numbers does each belong? Name as many as you can for each.

Answer

1 is a rational number, a counting number, a natural number and a positive integer.

There are others, e.g. odd, square, triangular.

$\sqrt{3}$ is an irrational number.
0 is a rational number, a natural number, an integer.
−5 is a rational number, a negative integer.

OPERATIONS ON REAL NUMBERS

In mathematics an **operation** is a way of combining numbers, sets, etc. The most well-known operations on real numbers are *addition, subtraction, multiplication* and *division.*

Commutative law

The operations of **addition** and **multiplication** on real numbers are **commutative.** This means that in the addition and multiplication of real numbers the order *does not matter.*

Changing the order does not change the result. For example, if a and b are real numbers, then:

$a + b = b + a$ *(addition is commutative)*
$ab = ba$ *(multiplication is commutative)*

(Try these yourself with some real numbers.)

Subtraction and **division** of real numbers are *not* commutative. For example, if a and b are real numbers, then:

$a - b \neq b - a$
$a \div b \neq b \div a$ } *(subtraction and division are* ***not*** *commutative)*

(Try these yourself with some real numbers.)

Associative law

Addition and **multiplication** of real numbers are also **associative.** This means that when three real numbers are added or multiplied, they may be grouped using brackets in any way and the value is the same. For example, for real numbers a, b and c,

$(a + b) + c = a + (b + c)$ *(addition is associative)*
$a(bc) = (ab)c$ *(multiplication is associative)*

(Try these for yourself with some real numbers.)

Subtraction and **division** of real numbers are *not* associative. For example, for real numbers a, b and c,

$(a-b)-c \neq a-(b-c)$ $\}$ *(subtraction and division*
$(a \div b) \div c \neq a \div (b \div c)$ $\}$ *are **not** associative)*

(Try these yourself with some real numbers.)

Distributive law

For real numbers, **multiplication** is **distributive over addition** (and subtraction). This means that *each* number *inside* a bracket is multiplied by the number *outside* the bracket. For example, if a, b and c are real numbers, then:

$a(b+c) = ab + ac$ *(left distributive law)*
$(b+c)a = ba + ca$ *(right distributive law)*

(Try these yourself with some real numbers.)

IDENTITY AND INVERSE

An **identity** is something which when combined with other things leaves them unchanged.

An **inverse** of something combines with it to give the *identity*.

The **identity for addition** is zero (0). If you add zero (0) to any real number, then the real number is unchanged. For example, if p is any real number, then:

$p + 0 = 0 + p = p$

The **additive inverse** of any real number p is ^-p, called '**negative** p'. This is because

$p + {}^-p = {}^-p + p = 0$ *(the identity for addition)*

For example, the additive inverse of 3 is $^-3$ because

$3 + {}^-3 = {}^-3 + 3 = 0$

Also the additive inverse of $^-3$ is 3.

The **identity for multiplication** is 1. If you multiply any real number by 1, then the real number is unchanged. For example, if q is any real number, then:

$q \times 1 = 1 \times q = q$

The **multiplicative inverse** of any real number q (except zero) is $\frac{1}{q}$, the **reciprocal** of q.

This is because

$q \times \frac{1}{q} = \frac{1}{q} \times q = 1$ *(the identity for multiplication)*

For example, the multiplicative inverse of 3 is $\frac{1}{3}$ because

$3 \times \frac{1}{3} = \frac{1}{3} \times 3 = 1$.

Also the multiplicative inverse of $\frac{1}{3}$ is 3.

FACTORS AND MULTIPLES

Common factors

If two or more integers have a factor in common, then the factor is called a **common factor**. For example,

2 is a factor of 6 since $6 \div 2 = 3$ (see Unit 1.5)
2 is a factor of 8 since $8 \div 2 = 4$
So 2 is a common factor of 6 and 8.

Since 1 is a factor of every number, 1 is always a common factor. Some sets of numbers may have more than one common factor.

The **highest common factor (HCF)** of two or more numbers is the largest factor they have in common.

Question

Find the common factors of 12 and 18. What is their highest common factor?

Answer

$12 = 1 \times 12$	$18 = 1 \times 18$
$= 2 \times 6$	$= 2 \times 9$
$= 3 \times 4$	$= 3 \times 6$

So the factors of 12 are (1), (2), (3), 4, (6) and 12,
and
the factors of 18 are (1), (2), (3), (6), 9 and 18.
The common factors of 12 and 18 are 1, 2, 3 and 6.
The highest common factor of 12 and 18 is 6.

Prime factors

A **prime factor** is a factor which is a **prime number**. For example, the factors of 24 are

1, (2), (3), 4, 6, 8, 12 and 24. (See Unit 1.5.)

2 and 3 are also prime numbers.
So 2 and 3 are prime factors of 24.

Every integer greater than 1 can be written as a product of prime factors only. The prime factors are usually written in order of size, smallest first. For example

$3410 = 2 \times 5 \times 11 \times 31$.

When a number is given as a product of prime numbers it is said to be **factorized completely**.

You can use a **factor tree** to work out the prime factors of a number. Start with a factor pair of the number. Then find factor pairs of each number you obtain until you reach prime numbers.

Question

Factorize 72 completely into its prime factors.

Answer

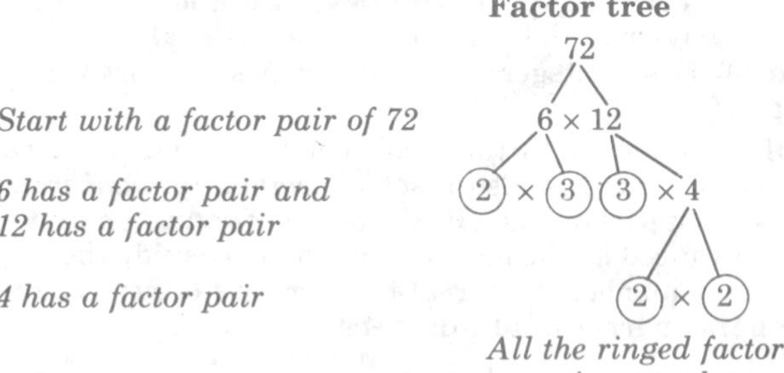

So $72 = \underbrace{2 \times 2 \times 2 \times 3 \times 3}_{\text{prime factors}}$

Often there are different factor trees for a number. But all factor trees of a number lead to the same set of prime factors. For example,

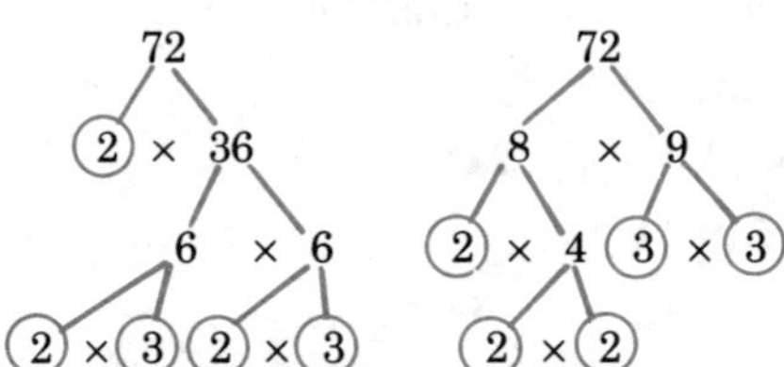

(Try to find some more yourself.)

You can also find prime factors by repeatedly dividing by the prime numbers in turn. Start dividing with the smallest prime number you can. Stop when you are left with just 1.

Question

Factorize 294 into its prime factors.

Answer

			Prime factors
Try 2. It works.✓	2	294	2
Try 2. × Try 3 (the next prime).✓	3	147	3
Try 3. × Try 5. × Try 7.✓	7	49	7
Try 7.✓	7	7	7
The end!		1	

So $294 = 2 \times 3 \times 7 \times 7$

Common multiples

If the multiples of two or more integers have a number in common, then the number is called a **common multiple**. For example,

the multiples of 2 are 2, 4, (6), 8, 10, ... (see Unit 1.5)

the multiples of 3 are 3, (6), 9, 12, ...

So 6 is a common multiple of 2 and 3.

Two or more integers may have more than one common multiple. The **lowest common multiple (LCM)** is the smallest multiple they have in common.

Question

Find the lowest common multiple of 15 and 18.

Answer

Multiples of 15: 15, 30, 45, 60, 75, (90), 105, ...

Multiples of 18: 18, 36, 54, 72, (90), ...

So the lowest common multiple of 15 and 18 is 90.

2.2 Directed numbers: four rules

Positive and negative numbers are often called **directed numbers** (see Unit 1.8).

Positive numbers are sometimes marked with a $^+$ positive sign. For example, $^+3$ is **positive 3**. Often the positive sign is omitted. But you know that a number *without* a sign is *always* positive. Negative numbers are marked with a $^-$ negative sign. For example, $^-6$ is **negative 6**. A negative number *must* have a sign in front of it.

Many people and books do not put positive and negative signs at the 'top' of the number. They write them on the line like plus and minus signs, for example +3 and −6, but they mean 'positive 3' and 'negative 6'. In this unit, positive and negative signs are written at the top of each number to help you to see the working.

ADDITION AND SUBTRACTION

Students are taught many different ways to add and subtract directed numbers. If you are sure that you understand and can use your method successfully, then use it. If you have difficulties, then here is a method for you to try.

Think of directed numbers as temperatures:

positive numbers as *hot* air,
negative numbers as *cold* air.

Use a number line (like a thermometer) to help you to do the working.

← negative positive →

$^-5$ $^-4$ $^-3$ $^-2$ $^-1$ 0 1 2 3 4 5

To help you do an addition or subtraction, ask yourself:

(a) What is the starting temperature (the first number)?
(b) Does it go up or down?
Use your common sense to work it out:
add hot air → it goes up,
add cold air → it goes down,
subtract hot air → it goes down,
subtract cold air → it goes up.
(c) By how much does it change?
(d) What is the final temperature?

For example, you can work out $5 + {}^-8$ like this:

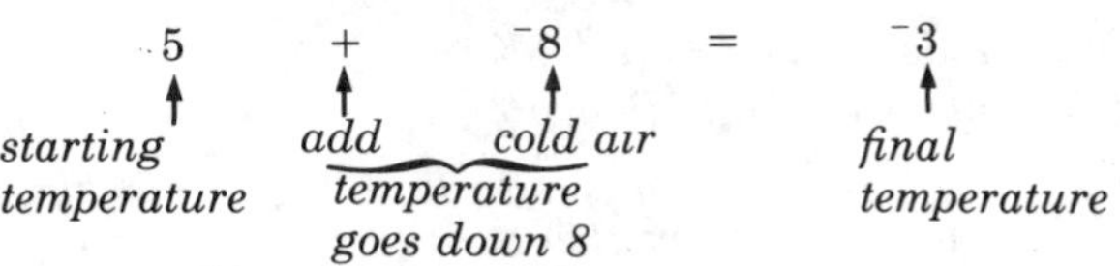

Number line work

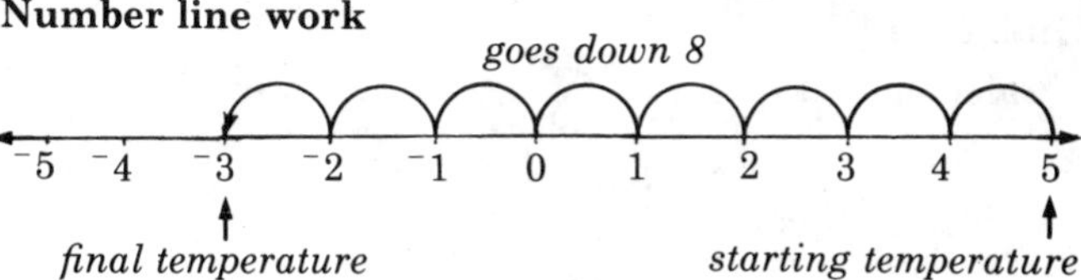

You can work out $^-2 - 3$ like this:

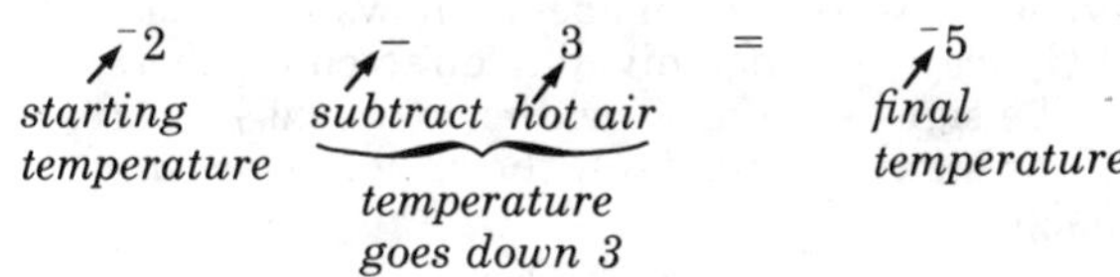

Number line work

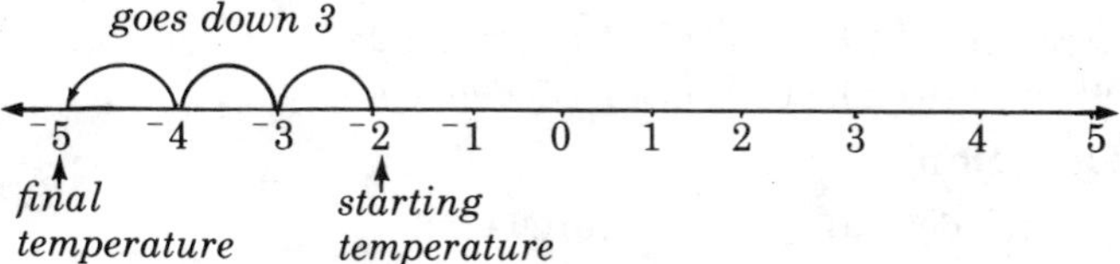

With practice you should be able to do these calculations without a number line.

Always **check** whether your answer makes sense. Adding a $^+$ number to a number increases the number. For example,

$^-3 + 2 = {}^-1$ ($^-1$ is bigger than $^-3$)

Adding a $^-$ number to a number decreases the number. For example,

$^-3 + {}^-2 = {}^-5$ ($^-5$ is smaller than $^-3$)

Subtracting a $^+$ number from a number decreases the number. For example,

$^-3 - 2 = {}^-5$ ($^-5$ is smaller than $^-3$)

Subtracting a $^-$ number from a number increases the number. For example,

$^-3 - {}^-2 = {}^-1$ ($^-1$ is bigger than $^-3$)

It may help you to remember the following, too.

Subtracting a positive **or** adding its negative } give the same answer.

For example, $2 - 7 = {}^-5$
$2 + {}^-7 = {}^-5$

Subtracting a negative **or** adding its positive } give the same answer.

For example, $^-3 - {}^-2 = {}^-1$
$^-3 + 2 = {}^-1$

MULTIPLICATION AND DIVISION

When **multiplying** directed numbers,
if the signs are the *same*, the answer is *positive*,
if the signs are *different*, then the answer is *negative*.

This gives:

same signs	$(+) \times (+) \rightarrow (+)$ $(-) \times (-) \rightarrow (+)$	*positive answer*
different signs	$(+) \times (-) \rightarrow (-)$ $(-) \times (+) \rightarrow (-)$	*negative answer*

Question

Work out: (a) $^-2 \times 7$ (b) $^-3 \times {}^-4$

Answer

(a) $^-2 \times 7 = {}^-(2 \times 7) = {}^-14$
different signs → negative

(b) $^-3 \times {}^-4 = {}^+(3 \times 4) = {}^+12$
same signs → positive

Sometimes you have to multiply more than two numbers. Multiply them 'two at a time'.

Question

Calculate: $3 \times {}^{-}2 \times {}^{-}4$

Answer

$3 \times {}^{-}2 \times {}^{-}4$

put in twos $= {}^{-}6 \quad \times {}^{-}4$

$= {}^{+}24$

Division of directed numbers follows the same pattern as multiplication. When dividing directed numbers,

if the signs are the *same*, the answer is *positive*,

if the signs are different, the answer is *negative*.

This gives:

same signs $\left\{\begin{array}{l}(+)\div(+)\rightarrow(+)\\(-)\div(-)\rightarrow(+)\end{array}\right\}$ *positive answer*

different signs $\left\{\begin{array}{l}(+)\div(-)\rightarrow(-)\\(-)\div(+)\rightarrow(-)\end{array}\right\}$ *negative answer*

Question

Work out: (a) ${}^{-}15 \div {}^{-}3$ (b) $20 \div {}^{-}2$

Answer

(a) ${}^{-}15 \div {}^{-}3 = {}^{+}(15 \div 3) = {}^{+}5$

same signs → positive

(b) $20 \div {}^{-}2 = {}^{-}(20 \div 2) = {}^{-}10$

different signs → negative

USING A CALCULATOR

If your calculator has a **sign change key** such as [+/−] or [+ −], then you can use it to enter directed numbers. Pressing this key changes the sign of the number on the display.

To enter a negative number, press its digit(s) and then the [+/−] key. For example, to enter ${}^{-}16$

Press: [1] [6] [+/−]

Display: [16.] [${}^{-}$16.]

You can use this to do calculations with directed numbers. Always check that the numbers on the display have the sign you want each time.

Question

Work out: (a) ${}^{-}6 + {}^{-}3$ (b) ${}^{-}21 \div {}^{-}7$

Answer

(a) ${}^{-}6 + {}^{-}3 = {}^{-}9$

Press: [C] [6] [+/−] [+] [3] [+/−] [=]

Display: [6.] [${}^{-}$6.] [3.] [${}^{-}$3.] [${}^{-}$9.]

(b) ${}^{-}21 \div {}^{-}7 = 3$

Press: [C] [2] [1] [+/−] [÷] [7] [+/−] [=]

Display: [21.] [${}^{-}$21.] [7.] [${}^{-}$7.] [3.]

You may find that, with practice, you can do these calculations faster in your head. When you are practising these skills you can use your calculator to check your answers.

2.3 Square and cube roots

MORE SQUARES AND SQUARE ROOTS

The **square** of any number is the number multiplied by itself, i.e. $n^2 = n \times n$.

Find the best way to square a number on your calculator. For example, to square 3.7, i.e. $(3.7)^2 = 3.7 \times 3.7$, try: [C] [3] [·] [7] [×] [=] or [C] [3] [·] [7] [x^2].

The **square root** of any *positive* number multiplied by itself gives the number, i.e. $\sqrt{n} \times \sqrt{n} = n$.

To find a square root use the [√] on your calculator.

Question

Work out $\sqrt{(19.4)}$ giving your answer correct to 2 significant figures.

Answer

$\sqrt{(19.4)} = 4.4$ (to 2 s.f.)

Press: [C] [1] [9] [·] [4] [√] **Display:** [4.404543109]

Check: [×] [=] **Display:** [19.4]

Note To check your answer on the calculator, press [×] [=] after you have obtained your display answer. Sometimes the number you get may not be *exactly* the number you started with ... but it may be very close to it. This happens when your display is too small to show all the digits in the square root.

CUBE ROOTS

A **cube number** (perfect cube) can be shown as a cube of dots. The number of dots along each *edge* gives the **cube root** of the cube number.

$\sqrt[3]{}$ means *the cube root of.*

Cube number	Cube root
1	$\sqrt[3]{1} = \sqrt[3]{1 \times 1 \times 1} = 1$
8	$\sqrt[3]{8} = \sqrt[3]{2 \times 2 \times 2} = 2$
27	$\sqrt[3]{27} = \sqrt[3]{3 \times 3 \times 3} = 3$

Here are the first ten cube numbers and their cube roots.

Cube number	1	8	27	64	125	216	343	512	729	1000
Cube root	1	2	3	4	5	6	7	8	9	10

It is useful to know some of these, especially $\sqrt[3]{1000} = 10$.

The cube root of a number multiplied by itself and by itself again gives the number. You can use this to help you to find cube roots and to check that a value is a cube root.

Question

Find $\sqrt[3]{512}$.

Answer

$\sqrt[3]{1000} = 10$ ... we know that because $10 \times 10 \times 10 = 1000$

512 is smaller than 1000

So $\sqrt[3]{512}$ is smaller than $\sqrt[3]{1000}$

Try a number smaller than 10

Try 5. $5 \times 5 \times 5 = 125$ *Too small. Try a bigger number, smaller than 10*

Try 7. $7 \times 7 \times 7 = 343$ *Still too small.*
Try 8. $8 \times 8 \times 8 = 512$ *That's it!*
So $\sqrt[3]{512} = 8$ (because $8 \times 8 \times 8 = 512$)

The cube root of the volume of a cube gives the length of the edge of the cube. Check that you give the correct unit in the answer. (**Remember** cm^3 will give a length in cm; m^3 will give a length in m, and so on ...).

Question

A packing box in a warehouse is a cube with volume 64 m^3. What is the length of each edge of the cube?

Answer

Volume of cube = 64 m^3.
$\sqrt[3]{64} = 4$. (**Check** $4 \times 4 \times 4 = 64$)
So the length of each edge = 4 m.
(Check units: $m \times m \times m \rightarrow m^3$)

4 m
4 m
4 m

2.4 Number patterns

FINDING RULES

Look carefully at this **number pattern**.

1st line: $1 + 1 = 2 \times 1$
2nd line: $2 + 2 = 2 \times 2$
3rd line: $3 + 3 = 2 \times 3$

If you were asked for the next three lines in this pattern, then you would write:

4th line: $4 + 4 = 2 \times 4$
5th line: $5 + 5 = 2 \times 5$
6th line: $6 + 6 = 2 \times 6$

The 10th line in the pattern is easy to write too.

10th line: $10 + 10 = 2 \times 10$

The pattern goes on for ever. But you can write a general rule to give the pattern.

For any line, the rule is:

line number + *line number* = 2 × *line number*

You can use a letter for the 'line number'. This gives a shorter way to write the rule.

If n is the line number, then the rule is:

nth line: $n + n = 2 \times n$
or $n + n = 2n$

It is a good idea to **check** that a rule works. Try putting different numbers instead of the letter(s). See if you get the answer(s) you expect.

Question

Look at this number pattern:

$1^3 + 1 = (1 + 1)(1^2 - 1 + 1)$
$2^3 + 1 = (2 + 1)(2^2 - 2 + 1)$
$3^3 + 1 = (3 + 1)(3^2 - 3 + 1)$

(a) Write the next three lines of the pattern.
(b) Give a general rule for the pattern for any number n.

Answer

(a) $4^3 + 1 = (4 + 1)(4^2 - 4 + 1)$
$5^3 + 1 = (5 + 1)(5^2 - 5 + 1)$
$6^3 + 1 = (6 + 1)(6^2 - 6 + 1)$

(b) For any number n, the pattern is:
$n^3 + 1 = (n + 1)(n^2 - n + 1)$
Check for $n = 10$,
$10^3 + 1 = (10 + 1)(10^2 - 10 + 1)$
LHS $10^3 + 1 = 1001$
RHS $(10 + 1)(10^2 - 10 + 1) = (11)(91) = 1001$
} equal ✓

You can work out a general rule for many number patterns this way.

SEQUENCES

A **sequence** is a pattern of numbers in a definite order. For example,

2, 4, 6, 8, 10, ... is the sequence of even numbers.

You can often find a rule connecting each number with its place in the order. Putting the numbers in a table can often help you to do this.

Here are some well-known sequences and their *place rules.* Each rule gives the nth number in the sequence. **Check** that each rule works with some numbers of your own.

Even numbers

nth even number is $2n$

Look at this table to see how this rule can be worked out.

Place number	Even number	Working
1	2	$= 2 \times 1$
2	4	$= 2 \times 2$
3	6	$= 2 \times 3$
4	8	$= 2 \times 4$
⋮	⋮	⋮
n	$2n$	$= 2 \times n$

Multiply place number by 2

Odd numbers

nth odd number is $2n - 1$

Odd and even numbers are related. You can use this fact to work out any odd number. Look at this table to see this relationship.

Place number	Even number	Odd number	Working
1	2	1	$= 2 - 1$
2	4	3	$= 4 - 1$
3	6	5	$= 6 - 1$
4	8	7	$= 8 - 1$
⋮	⋮	⋮	⋮
n	$2n$	$2n - 1$	$2n - 1$

Each odd number is its matching even number − 1

Square numbers

nth square number is n^2

Place number	Square number	Working
1	1	$= 1 \times 1 = 1^2$
2	4	$= 2 \times 2 = 2^2$
3	9	$= 3 \times 3 = 3^2$
4	16	$= 4 \times 4 = 4^2$
⋮	⋮	⋮
n	n^2	$= n \times n = n^2$

Multiply place number by itself, i.e. square it

Cubic numbers

nth cubic number is n^3

Place number	Cubic number	Working
1	1	$= 1 \times 1 \times 1 = 1^3$
2	8	$= 2 \times 2 \times 2 = 2^3$
3	27	$= 3 \times 3 \times 3 = 3^3$
4	64	$= 4 \times 4 \times 4 = 4^3$
⋮	⋮	⋮
n	n^3	$= n \times n \times n = n^3$

Cube each place number

You can try to work out the rule for any number sequence. The way the sequence is built up can give you a clue to the rule.

Question

(a) Write down the next three numbers in this sequence:
8, 13, 18, 23, 28, ...

Show how you worked them out.

(b) Work out a rule for the nth number in the sequence. Check your rule for the three numbers you found in (a).

Answer

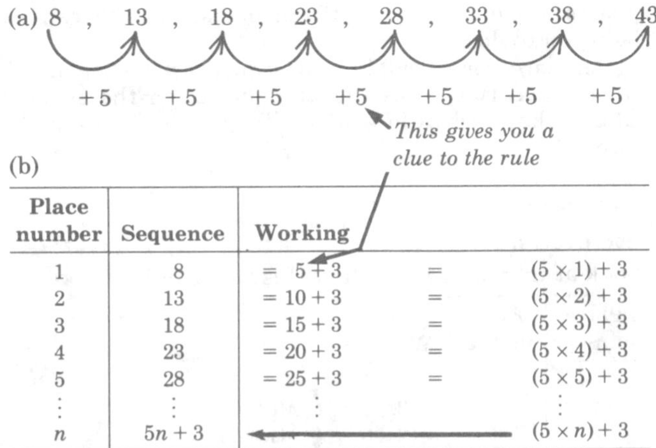

(b)

Place number	Sequence	Working		
1	8	= 5 + 3	=	(5 × 1) + 3
2	13	= 10 + 3	=	(5 × 2) + 3
3	18	= 15 + 3	=	(5 × 3) + 3
4	23	= 20 + 3	=	(5 × 4) + 3
5	28	= 25 + 3	=	(5 × 5) + 3
⋮	⋮	⋮		⋮
n	$5n + 3$	←		$(5 \times n) + 3$

So the nth number in the sequence is $5n + 3$.

Check 6th number → (5 × 6) + 3 = 30 + 3 = 33✓
7th number → (5 × 7) + 3 = 35 + 3 = 38✓
8th number → (5 × 8) + 3 = 40 + 3 = 43✓

COORDINATE PATTERNS

Coordinates are an ordered pair of numbers. They give the position of a point using a grid, axes and an origin. For example, the coordinates of Q are: (5, 2)

across 5 *up 2*

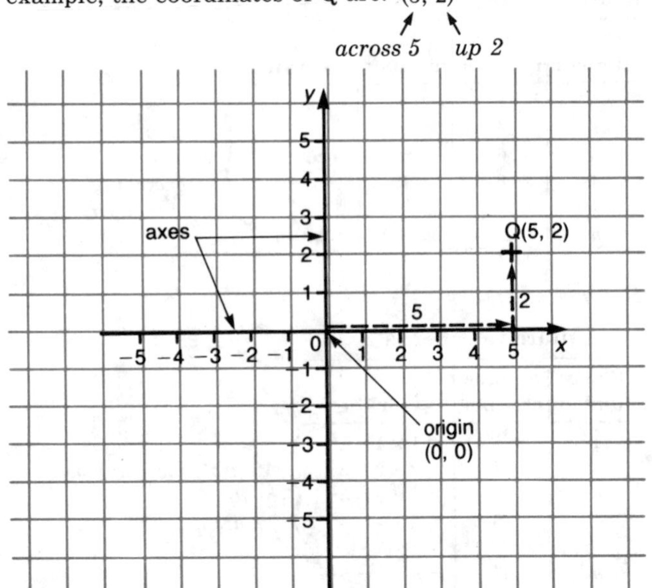

The coordinates of any point P are: (x, y)

x-coordinate *y-coordinate*

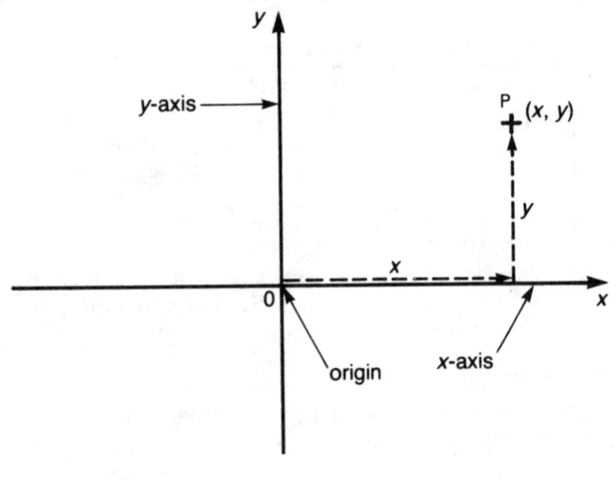

The first number is *always* 'across'. The 'across' axis is the x-axis. So the first number is called the **x-coordinate**.

The second number is *always* 'up or down'. The 'up and down' axis is the y-axis. So the second number is called the **y-coordinate**.

In a set of points there may be the same **relationship** (connection) between the x-coordinate and the y-coordinate in each point. If there is a **coordinate pattern**, then you can try to write a **rule** to show the pattern. Look for a rule that shows how to get the y-coordinate from the x-coordinate if you can.

For example, in these points:

A(−3, −3), B(−1, −1), C(0, 0), D(2, 2), E(5, 5),
equal equal equal equal equal

the y-coordinate is equal to the x-coordinate.

Using letters the rule is:

$y = x$

Points with a coordinate pattern usually make a pattern on the grid too.

For example, points A, B, C, D and E lie in a straight line on the grid.

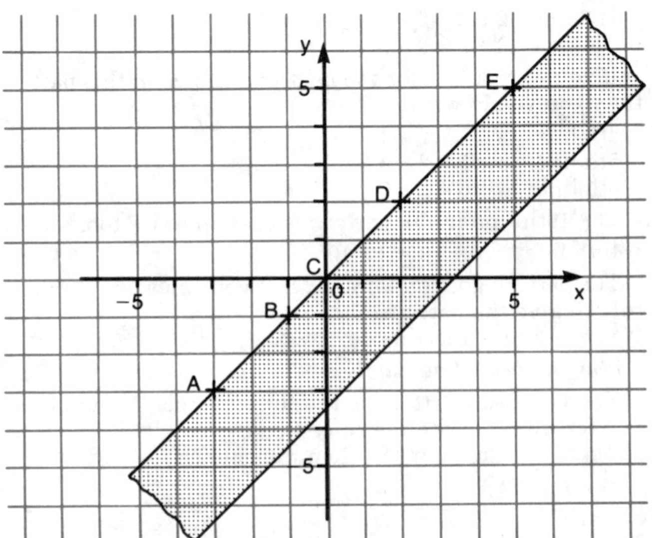

They make a **linear pattern**. If you draw the line through the points, then all the points on the line obey the coordinate rule:

$y = x$

Check some yourself.

This rule is called the **equation** of the line.

It is often easier to spot the coordinate pattern if you list the coordinates in a table.

Question

These points lie on three lines:

line ① (0, 3) (−1, 3) (8, 3) (−6, 3) (2, 3)

line ② (5, 1) (5, 7) (5, 0) (5, −2) (5, −3)

line ③ (3, 7) (−1, 11) (10, 0) (12, −2) (6, 4)

Look for a coordinate pattern for each line.

(a) Here are the coordinates of some more points.
(1, 3), (2, 2), (0, 10), (5, 2), (2, 8), (5, −5), (7, 8), (3, 3), (5, 5), (9, 8), (7, 3), (6, 2), (−4, 14), (5, 3)
Without plotting these points, predict:
(i) which points are on line ①,
(ii) which points are on line ②,
(iii) which points are on line ③,

(iv) which points are not on any of these lines.
Some points may be on more than one line.

(b) Write down a rule using x and y for the points on each line.

Answer

Points given on line (1)

x	y
0	3
−1	3
8	3
−6	3
2	3

y-coordinate is always 3

Points given on line (2)

x	y
5	1
5	7
5	0
5	−2
5	−3

x-coordinate is always 5

Points given on line (3)

x	y	
3	7	◀ *3 + 7 = 10*
−1	11	◀ *−1 + 11 = 10*
10	0	◀ *10 + 0 = 10*
12	−2	◀ *12 + −2 = 10*
6	4	◀ *6 + 4 = 10*

x- and y-coordinates always add up to 10

(a) Predictions:

(i) on line (1) : (1, 3), (3, 3), (7, 3), (5, 3)
y-coordinate is 3

(ii) on line (2) : (5, 2), (5, −5), (5, 5), (5, 3)
x-coordinate is 5

(iii) on line (3) : (0, 10), (2, 8), (5, 5), (7, 3), (−4, 14)
0 + 10 = 10, 2 + 8 = 10, 5 + 5 = 10, 7 + 3 = 10, −4 + 14 = 10

(iv) not on any of these lines: (2, 2), (7, 8), (9, 8), (6, 2)

(b) For line (1) : y-coordinate is 3
or $y = 3$

For line (2) : x-coordinate is 5
or $x = 5$

For line (3) : x- and y-coordinates add up to 10
or $x + y = 10$

Not all coordinate patterns give a linear pattern on a grid. Many of them give a **curved pattern**.

(−3, 9) (−1, 1) (0, 0) (2, 4) (3, 9)

The y-coordinate is the x-coordinate squared. So the rule is:

$y = x^2$

On a grid this gives a curve called a *parabola*.

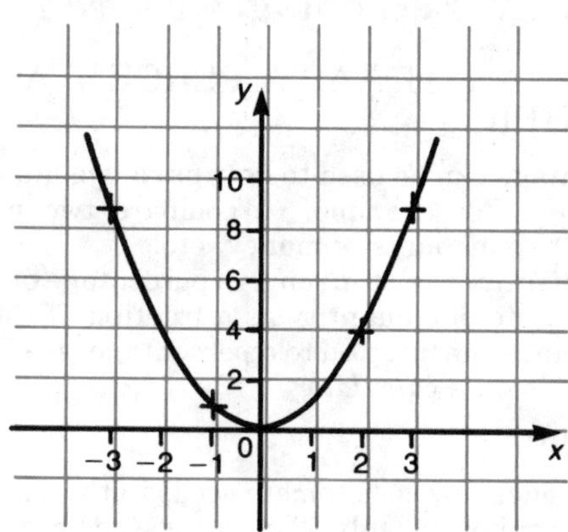

2.5 Fractions: four rules

ADDITION AND SUBTRACTION

You can only **add** or **subtract** fractions when their **denominators** (bottom numbers) are the same. The result is a fraction with the same denominator.

For example,

$\frac{2}{7} + \frac{3}{7} = \frac{5}{7}$

or 2 sevenths + 3 sevenths = 5 sevenths

When the denominators are *different*, use **equivalent fractions** to rewrite the fractions with the same denominators. Sets of equivalent fractions can be used to do this. A quicker way is to find the **lowest common multiple** (see Unit 2.1) of the denominators. This gives you the denominator of the equivalent fractions you need. When you get an answer, always:

(a) cancel if you can,

(b) change any improper fractions to mixed numbers.

Question

Express each of these as a single fraction.

(a) $\frac{3}{5} + \frac{2}{3}$ (b) $\frac{8}{9} - \frac{4}{7}$

Answer

(a) The LCM of 5 and 3 is 15.

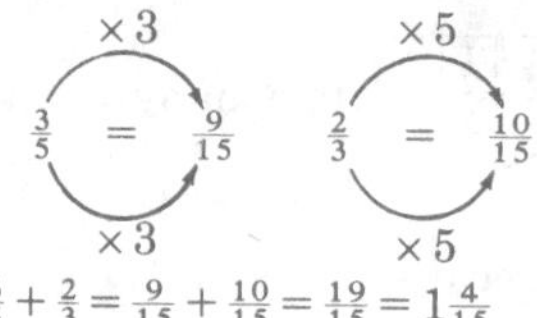

$\frac{3}{5} + \frac{2}{3} = \frac{9}{15} + \frac{10}{15} = \frac{19}{15} = 1\frac{4}{15}$

(b) The LCM of 9 and 7 is 63.

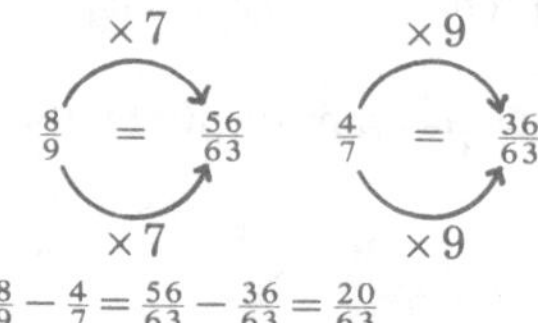

$\frac{8}{9} - \frac{4}{7} = \frac{56}{63} - \frac{36}{63} = \frac{20}{63}$

MULTIPLICATION

To **multiply** two fractions, multiply their numerators and multiply their denominators. For example,

$$\frac{2}{3} \times \frac{4}{5} = \frac{2 \times 4}{3 \times 5} = \frac{8}{15}$$

(Look at the diagram to see a 'picture' of this.)

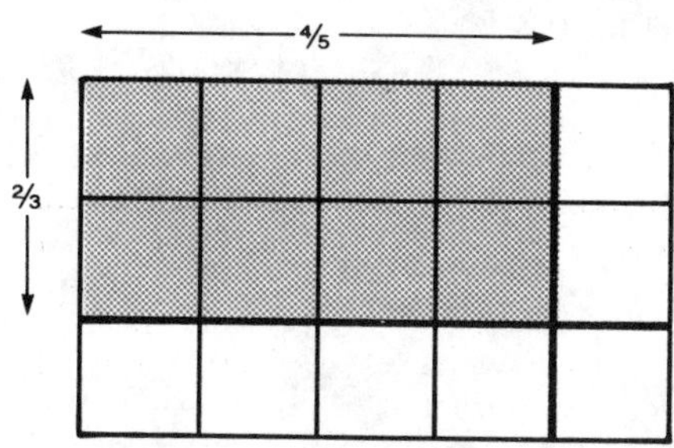

8/15 shaded

Always **cancel** if you can before multiplying. So look for factors which are common to the numerator and denominator.

Question

Work these out.

(a) $\frac{3}{8} \times \frac{4}{5}$ (b) $\frac{14}{15} \times \frac{12}{35}$

Answer

(a) $\frac{3}{8} \times \frac{4}{5} = \frac{3}{\cancel{8}_2} \times \frac{\cancel{4}^1}{5} = \frac{3 \times 1}{2 \times 5} = \frac{3}{10}$

4 and 8 are both divided by 4

(b) $\frac{14}{15} \times \frac{12}{35} = \frac{{}^2\cancel{14}}{{}_5\cancel{15}} \times \frac{\cancel{12}^4}{\cancel{35}_5} = \frac{2 \times 4}{5 \times 5} = \frac{8}{25}$

14 and 35 are both divided by 7
15 and 12 are both divided by 3

Change any **mixed numbers** to improper fractions before multiplying.

Question

Evaluate $2\frac{5}{8} \times \frac{5}{7}$

Answer

	$2\frac{5}{8} \times \frac{5}{7}$
Change $2\frac{5}{8}$ to an improper fraction	$= \frac{21}{8} \times \frac{5}{7}$
Divide 7 and 21 by 7	$= \frac{{}^{3}\not{21}}{8} \times \frac{5}{\not{7}_{1}}$
Multiply top and bottom	$= \frac{15}{8}$
Change to a mixed number	$= 1\frac{7}{8}$

DIVISION

Dividing by a number and **multiplying by its inverse** give the same answer. For example,

$6 \div \frac{1}{2} = 12$ [$\frac{1}{2}$ $\frac{1}{2}$ $\frac{1}{2}$ $\frac{1}{2}$ $\frac{1}{2}$ $\frac{1}{2}$ / $\frac{1}{2}$ $\frac{1}{2}$ $\frac{1}{2}$ $\frac{1}{2}$ $\frac{1}{2}$ $\frac{1}{2}$] 'How many $\frac{1}{2}$s in 6?'

$6 \times 2 = 12$

The inverse of $\frac{1}{2}$ is $\frac{2}{1}$ (or 2) because
$\frac{1}{2} \times \frac{2}{1} = 1$ (see Unit 2.1).

You can use this fact to change *any* division into a multiplication.

To **divide by a fraction** (such as $\frac{a}{b}$), multiply by its inverse (i.e. $\frac{b}{a}$).

Question

Divide $\frac{2}{5}$ by $\frac{3}{4}$.

Answer

	$\frac{2}{5} \div \frac{3}{4}$
The inverse of $\frac{3}{4}$ is $\frac{4}{3}$	
Change $\div$ to $\times$ by inverse	$= \frac{2}{5} \times \frac{4}{3}$
Multiply top and bottom	$= \frac{8}{15}$

If a **mixed number** is involved, then change it to an improper fraction first.

Question

Divide $3\frac{1}{7}$ by $\frac{2}{5}$.

Answer

	$3\frac{1}{7} \div \frac{2}{5}$
Change $3\frac{1}{7}$ to an improper fraction	$= \frac{22}{7} \div \frac{2}{5}$
The inverse of $\frac{2}{5}$ is $\frac{5}{2}$	
Change $\div$ to $\times$ by inverse	$= \frac{22}{7} \times \frac{5}{2}$
Cancel by 2	$= \frac{{}^{11}\not{22}}{7} \times \frac{5}{\not{2}_{1}}$
Multiply top and bottom	$= \frac{55}{7}$
Change to a mixed number	$= 7\frac{6}{7}$

2.6 Fractions, decimals and percentages

FRACTIONS TO DECIMALS

To change a fraction to a decimal, divide the top number by the bottom number (see Unit 1.13). For example,

$\frac{5}{8} = 5 \div 8$ [C] [C] [5] [÷] [8] [=]
$= 0.625$

At Level 1 all the fractions give **terminating decimals.** Each division works out exactly and the decimal comes to an end (terminates). Not all fractions give terminating decimals. Some decimals continue without end.
These are called **non-terminating decimals.**

Some fractions give **recurring** or **repeating decimals.** In a recurring decimal a digit or group of digits is repeated for ever. For example,

$\frac{1}{3} = 0.333\,333\,333\ldots$ the 3s repeat for ever.
$\frac{3}{11} = 0.272\,727\,272\,7\ldots$ the 27s repeat for ever.
$\frac{4}{7} = 0.571\,428\,571\,428\ldots$ the 571428s repeat for ever.

A short way to write these is:

$\frac{1}{3} = 0.\dot{3}$
$\frac{3}{11} = 0.\dot{2}\dot{7}$
$\frac{4}{7} = 0.\dot{5}71\,42\dot{8}$

The dots show the repeating pattern. A dot is placed over the first and last digit of the group of repeating digits.

Question

Write these fractions in recurring decimal form.
(a) $\frac{2}{3}$ (b) $\frac{5}{6}$ (c) $\frac{5}{22}$ (d) $\frac{21}{37}$ (e) $\frac{3}{7}$

Answer

(a) $\frac{2}{3} = 2 \div 3 = 0.666\,666\,666\ldots = 0.\dot{6}$
(b) $\frac{5}{6} = 5 \div 6 = 0.833\,333\,333\ldots = 0.8\dot{3}$
(c) $\frac{5}{22} = 5 \div 22 = 0.227\,272\,727\ldots = 0.2\dot{2}\dot{7}$
(d) $\frac{21}{37} = 21 \div 37 = 0.567\,567\,567\ldots = 0.\dot{5}6\dot{7}$
(e) $\frac{3}{7} = 3 \div 7 = 0.428\,571\,428\ldots = 0.\dot{4}28\,57\dot{1}$

FRACTIONS AND DECIMALS TO AND FROM PERCENTAGES

A percentage gives a number 'out of 100'.
To **change a percentage to a fraction or decimal**, divide the number by 100.
For example, $7\% = \frac{7}{100}$ or $7 \div 100 = 0.07$.
To **change a fraction or decimal to a percentage**, multiply it by 100%.
For example, $0.35 = 0.35 \times 100\% = 35\%$.

Question

Change these to percentages correct to 1 d.p.
(a) $\frac{2}{3}$ (b) $\frac{5}{11}$ (c) $\frac{7}{27}$

Answer

[C]

(a) $\frac{2}{3} = \frac{2}{3} \times 100\% = 66.666\ldots\%$
$= 66.7\%$ (to 1 d.p.)
(b) $\frac{5}{11} = \frac{5}{11} \times 100\% = 45.4545\ldots\%$
$= 45.5\%$ (to 1 d.p.)
(c) $\frac{7}{27} = \frac{7}{27} \times 100\% = 25.925\,92\ldots\%$
$= 25.9\%$ (to 1 d.p.)

2.7 Percentages 2

ONE QUANTITY AS A PERCENTAGE OF ANOTHER

A percentage can be used to **compare** two quantities of the same kind. For example, to compare two numbers, two lengths, two amounts of money, etc.

One quantity can be given as a percentage of the other. To do this, write one quantity as a fraction of the other first. Then change the fraction to a percentage (see Unit 2.6). You can do this on a *calculator*.

Question

A gardener sowed 48 tomato seeds in the same conditions in a greenhouse. Only 39 of these seeds grew into plants. What percentage of the tomato seeds sown in the greenhouse grew into plants?

Answer

As a fraction: $\frac{39}{48}$
As a percentage: $\frac{39}{48} \times 100\% = 81.25\%$ [C]
So 81.25% of the sown seeds grew into plants.

Calculator work

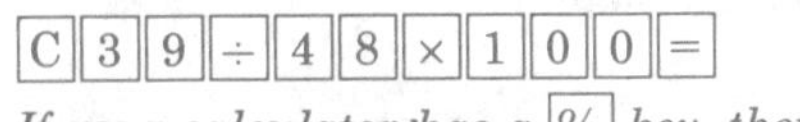

If your calculator has a [%] *key, then try this:*

[C] [3] [9] [÷] [4] [8] [%]

On some calculators this gives the same answer.

Percentages are often used to compare several sets of quantities; for example, to compare marks from different tests, results from different parts of a survey, etc.

Question

At the end of term Jane got 14 marks out of 20 in the mathematics test and 56 marks out of 70 in the science test. For which test did Jane get the higher percentage mark?

Answer

Mathematics

As a fraction: $\frac{14}{20}$

As a percentage: $\frac{14}{20} \times 100\%$
$= 70\%$

C 1 4 ÷ 2 0 × 1 0 0 =

or try:

C 1 4 ÷ 2 0 %

Science

As a fraction: $\frac{56}{70}$

As a percentage: $\frac{56}{70} \times 100\%$
$= 80\%$

C 5 6 ÷ 7 0 × 1 0 0 =

or try:

C 5 6 ÷ 7 0 %

So Jane got a higher percentage mark in the Science test.

When comparing quantities any units of measure **must** be the same. If the quantities are given in different units, then change them to the *same* unit before doing the calculation.

Question

At the beginning of the year Winston's height was 1.24 metres. During the year he grew 6 cm. What was the percentage increase in Winston's height?
Give your answer to the nearest 1%.

Answer

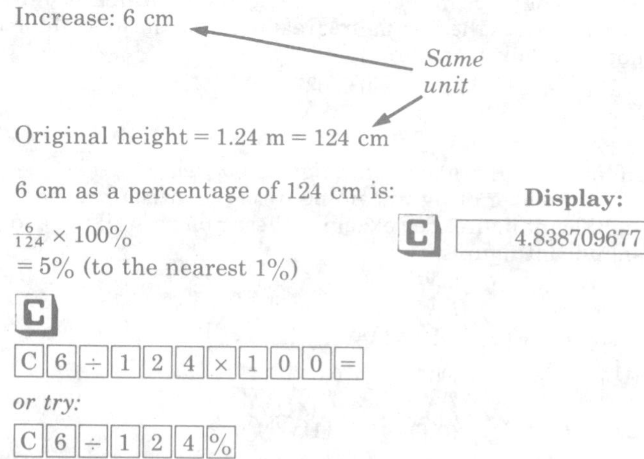

6 cm as a percentage of 124 cm is:

$\frac{6}{124} \times 100\%$
$= 5\%$ (to the nearest 1%)

Display: 4.838709677

C 6 ÷ 1 2 4 × 1 0 0 =

or try:

C 6 ÷ 1 2 4 %

PERCENTAGE CHANGES

The **change** (increase or decrease) in a quantity is often described as a percentage; for example, profit and loss, price rises and discounts, etc.

To **increase** a quantity by a percentage, you can work out the actual increase and then add it to the original quantity to find the actual new quantity.

You can also work out the new quantity as a percentage of the original quantity and then find the actual new quantity. For example, if you start with a certain amount (100%) and increase it by $x\%$, then you end up with $(100 + x)\%$ of the original amount.

You can use this way because they are all percentages of the original amount. (**Remember** your answer is the new quantity *after* the increase *not* the increase itself.)

Question

Sarah earns £120 a week. She receives a pay rise of 7%. How much does she earn each week after the pay rise?

Answer

Sarah's wage is 100%.
Sarah's new wage = 100% + 7% = 107%
New wage = 107% of £120
= £128.40

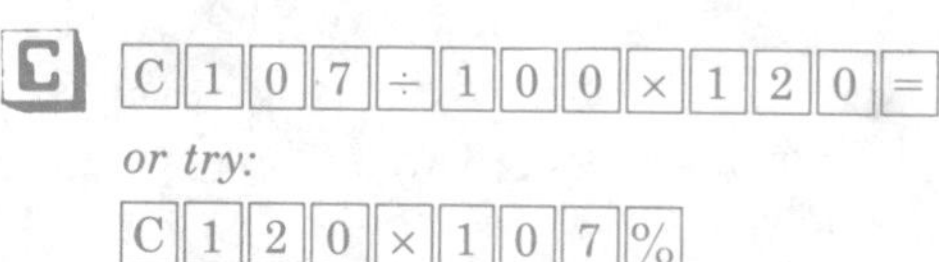

C 1 0 7 ÷ 1 0 0 × 1 2 0 =

or try:

C 1 2 0 × 1 0 7 %

The new quantity after a **decrease** can be worked out in a similar way but the decrease is **subtracted**. For example, if you start with a certain amount (100%) and decrease it by $x\%$, then you end up with $(100 - x)\%$ of the original amount. (**Remember** your answer is the new quantity *after* the decrease, not the decrease itself.)

Question

A car journey uses 12.5 litres of petrol. A new additive reduces consumption by 4%. How much of the new type of petrol would be needed for the same journey?

Answer

Original amount of petrol is 100%.
New amount is 100% − 4% = 96%
96% of 12.5 litres = 12 litres
So 12 litres of new petrol are needed.

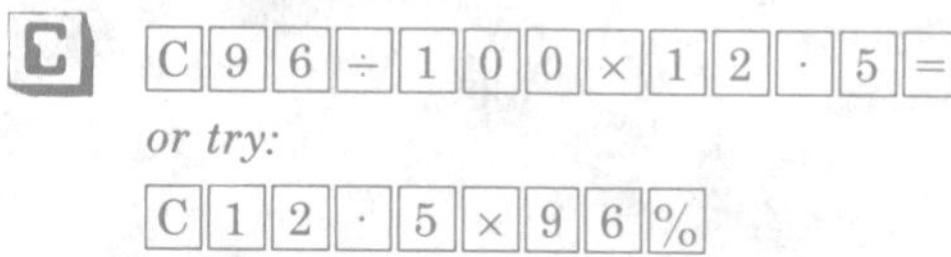

C 9 6 ÷ 1 0 0 × 1 2 · 5 =

or try:

C 1 2 · 5 × 9 6 %

If you know a percentage change and its result, i.e. the new quantity, then you can find the original quantity.
The new quantity will be:

$(100 + x)\%$ of the original after an *increase*,
$(100 - x)\%$ of the original after a *decrease*.

You can use these to find 1% and then 100% (the whole) of the original.

Question

A wine merchant sells a case of wine for £72 and makes a profit of 20%. How much did he pay for the wine?

Answer

If the cost price is 100%
then the selling price is 100% + 20% = 120%.
So 120% represents the selling price of £72.

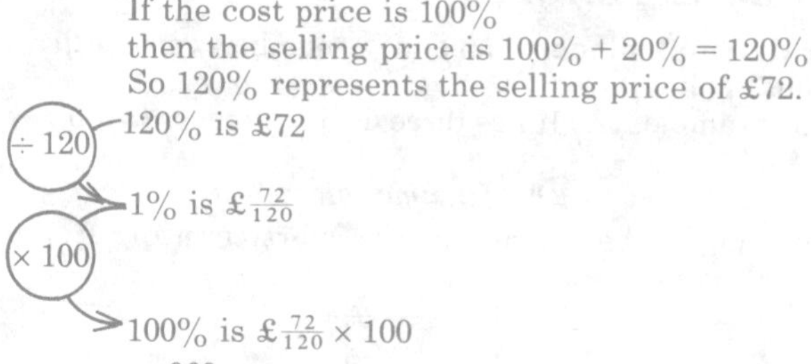

120% is £72

1% is £$\frac{72}{120}$

100% is £$\frac{72}{120} \times 100$
= £60

C 7 2 ÷ 1 2 0 × 1 0 0 =

So the cost price of the wine was £60.

It is important to realize that an increase of $x\%$ is **not** 'cancelled' by a decrease of $x\%$. This is because percentage change is always found as a *percentage of the original quantity*. The following example illustrates this.

Question

A dealer bought a car for £3000 and sold it at a profit of 25%. The buyer then had to sell it back to the dealer at a loss of 25%. How much did the buyer get for the car?

Answer

For the dealer:

Cost price = £3000

Selling price = (100% + 25%) of £3000
= 125% of £3000
= £3750

For the buyer:

Cost price = £3750

Selling price = (100% − 25%) of £3750
= 75% of £3750
= £2812.50

C

PERCENTAGE ERROR

The percentage error of a given measurement may be worked out using:

$$\text{percentage error} = \frac{\text{error}}{\text{true measurement}} \times 100\%$$

The error and measurement must be in the same unit.

Question

The error in weighing a 2.5 kg mass is 10 g. What is the percentage error?

Answer

Error = 10 g ← *Same unit*

True measurement = 2.5 kg = 2500 g

$$\text{Percentage error} = \frac{10\text{ g}}{2500\text{ g}} \times 100\% = 0.4\%$$

C

2.8 Approximation

Rounding off is a simple way to find **approximate** values. You should be able to round off values to the nearest 1, 10, 100, 1000, ... Values can also be rounded off to a stated number of *decimal places* or *significant figures*.

Answers, especially when found on a calculator, may have more decimal places or figures than is sensible. Examination questions will often tell you the number of decimal places or significant figures to give in an answer. Sometimes you will have to decide what size of an answer is sensible.

DECIMAL PLACES

The **decimal places** (d.p.) in a number come *after* the decimal point.

For example, 72.591 has three decimal places (3 d.p.).

①②③ *decimal places*

To number the decimal places, start counting from the decimal point.

·	t	h	th
·			
	①	②	③

The digit in the *1st* decimal place is *tenths*,
in the *2nd* decimal place is *hundredths*,
in the *3rd* decimal place is *thousandths*,

and so on ...

The rules used to correct a number to a stated number of decimal places are like those used to round whole numbers.

To correct a number:
to 1 d.p., look at the 2nd d.p.,
to 2 d.p., look at the 3rd d.p.,
to 3 d.p., look at the 4th d.p.,

and so on ...

If the digit (figure) you look at is:

less than 5 – forget it and round down,
5 or more – round up by adding 1 to the figure in front of it.

Question

Correct 27.0475 to:

(a) 1 d.p. (b) 2 d.p. (c) 3 d.p.

Answer

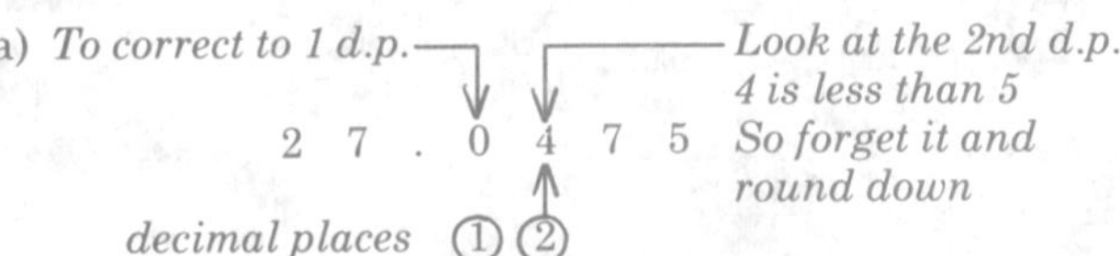

So 27.0475 is 27.0 (correct to 1 d.p.)

(b) *To correct to 2 d.p.* — *Look at the 3rd d.p. 7 is more than 5 So round up by adding 1 to 4*

2 7 . 0 4 7 5

decimal places ① ② ③

So 27.0475 is 27.05 (correct to 2 d.p.)

(c) *To correct to 3 d.p.* — *Look at the 4th d.p. It is 5 So round up by adding 1 to 7*

2 7 . 0 4 7 5

decimal places ① ② ③ ④

So 27.0475 is 27.048 (correct to 3 d.p.)

SIGNIFICANT FIGURES

The value of a figure (digit) in a number depends upon its position or place in the number. The first **significant figure** in a number is the first figure (reading from the left) which is not zero. For example,

251	0.0152	0.00032
1st s.f. (2)	1st s.f. (1)	1st s.f. (3)

s.f. or sig. fig. are short for *significant figures*.

The number of significant figures is counted *from* the first significant figure. For example, these numbers all have four significant figures.

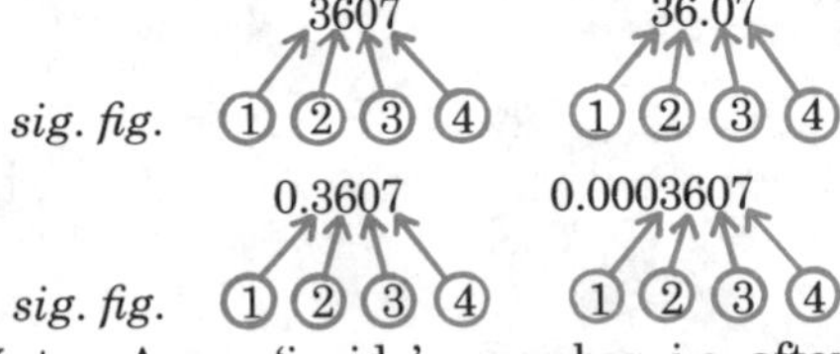

Note A zero 'inside' a number, i.e. after the 1st significant figure, counts as a significant figure.

Numbers can be corrected to a given number of significant figures in a similar way to that used for decimal places.

To correct a number:
to 1 s.f., look at the 2nd s.f.,
to 2 s.f., look at the 3rd s.f.,
to 3 s.f., look at the 4th s.f.,

and so on ...

If the figure (digit) you look at is:

less than 5 – forget it and round down,
5 or more – round up by adding 1 to the figure in front of it.

Question

Correct: (a) 18.073 to 3 s.f. (b) 0.3651 to 2 s.f.
(c) 0.002 179 to 1 s.f.

Answer

(a) 1 8 . 0 7 3 — sig. fig. ① ② ③ ④

To correct to 3 s.f. look at the 4th s.f. 7 is more than 5 So round up by adding 1 to 0

So 18.073 is 18.1 (to 3 s.f.)

(b) 0 . 3 6 5 1 — sig. fig. ① ② ③

To correct to 2 s.f. look at the 3rd s.f. It is 5 So round up by adding 1 to 6

So 0.3651 is 0.37 (to 2 s.f.)

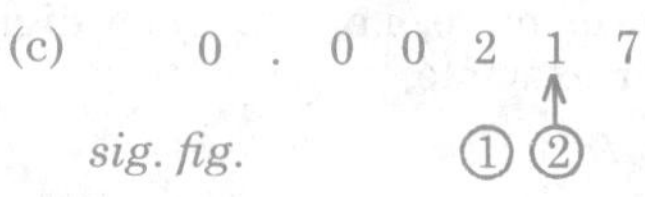

(c) 0 . 0 0 2 1 7 9 — sig. fig. ① ②

To correct to 1 s.f. look at the 2nd s.f. 1 is less than 5 So forget it and round down

So 0.002 179 is 0.002 (to 1 s.f.)

Sometimes you will have to fill in some 'places' with zero(s) to keep the place value of each figure correct.

Question

Correct the number 187 540 to
(a) 4 s.f. (b) 3 s.f. (c) 2 s.f. (d) 1 s.f.

Answer

(a) 1 8 7 5 4 0 is 187 500 (to 4 s.f.)
sig. fig. ① ② ③ ④ ⑤

(b) 1 8 7 5 4 0 is 188 000 (to 3 s.f.)
sig. fig. ① ② ③ ④

(c) 1 8 7 5 4 0 is 190 000 (to 2 s.f.)
sig. fig. ① ② ③

(d) 1 8 7 5 4 0 is 200 000 (to 1 s.f.)
sig. fig. ① ②

APPROXIMATE ANSWERS

Approximate answers are often all you need when working out real life problems. They can also be used to check answers to see if they are sensible.

The numbers used in a calculation can be rounded off to the nearest 1, 10, 100, ... or to a number of decimal places or significant figures. These rounded numbers can then be used in the calculation to get an approximate answer.

Question

Correct each number to 1 significant figure to find an approximate answer to

$$\frac{0.63 \times 7.8}{0.036}$$

Answer

$$\frac{0.63 \times 7.8}{0.036} \approx \frac{0.6 \times 8}{0.04} = 120$$

LIMITS OF ACCURACY

When a quantity is measured, the measurement cannot be exact. It is always an approximation. This means that there is always an **error** in any measurement.

A measurement should be made correct to the most suitable unit. This depends on the quantity being measured and the degree of accuracy of the measuring instrument used. For example, using this ruler it is only possible to measure lengths 'to the nearest centimetre'.

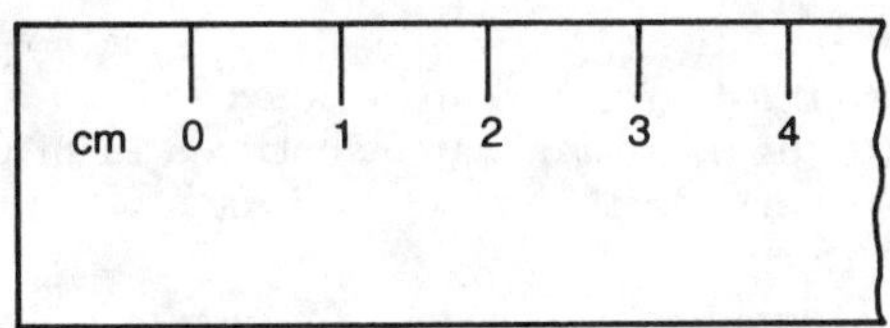

The length of each of these pencils would be given as 8 cm (to the nearest cm).

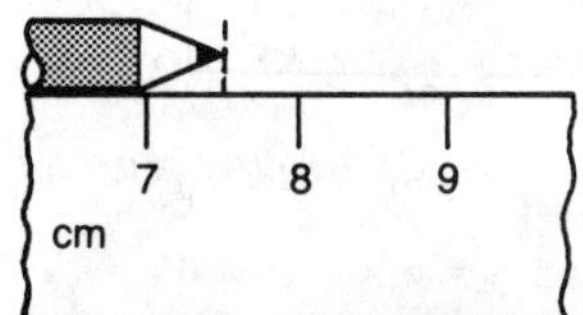

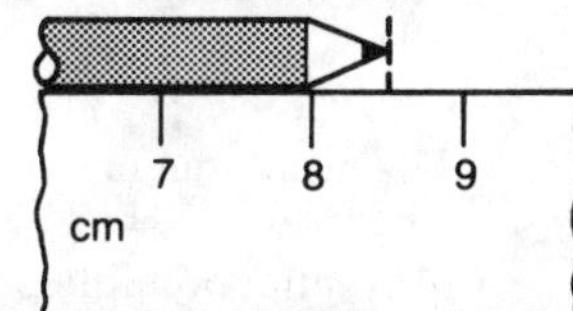

If a length is given as 8 cm (to the nearest cm), then it may actually be only 7.5 cm long or it could be almost 8.5 cm long. So its true length can be anywhere between 7.5 cm and 8.5 cm.

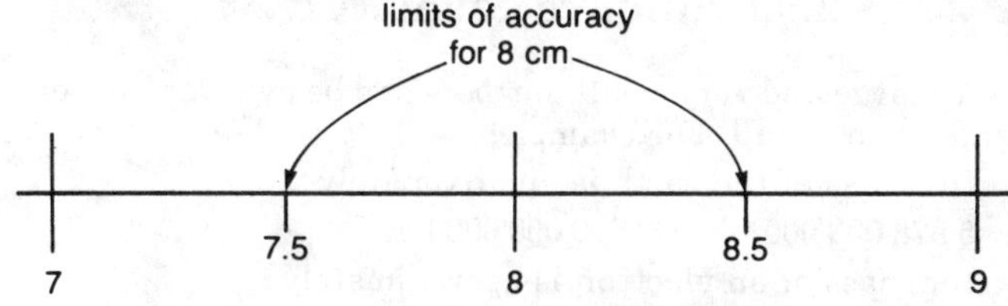

These are called the **limits of accuracy** for the measurement 8 cm. The error is 0.5 cm, i.e. the given measurement could be 0.5 cm too large or 0.5 cm too small.

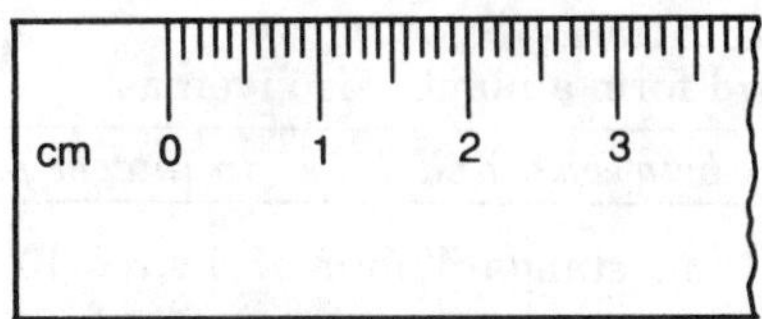

Using this ruler, it is possible to measure lengths 'to the nearest 0.1 cm' (i.e. mm).

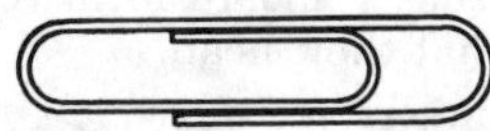

If the length of a paperclip is given as 3.2 cm (to the nearest 0.1 cm), then its true length can be anywhere between 3.15 cm and 3.25 cm. These are the limits of accuracy for the measurement 3.2 cm. The error is 0.05 cm.

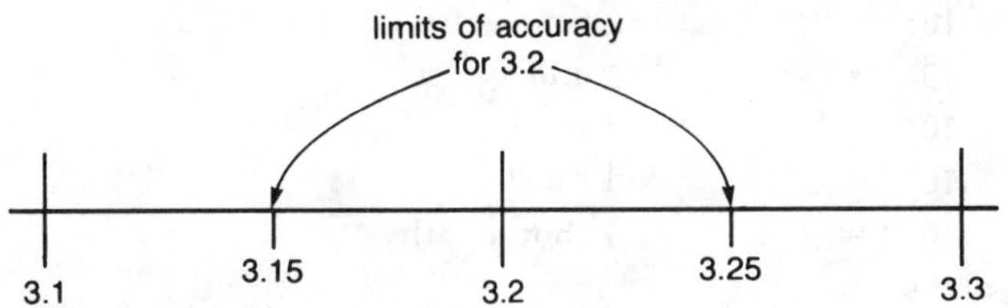

Question

A rectangular plot of land has its sides measured to the nearest metre. The measurements recorded are 6 m and 2 m. Find:

(a) the limits of accuracy of each measurement,
(b) the maximum possible value for the area of the plot,
(c) the minimum possible value for the perimeter of the plot.

Answer

(a) 6 m (to the nearest m) can lie between 5.5 m and 6.5 m. 2 m (to the nearest m) can lie between 1.5 m and 2.5 m. These are the limits of accuracy for each measurement.

(b) The maximum (largest) area of the plot is given when the sides are 6.5 m and 2.5 m.
Maximum possible area
$= 6.5\text{ m} \times 2.5\text{ m}$
$= 16.25\text{ m}^2$

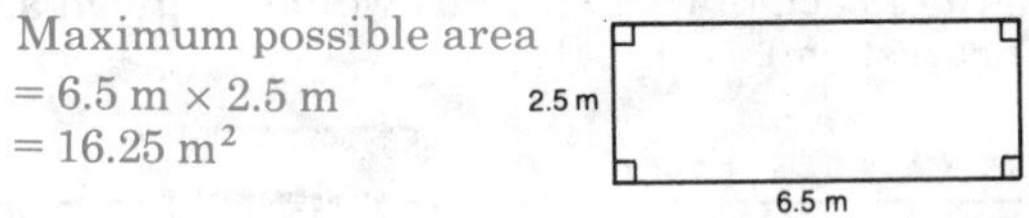

(c) The minimum (smallest) perimeter of the plot is given when the sides are 5.5 m and 1.5 m.
Minimum possible perimeter $= 2(5.5\text{ m} + 1.5\text{ m})$
$= 2(7\text{ m})$
$= 14\text{ m}$

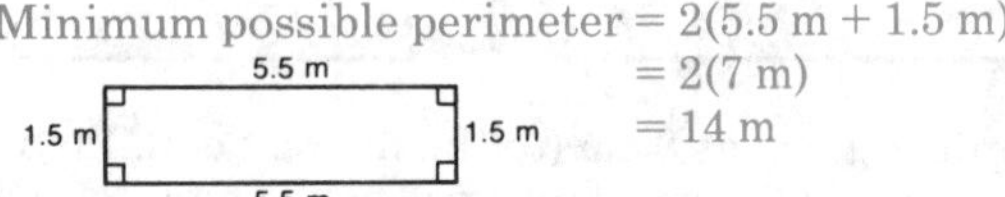

2.9 Standard form

Very large and very small numbers can be awkward to read and write in full. For example,
the mass of the earth is approximately
5 978 000 000 000 000 000 000 000 kg,
the mass of an electron is approximately
0.000 000 000 000 000 000 000 000 000 000 911 kg.

Standard form (or **standard index form**) is a concise way to give such numbers. For example, in standard form:
the earth's mass $\approx 5.978 \times 10^{24}$ kg
electron's mass $\approx 9.11 \times 10^{-31}$ kg

Standard form is often used in science, so it is also called **scientific notation**.

In standard form a number is given as:

(a number between 1 and 10) $\times$ *(an integer power of 10)*

So $a \times 10^n$ is in standard form if $1 \leqslant a < 10$ and n is an integer. For example,
3.21×10^7 and 1.6×10^{-3} are in standard form.
32.1×10^6 and 0.16×10^{-2} are *not* in standard form.

These numbers are *not* between 1 and 10.

To understand and use standard form you must know the powers of 10 and what they mean.
Here are some reminders.

10^6	$= 1\,000\,000$	1 million
10^5	$= 100\,000$	1 hundred thousand
10^4	$= 10\,000$	1 ten thousand
10^3	$= 1000$	1 thousand
10^2	$= 100$	1 hundred
10^1	$= 10$	1 ten
10^0	$= 1$	1 unit
10^{-1}	$= \frac{1}{10}$	1 tenth
10^{-2}	$= \frac{1}{100}$	1 hundredth
10^{-3}	$= \frac{1}{1000}$	1 thousandth

and so on ...

You must also be able to multiply and divide by powers of 10.

Remember

Multiplying by a *positive* power of 10, i.e. 10^n, moves each digit n places to the *left*. For example,

$3.251 \times 10^2 = 325.1$

			3	2	5	1
3	2	5	1			

2 places to the left

Multiplying by a *negative* power of 10, i.e. 10^{-n}, moves each digit n places to the *right*.

This is the same as dividing by a positive power of 10. For example,

3.251×10^{-2}
or $\Bigg\} = 0.032\,51$
$3.251 \div 10^2$

3	2	5	1		
0	0	3	2	5	1

2 places to the right

Dividing by a *negative* power of 10, i.e. 10^{-n}, is the same as multiplying by a positive power of 10, i.e. 10^n. Each digit moves n places to the *left*. For example,
$3.251 \div 10^{-2}$
$= 3.251 \times 10^2$
$= 325.1$

CHANGING NUMBERS TO STANDARD FORM

To **change** a number to standard form, first write down the number between 1 and 10 and work out the power of 10. A number *greater than 1* always has a **positive power** of 10 in standard form.

Question

Jupiter is about 778 million miles from the sun. Write this distance in standard form.

Answer

778 million $= 778\,000\,000$
$= 7.78 \times 100\,000\,000$
$= 7.78 \times 10^8$

Move 8 places
7|7 8 0 0 0 0 0 0|

So 778 million miles is 7.78×10^8 miles.

A number *smaller than 1* always has a **negative power** of 10 in standard form.

Question

The mass of a pygmy shrew is approximately 0.0025 kg. Write this mass in standard form.

Answer

$0.0025 = 2.5 \div 1000$
$= 2.5 \div 10^3$
$= 2.5 \times 10^{-3}$

Move 3 places
0|0 0 2|5

So 0.0025 kg is 2.5×10^{-3} kg.

A place value table can be used to check numbers in standard form. For example,

Place value table

	10^8	10^7	10^6	10^5	10^4	10^3	10^2	10^1	10^0
7.78×10^8 $= 778\,000\,000$	**7**	7	8	0	0	0	0	0	0

	10^0	10^{-1}	10^{-2}	10^{-3}	10^{-4}
2.5×10^{-3} $= 0.0025$	0	0	0	**2**	5

CHANGING STANDARD FORM TO ORDINARY NUMBERS

It is important to be able to work out the value of a number given in standard form. You need to be able to write it as an ordinary number.

Question

The radius of Saturn is approximately 6.04×10^7 metres. The diameter of a red blood cell is approximately 7×10^{-6} metres. Write each of these lengths as 'ordinary numbers'.

Answer

Radius of Saturn:
6.04×10^7 m
$= 6.04 \times 10\,000\,000$ m
$= 60\,400\,000$ m

Move 7 places
6·0 4 0 0 0 0 0

Place value table

10^7	10^6	10^5	10^4	10^3	10^2	10^1	10^0
6	0	4	0	0	0	0	0

Diameter of a red blood cell:
7×10^{-6} m
$= 7 \div 10^6$ m
$= 7 \div 1\,000\,000$
$= 0.000\,007$

Move 6 places
0 0 0 0 0 7·

Place value table

10^0	10^{-1}	10^{-2}	10^{-3}	10^{-4}	10^{-5}	10^{-6}
	0	0	0	0	0	7

WITH A CALCULATOR

Some *calculators* will work with numbers in standard form. They are usually called **scientific calculators**. These *calculators* automatically put an answer into standard form if the number has too many digits for its display to show. Sometimes they show very small answers (a thousandth or less) only in standard form.

To show a number in standard form, a *calculator* displays the first number (between 1 and 10) and the index. For example,

2.5×10^{-4} is shown as:

[2.5 −04] or [2.5 E −04]

E stands for *exponent* (another word for power)

To find out if your *calculator* works in standard form, try this calculation on it.

$3\,000\,000 \times 5\,000\,000 =$

After pressing [=], if your display shows [1.5 13] then your *calculator* works in standard form.

This means 1.5×10^{13}

If your *calculator* 'overflows' (it may show 0, or start flashing, or 'lock', or show E for error), then it does *not* work in standard form.

To **enter** a number in standard form, you must use the **exponent key**. This will be marked

[EXP] or [E] or [EE]

Enter Exponent

For example, to enter the number 3.7×10^3,

Press: [C][3][·][7][EXP][3] **Display:** [3.7 03]

Pressing [=] next gives: **Display:** [3700.]

i.e. the 'ordinary number'.

Similarly, to enter 2.9×10^{-4},

Press: [C][2][·][9][EXP][4][+/−] **Display:** [2.9 −04]

Pressing [=] this time usually leaves the number still in standard form. Try it and see what happens.

COMPARING NUMBERS

Numbers given in standard form are easy to **compare**. It is easy to compare the powers of 10 if you know what they mean. The largest number has the highest power of 10. The smallest number has the smallest power of 10.

Question

Put these numbers in order of size, largest first.

3.21×10^5 8.9×10^{-3} 9.65×10^4
6.3×10^9 3.5×10^4 7.62×10^{-1}

Answer

The order is:

largest 6.3×10^9 — *9 is the highest power of 10 here*
3.21×10^5
9.65×10^4 } *Both numbers have the power 4*
3.5×10^4 } *Compare the first numbers: 9.65 is larger than 3.5*
7.62×10^{-1}
smallest 8.9×10^{-3} — *$^-3$ is the smallest power of 10 here*

CALCULATIONS IN STANDARD FORM

Multiplications and divisions are sometimes easier to do in standard form. To do this *without* a calculator you use the laws of indices (see Unit 2.28).

Question

Without a calculator work out:
(a) $(6 \times 10^{-3}) \div (4 \times 10)$ (b) $(3 \times 10^{-4}) \times (4 \times 10^6)$

Answer

(a) $(6 \times 10^{-3}) \div (4 \times 10)$

Group numbers and powers of 10 $= (6 \div 4) \times (10^{-3} \div 10^1)$
Work out divisions $= 1.5 \times 10^{-3-1}$
Use laws of indices $= 1.5 \times 10^{-4}$

(b) $(3 \times 10^{-4}) \times (4 \times 10^6)$

Group numbers and powers of 10 $= (3 \times 4) \times (10^{-4} \times 10^6)$
Work out multiplications $= 12 \times 10^{-4+6}$
Use laws of indices $= 12 \times 10^2$
Put numbers into standard form $= (1.2 \times 10^1) \times 10^2$
Use laws of indices $= 1.2 \times 10^3$

You can use your *calculator* to do calculations in standard form. Just enter the numbers in standard form and press the correct operation keys. The answer you get may not be given in standard form.

Question

In astronomy very large distances are measured in light years. A light year is the distance travelled by light in 1 year ($365\frac{1}{4}$ days).

(a) The speed of light is approximately 2.998×10^8 metres per second. Work out the approximate length of a light year in metres (to 4 s.f.).
(b) The earth is approximately 1.496×10^{11} metres from the sun. How many light years is this? Use your approximate length of a light year to work it out to 4 s.f.

Answer

(a) Distance travelled by light:
in 1 second $\approx 2.998 \times 10^8$ m
in 60 seconds $\approx 2.998 \times 10^8 \times 60$ m

in 60 minutes $\approx 2.998 \times 10^8 \times 60 \times 60$ m
in 24 hours $\approx 2.998 \times 10^8 \times 60 \times 60 \times 24$ m
in $365\frac{1}{4}$ days $\approx 2.998 \times 10^8 \times 60 \times 60 \times 24 \times 365.25$ m

So 1 light year $\approx 9.461 \times 10^{15}$ m (to 4 s.f.) | 9.4609684 15 |

(b) Distance from earth to sun:
$\approx 1.496 \times 10^{11}$ metres
$\approx (1.496 \times 10^{11}) \div (9.461 \times 10^{15})$ light years

$\approx 1.581 \times 10^{-5}$ light years (to 4 s.f.) | 1.5812334 -05 |

2.10 Compound interest

When you leave money in a savings account you are paid interest on that money. If you withdraw only the interest each year, then the interest is called **simple interest** (see Unit 1.21). The **principal** (the money invested) and the **annual interest** will be the same each year.

For **compound interest**, the interest for a year must be left in the savings account and added to that year's principal. So each year the money in the account and the annual interest both increase.

STEP BY STEP CALCULATIONS

Compound interest can be calculated step by step. Work out the interest for a year, then add it to the principal for that year. This gives you the new principal for the next year. Repeat these steps for each year the money is invested. To find the total interest, work out:

total interest = final amount − first principal

Question

Find the compound interest on £3000 at 6% for three years and the amount at the end of that time.

Answer

Principal for the 1st year = £3000
Interest for the 1st year = 6% of £3000 = £ 180

Principal for the 2nd year = £3180
Interest for the 2nd year = 6% of £3180 = £ 190.80

Principal for the 3rd year = £3370.80
Interest for the 3rd year = 6% of £3370.80 = £ 202.25
£3573.05
(to the nearest p)

So the amount at the end of 3 years is £3573.05 (to the nearest p).

The compound interest is £3573.05 − £3000
= £573.05 (to the nearest p)

Each step in a *compound interest* calculation can be worked out on a calculator. The answers can be written down as in the answer above.

If your calculator has a constant function facility, then it is easier and more efficient to use this. To do this you must use the method of calculating percentage change given in Unit 2.7. For example, if you begin with a certain sum of money (this is 100%) and increase it by 6%, you end up with (100% + 6%) = 106% of the original sum of money.

In this case,
the principal is the original sum of money (i.e. 100%),
the year's interest is the increase (i.e. 6%),
the amount for a year is the money you end up with (i.e. 106%).

So at the end of each year the amount is 106% of the principal for that year. Changing 106% to a decimal gives 1.06 and the compound interest calculation becomes:

amount at the end of 1 year = 1.06 × £3000
= £3180
amount at the end of 2 years = 1.06 × £3180
= £3370.80
amount at the end of 3 years = 1.06 × £3370.80
= £3573.05
(to the nearest p)

The **constant multiplier** on a calculator will do this repeated multiplication by 1.06 automatically for you. It multiplies the number on the display each time by the number entered as the **constant**.

On most calculators, pressing the × key twice sets up this constant multiplier function. So to work out the amount at the end of 3 years if £3000 is invested at compound interest of 6%:

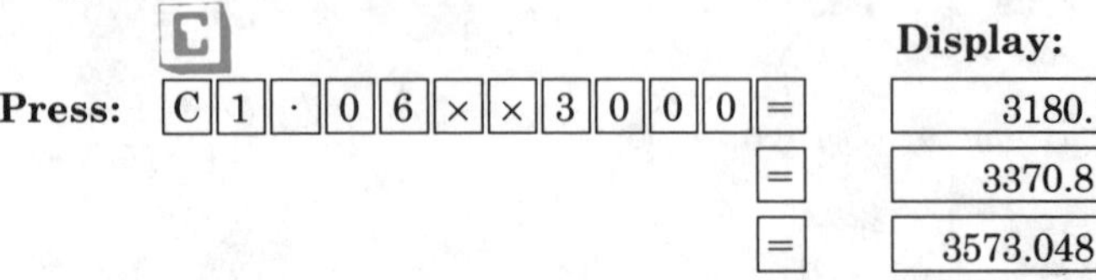

Always write down and explain your calculator answers in your answer. Do not correct any answers until the end of the calculation.

APPRECIATION AND DEPRECIATION

Some things **appreciate** or go up in value with time. For example, good antiques and many houses have appreciated in value in recent years. Most things which people buy **depreciate** or go down in value over the years. For example, most cars and household goods depreciate with time.

Companies often have to calculate the appreciation or depreciation of their **assets** (the things they own). The amount of appreciation or depreciation is usually described in percentages. At the end of each year the companies work out the appreciation or depreciation as a percentage of the value of each item at the beginning of that year. So in a sense, appreciation and depreciation are worked out in a similar way to compound interest.

For example, if an item worth a certain sum of money at the beginning of the year (this is 100%) depreciates (goes down) by 5%, then its value at the end of the year is (100% − 5%) = 95%. Changing this to a decimal gives you a constant multiplier of 0.95. So,
for a **depreciation** the constant multiplier will be *less than 1,*
for an **appreciation** the constant multiplier will be *more than 1.*

Question

A company estimates that a car depreciates in value by 20% each year. How much does it estimate that a car it buys for £4250 is worth at the end of 4 years?

Answer

To decrease a sum of money by 20%, use a constant multiplier of 0.80 (i.e. 100% − 20% = 80% changed to a decimal).

Using a calculator:

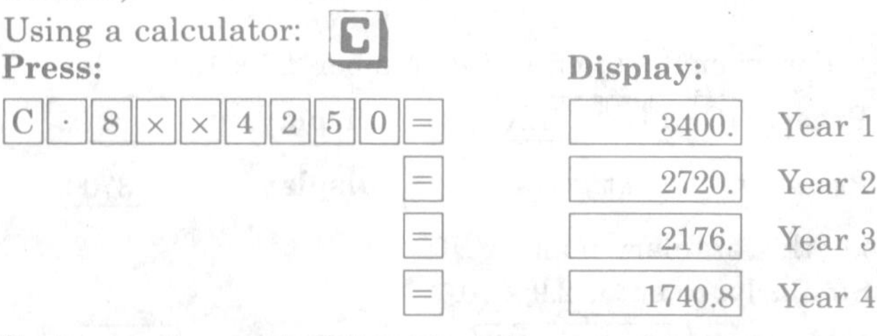

So the car is worth £1740.80 at the end of 4 years.

2.11 Proportional division

Proportional division is about sharing something in a *given ratio*. The ratio tells you how to do the sharing. For example, if cement and sand are mixed in the ratio of 1:2, then:

1 shovel of cement and 2 shovels of sand
→ 3 shovels of concrete,

1 bucket of cement and 2 buckets of sand
→ 3 buckets of concrete,

1 tonne of cement and 2 tonnes of sand
→ 3 tonnes of concrete,

⋮

1 part of cement and 2 parts of sand
→ 3 parts of concrete.

DIVIDING A QUANTITY

To divide something in a given ratio, find:

(a) the total number of parts from the ratio,
(e.g. the ratio $a:b$ gives $(a+b)$ parts,
the ratio $a:b:c$ gives $(a+b+c)$ parts, and so on ...)

(b) what one part is,

(c) the amounts for the ratio.

The something can be a number, an amount of money, a measurement, ...

Question

A green paint is mixed from blue and yellow paint in the ratio 3:5. How much of each colour is needed to make 40 litres of this green paint?

Answer

The ratio 3:5 gives (3 + 5) = 8 parts.
40 litres of green paint are needed.
Green paint: 8 parts → 40 litres
1 part → (40 ÷ 8) litres = 5 litres
Blue paint: 3 parts → 3 × 5 litres = 15 litres
Yellow paint: 5 parts → 5 × 5 litres = 25 litres
Check 15 litres + 25 litres = 40 litres
So 15 litres of blue paint and 25 litres of yellow paint are needed.

Sometimes the ratio is *not* in its simplest form. It is usually easier to simplify it first.

Question

Three workers, Mr Allan, Miss Brown and Mrs Cork, hold 120, 200 and 40 shares respectively in their company. A total dividend of £1800 is paid to the three workers in the same ratio as their shares. How much does each worker receive?

Answer

The ratio of the shares is 120 : 200 : 40
÷40 ↓ ÷40 ↓ ÷40 ↓
In its simplest form this is 3 : 5 : 1
This ratio gives (3 + 5 + 1) = 9 parts
Total dividend: 9 parts → £1800
1 part → £1800 ÷ 9 = £200
Mr Allan's dividend: 3 parts → 3 × £200 = £600
Miss Brown's dividend: 5 parts → 5 × £200 = £1000
Mrs Cork's dividend: 1 part → £200
Check £600 + £1000 + £200 = £1800

DIVIDING A LINE

This is a special example of proportional division. To divide a line in the ratio $a:b$,

(a) divide the line into $(a+b)$ equal parts,

(b) mark a parts and b parts on the line.

To do this you must be able to divide a line into a number of equal parts. These steps show you how to divide a line AB into n equal parts.

1 Draw a line AC at an acute angle to AB.

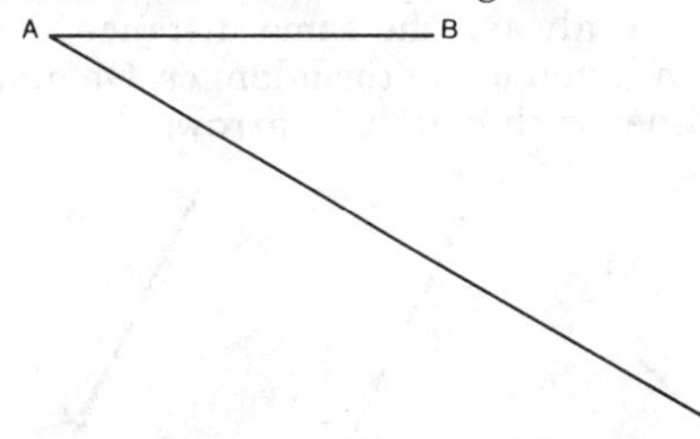

2 Using compasses, step off n equal lengths along AC. (The length can be any size.)

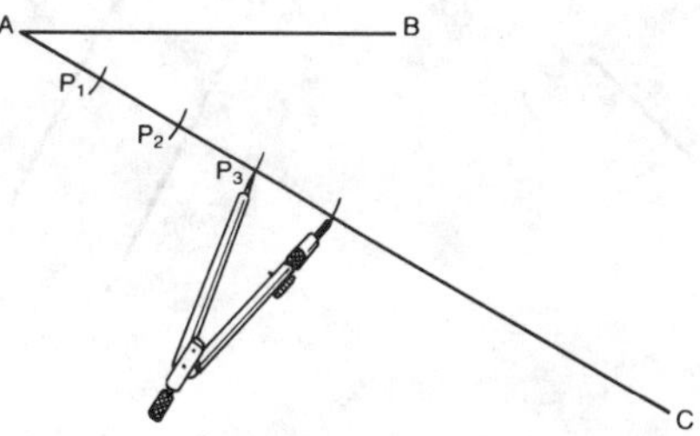

3 Mark the points $P_1, P_2, P_3, \ldots, P_n$. Join the last point P_n to B.

4 Using a set square draw lines parallel to BP_n through P_1, P_2, P_3, ... Each line must cut AB. AB will be divided into n equal parts.

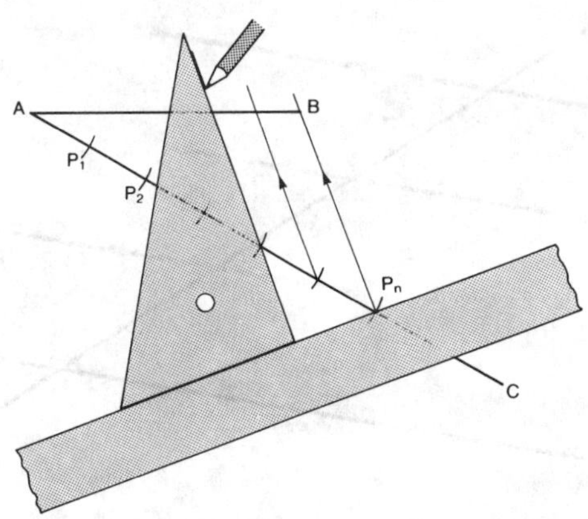

Question

Divide this line AB in the ratio 2:3.

A ———————————————— B

Answer

AB must be divided into (2 + 3) = 5 equal parts first. Then mark 2 parts and 3 parts on AB.

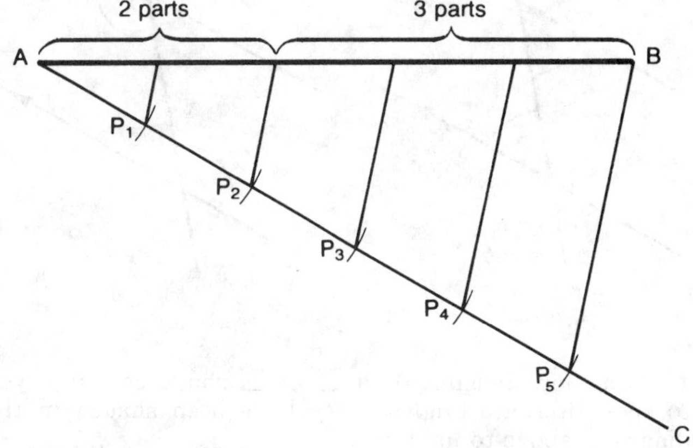

2.12 Parallels and angles

PARALLELS

Parallel lines are always the same distance apart. They never meet, even if you make them longer. On diagrams we mark parallel lines with matching arrows.

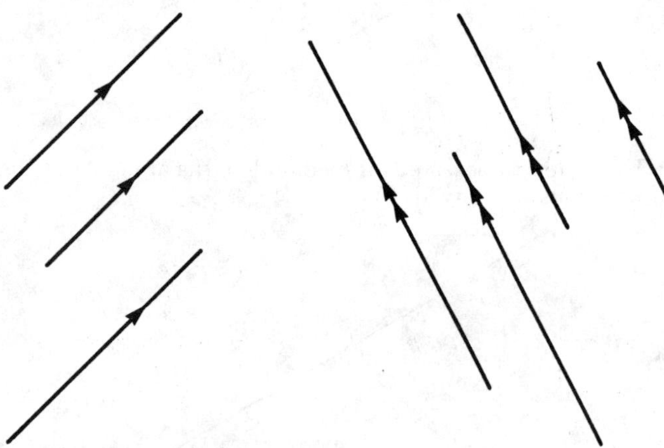

A straight line which cuts parallel lines is called a **transversal**. Some of the angles it makes with the parallels are equal. They have special names.

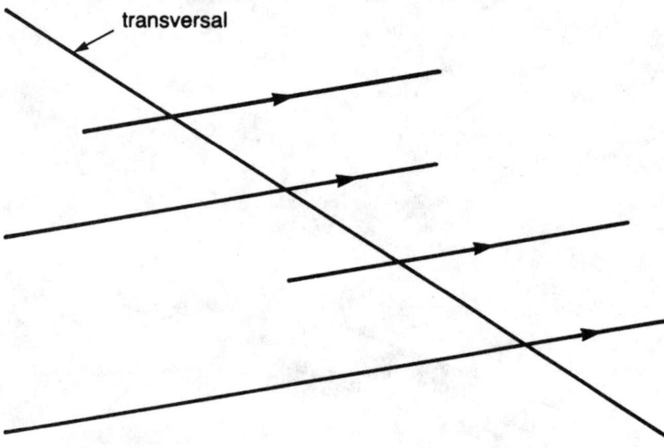

ALTERNATE ANGLES

Alternate angles are formed when a transversal cuts parallel lines. (They are on *alternate* sides of the transversal and *between* the parallel lines.) These alternate angles are *equal*.

A pair of equal alternate angles are marked on each diagram below.

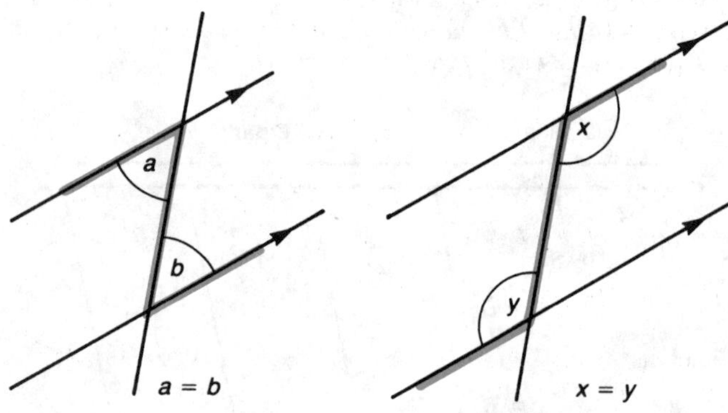

Marking (or imagining) a Z or ⅀ shape can help you to spot alternate angles. They have been shaded in the diagrams above to help you.

Question

Find the size of the lettered angles in this diagram.

Answer

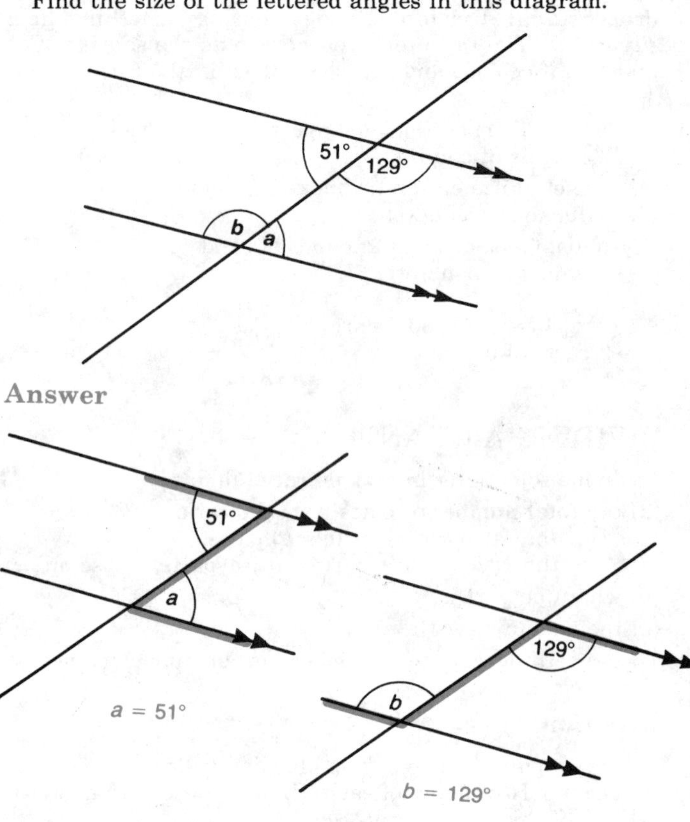

CORRESPONDING ANGLES

Corresponding angles are also formed when a transversal cuts parallel lines. (They are in *corresponding* or *matching* positions *between* the parallel lines and the transversal.) These corresponding angles are *equal*.

A pair of equal corresponding angles are marked on each diagram below.

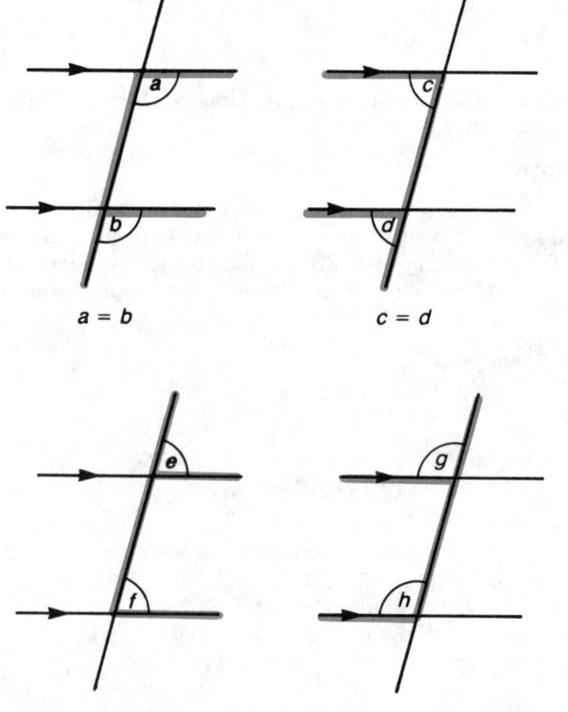

Marking (or imagining) an F or ꟻ shape can help you to spot corresponding angles. They have been shaded in the diagrams above to help you.

Question

Find the size of the lettered angles in this diagram.

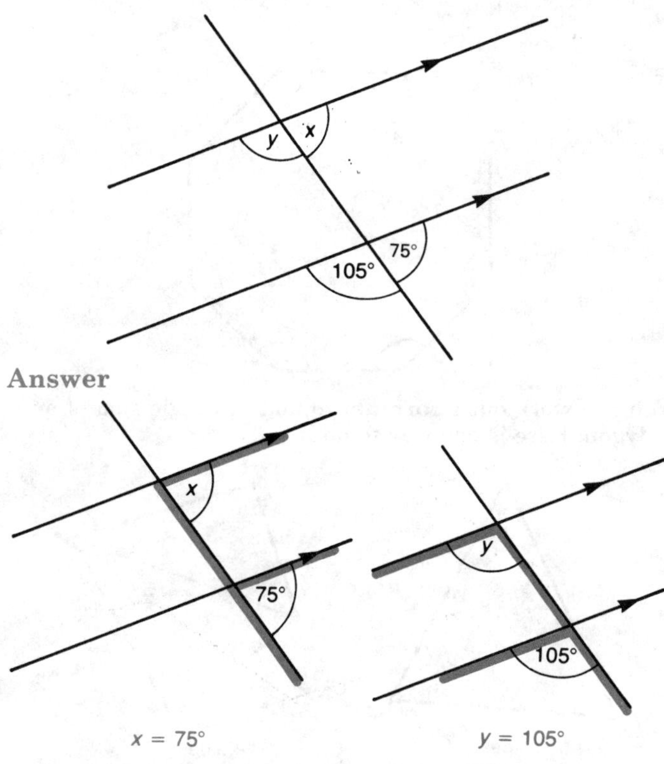

$x = 75°$ $y = 105°$

In this diagram a transversal cuts a pair of parallel lines. If you know *one* angle, then you can work out *all* the others.

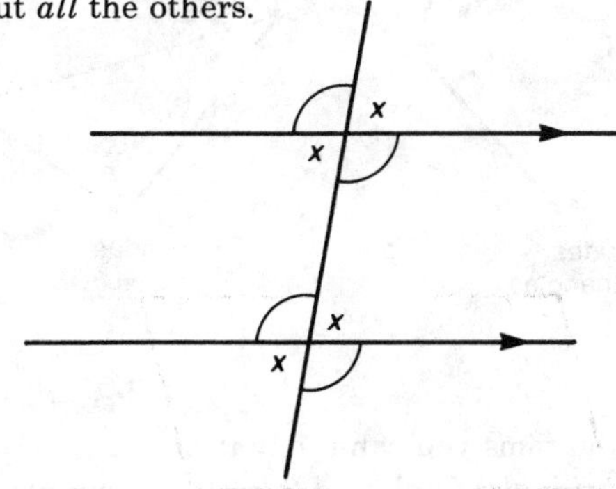

Question

Calculate the size of the lettered angles in this diagram. Give a reason for each answer.

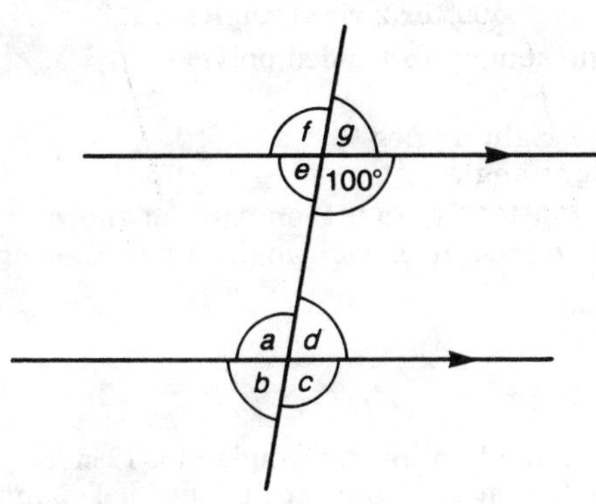

Answer

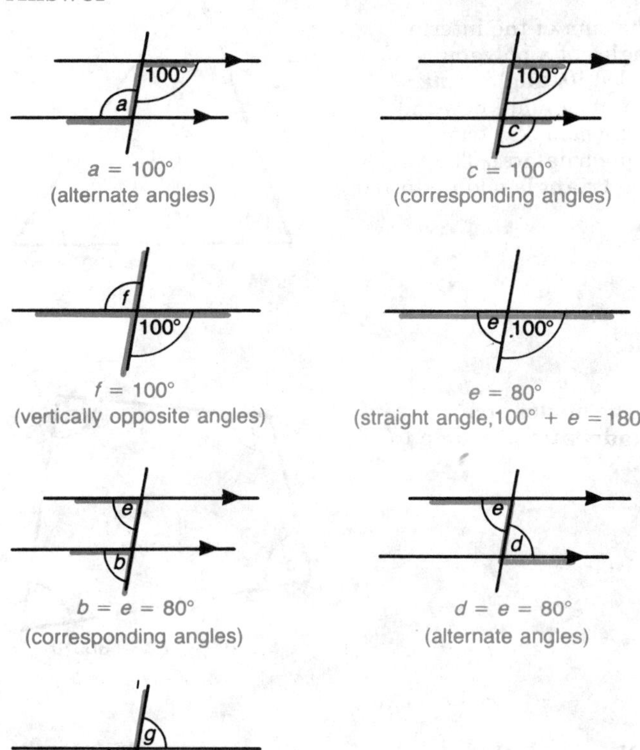

$a = 100°$
(alternate angles)

$c = 100°$
(corresponding angles)

$f = 100°$
(vertically opposite angles)

$e = 80°$
(straight angle, $100° + e = 180°$)

$b = e = 80°$
(corresponding angles)

$d = e = 80°$
(alternate angles)

$g = e = 80°$
(vertically opposite angles)

This is one way to work out all the lettered angles. There are others.

CALCULATING ANGLES

To calculate the size of angles in a diagram you will often have to use *more than one* **angle fact**. Here are some useful ones to *look for*. Mark the angles you find on the diagram.

Angle check-list

Look for:

(a) angles making a right angle (90°),
(b) angles making a straight angle (180°),
(c) angles making a full turn (360°),
(d) opposite angles,
(e) regular polygons, (see Unit 1.33),
(f) triangles, (see Unit 1.34),
(g) quadrilaterals, (see Unit 1.35),
(h) parallel lines and a transversal, (this unit),
(i) circles (see Unit 2.14).

2.13 Angles and polygons

INTERIOR ANGLES

The angles of a polygon are its **interior** angles.

They are *inside* the polygon.

Each interior angle is *at* a vertex and *between* two sides of the polygon.

The polygon's name tells you the number of interior angles it has.

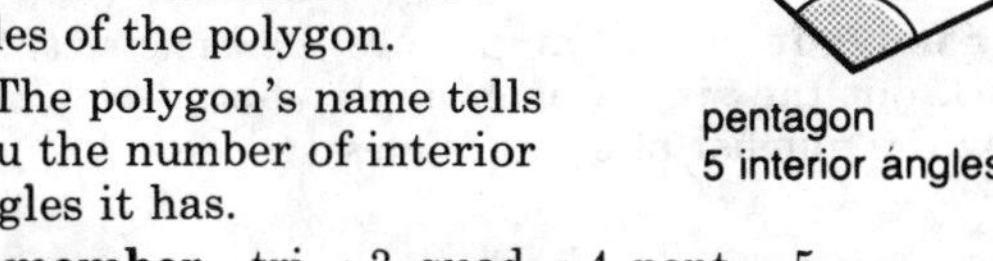

Remember tri → 3, quad → 4, pent → 5, hex → 6, hept → 7, oct → 8.

ANGLE SUM OF A POLYGON

The sum of the interior angles of a polygon is often called its **angle sum**.

You should know the angle sum of a triangle and a quadrilateral. The angles of a **triangle** add up to 180°.

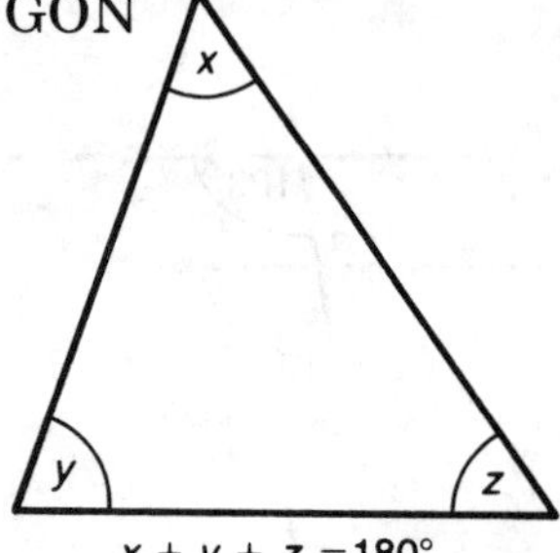

The angles of a **quadrilateral** add up to 360°.

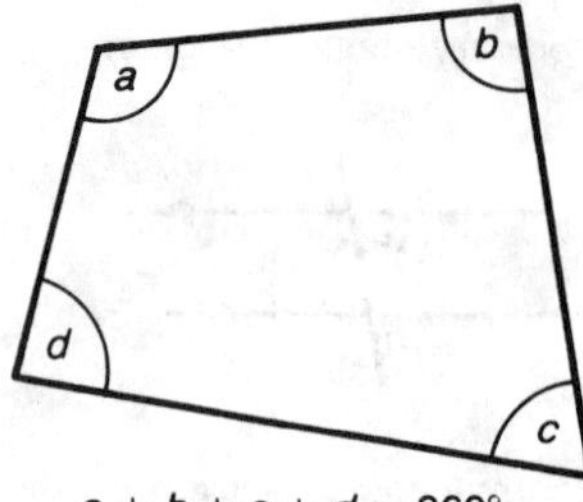

You can find the angle sum of **any polygon**. Here is one way to do it.

Split the polygon into triangles by drawing all the diagonals from just one vertex (corner).

Count the number of triangles made. Then use the angle sum of a triangle.

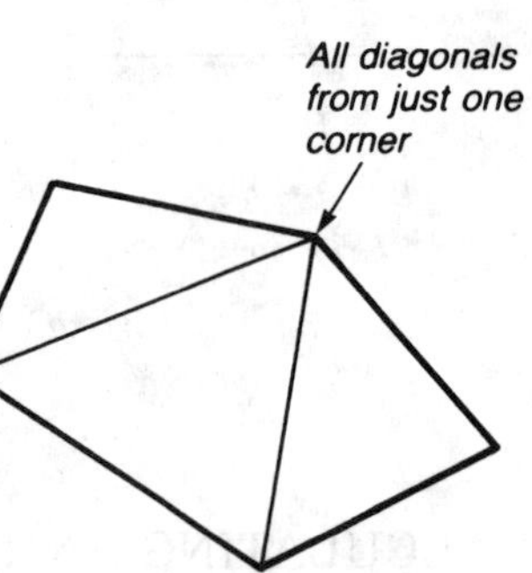

Question

Find the angle sum of an octagon. Show all your working.

Answer

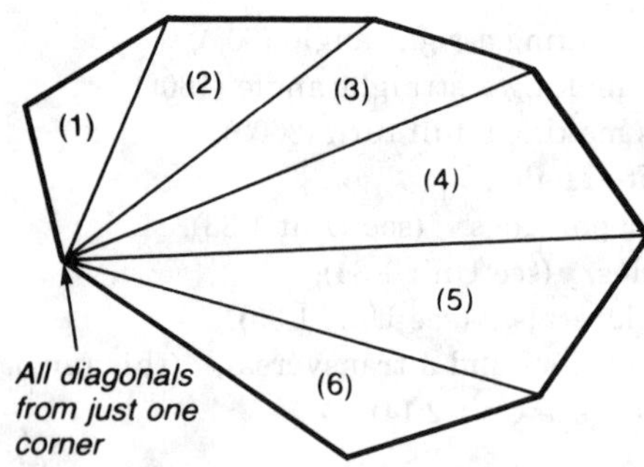

This octagon has been split into 6 triangles.
Angle sum of 1 triangle = 180°
Angle sum of 6 triangles = 6 × 180° = 1080°
So the angles of the octagon add up to 1080°.

In a **regular polygon**, all the angles are the *same* size. So you can work out the size of each angle. Just divide the angle sum by the number of equal angles.

Question

Find the size of each angle in a regular octagon.

Answer

The angle sum of a regular octagon is 1080°.
A regular octagon has 8 equal angles.
So each angle is $\frac{1080°}{8} = 135°$.

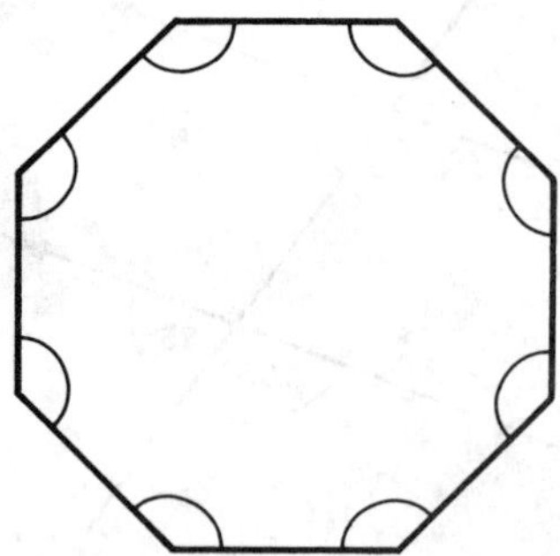

You can work out a **formula** to find the angle sum of any polygon. Here is one way to do it.

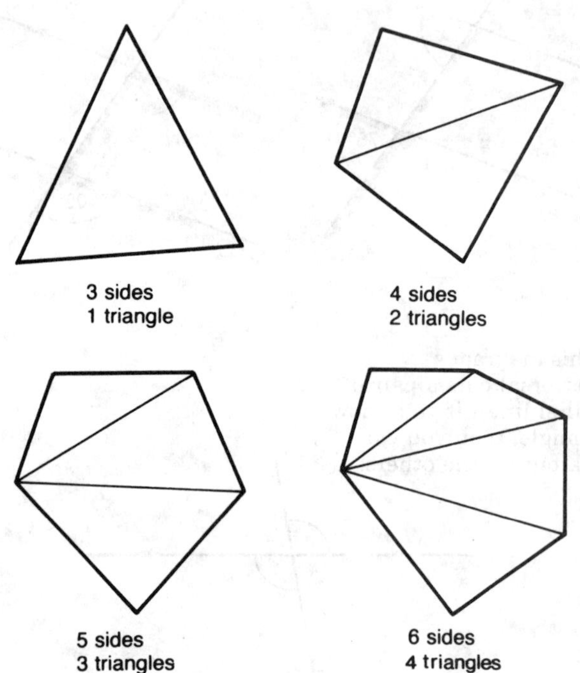

and so on …

From these diagrams you can see that:

number of triangles is always *2 less* than the *number of sides.*

So for a polygon with n sides, the number of triangles is $(n - 2)$.

Angle sum of 1 triangle = 180°
Angle sum of $(n - 2)$ triangles = $(n - 2) \times 180°$

So the angles of a polygon with n sides add up to $(n - 2) \times 180°$.

This formula is often given using *right angles* instead of degrees. 180° is 2 × 90° or 2 right angles.

So the angle sum of an n-sided polygon
$= (n - 2) \times 180°$
$= (n - 2) \times 2$ right angles
$= 2n - 4$ right angles.

If the polygon is **regular**, then each of the n angles is equal. So to find the size of each angle, divide the angle sum by n.

Question

What is the size of an interior angle of a 12-sided regular polygon? (The angle sum of an n-sided polygon is $2n - 4$ right angles.)

Answer

The polygon has 12 sides, so $n = 12$.

The angle sum of the polygon

$= 2n - 4$ right angles

$= (2 \times 12) - 4$ right angles

$= 24 - 4$ right angles

$= 20$ right angles or $20 \times 90°$

$= 1800°$

Since the polygon is regular, it has 12 equal angles.

So each angle is $1800° \div 12 = 150°$.

EXTERIOR ANGLES

The **exterior** angles of a polygon are *outside* the polygon. An exterior angle is formed when a side of the polygon is made longer (**produced**).

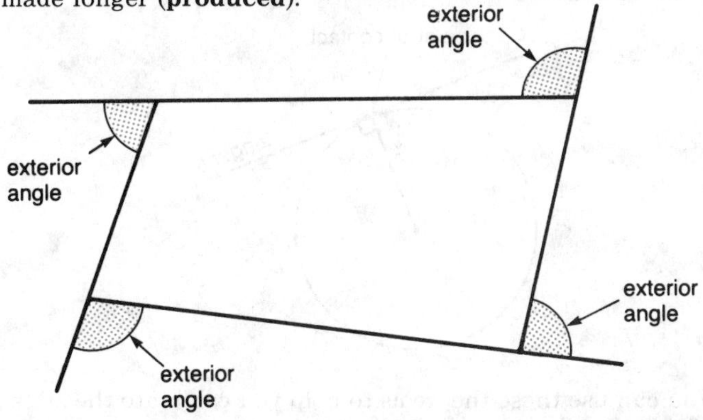

If you make each side of the polygon longer in turn, then you get all the exterior angles of the polygon. An exterior angle and its **interior angle** always make a *straight angle*. So they add up to 180°.

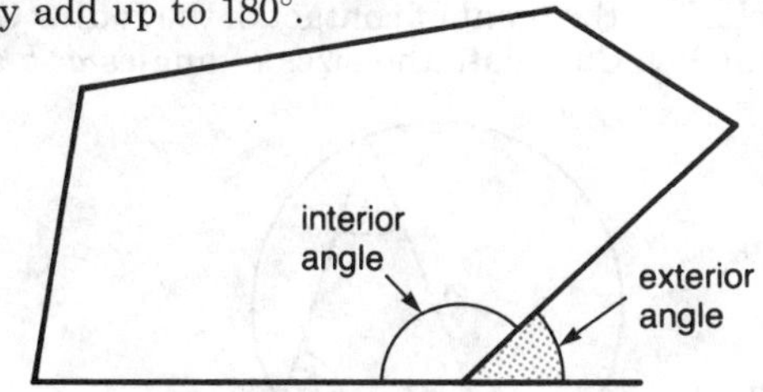

SUM OF THE EXTERIOR ANGLES OF A POLYGON

The exterior angles of any polygon add up to 360°.

Use your pencil to help you to see that this is true for this pentagon.

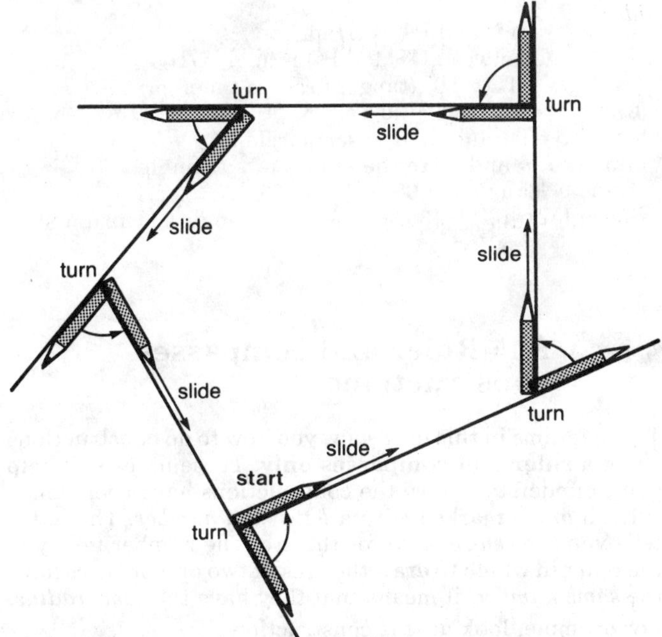

Take it 'for a walk' around the pentagon as shown in the diagram.

Your pencil will turn through each exterior angle.

So at the end of its 'walk', it will have turned through the sum of the exterior angles.

You can see that your pencil has made a complete turn (360°) during its 'walk'.

So the sum of the exterior angles of this pentagon is 360°.

Try taking your pencil 'for a walk' like this around some other polygons. See what results you get.

An n-sided regular polygon has n equal angles. So each of its exterior angles is $(360° \div n)$.

Question

What is the size of each exterior angle of a regular octagon?

Answer

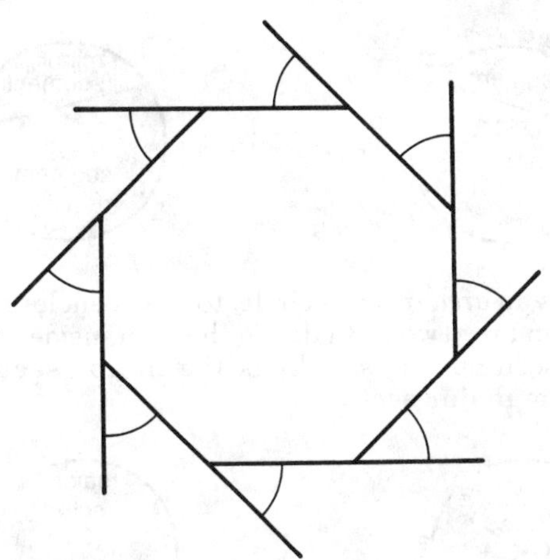

The exterior angles of an octagon add up to 360°.
A regular octagon has 8 equal angles.
So each exterior angle is $360° \div 8 = 45°$.

2.14 Circles 2

The basic circle words and facts you should know are given in unit 1.36.

MORE CIRCLE WORDS

A **chord** is a straight line joining any two points on a circle.

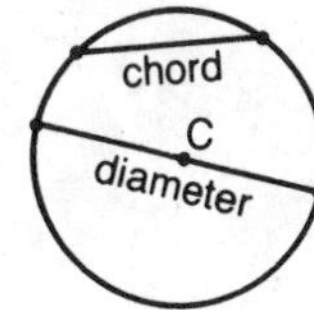

A **diameter** is a special chord. It passes through the centre of the circle. A diameter is the longest chord for a circle.

A **tangent** is a straight line which touches a circle at *one point only*. This point is called the **point of contact**. If a tangent is made longer, it still will not cut the circle.

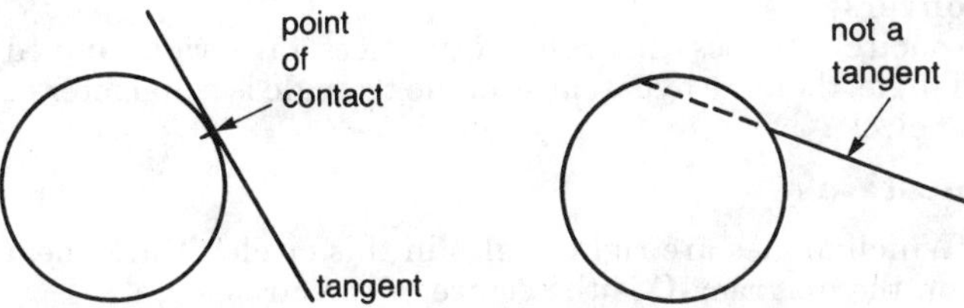

An **arc** is part of a circle. Two points on a circle will give either a **minor arc** and a **major arc** or two **semicircles**.

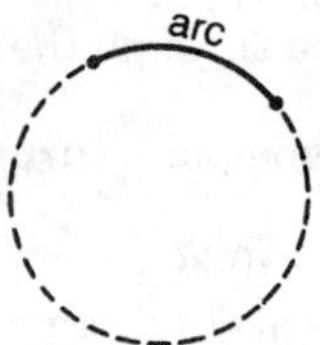

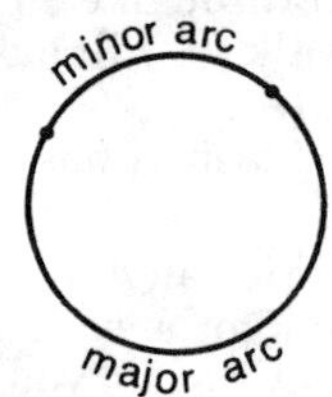

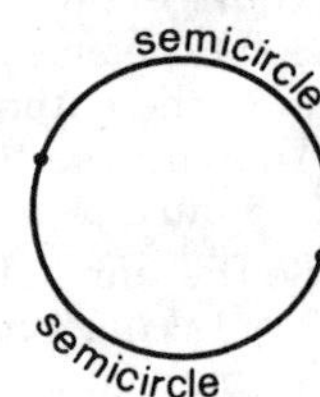

A *minor* arc is always *smaller* than a semicircle. A *major* arc is always *larger* than a semicircle.

A **segment** is an *area* inside a circle. It is enclosed by an arc and a chord. Any chord divides the area inside a circle into two segments. The *smaller* one is the **minor segment**. The *larger* one is the **major segment**.

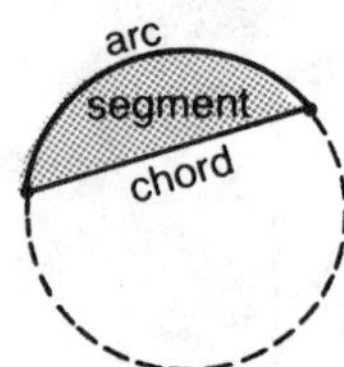

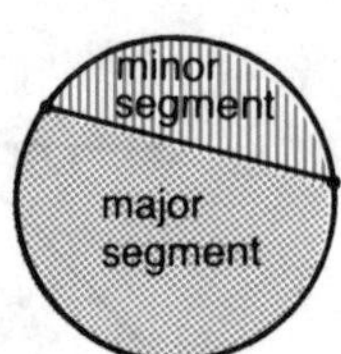

A **sector** is an *area* inside a circle, too. It is enclosed by two radii and an arc. Two radii divide the area inside the circle into two sectors. The *smaller* is the **minor sector**. The *larger* is the **major sector**.

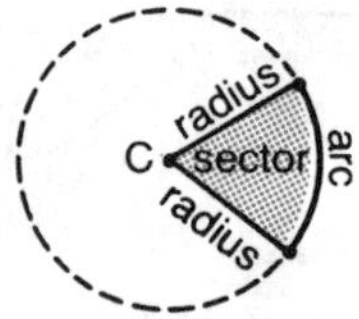

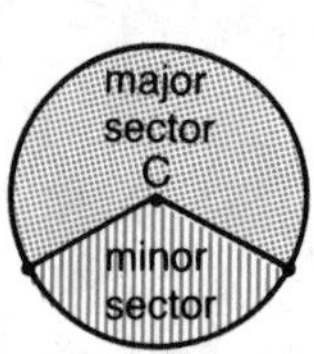

CIRCLE THEOREMS

Here are two important **circle theorems** (rules). The **converse** of theorem 1 is also useful. The converse of a theorem is the theorem put the other way round. For example, the converse of

'a polygon with three sides has three angles'
is 'a polygon with three angles has three sides'.

Not all theorems have converses which are true.

1 Angle in a semicircle

An angle in a semicircle is a right angle.

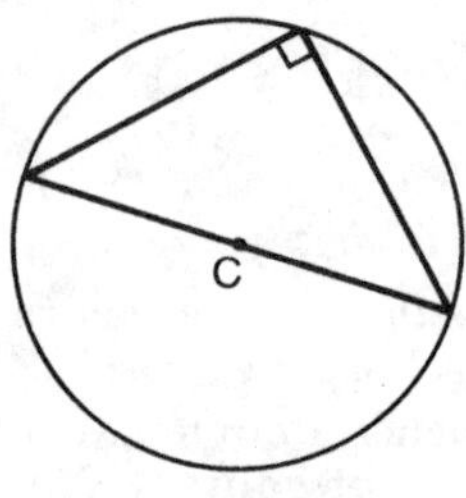

Theorem

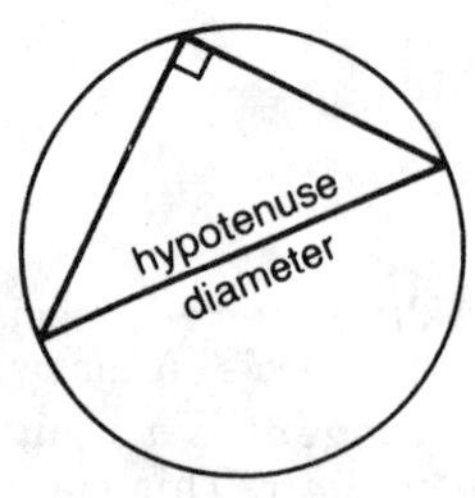

Converse

Converse
If a circle passes through the vertices of a right-angled triangle, then the hypotenuse of the triangle is a diameter of the circle.

Question

Which angles are right angles in this circle? Mark them on the diagram. C is the centre of the circle.

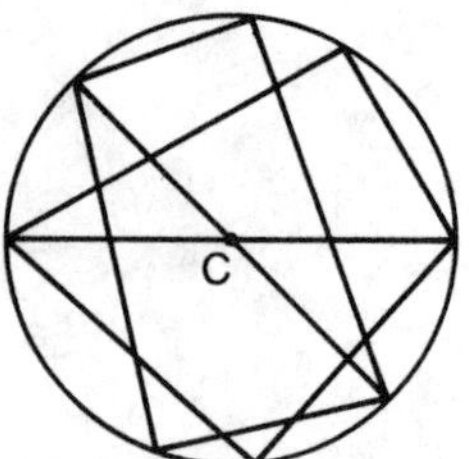

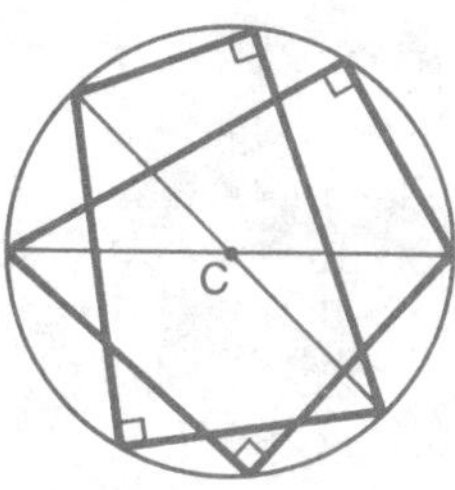

Answer

Each right angle is an angle in a semicircle.

2 Tangent-radius theorem

A tangent to a circle is perpendicular to the radius at the point of contact.

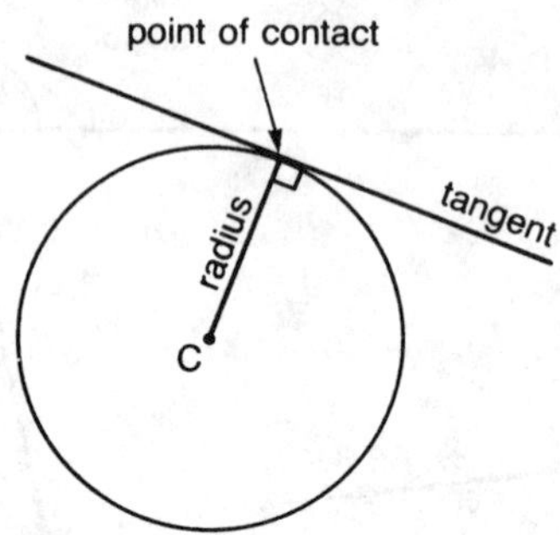

You can use these theorems to help you calculate the sizes of other angles in a circle diagram.

Question

This diagram shows a circle, centre O, and a tangent PQ to the circle. T is the point of contact of the radius OT and the tangent PQ. Calculate the sizes of angles a, b and c.

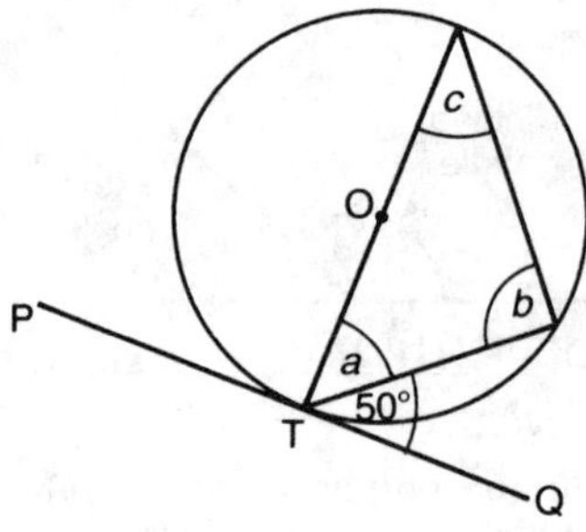

Answer

OT is a radius and PQ is a tangent.
The angle between OT and PQ is angle OTQ.
So angle OTQ = 90° (tangent-radius theorem)
Angle $a = 90° - 50° = 40°$
Angle $b = 90°$ (angle in a semicircle)
Angles a, b and c are the angles of a triangle.
Angle a + angle $b = 90° + 40° = 130°$
So angle $c = 180° - 130°$ (angles of a triangle add up to 180°)
$= 50°$

2.15 Ruler and compasses constructions

The diagrams in this unit show you how to do constructions using a **ruler and compasses only**. These notes will help you to understand how the constructions have been done.

Each *arc* is marked with a *letter* and *number*. The letter tells you the *centre point* for the arc. The number tells you the *order* in which to draw the arcs. If two or more arcs have the *same number*, it means that they have the *same radius*. For example, look at this construction.

The arcs (P)$_1$:
were drawn *first*,
have the *same* radius
(3 cm in this case),
have centre, *point* P.
The arcs marked (A)$_2$ and (B)$_2$:
were drawn *second*,
have the *same* radius
(2 cm in this case),
have centres A and B
respectively.

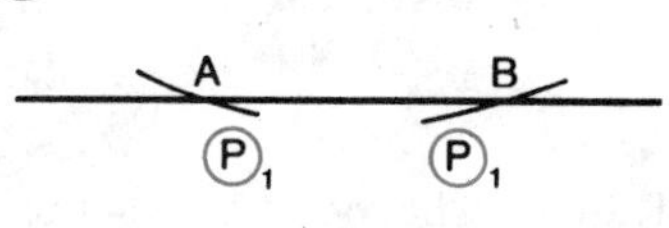

To **check** that you understand this, use these instructions to draw the construction yourself. Try to draw all these constructions yourself.

Remember A *perpendicular* is a line at right angles to another line. A *bisector* is a line that cuts another line or angle into two equal parts. *Bisect* means 'to cut into two equal parts'.

1 TO CONSTRUCT THE PERPENDICULAR BISECTOR OF A GIVEN LINE AB

(a) Draw arcs (A)$_1$.

(b) Draw arcs (B)$_1$.

(c) Draw a line through the intersecting arcs. This line is the perpendicular bisector of AB.

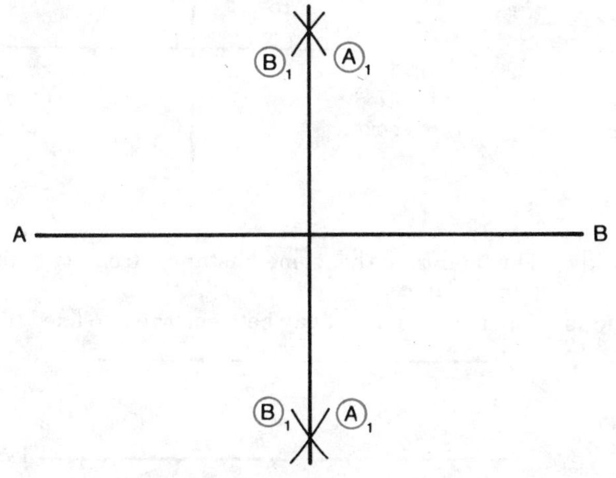

2 TO CONSTRUCT A PERPENDICULAR TO A GIVEN LINE AB, FROM A GIVEN POINT P

(a) Draw arcs (P)$_1$ to cut AB at C and D.

(b) Draw arcs (C)$_2$ and (D)$_2$.

(c) Join P to the point of intersection of arcs (C)$_2$ and (D)$_2$.

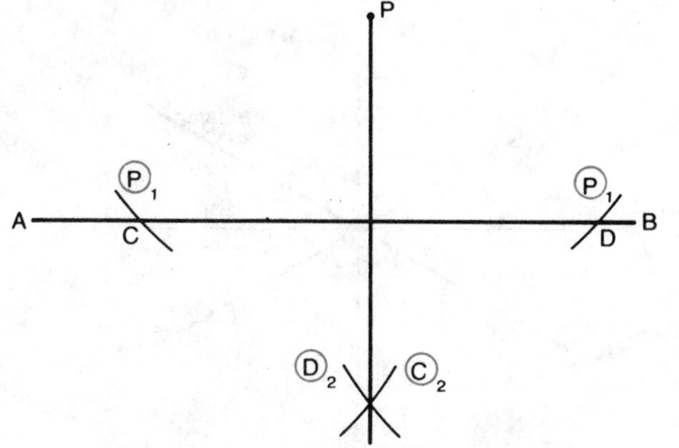

The construction is the same if P lies on AB. Try this construction too.

3 TO BISECT A GIVEN ANGLE, ∠A

(a) Draw arcs (A)$_1$ to cut at B and C.

(b) Draw arcs (B)$_2$ and (C)$_2$.

(c) Join A to the point of intersection of (B)$_2$ and (C)$_2$.

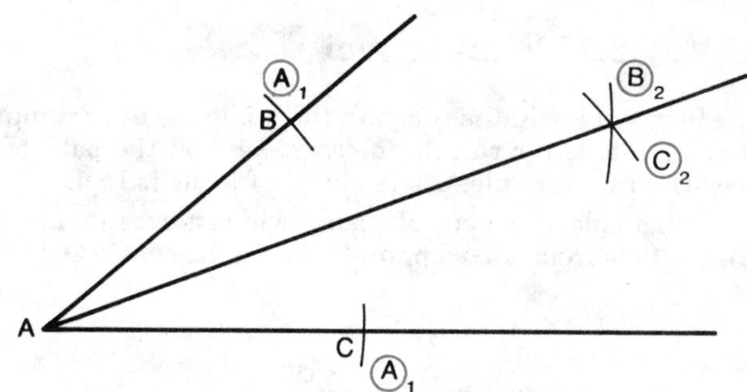

4 TO CONSTRUCT AN ANGLE OF 90° AT A POINT, A, ON A LINE

(a) Draw arcs (A)$_1$ to cut the line at C and D.

(b) Draw arcs (C)$_2$ and (D)$_2$.

(c) Join A to the point of intersection of arcs (C)$_2$ and (D)$_2$.

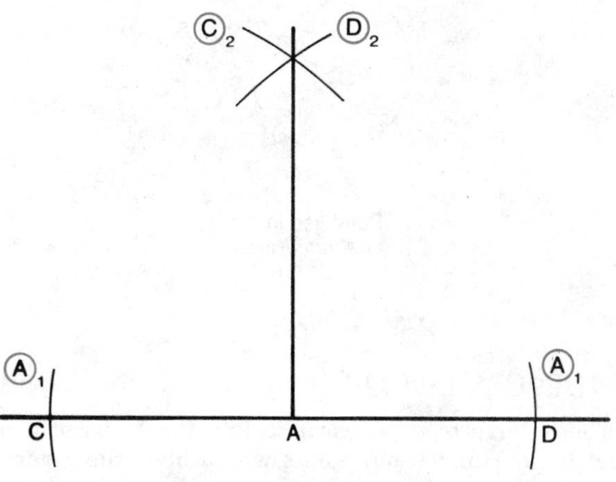

5 TO CONSTRUCT AN ANGLE OF 45°

(a) Construct an angle of 90°.

(b) Bisect the angle of 90°.

6 TO CONSTRUCT AN ANGLE OF 60° AT A POINT, A, ON A LINE

(a) Draw the 'large' arc (A)$_1$ to cut the line at B.

(b) Draw arc (B)$_1$ to cut the large arc (A)$_1$.

(c) Join A to the point C of intersection of arcs (A)$_1$ and (B)$_1$.

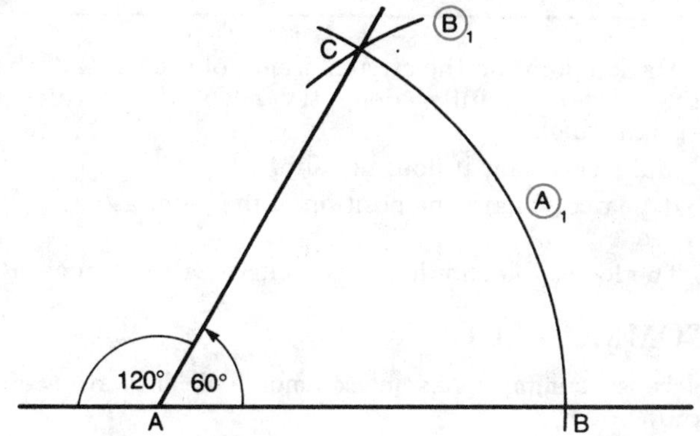

The angle 120° (= 180° − 60°), is obtained as a bonus from the same construction. Also if B is joined to C, then △ ABC is an equilateral triangle. So this method can be used to construct an equilateral triangle.

7 TO CONSTRUCT AN ANGLE OF 30°

(a) Construct an angle of 60°.
(b) Bisect the angle of 60°.

2.16 Simple loci

The **locus** of a point is the path the point traces as it moves obeying a rule (or rules). So *everywhere* on the path must obey the rule (or rules). The plural of locus is **loci**.

For example, the locus of a point which moves so that it is always 1 cm from a fixed point O is a circle, centre O, radius 1 cm.

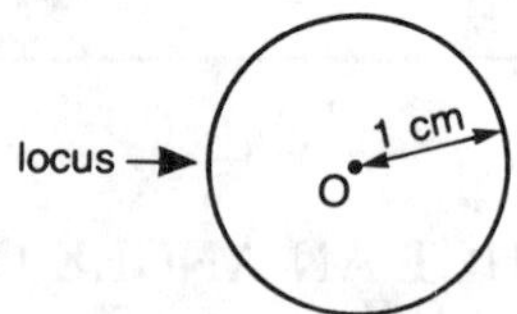

If a point moves so that it is always *less than* 1 cm from the fixed point O, then the point will always be *inside* the circle, centre O, radius 1 cm.

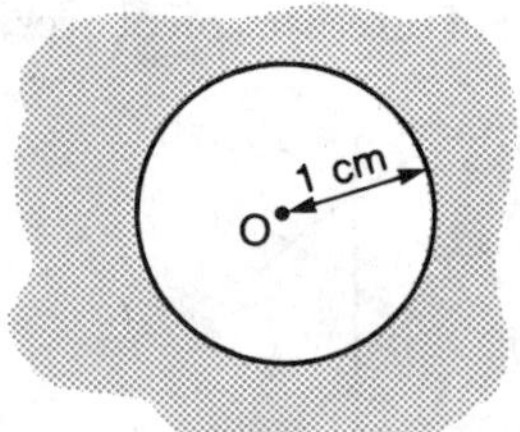

Point lies in the *unshaded* area

FINDING A LOCUS

You may have to *experiment* to find the locus of a point. Start by marking some points which obey the given rule. You may recognize the path being traced after marking only a few points. Sometimes you will need to mark many points before you get a clear idea of what the locus looks like. For example, you can use a circular lid and a ruler to investigate the locus of a point on the circumference of a circle as the circle rolls along a straight line.

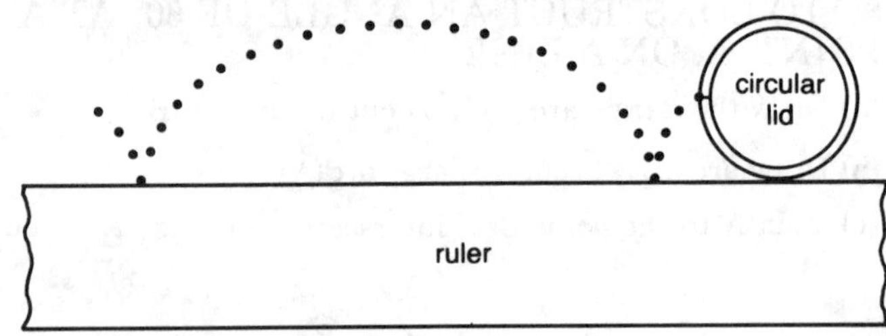

Mark a point on the circumference of the lid. Roll the lid (the circle) carefully along, the edge of the ruler (the straight line).

Make sure that it does not slip.

Repeatedly mark the position of the point as you roll the circle.

The locus you should get is a curve called a **cycloid**.

COMMON LOCI

Here is a summary of some common loci. They are useful to know.

Rule The point stays the same distance from a fixed point.

Locus A circle with the fixed point as centre and radius the given distance.

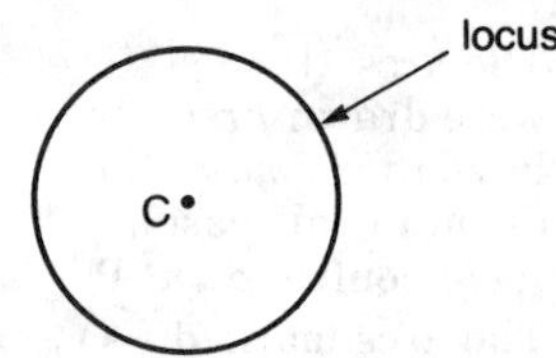

Rule The point stays the same distance from a fixed straight line.

Locus Two parallel lines, one on each side of the fixed line and the given distance from the line.

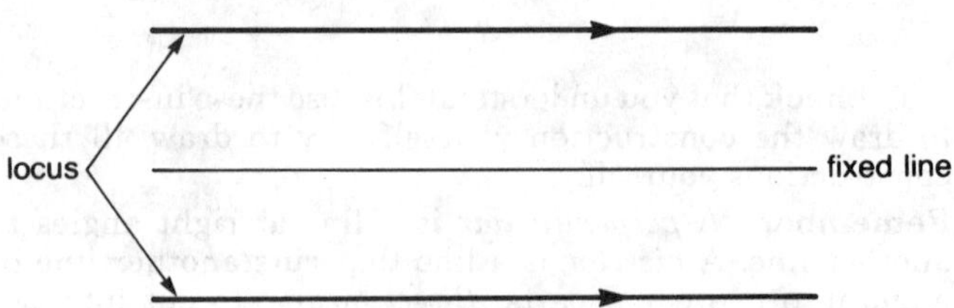

Rule The point is the same distance from two fixed points.

Locus The perpendicular bisector of the line joining the points.

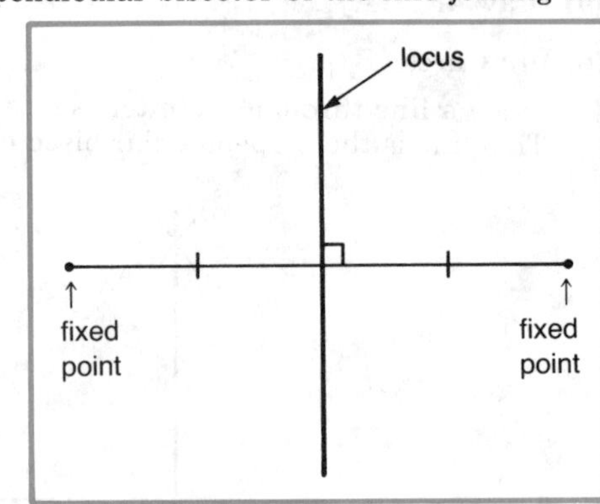

Rule The point is the same distance from two fixed parallel lines.

Locus A parallel line halfway between the two fixed lines.

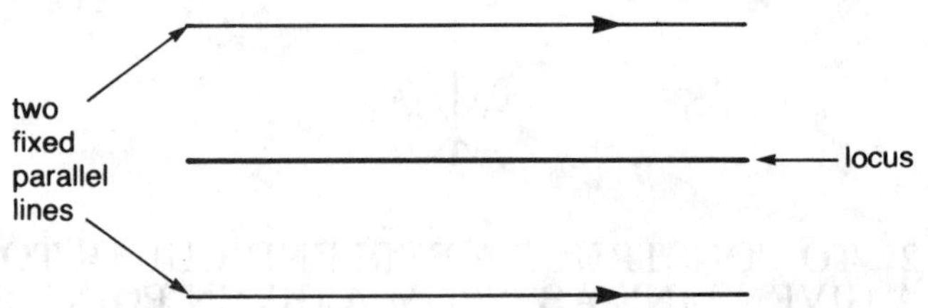

Rule The point is the same distance from two straight intersecting lines.

Locus The bisectors of the angles between the lines.

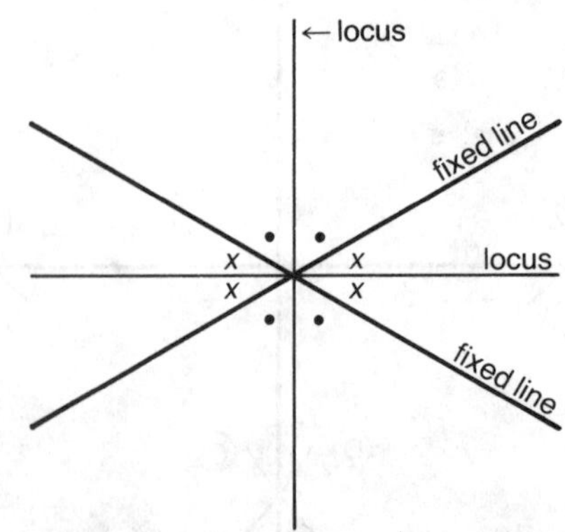

DRAWING LOCI

You may need to use drawing instruments, e.g. ruler, compasses, set square, protractor, to draw a locus. Some loci can be drawn using ruler and compasses only (see Unit 2.15).

In some loci problems you will be given several rules to fix the position or path of a point. Deal with each rule separately. The points which obey *all* the rules, e.g. where the loci **intersect**, will give you all the possible positions or path.

Question

The scale drawing below shows a plan of Mrs O'Neil's rectangular garden. She wants to put a clothes drier in her garden. It must be more than 3 m from the house but an equal distance from the two pillars. She wants it to be more than 10 m from the apple tree. On the plan, show the possible positions for the clothes drier.

Answer

Scale: 1 cm represents 2 m.

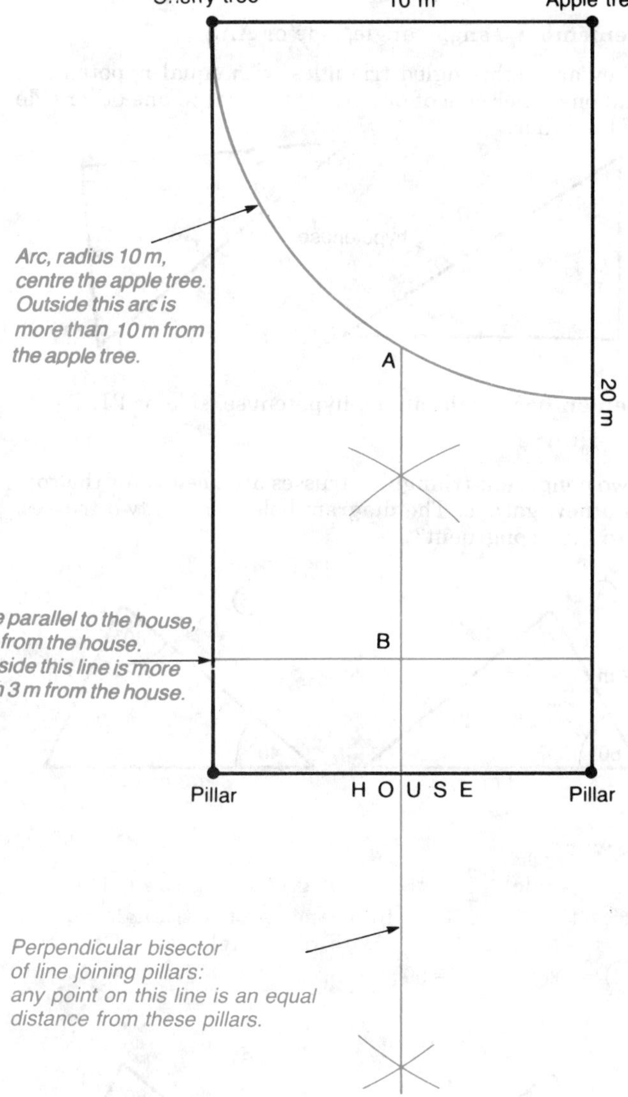

All the points on the line AB obey all three rules. The clothes drier can go anywhere on the straight line AB.

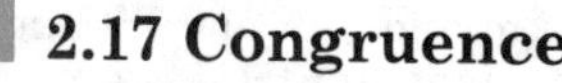

2.17 Congruence

Congruent shapes are the *same shape* and *size*.

For example,

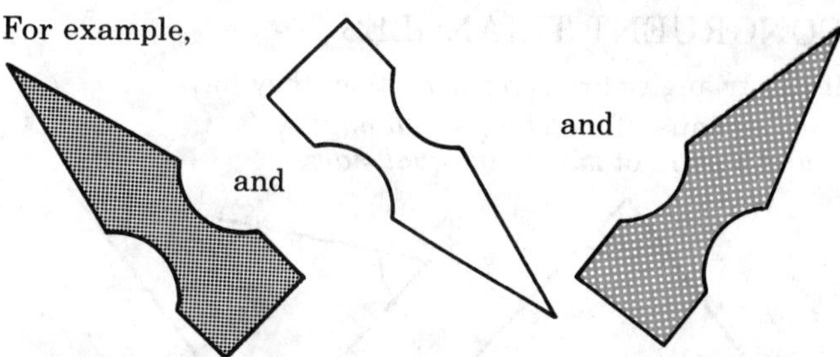

are congruent. The different colours do not matter

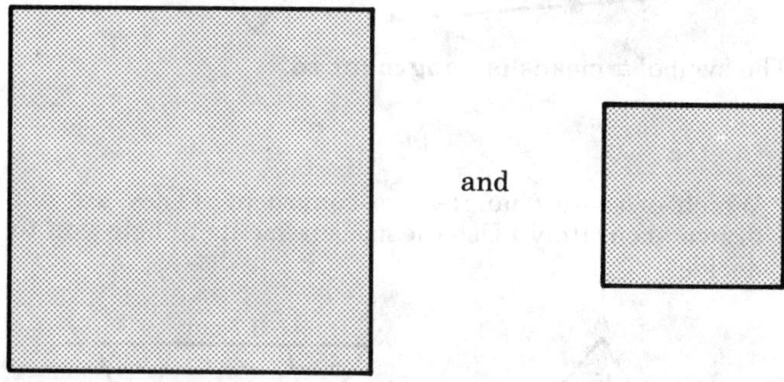

are *not* congruent. They are *not* the same size.

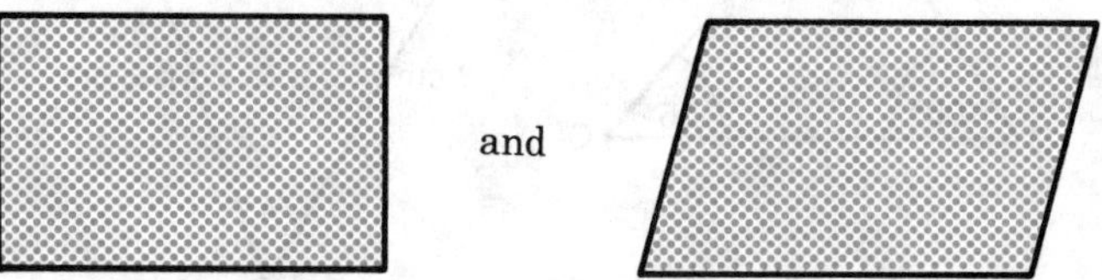

are *not* congruent. They are *not* the same shape.

Congruent shapes will fit over each other exactly. You can check congruent shapes by tracing or cutting out the shapes. Turn the shapes round or over if you need to.

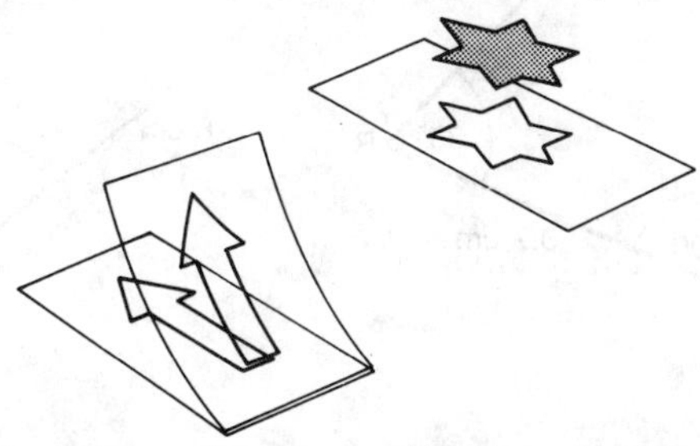

Matching sides and angles are *equal* in congruent shapes. You can check by measuring their sides and angles.

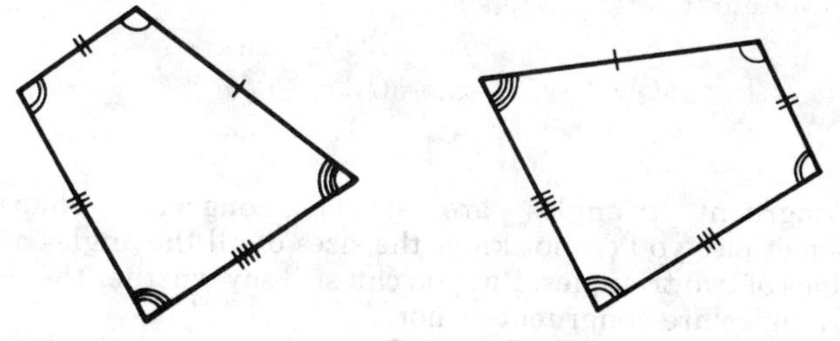

Solids which are exactly the same shape and size are congruent too.
For example, in a tea set
all the cups are congruent,
all the saucers are congruent,
and so on ...

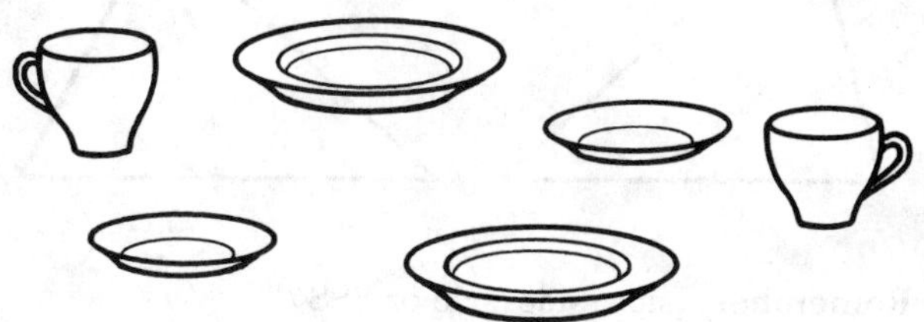

CONGRUENT TRIANGLES

If two triangles are congruent, then they have
3 pairs of *matching equal angles*,
and 3 pairs of *matching equal sides*.

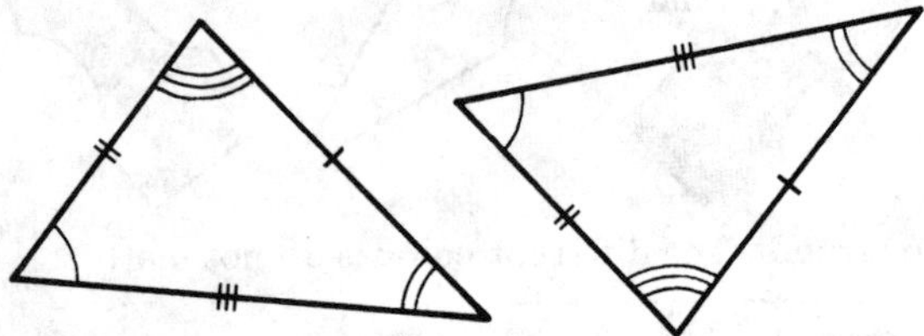

The symbol ≡ means **is congruent to.**

Question

Which of these triangles are congruent? (They are not drawn accurately.) Use the measurements to help you to decide.

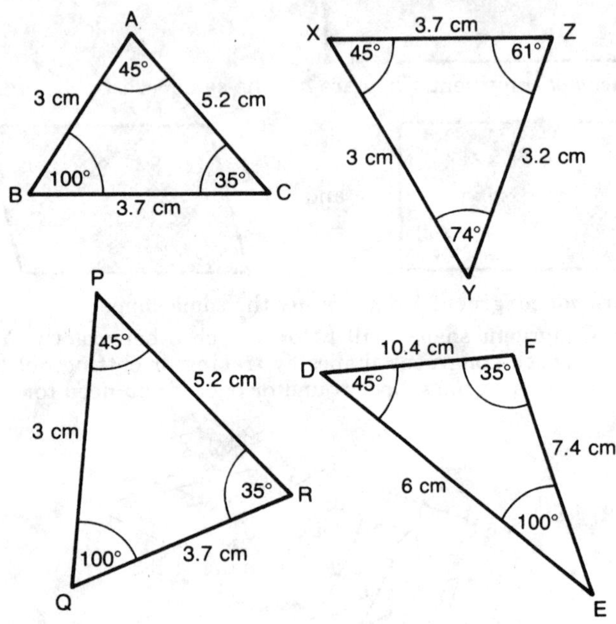

Answer

Triangles ABC and PQR are congruent, i.e.
$\triangle ABC \equiv \triangle PQR$.
Matching angles and sides are equal.

$\angle A = \angle P = 45°$ $AB = PQ = 3$ cm
$\angle B = \angle Q = 100°$ $BC = QR = 3.7$ cm
$\angle C = \angle R = 35°$ $AC = PR = 5.2$ cm

Congruent triangles are special congruent shapes. Sometimes you do not know the sizes of all the angles and sides of two triangles. But you can still say whether the two triangles are congruent or not.

If you can show that *one* of the following conditions is true for two triangles, then the two triangles are congruent.

1 Three sides of one triangle are equal to the three sides of the other.

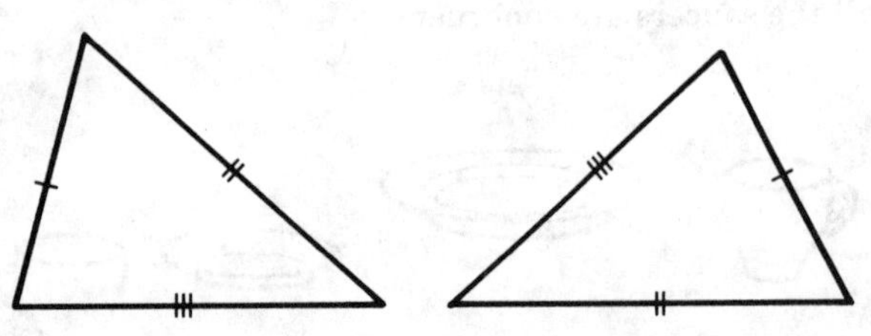

Remember side, side, side or SSS

2 Two sides of one triangle and the angle between the sides (the *included* angle) are equal to two sides and the included angle in the other.

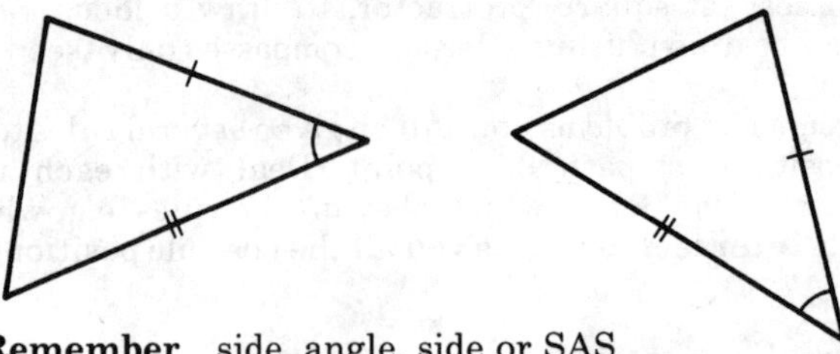

Remember side, angle, side or SAS

3 Two angles and a matching side of each triangle are equal.

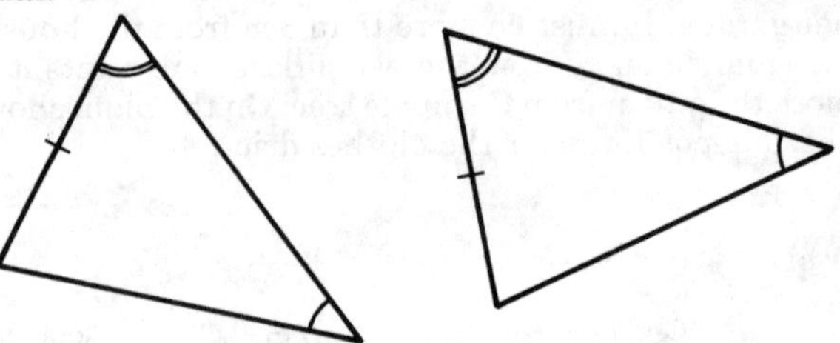

Remember angle, angle, side or AAS

4 They are right-angled triangles with equal hypotenuses and one other side of one triangle equal to one other side of the other.

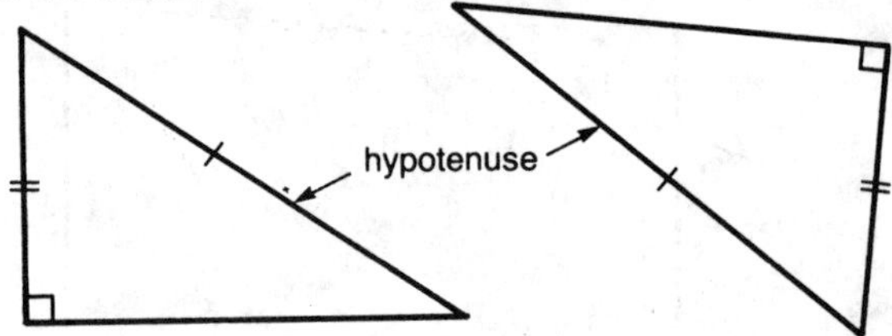

Remember right angle, hypotenuse, side or RHS

Question

Two congruent triangular trusses are needed for the roof of a new garage. The diagram below shows two trusses. Are they congruent?

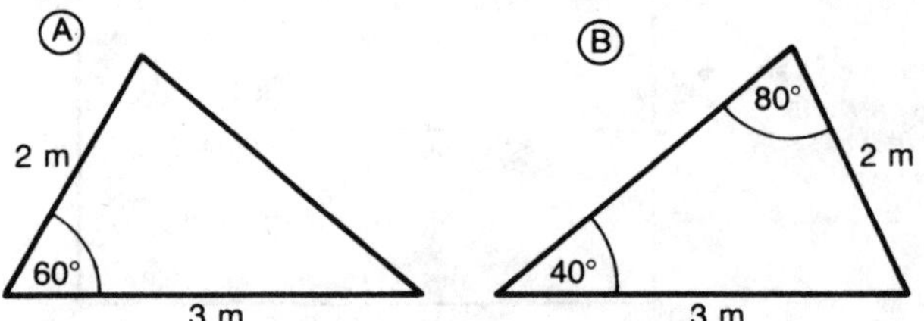

Answer

In triangle Ⓑ, the two given angles add up to $80° + 40° = 120°$. The three angles of a triangle add up to 180°. So the third angle of triangle Ⓑ $= 180° - 120° = 60°$.

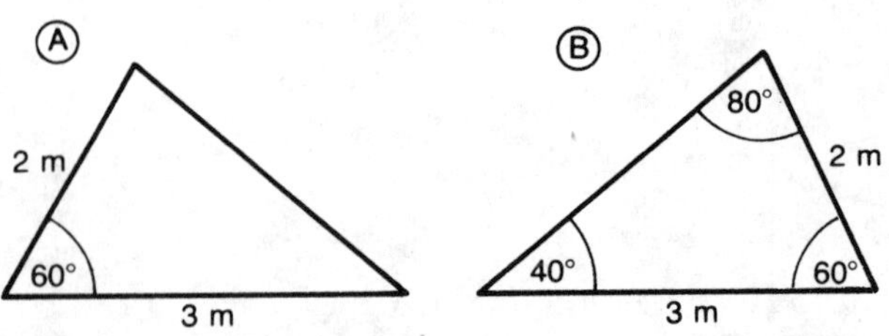

Each triangle has sides 2 m and 3 m and an angle of 60° between them. So the two triangular trusses are congruent (SAS).

2.18 Enlargement

When you **enlarge** something, you change its *size*.

Its shape stays the same. So the original shape and its enlargement are **similar**. Matching lengths change in size. But matching angles stay the same.

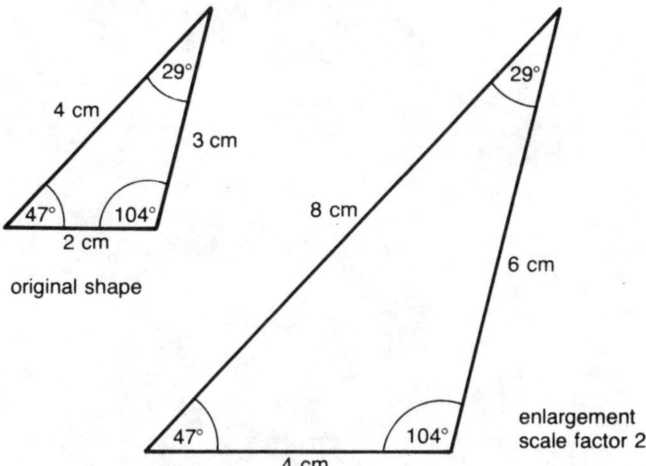

The **object** (the starting shape) and the **image** (the enlarged shape) in this diagram have been labelled in a special way. The object is ABCD. The same letters are used for matching points on the image but with a dash (′) after each. So the image is A′B′C′D′.

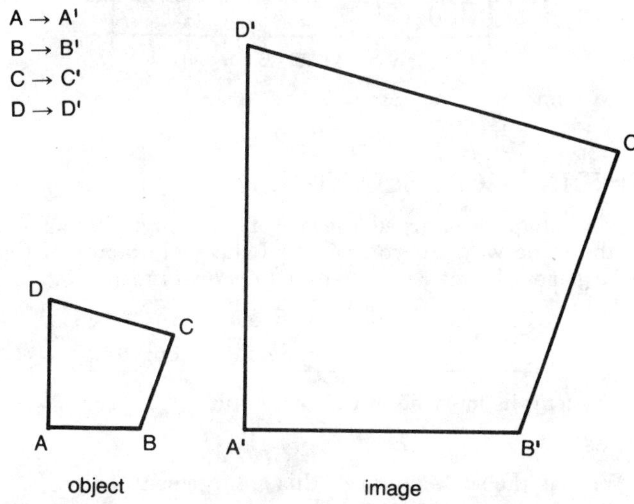

An object and its image are often labelled this way. It is also used for other transformations e.g. in Unit 2.19.

DRAWING ENLARGEMENTS

A grid (or dotted paper) can be used to enlarge shapes.

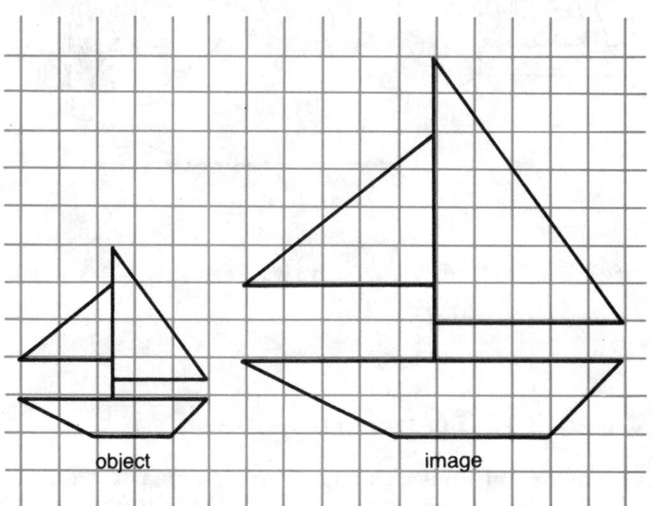

You can also enlarge a shape using a **centre of enlargement** and a **scale factor**. This is often called the *spider method* or *ray method*. You should be able to see why. Follow these steps to draw an enlargement this way.

1 Mark the centre of enlargement O.

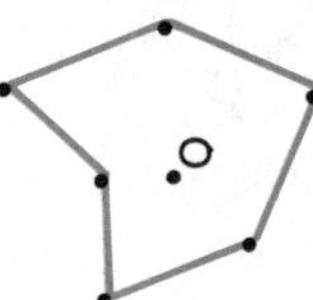

2 Draw a straight line from O through each **vertex** (corner point) of the shape in turn.

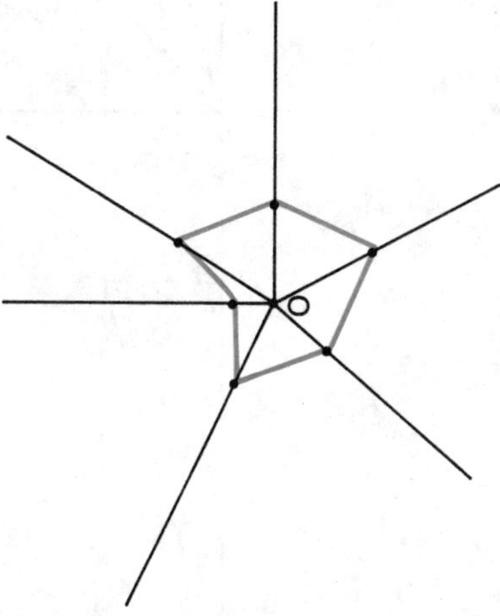

3 Measure the distance from O to each vertex. Put your measurements in a table.

4 Multiply each length by the scale factor. Put your answers in the table too.

5 Use your 'enlarged lengths' to mark the image of each vertex.

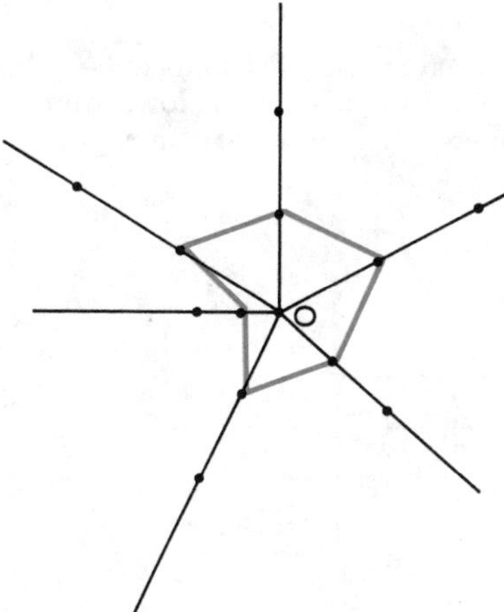

6 Join up the 'image points' in the correct order to make the image shape.

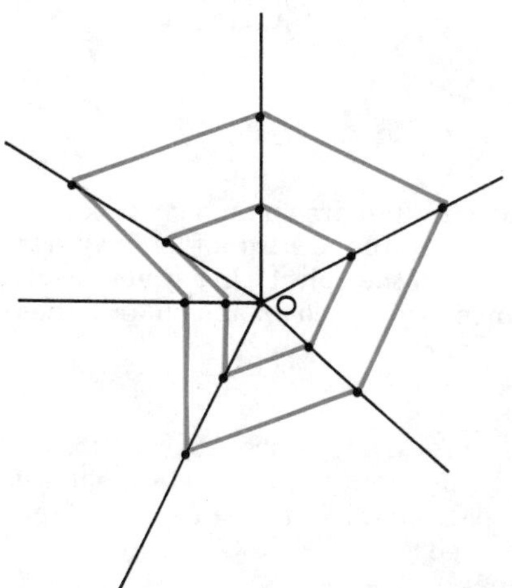

The centre of enlargement does not have to be *inside* the object. It can be *outside* or on the *edge* of the object.

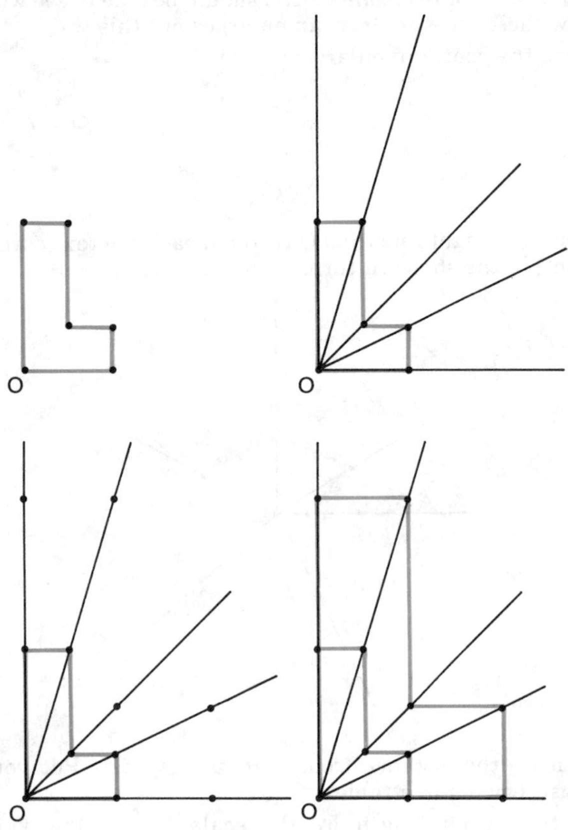

Question

A metal L-shaped bracket PQR has to be enlarged using a scale factor 3. On the diagram below, enlarge the bracket using the given centre of enlargement C.

Answer

Distances

Object		Image	
C to P	1.8 cm	C to P′	3 × 1.8 cm = 5.4 cm
C to Q	1.4 cm	C to Q′	3 × 1.4 cm = 4.2 cm
C to R	2.7 cm	C to R′	3 × 2.7 cm = 8.1 cm

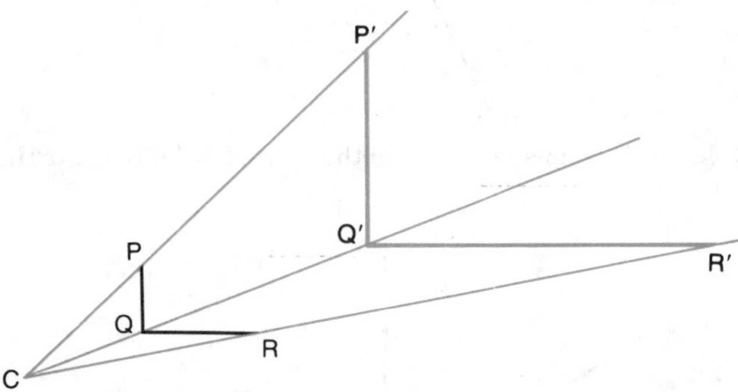

Enlargements are often drawn on a *grid*. You may be given the coordinates of the centre of enlargement and the vertices (corners) of the object. On a grid it is often easier to find the distances *along* and *up* and enlarge these using the scale factor.

Question

The vertices of a triangle are A(5, 2), B(5, 4) and C(2, 3). Draw this triangle on the grid below. Enlarge it on the grid using scale factor 2 and centre of enlargement (1, 1). Label the image triangle A′B′C′ and give the coordinates of its vertices.

Answer

Distances

Object	Image
Centre to A 4 along, 1 up	Centre to A′ 8 along, 2 up
Centre to B 4 along, 4 up	Centre to B′ 8 along, 8 up
Centre to C 1 along, 2 up	Centre to C′ 2 along, 4 up

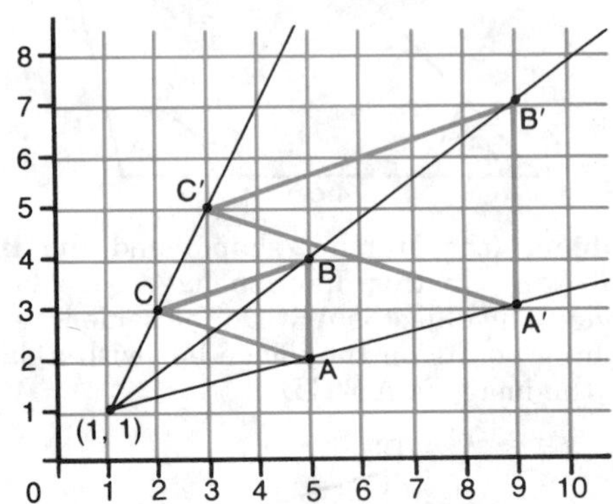

Coordinates of vertices of A′B′C′ are:
A′(9, 3), B′(9, 7), C′(3, 5).

FINDING SCALE FACTORS

When a shape is enlarged, the size of each length is changed in the same way. So you can find the scale factor of the enlargement by measuring any two *matching lengths*.

$$\text{scale factor} = \frac{\text{image length}}{\text{matching object length}}$$

The lengths must be in the *same* unit.

Question

What is the scale factor of this enlargement?

Answer

On the object, AB = 2 cm   On the image, A′B′ = 5 cm

$$\text{Scale factor} = \frac{A'B'}{AB} = \frac{5\text{ cm}}{2\text{ cm}} = 2.5$$

2.19 Transformations

A **transformation** is a change. **Translation, rotation** and **reflection** are transformations. Each changes (moves) the position of an object. This unit is about these three transformations.

Enlargement is also a transformation. It changes the size of an object. Enlargements are described in unit 2.18.

Sometimes you will find the words '*map*' or '*mapping*' used instead of '*transform*' or '*transformation*'. This is because a transformation is a special mapping.

TRANSLATION

A **translation** is a *sliding* movement (without rotation or reflection). In a translation every point is moved the same amount in the same direction.

To describe a translation, you must give:

(a) the *distance* moved,

(b) the *direction* of the movement.

Question

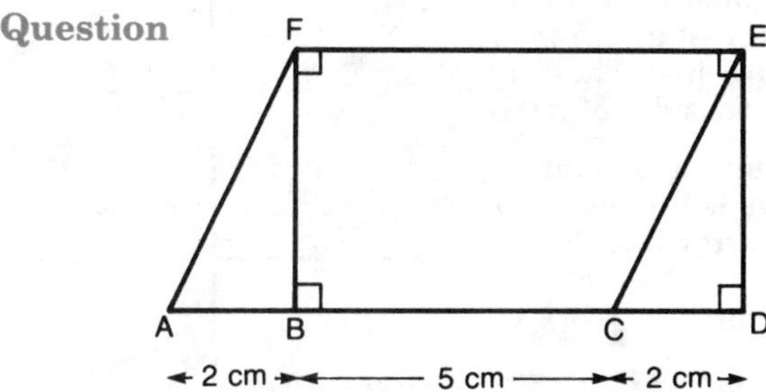

In the diagram, BDEF is a rectangle. Describe fully the transformation which maps triangle ABF on to triangle CDE.

Answer

The transformation is a translation of 7 cm in a direction parallel to AD.

A *grid* makes a translation easy to describe. You can use '*steps across*' and '*steps up or down*' or a *vector*.

Remember that moves right or up are positive$^+$,
moves left or down are negative$^-$.

For example, on the grid below the translation which maps triangle ABC to A′B′C′ is:

7 right,
3 down

or vector $\binom{7}{-3}$

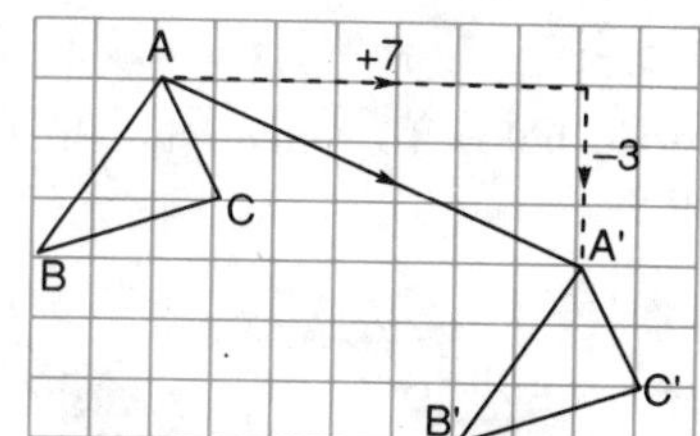

Here are some important **properties** of translation.

1 It does *not* change size and shape. An object and its image are *directly congruent* (i.e. one can be fitted exactly on top of the other, without turning it over).

2 Lines drawn from 'object points' to 'image points' are all *parallel* and *equal* in length.

For example, triangle ABC (the object) has been translated to triangle A′B′C′ (the image).

ROTATION

A **rotation** is a *turning* movement. In a rotation every point turns through the same angle (the angle of rotation) about a fixed point (the centre of rotation).

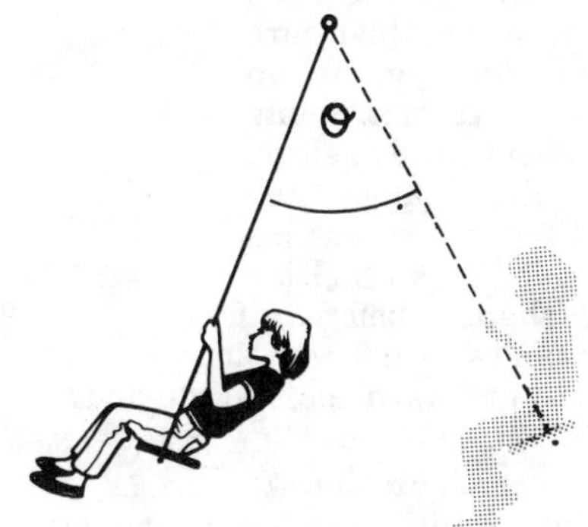

To describe a rotation, you must give:

(a) the *centre* of rotation,

(b) the *angle* of rotation,

(c) the *direction* of rotation, (anticlockwise is positive $^+$, clockwise is negative $^-$).

Here are some important **properties** of rotation.

1 It does *not* change size and shape. An object and its image are *directly congruent.*

2 The centre of rotation is the only *fixed* (**invariant**) point. All other points move.

3 The centre of rotation can be anywhere in the plane.

4 Every line turns through the *same* angle. This is the **angle of rotation.**

The easiest rotations you are likely to be given are ±90° and 180°. Here are two ways to do these rotations **on a grid**.

1 *By tracing*

Trace the object shape in pencil. Put a cross (+) on your tracing paper at the centre of rotation (draw along the grid lines). With a pencil point holding the tracing paper at the cross, turn the tracing paper through the ±90° or 180° angle needed (the cross will sit over the grid lines again). Press your pencil point through each corner point of the traced shape – this should leave pencil dots at the corner points of the image. Join up the pencil dots to give the image shape.

Question

On the given grid show the position of triangle ABC after a rotation of $^+$90° about the point P. Label the image A′B′C′.

Answer

A positive rotation is anticlockwise.

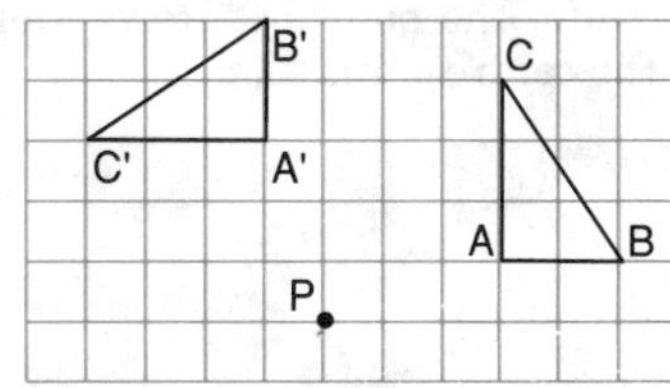

2 *Using displacements*

Look at the previous question again. Note where point A is in relation to the centre of rotation P. It is:

3 units right,
1 unit up

After the rotation of $^+$90°, the image point A′ is:

1 unit left,
3 units up

1 left
A'
3 up
A
1 up
P
3 right

Check that the same idea works for points B and C too. With practice, you should be able to use this pattern to do rotations on a grid. It is quicker than tracing.

When the shape to be rotated is **not on a grid**, the easiest way to do the rotation is with a *tracing*. Before tracing the shape, draw a line from an object point to the centre of rotation. Use a protractor to 'rotate' this line through the given angle. Trace the shape, the centre point and your line joining an object point to the centre. Rotate the tracing about the centre, through the given angle (by turning it until your traced line and 'rotated line' match). Then draw the image shape as before.

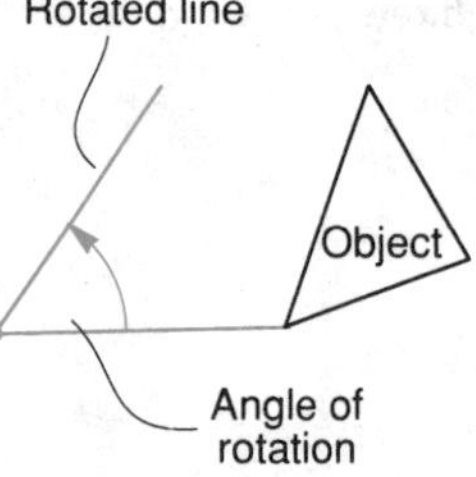

This method can be used for *any* angle of rotation.

Given an object and its image, you can find the centre and angle of rotation.

To find the centre of rotation:
Join two matching points on the object and image and draw the perpendicular bisector of this line. Repeat this for two other matching points. The centre of rotation is where the two perpendicular bisectors cross.

To find the angle of rotation:

1 If you have the centre of rotation, then draw two lines joining an object point and its image point to the centre. The angle between these two lines is the angle of rotation. You can measure it with a protractor.

Question

Find the centre and angle of the rotation which maps triangle ABC onto triangle A′B′C.

Answer

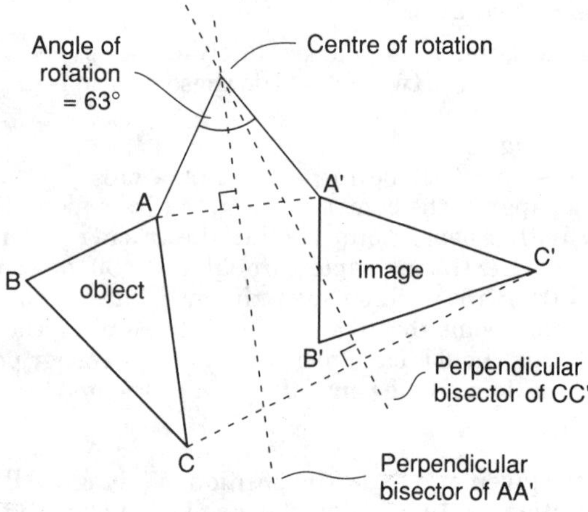

2 To find the angle of rotation, *without* the centre of rotation, extend any object line and its matching image line until they cross. The angle between these lines is the angle of rotation. (Note: the point of intersection of the lines is *not* usually the centre of rotation.)

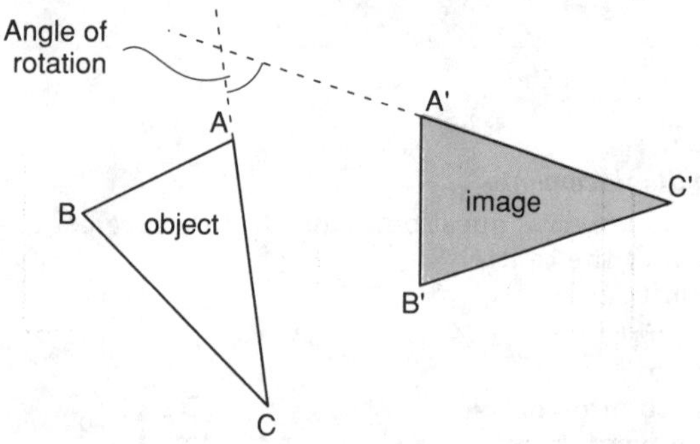

REFLECTION

In a **reflection** an object is changed into its **mirror image**. To obtain or describe a reflection you must know the position of the **mirror line**.

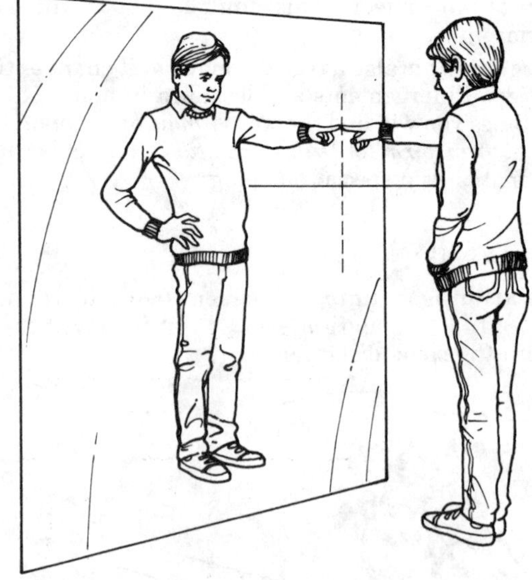

Here are some important **properties** of reflection:

1 It does *not* change size and shape. But it does *'flip'* the shape over. An object and its image are *oppositely congruent* (i.e. one can be fitted exactly on top of the other after being 'flipped' over).

2 A point and its image are the *same* distance from the mirror line. They are on *opposite* sides of it.

3 A line joining a point to its image is *perpendicular* to the mirror line. It is also *bisected* by the mirror line.

4 The image of a point *on* the mirror line is the point itself.

5 The angle between a line and the mirror line is *equal* to the angle between its image and the mirror line (i.e. the mirror line bisects the angle between a line and its image).

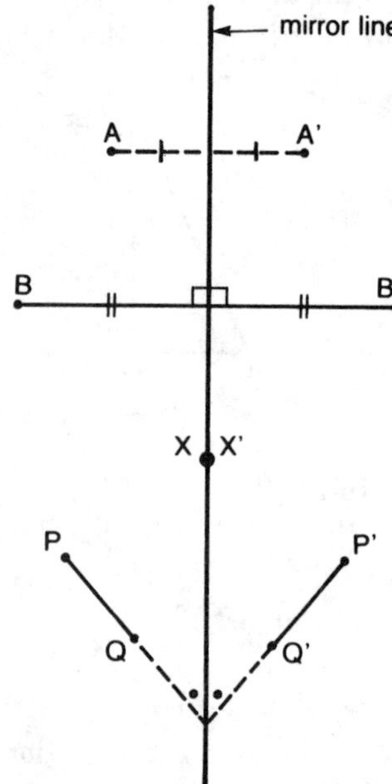

When reflecting an object in a mirror line, reflect each vertex (corner point) in turn. Make each image point the same perpendicular distance from the mirror line as its object point, but on the opposite side. You may find it easier to draw mirror images if you turn your paper round so the mirror line looks vertical.

Question

Use the grid below to reflect the shaded L-shape in the mirror line.

Answer

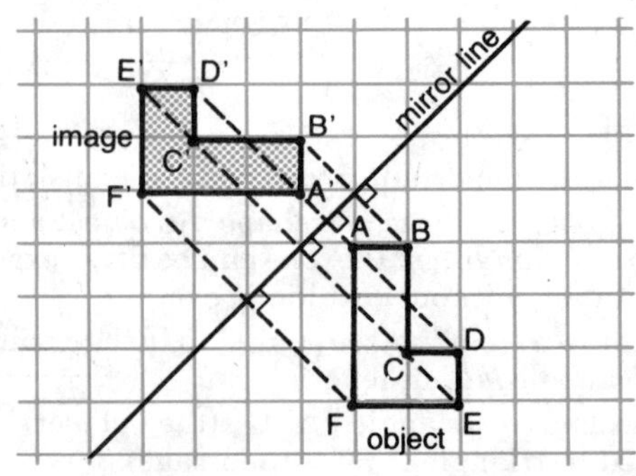

The position of a mirror line on a grid may be given using the equation of the straight line (see Unit 2.33).

Question

On the grid below find the coordinates of the point (4, 2), after reflection in:

(a) the x-axis (b) the y-axis

(c) $y=x$ (d) $y=-x$

Answer

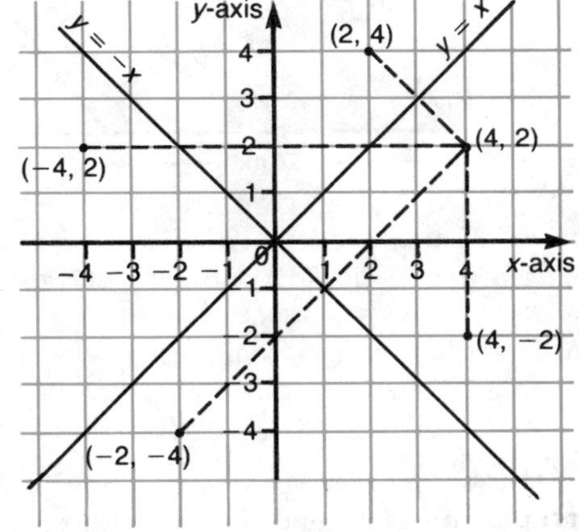

Object	→ Image	Object	→ Image
(a) (4, 2)	→ (4, −2)	(b) (4, 2)	→ (−4, 2)
(c) (4, 2)	→ (2, 4)	(d) (4, 2)	→ (−2, −4)

You can find the mirror line given an object and its image. Join two matching points on the object and its image. Draw the perpendicular bisector of this line. The perpendicular bisector is the mirror line.

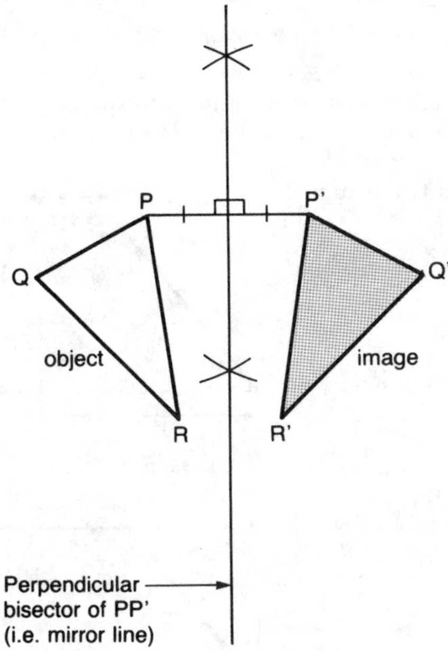

2.20 Plane symmetry

A **plane of symmetry** divides a solid into two *matching* halves. For example, a **square-based pyramid** has 4 planes of symmetry.

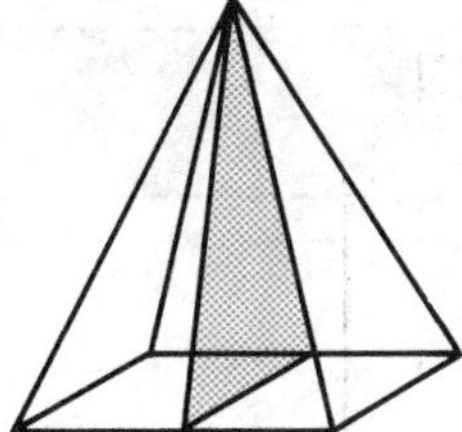

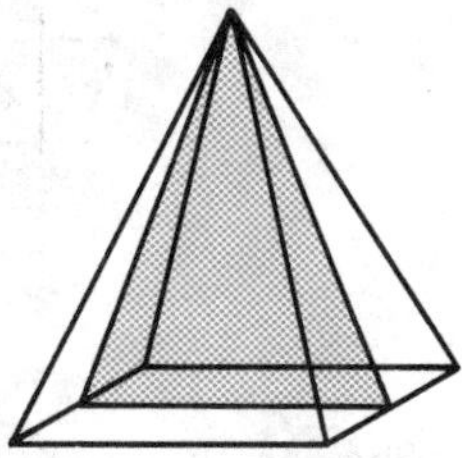

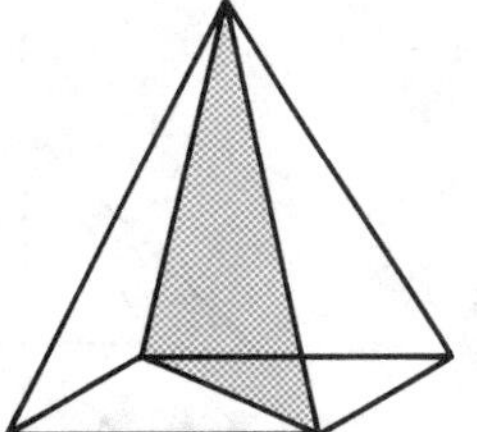

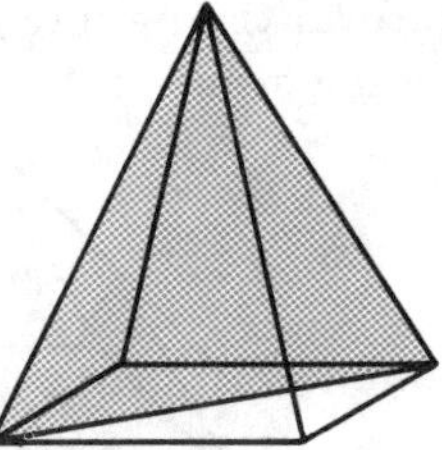

Each shaded shape shows where a plane of symmetry cuts the solid

Imagine that the plane of symmetry is a mirror.
Half of the solid and its reflection look like the full solid.

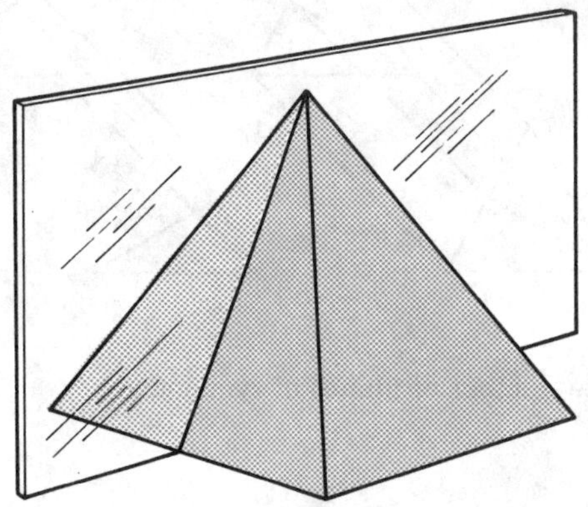

Some other well known solids which have plane symmetry are:

Cuboid
(3 planes of symmetry)

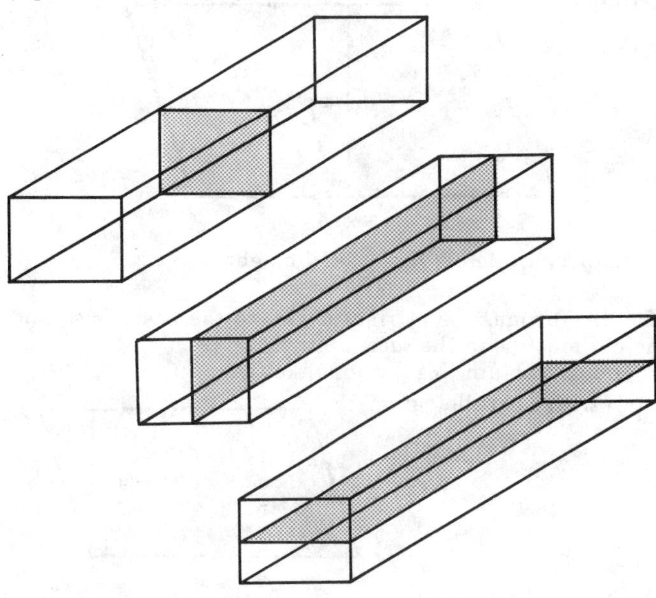

Cube
(9 planes of symmetry; here are 5, find the rest)

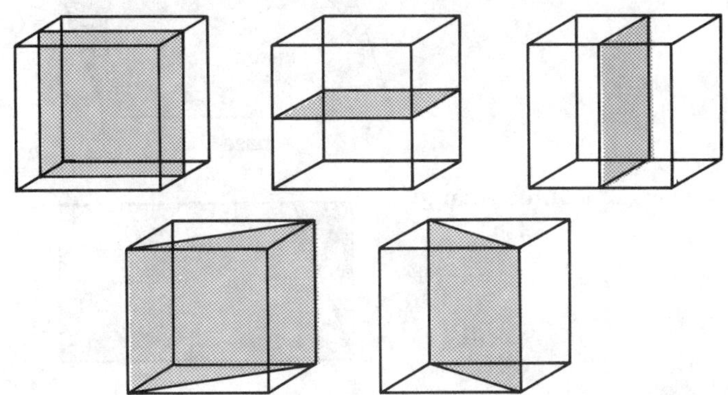

Equilateral triangular prism
(4 planes of symmetry)

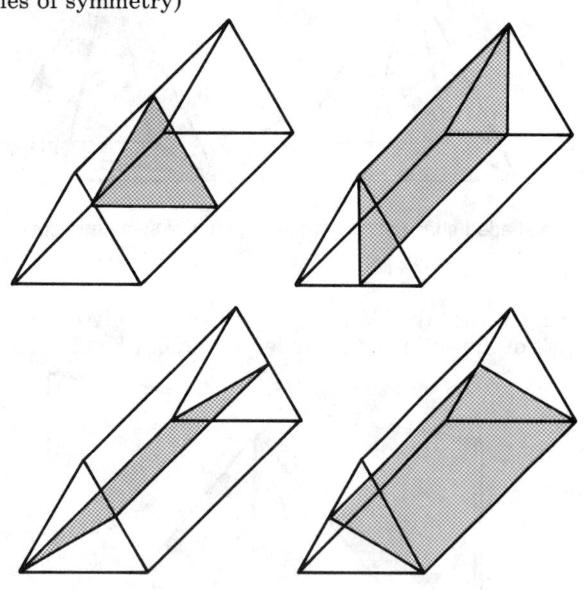

Sphere
(an infinite number of planes of symmetry)

2.21 Area 2

PARALLELOGRAM

A **parallelogram** is a quadrilateral with opposite sides parallel.

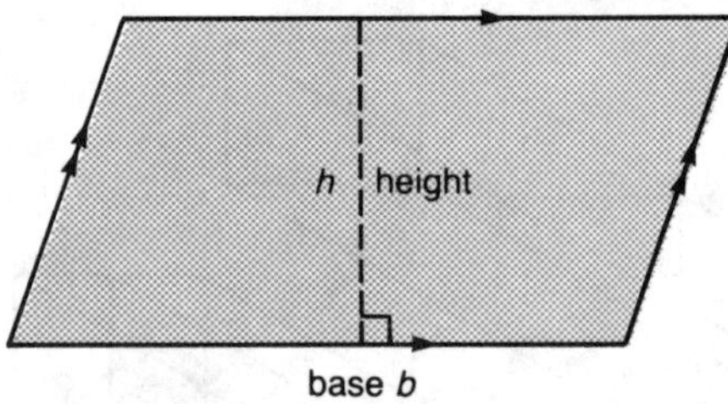

Area of a parallelogram = base × height
$= bh$

The height must be at *right angles* to the base. Base and height must be in the *same* unit.

You can obtain this formula like this:

Start with a parallelogram ...

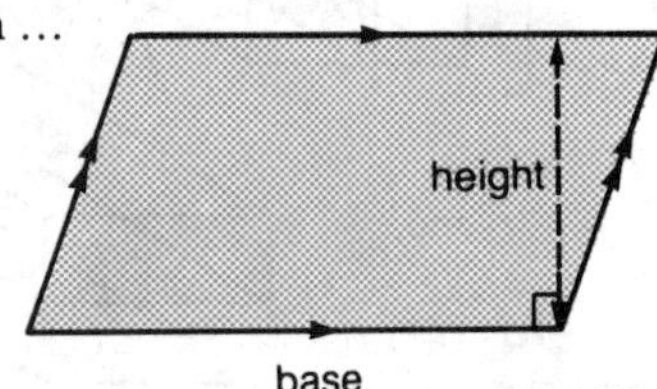

cut it up like this ...

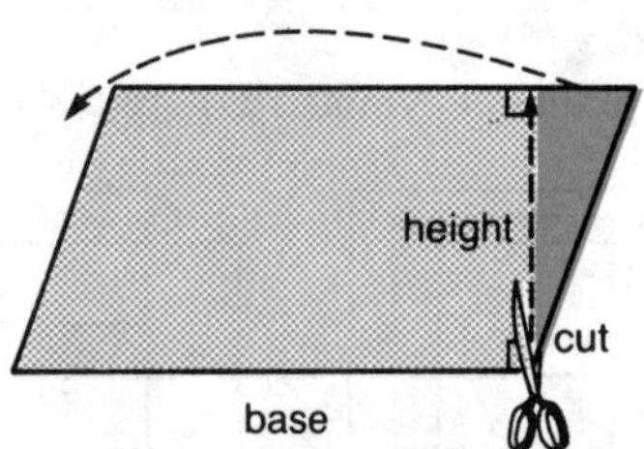

and make it into rectangle.

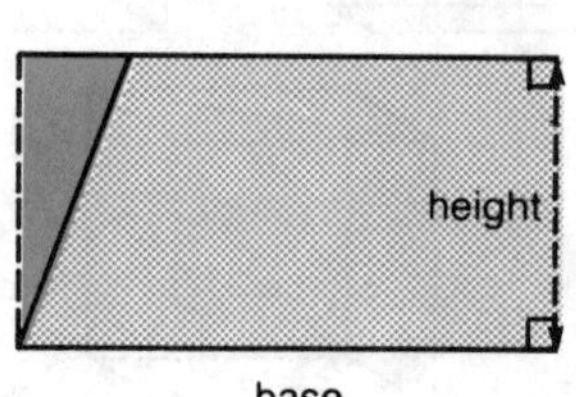

The rectangle has been made from the parallelogram. So their areas must be the same.

The area of this rectangle = base × height
So the area of parallelogram = base × height

Question

What is the area of this parallelogram?

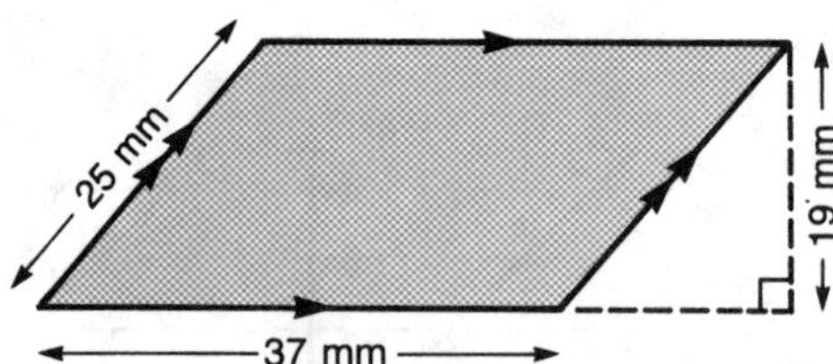

Answer

base = 37 mm, height = 19 mm

(The 'height' is 19 mm because it is at right angles to the base. 25 mm is the 'slant height'.)

Area of the parallelogram = base × height
= 37 mm × 19 mm
= 703 mm^2

C

TRAPEZIUM

A **trapezium** is a quadrilateral with one pair of parallel sides.

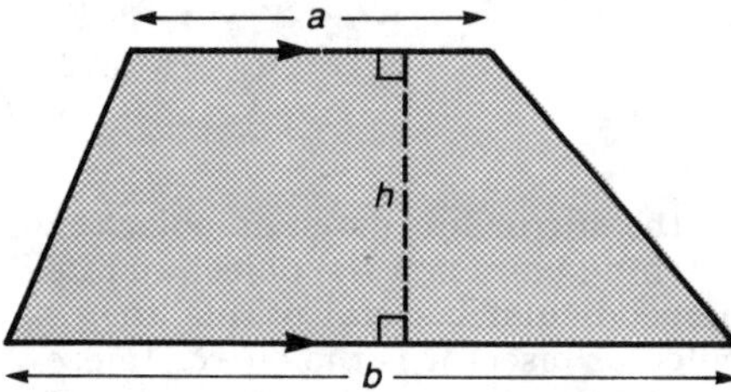

Area of a trapezium $= \frac{1}{2} \times$ (sum of parallel sides) × height
$= \frac{1}{2}(a+b)h$

The height must be at right angles to the parallel sides.
All the measurements must be in the same unit.
Here is one way to obtain this formula:

Start with a trapezium ...

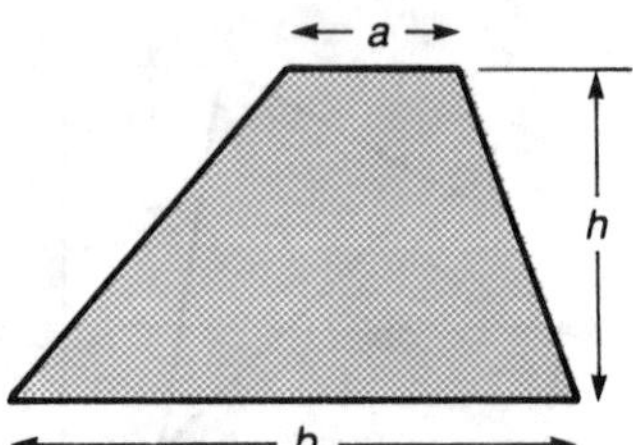

cut it up like this ...

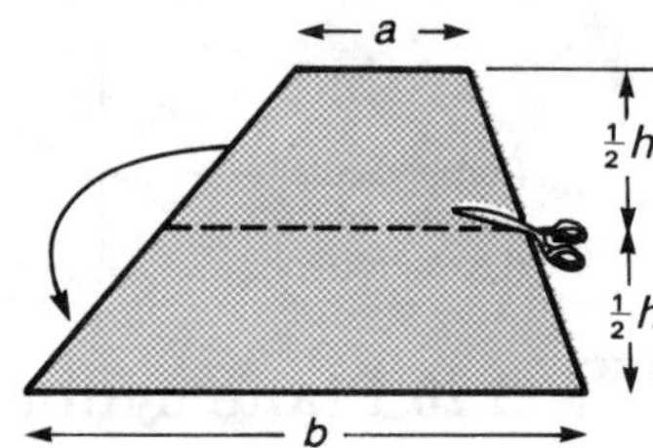

and make it into a parallelogram.

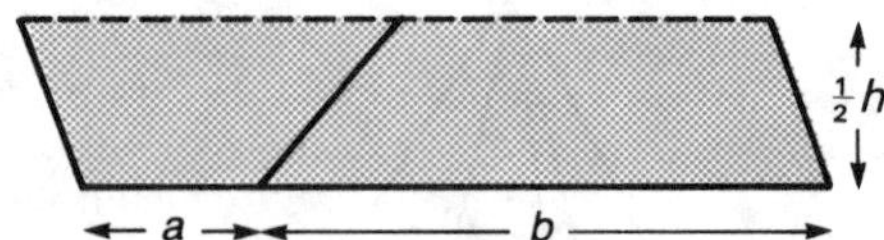

The parallelogram and the trapezium must have the same area.

The area of the parallelogram = base × height

$= (a + b) \times \frac{1}{2}h$

$= \frac{1}{2}(a + b)h$

So the area of the trapezium $= \frac{1}{2}(a + b)h$

Question

This trapezium shows the shape of a special DIY knife blade. What is its area?

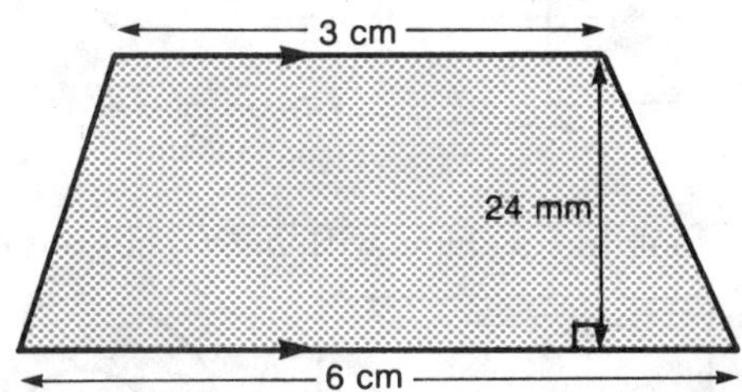

Answer

parallel sides: 3 cm and 6 cm, height = 24 mm = 2.4 cm

Area of the trapezium

$= \frac{1}{2} \times$ (sum of parallel sides) × height

$= \frac{1}{2} \times (3\text{ cm} + 6\text{ cm}) \times 2.4\text{ cm}$

$= \frac{1}{2} \times 9\text{ cm} \times 2.4\text{ cm}$

$= 10.8\text{ cm}^2$

CIRCLE

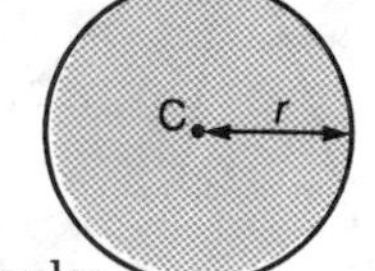

Area of a circle $= \pi \times (\text{radius})^2$

$= \pi r^2$

Here is a way to obtain this formula:

Cut a circle into 16 equal sectors …

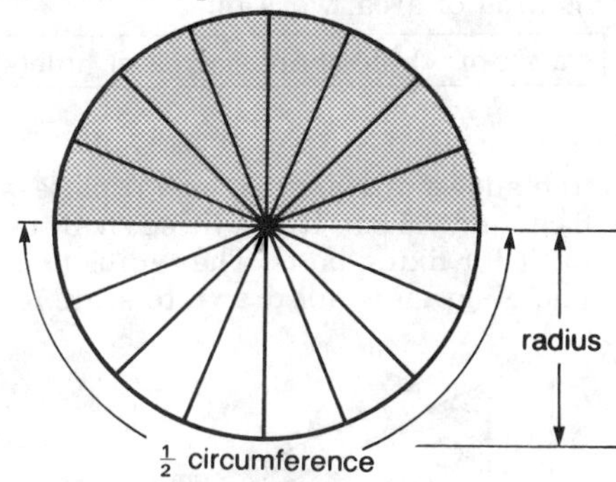

put them together like this:

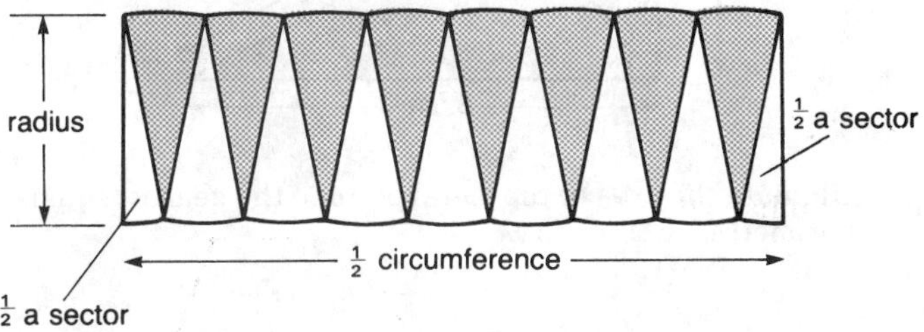

The shape you make is almost a rectangle. (Cutting the circle into more sectors makes it even more like a rectangle.)

Its length $= \frac{1}{2}$ circumference $= \frac{1}{2} \times 2\pi r = \pi r$

Its width = radius = r

Area of the rectangle = length × width $= \pi r \times r = \pi r^2$

So the area of the circle $= \pi r^2$

If you know the radius of a circle, then you can use this formula to find its area. π (the Greek letter *pi*) is the same for all circles. Its value cannot be stated exactly. So in calculations you must use an approximate value for π. You can use $\pi = 3$ for very approximate calculations. Usually you will be given the value of π to use.

When using decimals, π is often given as 3.14 or 3.142. When using fractions, π is given as $3\frac{1}{7}$ or $\frac{22}{7}$.

Your calculator may have a $\boxed{\pi}$ key. You can just press this key instead of entering the approximate value yourself.

Your $\boxed{\pi}$ key may give the value of π correct to six or more decimal places. So always check whether you may use this key to answer a 'circle question'.

Sometimes you will be given the diameter instead of the radius.

Remember radius $= \frac{1}{2}$ diameter

Question

A circular badge was made out of fabric. It has a diameter of 5 cm. What is its area? Give your answer to 1 decimal place. (Use the $\boxed{\pi}$ key on your calculator. If you do not have a $\boxed{\pi}$ key, use $\pi = 3.14$.)

Answer

diameter = 5 cm, radius $= \frac{1}{2}$ of 5 cm = 2.5 cm

Area of the circle $= \pi r^2$

$= \pi \times 2.5^2\text{ cm}^2$

$= \pi \times 2.5 \times 2.5\text{ cm}^2$

$= 19.6\text{ cm}^2$ (to 1 d.p.)

Display using $\boxed{\pi}$ 19.63495408

Display using $\pi = 3.14$ 19.625

OTHER SHAPES

Many *complicated* shapes can be split into *simple* shapes. This helps you to find their areas. For example,

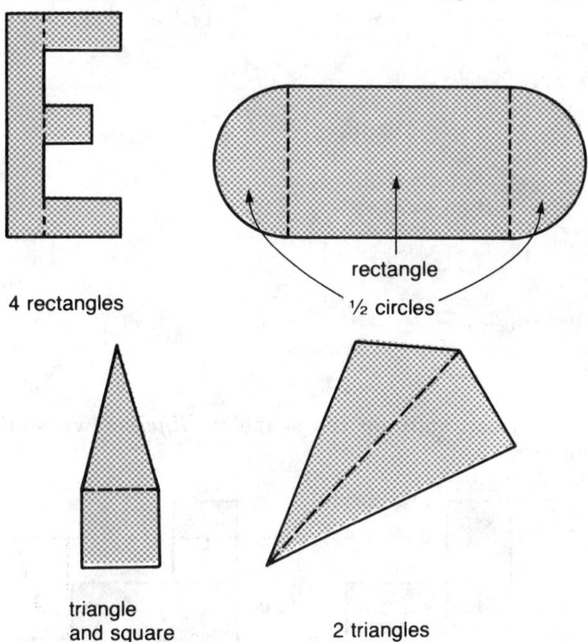

To find the total area, work out the area of each simple shape and add them together.

Question

The sketch shows the shape of a formica work surface (not drawn to scale). The surface is made from a rectangle of sides 40 cm and 68 cm and half a circle of diameter 40 cm.

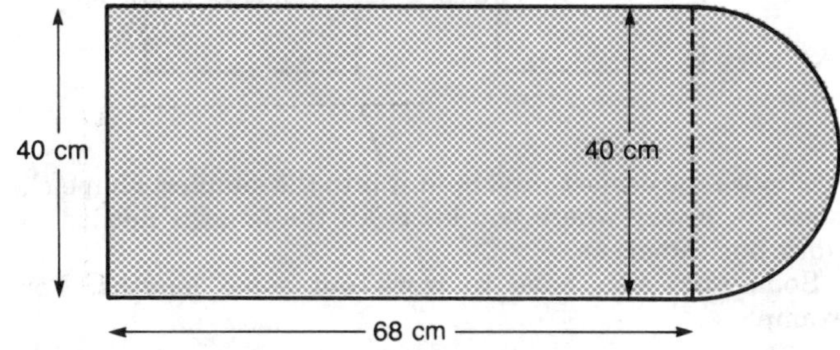

Calculate the area of the work surface. (Take π to be 3.14.)

Answer

Area of the work surface
$= \text{area of rectangle} + \text{area inside half a circle}$

Area of rectangle = length × width
$= 68 \text{ cm} \times 40 \text{ cm} = 2720 \text{ cm}^2$ C

diameter of circle = 40 cm

radius of circle $= \frac{1}{2}$ of 40 cm
$= 20$ cm

Area inside a circle $= \pi r^2$

Area inside half a circle $= \frac{1}{2}\pi r^2$
$= \frac{1}{2} \times 3.14 \times 20^2 \text{ cm}^2$
$= 628 \text{ cm}^2$

So area of the work surface $= 2720 \text{ cm}^2 + 628 \text{ cm}^2$
$= 3348 \text{ cm}^2$

Here is one way to do this on a calculator. Try it. Then see if there is a better way to do it on your calculator.

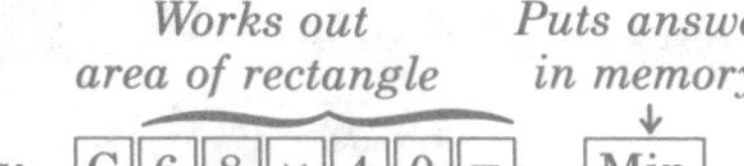

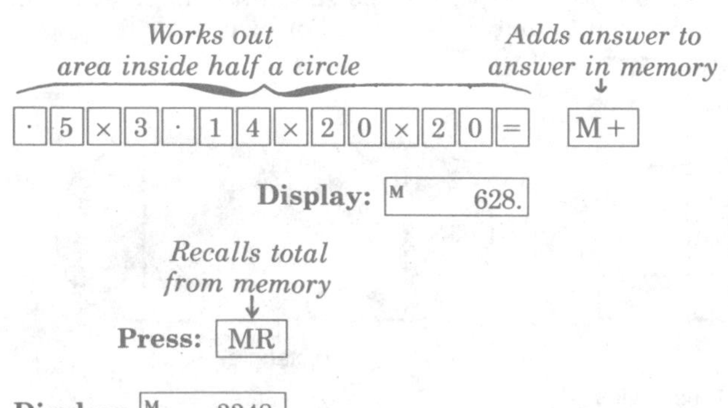

Often you can split up the shape in *different* ways. For example,

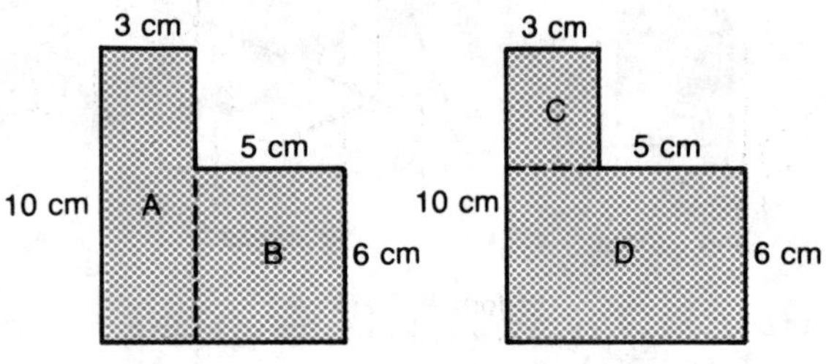

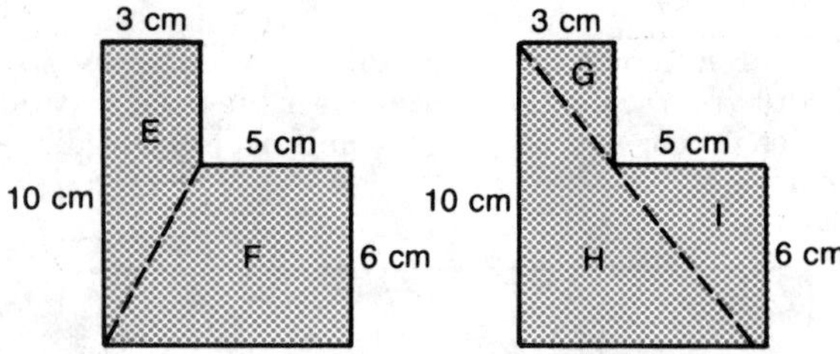

Choose the easiest way. Split it into the simplest shape(s). Look for a way where you know all the lengths needed to work out the areas.

Sometimes you have to work out some lengths. For example,

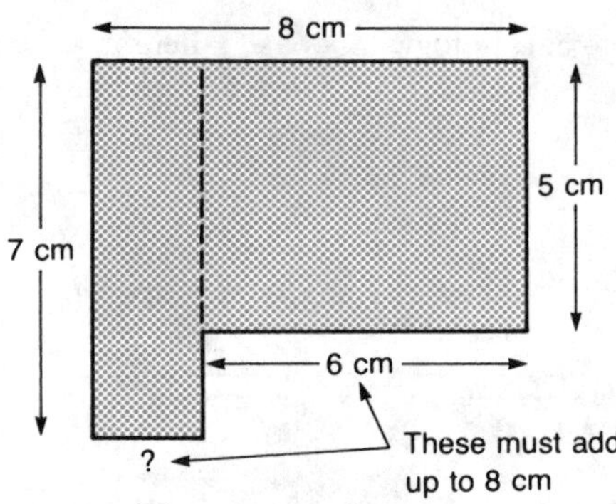

Some areas look like a shape with *hole(s)* cut out of it. For example,

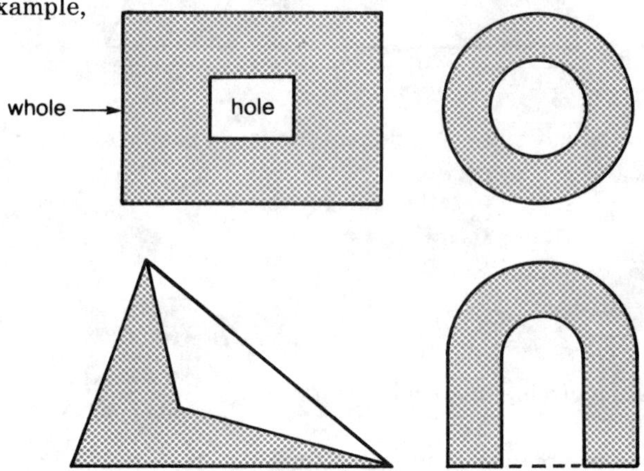

To find this kind of area, work out:

area of whole shape – area of hole(s)

Question

The sketch shows a triangular metal plate with sides of 4.5 cm, 6 cm and 7.5 cm. It has three small circular holes cut out of it for fixing bolts. The radius of each circle is 4 mm. (The diagram is not drawn to scale.)

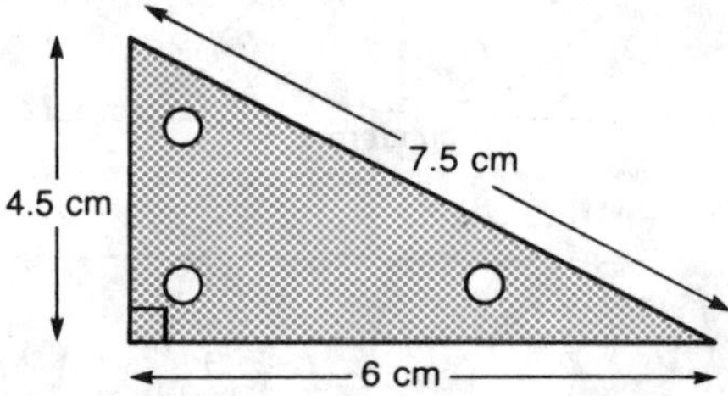

Calculate the area of the metal plate to the nearest square centimetre. (Use $\pi = 3.14$.)

Answer

Area of metal plate
$= \text{area of whole triangle} - \text{area of 3 circular holes}$

Area of circle $= \pi r^2$
$= 3.14 \times 0.4^2 \text{ cm}^2$ (4 mm = 0.4 cm)

Area of 3 circular holes $= 3 \times 3.14 \times 0.4^2 \text{ cm}^2$
$= 1.5072 \text{ cm}^2$ C

Area of whole triangle $= \frac{1}{2} \times \text{base} \times \text{height}$
$= \frac{1}{2} \times 6 \text{ cm} \times 4.5 \text{ cm}$
$= 13.5 \text{ cm}^2$

Area of metal plate $= 13.5 \text{ cm}^2 - 1.5072 \text{ cm}^2$
$= 12 \text{ cm}^2$ (to the nearest cm^2)

Display: 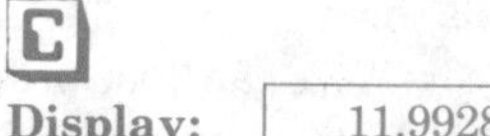

You can use the memory on a calculator to do this. Try this way if you can.

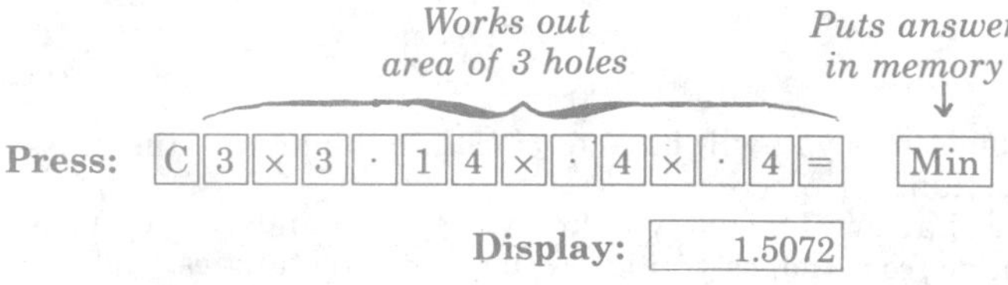

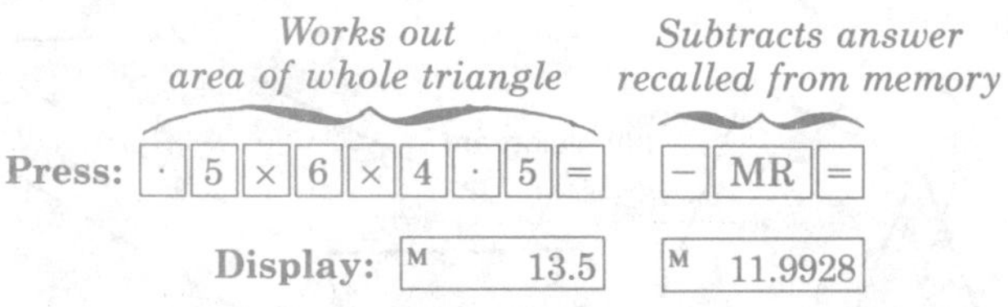

There may be another way to do this on your calculator. Experiment to find out if there is. Choose the best way to do this on your calculator.

SURFACE AREA OF A CYLINDER

The surface area of a cylinder is made up of 2 equal ends and 1 curved face.

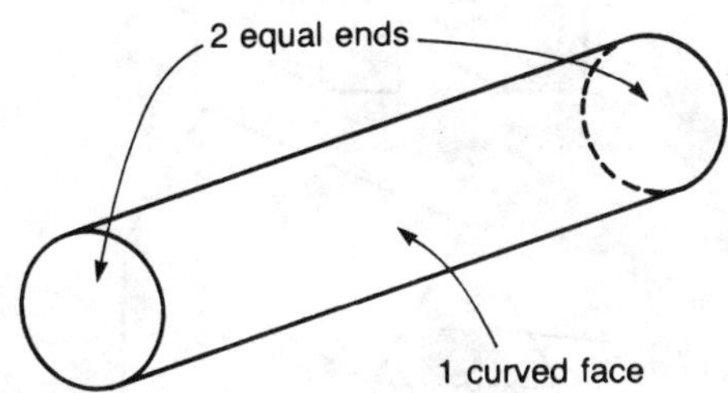

Each end is a circle.
So the area of the 2 circular ends = 2 × area of a circle
$= 2\pi r^2$

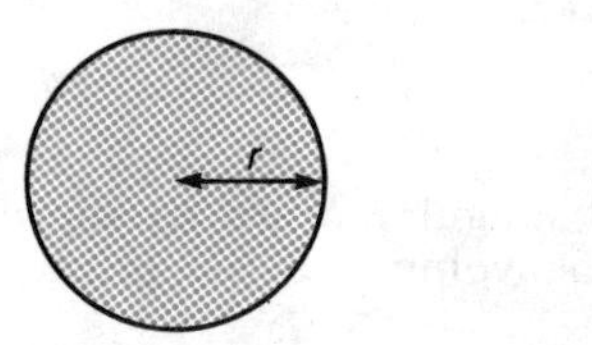

The curved surface can be cut open to make a rectangle.

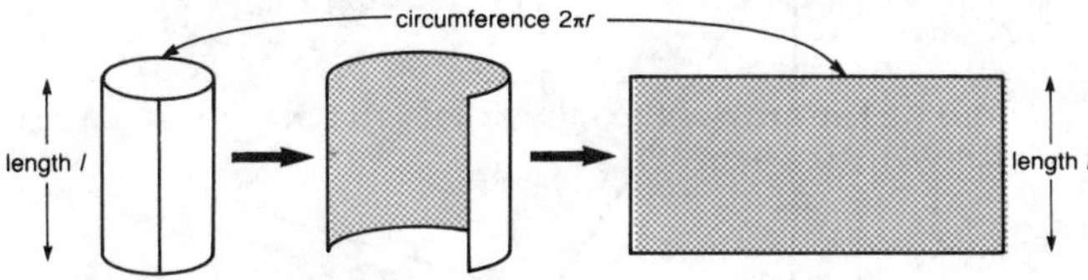

Area of curved surface
= circumference of end face × length of cylinder
$= 2\pi r \times l$
$= 2\pi rl$

Total surface area of cylinder
= area of two circular ends + area of curved surface
$= 2\pi r^2 + 2\pi rl$
$= 2\pi r(r + l)$

Question

A cylindrical hot water tank is closed at both ends. The radius of the tank is 0.5 m and the height is 0.75 m. Calculate the total surface area of the tank to the nearest square metre. (Take $\pi = 3.14$.)

Answer

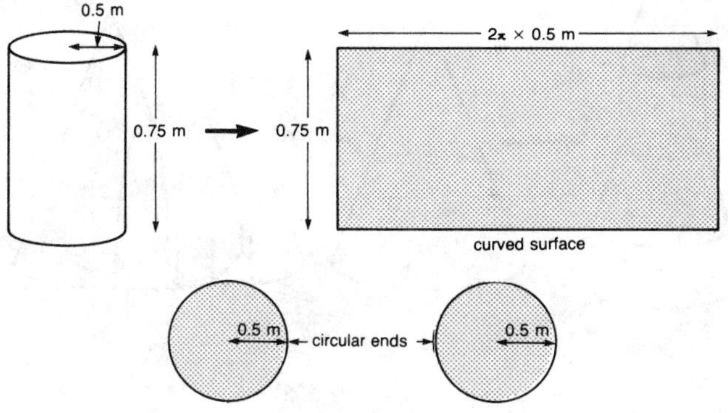

Surface area of tank
= area of two circular ends + area of curved surface
$= 2\pi r^2 + 2\pi rl$

Area of 2 circular ends $= 2\pi r^2$
$= 2 \times 3.14 \times 0.5^2 \text{ m}^2$
$= 1.57 \text{ m}^2$

C

Area of curved surface $= 2\pi rl$
$= 2 \times 3.14 \times 0.5 \times 0.75 \text{ m}^2$
$= 2.355 \text{ m}^2$

Total surface area of tank
$= 1.57 \text{ m}^2 + 2.355 \text{ m}^2$
$= 3.925 \text{ m}^2$ **Display:** 3.925
$= 4 \text{ m}^2$ (to the nearest square metre)

This calculation is easy to do using a calculator memory. Work out the best way to do it on your calculator.

2.22 Volumes of prisms

PRISMS

A **prism** is a solid with a uniform **cross-section**. This means that you can cut a prism into 'slices' like this:

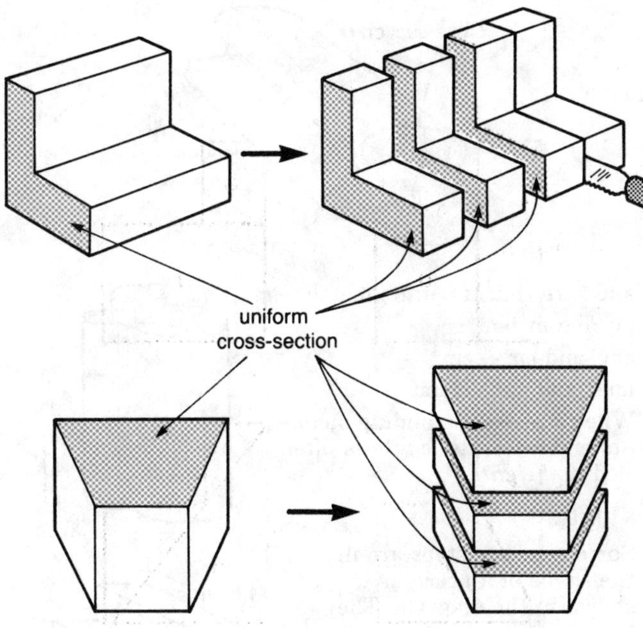

Each 'cut' is parallel to an end-face. The ends of each slice are all the same shape and size. This is called the **cross-section** of the prism.

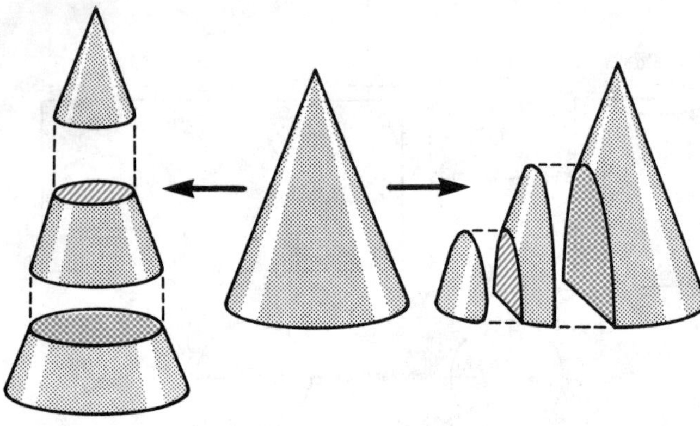

This solid is *not* a prism.

You cannot cut it into slices which have the same cross-section.

A prism usually takes its name from the shape of its cross-section.

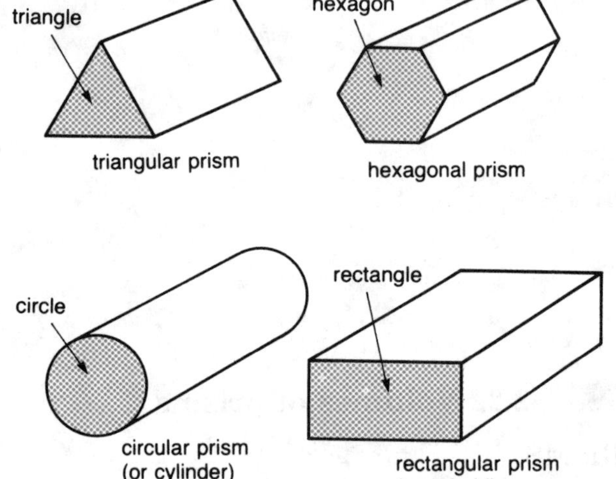

VOLUME OF ANY PRISM

Volume of any prism = (area of cross-section) × length

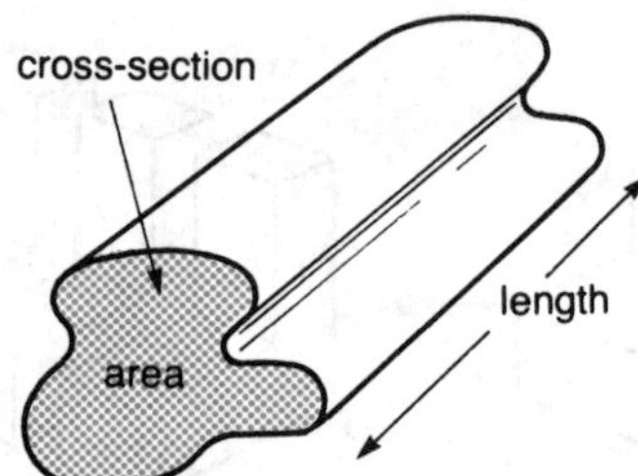

Make sure that the units match, e.g.

m^2 and m → m^3

cm^2 and cm → cm^3

mm^2 and mm → mm^3

When a prism is standing on one of its end-faces, its *length* is often called its *height*.

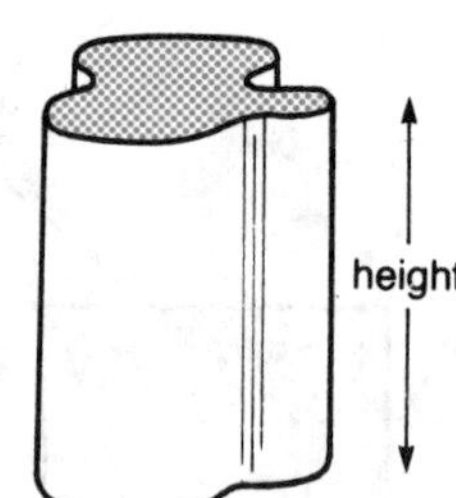

Question

Some concrete steps are in the shape of a prism as shown in the diagram. They have a cross-sectional area of 864 cm^2 and are 1.06 m long.

What is the volume of the prism in cubic centimetres?

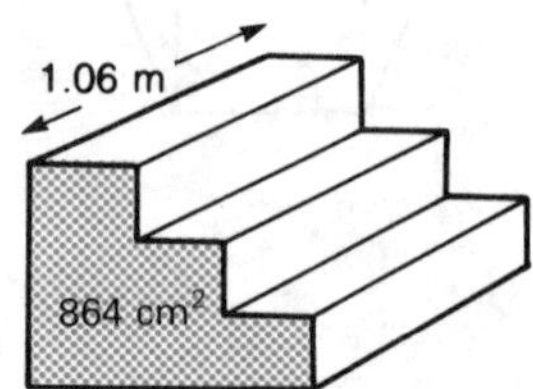

Answer

area of cross-section = 864 cm^2

length = 1.06 m = 106 cm

volume of prism = area of cross-section × length

= 864 cm^2 × 106 cm

= 91 584 cm^3

Sometimes you will have to *calculate* the area of the cross-section.

Its shape will be one you know, e.g. a triangle, or it will be *made from* shapes you know, e.g. from rectangles.

Remember All the measurements must be in the *same* unit.

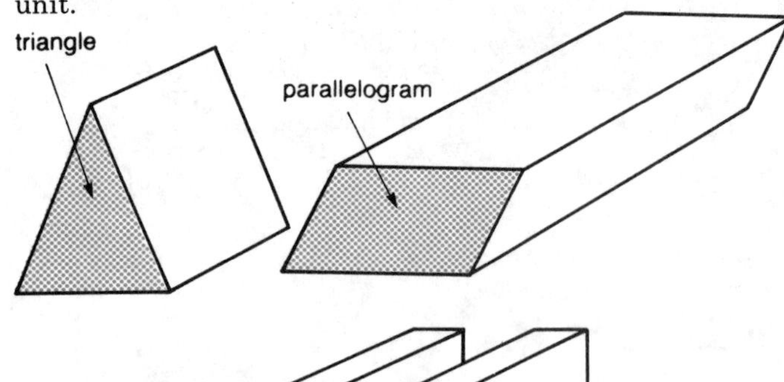

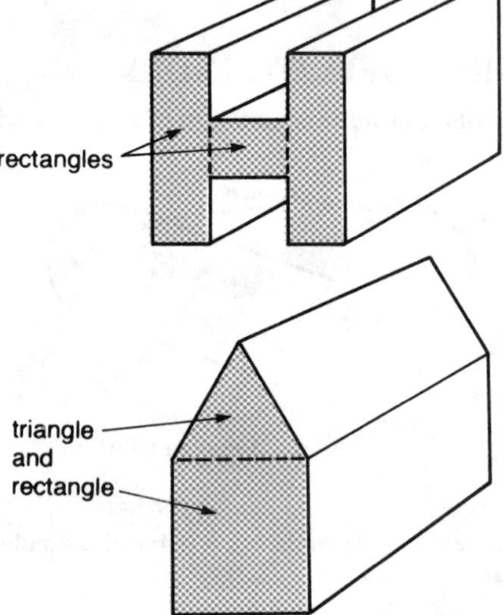

Question

A lean-to shed is a triangular prism as shown in the diagram. Calculate the volume of the prism in cubic metres.

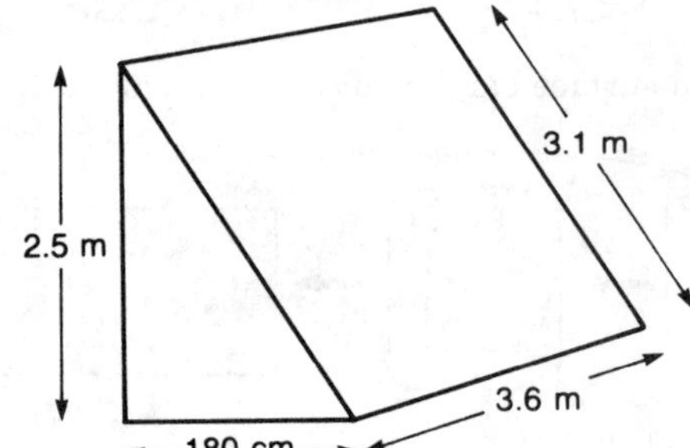

Answer

base of triangle = 180 cm = 1.8 m

volume of prism

= (area of triangular cross-section) × length

= ($\frac{1}{2}$ × base × height of triangle) × length

= ($\frac{1}{2}$ × 1.8 m × 2.5 m) × 3.6 m

= 8.1 m^3

VOLUME OF A CYLINDER

A **cylinder** is a special prism. Its cross-section is a *circle*.

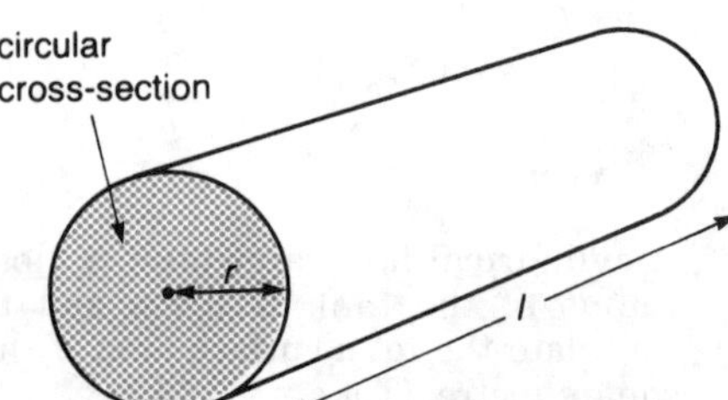

Volume of a cylinder
$= (\text{area of circular cross-section}) \times \text{length}$
$= \pi r^2 \qquad\qquad\qquad\qquad \times \quad l$
$= \pi r^2 l$

Question

An oil storage tank is a cylinder of height 4.5 m and radius 1.8 m. Estimate its volume to the nearest cubic metre. (Take $\pi = 3.14$.)

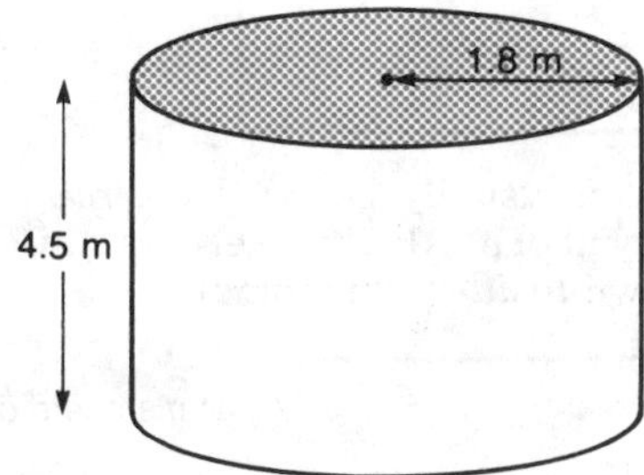

Answer

volume of cylindrical tank
$= \text{area of circular cross-section} \times \text{height}$
$= \pi r^2 \times \text{height}$
$= 3.14 \times 1.8^2 \times 4.5 \text{ m}^3$
$= 46 \text{ m}^3$ (to nearest m^3)

Display: 45.7812

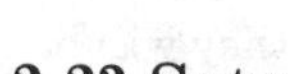

2.23 Sets

A **set** is a *collection* of things. The things have something in common; for example, a set of stamps, a set of chairs, a set of numbers.

The things in a set are called its **members** or **elements**. For example,
a 'Penny Black' is a member of the set of stamps,
an armchair is a member of the set of chairs,
21 is a member of the set of numbers.

A set is usually named or labelled with a capital letter. Curly brackets or *braces* { } often replace the words 'the set of'.
For example, X is 'the set of even numbers' can be written as $X = \{\text{even numbers}\}$.

The members of a set can be either **described** or **listed**.
For example, $A = \{\text{vowels}\}$ – *description*
or $A = \{a, e, i, o, u\}$ – *list*

When members are listed the order does not matter. Commas must be placed between members. The word 'and' is not used (unless it is a member of the set!).

Some sets have an infinite number of members. They go on for ever so it is impossible to list all their members. You can list the first few members and use three dots to show that the list continues. For example,

$X = \{\text{counting numbers}\}$
$X = \{1, 2, 3, 4, 5, \ldots\}$

First few members (1, 2, 3, 4, 5) — *The three dots show that it goes on for ever*

Some sets have too many members to list. But they do not go on for ever. You can list the first few members, put three dots to show that the pattern continues, then list the last few members. For example,

$Y = \{\text{even numbers between 1 and 301}\}$
or $Y = \{2, 4, 6, 8, \ldots, 298, 300\}$

First few members (2, 4, 6, 8) — *Pattern continues* (…) — *Last few members* (298, 300)

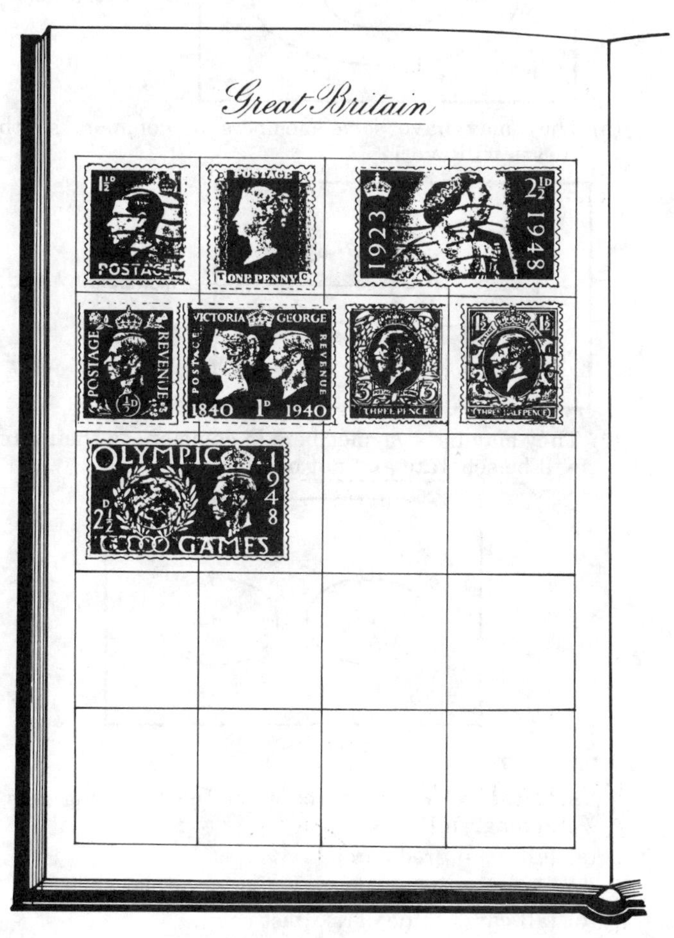

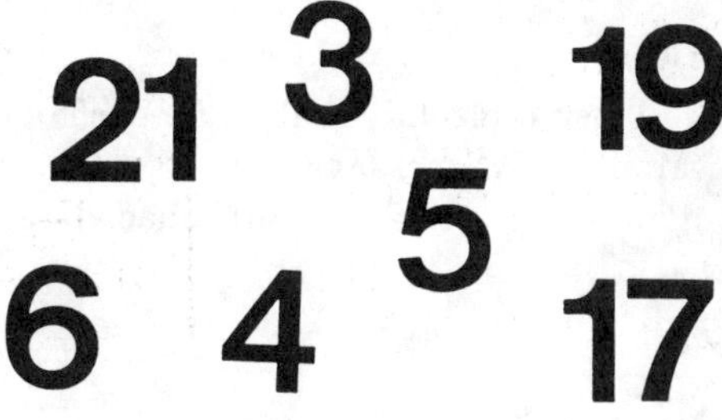

Question

(a) Write the members of each set as a **list**.
A = {negative integers}
B = {odd numbers greater than 1 but less than 11}
C = {multiples of 3 between 1 and 151}

(b) **Describe** the members listed in each of these sets.
D = {London, Washington, Moscow, Lisbon, … Madrid, Paris}
E = {1, 4, 9, 16, 25, …}
F = {January, March, May, July, August, October, December}

Answer

(a) $A = \{^-1, ^-2, ^-3, ^-4, ^-5, ^-6, \ldots\}$
$B = \{3, 5, 7, 9\}$
$C = \{3, 6, 9, 12, \ldots, 147, 150\}$

(b) D = {capital cities}
E = {square numbers}
F = {months with 31 days}

SUBSETS

A **subset** is a set within a set. All its members are also members of another set. For example
all even numbers are also counting numbers,
so {even numbers} is a subset of {counting numbers}.

So if all the members of a set A are also members of set B, then A is a subset of B.

Question

Is {rectangles} a subset of:

(a) {quadrilaterals}, (b) {solids},
(c) {polygons}, (d) {circles},
(e) {parallelograms}, (f) {squares}?

Explain each of your answers.

Answer

(a) Yes; all rectangles are quadrilaterals.
(b) No; rectangles are plane shapes not solids.
(c) Yes; all rectangles are polygons.
(d) No; a rectangle cannot be a circle.
(e) Yes; all rectangles are parallelograms.
(f) No; only some, not all, rectangles are squares.

UNIVERSAL SET

The **universal set** is the set which contains everything under discussion. The symbol used for the universal set is $\mathscr{E}$. For example, if you are talking about different dogs – black dogs, curly-haired dogs, sheep-dogs, terriers, poodles, …, then the universal set would be the set of all dogs or $\mathscr{E}$ = {all dogs}.
All other sets in the discussion will be *subsets* of the universal set $\mathscr{E}$. For example,

{black dogs}, {curly-haired dogs}, {sheep-dogs} are all subsets of $\mathscr{E}$ = {all dogs}.

In a problem it is usually clear what the universal set should be.

Question

Suggest a suitable universal set for each of the following.

(a) {Monday, Wednesday} (b) $\{^+3, ^-1, 0, ^-5\}$
(c) {vowels} (d) {quadrilaterals}

Answer

(a) $\mathscr{E}$ = {days of the week} (b) $\mathscr{E}$ = {integers}
(c) $\mathscr{E}$ = {letters of the alphabet} (d) $\mathscr{E}$ = {polygons}

VENN DIAGRAMS

Venn diagrams are pictures which help you to see sets and the relationships between sets.

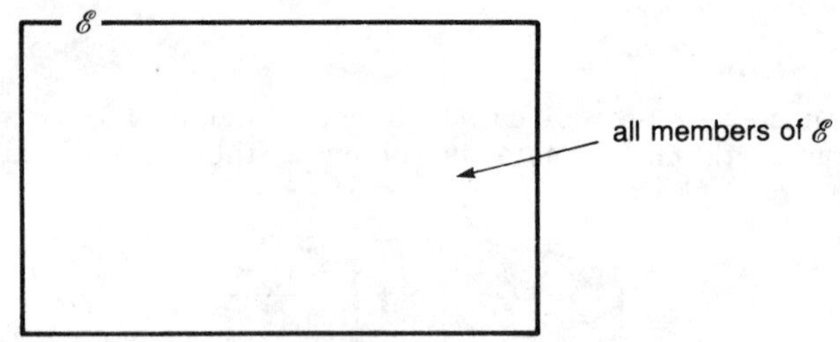

The *universal set* is usually shown by a *rectangle*. It is labelled with its symbol $\mathscr{E}$. All other sets are subsets of $\mathscr{E}$, so they must be drawn *inside* the rectangle.

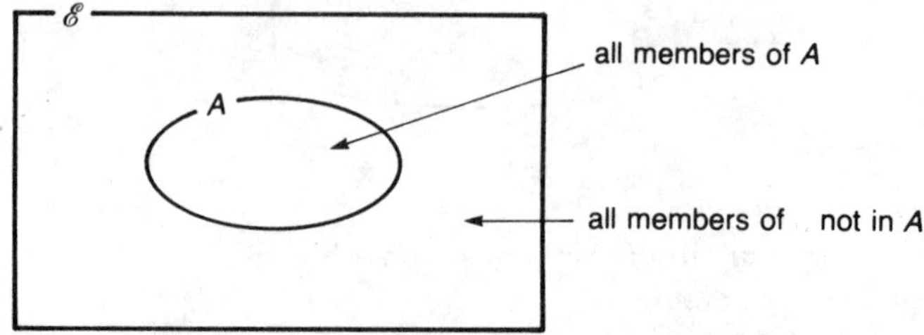

Other sets are shown by *closed curves*, such as circles or ovals. Each is usually labelled with its capital letter.

If there are two sets inside $\mathscr{E}$, then they will be related in one of these ways:

(a) One may be a *subset* of the other, so its curve will be inside the other.

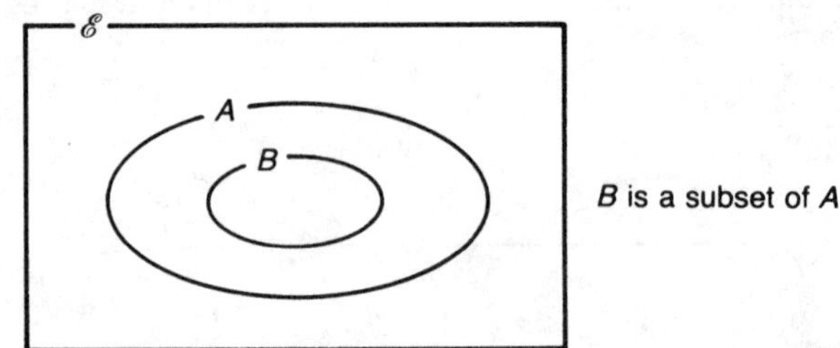

(b) They may have *some* members in common, so their curves will overlap.

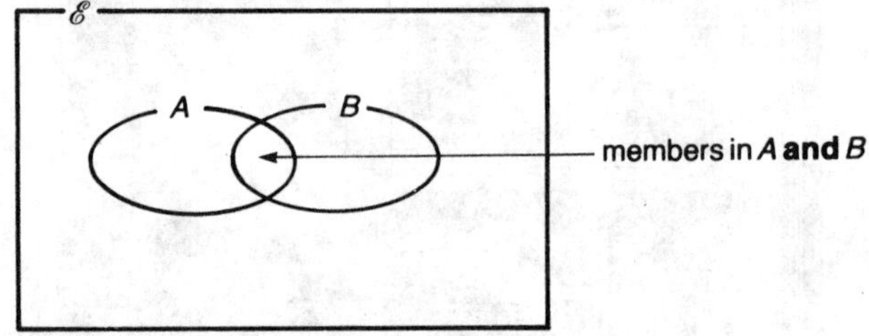

(c) They may have *no* members in common, so their curves will be separate and not overlap.

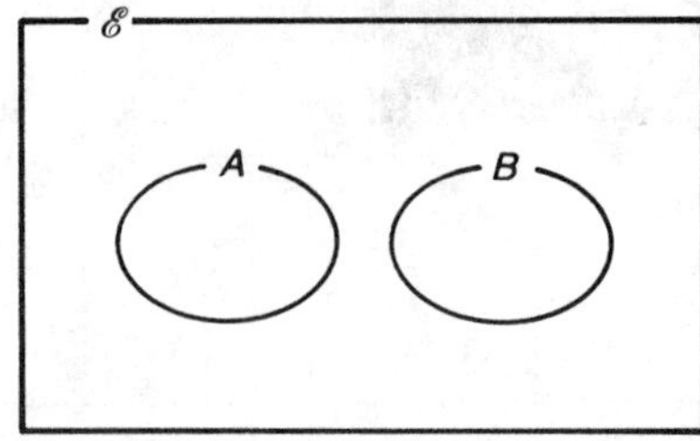

Question

Show the relationships between the following sets on Venn diagrams.

(a) {all cars}, {red cars};
(b) {Jersey cows}, {Guernsey cows}, {all cows};
(c) {all cars}, {blue cars}, {fast cars};
(d) {squares}, {rectangles}, {quadrilaterals}

Indicate on your Venn diagrams what each region represents.

Answer

(a) $\mathscr{E}$ = {all cars}, R = {red cars}

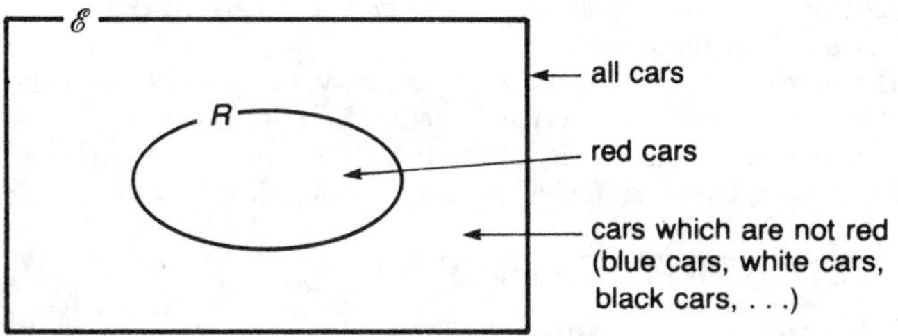

(b) $\mathscr{E}$ = {all cows}, J = {Jersey cows}, G = {Guernsey cows}.

Jersey cows cannot be Guernsey cows. So the two sets do not overlap.

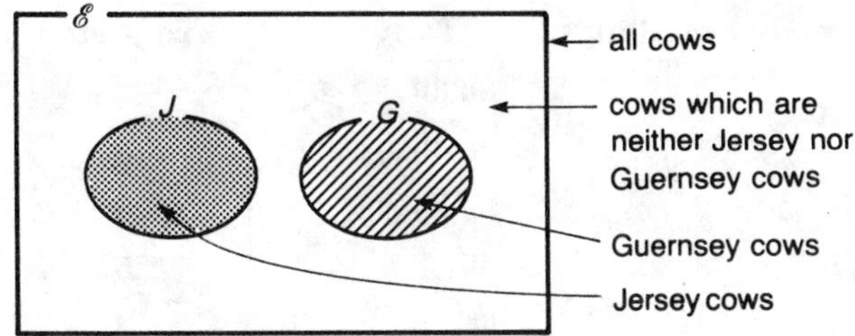

(c) $\mathscr{E}$ = {all cars}, B = {blue cars}, F = {fast cars}.

Cars can be both blue and fast. So the two sets overlap.

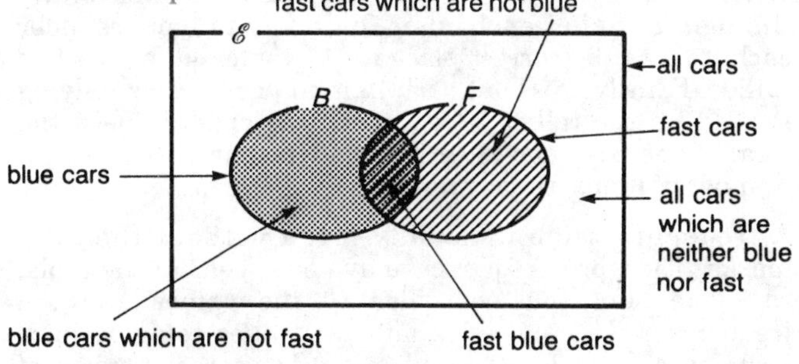

(d) $\mathscr{E}$ = {quadrilaterals}, S = {squares}, R = {rectangles}.

All squares are rectangles. So {squares} is a subset of {rectangles}.

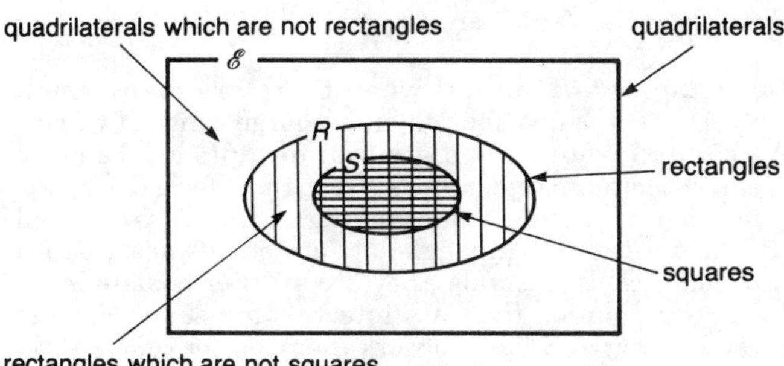

Sets can be shown on a Venn diagram in several ways. Sometimes the *actual* members of each set are shown in each region of the Venn diagram. For example, this Venn diagram shows:

$\mathscr{E}$ = {months}

A = {months beginning with J}

B = {months with 31 days}

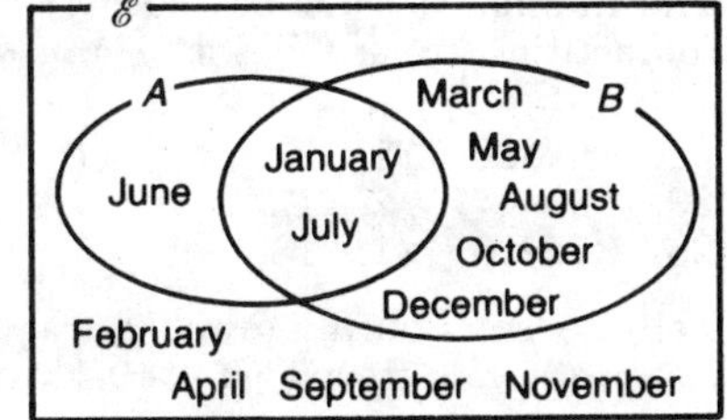

You can see that:

A = {January, June, July}

B = {January, March, May, July, August, October, December}

February, April, September and November are in *neither* set.

January and July are in *both* A and B, i.e. each begins with J and has 31 days.

June is in A **only**, i.e. it begins with J but does not have 31 days.

March, May, August, October, December are in B **only**, i.e. each has 31 days but does not begin with J.

Often the *number* of members in each set is shown in each region of the Venn diagram. For example, this Venn diagram is about the same sets $\mathscr{E}$, A and B.

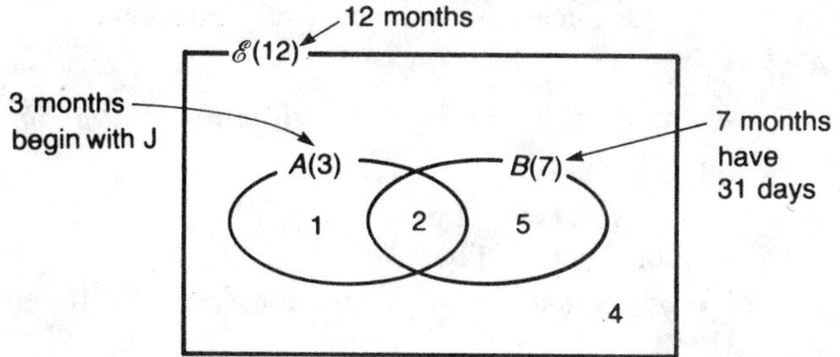

In brackets after the letter of each set is the number of members in the *whole* of that set.

Always **check** whether a Venn diagram is showing the actual members or the number of members in each region.

PROBLEM SOLVING

Sets and Venn diagrams can be used to solve some problems. Often the problems involve two sets and a universal set $\mathscr{E}$. Before attempting to solve any problems, it is important to understand what a Venn diagram shows you.

For example, this Venn diagram shows some information about the students in class 5. The numbers tell you the number of students shown by that region.

$\mathscr{E}$ = {students in class 5}

T = {tennis players}

C = {cricketers}

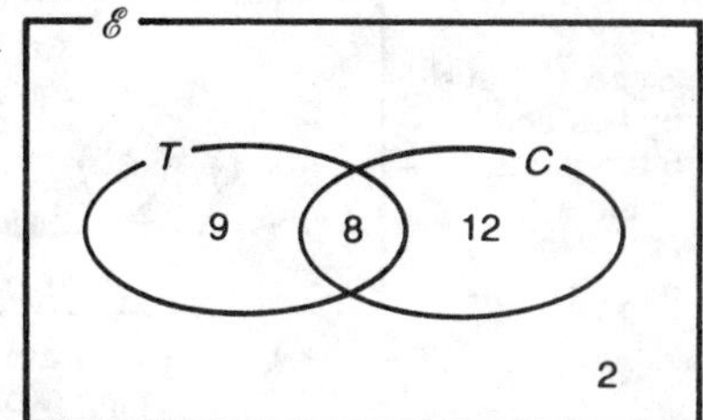

Here is what the diagram tells you:

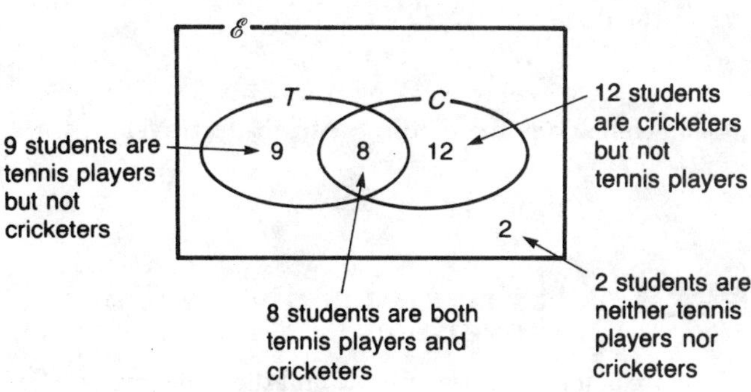

You can work out more information from the diagram too.

The number of tennis players = 9 + 8 = 17

The number of cricketers = 12 + 8 = 20

The total number of students in class 5 = 9 + 8 + 12 + 2 = 31.

A thorough understanding of this diagram will help you to tackle these problems with confidence. When solving such a problem, follow these steps:

(a) Draw a Venn diagram to show how the sets in the

problem are related. (Ask yourself: Is one a subset of another? Do they overlap? Are they separate? If you are not sure, then show them overlapping.)

(b) Write the given information in the correct region(s). When you know the number of members in a whole set, write the number in brackets after the letter of the set.

(c) Work out the missing numbers in the Venn diagram.

Question

Twenty-eight office workers were asked in a survey how they travelled to work. Seventeen of them travelled by bus and fourteen travelled by train. Six people travel by both bus and train. How many office workers in the survey

(a) travel to work by bus only,

(b) travel to work by train only,

(c) do not use buses or trains to travel to work?

Answer

Draw a Venn diagram. Write the given information on it

$\mathscr{E}$ = {office workers in the survey}

B = {people who travel by bus}

T = {people who travel by train}

Some people travel by both bus and train. So the sets overlap.

Work out the missing numbers

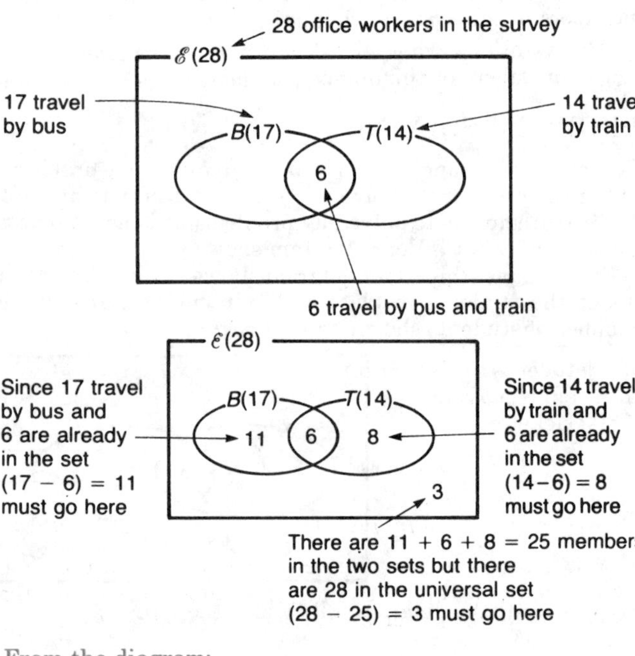

From the diagram:

(a) 11 people travel to work by bus only,

(b) 8 people travel to work by train only,

(c) 3 people do not use buses or trains to travel to work.

2.24 Frequency distributions and averages

Here are some 'statistics words' and their meanings.

Discrete data: values restricted to only certain, exact *distinct numbers* (but not measurements) e.g. a number of pupils can be 0, 1, 2, 3... but not 2½, -3, 4, 7... Do not have to be whole numbers. Usually found by counting.

Continuous data: can be any *real values*. Usually found by measuring (not counting) and rounded to a suitable degree of accuracy, e.g. times can be measured to the nearest second, minute, hour... but not exactly.

Frequency: the number of times an item or event occurs.
Range: the difference between the highest and lowest values.
Average: an item used to represent all items in the data. Three common averages are mode, median and mean.
Mode: the item which occurs *most frequently* in the data. Not all data have a mode.
Median: the *'middle value'* (or mean of the two 'middle values') when the data are in order of size.
Mean: (or Arithmetic Mean): the *'total of the values'* divided by the *'number of values'*; for the data.

FREQUENCY DISTRIBUTIONS

A **frequency distribution** shows the *frequency* of each item in data. It helps you to see how data are *distributed* (spread). A **tally table** is a simple frequency distribution table. For example, this table is about the fillings in the teeth of 45 boys.

Number of fillings	Tally	Frequency
0	卌 IIII	9
1	卌 卌 卌	15
2	卌 卌 III	13
3	卌	5
4	III	3
	Total	45

When making a tally table, you must work carefully through the data item by item, putting a tally mark, I, for each item in the correct place in the table. 卌 shows five tallies. Faintly cross out each item in pencil after tallying it. Add up the tallies to give each frequency. Check the total of the frequencies (if it is not the same as the total number of items, then you need to tally again).

A frequency table is usually given without the tally marks. The word 'frequency' may not appear in the table, so make sure that you identify the values and the frequencies. The table can have the values going down or across the page. For example, here is another version of the frequency table given above:

Values →	**Number of fillings**	0	1	2	3	4
Frequencies →	**Number of boys**	9	15	13	5	3

Grouping data is useful when there are many small frequencies in a distribution and/or large range of values. A **grouped frequency distribution table** can be made to show the number of values (frequency) for each group. The range of possible values for a group or class is called its **class interval**. Although data are not always grouped into *equal* class intervals, they are at Intermediate level. In an examination the class intervals to use are usually given but you may have to work them out for coursework. Take care: too many or too few groups can make it difficult to see any patterns, where these exist. There must be no doubt about the class interval in which each value should be placed.

Question

The number of runs scored by 36 batsmen in a cricket competition are as follows:

31, 40, 20, 35, 21, 12, 11, 39, 16, 0, 28, 49,
29, 32, 17, 2, 12, 24, 14, 1, 10, 23, 19, 13,
25, 30, 10, 21, 18, 0, 15, 11, 29, 8, 12, 1

Tally these data in a grouped frequency table. Use equal class intervals starting 0-9, 10-19,...

Answer

Number of runs	Tally	Frequency
0- 9	𝍸 I	6
10-19	𝍸 𝍸 IIII	14
20-29	𝍸 IIII	9
30-39	𝍸	5
40-49	II	2
	Total	36

Class limits are often used to describe class intervals.

Class boundaries separate one class from another. For each group they are the smallest and largest values an item in that class can have. Each class boundary is usually half-way between the upper limit of one class and the lower limit of the next.

Width of class interval
= upper class boundary – lower class boundary

Mid-value of class interval
= ½(lower class boundary + upper class boundary)

For example, in this frequency table of masses measured to the nearest kg (i.e. continuous data), any mass from 59.5kg to 64.499…kg will go into the group 60 - 64 kg.

Mass (to nearest kg)	Frequency
55-59	2
60-64	7
65-69	11

For this group:

class limits : lower 60kg, upper 64kg
class boundaries : lower 59.9kg, upper 64.5 kg
class width : (64.5 – 59.5) = 5kg
class mid-value : 1/2(59.5 + 64.5) = 62kg

AVERAGES OF FREQUENCY DISTRIBUTIONS

To find the mode, median and mean of a frequency distribution you can use the raw (unsorted) data but this can take a long time for a lot of data. It is usually easier and quicker to use the data directly from the frequency table.

MODE

Ungrouped data: you can read the **mode** (the value with the largest frequency) directly from the table. Remember that the mode is the value, not the frequency.

Question

This frequency table shows the number of children in each of thirty families. What is the mode of these data?

Values →	**Number of children**	0	1	2	3	4	5
Frequency →	**Number of families**	3	9	11	4	2	1

Answer

The largest frequency is 11. 11 families each had 2 children. So the mode of the data is 2 children

Grouped data: The **modal class** is the class with the largest frequency. For example, in the table of runs scored in a cricket competition, the modal class, is 10-19 runs.

MEDIAN

Ungrouped data: To find the **median** the data must be in order of size This is usually done already in a frequency table, but check just is case. Use the total of frequencies (n) to work out where the middle value, i.e. the ½(n + 1)th value occurs (or the two middle values if n is even). A 'running total' of the frequencies help you to find the value(s) to want. Remember that the median is the value not the frequency.

Question

The table gives the number of accidents had by 60 drivers in the last 5 years. What is the median of these data?

Number of accidents	0	1	2	3	4	5	6	7
Number of drivers	15	9	6	19	5	3	2	1

Answer

Values Frequency

Number of accidents	Number of drivers	
0	15	
1	9	15+9=24
2	6	24+6=30 ← 30th driver is in here.
3	19	← 31st driver must be in here.

Total frequency = 60
Median is the mean of the values for the 30th and 31st drivers

The 30th driver had 2 accidents
The 31st driver had 3 accidents
So the median number of accidents is ½ (2 + 3) = 2.5

Grouped data: An **estimate** of the median can be found (see p104). This is usually needed only at Higher level.

MEAN

Ungrouped data: The **mean** of a set of values is given by:

$$\text{Mean value} = \frac{\text{total of all the values}}{\text{total of the frequencies}}$$

You can find these totals from the frequency table. To find the total of all the values, you must take the frequency of each value into account. To do this, multiply each value by its frequency. It is usually easier to set down the working in a table like this.

Value	Frequency	Frequency × value
Total		
	↑ *total of frequencies*	↑ *total of all the values*

The totals are then simple to calculate from the table. you can do all this work on a calculator. Make sure that you show your method as well as your final answer.

Question

The frequency table shows the results of a survey into the number of people living in each house in a village. Calculate the mean of the data (to 1.d.p.)

Number of residents	1	2	3	4	5	6
Number of houses	5	24	14	20	3	4

Answer

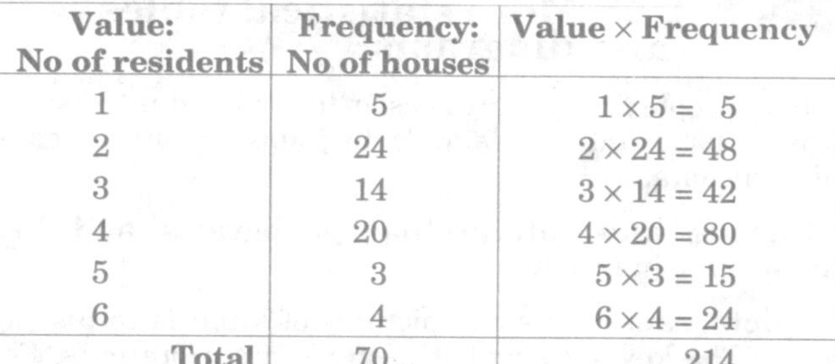

Value: No of residents	Frequency: No of houses	Value × Frequency
1	5	1 × 5 = 5
2	24	2 × 24 = 48
3	14	3 × 14 = 42
4	20	4 × 20 = 80
5	3	5 × 3 = 15
6	4	6 × 4 = 24
Total	70	214

$$\text{Mean number of residents} = \frac{\text{total number of residents}}{\text{total of frequencies}}$$

$= \frac{214}{70}$ C 3.0571429

= 3.1 (to 1 d.p.)

You can work out each multiplication in the table one at a time on a calculator. Write each answer in the table. Then add up these answers at the end to give a total of all the ***values.*** *If your calculator has a memory then you can use it to find the total of* ***values,*** *like this:*

c 1 x 5 = M+ 2 x 2 4 = M+ ... MR

Puts answer in memory **Adds answer to memory**

The answer to each multiplication appear on the display when you press = *So you can write each answer in the table. Pressing* MR *at the end brings the final total from the memory. Use your calculator in the usual way to find the total of frequencies and to work out the mean.*

Grouped data: An *estimate* of the **mean** can be found from a grouped frequency distribution. (The actual mean cannot be calculated unless the actual values in the groups are used.) The mid-value of each group is chosen to represent all the values in the group. Then the working is like that for ungrouped data. As before, a table is an easy way to the working.

	Mid-value	Frequency	Mid-value × Frequency

Dividing the total of the 'Mid-value × Frequency' column by the total of the Frequency column gives an estimate of the mean.

Question

The table shows a grouped frequency distribution of the heights of 60 girls. Each height was measured to the nearest centimetre. Calculate an estimate of the mean height (to the nearest cm) of these girls.

Height(cm)	Frequency
140-144	2
145-149	6
150-154	15
155-159	14
160-164	13
165-169	7
170-174	3

Answer

Heights	Mid-value	Frequency	Mid-value x Frequency
140-144	142	2	142 × 2 = 284
145-149	147	6	147 × 6 = 882
150-154	152	15	152 × 15 = 2280
155-159	157	14	157 × 14 = 2198
160-164	162	13	162 × 13 = 2106
165-169	167	7	167 × 7 = 1169
170-174	172	3	172 × 3 = 516
		60	9435

Estimated mean height $= \frac{9435}{60}$ C 157.25

= 157 cm (to nearest cm)

2.25 More statistical tables and diagrams

Many people find pictures easier to read and understand than a list or table of data. So diagrams are often used to display data.

Drawing and interpreting pictograms and bar charts are in List 1.

A **pictogram** uses small pictures of symbols to display data. The key shows what each picture represents. For example from this pictogram you can work out the number of each types of LP borrowed.:

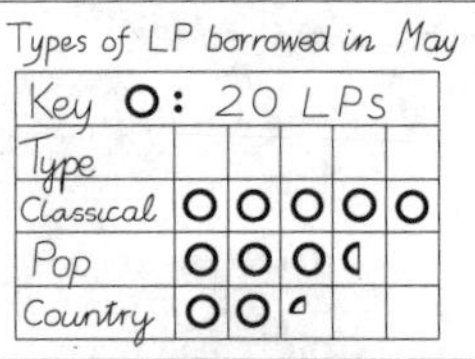

Classical 5 × 20 = 100
Pop: 3½ × 20 = 70
Country: 2¼ × 20 = 45

A **bar chart** uses bars to display data. The length of a bar shows the frequency for its item. For example, from this bar chart you can work out that the total number of votes in the survey is

15 + 12 + 9 + 9 + 5 = 50.

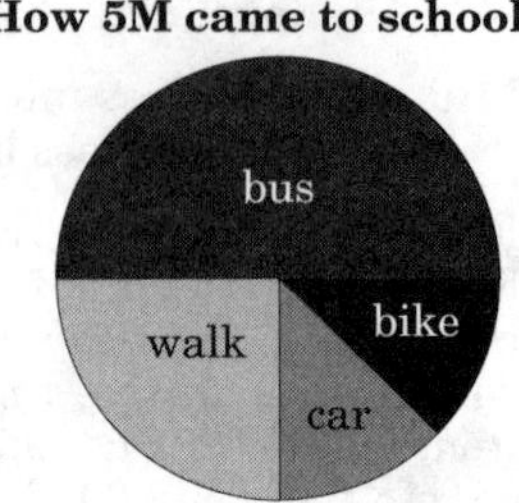

PIE CHART

A **pie chart** is a circular diagram. It shows how the data are divided into parts (just like a pie cut into portions). The whole circle area (the whole pie) shows the whole data. Each *sector* (a portion) shows a *fraction* of the data. For example from this pie chart you can see that about ½ of 5M came to school by bus, about ¼ by walking, about ⅛ by car and about ⅛ by bike. **Interpreting pie charts** is in List 1. Often you cannot find the fractions just by looking at the pie chart. But you can work out the size of each fraction from the angle at the 'centre' of its portion.

How 5M came to school

bus
walk
bike
car

There are 360° at the 'centre of a circle',
so 360°show all of the data,
1°shows 1/360 of the data,
and so on...

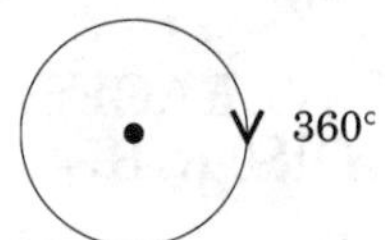

For example, on this pie chart the angle for PE is 80°,

so $\frac{80}{360}$ of 5P chose PE.

There are 27 pupils in 5P,

so $\frac{80}{360} \times 27$

= 6 pupils chose PE.

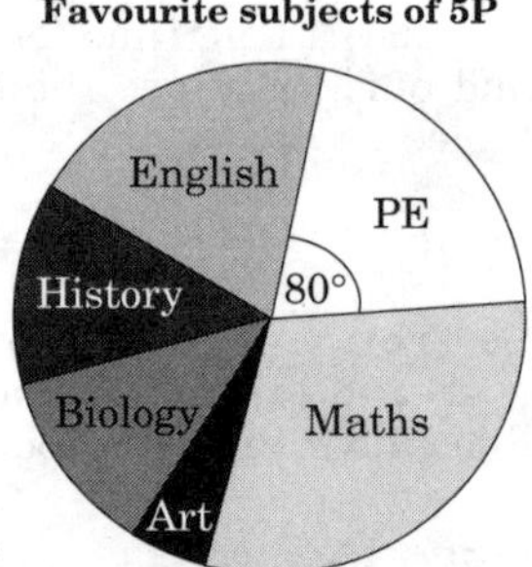

In an examination you may be given the angle for each portion on the diagram. Sometimes you will have to measure the angles.

Drawing pie charts is in List 2. Here are some hints to help you with this.

1 Find the *angle* for each sector by working out:

(a) the fraction for each sector, i.e.

$$\frac{\text{number shown by the sector}}{\text{total shown by the pie chart}}$$

(b) this fraction of 360°.

Check that the angles add up to 360!

2 Use a pair of compasses to *draw a circle*. Make the radius as large as possible.

3 Use a protractor to *draw the angle* of each sector at the *centre* of the circle. Turn your page around for each angle if it is easier.

Draw the smallest angle first, then the next smallest eg.

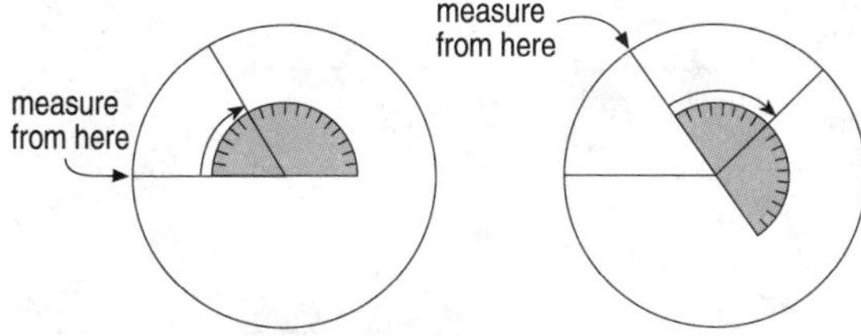

and so on..., so that the largest angle is last.

4 *Label* each sector and angle carefully (In coursework you can shade the sector in different colours if you want to make them easier to see.)

5 Give the pie chart a suitable *title*.

Question

In a survey 400 people were asked which Sunday paper they preferred to read. The number of people naming each paper was

Sunday Times	75	*Observer*	50
News of the World	150	*Sunday Telegraph*	25
Sunday Mirror	100		

Draw a pie chart for these data.

Answer

In the pie chart, the full circle (360°) represents 400 people.

Sunday Times $\frac{75}{400} \times 360° = 67\frac{1}{2}°$

News of the World $\frac{150}{400} \times 360° = 135°$

Sunday Mirror $\frac{100}{400} \times 360° = 90°$

Observer $\frac{50}{400} \times 360° = 45°$

Sunday Telegraph $\frac{25}{400} \times 360° = 22\frac{1}{2}°$

Total = 360°

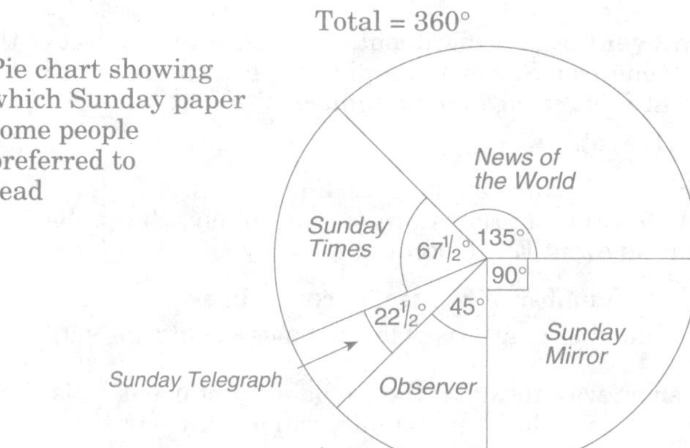

Pie chart showing which Sunday paper some people preferred to read

HISTOGRAM

Histograms are often used to illustrate **grouped frequency distributions**. A histogram uses bars and two axes to show data, so it looks similar to a bar chart. However there are *important differences*. Histograms always represent quantitative data, e.g. numbers, measurements. So both axes in a histogram are numbered. A bar chart may show qualitative data, e.g. car makes, colours. If it does, then only the frequency axis of the car chart will be numbered, the other axis will be labelled with these other items. In a histogram the *area* of a bar represents *frequency*. In a bar chart the *'height'* of a bar shows *frequency*.

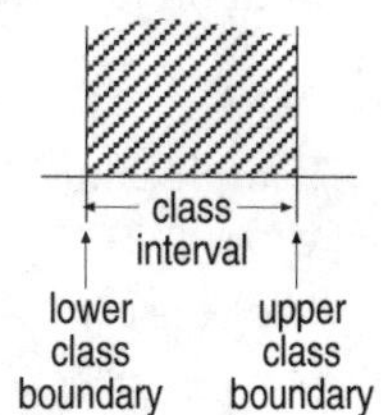

In histograms showing grouped data, the width of each bar represents the size of the interval it shows. (it is proportional to it.) So if the class intervals are equal, then the bars of the histogram are of equal width. The 'edges' of each bar will be on the class boundaries for its group.

(At Intermediate level the bars and classes in a histogram will always be of equal width. Some Higher level candidates may have to deal with histograms showing unequal class intervals. Ask your teacher about this.)

The axes of a histogram must be labelled and numbered carefully.

Horizontal axis: The bars of a histogram are drawn vertically, so the horizontal axis tells you about the range of values in the data. It should be labelled with a description of the values. There are several correct ways to mark and number the scale on the horizontal axis. Here are some of the most common of them. Use the way(s) you know and understand.

The scale can be numbered:

- with the class boundaries... e.g. → ...and the edges of the bars must be on these values; 19.5 29.5 39.5
- with the class mid-values... e.g. → ...and these values must be at the middles of the bars; 24.5 34.5
- as an 'ordinary number line'...e.g.→ ...and the edges of the bars must be placed correctly on the class boundaries using the scale; 20 30 40
- with each bar labelled with its class interval. e.g. → 20-29 30-39

The numbering on the scale can begin at any suitable number (depending upon the data). It does not have to start at zero.

Vertical axis: In a histogram the area of each bar is proportional to the frequency it represents. When the bars (and classes) are of equal width, then the height of each bar will also be proportional to the frequency. For this reason the vertical axis of a histogram showing equal class intervals is sometimes labelled simply 'Frequency'. However, since data are not always grouped into equal class intervals, this can be misleading. A label which applies to any histogram (not just a special case) is often preferred. One such label is:

'Frequency for a class interval of _____'

with the size of the class interval _____ chosen from the frequency distribution. The answer to the following question illustrates this. Note that a histogram must not have spaces between the bars.

Question

The table shows a grouped frequency distribution of the masses of 125 fifth year students, each measured to the nearest kilogram.

(a) What is the modal class of these data?

(b) What is the least mass which would be put in the class 40-44?

(c) Draw a histogram illustrating these data.

Mass (in kg)	**Number of students**
40-44	3
45-49	13
50-54	22
55-59	27
60-64	29
65-69	24
70-74	7

Answer

(a) 60 - 64kg (b) 39.5 kg (c) see below

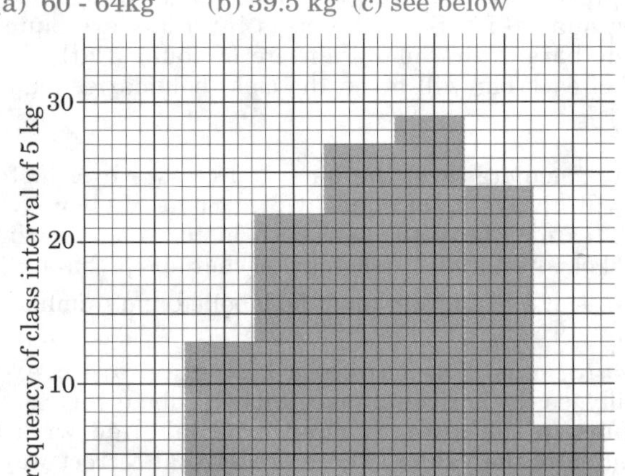

SCATTER DIAGRAMS

Sometimes the data you collect has *more than one* measurement connected with it. For example, to investigate the question, 'In general, does a taller person weight more than a shorter person?', you could collect the heights and weights of a number of people and compare them. One way to compare two sets of connected data is to plot them on a **scatter diagram**. In this case, you can plot the height against the weight for each person. So each point on the scatter diagram shows a connected height and weight. The '*look*' of the scatter diagram can help you to see if any *relationship* exists between the two sets of data.

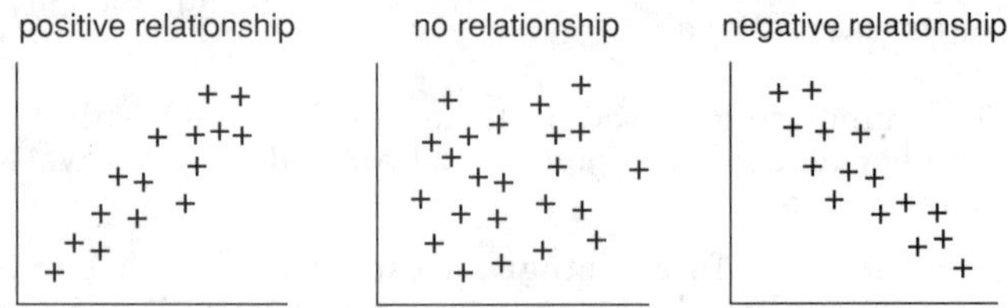

For example, on a height/weight scatter diagram:

(a) a *positive relationship* suggests that 'a taller person weighs *more than* a shorter person',

(b) a *negative relationship* suggests that 'a taller person weighs *less than* a shorter person'.

If the points on a scatter diagram lie in a narrow band around an imaginary line, then you can draw in the line *by eye*. This is called the **line of best fit**. You can use the line of best fit to *predict* possible values in the data. For example, it could help you to answer questions such as 'What would you expect the height of a person who weighs 65 kg to be?' or 'How heavy would you expect a person who is 155 cm tall to be?'

Question

The heights and weights of 10 men, described as being of the same body frame, are given in the table.

Height(cm)	168	178	183	158	162	189	152	191	172	175
Weight (kg)	65	77	78	68	63	82	57	86	69	74

Use the grid below to plot these data on a scatter diagram and draw a line of best fit for these points.

Use your line to suggest, for men of similar body frame,
(a) the possible height of a man weighing 73 kg,
(b) the possible weight of a man 188 cm tall.

Answer

Scatter diagram showing heights and weights of 10 men

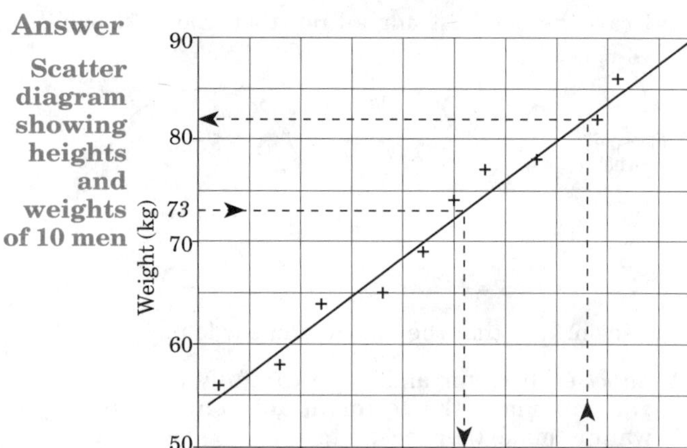

From the scatter diagram: (a) A possible height for a man weighting 73 kg could be 176cm; (b) A possible weight for a man of height 188 cm could be 82 kg.

2.26 Probability

Set language is often used in probability work, so some ofthe basic ideas of probability are given again in simple set language in this unit. These ideas are then developed further.

BASIC IDEAS

The **outcome** of an experiment or action is a *single* result of the experiment or action. For example, one outcome of tossing a coin is *getting a head*.

The set of *all* possible outcomes of an experiment or action is called the **outcome set** or **sample space**. This set is usually called S. For example, the outcome set (sample space) for rolling a die is

$S = \{1, 2, 3, 4, 5, 6\}$.

The number of members in any set X is written as $n(X)$. For example, when rolling a die, the outcome set S contains 6 outcomes.

So $n(S) = 6$.

An **event** of an experiment or action is any subset of the outcome set S. For example, when a die is rolled, one event E is *getting an odd number*.

$E=\{1, 3, 5\}$.

This set contains 3 outcomes. So $n(E) = 3$.

When the outcomes are equally likely, the probability that an event E will occur is given by:

$$\frac{\text{number of wanted outcomes in event set } E}{\text{number of all possible outcomes in outcome set } S}$$

A short way to write 'the probability of event E' is $P(E)$. So this formula for probability can be written as:

$$P(E) = \frac{n(E)}{n(S)}.$$

Question

The letters of the word MATHEMATICS are each written on a separate piece of paper and put in a bag. What is the probability of picking a piece of paper with:

(a) an M on it, (b) a vowel on it?

Answer

The sample space S is:

S= {M, A, T, H, E, M, A, T, I, C, S}

It has 11 outcomes. So n(S)= 11.

(a) The letter M occurs 2 times. So $n(M) = 2$.

$P(M) = \frac{n(M)}{n(S)} = \frac{2}{11}$

(b) The letters which are vowels= {A, E, A, I}

So $n(\text{vowels}) = 4$

and $P(\text{vowels}) = \frac{n(\text{vowels})}{n(S)} = \frac{4}{11}$

When an event is **certain** to happen, its probability is 1.

So P(certainty) = 1.

For example, when picking a card at random from an ordinary pack,

P(red or black card) = 1

because you are certain to get either a red or black card. When an event is impossible, its probability is 0. This means that P (impossibility) = 0. For example when rolling two ordinary dice

P(total 1) = 0

because it is impossible to get a total of 1.

All other probabilities must be between 0 and 1, so they must be a fraction or decimal between 0 and 1.

The sum of the probabilities of all possible outcomes in a sample space is 1. For example, when rolling a die,

$S = \{1, 2, 3, 4, 5, 6\}$.

$P(1) = \frac{n(1)}{n(S)} = \frac{1}{6}$ $P(4) = \frac{n(4)}{n(S)} = \frac{1}{6}$

$P(2) = \frac{n(2)}{n(S)} = \frac{1}{6}$ $P(5) = \frac{n(5)}{n(S)} = \frac{1}{6}$

$P(3) = \frac{n(3)}{n(S)} = \frac{1}{6}$ $P(6) = \frac{n(6)}{n(S)} = \frac{1}{6}$

The sum of the probabilities is:

P(1) + P(2) + P(3) + P(4) + P(5) + P(6)

$= \frac{1}{6}+\frac{1}{6}+\frac{1}{6}+\frac{1}{6}+\frac{1}{6}+\frac{1}{6} = \frac{6}{6} = 1$

COMPLEMENTARY EVENTS

In a sample space, an event can either *take place* (E) or *not take place* (not E). Pairs of events like E and 'not E' are called **complementary events**. For example, when you pick a card at random from a pack of playing cards, the event E='getting a picture card, i.e. J, Q, K' has the complementary event 'not E', and

'not E' = 'not getting a picture card,
i.e. getting A, 2, 3, 4, 5, 6, 7, 8, 9,10'

The sum of complementary events gives the total sample space, i.e. all the possible outcomes. Complementary events can be shown clearly on a Venn diagram.

For example,

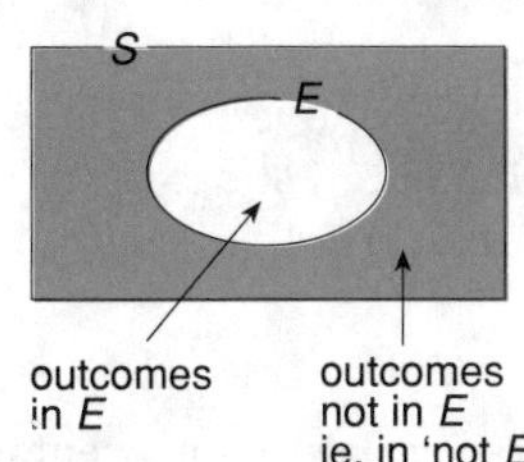

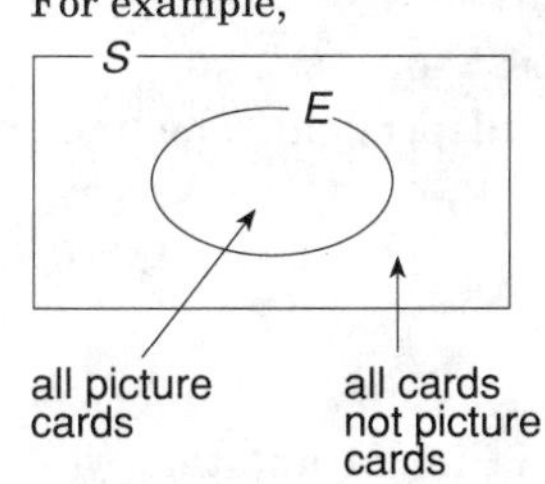

It is certain that an event either takes place (E) or does not take place (not E). The probability of a certainty is 1. So the probabilities of E and 'not E' must add up to 1. i.e. $P(E) + P(\text{not } E) = 1$. Rearranging this equation gives: $P(\text{not } E) = 1 - P(E)$. This is very useful if you know (or can find easily) the probability of an event happening and you want to find the probability of the event *not* happening.

Question

What is the probability of: (a) not rolling a 6 with a die? (b) not picking an ace from a pack of cards?

Answer

(a) $P(6) = \frac{1}{6}$

$P(\text{not } 6) = 1 - P(6)$

$= 1 - \frac{1}{6} = \frac{6}{6} - \frac{1}{6} = \frac{5}{6}$

(b) $P(\text{ace}) = \frac{4}{52} = \frac{1}{13}$

$P(\text{not ace}) = 1 - P(\text{ace})$

$= 1 - \frac{1}{13} = \frac{13}{13} - \frac{1}{13} = \frac{12}{13}$

COMBINED EVENTS

Two or more simple events can occur together (or one after the other). They give a **combined** or **compound event**. For example, the result of tossing a coin and picking a card is a combined or compound event. So a *head and an ace* is a combined event. The outcomes in the combined sample space are formed by combining the outcomes of the separate sample spaces. A **table** is a useful way to show all the possible outcomes when *two* sample spaces are combined. Each entry in the table shows an outcome in the combined sample space. This table is helpful when you have to calculate the probability of two combined events taking place.

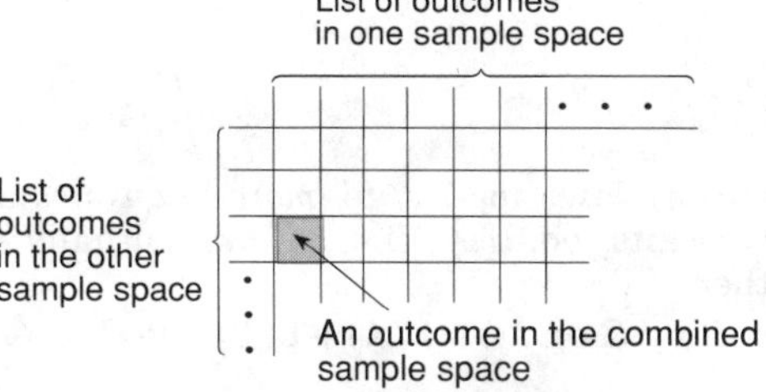

Question

In an experiment, David tosses a coin and Bob throws a die. (a) What is the probability that the outcome will be a head on the coin and a 5 on the die? (b) What is the probability of getting a tail and an even number?

Answer

(a) Table of possible outcomes in combined sample space.

		Die					
		1	2	3	4	5	6
Coin	H	H1	H2	H3	H4	H5	H6
	T	T1	T2	T3	T4	T5	T6

From the table, the combined sample space S is:

S = {H1, H2, H3, H4, H5, H6, T1, T2, T3, T4, T5, T6}

There are 12 outcomes. So $n(S)$= 12. The event E we are interested in is the outcome *a head and a 5*, i.e. H5.

So E_1 = H5 and $n(E_1) = 1$

$P(E_1) = \frac{n(E_1)}{n(S)} = \frac{1}{12}$

So the probability of getting a head and a 5 is $\frac{1}{12}$

(b) The event E_2 we are interested in is a tail and an even number. From the table, E_2 = {T2, T4, T6}
So $n(E_2)$= 3

$P(E_2) = \frac{n(E_2)}{n(S)} = \frac{3}{4} = \frac{1}{4}$

So the probability of getting a tail and an even number is ¼.

MUTUALLY EXCLUSIVE EVENTS

Events are said to be **mutually exclusive** if they cannot happen at the same time. For example, when you toss a coin, you can get either a head or a tail, not both at the same time. So the events *getting a head* and *getting a tail* are mutually exclusive. On a Venn diagram the sets of outcomes for mutually exclusive events do *not* overlap (intersect).

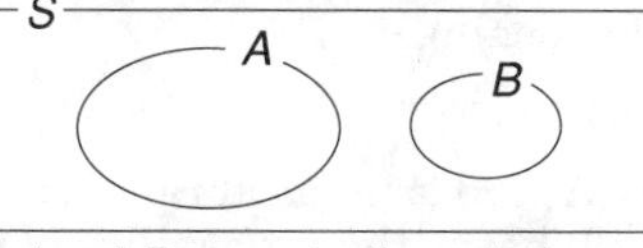

A and *B* are mutually exclusive

An **addition law** applies to mutually exclusive events. It is sometimes called the **'or' law** because it gives you the probability that one event **or** another happens. If A and B are mutually exclusive events, then:

$P(A \textbf{ or } B) = P(A) + P(B)$

A probability is usually worked out as a fraction and cancelled to its simplest form. In these questions it is usually easier to leave any cancelling to the very end of the calculation. Adding fractions is easy if the denominators are the same.

Question

Mary picks a card at random from a well-shuffled pack of 52 playing cards (no jokers). What is the probability that the card picked is the king of spades or an ace?

Answer

The two events are mutually exclusive. You can pick the king of spades **or** an ace, not *both* at the same time.

The addition law gives:

P(king of spades or an ace)

$= $ P(king of spades) + P(an ace)

$= \frac{1}{52} + \frac{4}{52}$ *Do not cancel here!*

$= \frac{5}{52}$

This addition law applies to *more than two* mutually exclusive events too. If A, B, C, ... are mutually exclusive events, then

$P(A \textbf{ or } B \textbf{ or } C \textbf{ or } \ldots) = P(A) + P(B) + P(C) + \cdots$

Question

During a game of Scrabble the bag contained 30 tiles. The letters were:

AAAAAA EEEEEEEEEE NNN RRRR TTTTT WW

Dapinder can complete a word if he picks an A or E or R. He picks one letter tile out of the bag at random. What is the probability that Dapinder can complete a word after picking this letter tile?

Answer

The three events *picking an A or E or R* are mutually exclusive. Each tile has one letter on it. So when you pick one letter tile you can pick only one letter.

The addition law gives:

P(A or E or R) $= $ P(A) + P(E) + P(R)

Do not cancel here $= \frac{6}{30} + \frac{10}{30} + \frac{4}{30}$

Cancel by 10 now $= \frac{20}{30}$

$= \frac{2}{3}$

It is important that you can recognize when events are *not* mutually exclusive. For example, when you take a card at random from a pack, the two events *taking an ace* and *taking a heart* are *not* mutually exclusive because if you take the ace of hearts then both events have happened together.

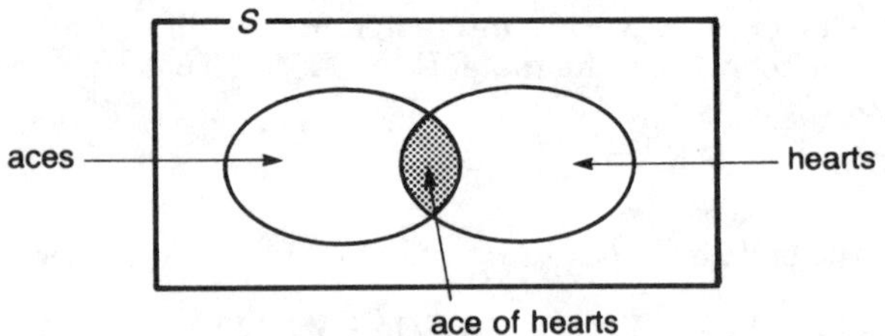

On a Venn diagram, the sets of outcomes for events that are not mutually exclusive overlap **(intersect)**.

When events are **not mutually exclusive** you can use the sample space to work out the probability of one or the other happening.

Question

A card is taken at random from a pack of 52 playing cards. What is the probability of taking a diamond or a 10?

Answer

This table shows the sample space for these cards. Each × stands for a card.

	A	2	3	4	5	6	7	8	9	10	J	Q	K
Clubs	×	×	×	×	×	×	×	×	×	⊗	×	×	×
Diamonds	⊗	⊗	⊗	⊗	⊗	⊗	⊗	⊗	⊗	◎	⊗	⊗	⊗
Hearts	×	×	×	×	×	×	×	×	×	⊗	×	×	×
Spades	×	×	×	×	×	×	×	×	×	⊗	×	×	×

Each diamond is ringed. Each 10 is ringed.

Note One card, the 10 of diamonds, is ringed twice. So the events *a diamond* and *a 10* are *not* mutually exclusive.

There are 16 cards out of the 52 cards ringed.

P(diamond or 10) $= \frac{16}{52} = \frac{4}{13}$

INDEPENDENT EVENTS

Events are said to be **independent** if they have no effect on each other. For example, when you roll a die twice, the event *getting a six* on the first roll does not affect the event *getting a one* on the second roll. These two events are independent.

A **multiplication** law applies to independent events. It is sometimes called the **and law** because it gives you the probability that one event **and** another happens. If A and B are independent events, then

$P(A \textbf{ and } B) = P(A) \times P(B)$

Question

Patrick throws a die and picks a card at random from a pack. What is the probability that he throws a six on the die and picks the ace of hearts?

Answer

Clearly these are two independent events. The result of rolling the die does not affect the result of picking the card. The multiplication law gives:

P(six **and** ace of hearts) = P(six) × P(ace of hearts)

$= \frac{1}{6} \times \frac{1}{52}$

$= \frac{1}{312}$

This multiplication law can be used for *more than two* independent events. If A, B, C, ... are independent events, then

$P(A \textbf{ and } B \textbf{ and } C \textbf{ and } \ldots) = P(A) \times P(B) \times P(C) \times \cdots$

Question

Four coins are tossed together. What is the probability of getting four tails?

Answer

The four events (i.e. tossing a tail on each coin) are independent. The multiplication law gives:

P(four tails) = P(tail and tail and tail and tail)

= P(tail) × P(tail) × P(tail) × P(tail)

$= \frac{1}{2} \times \frac{1}{2} \times \frac{1}{2} \times \frac{1}{2}$

$= \frac{1}{16}$

It is important that you can recognize when events are independent. Sometimes it is obvious. For example, it is obvious that the result of tossing a coin and the result of throwing a die are independent events.

Sometimes you will have to think carefully about the events to decide whether they are independent or not. For example, if you draw a card at random from a pack, replace it and draw another card at random from the pack, then the event of *drawing an ace* on the first draw and the event of *drawing a king* on the second draw *are* independent events. The result of the first draw does not affect the result of the second draw. There are the same 52 cards to draw from each time. However, if you draw a card from the pack and *then* take another, without replacing the first, then the two results are *not* independent events. There are not the same 52 cards to draw from the second time. Only 51 cards are left in the pack to draw from.

In examples like these the words *replaced* or *with replacement* can often give you a clue that independent events are taking place.

TREE DIAGRAMS

A **probability tree diagram** can be used to solve problems involving combined events. Use these notes to help you.

(a) For each 'action' in the problem, show the possible outcomes (or events) at the end of a branch of the tree. For example, when you toss a die the outcomes can be shown on the tree diagram like this.

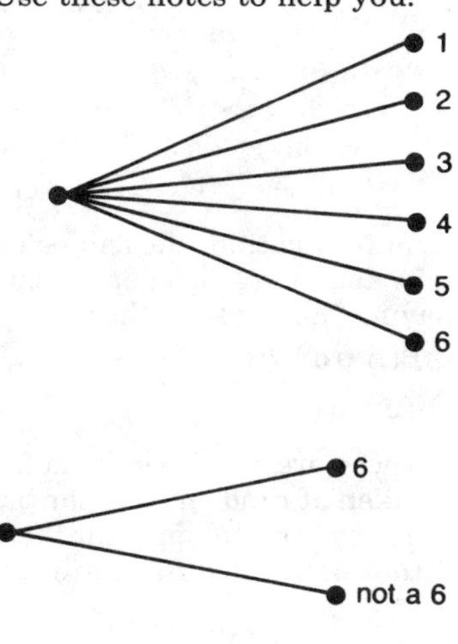

Sometimes you do not need to show all the individual outcomes. For example, you may be interested only in whether you toss a *six* or *not a six*, so you can draw this simpler tree diagram.

(b) Each 'action' in the problem is shown by a 'stage' in the diagram. For example, for two actions there will be two stages.

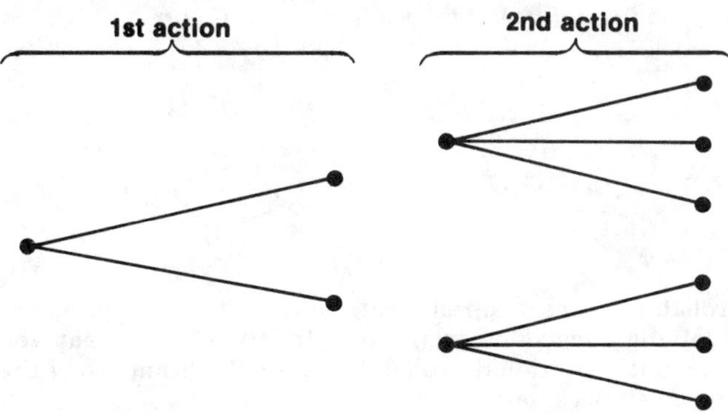

(c) At the end of each route along the branches of the tree, write its final outcome.

(d) Work out the probability of each outcome (or event) shown by a branch on the diagram. (Make sure that you check whether the events are independent or not.) Write each probability on its branch of the tree.

The probabilities on adjacent branches of the tree must add up to 1. This is a useful check that you have worked out the probabilities correctly.

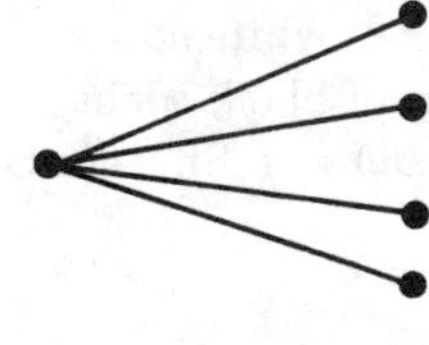

(e) To find the probability of a final outcome, find the route along the branches which lead to that outcome. Multiply together the probabilities from any branch you go along (i.e. use the multiplication law).

(f) An event may involve more than one of these final outcomes. To find the probability of that event happening, add together the probabilities of these final mutually exclusive outcomes (i.e. use the addition law).

Here is a question containing a mixture of independent events and mutually exclusive events.

Question

There are 20 books on a shelf in a hotel room. Nine of the books are fiction, eleven are non-fiction. A hotel guest takes a book at random from the shelf and looks at it. She then replaces it on the shelf and takes a book again at random. Draw a probability tree diagram to show the possible outcomes. What is the probability that the two books taken are:

(a) both fiction, (b) both non-fiction,

(c) one of each kind?

Explain how you obtained each answer.

Answer

The events in this example are independent. The first book is replaced before the second is taken. So the type of book taken first does not affect the type taken second.

Let F stand for a fiction book

and N for a non-fiction book.

$P(F) = \frac{9}{20}$, $P(N) = \frac{11}{20}$

Probability tree diagram

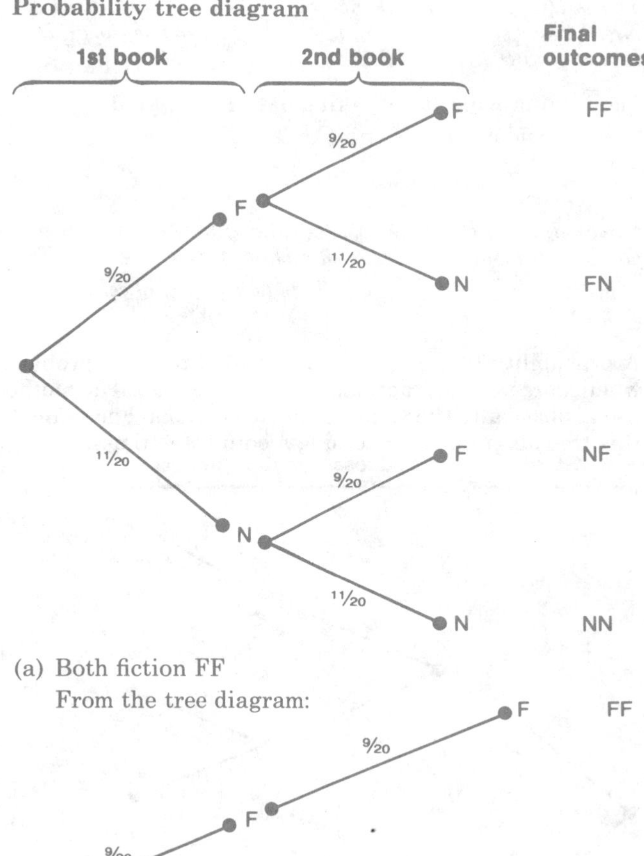

(a) Both fiction FF

From the tree diagram:

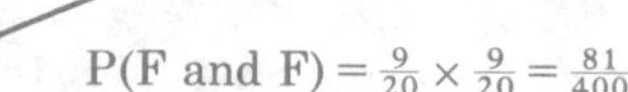

$P(F \text{ and } F) = \frac{9}{20} \times \frac{9}{20} = \frac{81}{400}$

So the probability of both books being fiction is $\frac{81}{400}$.

(b) Both non-fiction NN

From the tree diagram:

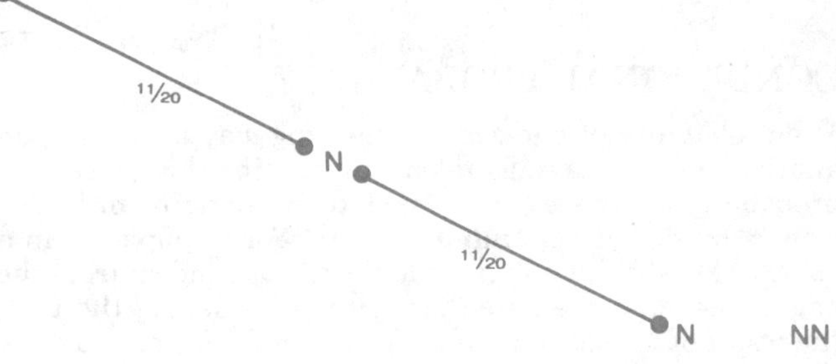

$P(N \text{ and } N) = \frac{11}{20} \times \frac{11}{20} = \frac{121}{400}$

So the probability of both books being non-fiction is $\frac{121}{400}$.

(c) One of each kind

Two final outcomes give this. They are FN and NF.

For FN

From the tree diagram:

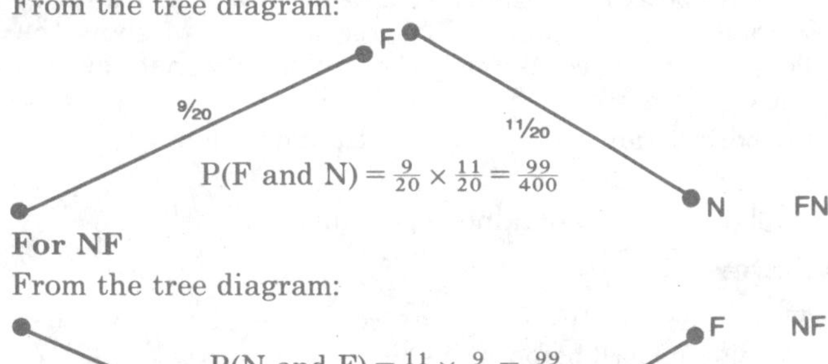

For NF

From the tree diagram:

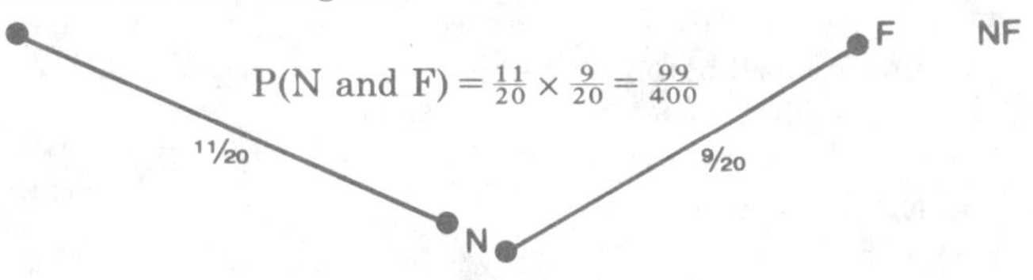

To take two books, one of each kind, she can take either FN or NF. These events are mutually exclusive, so use the addition law to find P(FN or NF).

The total probability of taking one of each kind

$= P(F \text{ and } N) \text{ or } P(N \text{ and } F)$

$= \frac{99}{400} + \frac{99}{400} = \frac{198}{400} = \frac{99}{200}$

Note *In this example results (a), (b) and (c) cover all the possible outcomes. So their sum should be 1.*

$\frac{81}{400} + \frac{121}{400} + \frac{198}{400} = \frac{400}{400} = 1$ ✓ *This is a useful check.*

A probability tree diagram can be used to solve problems when *more than two* actions are combined too. The method used is basically the same as for two actions. For example, this tree diagram is for tossing a coin three times.

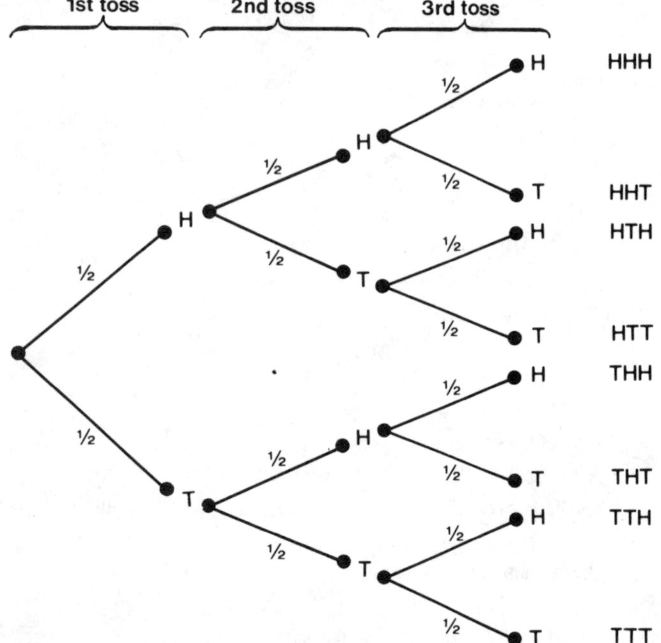

CONDITIONAL PROBABILITY

The probability of one event happening may **depend** upon another event having taken place. In this case the probability of the event is said to be **conditional**. The events are called **dependent events**. For example, if, in a game of Scrabble, you take a letter tile at random from the bag of tiles and then another, without replacing the first, the result of the second draw depends on the letter you drew the first time. In probability problems the words *without replacement* or *not replaced* can give you a hint that conditional probability is involved.

Question

A card is picked at random out of a pack of 52 playing cards and not replaced. A second card is then picked at random. What is the probability that the second card is an ace if the first card is:

(a) an ace, (b) not an ace?

Explain your answers.

Answer

The events in this question are dependent. After the first card is picked, 51 cards are left.

(a) If the first card is an ace, then only 3 aces are left in the 51 cards. So the probability of getting an ace after an ace is:

$P(\text{ace after an ace}) = \frac{3}{51} = \frac{1}{17}$

(b) If the first card is not an ace, then all 4 aces are left in the 51 cards. So the probability of getting an ace after not an ace is:

$P(\text{ace after not an ace}) = \frac{4}{51}$

A multiplication rule can be used for dependent events too. If A and B are two dependent events and B depends on A having taken place, then:

$P(A \textbf{ and } B) = P(A) \times P(B \textit{ after } A \textit{ has taken place})$

Question

There are 5 red pens and 2 blue pens in a bag. A pen is taken at random from the bag but not replaced. A second pen is then taken from the bag. What is the probability that both pens taken are red?

Answer

The events in this question are dependent.

First pen: 5 out of the 7 pens in the bag are red.

$P(\text{red}) = \frac{5}{7}$

Second pen: *If the first pen is red, then there are only 4 red pens left in the bag. There are 6 pens in the bag.*

$P(\text{red after red}) = \frac{4}{6}$

The probability that both pens are red is given by:

$P(\text{red and red after red}) = P(\text{red}) \times P(\text{red after red})$

$= \frac{5}{7} \times \frac{4}{6}$

$= \frac{20}{42} = \frac{10}{21}$

Probability tree diagrams can be used to solve problems involving dependent events too. It is important that you work out conditional probabilities for the branches of the tree when necessary.

Question

Andrew has 6 white socks and 10 black socks of the same kind in a drawer. In the dark, he takes two socks at random, one after the other, out of the drawer. Draw a probability tree diagram to show the possible outcomes. What is the probability that he takes out:

(a) a pair of white socks,

(b) a pair of black socks,

(c) two socks of different colours?

Answer

The colour of the second sock depends on the colour of the first. So this example contains dependent events and conditional probabilities. The events are mutually exclusive: a sock is not black and white at the same time.

Let W stand for a white sock and B stand for a black sock.

$P(W) = \frac{6}{16}$ $P(B) = \frac{10}{16}$

The probabilities for the second sock are dependent upon the result of the first. After a sock has been taken, 15 socks are left. After a white sock has been taken, 5 white socks and 10 black socks are left.

$P(W \text{ after } W) = \frac{5}{15}$ $P(B \text{ after } W) = \frac{10}{15}$

After a black sock has been taken, 6 white socks and 9 black socks are left.

$P(W \text{ after } B) = \frac{6}{15}$ $P(B \text{ after } B) = \frac{9}{15}$

Probability tree diagram

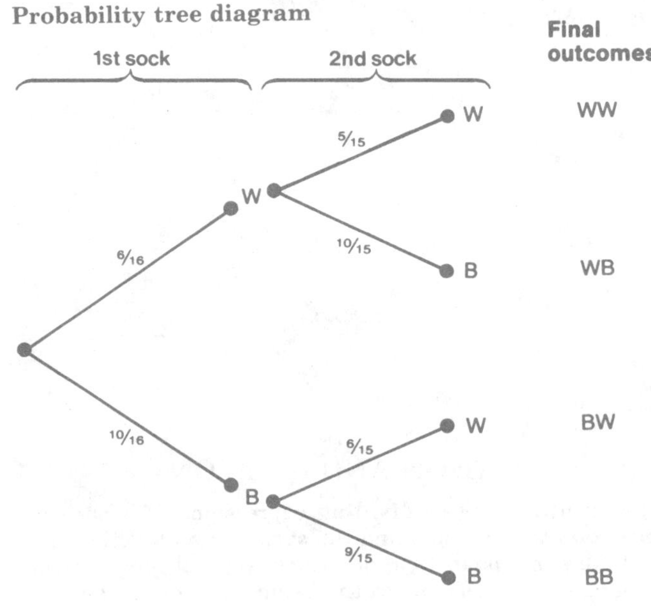

(a) P(W and W) $= \frac{6}{16} \times \frac{5}{15} = \frac{1}{8}$
(b) P(B and B) $= \frac{10}{16} \times \frac{9}{15} = \frac{3}{8}$
(c) To take two socks of different colours, he can take either WB or BW. These events are mutually exclusive, so use the addition law to find P(WB or BW).
P(W and B) $= \frac{6}{16} \times \frac{10}{15} = \frac{1}{4}$ P(B and W) $= \frac{10}{16} \times \frac{6}{15} = \frac{1}{4}$
P(WB and BW) = P(W and B) + P(B and W) $= \frac{1}{4} + \frac{1}{4} = \frac{1}{2}$

Note *In this example, results (a), (b) and (c) cover all the possible outcomes so their sum should be 1.*
$\frac{1}{8} + \frac{3}{8} + \frac{1}{2} = \frac{1}{8} + \frac{3}{8} + \frac{4}{8} = \frac{8}{8} = 1$✓ *This is a useful check.*

2.27 Simple algebra

In **algebra** letters are used to stand for numbers. It is important that you know and understand the 'shorthand' used in algebra. For example,

a means $1 \times a$ or $1a$
$-a$ means $-1 \times a$ or $-1a$
$3a$ means $3 \times a$ or $(a+a+a)$
$\frac{a}{3}$ means $a \div 3$ or $\frac{1}{3}$ of a
ab means $a \times b$
$2ab$ means $2 \times a \times b$ or $(ab+ab)$
a^2 means $a \times a$
a^3 means $a \times a \times a$
$3a^2$ means $3 \times a^2$ or $3 \times a \times a$ or $(a^2 + a^2 + a^2)$
$(3a)^2$ means $3a \times 3a$ or $3 \times a \times 3 \times a$
$3ab^2$ means $3 \times ab^2$ or $3 \times a \times b \times b$ or $(ab^2 + ab^2 + ab^2)$
$a^{\frac{1}{3}}$ means $\sqrt[3]{a}$
and so on ...

Note The number always goes in front of the letter.

The **basic laws of arithmetic** (see Unit 2.1) are also true in algebra. For example,

Laws	Examples: arithmetic	Examples: in algebra
Commutative laws		
+ is commutative	$3+5=5+3$	$a+b=b+a$
× is commutative	$3 \times 5 = 5 \times 3$	$ab = ba$
− is not commutative	$3-5 \neq 5-3$	$a-b \neq b-a$
÷ is not commutative	$3 \div 5 \neq 5 \div 3$	$\frac{a}{b} \neq \frac{b}{a}$
Associative laws		
+ is associative	$(3+5)+2 = 3+(5+2)$	$(a+b)+c = a+(b+c)$
× is associative	$(3 \times 5) \times 2 = 3 \times (5 \times 2)$	$(ab)c = a(bc)$
− is not associative	$(3-5)-2 \neq 3-(5-2)$	$(a-b)-c \neq a-(b-c)$
÷ is not associative	$(3 \div 5) \div 2 \neq 3 \div (5 \div 2)$	$\frac{a}{b} \div c \neq a \div \frac{b}{c}$
Distributive laws		
× over + or −: left	$3 \times (5+2) = 3 \times 5 + 3 \times 2$	$a(b+c) = ab + ac$
right	$(3+5) \times 2 = 3 \times 2 + 5 \times 2$	$(a+b)c = ac + bc$

The **rules for signs** are also the same in arithmetic and algebra (see Unit 2.2). For example,

when multiplying	when dividing
$(+) \times (+) \rightarrow (+)$	$(+) \div (+) \rightarrow (+)$
$(+) \times (-) \rightarrow (-)$	$(+) \div (-) \rightarrow (-)$
$(-) \times (+) \rightarrow (-)$	$(-) \div (+) \rightarrow (-)$
$(-) \times (-) \rightarrow (+)$	$(-) \div (-) \rightarrow (+)$

WORDS TO KNOW

When letters are used to stand for *different* numbers, they are called **variables**.

Letters which have *fixed* values are called **constants**. All numbers are constants. For example,

in $\frac{1}{3}\pi r^2 h$
r and h are **variables** (their values can change),
$\frac{1}{3}$ and π are **constants** (their values stay the same).

An **algebraic expression** is a calculation written using letters. So it is a collection of letters and symbols combined by at least one of the operations +, −, ×, ÷. For example,

$6x + 5 - 3y$, $2ab^3c^4$, $\frac{x^2 - 1}{x + 2}$

are all **expressions**.

Remember × and ÷ signs are not usually written in algebraic expressions but you know that ab means $a \times b$ and $\frac{a}{b}$ means $a \div b$.

The **terms** of an expression are linked by plus (+) or minus (−) signs. For example,

the terms of $7x - 3y + 2$ are $7x$, $3y$ and 2.

A number on its own or a letter standing for a constant is called a **constant term**. For example,

in $7x - 3y + 2$, the number 2 is a **constant term**.

A term can consist of a number, letters and powers of letters. For example,

the terms of $2xy + 3x^2 - 7x^2y^3$ are $2xy$, $3x^2$, $7x^2y^3$.

(**Note** that $2xy$, for instance, is only *one* term. x and y are not separate terms here.)

In a term the number always comes *first*. The letters are usually written in *alphabetical* order. For example,

we write $14xy^2z$ rather than $y^2 14zx$.

The number placed *in front of*, and thus *multiplying*, a letter or group of letters is called a **coefficient**. For example,

in $3x$, the x has a coefficient of 3.

In an expression, the + or − sign goes with the term which follows it. For example,

in $9x^2 - 4xy$, 9 is the coefficient of x^2,
−4 is the coefficient of xy.

Like terms contain the *same* 'algebraic quantity'. For example

$7x$, $5x$ and $-x$ are like terms,
but $7x$, $5y$ and $-z$ are *not* like terms.

In like terms, the letters and the powers of each letter must be the same. For example,

$4b^2c$ and $-7b^2c$ are like terms,
but $4b^2c$ and $-7bc^2$ are *not* like terms
(b^2c and bc^2 are different!).

When looking for like terms, remember that the order of the letters in a term is *not* important. For example,

$ab^2c = acb^2 = b^2ac = b^2ca = cab^2 = cb^2a$

Writing the letters in each term in alphabetical order may help you to spot like terms.

Answers are usually given in this way too. For example, rewriting $3ab^2c$, $-5b^2ca$ and $6cab^2$ gives $3ab^2c$, $-5ab^2c$ and $6ab^2c$.

Now it is easy to see that these are like terms.

SIMPLIFICATION

Algebraic expressions can often be **simplified**. This makes them shorter and easier to read. The **four rules** of addition, subtraction, multiplication and division may be used to simplify expressions. Since the terms may be positive (+) or negative (−), the four rules of directed numbers (see Unit 2.2) will apply.

ADDITION AND SUBTRACTION

Only **like terms** can be **added** or **subtracted** to give a single term. This is often called **collecting like terms**. For example,

$5x + 3x + x = 9x$ (**Remember** x means $1x$)
$7y - 2y = 5y$

Unlike terms *cannot* be collected together and written as a single term. For example,

$3x - 7y$ and $5x + 3x^2 - 9x^4$ cannot be simplified.

Each is in its *simplest form.*

When collecting like terms, group together the positive (+) and negative (−) like terms. This makes them easier to work out.

Remember that the + or − sign goes with the term that follows it.

Question

Simplify:

(a) $7x - 8x + 5x - x$ (b) $-3a^2 + 9a^2 - 11a^2 - 5a^2$
(c) $4bac + 11cab - 2bca$

Answer

(a) $7x - 8x + 5x - x$

Group + and − terms $= 7x + 5x - 8x - x$

Work them out $= 12x \quad -9x$
$= 3x$

(b) $-3a^2 + 9a^2 - 11a^2 - 5a^2$

Group + and − terms $= 9a^2 - 3a^2 - 11a^2 - 5a^2$

Work them out $= 9a^2 \quad -19a^2$
$= -10a^2$

(c) $4bac + 11cab - 2bca$

Rewrite letters in alphabetical order $= 4abc + 11abc - 2abc$

Work them out $= 15abc \quad -2abc$
$= 13abc$

Expressions often contain *several* sets of like terms. Each set can be simplified *separately*. This is easier to do if you rewrite the expression with like terms next to each other.

Question

Simplify:

(a) $7x + 5 - 6y + 2x + 3y - y - 8$
(b) $3xy^2 + 2x^2y - 4y^2x + 6yx^2$

Answer

(a) $7x + 5 - 6y + 2x + 3y - y - 8$

Group like terms $= 7x + 2x + 3y - 6y - y + 5 - 8$

Work them out $= 9x \quad -4y \quad -3$
$= 9x - 4y - 3$

(b) $3xy^2 + 2x^2y - 4y^2x + 6yx^2$

Rewrite letters in alphabetical order $= 3xy^2 + 2x^2y - 4xy^2 + 6x^2y$

Group like terms $= 3xy^2 - 4xy^2 \quad + 2x^2y + 6x^2y$

Work them out $= -xy^2 \quad +8x^2y$
$= -xy^2 + 8x^2y$

MULTIPLICATION AND DIVISION

When **multiplying** or **dividing** expressions, it is easier if you group the numbers and the *same* letters together. Put the letters in alphabetical order. Always multiply or divide the numbers first. Then use the **basic rules of indices** (see Unit 2.28) to simplify sets of the same letter.

Remember A bracket may be used to show a multiplication. For example,

$a(bc)$ means $a \times (bc)$

Question

Write these as simply as possible.

(a) $-4c \times 2a \times 3b$ (b) $2ab(-3bc)$
(c) $6mn^2 \times 5m^3n^4$ (d) $8a^3b^2 \div 4$

Answer

(a) $-4c \times 2a \times 3b = -4 \times 2 \times 3 \times a \times b \times c$
$= -24 \times abc$
$= -24abc$

(b) $2ab(-3bc) = 2 \times -3 \times a \times b \times b \times c$
$= -6 \times a \times b^2 \times c$
$= -6ab^2c$

(c) $6mn^2 \times 5m^3n^4 = 6 \times 5 \times m \times m^3 \times n^2 \times n^4$
$= 30 \times m^4 \times n^6$
$= 30m^4n^6$

(d) $8a^3b^2 \div 4 = \frac{8}{4}a^3b^2$
$= 2a^3b^2$

SUBSTITUTION

A *substitute* replaces something or someone. For example, in football a substitute replaces another player.

In algebra, **substitution** is replacing letters by numbers. This is used to find a **numerical value** for an expression.

When substituting numbers in an expression, it often helps to write out what the expression means.

Question

If $x = 2$ and $y = 5$, find the values of:

(a) $3x$ (b) x^3 (c) $4xy$
(d) $(4y)^2$ (e) $x + 6y$ (f) $4x^2 + 1$

Answer

(a) $3x = 3 \times x$
$= 3 \times 2$
$= 6$

(b) $x^3 = x \times x \times x$
$= 2 \times 2 \times 2$
$= 8$

(c) $4xy = 4 \times x \times y$
$= 4 \times 2 \times 5$
$= 40$

(d) $(4y)^2 = 4y \times 4y$
$= 4 \times y \times 4 \times y$
$= 4 \times 5 \times 4 \times 5$
$= 400$

(e) $x + 6y = x + (6 \times y)$
$= 2 + (6 \times 5)$
$= 2 + 30$
$= 32$

(f) $4x^2 + 1 = (4 \times x \times x) + 1$
$= (4 \times 2 \times 2) + 1$
$= 16 + 1$
$= 17$

Take special care when negative (−) numbers are involved. **Remember** the rules for dealing with signs (see Unit 2.2). Do not try to do too much in each step. **Remember** also that *multiplication by zero gives zero.*

Question

If $a = 2$, $b = -1$, $c = -3$ and $d = 0$, evaluate the following.

(a) $a - b - c$ (b) acd (c) $3a^2 - 2bc + d$

Answer

(a) $a - b - c = 2 - (-1) - (-3)$
$= 2 + 1 + 3$
$= 6$

(b) $acd = a \times c \times d$
$= 2 \times -3 \times 0$
$= 0$

(c) $3a^2 - 2bc + d = (3 \times a \times a) - (2 \times b \times c) + d$
$= (3 \times 2 \times 2) - (2 \times -1 \times -3) + 0$
$= 12 - (+6)$
$= 6$

Sometimes an expression is *not* in its simplest form. It is usually easier to substitute values into it *before* simplifying rather than vice versa.

Question

Evaluate the expression $2x^3 - 5x^2$ when $x = -1$.

Answer

$2x^3 - 5x^2 = 2 \times (-1)^3 - 5 \times (-1)^2$
$= 2 \times (-1) - 5 \times (+1)$
$= -2 - 5$
$= -7$

$(-1)^3 = -1 \times -1 \times -1 = -1$
$(-1)^2 = -1 \times -1 = 1$

FORMING EXPRESSIONS

Statements *in words* are often written as algebraic expressions in mathematics. *Any* letter may be used to stand for the unknown number, but a *different* letter must be used for each different unknown.
For example,

if n represents an unknown number, then:

3 more than the number → $n + 3$
7 less than the number → $n - 7$
5 times the number → $5n$
a quarter of the number → $\frac{n}{4}$
the number subtracted from 2 → $2 - n$
6 divided by the number → $\frac{6}{n}$
y more than the number → $n + y$
y less than the number → $n - y$
y times the number → ny or yn
the number divided by y → $\frac{n}{y}$

and so on ...

Using a **flow diagram** is one way to form an expression. Sometimes you have to use brackets.

Question

Here are some instructions.

Think of a number. Multiply it by 3. Subtract 7. Multiply the result by 5. Add the number you first thought of.
Draw a flow diagram to help form an expression for these instructions.

Answer

Let the number be n.

n → [×3] → $3n$ → [−7] → $3n - 7$ → [×5] → $5(3n - 7)$ → [+n] → $5(3n - 7) + n$

think n — *multiply by 3* — *subtract 7* — *multiply result by 5* — *add n* — *expression*

Working out how to solve a *matching* problem in arithmetic can often help you to form an expression. You can also use this as a check.

Question

A student buys x books at £a each and y books at £b each. Write an expression for the average (mean) cost of these books.

Answer

'Matching problem'
A student buys 2 books at £5 each and 4 books at £3 each. What is the average cost of these books?
Cost of 2 books at £5 each = £2 × 5 = £10
Cost of 4 books at £3 each = £4 × 3 = £12
Total cost of books = £(10 + 12) = £22
Total number of books bought = 2 + 4 = 6
Average cost of these books
$= \frac{\textit{total cost}}{\textit{total number}} = £\frac{22}{6}$.

Cost of x books at £a each = £$x \times a$ = £xa
Cost of y books at £b each = £$y \times b$ = £yb
Total cost of books = £$(xa + yb)$
Total number of books bought = $(x + y)$
Average cost of these books
$= \frac{\text{total cost of books}}{\text{total number of books}} = \frac{£(xa + yb)}{(x + y)}$

To solve some problems you may need to form an expression and then solve an equation. This is dealt with in Unit 2.30.

2.28 Simple indices

INDEX FORM

Index form or **index notation** is a simple way to write some numbers. For example,

the number 2^5 is in index form.
The small ^{5} is the **index**.
The 2 is called the **base**.

Index form
2^5 ← index
↑ base

An index tells you how many of the base number to multiply together. For example,

$$2^5 = 2 \times 2 \times 2 \times 2 \times 2$$
(5)

The ^{5} tells you how many 2s to multiply together.
You have 5.

Power is another word used for index. You use it when you 'say' a number in index form. For example,

for 2^5 you say, *2 to the power 5.*

A number *to the power 2* is usually called a **square**. For example,

7^2 is *7 to the power 2* **or** *7 squared* **or** *the square of 7*.
$7^2 = 7 \times 7$

A number *to the power 3* is usually called a **cube**. For example,

8^3 is *8 to the power 3* **or** *8 cubed* **or** *the cube of 8*.
$8^3 = 8 \times 8 \times 8$

When the base number is a decimal or fraction, it is usually written in brackets with the index outside. For example,

$(2.5)^3 = 2.5 \times 2.5 \times 2.5$
$(\frac{1}{2})^2 = \frac{1}{2} \times \frac{1}{2}$

Any number written *without* an index can be written with the index 1. For example,

$6 = 6^1,\ 3 = 3^1,\ \ldots$

Any number *to the power 0* is equal to 1. For example,

$5^0 = 1, \quad 9^0 = 1, \quad 127^0 = 1, \quad \ldots$

An index can be **negative** as well as positive. A negative index has a special meaning. For example,

$$3^{-2} = \frac{1}{3^2} \left(= \frac{1}{3 \times 3} \right)$$

$$2^{-5} = \frac{1}{2^5} \left(= \frac{1}{2 \times 2 \times 2 \times 2 \times 2} \right)$$

Question

Write each of the following in index form.

(a) $5 \times 5 \times 5 \times 5 \times 5 \times 5 \times 5$ (b) 1.7×1.7
(c) 10 (d) $\frac{1}{9} \times \frac{1}{9} \times \frac{1}{9}$
(e) $\dfrac{1}{6 \times 6 \times 6 \times 6 \times 6}$

Answer

(a) $5 \times 5 \times 5 \times 5 \times 5 \times 5 \times 5 = 5^7$
(b) $1.7 \times 1.7 = (1.7)^2$
(c) $10 = 10^1$
(d) $\frac{1}{9} \times \frac{1}{9} \times \frac{1}{9} = (\frac{1}{9})^3$
(e) $\dfrac{1}{6 \times 6 \times 6 \times 6 \times 6} = \dfrac{1}{6^5} = 6^{-5}$

FINDING VALUES

You can work out the **value** of a number written in index form. One way is to write out what the number means and then work out the multiplication. This can be done with or without a *calculator*. It depends on the numbers!

Question

Find the value of:

(a) 3^4 (b) 2^5 (c) $(1.5)^3$ (d) 4^{-2}

Answer

(a) $3^4 = 3 \times 3 \times 3 \times 3$
$= 9 \times 9 = 81$

(b) $2^5 = 2 \times 2 \times 2 \times 2 \times 2$
$= 4 \times 4 \times 2 = 32$

(c) $(1.5)^3 = (1.5) \times (1.5) \times (1.5)$ [C]
$= 3.375$
[C] [1] [·] [5] [×] [1] [·] [5] [×] [1] [·] [5] [=]

(d) $4^{-2} = \dfrac{1}{4^2}$
$= \dfrac{1}{4 \times 4} = \dfrac{1}{16}$ [C] [C] [1] [6] [1/x]
$= 0.0625$

It is useful to know and to recognize **powers of 10**. For example,

$10^0 = 1$
$10^1 = 10$
$10^2 = 10 \times 10 = 100$
$10^3 = 10 \times 10 \times 10 = 1000$
$10^4 = 10 \times 10 \times 10 \times 10 = 10\,000$
$10^5 = 10 \times 10 \times 10 \times 10 \times 10 = 100\,000$
$10^6 = 10 \times 10 \times 10 \times 10 \times 10 \times 10 = 1\,000\,000$

and so on ...

Negative powers of 10 are useful to know too. For example,

$$10^{-1} = \frac{1}{10} \text{ or } 0.1$$

$$10^{-2} = \frac{1}{10^2} = \frac{1}{10 \times 10} = \frac{1}{100} \textbf{ or } 0.01$$

$$10^{-3} = \frac{1}{10^3} = \frac{1}{10 \times 10 \times 10} = \frac{1}{1000} \textbf{ or } 0.001$$

$$10^{-4} = \frac{1}{10^4} = \frac{1}{10 \times 10 \times 10 \times 10} = \frac{1}{10\,000} \textbf{ or } 0.0001$$

and so on ...

SPECIAL CALCULATOR METHODS

There are several special ways to use a **calculator** to find a power of a number. Here are two of them. Try them if you can on your calculator.

Do not worry if you cannot use your calculator in these ways.

Remember that you can always use simple multiplication.

Using a constant multiplier

If your calculator has a **constant function** facility, then you can use this to find powers. On some calculators, pressing [×][×] makes the number on the display a 'constant'. Each press of [=] then gives a power of this number. For example, try this to work out 3^4:

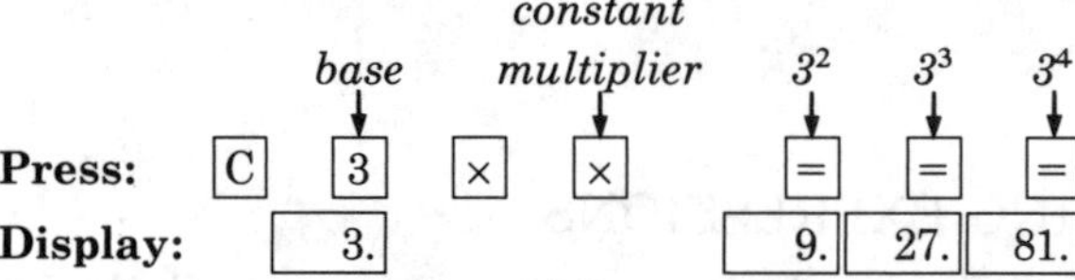

so $3^4 = 81$.

If your 'constant multiplier' does *not* work this way, then find out how it does work. Look it up in your calculator booklet or experiment to find out yourself.

Using a power key

Scientific calculators usually have a **power key**. It is often labelled [x^y] or [y^x]. It is very easy to use it to find the power of a number. Enter the number (the base) first, press the power key, enter the index and then press [=].

Question

Find the value of:

(a) 7^{11} (b) 0.6^9

Answer

(a) $7^{11} = 1\,977\,326\,750$ [C]

Press: [C] [7] [x^y] [1] [1] [=]
(7 = *base*, x^y = *power key*, 11 = *index*)

(b) $0.6^9 = 0.010\ 077\ 696$

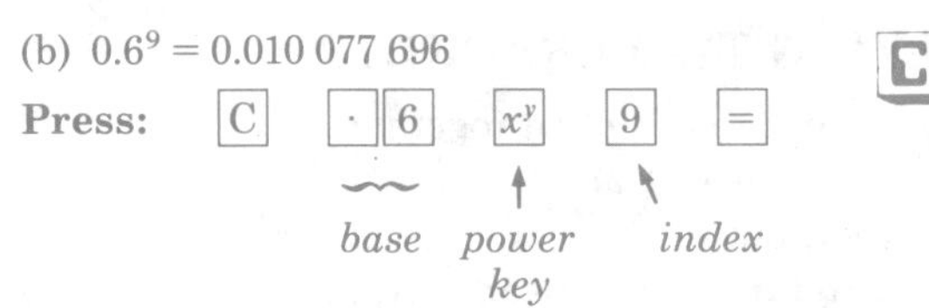

MULTIPLICATION AND DIVISION

Numbers in index form are often easier to use in calculations. The following **laws of indices** are used in multiplications and divisions.

1 To **multiply** numbers written with the *same* base, add the indices. For example,

$2^3 \times 2^4 = 2^{3+4} = 2^7$

You can check this by writing out the numbers in full.

$2^3 = 2 \times 2 \times 2$ and $2^4 = 2 \times 2 \times 2 \times 2$

so $2^3 \times 2^4 = (2 \times 2 \times 2) \times (2 \times 2 \times 2 \times 2)$
$= 2 \times 2 \times 2 \times 2 \times 2 \times 2 \times 2$
$= 2^7$

2 To **divide** numbers written with the *same* base, subtract the indices. For example,

$3^5 \div 3^4 = 3^{5-4} = 3^1 = 3$

You can check this too, since

$3^5 = 3 \times 3 \times 3 \times 3 \times 3$ and $3^4 = 3 \times 3 \times 3 \times 3$

so $3^5 \div 3^4 = \dfrac{3^5}{3^4} = \dfrac{\not{3} \times \not{3} \times \not{3} \times \not{3} \times 3}{\not{3} \times \not{3} \times \not{3} \times \not{3}} = 3$

You can use this law to show that a number to the power 0 is 1. For example,

$9^5 \div 9^5 = 9^{5-5} = 9^0$
but $9^5 \div 9^5 = \dfrac{9^5}{9^5} = 1$
These answers must be the same. So $9^0 = 1$

This law also can show you the meaning of a negative index. For example,

$7^3 \div 7^5 = 7^{3-5} = 7^{-2}$

but $7^3 \div 7^5 = \dfrac{7^3}{7^5} = \dfrac{\not{7} \times \not{7} \times \not{7}}{\not{7} \times \not{7} \times \not{7} \times 7 \times 7} = \dfrac{1}{7 \times 7} = \dfrac{1}{7^2}$

These two answers must be the same. So $7^{-2} = \dfrac{1}{7^2}$.

You can multiply and divide numbers with *negative* indices using the same laws too.

Remember The base must be the same in each number.

Question

Work these out in index form.
(a) $2^{-3} \times 2^4$ (b) $5^2 \div 5^{-2}$

Answer

(a) $2^{-3} \times 2^4 = 2^{-3+4} = 2^1 = 2$
(b) $5^2 \div 5^{-2} = 5^{2--2} = 5^{2+2} = 5^4$

These laws of indices can *only* be used if the numbers are written with the *same* base. If the numbers in a calculation have *different* bases, then you must work out the value of each number.

Question

Work out $\dfrac{5^4}{3^2 \times 2^3}$. Leave your answer as a fraction.

Answer

$5^4 = 5 \times 5 \times 5 \times 5 = 625$
$3^2 = 3 \times 3 = 9$
$2^3 = 2 \times 2 \times 2 = 8$
So $\dfrac{5^4}{3^2 \times 2^3} = \dfrac{625}{9 \times 8} = \dfrac{625}{72}$

INDICES IN ALGEBRA

Indices have the same meaning in algebra as in arithmetic. For example,

$a^3 = a \times a \times a$
$a^{-2} = \dfrac{1}{a^2} \quad \left(= \dfrac{1}{a \times a}\right)$
$a^0 = 1$
In these examples the base is a.

In terms such as $2xy^5$, only the y is 'to the power 5'.
So $2xy^5 = 2 \times x \times y \times y \times y \times y \times y$

If the power of a term is needed, then brackets are used. The index goes outside the brackets. For example,

$(3yz)^4 = (3yz) \times (3yz) \times (3yz) \times (3yz)$
$= 81y^4z^4$

You can write out the meaning of a term written in index form. However, you cannot find its value *unless* you know the value of each letter in the term.

Question

(a) Write out the meaning of $3a^2b^4$ in full.

(b) If $a = -1$ and $b = 2$, work out the value of $7a^3b^2$.

Answer

(a) $3a^2b^4 = 3 \times a^2 \times b^4$
$= 3 \times a \times a \times b \times b \times b \times b$

(b) If $a = -1$ and $b = 2$, then
$7a^3b^2 = 7 \times (-1)^3 \times (2)^2$ $\quad 2^2 = 2 \times 2 = 4$
$= 7 \times (-1) \times (4)$ $\quad (-1)^3 = (-1) \times (-1) \times (-1)$
$= -28$ $\quad = -1$

The **basic laws of indices** are true in algebra too. You can use them to simplify multiplications and divisions. It is easier if you group indices with the same base together.

Question

Simplify these as far as possible.
(a) $x^2 \times x^3$ (b) $y^{-3} \times y^5$ (c) $x^2y^3 \times xy^{-2}$
(d) $a^7 \div a^2$ (e) $b^{-6} \div b^{-4}$ (f) $a^5b^3 \div a^4b^4$

Answer

(a) $x^2 \times x^3 = x^{2+3} = x^5$

(b) $y^{-3} \times y^5 = y^{-3+5} = y^2$

(c) $x^2y^3 \times xy^{-2} = (x^2 \times x) \times (y^3 \times y^{-2})$
$= (x^{2+1}) \times (y^{3+-2})$
$= x^3 \times y$
$= x^3y$

(d) $a^7 \div a^2 = a^{7-2} = a^5$

(e) $b^{-6} \div b^{-4} = b^{-6--4} = b^{-6+4} = b^{-2}$

(f) $a^5b^3 \div a^4b^4$
$= ab^{-1}$
$\left(\begin{array}{l} a^5 \div a^4 = a^{5-4} = a \\ b^3 \div b^4 = b^{3-4} = b^{-1} \end{array}\right)$

2.29 Brackets and common factors

REMOVING BRACKETS

Brackets are used to group terms together. An expression *with* brackets in it can be replaced by an equivalent one *without* brackets. This is called **removing the brackets** or **expanding the expression**. To remove brackets you use the **distributive law** (see Unit 2.1). Multiply the term *outside* the bracket by each of the terms *inside* the brackets. Write out each multiplication in full if it helps. For example,

$5(x+3) = 5 \times x + 5 \times 3$
$= 5x + 15$

Take care with the signs when removing brackets. You must use the rules for signs when multiplying.

Remember a letter or number without a sign is +. For example,

x means $+x$, 3 means $+3$,

and so on ...

$(+) \times (+) \to +$
$(+) \times (-) \to -$
$(-) \times (+) \to -$
$(-) \times (-) \to +$

When there is a − sign in front of the brackets, the signs that were *inside* the brackets *change* when the brackets are removed. For example,

$-a(b - c + d)$ *Working* $-a \times +b = -ab$

$-a \times -c = +ac$

$= -ab + ac - ad$ $\quad -a \times +d = -ad$

Question

Remove the brackets from these expressions.

(a) $2y(y + 4)$ (b) $-3(2x - 5)$ (c) $2x^2(x^3 + 2xy - y^2)$

Answer

(a) $2y(y + 4)$ *Working* $2y \times y = 2y^2$

$= 2y^2 + 8y$ $\quad 2y \times 4 = 8y$

(b) $-3(2x - 5)$ *Working* $-3 \times +2x = -6x$

$= -6x + 15$ $\quad -3 \times -5 = +15$

(c) $2x^2(x^3 + 2xy - y^2)$ *Working* $2x^2 \times x^3 = 2x^5$

$= 2x^5 + 4x^3y - 2x^2y^2$ $\quad 2x^2 \times 2xy = 4x^3y$

$2x^2 \times -y^2 = -2x^2y^2$

When you have to simplify an expression with brackets in it, remove the brackets first and then collect like terms together (see Unit 2.27). Do not try to do both in one step.

Question

Simplify these expressions.

(a) $5a + 2(2a - 3) + 4$ (b) $12b - (5 + b) - 6$

(c) $15y - 7(3x - 2y)$

Answer

(a) $5a + 2(2a - 3) + 4$

Remove brackets $= 5a + 4a - 6 + 4$

Collect like terms $= 9a \quad -2$

(b) $12b - (5 + b) - 6$

Remove brackets $= 12b - 5 - b - 6$

Put like terms together $= 12b - b - 5 - 6$

Collect like terms $= 11b \quad -11$

(c) $15y - 7(3x - 2y)$

Remove brackets $= 15y - 21x + 14y$

Put like terms together $= 15y + 14y - 21x$

Collect like terms $= 29y \quad -21x$

Sometimes there are brackets *inside* brackets in an expression. Always remove the *inside* brackets first. Then collect any like terms before removing the other brackets. It is safer to keep each step separate.

Question

Expand $2a[(a + 2b) + 3(2a - b)]$

Answer

$2a[(a + 2b) + 3(2a - b)]$

Remove inside brackets $= 2a[a + 2b + 6a - 3b]$

Put like terms together $= 2a[a + 6a + 2b - 3b]$

Collect like terms $= 2a[\ 7a \quad -b\ ]$

Remove other brackets $= 14a^2 - 2ab$

MULTIPLYING TWO BRACKETS

Two brackets may be multiplied together. For example,

$(x + 2)(x + 3)$ means $(x + 2) \times (x + 3)$

The × sign is left out.

To find the **product of two brackets**, multiply *each term* in one bracket by *each term* in the other bracket. For example,

$(a + b)(c + d) = a(c + d) + b(c + d)$

$= ac + ad + bc + bd$

You may remember the working like this:

$(a + b)(c + d) = ac + ad + bc + bd$

After removing the brackets always collect any *like* terms together.

Question

Expand:

(a) $(x + 2)(x - 5)$ (b) $(a - b)(a^2 + b^2)$

Answer

(a) $(x + 2)(x - 5)$

Rewrite the multiplication $= x(x - 5) + 2(x - 5)$

Remove brackets $= x^2 - 5x + 2x - 10$

Collect like terms $= x^2 \quad -3x \quad -10$

(b) $(a - b)(a^2 + b^2)$

Rewrite the multiplication $= a(a^2 + b^2) - b(a^2 + b^2)$

Remove brackets $= a^3 + ab^2 - a^2b - b^3$

Note *There are no like terms here.* ab^2 *and* a^2b *are different.*

Here are three important expansions:

$(a + b)(a - b) = a^2 - b^2$ (the difference between two perfect squares)

$(a + b)^2 = (a + b)(a + b) = a^2 + 2ab + b^2$ (a perfect square)

$(a - b)^2 = (a - b)(a - b) = a^2 - 2ab + b^2$ (a perfect square)

These expansions are useful to know. But you should be able to work them out. Check that you can. Take careful note of the signs.

Question

Expand:

(a) $(x - 3)^2$ (b) $(y + 5)(y - 5)$ (c) $(a + 4)^2$

Answer

(a) $(x - 3)^2$ *a perfect square*

$= x^2 - (2 \times x \times 3) + 3^2$

$= x^2 - 6x + 9$

(b) $(y + 5)(y - 5)$

$= y^2 - 5^2$ *difference between two perfect squares*

$= y^2 - 25$

(c) $(a + 4)^2$ *a perfect square*

$= a^2 + (2 \times a \times 4) + 4^2$

$= a^2 + 8a + 16$

FACTORS

In *arithmetic*, two **factors** of a number multiply together to give that number (see Unit 2.1). For example,

$12 = 1 \times 12$

$12 = 2 \times 6$

$12 = 3 \times 4$

So 1, 2, 3, 4, 6 and 12 are **factors** of 12.

Remember 1 and the number itself are *always* factors of the number.

In *algebra*, two **factors** of a term multiply together to give that term. For example,

$$\left.\begin{array}{l} 7xy = 1 \times 7xy \\ 7xy = 7 \times xy \\ 7xy = 7x \times y \\ 7xy = 7y \times x \end{array}\right\} \text{ So } 1, 7, 7x, 7y, x, y, xy \text{ and } 7xy \text{ are } \textbf{factors} \text{ of } 7xy.$$

Remember 1 and the term itself are *always* factors of the term.

A term and its factors can have + or − signs. **Remember** the + or − sign goes with the term that follows it in an expression. For example,

$$\left.\begin{array}{l} -3x = 1 \times -3x \\ -3x = -1 \times 3x \\ -3x = 3 \times -x \\ -3x = -3 \times x \end{array}\right\} \text{ So } 1, -1, 3, -3, x, -x, 3x \text{ and } -3x \text{ are all } \textbf{factors} \text{ of } -3x.$$

In arithmetic, a factor of a number divides *exactly* into that number. The answer is another factor of the number. For example,

$20 \div 5 = 4.$ So 5 and 4 are factors of 20.

In algebra, a factor of a term divides *exactly* into that term. The answer is another factor of the term. For example,

$\dfrac{6x^2y}{3x} = 2xy.$ So $3x$ and $2xy$ are factors of $6x^2y$.

You can **check** by multiplying the factors together.

$3x \times 2xy = 6x^2y$ **Check✓**

COMMON FACTORS

In *arithmetic* a **common factor** is a factor of several numbers (see Unit 2.1). For example,

the factors of 12 are (1), (2), 3, (4), 6 and 12.

the factors of 20 are (1), (2), (4), 5, 10 and 20.

The common factors are 1, 2 and 4. The **highest** common factor is 4.

In *algebra*, a **common factor** is a factor of each term in an expression. For example,

the expression $6xy^2 + 8zy$ has common factors 1, 2, y and $2y$.

The **highest** common factor is $2y$.

When looking for common factors in an expression, look at the number and sign of each term first, then look for the same letter(s) in each term.

If an expression has a common factor, then write it in front of some brackets. Write the other factor inside the brackets. You can find this 'other factor' by dividing each term in the original expression by the common factor. For example,

$$6xy^2 + 8zy = 2y \times 3xy + 2y \times 4z$$
$$= 2y(3xy + 4z)$$

common factor ($2y$)

$$\frac{6xy^2}{2y} = 3xy \qquad \frac{8zy}{2y} = 4x$$

You can **check** your factorization by multiplying the factors. For example,

$2y(3xy + 4z) = 6xy^2 + 8yz$ **Check✓**

With practice it is possible to spot the common factor and other factor of an expression just by looking at it. So you need to practise. Always check that there is no common factor left inside the brackets.

Question

Factorize:

(a) $ab + a$ (b) $3x - 15y$

(c) $-4xy - 12yz$ (d) $3a^2 + 12a^2b^2 - 6a^3b$

Answer

(a) $ab + a = a \times b + a \times 1 = a(b + 1)$

(b) $3x - 15y = 3 \times x - 3 \times 5y = 3(x - 5y)$

(c) $-4xy - 12yz = -4y \times x - 4y \times 3z = -4y(x + 3z)$

Remember $(-) \times (+) \rightarrow (-)$

(d) $3a^2 + 12a^2b^2 - 6a^3b = 3a^2 \times 1 + 3a^2 \times 4b^2 - 3a^2 \times 2ab$
$= 3a^2(1 + 4b^2 - 2ab)$

Sometimes the common factor has more than one term in it. In this case it is usually written in a bracket. For example,

$$2(y-3) + x(y-3) = 2 \times (y-3) + x \times (y-3)$$
$$= (y-3)(2+x)$$

common factor

2.30 Simple linear equations

An **equation** is a true statement containing an equals sign (=). It shows that two quantities (the *left-hand side* and the *right-hand side*) are equal. For example,

$7 + 5 = 12$ and $5 + 2 = 10 - 3$ are *arithmetic* equations.

An **algebraic equation** contains letter(s) standing for unknown value(s). For example,

$x + 4 = 7$ and $y = 5 - x$ are *algebraic* equations.

This unit is about algebraic equations. A **linear equation** has *no* squares or *higher* powers of the unknown(s). For example,

$y = 7x + 1$ and $x - 9 = 10$ are linear equations.

The *simplest* type of linear equation has only *one* unknown, i.e. only one letter. All the terms are 'letter terms in that unknown' and numbers. For example,

$x - 9 = 10$ is a linear equation in x,
$2y + 7 = 3y$ is a linear equation in y.

SOLUTION OF LINEAR EQUATIONS

A **solution** of an equation is a number which, when put instead of the letter, makes the equation true. A linear equation with only *one* unknown has only *one* solution. For example,

$4 + x = 11$ has the solution $x = 7$ because $4 + 7 = 11$.

A solution of an equation is said to **satisfy** the equation. To **check** the solution of an equation, substitute the value for the letter in the equation. The left-hand side and right-hand side should be equal in value.

SOLVING BY BALANCING

An equation is like a set of scales *in balance*.

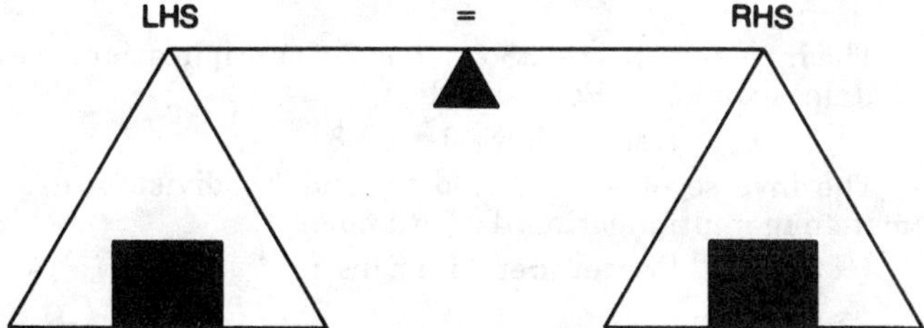

The quantities on the left-hand side (LHS) balance and are equal to the quantities on the right-hand side (RHS).

The equation, like the scales, will still balance if you do *exactly the same to each side*. The balance will be unchanged if you:

(a) add the same quantity to each side,
(b) subtract the same quantity from each side,
(c) multiply each side by the same quantity,
(d) divide each side by the same quantity.

You can use these 'common sense' ideas of balancing to help you to solve equations.

When solving an equation you want all the 'letter terms' on one side of the equals sign and all the 'number terms' on the other.

i.e. 'letter terms' = 'number terms'

To obtain this you may need to get rid of some unwanted terms from each side of the equation. You must decide whether to add or subtract to get rid of these terms.

The **inverses** of + and − help you to do this.

The inverse of + is −. So to get rid of a '+ term', use the matching '− term'. For example,

to get rid of '+2', use '−2' because $+2-2=0$.

The inverse of − is +. So to get rid of a '− term', use the matching '+ term'. For example,

to get rid of '−5', use '+5' because $-5+5=0$.

Remember You must do the same to each side of the equation to keep it 'in balance'.

Always **check** your answer by substitution.

Question

Solve:

(a) $x+3=7$ (b) $x-4=10$

Answer

(a) $x+3=7$

To get rid of +3, use −3
So subtract 3 from each side $x+3-3=7-3$

+3 − 3 = 0 $x=4$

Check LHS: $x+3=4+3=7$; RHS: 7 } LHS = RHS ✓

(b) $x-4=10$

To get rid of −4, use +4
So add 4 to each side $x-4+4=10+4$

−4 + 4 = 0 $x=14$

Check LHS: $x-4=14-4=10$; RHS: 10 } LHS = RHS ✓

These examples (and the next two) are very simple. You can easily work them out in your head. However they show you how the 'balance method' works. You can use it to solve more 'difficult' equations

When solving an equation you want to have the letter 'on its own'.

Remember x means $1x$.

The 'letter term' may have a coefficient that is not 1. For example,

$3x$ has a coefficient of 3; it means $3\times x$

$\frac{x}{2}$ has a coefficient of $\frac{1}{2}$; it means $x\div 2$.

You must decide whether to multiply or divide to make the coefficient equal to 1. The **inverses** of × and ÷ help you to do this.

The inverse of × is ÷. So to 'undo' a multiplication, use a matching division. For example,

$3\div 3=1$ **Remember** $3=1\times 3$

The inverse of ÷ is ×. So to 'undo' a division, use a matching multiplication. For example,

$\frac{1}{5}\times 5=1$ **Remember** $\frac{1}{5}$ means $1\div 5$

Question

Solve:

(a) $4x=8$ (b) $\frac{x}{7}=3$

Answer

(a) $4x=8$

To 'undo' ×4, use ÷4

So divide each side by 4 $\frac{4x}{4}=\frac{8}{4}$

4 ÷ 4 = 1 $x=2$

Check LHS: $4x=4\times 2=8$; RHS: 8 } LHS = RHS ✓

(b) $\frac{x}{7}=3$

To 'undo' ÷7, use ×7

So multiply each side by 7 $\frac{x}{7}\times 7=3\times 7$

$\frac{1}{7}\times 7=1$ $x=21$

Check LHS: $\frac{x}{7}=\frac{21}{7}=3$; RHS: 3 } LHS = RHS ✓

Linear equations often involve more than one operation. For example,

$2x-3=15$

involves multiplication $(2\times x)$ and subtraction (-3).

So more than one inverse operation is needed to solve such an equation. The order in which the operations are 'undone' is important.

Get rid of 'unwanted terms' by adding or subtracting first. Then get the letter 'on its own' by multiplying or dividing. Write out each step in full. This may help you to avoid making mistakes.

Question

Solve $2x+5=11$

Answer

$2x+5=11$

To get rid of +5, use −5
Subtract 5 from each side $2x+5-5=11-5$

+5 − 5 = 0 $2x=6$

To 'undo' ×2, use ÷2
Divide each side by 2 $\frac{2x}{2}=\frac{6}{2}$

2 ÷ 2 = 1 $x=3$

Check LHS: $2x+5=2\times 3+5=6+5=11$; RHS: 11 } LHS = RHS ✓

Sometimes letters and numbers are on *both* sides of an equation. For example,

$4x+5=14+x$

In these examples, group all the 'letter terms' on one side of the equation first. Then solve the equation as before. Always check your solution.

Question

Solve $3x+4=7-2x$

Answer

$3x+4=7-2x$

To get rid of −2x, use +2x
Add 2x to each side $3x+2x+4=7-2x+2x$

−2x + 2x = 0 $5x+4=7$

To get rid of +4, use −4
Subtract 4 from each side $5x+4-4=7-4$
To undo ×5, use ÷5 $5x=3$

Divide each side by 5 $\frac{5x}{5}=\frac{3}{5}$

$x=\frac{3}{5}$ or 0.6

Check LHS: $3x+4=3\times 0.6+4=1.8+4=5.8$; RHS: $7-2x=7-2\times 0.6=7-1.2=5.8$ } LHS = RHS ✓

Usually we group all the 'letter terms' on the left-hand side. Sometimes it is easier to group them on the right-hand side. With practice you will be able to spot which side to choose. Often it is the side with the 'larger letter term'. This will give you a '+ letter term' which is easier to deal with.

Question

Solve $3 - x = 8x + 12$

Answer

$$3 - x = 8x + 12$$

To get rid of $-x$, use $+x$
Add x to each side $3 - x + x = 8x + x + 12$
$3 = 9x + 12$

To get rid of $+12$, use -12
Subtract 12 from each side $3 - 12 = 9x + 12 - 12$
$-9 = 9x$

To undo $\times 9$, use $\div 9$
Divide each side by 9 $\frac{-9}{9} = \frac{9x}{9}$
$-1 = x$

Check LHS: $3 - x = 3 - -1 = 3 + 1 = 4$
RHS: $8x + 12 = 8 \times -1 + 12 = -8 + 12 = 4$
LHS = RHS✓

EQUATIONS WITH BRACKETS

To solve an equation with brackets, remove the brackets first (see Unit 2.29). Collect any like terms together. Then solve the equation and check your solution as usual.

Question

Solve $2(x + 5) = 5(x - 7)$

Answer

$$2(x + 5) = 5(x - 7)$$

Remove brackets $2x + 10 = 5x - 35$
Subtract $2x$ from each side $2x - 2x + 10 = 5x - 2x - 35$
$10 = 3x - 35$
Add 35 to each side $10 + 35 = 3x - 35 + 35$
$45 = 3x$
Divide each side by 3 $\frac{45}{3} = \frac{3x}{3}$
$15 = x$

Check LHS: $2(x + 5) = 2(15 + 5) = 2(20) = 40$
RHS: $5(x - 7) = 5(15 - 7) = 5(8) = 40$
LHS = RHS✓

Take extra care when there is a − sign outside the bracket. When this happens the signs that were *inside* the brackets change when the brackets are removed.

Question

Solve the equation $8 = 20 - 3(5 - x)$

Answer

$$8 = 20 - 3(5 - x)$$

Remove brackets $8 = 20 - 15 + 3x$
$8 = 5 + 3x$
Subtract 5 from each side $8 - 5 = 5 - 5 + 3x$
$3 = 3x$
Divide each side by 3 $\frac{3}{3} = \frac{3x}{3}$
$1 = x$

Check LHS: 8
RHS: $20 - 3(5 - x) = 20 - 3(5 - 1) = 20 - 3(4) = 20 - 12 = 8$
LHS = RHS✓

EQUATIONS INVOLVING FRACTIONS

An equation involving a fraction is easier to solve when the fraction has been removed. You can do this by multiplying every term in the equation by the denominator of the fraction. Do not try to do too many steps at a time. **Check** your solution as before.

Question

Solve $\frac{(2x - 1)}{3} = 7$

Answer

$$\frac{(2x - 1)}{3} = 7$$

Multiply every term by denominator 3 $3 \times \frac{(2x-1)}{3} = 3 \times 7$
$(2x - 1) = 21$
Add 1 to each side $2x - 1 + 1 = 21 + 1$
$2x = 22$
Divide each side by 2 $\frac{2x}{2} = \frac{22}{2}$
$x = 11$

Check
LHS: $\frac{(2x - 1)}{3} = \frac{(2 \times 11 - 1)}{3} = \frac{22 - 1}{3} = \frac{21}{3} = 7$
RHS: 7
LHS = RHS✓

2.31 Formulae

FORMULAE AND EQUATIONS

A **formula** is basically an **equation**. It is a *true statement* containing an equals sign.

In an algebraic equation, letters stand for unknown values. For example, the equation $y = 3x + 2$ shows the relationship between two unknown values, x and y. In a formula, letters stand for unknown values which are definite quantities. In the formula $A = lw$, A stands for the *A*rea of a rectangle, l for the *l*ength and w for the *w*idth.

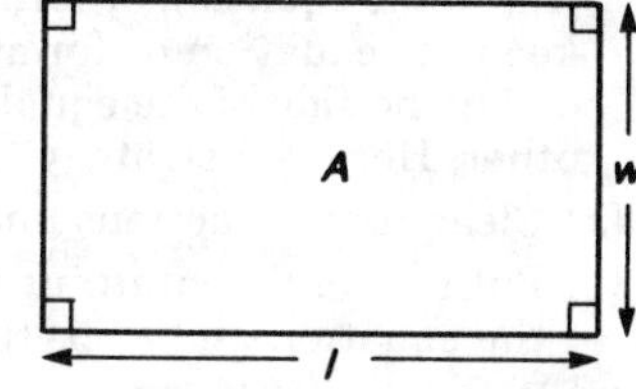

Equations (and formulae) are often written with one letter isolated on one side of the equals sign. This letter is called the **subject** of the equation or formula. Any other letters and numbers are all on the other side of the equals sign. For example, in the equation $y = 2x - 3$ the subject is y.

But in the equation $y = 2x - 4y + 6$, the subject is *not* y because there is a y term on both sides of the equation.

If a letter, y say, is the subject of an equation, then the equation is written as:

y = (an expression not including y)
or (an expression not including y) = y

The subject may be on either the left or right hand side of the equation. It is usually written on the left.

REARRANGING EQUATIONS OR FORMULAE

An equation or formula can be rearranged so that a different letter becomes its subject. For example, the

formula $A = lw$ (subject A)

can be written as $l = \frac{A}{w}$ (subject l)

or $\frac{A}{l} = w$ (subject w)

This is often called **changing the subject** of the equation or formula, or **transforming** or **transposing** the equation or formula. At this level the new subject appears only *once* in the equation or formula. Here are two ways to rearrange such an equation or formula.

1 The simplest way to rearrange an equation or formula at this level is to use **flow diagrams**. To rearrange an equation or formula:

(a) Start with the new subject. Build up the equation or formula step by step with a flow diagram.

(b) Draw the inverse flow diagram. End up with the expression equal to the new subject.

Question

The formula $s = \frac{(u+v)t}{2}$ is used in Physics to find the distance (in metres) an object travels if it moves in a straight line with constant acceleration. u is the starting speed (in m/s), v the final speed (in m/s) and t (in seconds) is the time for which it travels. If s, u and t are known, find a formula which will give v (i.e. make v the subject).

Answer

Flow diagram

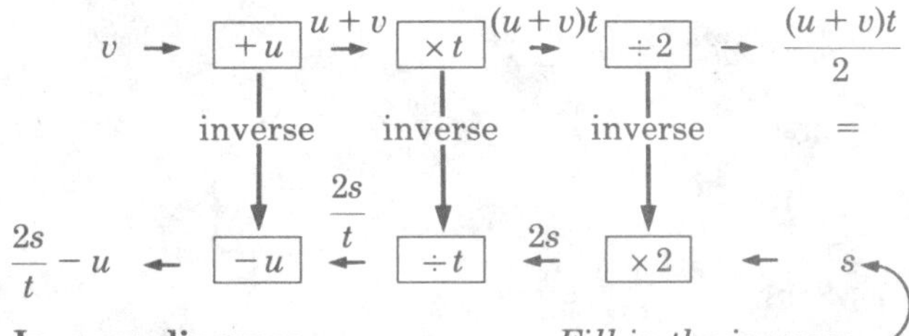

Inverse diagram

Fill in the inverses Then go back along the inverse diagram

From the inverse diagram: $v = \frac{2s}{t} - u$

2 Another way to rearrange an equation or formula is **by balancing**. This method is like solving an equation (see Unit 2.30) but you will have letters as well as numbers in the solution. Your aim is to *isolate* the new subject on one side of the equation or formula. When doing this you must keep the equation or formula *balanced*. So whatever you do on one side of the equals sign, you must also do on the other. Here is a strategy to help you.

(a) Clear roots, fractions and brackets (if there are any).

(b) Put the term containing the new subject on one side of the equation and everything else on the other side.

(c) Simplify any terms if you can.

(d) Reduce the term containing the new subject to a single letter. You may have to divide, multiply or take a root.

(e) Write the equation or formula with the subject on the left hand side.

When rearranging simple equations or formulae you may need only a few of the steps in this strategy.

Question

Rewrite the linear equation $2y + 4x = 10$ in the standard form $y = mx + c$.

Answer

$$2y + 4x = 10$$

Subtract 4x from both sides $\quad 2y + 4x - 4x = 10 - 4x$

$$2y = 10 - 4x$$

Divide each term by 2 $\quad \frac{2y}{2} = \frac{10}{2} - \frac{4x}{2}$

$$y = 5 - 2x$$

Put in standard form $\quad y = -2x + 5$

Here is a more difficult example. It uses most of the steps in the strategy.

Question

In Physics $s = ut + \frac{1}{2}at^2$ is called an equation of motion. It can be used whenever an object is travelling with constant, uniform acceleration in a straight line.

s = distance travelled (m) $\quad u$ = initial velocity (m/s)

a = acceleration (m/s^2) $\quad t$ = time taken (s)

Make a the subject of this equation of motion.

Answer

$$s = ut + \tfrac{1}{2}at^2$$

Multiply each term by 2 $\quad 2s = 2ut + 2 \times \tfrac{1}{2}at^2$

$$2s = 2ut + at^2$$

Subtract 2ut from both sides $\quad 2s - 2ut = 2ut - 2ut + at^2$

$$2s - 2ut = at^2$$

Simplify by taking out a common factor of 2 $\quad 2(s - ut) = at^2$

Divide by t^2 $\quad \frac{2(s-ut)}{t^2} = \frac{at^2}{t^2}$

$$\frac{2(s-ut)}{t^2} = a$$

Rewrite with a on the LHS $\quad a = \frac{2(s-ut)}{t^2}$

SOLVING PROBLEMS

Algebra is often used to **solve problems** given in words and sentences. To do this you need to understand the other algebra units in Lists 1 and 2 (see units 1.62, 1.63, 2.27–2.30). Here is a useful strategy to help you to solve such problems.

1 Read the information given carefully. Decide on what are the unknown quantities that you have to find. Use diagrams if they help to sort out the information.

2 Choose a letter to stand for one unknown quantity you have to find. Sometimes there is more than one unknown. Try to use the information given to write each unknown in terms of this letter. Some problems will have units of measurement such as metres or centimetres, in them. Make sure that all the expressions are in the same units.

3 Use the information given to find two equal expressions. At least one must use the letter you have chosen. Write these expressions as an equation.

4 Solve the equation you have made (see Unit 2.30 for linear equations). Use the solution to answer the question, in words.

5 **Check** your answer. Use the original information in the problem in your check. Do not simply check your answer in your equation! You may have made a mistake when you formed the equation.

When making up an equation or formula you may be able to use a relationship or rule you know. For example,

the perimeter of a shape is the sum of the lengths of its sides,

the angles of a quadrilateral add up to 360°,

the area of a rectangle is its length × its width.

So look for relationships like these in the question.

Question

The length of a rectangular field is 25 metres more than its width. The perimeter of the field is 450 metres. What is the actual width and length of the field?

Answer

Let the width of the field be x metres. The length is 25 metres more than the width. So the length of the field is $(x + 25)$ metres.

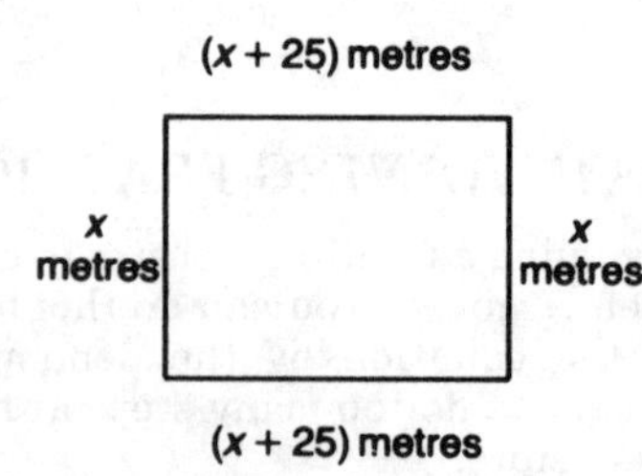

The perimeter of the field in metres is

$(x + 25) + x + (x + 25) + x$

But the actual perimeter is given as 450 metres. So

$(x + 25) + x + (x + 25) + x = 450$

Solve this equation to find x

Remove brackets $x + 25 + x + x + 25 + x = 450$

Collect like terms $4x + 50 = 450$

Subtract 50 from each side $4x + 50 - 50 = 450 - 50$

$4x = 400$

Divide each side by 4 $\frac{4x}{4} = \frac{400}{4}$

$x = 100$

The width of the field is 100 metres. The length of the field is (100 + 25) metres = 125 metres.

Check The perimeter of the field is
100 m + 125 m + 100 m + 125 m = 450 m.

Sometimes you will have to work out a relationship or rule yourself from the information given. Diagrams are often helpful here too.

Question

A new town has houses built on one side of a road only. The houses are built in blocks of 10. Between each block of 10 houses there is a lamp post. There is always a lamp post at the end of each road.

(a) How many lamp posts are there in a road with
 (i) 20 houses (ii) 30 houses (iii) 50 houses?

(b) Find an equation which gives the number (L) of lamp posts needed for a road with H houses.

(c) Use your rule to find how many lamp posts are needed for a road with 150 houses.

(d) How many houses are there on a road with 22 lamp posts?

Answer

(a) 10 houses → 1 block

 (i) 20 houses → $\frac{20}{10}$ blocks → 2 blocks

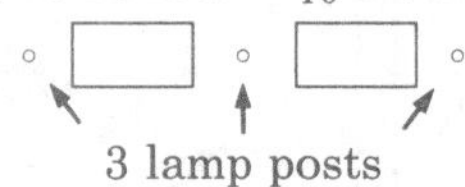

 (ii) 30 houses → $\frac{30}{10}$ blocks → 3 blocks

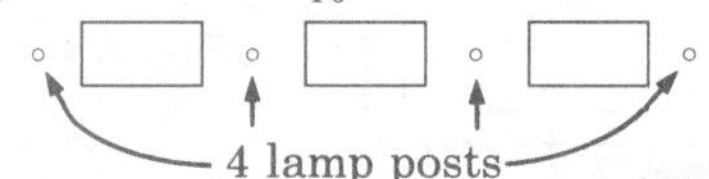

 (iii) 50 houses → $\frac{50}{10}$ blocks → 5 blocks

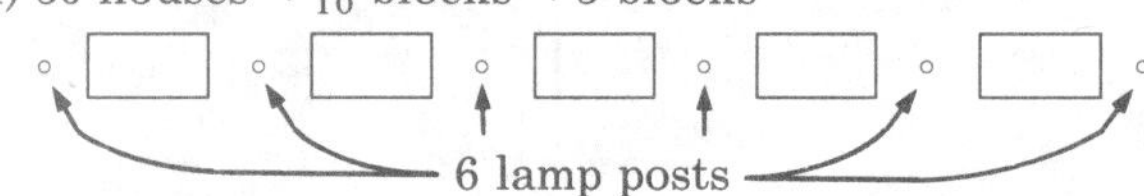

(b) The number (L) of lamp posts is one more than the number of blocks of houses.

So L = (number of blocks of houses) + 1

The number of blocks of houses

= (number of houses) ÷ 10

$= H \div 10$ or $\frac{H}{10}$

So $L = \frac{H}{10} + 1$

(c) In a road with 150 houses, $H = 150$.

So $L = \frac{150}{10} + 1$
$= 15 + 1$
$= 16$

So 16 lamp posts are needed.

(d) In a road with 22 lamp posts, $L = 22$.

So, $22 = \frac{H}{10} + 1$

Subtract 1 from both sides $22 - 1 = \frac{H}{10} + 1 - 1$

$21 = \frac{H}{10}$

Multiply both sides by 10 $21 \times 10 = \frac{H}{10} \times 10$

$210 = H$

So there are 210 houses in the road.

2.32 Gradient

IDEA OF GRADIENT

A **gradient** is a slope. In mathematics a gradient must have a **sign** and a **size**.

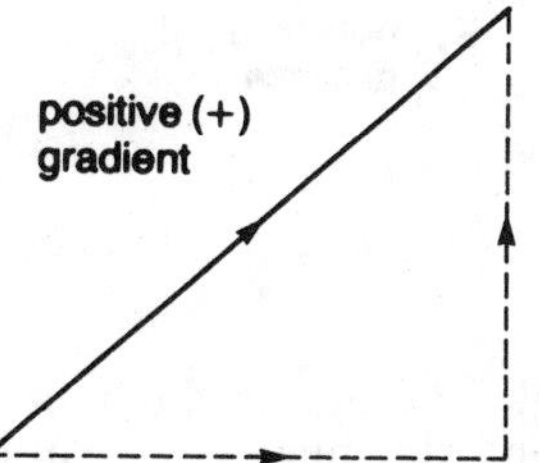

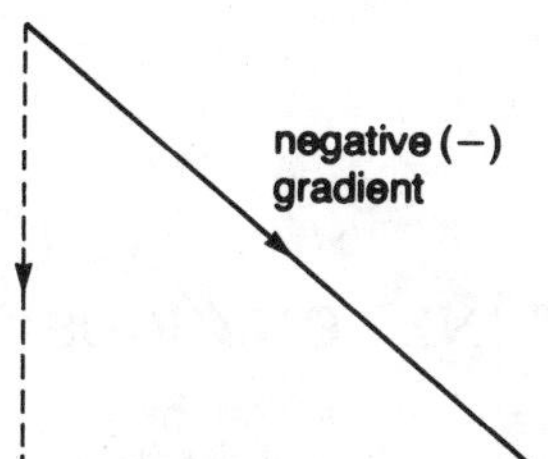

The sign tells you the **direction** of the slope.
An *up slope* (↗) has a *positive* (+) gradient.
A *down slope* (↘) has a *negative* (−) gradient.
The size tells you the **steepness** of the slope.
The steeper the slope, the larger the size of the gradient.

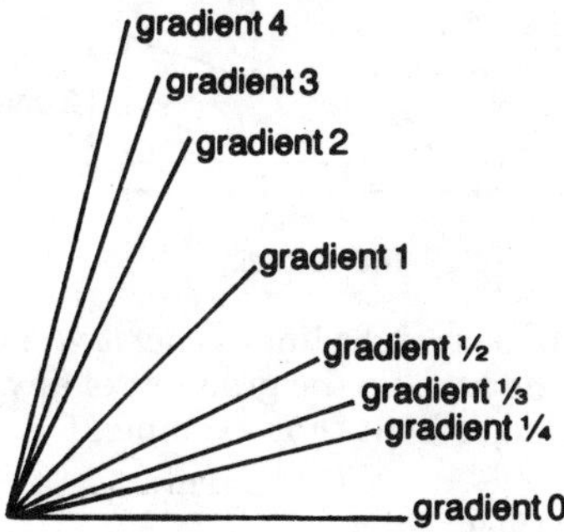

The *flat* (horizontal) has *no* slope so its gradient is zero (0).

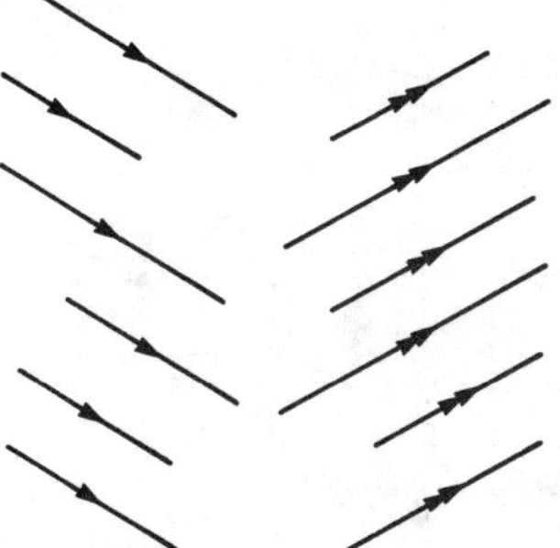

Lines with the *same* gradient are *parallel.*

The size of a gradient can be worked out from

size of a gradient = $\frac{\text{vertical distance}}{\text{horizontal distance}}$

vertical distance

horizontal distance

Take care to **match the units** of the distances. A gradient itself has no units.

You may have to measure the vertical and horizontal distances before working out the gradient. Often you will be given them in a question.

Question

The cable of a ski lift rises 12 m vertically for every horizontal 8 m distance. What is the gradient of the cable?

Answer

$$\text{size of gradient} = \frac{\text{vertical distance}}{\text{horizontal distance}} = \frac{12\text{ m}}{8\text{ m}} = 1.5$$

12 m vertical distance

8 m horizontal distance

Since the cable is an 'up slope', the gradient is positive. So the gradient of the cable is $^{+}1.5$.

LINES ON GRIDS

Grid lines can help you to work out the gradient of a straight line. It is easy to count the number of units *vertically* and *horizontally*. For example,

the gradient of PQ

$$= \frac{2\text{ units}}{6\text{ units}} = \tfrac{1}{3}$$

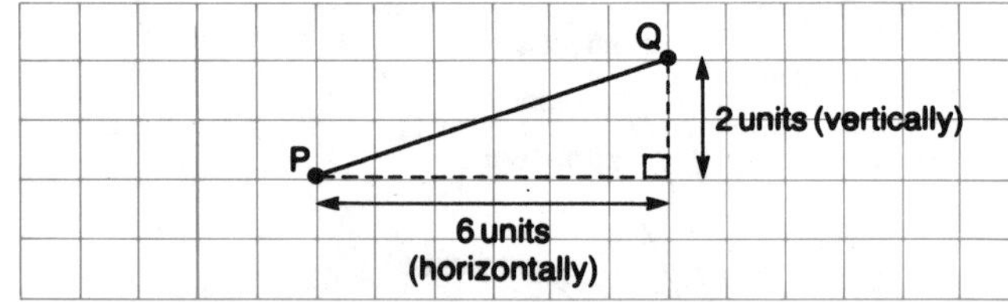

The gradient of a straight line is *constant*, i.e. it is the same anywhere on the line. So the gradient of any part of the line gives the line's gradient. For example, for the line on this grid,

using AB, the gradient $= \frac{1}{2}$
using CD, the gradient $= \frac{2}{4} = \frac{1}{2}$
using EF, the gradient $= \frac{3}{6} = \frac{1}{2}$

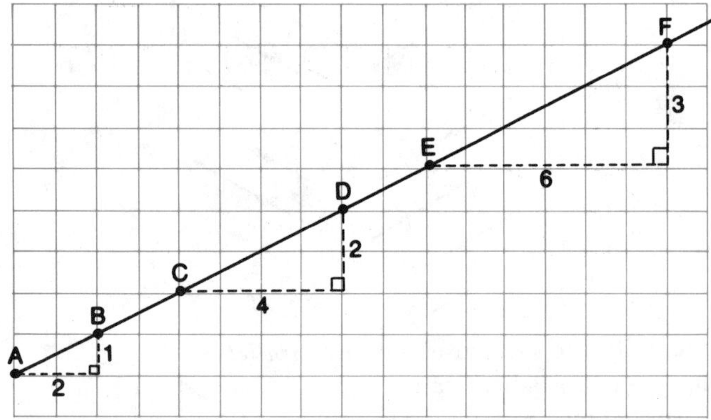

Often, the gradient of a **straight line graph** is needed. Here is one way to work it out.

1 Mark two points on the line.

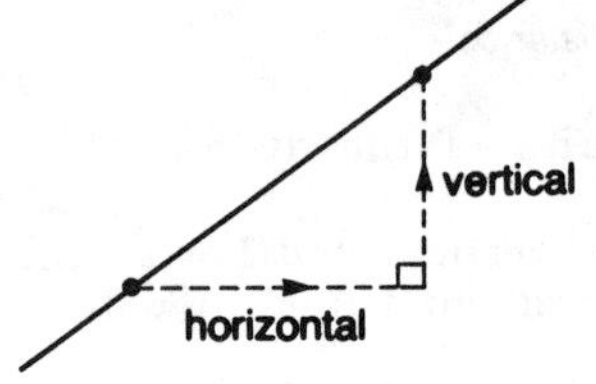

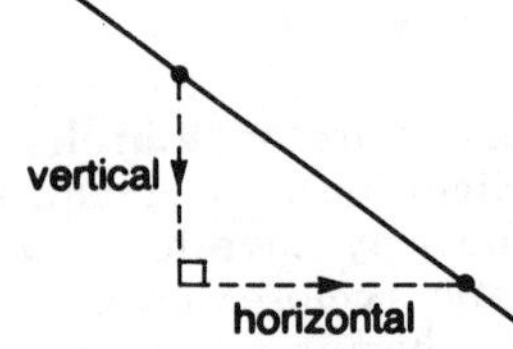

2 Work out the *vertical distance* and *horizontal distance* between the two points. Choose the points to make these 'easy' values to work with.

Remember When moving from one point to the other,
right (→) is positive (+), *left* (←) is negative (−),
up (↑) is positive (+), *down* (↓) is negative (−),

3 Find the gradient using
$$\frac{\text{vertical distance}}{\text{horizontal distance}}$$
Always **check** that the sign of the gradient makes sense.

Remember ↗ *up slopes* are positive (+)
↘ *down slopes* are negative (−).

Question

Calculate the gradients of these straight line graphs.

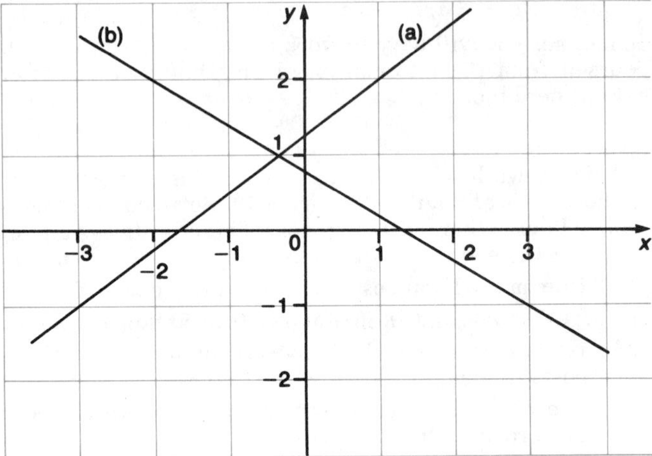

Answer

(a)

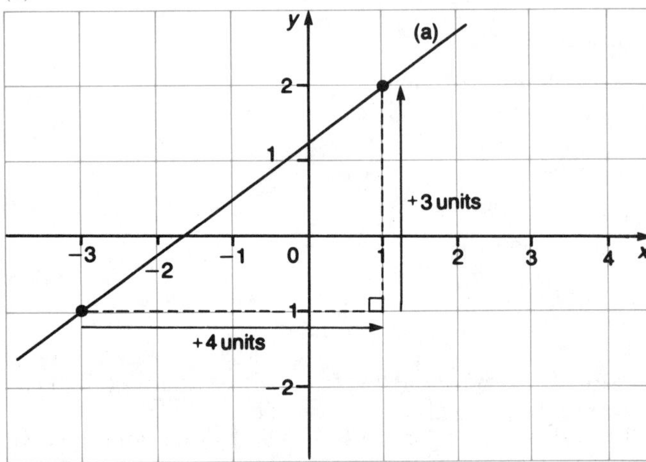

$$\text{gradient} = \frac{+3\text{ units}}{+4\text{ units}} = {}^{+}\tfrac{3}{4}\text{ or }{}^{+}0.75$$

Check: the line is an *up slope*, so the gradient is +

(b)

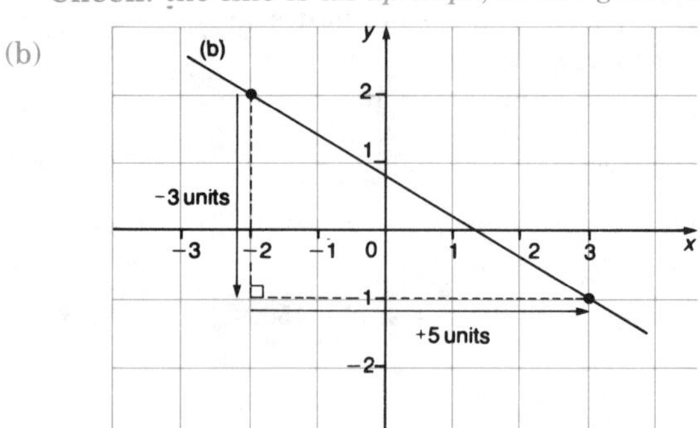

$$\text{gradient} = \frac{-3\text{ units}}{+5\text{ units}} = {}^{-}\tfrac{3}{5}\text{ or }{}^{-}0.6$$

Check: the line is a *down slope*, so the gradient is −.

The gradient of a straight line graph is used in many practical situations. For example, when finding speeds on travel graphs.

2.33 Drawing algebraic graphs

An **algebraic graph** gives a picture of an algebraic equation. It consists of a set of points whose coordinates fit the given algebraic equation. In mathematics algebraic equations are usually given in terms of x and y. So all equations in this unit are given using these letters. Other letters may be used in practical examples but their graphs may be drawn as shown in this unit.

RECOGNIZING COMMON GRAPHS

When drawing graphs, being able to **predict** the shape and some features is useful. This can help you to avoid producing graphs which are obviously incorrect. It is also a useful check on the points calculated and plotted. Any points that look as if they are not on the expected shape can be checked. Fortunately the algebraic equation itself can give some clues to help you here ... if you know what to look for!

The graphs of simple equations are either **straight lines** or **smooth curves**. At this level the graphs you may have to draw are usually of the following standard types.

Straight line

The graph of a **linear equation** (see Unit 2.30) is a straight line. You must be able to recognize a linear equation. Compare these two sets of equations.

Linear equations		**Not linear equations**	
$y = 3x$	$y = 2x - 1$	$y = 5x^2$	$x^2 + y^2 = 4$
$x = 5$	$y = 7$	$y = 3x^2 - x + 1$	$y = x^3$
$4y = 5x - 3$	$x + y = 6$	$y = \frac{1}{x}$	$\frac{1}{x} - \frac{1}{y} = 3$
$\frac{x}{2} + \frac{y}{3} + = 1$		$y = \sqrt{x}$	

The equation of each straight line contains an x (i.e. x^1) term and/or a y (i.e. y^1) term. Some of them contain constants, for example a number, too. In the linear equations there are no other powers of x and y except x^1 and y^1. For example, there are no terms in x^2, x^3, $\sqrt{x}$, $\frac{1}{x}$ (i.e. x^{-1}), etc. Any linear equation can be written in the form

$\boldsymbol{y = mx + c}$

where m and c are constants.

You may have to rearrange the equation (see p. 61) to put it in this form. Check that you can write all the linear equations in the set above as $y = mx + c$.

The values of the constants m and c in this equation give you some features of the straight line.

$y = \boldsymbol{m}x + \boldsymbol{c}$

gradient or **slope** (m) — **y-intercept** (c)

The constant m gives the **gradient** or **slope** of the line (see Unit 2.32).

The *sign* of m tells you the *direction* of the slope of the line.

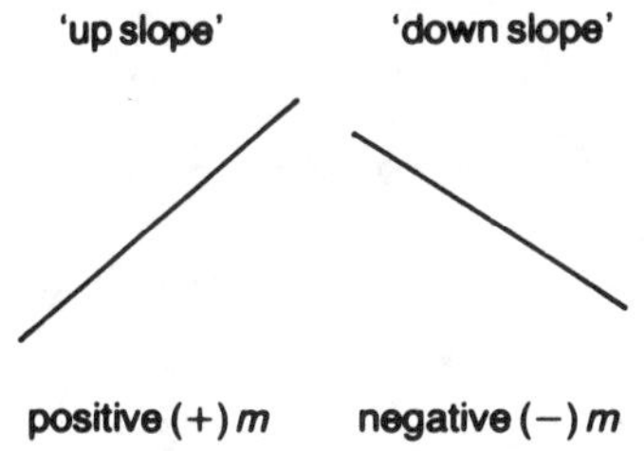

A *positive* value (+) gives an *up slope*. A *negative* value (−) gives a *down slope*. For example,

in $y = 2x$, $m = +2$, i.e. *up* ↗
in $y = 7x - 5$, $m = +7$, i.e. *up* ↗
in $y = -3x$, $m = -3$, i.e. *down* ↘
in $y = -5x + 7$, $m = -5$, i.e. *down* ↘

Remember

$y = x + 2$ means $y = 1x + 2$, so $m = +1$, i.e. *up* ↗
$y = -x + 7$ means $y = -1x + 7$, so $m = -1$, i.e. *down* ↘

The *size* of m tells you about the *steepness* of the slope. The larger the figure, the steeper the slope.

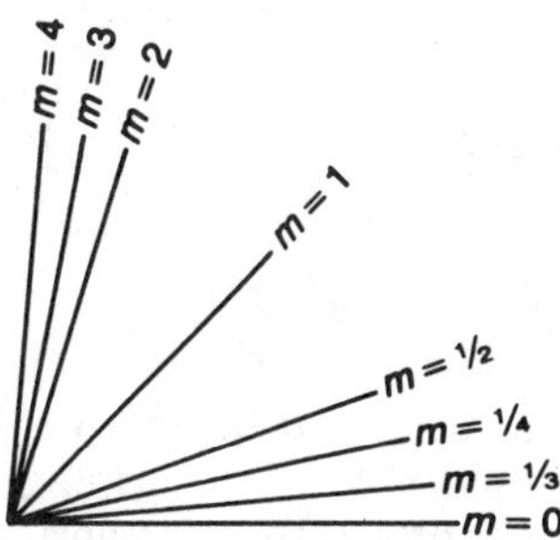

All lines with the **same value** of m, i.e. *the same gradient*, are **parallel**. For example, all the lines on this graph have $m = \frac{1}{2}$, i.e. gradient $\frac{1}{2}$.

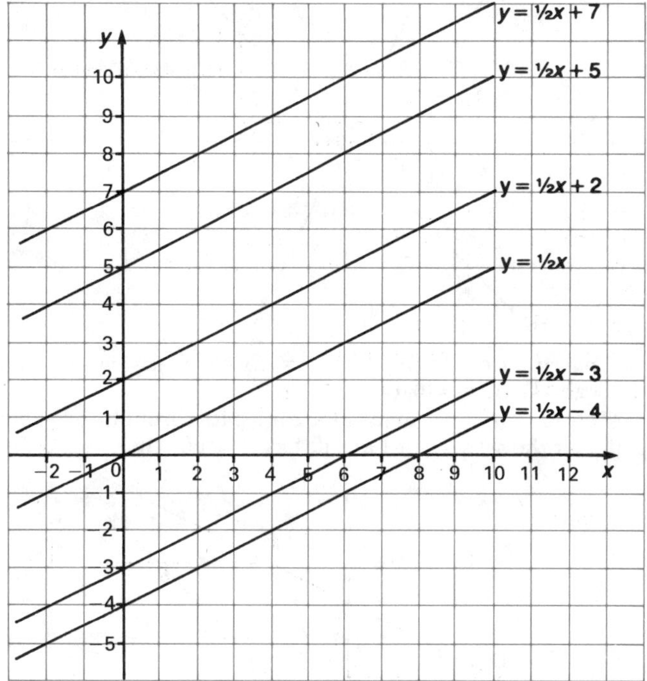

The constant $\boldsymbol{c}$ tells you where the line cuts the y-axis. This is often called the **y-intercept**. It is the value of y when $x = 0$.

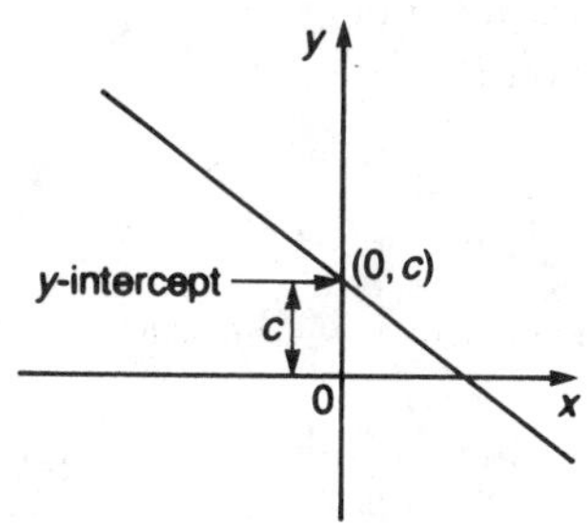

For example,
the line $y = -\frac{1}{3}x + 2$ cuts the y-axis at $y = +2$,
the line $y = 2x - 3$ cuts the y-axis at $y = -3$.

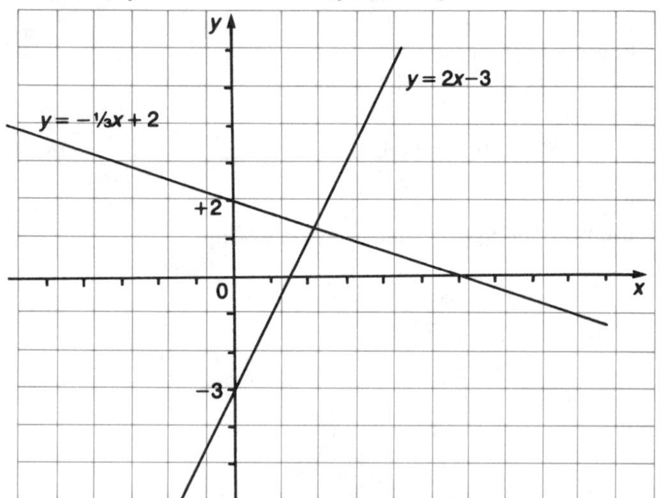

When the y-intercept, c, is 0, then the lines passes through the origin (0, 0). For example,
$y = x$ and $y = -2x$ pass through the origin.

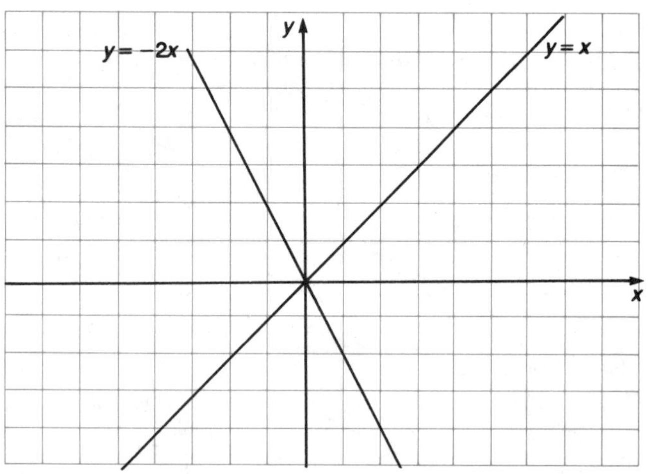

So any equation of the form $\boldsymbol{y = mx}$ gives a straight line through the origin (0, 0).

All lines with the same value for c pass through the same point on the y-axis but have different gradients.

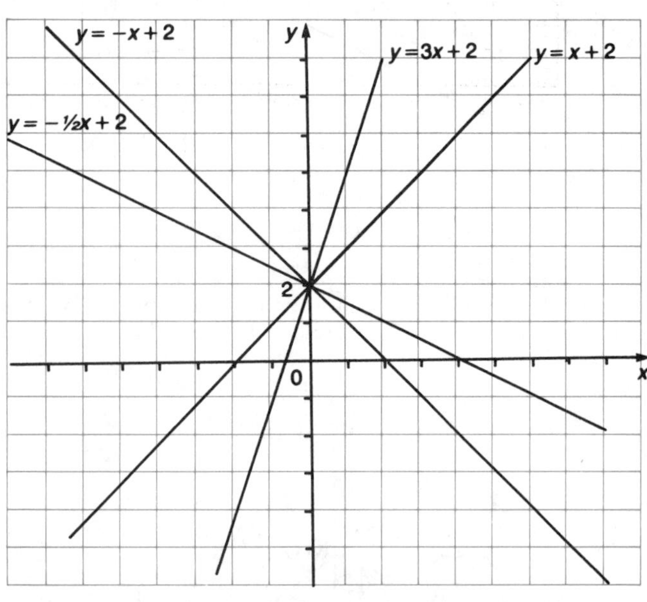

For example, the lines given by $y = 3x + 2$, $y = x + 2$, $y = -\frac{1}{2}x + 2$, $y = -x + 2$ all pass through (0, 2).

Lines parallel to the axes have simple equations. These are easy to spot too.

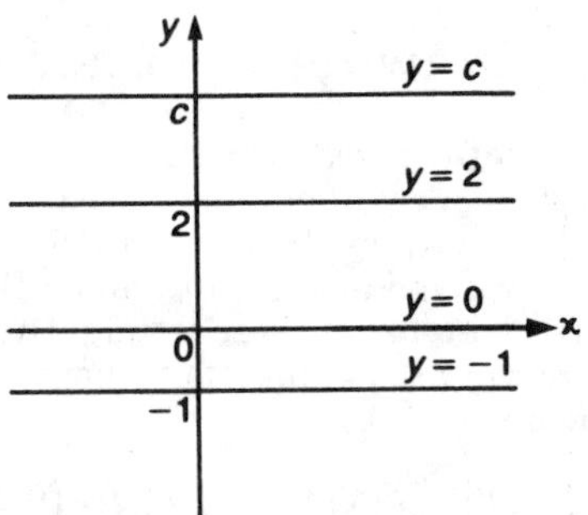

$\boldsymbol{y = 0}$ is the equation of the x-axis. $\boldsymbol{y = c}$ (where c is a constant) is the equation of any line parallel to the x-axis. It cuts the other axis where $y = c$. For example, the lines given by $y = 2$ and $y = -1$ are both parallel to the x-axis.

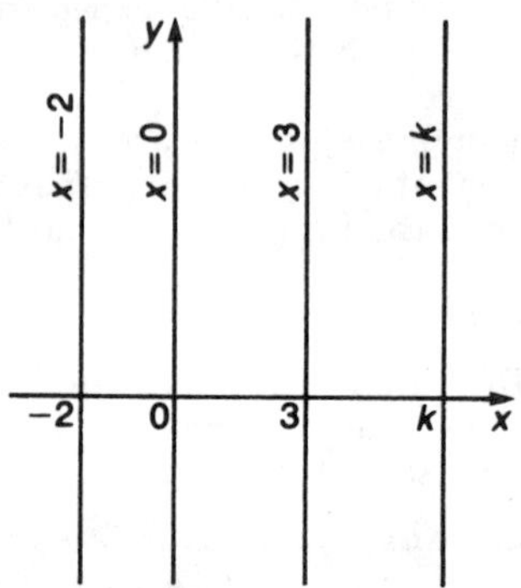

$\boldsymbol{x = 0}$ is the equation of the y-axis. $\boldsymbol{x = k}$ (where k is a constant) is the equation of any line parallel to the y-axis. It cuts the other axis where $x = k$. For example, the lines given by $x = 3$ and $x = -2$ are both parallel to the y-axis.

PARABOLA

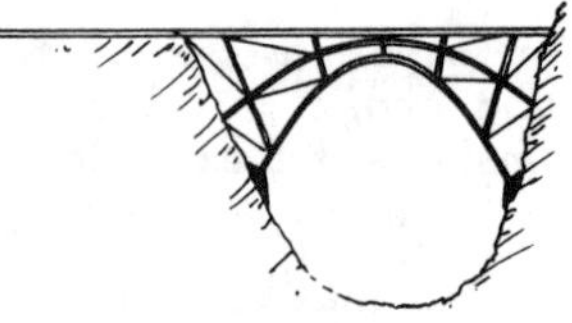

The **parabola** is a simple curve. Its shape is easy to recognize. Parabolas often occur in science and practical situations.

Any equation which can be written in the form:

$\boldsymbol{y = ax^2}$

(where a is a constant but not zero), gives a parabola as its graph. For example,

$y = x^2$, $y = 5x^2$, $y = -x^2$ and $y = -2x^2$

are all equations of parabolas. The sign of the coefficient a tells you *which way up* the parabola is drawn.

If a is positive (+), the curve *points down.* The **turning point** is at the **minimum** value of y on the curve. For example, the graphs of $y = x^2$ and $y = 5x^2$ *point down.*

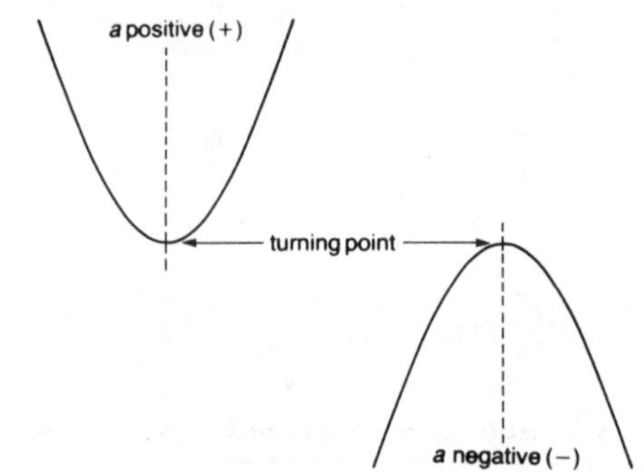

If a is negative (−), then the curve *points up*. The **turning point** is at the **maximum** value of y on the curve. For example, the graphs of $y = -x^2$ and $y = -2x^2$ *point up*.

The graph of $y = ax^2$ always has the origin (0, 0) as its turning point. The y-axis is its **line of symmetry**. For example,

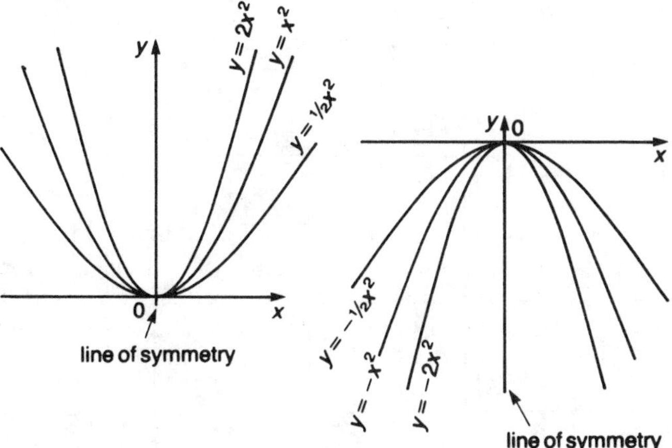

Other parabolas have more complicated equations. Any equation which can be written as

$$y = x^2 + bx + c$$

(where b and c are constants) also gives a parabola as its graph. For example,

$y = x^2 + 3x - 1$, $y = x^2 + 2x + 5$, $y = x^2 - 3x$ and $y = x^2 + 1$

are all equations of parabolas.

These parabolas all have minimum turning points, i.e. they *point down*. The line of symmetry of each parabola passes through its turning point. It is parallel to the y-axis.

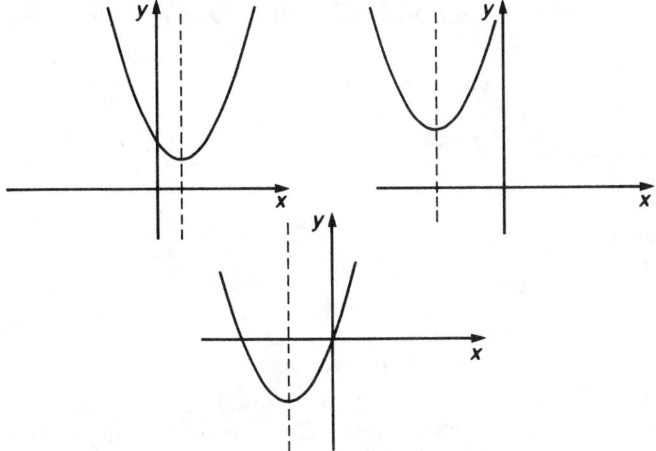

RECTANGULAR HYPERBOLA

The smooth curve in this diagram is called a **rectangular hyperbola**.

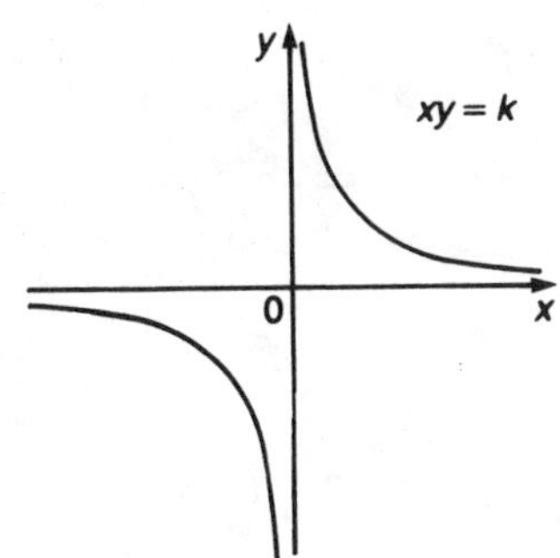

Note The curve does not cut either the x-axis or the y-axis.

Any equation which can be written as

$$xy = k$$

(where k is a constant but not zero) gives this kind of rectangular hyperbola as its graph. For example,

$$xy = 10,\ y = \frac{3}{x},\ x = \frac{1}{y}$$

all give graphs like this.

A rectangular hyperbola has two lines of symmetry.

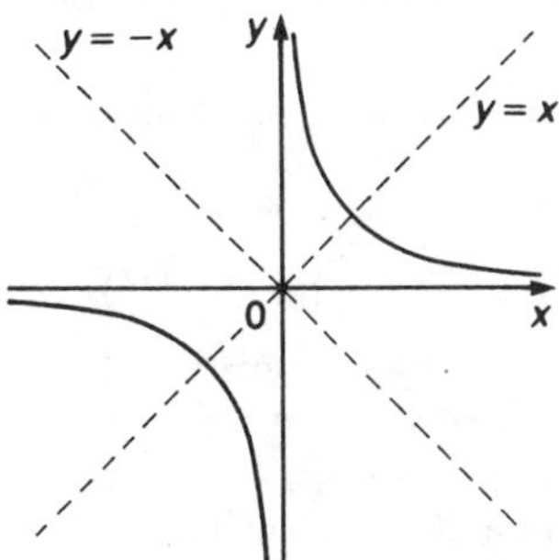

For $xy = k$, the equations of the lines of symmetry are $y = x$ and $y = -x$.

Question

The diagram below shows part of eight graphs. Here are their equations.

$xy = 10$, $y = 3$, $x + y = 10$, $y = x + 3$,
$x = 10$, $4y = x^2$, $y = x + 7$, $y = 2x + 10$

Match each equation to a graph. Explain how you worked out your answers.

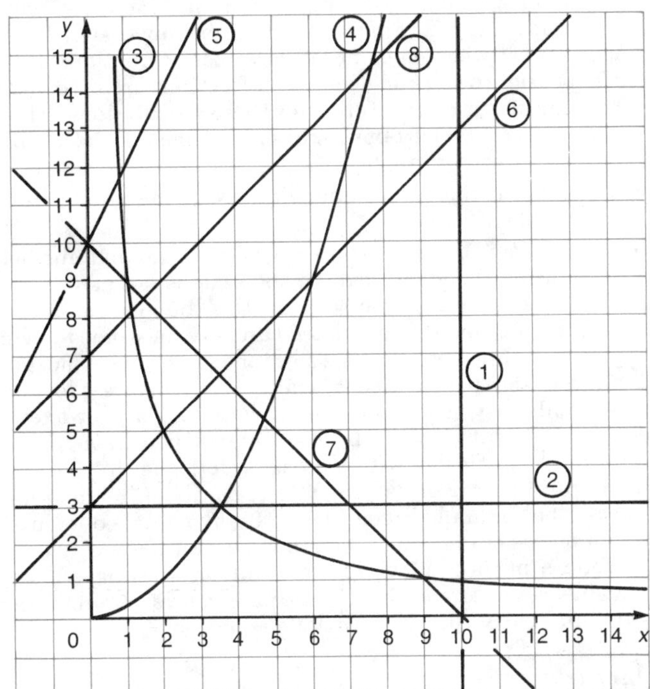

Answer

Straight lines

①, ②, ⑤, ⑥, ⑦ and ⑧ are straight lines. The linear equations are

$y = 3$, $x + y = 10$, $y = x + 3$, $x = 10$, $y = x + 7$, $y = 2x + 10$.

① is $x = 10$. It is a straight line parallel to the y-axis through (10, 0).

② is $y = 3$. It is a straight line parallel to the x-axis through (0, 3).

⑥ and ⑧ are parallel, i.e. have the same gradient. $y = x + 3$ and $y = x + 7$ have the same gradient.

⑥ has y-intercept 3, so it is $y = x + 3$.

⑧ has y-intercept 7, so it is $y = x + 7$.

⑤ and ⑦ have the same y-intercept 10. $y = 2x + 10$ and $x + y = 10$ (i.e. $y = -x + 10$) have this same y-intercept.

⑤ has a positive gradient (up slope), so it is $y = 2x + 10$.

⑦ has a negative gradient (down slope), so it is $y = -x + 10$ (i.e. $x + y = 10$).

Curves

③ is a rectangular hyperbola. The equation which gives a rectangular hyperbola is $xy = 10$.

④ is a parabola. The equation which gives a parabola is $4y = x^2$.

DRAWING GRAPHS FROM EQUATIONS

These notes apply to the **drawing** of *any* algebraic graph from its equation. Use them to help you.

1 You need squared paper, a sharp pencil, a rubber and a ruler (preferably a 30 cm ruler).

2 Make sure that the equation is in its *standard form*. For example, $y = mx + c$, $y = ax^2$, $y = x^2 + bx + c$, $xy = k$ are all standard forms you should know. Rearrange the equation (see p. 61) if you need to. The standard form will help you to predict the type of curve it should be. It will also make it easier to calculate values of y.

3 You need a *table* of corresponding values of x and y which fit the equation. The question may give you a table of values to use or to complete. You may have to make your own table. When calculating values for the table, use the given **domain** (values of x) and find the corresponding values of y using the given equation. Choose simple values for x, if you can, to make the working easier. Take special care when using negative values or fractions. It is often easier to work in decimals if fractions are involved. You can use a calculator to do these calculations. This table is a crucial part of your answer. A mistake here will give an incorrect graph.

4 Write down the **(x, y) coordinates** of the points from your table of values.

5 If the *scale* is given, draw and label the axes and number them using the given scale. If the scale is not given, you have to choose suitable scale(s). Use the given **domain** (values of x) and the calculated **range** (values of y) to help you. Your aim is to produce a graph which covers most of your graph paper. Use a scale which makes plotting decimals easy. Then you can draw and label your axes.

6 *Plot* the points with the coordinates you have listed. Mark them clearly with a cross or dot. The shape of the curve to be drawn (straight line, parabola, rectangular hyperbola) should become clear. If any point is obviously not on the curve you expect, then check it. You may have made a mistake plotting the point or working out the value of y. Draw the appropriate curve through the points. Label the curve with its equation.

Linear graphs

When given a **linear equation** to graph, find the (x, y) values for *three* points only. Two of these points give you the line. The third acts as a check. Two easy points to find are usually where $x = 0$ and $y = 0$. These are the points where the line cuts the axes.

After drawing the line, check that the gradient and y-intercept are what you expect from the equation.

Question

Draw the graph of $2y = x - 2$ for $-2 \leqslant x \leqslant 4$.

Answer

The equation is $2y = x - 2$

$$y = \tfrac{1}{2}x - 1$$

The expected graph is a straight line, with gradient $\frac{1}{2}$, i.e. positive so an 'up slope', and y-intercept of -1

Table of values

x	-2	0	4
y	-2	-1	1

The points to be plotted are

$(-2, -2)$, $(0, -1)$, $(4, 1)$

From the table of values:
the x-axis must go at least from -2 to 4,
the y-axis must go at least from -2 to 1

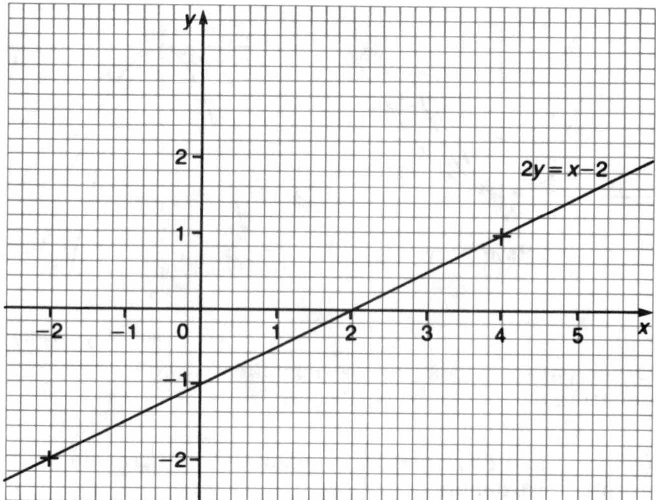

Check *The line has an 'up-slope'*
It cuts the y-axis at $y = -1$

Non-linear graphs

When you have a **non-linear equation** to graph, you need a more detailed table of values. It is usually easier to set down the table like this.

given domain (values of x)

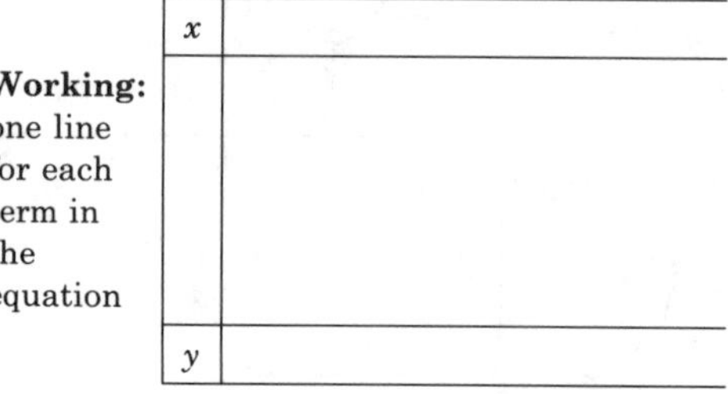

calculated range

Leave the right-hand side of the table open in case you need to find any extra points. This is usually helpful when the curve is near a turning point, **or** a large change has occurred in the value of y **or** it is not clear what is happening to the curve between two points already plotted.

Drawing a smooth curve through points needs practice.

You may find it difficult to do at first. Begin by drawing the line very lightly. When the shape is clear go over the line clearly. You may find it easier if you keep your hand 'inside' the curve when drawing. Turn your graph paper round if you need to.

Question

Draw the graph of $y = x^2 - 3x - 4$ for $-2 \leqslant x \leqslant 5$. Comment on its shape and any special features it may have.

Answer

From the equation $y = x^2 - 3x - 4$, the expected graph is a ∪-shaped parabola.

Table of values

x	-2	-1	0	1	2	3	4	5	1.5
x^2	4	1	0	1	4	9	16	25	2.25
$-3x$	6	3	0	-3	-6	-9	-12	-15	-4.5
-4	-4	-4	-4	-4	-4	-4	-4	-4	-4
y	6	0	-4	-6	-6	-4	0	6	-6.25

C Extra point

This extra point is needed because the graph turns between $x = 1$ and $x = 2$

The points to be plotted are
$(-2, 6)$, $(-1, 0)$, $(0, -4)$, $(1, -6)$, $(2, -6)$, $(3, -4)$, $(4, 0)$, $(5, 6)$.

The extra point is $(1.5, -6.25)$.

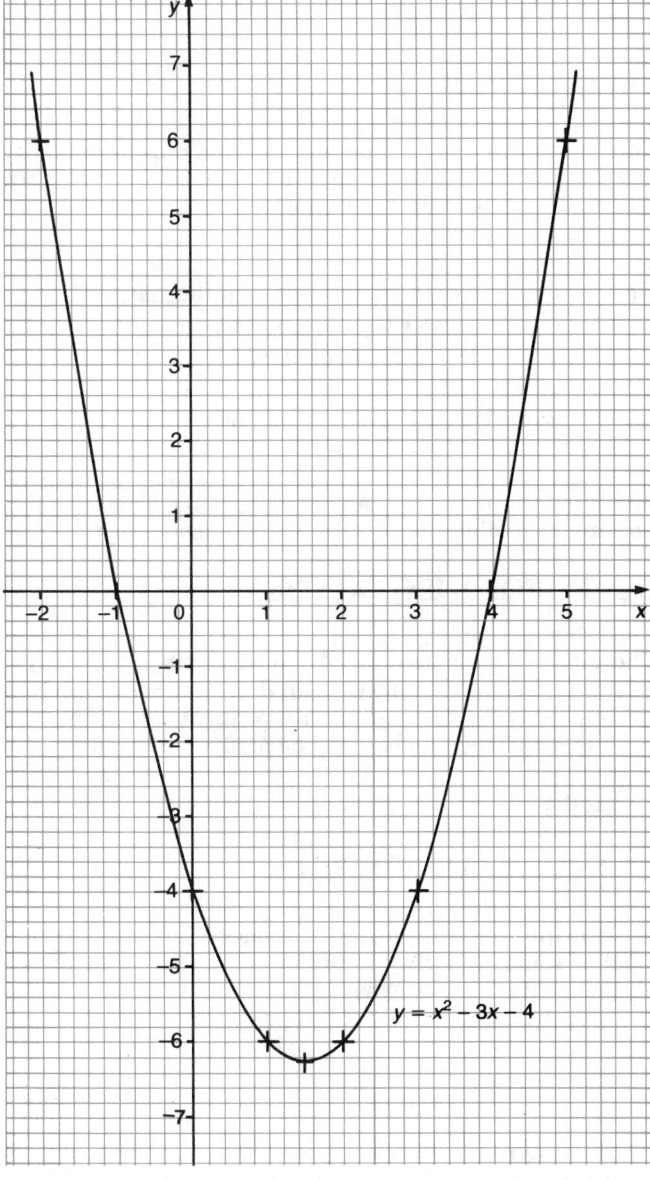

The graph is a parabola. It has a turning point at $(1.5, -6.25)$. At this point the y value is at a minimum on the curve. The axis of symmetry is parallel to the y-axis. It is the line $x = 1.5$.

2.34 Solving equations with graphs

Algebraic equations may be solved by using *graphs*. This is particularly useful when the equation cannot be solved any other way. However it is important to remember that solutions obtained from graphs are only approximate.

LINEAR EQUATIONS

You can solve a **linear equation** by drawing a **straight line graph**. The x-coordinate of the point where the line cuts the x-axis (i.e. $y = 0$) gives the solution. The graph of the straight line $y = mx + c$ cuts the x-axis ($y = 0$) where $mx + c = 0$. The x-coordinate of this point of intersection is the solution of the equation $mx + c = 0$.

Check your answer by substituting the value into the original equation.

Question

The diagram shows the graph of $y = 2x - 3$.

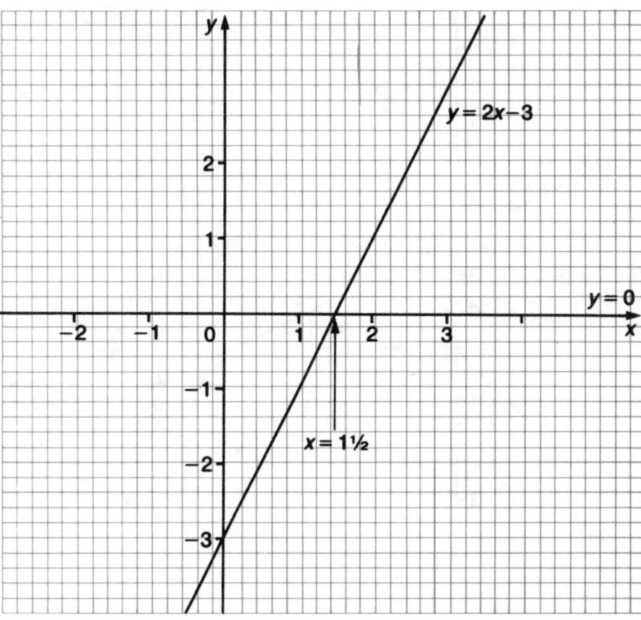

Explain how to use the graph to solve the equation
$2x - 3 = 0$

Answer

The graph of $y = 2x - 3$ cuts the x-axis where $y = 0$. So the solution of the equation $2x - 3 = 0$ is the x-coordinate of the point where the line cuts the x-axis.

The line cuts the x-axis where $x = 1\frac{1}{2}$. So $x = 1\frac{1}{2}$ is the solution of $2x - 3 = 0$.

Check $y = 2x - 3 = (2 \times 1\frac{1}{2}) - 3 = 3 - 3 = 0$ ✓

SIMULTANEOUS LINEAR EQUATIONS

To solve two simultaneous linear equations you must find the values of x and y which make both equations true **simultaneously** (at the same time).

You can do this by drawing the two straight lines on the same axes. When the two lines cross, the point of intersection is on both lines. So its coordinates satisfy both equations simultaneously and give the solution of the equations.

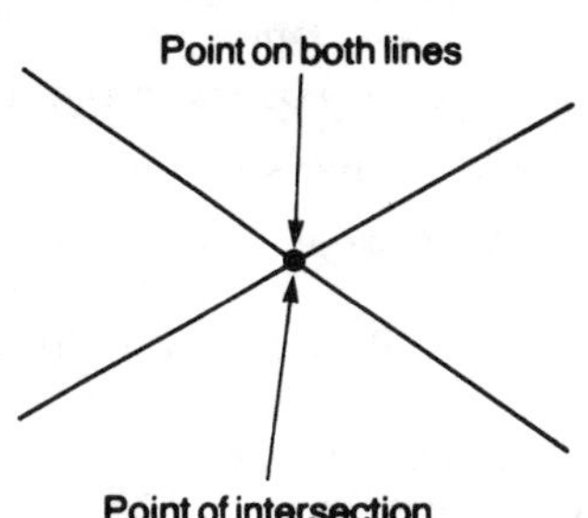

You can **check** your answer by substituting the values into the original equations.

Question

Solve the equations $y = x + 1$ and $2y = 8 - x$ graphically.

Answer

For $y = x + 1$ **Table of values**

x	-1	0	5
y	0	1	6

Points to be plotted are $(-1, 0)$, $(0, 1)$, $(5, 6)$.

For $2y = 8 - x$ Rearranging gives $y = 4 - \frac{1}{2}x$

Table of values

x	8	0	-2
y	0	4	5

Points to be plotted are $(8, 0)$, $(0, 4)$, $(-2, 5)$.

Graph of the lines

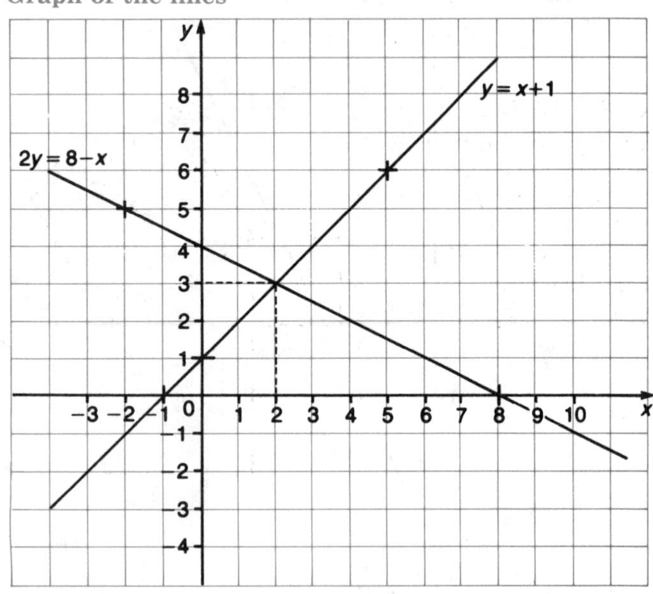

The point of intersection is (2, 3), i.e. $x = 2$, $y = 3$. So the solution of $y = x + 1$ and $2y = 8 - x$ is $x = 2$, $y = 3$.

Check

For $y = x + 1$, when $x = 2$, $y = 2 + 1 = 3$ ✓

For $2y = 8 - x$, when $x = 2$, $2y = 8 - 2 = 6$. So $y = 3$ ✓

2.35 Simple inequalities

INEQUALITIES

An **inequality** is a statement that one quantity is *greater than* or *less than* another. For example,

10 is greater than 3
7 is less than 9
} are inequalities.

The symbols > and < are used to show inequalities.

> means *is greater than.*
< means *is less than.*

For example,

$10 > 3$ means *10 is greater than 3*
$7 < 9$ means *7 is less than 9.*

Note The symbol always *points* to the smaller quantity.

larger > smaller smaller < larger

Its *larger* end is at the *larger* value. Its *smaller* end is at the *smaller* value.

An inequality can always be rewritten in the reverse order. For example,

$5 > 3$, i.e. *5 is greater than 3*
and $3 < 5$, i.e. *3 is less than 5*
} mean the same.

NUMBER LINE

All real numbers can be represented on a **number line.** Their position on the number line helps you to compare their size.

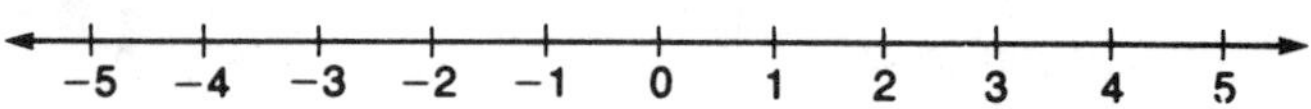

On this number line:

a number is *greater* than another, if it is on the *right* of that number;

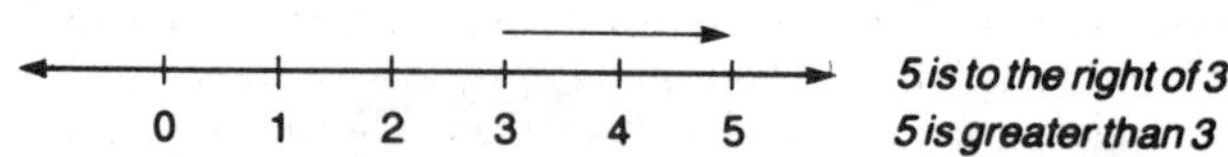

a number is *less* than another, if it is on the *left* of that number.

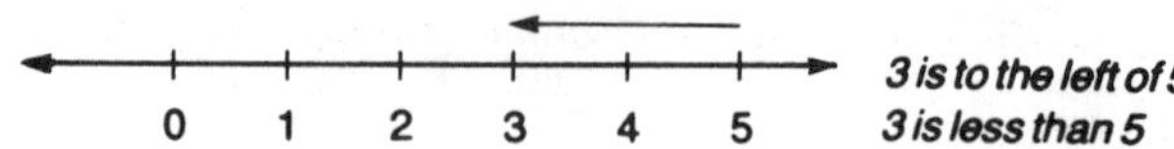

For example, from the numbers marked on the number lines above

$4 > 2$ and $2 < 4$
$2 > {}^{-}3$ ${}^{-}3 < 2$
${}^{-}3 > {}^{-}5$ ${}^{-}5 < {}^{-}3$

INEQUATIONS

An inequality may contain an unknown quantity represented by a letter. This kind of inequality is often called an **inequation**. For example,

$x < 4$, $y > -2$, $2x > 9$, $y - 1 < 6$

are all inequations.

The symbols $\geqslant$ and $\leqslant$ are also used in inequations.

$\geqslant$ means *is greater than or equal to,*
$\leqslant$ means *is less than or equal to.*

For example,

$x \geqslant 3$ means that x is greater than or equal to 3,
$y \leqslant 6$ means that y is less than or equal to 6.

Values for the unknown quantities in inequations may be found (rather like they can for equations). This is called **solving** or finding the **solutions** to the inequation.

RULES FOR INEQUALITIES

These rules can be used to solve inequations.

1 The same number may be **added** to or **subtracted** from both sides of an inequation without changing the inequality. The number may be positive or negative. For example,

addition	**subtraction**
$5 > -2$ True.✓	${}^{-}2 < 5$ True.✓
$5 + 1 > {}^{-}2 + 1$	${}^{-}2 - 1 < 5 - 1$
i.e. $6 > {}^{-}1$ True.✓	i.e. ${}^{-}3 < 4$ True.✓

2 **Multiplying** or **dividing** both sides of an inequation by the same **positive number** does *not* change the inequality. For example.

multiplication	**division**
${}^{-}6 < 4$ True.✓	$4 > {}^{-}6$ True.✓
$2 \times -6 < 2 \times 4$	$4 \div 2 > {}^{-}6 \div 2$
${}^{-}12 < 8$ True.✓	$2 > {}^{-}3$ True.✓

3 **Multiplying** or **dividing** both sides of an inequality by the same **negative** number *reverses* the sign of the inequality.

> changes to <   < changes to >
$\geqslant$ changes to $\leqslant$ $\leqslant$ changes to $\geqslant$

For example,

multiplication | **division**

$9 > 6$ True.✓ | $6 < 9$ True.✓

$^-3 \times 9 < {}^-3 \times 6$ *Reverse the sign* $6 \div {}^-3 > 9 \div {}^-3$

$^-27 < {}^-18$ True.✓ | $^-2 > {}^-3$ True.✓

SOLUTION OF INEQUATIONS

A **solution** of an inequation is a value which, when put instead of the letter, makes the inequation true. So when you solve an inequation you find possible values for the unknown. Often there are many values which make an inequation true. You may be asked to give one of them.

When solving an inequation you want the unknown on one side of the inequality sign and all the 'numbers' on the other. Use the rules for inequalities to achieve this.

Question

Find a possible integer value of x for each of these inequations.

(a) $x + 3 > 9$ (b) $x - 8 < {}^-1$ (c) $^-3x < 9$ (d) $\frac{x}{2} < {}^-4$

Answer

(a) $x + 3 > 9$

Subtract 3 from both sides $x + 3 - 3 > 9 - 3$

i.e. $x > 6$

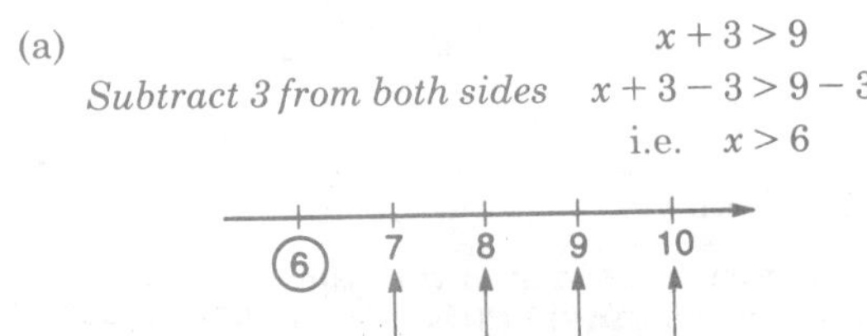

Any integer greater than 6 is a solution. So one value for x is 7.

(b) $x - 8 < {}^-1$

Add 8 to both sides $x - 8 + 8 < {}^-1 + 8$

i.e. $x < 7$

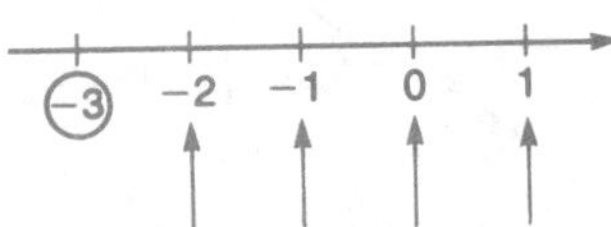

Any integer less than 7 is a solution. So one value for x is 6.

(c) $^-3x < 9$

Divide both sides by $^-3$ and reverse the sign $\frac{^-3x}{^-3} > \frac{9}{^-3}$

−3 −2 −1 0 1

Any integer greater than −3, i.e. to its right on this number line

i.e. $x > {}^-3$

Any integer greater than $^-3$ is a solution. So one value for x is 0.

(d) $\frac{x}{2} < {}^-4$

Multiply both sides by 2 $2 \times \frac{x}{2} < 2 \times {}^-4$

i.e. $x < {}^-8$

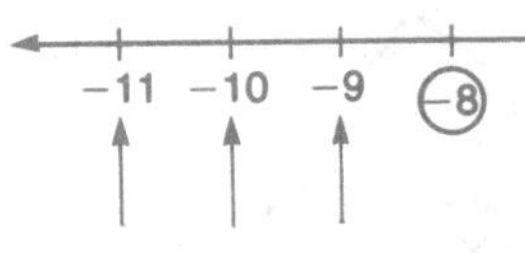

Any integer less than $^-8$ is a solution. So one value for x is $^-9$.

2.36 Pythagoras' theorem

Pythagoras' theorem is about *right-angled* triangles. A right-angled triangle has one of its angles a right angle. The side opposite the right angle is called the **hypotenuse**. It is always the *longest* side in the triangle.

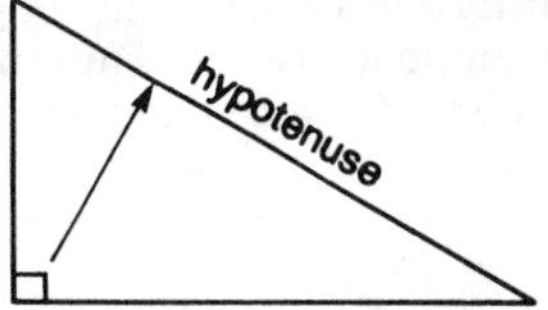

Pythagoras' theorem states:
In a right-angled triangle, the square on the hypotenuse equals the sum of the squares on the other two sides.

For triangle ABC in the diagram, Pythagoras' theorem gives
$c^2 = a^2 + b^2$

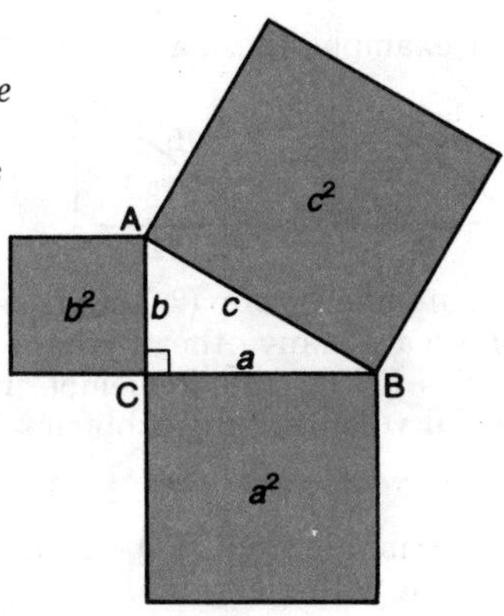

Note The sides of this triangle are labelled a, b and c.
side a is opposite angle A,
side b is opposite angle B,
side c is opposite angle C.

This is a standard way to label the sides of any triangle. An angle of the triangle can be named using the capital letter at its **vertex** (corner). A matching small letter stands for the side opposite the angle.

You can use Pythagoras' theorem to find any side of a right-angled triangle, if you know the lengths of the other two sides. Pythagoras' theorem gives you the *square on the side* not the side itself. So you must find its *square root* to get the length of the side. It may be a square root you know, or you may need to use the [√] key on your *calculator* (see Unit 2.3). Always draw a diagram and mark it with the information given. This can help you to *see* the problem. Marking the squares on the sides may help too.

Question

In triangle XYZ, YZ = 4 cm, XZ = 3 cm and angle $Z = 90°$. Find the length of XY.

Answer (*See overleaf for diagram*)

In triangle XYZ, XY is the hypotenuse.
By Pythagoras' theorem

$XY^2 = XZ^2 + YZ^2$
$= 3^2 + 4^2$
$= 9 + 16$

i.e. $XY^2 = 25$

So $XY = \sqrt{25} = 5$

So the length of XY is 5 cm.

The triangle in the question above is a special triangle. It is called a **(3, 4, 5) triangle** because of the lengths of its sides. Any right-angled triangle whose sides are in the same ratio, i.e. 3:4:5, is also called a (3, 4, 5) triangle.

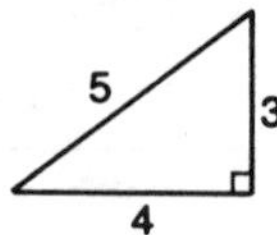

For example, these are all (3, 4, 5) triangles.

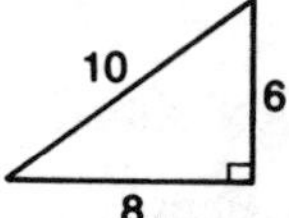

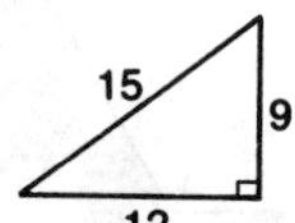

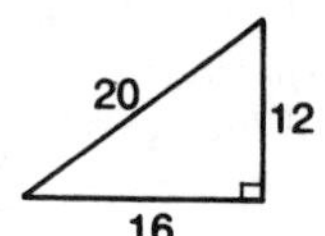

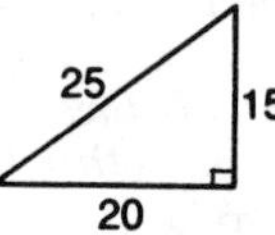

The number group (3, 4, 5) is called a **Pythagorean triple**. There are many other Pythagorean triples. Another simple one is (5, 12, 13). Remembering these two triples can be useful when solving problems.

Question

In triangle PQR, PQ = 26 cm, PR = 10 cm and $\angle R = 90°$. What is the length of QR?

Answer

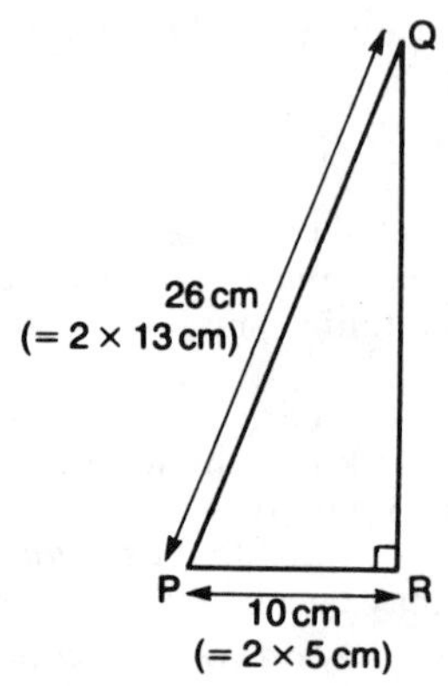

Triangle PQR is a (5, 12, 13) triangle.

PR = 10 cm = 2 × 5 cm
PQ = 26 cm = 2 × 13 cm
So QR = 2 × 12 cm = 24 cm

Check *this is true using Pythagoras' theorem.*

Pythagoras' theorem is often used to solve practical problems. Right angles are very common in real life. So it is often easy to find a right-angled triangle in a practical situation.

Question

A ladder is 4.5 m long. Its foot is standing on a horizontal path. Its top is resting against a vertical wall. The foot of the ladder is 2 m from the base of the wall. How far up the wall is the top of the ladder? Give your answer in metres, correct to 2 decimal places.

Answer

The horizontal path and the vertical wall are at right angles. So there is a right-angled triangle as shown in the diagram. The ladder is the hypotenuse = 4.5 metres. The distance on the path = 2 metres. Let the height up the wall = h metres.

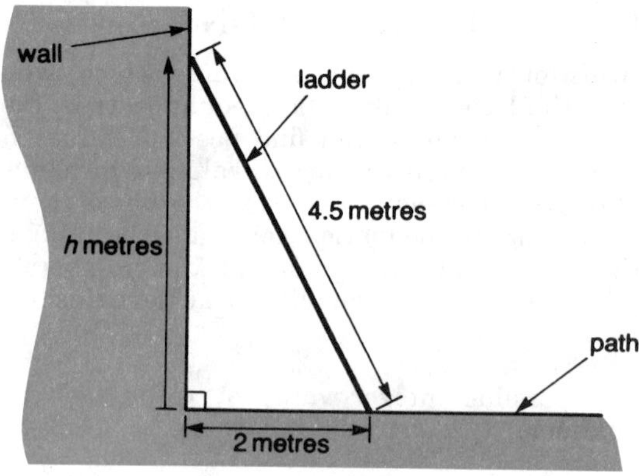

By Pythagoras' theorem:

$$4.5^2 = h^2 + 2^2$$
$$\text{So } h^2 = 4.5^2 - 2^2$$
$$= 20.25 - 4$$
$$h^2 = 16.25$$
$$h = \sqrt{16.25}$$
$$= 4.03 \text{ metres (to 2 d.p.) up the wall.}$$

C

Pythagoras' theorem is often used with the trigonometrical ratios **sine**, **cosine** and **tangent** to solve problems (see Unit 2.37).

2.37 Sine, cosine and tangent

TRIGONOMETRICAL RATIOS

Sine (sin), **cosine** (cos) and **tangent** (tan) are three trigonometrical ratios. To find them for an angle in a right-angled triangle, label its sides:

hypotenuse (always opposite the right angle),
opposite (opposite the angle you are using),
adjacent (adjacent or next to the angle you are using).

The ratios are given by:

$$\sin = \frac{\text{opposite}}{\text{hypotenuse}}$$

$$\cos = \frac{\text{adjacent}}{\text{hypotenuse}}$$

$$\tan = \frac{\text{opposite}}{\text{adjacent}}$$

In this right-angled triangle ABC, angle $B = 90°$ and AC is the hypotenuse.

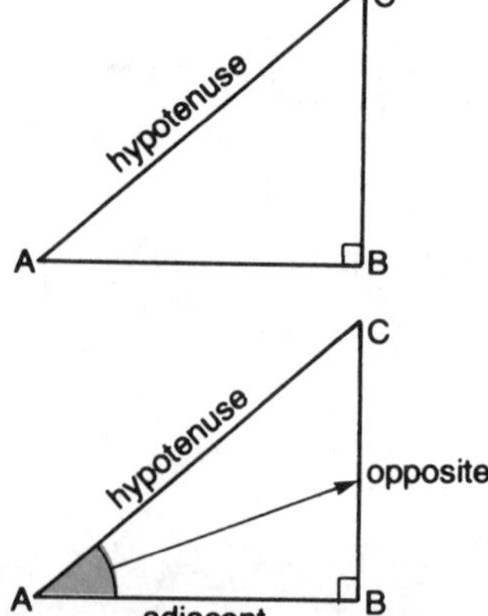

For angle *A*
CB is *opposite*
AB is *adjacent*

$$\sin A = \frac{CB}{AC} \quad \cos A = \frac{AB}{AC} \quad \tan A = \frac{CB}{AB}.$$

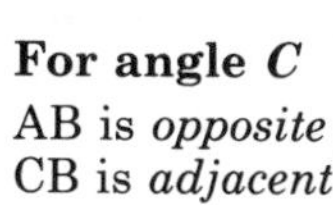

For angle *C*
AB is *opposite*
CB is *adjacent*

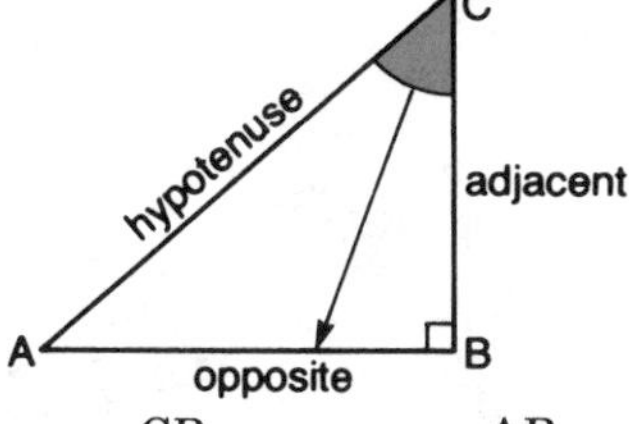

$\sin C = \dfrac{AB}{AC}$ $\cos C = \dfrac{CB}{AC}$ $\tan C = \dfrac{AB}{CB}$

Question

The diagram shows a right-angled triangle PQR. Calculate:

(a) $\sin P$ (b) $\cos P$ (c) $\tan P$.

Give your answers correct to 2 decimal places.

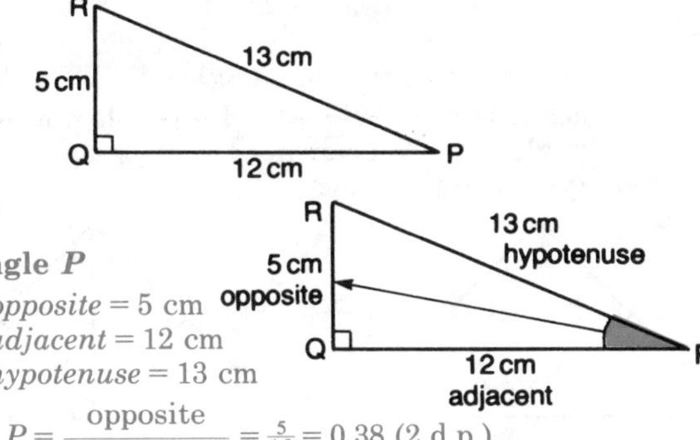

Answer

For angle *P*
RQ is *opposite* = 5 cm
PQ is *adjacent* = 12 cm
PR is *hypotenuse* = 13 cm

(a) $\sin P = \dfrac{\text{opposite}}{\text{hypotenuse}} = \frac{5}{13} = 0.38$ (2 d.p.)

 **Display:** 0.384615384

(b) $\cos P = \dfrac{\text{adjacent}}{\text{hypotenuse}} = \frac{12}{13} = 0.92$ (2 d.p.)

 **Display:** 0.923076923

(c) $\tan P = \dfrac{\text{opposite}}{\text{adjacent}} = \frac{5}{12} = 0.42$ (2 d.p.)

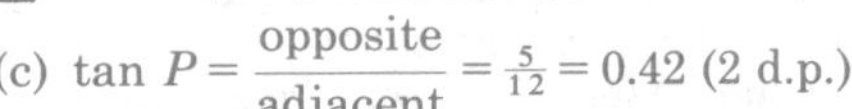

 **Display:** 0.416666666

ANGLES AND RATIOS

The sine, cosine and tangent of an angle can be found using a calculator with [sin], [cos] and [tan] keys.

You will usually have to *correct* your display answers to a given number of **decimal places** or **significant figures** (see Unit 2.8). For example, to find the sine, cosine and tangent for an angle of 56°, follow these steps.

for sin 56°,

Press: [C] [5] [6] [sin]

Display: 0.829037572 = 0.83 to 2 decimal places

for cos 56°,

Press: [C] [5] [6] [cos]

Display: 0.559192903 = 0.56 to 2 decimal places

for tan 56°,

Press: [C] [5] [6] [tan]

Display: 1.482560968 = 1.48 to 2 decimal places

You may need to do the **opposite (inverse)** and find an angle if you know one of the ratios. You can do this with your *calculator* too. For example, to find the angle whose sine is 0.5

Press: [C] [·] [5] [INV] [sin] **Display:** 30.

So the angle whose sine is 0.5 is 30°.

Question

Find, to 1 decimal place, the angles P and Q if:

(a) $\cos P = 0.66$ (b) $\tan Q = 2.3$

Answer

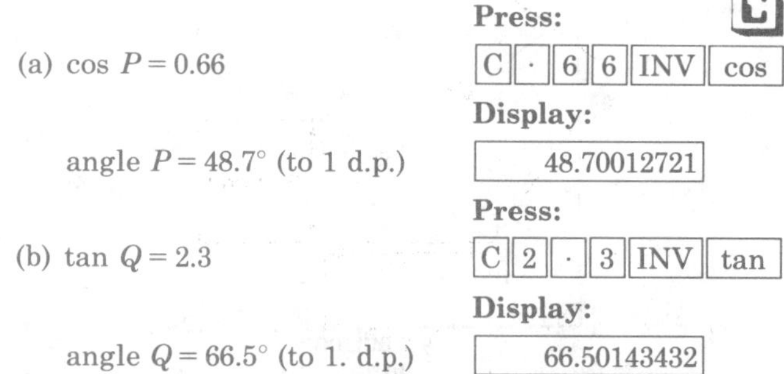

(a) $\cos P = 0.66$

Press: [C] [·] [6] [6] [INV] [cos]

Display:

angle $P = 48.7°$ (to 1 d.p.) 48.70012721

(b) $\tan Q = 2.3$

Press: [C] [2] [·] [3] [INV] [tan]

Display:

angle $Q = 66.5°$ (to 1. d.p.) 66.50143432

SOLVING RIGHT-ANGLED TRIANGLES

Solving a triangle means finding the sizes of the *unknown* sides and angles in the triangle. Sine, cosine and tangent can often be used to solve right-angled triangles. Always draw a diagram and mark it with the given information. Use the diagram to help you to decide what to do.

To find an angle, if you know two sides, use sin, cos or tan of the angle. Make sure that the trig ratio you choose uses the sides you know and the angle you want!

You can easily find the third angle. Use the fact that the three angles of a triangle must add up to 180°.

Question

In triangle PQR, $\angle R = 90°$, PQ = 7 cm and QR = 4.6 cm. Calculate the sizes of angles P and Q, each to the nearest degree.

Answer

For angle *P*
QR is *opposite* = 4.6 cm
PR is *adjacent*
PQ is *hypotenuse* = 7 cm

Use $\sin P = \dfrac{\text{opposite}}{\text{hypotenuse}}$

$= \dfrac{4.6 \text{ cm}}{7 \text{ cm}}$

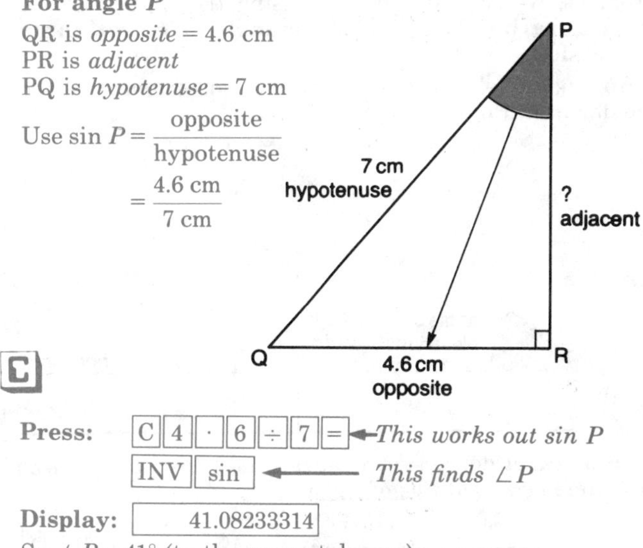

Press: [C] [4] [·] [6] [÷] [7] [=] ← *This works out sin P*
[INV] [sin] ← *This finds ∠P*

Display: 41.08233314

So $\angle P = 41°$ (to the nearest degree)

The angles of a triangle add up to 180°.

$\angle R + \angle P = 90° + 41° = 131°$

So $\angle Q = 180° - 131° = 49°$ (to the nearest degree)

You can find a side, if you know an angle and another side. To do this, it is easier to use the ratios in this form:

opposite = hypotenuse × sin $\left(\text{from } \dfrac{\text{opposite}}{\text{hypotenuse}} = \sin\right)$

adjacent = hypotenuse × cos $\left(\text{from } \dfrac{\text{adjacent}}{\text{hypotenuse}} = \cos\right)$

opposite = adjacent × tan $\left(\text{from } \dfrac{\text{opposite}}{\text{adjacent}} = \tan\right)$

Question

In triangle XYZ, angle $X = 90°$, angle $Z = 37.8°$ and YZ = 13.4 cm. Calculate the length of XZ to 3 significant figures.

Answer

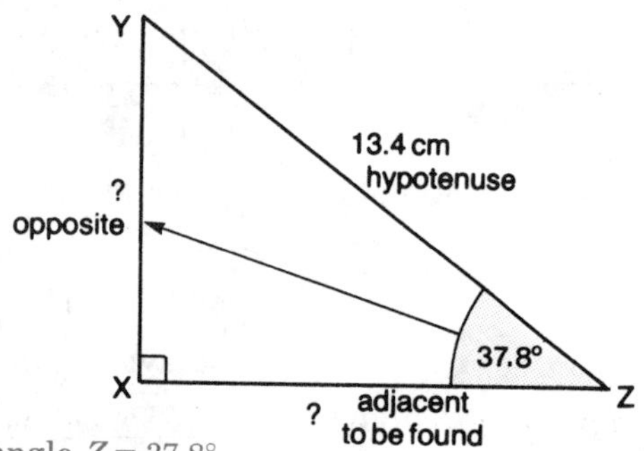

For angle $Z = 37.8°$
XY is *opposite*
XZ is *adjacent*, to be found
ZY is *hypotenuse* = 13.4 cm
Use adjacent = hypotenuse × cos
XZ = 13.4 cm × cos 37.8°
= 10.6 cm (to 3 s.f.)

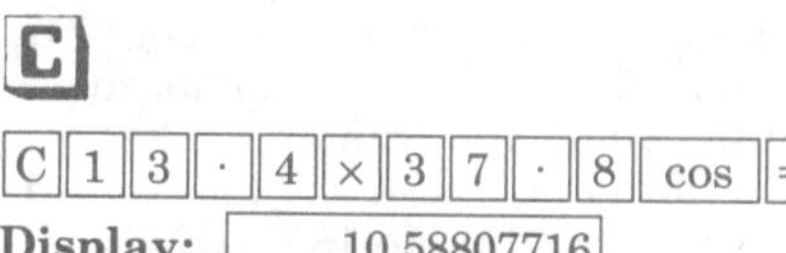

Note If you know two sides and have to find the third side in a right-angled triangle, then use Pythagoras' theorem (see Unit 2.36).

SOLVING PROBLEMS

Problems which you can solve using trigonometry often involve **bearings** (see Unit 1.32) or **angles of elevation** and **depression**.

An angle of elevation is always measured *upwards* from the horizontal *line of sight*.

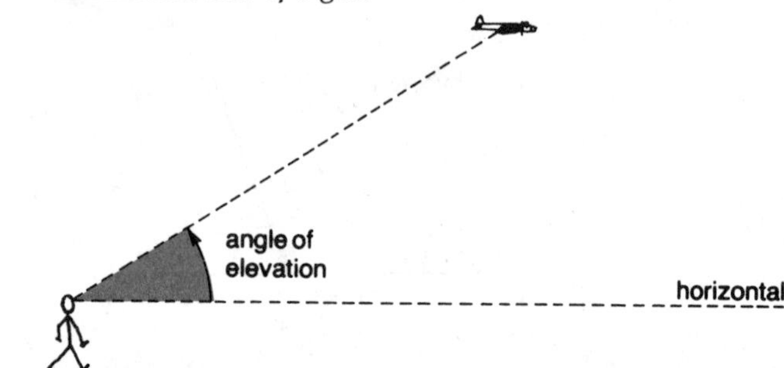

An angle of depression is always measured *downwards* from the horizontal *line of sight*.

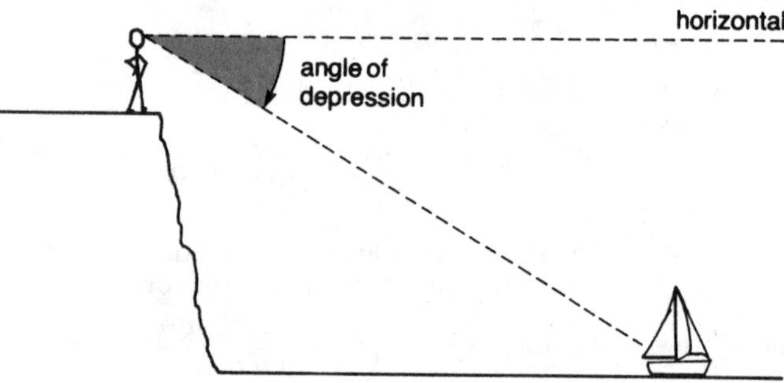

Question

A vertical radio mast stands in the middle of a flat horizontal field. The angle of elevation of the top of the mast from a point on the ground 65 m away from the foot of the mast is 25°. Calculate the height of the mast, to the nearest metre.

Answer

In the diagram, LM represents the mast, N is the point on the ground 65 m from the foot of the mast.

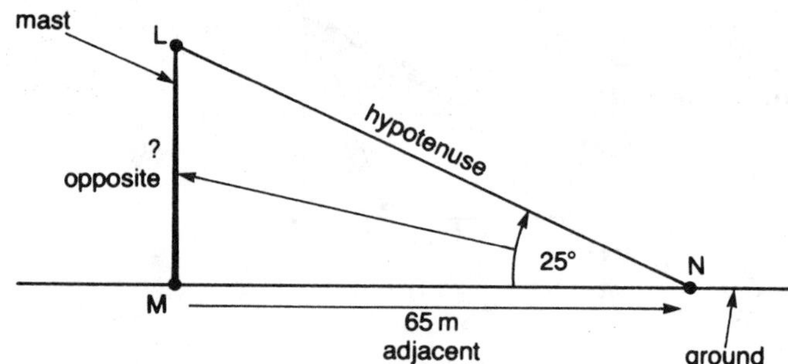

For angle $N = 25°$ LM is *opposite*, to be found
NM is *adjacent* = 65 m
LN is *hypotenuse*

Use opposite = adjacent × tan

LM = 65 m × tan 25°
= 30 m (to the nearest m)

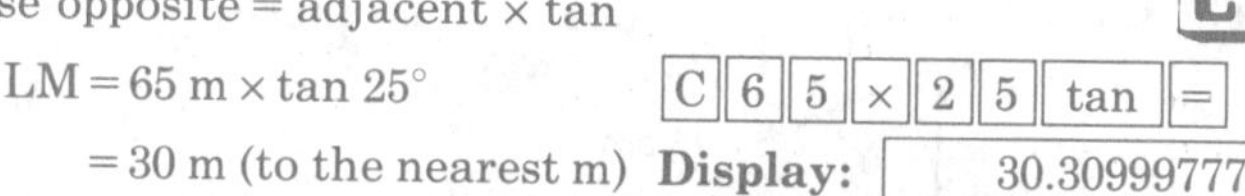

Sometimes it is not obvious that a problem has a right-angled triangle in it. You may need to draw a *perpendicular* to a line to get a right angle.

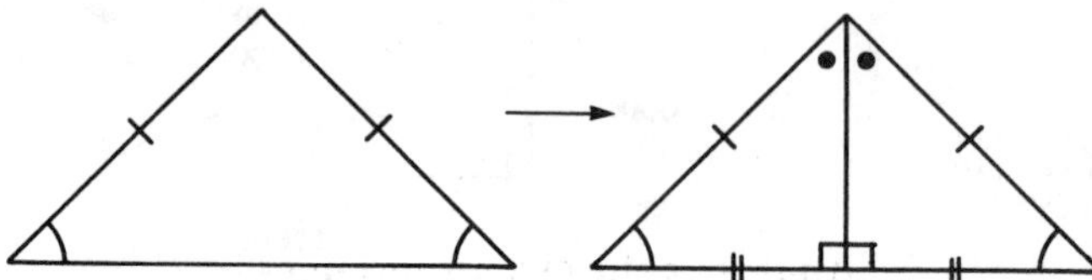

For example, an isosceles triangle can be split into two identical right-angled triangles. To do this, draw a perpendicular to the base. The perpendicular **bisects** (cuts in half) the base line and the top angle.

Question

The end-face of a tent is an isosceles triangle with base 3.4 m. The angle at the top of the face is 24°. Calculate the lengths of the two equal sides of the tent face. Give your answer to two significant figures.

Answer

Call the triangular face ABC. AB and AC are the lengths to be found.

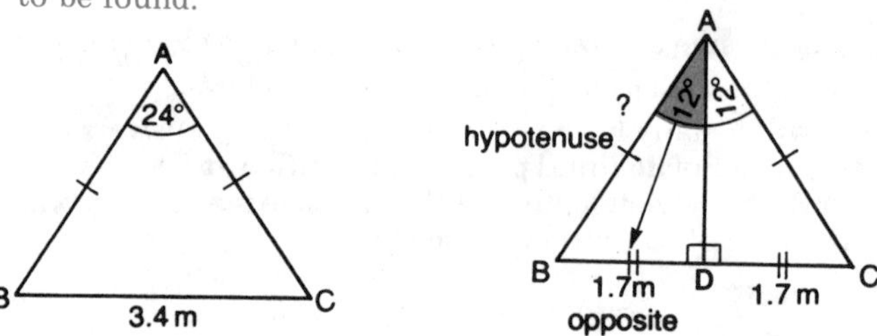

The diagram shows triangle ABC with the perpendicular AD drawn. AD divides △ ABC into two congruent right-angled triangles ABD and ACD.

In △ ABD, angle BAD = 12°
BD is *opposite* = 1.7 m
AD is *adjacent*
AB is *hypotenuse*, to be found

Use opposite = hypotenuse × sin
= AB × sin 12°
So AB = (1.7 ÷ sin 12°) m
= 8.2 m (to 2 s.f.)

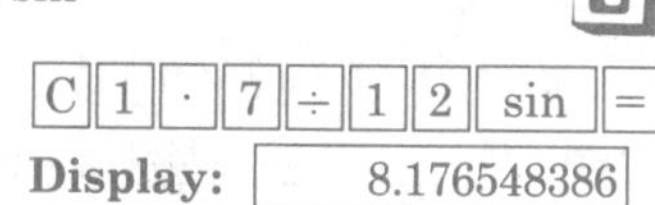

Knowing about right angles in shapes helps you to spot right-angled triangles too. For example, right-angles are found:

(a) as the angles of a square or rectangle,
(b) at the intersection of the diagonals of some quadrilaterals, } (see Unit 1.35)
(c) as the angle in a semicircle,
(d) as the angle between a tangent and a radius. } (see Unit 2.14)

LIST 3

3.1 Circle theorems

MORE CIRCLE WORDS

The following circle words or descriptions are used in some of the theorems in this unit. The other circle words used are given in units 1.36 and 2.14.

An **angle at the circumference** has its *vertex on* the circumference of the circle. Its arms *meet* or *cut* the circle. The angle can be either *acute* or *obtuse*.

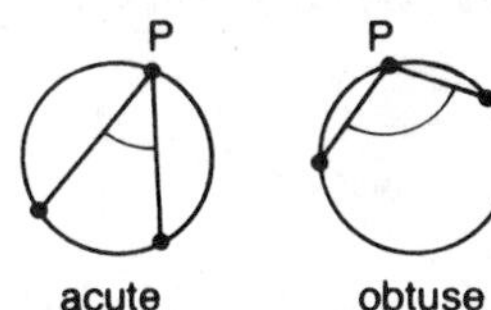

Angles at the circumference

An **angle at the centre** has its *vertex at* the centre of the circle. Its arms meet or cut the circle. The angle can be *acute, obtuse* or *reflex*.

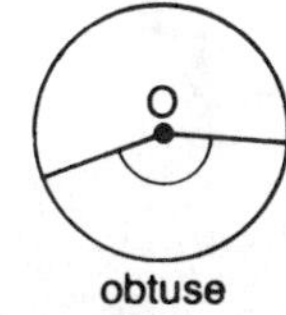

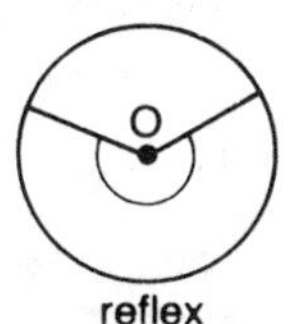

Angles at the centre O

An **angle subtended by an arc or chord** is an angle *opposite* to the arc or chord. It is usually an angle at the circumference or centre of the circle. The arc or chord can be major or minor. In the diagrams below, each angle APB is an *angle at the circumference subtended by the arc or chord AB.*

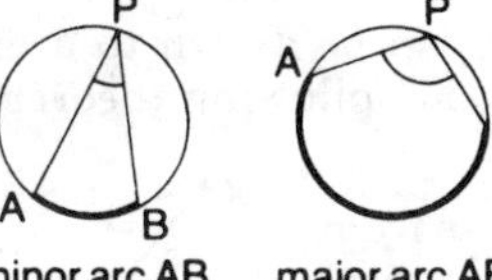

These angles are also described as
an *angle in the segment APB*, or
an *angle standing on the same side of the arc or chord AB.*
In the diagrams below, each angle AOB is an *angle at the centre subtended by the arc or chord AB.*

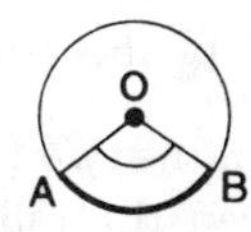

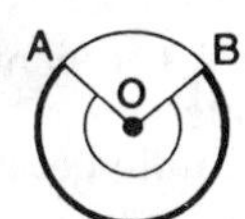

A **cyclic quadrilateral** is a quadrilateral drawn inside a circle. It has all four of its vertices on the circumference of the same circle. ABCD is a cyclic quadrilateral.

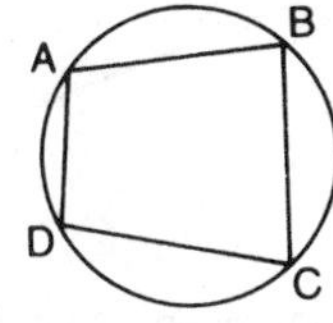

Concyclic points lie on the circumference of the same circle. V, W, X, Y, and Z are concyclic points.

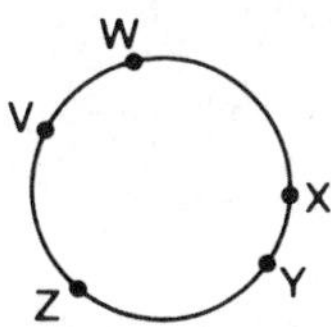

ANGLE THEOREMS

1 The angle at the centre of a circle is twice the angle at the circumference subtended by the same arc or chord.

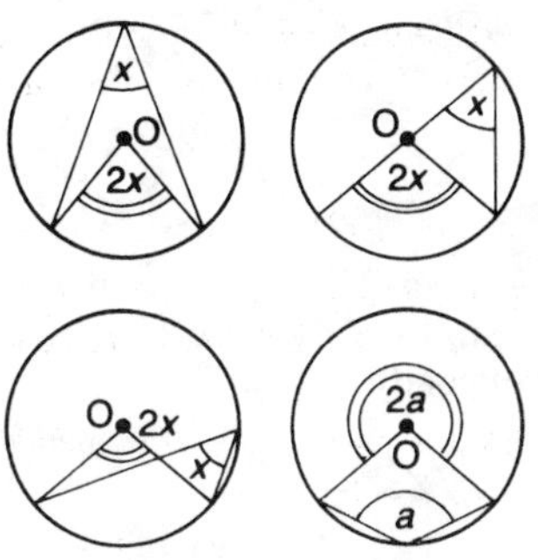

2 Angles at the circumference of a circle subtended by the same arc or chord are equal, **or**
Angles in the same segment of a circle are equal.

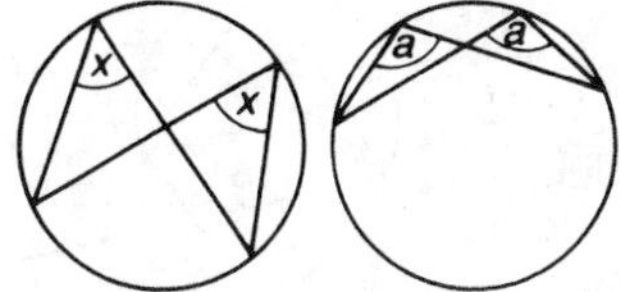

Converse If the line joining two points subtends equal angles at two other points on the same side of it, then the four points are concyclic.

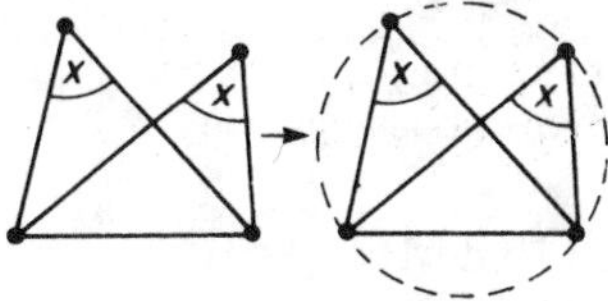

Question

Find the sizes of the angles marked with letters in the diagrams below. Give a brief reason for each answer. In each circle, O is the centre.

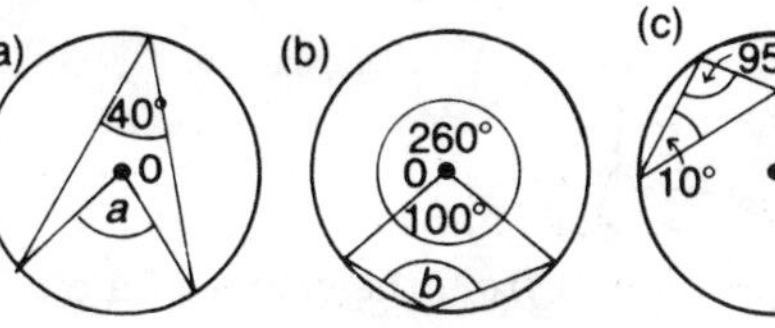

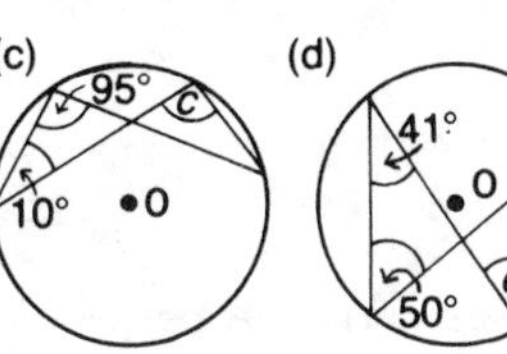

Answer

(a) $a = 2 \times 40°$ (Angle at centre
$= 80°$ $= 2 \times$ angle at circumference)

(b) $b = \frac{1}{2} \times 260°$ (Angle at circumference $= \frac{1}{2}$ angle at centre)
$= 130°$

(c) $c = 95°$ (Angles in the same segment are equal)

(d) $d = 41°$, $e = 50°$ (Angles in the same segment are equal)

CYCLIC QUADRILATERAL THEOREMS

1 The opposite angles of a cyclic quadrilateral are supplementary (i.e. they add up to 180°).

ABCD is a cyclic quadrilateral

$a + c = 180°$
$b + d = 180°$

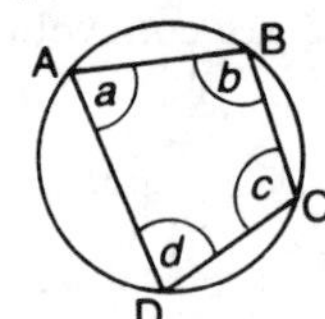

Converse A quadrilateral in which two opposite angles are supplementary (i.e. add up to 180°) is a cyclic quadrilateral.

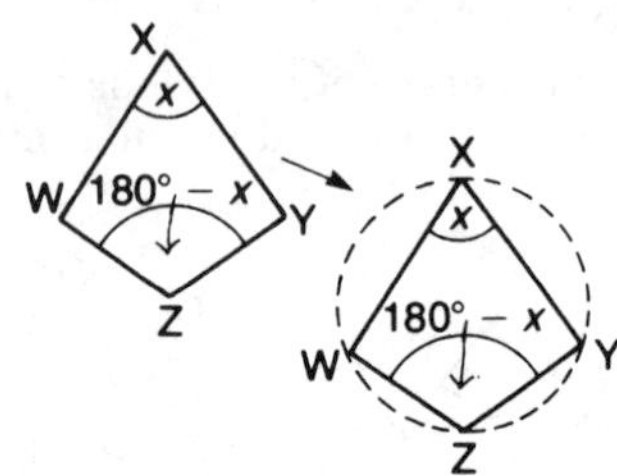

2 The exterior angle of a cyclic quadrilateral is equal to the interior opposite angle.

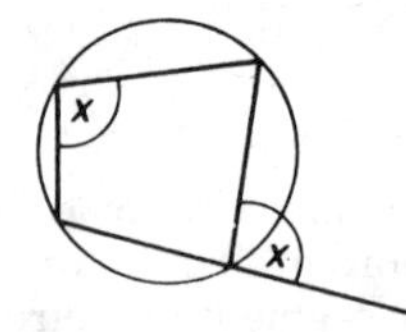

Question

Find the sizes of the lettered angles in this diagram. Give a brief reason for each answer.

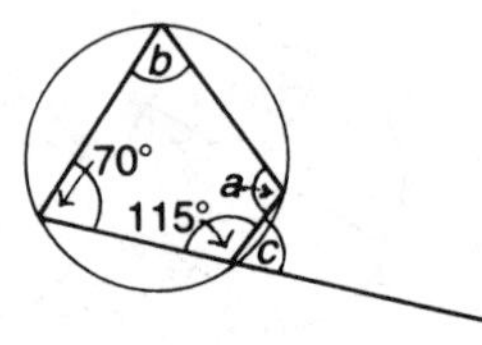

Answer

$a = 180° - 70° = 110°$
$b = 180° - 115° = 65°$ (Opposite angles of a cyclic quadrilateral are supplementary)

$c = b$
$= 65°$ (Exterior angle of cyclic quadrilateral equals interior opposite angle)

CHORD THEOREMS

1 A straight line joining the centre of a circle to the midpoint of a chord is perpendicular to the chord.

If AD = DB, then
$\angle ODA = \angle ODB = 90°$

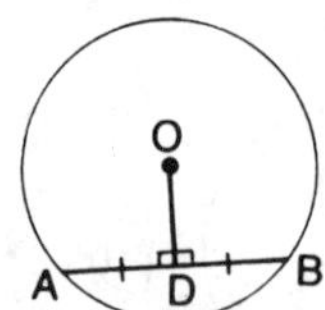

Converse A perpendicular from the centre of a circle to a chord bisects that chord.
If $\angle ODA = \angle ODB = 90°$, then AD = DB.

2 Equal chords of a circle are equidistant from its centre.

If AB = CD, then OX = OY.

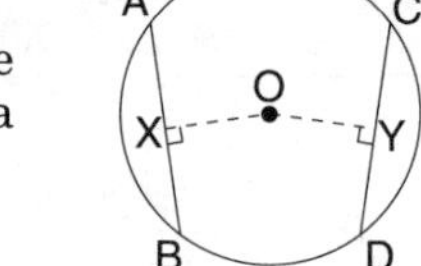

Converse Chords which are equidistant from the centre of a circle are equal in length.

If OX = OY, then AB = CD.

These theorems are often used with Pythagoras' theorem (see Unit 2.36) to calculate the length of a chord or its distance from the centre of the circle.

Question

A chord 24 cm long is drawn in a circle of radius 13 cm. Calculate the distance of the chord from the centre of the circle.

Answer

AB is the chord of the circle, centre O. OM is the distance from the centre to the chord. OM is the perpendicular from the centre to the chord.

OM is the perpendicular from the centre to the chord. So OM bisects the chord AB.

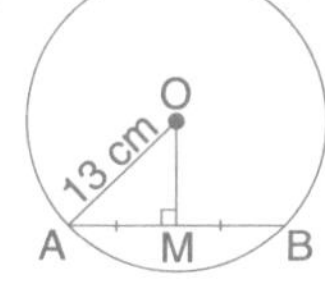

This gives $\angle OMA = 90°$
and $AM = \frac{1}{2} \times 24$ cm $= 12$ cm

OA = 13 cm (radius)

By Pythagorus' theorem in triangle OAM,

$OA^2 = OM^2 + AM^2$
So $OM^2 = OA^2 - AM^2$
$= 13^2 - 12^2$
$= 139 - 144 = 25$
$OM = \sqrt{25} = 5$ cm

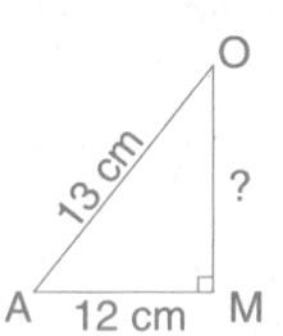

So the chord is 5 cm from the centre of the circle.

Note: You may have spotted that triangle OAM is a (5,12,13) triangle—a Pythagorean triple.

TANGENT THEOREMS

Two tangents only can be drawn to a circle from a point outside the circle. The following theorems are about these tangents.

1 The two tangents from a given point to a circle are equal in length.

AX = BX

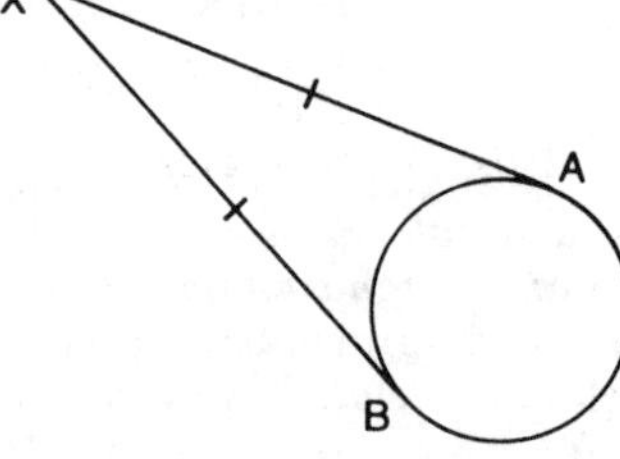

2 The line joining the centre of the circle to the point outside the circle:

(a) bisects the angle between the two tangents,

(b) bisects the angle between the radii drawn to the points of contact.

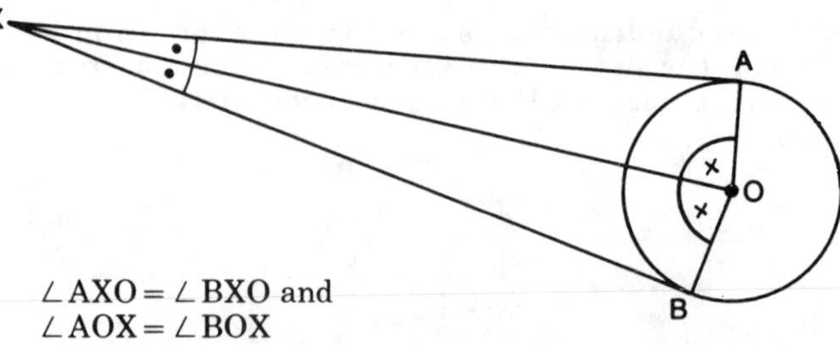

$\angle AXO = \angle BXO$ and
$\angle AOX = \angle BOX$

These theorems are often used with the **tangent-radius**

theorem (see p.26) and Pythagoras' theorem (see Unit 2.36).

Question

AT and BT are tangents to a circle, centre O. A and B lie on the circle and T is a point outside the circle. If ∠ATB = 50°, then find the sizes of ∠TAB and ∠TBA. Give brief reasons for your answers.

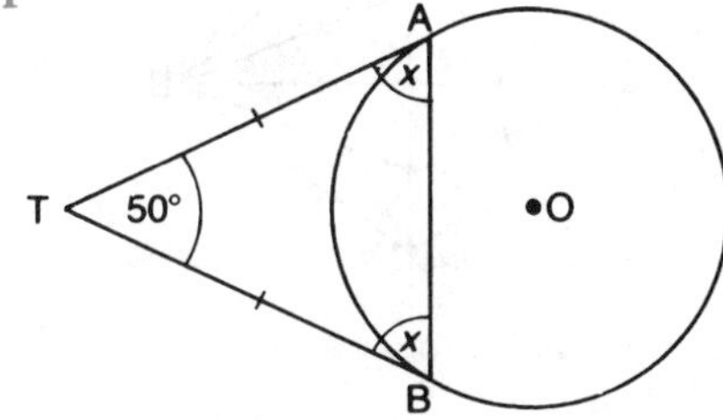

AT = BT (Equal tangents from the same point T)
So triangle ATB is an isosceles triangle.
∠TAB = ∠TBA (Base angles of an isosceles triangle)
Let ∠TAB = ∠TBA = x,

$x + x + 50° = 180°$ (Angle sum of a triangle)

$2x = 180° - 50°$

$x = \frac{130°}{2} = 65°$

So ∠TAB = ∠TBA = 65°.

SOLVING PROBLEMS

The theorems in this unit and Unit 2.14 are often used to solve problems involving circles. It is important to draw a large clear diagram. Fill in the given information carefully and mark any angles or lengths to be calculated. Give brief reasons to explain your answers. In most problems you will need to use more than one circle theorem. As well as knowing the theorems, you must be able to spot which one(s) to use. Words in the question, such as **tangent** and **chord**, can give you clues to the theorems to use.
Your diagram can also help you here. Mark on your diagram angles and lengths found using the theorems. It is often clearer if you use different colours to mark *given* and *found* values. These may help you to decide which is the best or shortest way to solve the problem. You may need to use other angle and length properties in your solution. For example, look for:

- related angles (see Unit 2.12)
- right angles (for Pythagoras' theorem)
- angle sum of polygons (see Unit 2.13)
- equal lengths such as radii or tangents (to make isosceles triangles)

and so on ...

In the answer below, a series of diagrams is drawn. These show the part of the diagram used to answer each part of the question. In your answer you would fill in the values step-by-step on the same diagram.

Question

XT and ZT are tangents to the circle WXYZ drawn below. O is the centre of the circle and ∠OZX = 25°. Calculate, giving brief reasons, the value of

(a) ∠OXZ (b) ∠XOZ (c) ∠XWZ (d) ∠XYZ (e) ∠XTZ

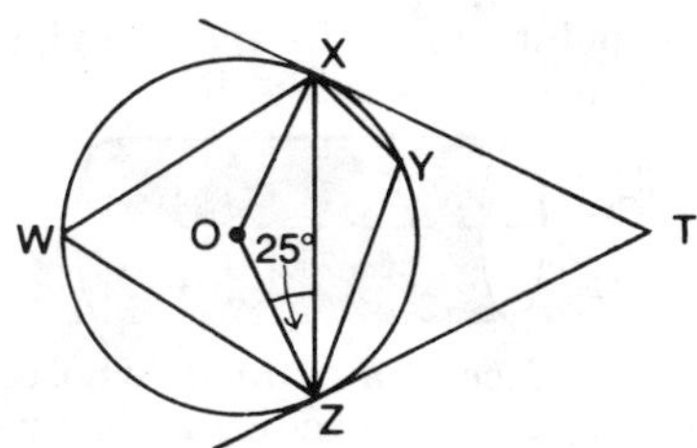

Answer

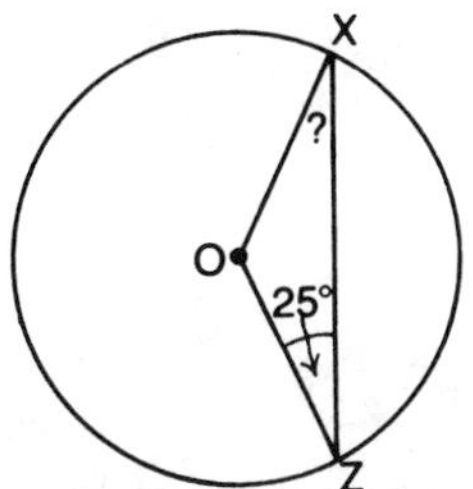

(a) Triangle OXZ is an isosceles triangle because OX = OZ (Equal radii)
So ∠OXZ = ∠OZX (Base angles of isosceles triangle)
= 25°

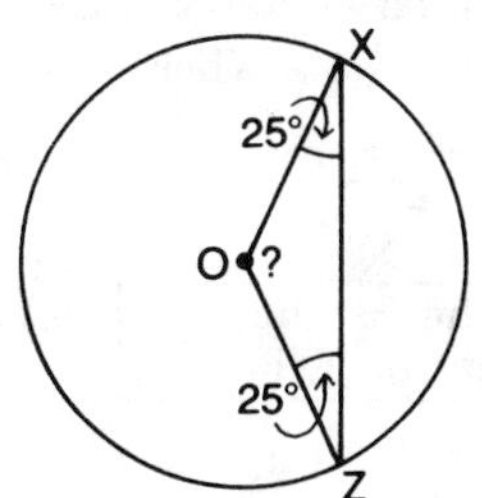

(b) In triangle OXZ,
∠XOZ + 25° + 25° = 180° (Angle sum of a triangle)
∠XOZ = 180° − 50°
= 130°

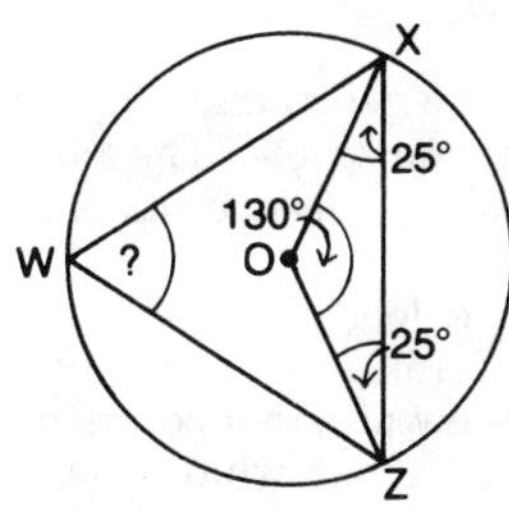

(c) ∠XWZ = $\frac{1}{2}$∠XOZ (Angle at circumference = $\frac{1}{2}$ angle at the centre)
= $\frac{1}{2} \times 130°$
= 65°

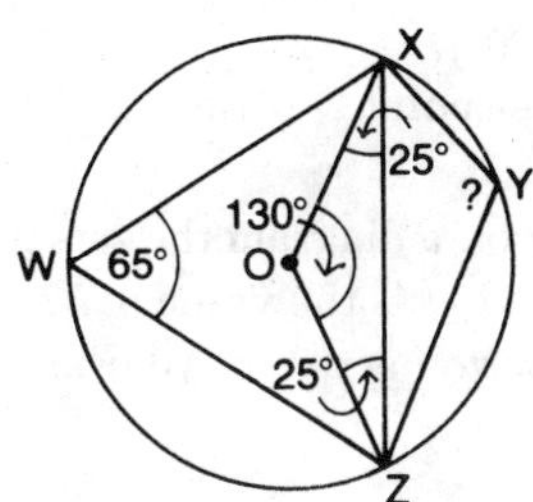

(d) ∠XYZ + ∠XWZ = 180° (Opposite angles of a cyclic quadrilateral)
∠XYZ = 180° − ∠XWZ
= 180° − 65°
= 115°

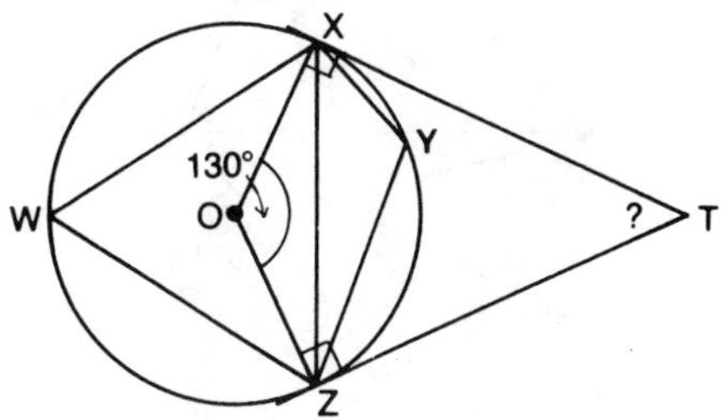

(e) In quadrilateral WXTZ,
∠OXT = 90° (Angle between tangent and radius)
∠OZT = 90° (Angle between tangent and radius)
∠XOZ = 130° (see (b))

So $90° + 90° + 130° + \angle XTZ = 360°$ (Angle sum of quadrilateral)

$$310° + \angle XTZ = 360°$$
$$\angle XTZ = 360° - 310°$$
$$= 50°$$

3.2 Loci

This unit extends the simple ideas of locus given in Unit 2.16. Set notation (see Unit 3.8) is used to describe some loci in this unit. You may meet this notation in examination questions. For example, the locus of a point P which moves in the plane so that it remains 2 cm from a fixed point O can be written using set notation as:

'the locus of point P is the set X where

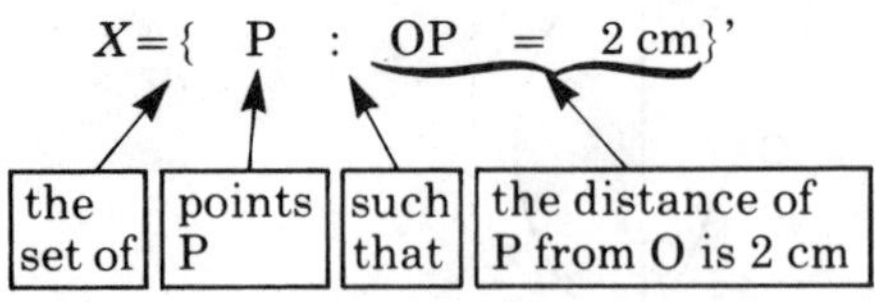

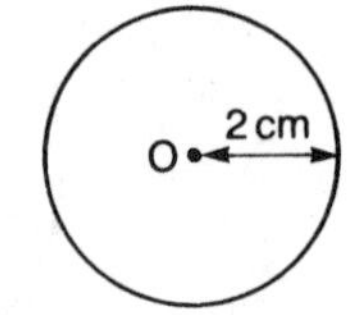

Sometimes you need more than one locus to find the solution to a problem. In set notation the *intersection* of two loci sets A and B is written as $(A \cap B)$. The number of points of intersection is given by $n(A \cap B)$.

2D LOCI

Many examples of loci use geometrical properties of lines, angles, shapes, ... that you know. The chord, angle and tangent properties of circles (see units 2.14 and 3.1) are often used.

You will recognize some loci and be able to draw them immediately (see Unit 2.16). If you do not recognize the locus, then sketching a few possible points using the given rule will help you to work out what it is. The following question illustrates this.

Question

The points A and B are fixed and are 5 cm apart. The locus of a point P is the set X where

$X = \{P : \angle APB = 90°\}$.

The locus of another point Q is the set Y where

$Y = \{Q : AQ = BQ\}$.

(a) Indicate clearly on a diagram the sets X and Y.

(b) If $n(X \cap Y) = k$, what is the value of k?

Explain clearly how you arrive at your answers.

Answer

$X = \{P : \angle APB = 90°\}$

This says that P must move so that $\angle APB$ must be 90°. The sketch shows some possible points for P.

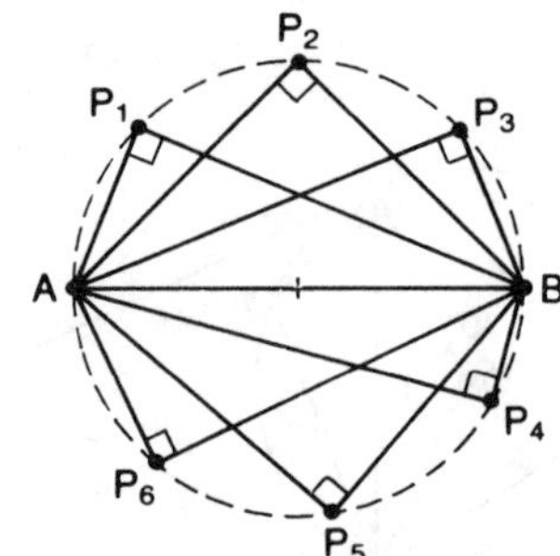

The angle in a semicircle is always 90°.
If AB is the diameter of a circle, then P must lie on that circle.
The centre of the circle is the midpoint of AB.
The radius of the circle is $\frac{1}{2}AB = \frac{1}{2}$ of 5 cm = 2.5 cm.

$Y = \{Q : AQ = BQ\}$

This says that Q must move so that it is the same distance from A and B.

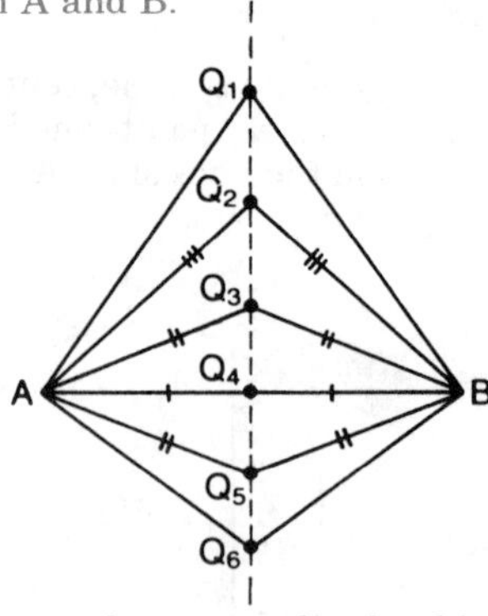

So Q must lie on the perpendicular bisector of the line AB.

(a) Construction of sets X and Y:

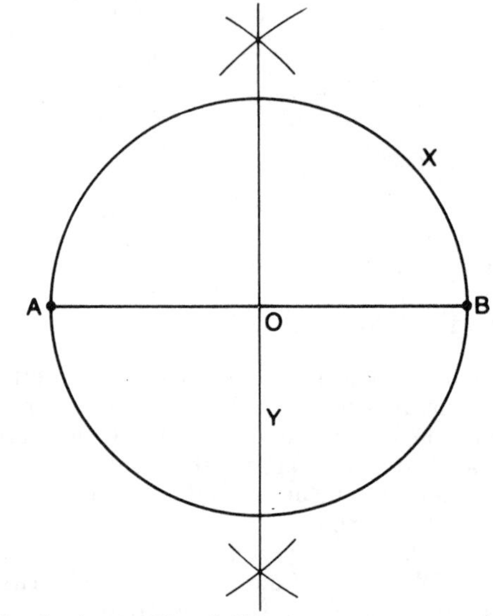

(b) The loci sets X and Y intersect at two points.
So $n(X \cap Y) = 2$, i.e. $k = 2$.

3D LOCI

A moving point is not necessarily restricted to moving in two dimensions, i.e. in the same plane. It could move in three dimensions, i.e. in space.

Here are two common loci in 3D which are useful to know.

1 *Rule* the point moves in space and stays the same distance from a fixed point.

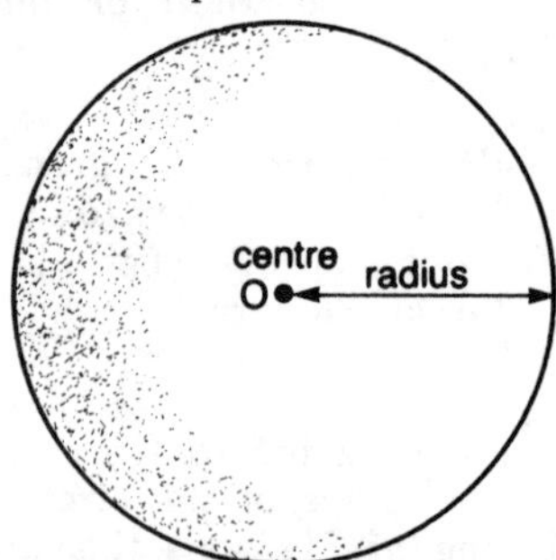

Locus the surface of a sphere with the fixed point as centre and radius the given distance.

2 *Rule* the point moves in space and stays the same distance from a fixed straight line.

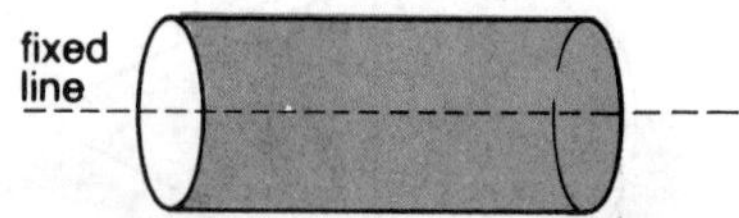

Locus the surface of a cylinder whose central axis is the fixed line and whose radius is the given distance.

3.3 Enlargement

Enlargement is a *transformation*, i.e. a change. In an enlargement the size of the object usually changes and the scale factor of the enlargement describes the size of the change. The shape of the object is always unchanged in an enlargement. So the object and its image are similar (see Unit 1.41). Matching angles in the object and image are equal, corresponding lengths are in proportion.
All the enlargements described in Unit 2.18 have scale factors greater than 1. For example, in this diagram triangle ABC (the object) has been enlarged to triangle A′B′C′ (the image) by the *spider* or *ray method.* It uses a centre of enlargement O and scale factor $k>1$.

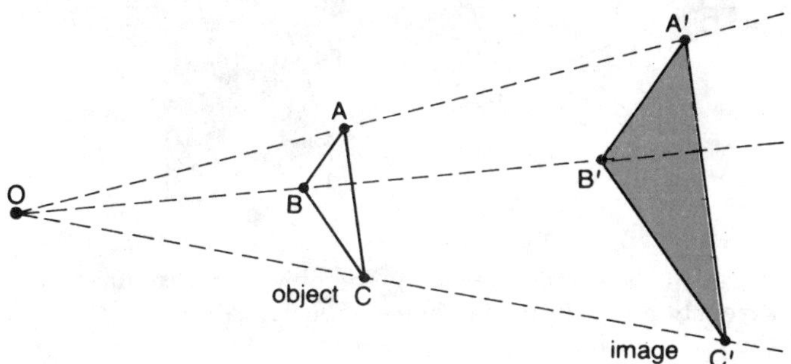

Matching lengths have been changed in the same way, i.e. by the scale factor k.

Lengths from centre	Lengths on shape
$OA' = kOA$	$A'B' = kAB$
$OB' = kOB$	$B'C' = kBC$
$OC' = kOC$	$C'A' = kCA$

Since $k>1$, all the *image lengths* are greater than the matching *object lengths.* So each change is an increase of size k.
Matching sides of the image and object are parallel.

A′B′ is parallel to AB,
B′C′ is parallel to BC,
C′A′ is parallel to CA.

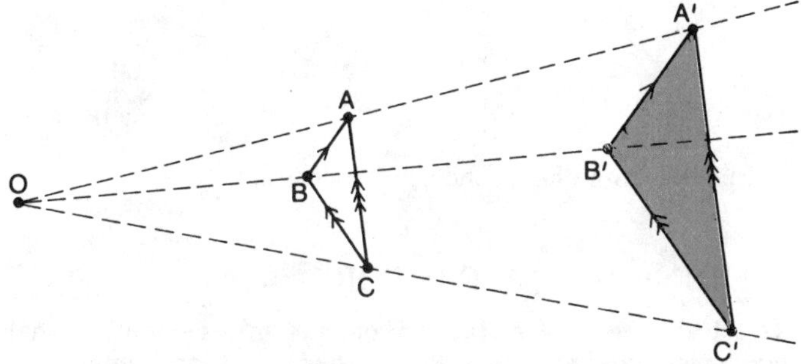

Not all scale factors are greater than 1. This unit also deals with enlargements with scale factors which are proper fractions or negative. The methods used to enlarge an object in Unit 2.18 are also used in this unit.

FRACTIONAL SCALE FACTORS

When the scale factor k is a **proper fraction**, i.e. $0<k<1$, the image is *smaller* than the object. Each length on the image is a fraction of the matching length on the object. This kind of enlargement is often called a **reduction** (for obvious reasons).

Question

Enlarge the given shape by a scale factor of $\frac{1}{3}$ on the given grid.

Answer

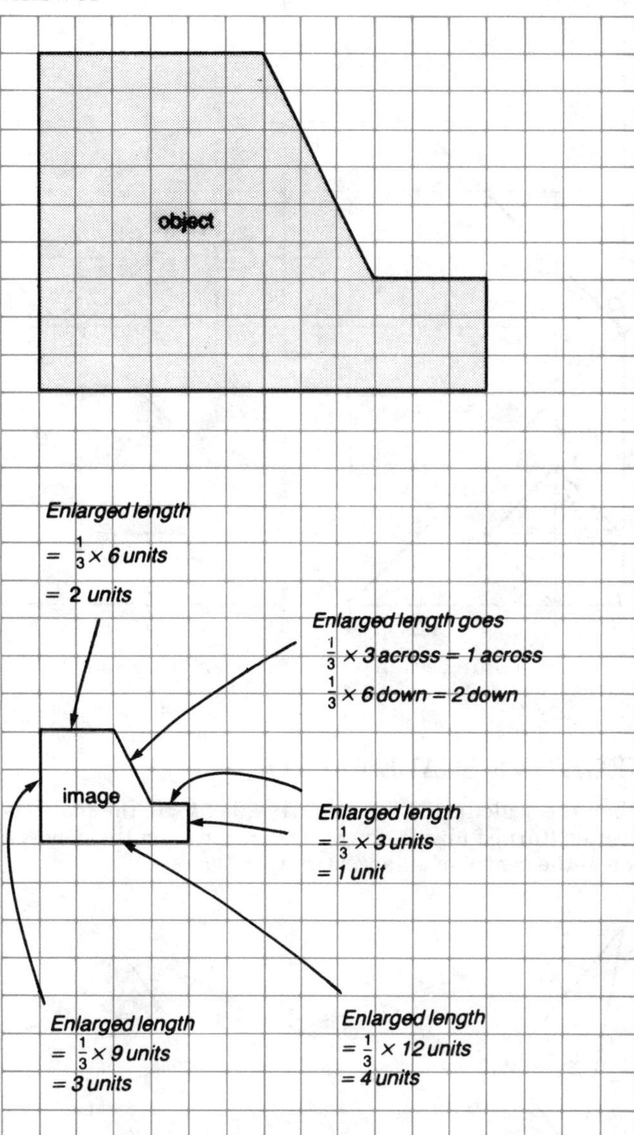

When you use a centre of enlargement O and a fractional scale factor, the image is on the *same* side of O as the object but *nearer* to O than the object.

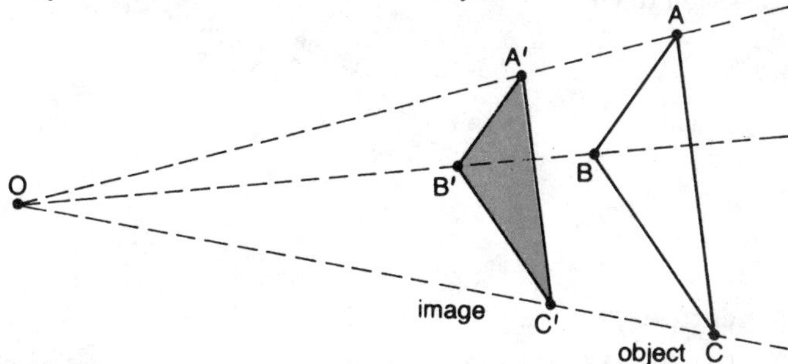

Question

The vertices of a quadrilateral are A(4, 0), B(8, 4), C(4, 8) and D(0, 4). Draw this quadrilateral on the given grid. Enlarge the quadrilateral using a scale factor $\frac{1}{4}$ and centre of enlargement (0, 0). Label the image A′B′C′D′ and give the coordinates of its vertices.

Answer

Object distance	Image distance
O to A : 4 along, 0 up	O to A′ : 1 along, 0 up
O to B : 8 along, 4 up	O to B′ : 2 along, 1 up
O to C : 4 along, 8 up	O to C′ : 1 along, 2 up
O to D : 0 along, 4 up	O to D′ : 0 along, 1 up

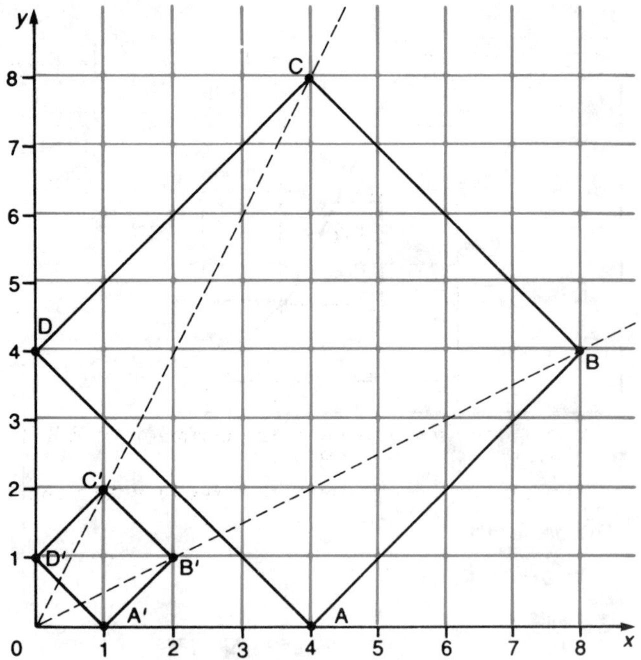

So the coordinates of the vertices A′B′C′D′ are A′(1, 0), B′(2, 1), C′(1, 2) and D′(0, 1).

NEGATIVE SCALE FACTOR

When the scale factor k is **negative**, i.e. $k<0$, the image is *inverted* (turned upside down). The image is on the *opposite* side of the centre of enlargement O to the object.

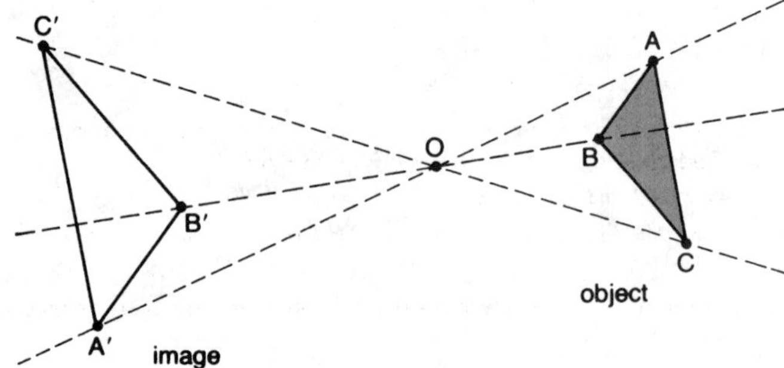

The *negative* sign tells you that to find the image of any point P, the length OP′ must be measured in the *opposite* direction to OP.

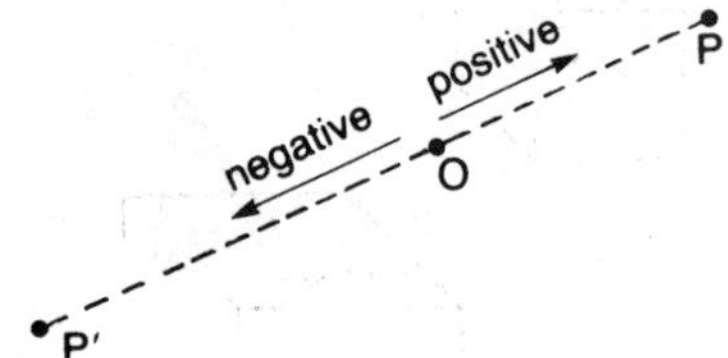

Question

Enlarge the given shape (PQRS) using a scale factor of -2 and centre of enlargement O.

Answer

Distances	
Object	**Image**
O to P = 1 cm	O to P′ = -2×1 cm $=-2$ cm
O to Q = 2 cm	O to Q′ = -2×2cm $=-4$ cm
O to R = 3 cm	O to R′ = -2×3 cm $=-6$ cm
O to S = 1.5 cm	O to S′ = -2×1.5 cm $=-3$ cm

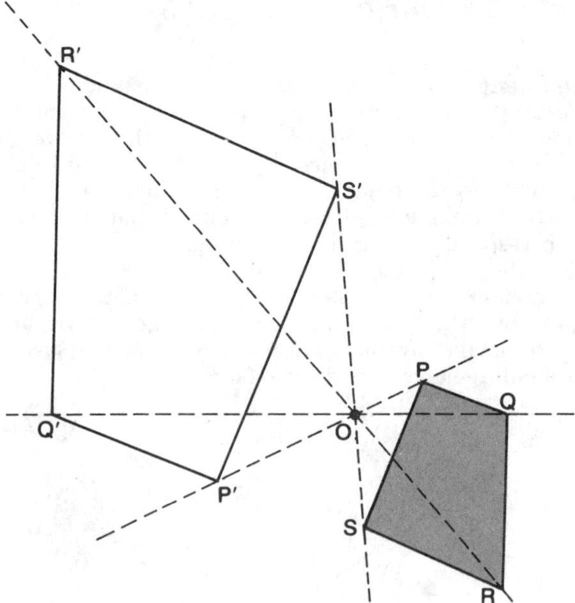

When the scale factor $k=-1$, the object and its image are **directly congruent**, i.e. one can be fitted exactly on top of the other without being ‘flipped over’.

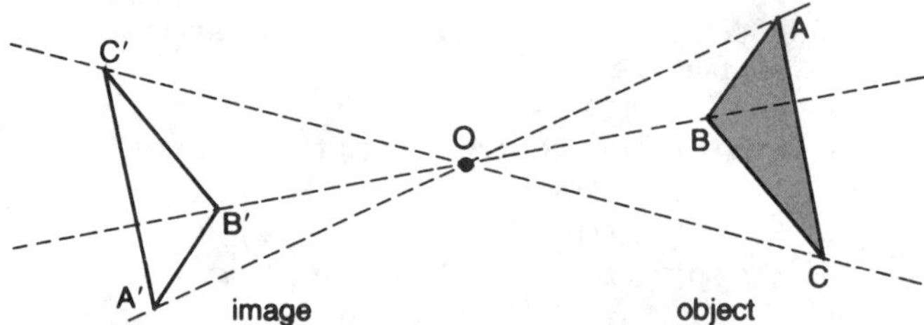

The scale factor k may be *both* negative *and* a proper fraction, i.e. $-1<k<0$. In this case, the image is inverted (because $k<0$) and is a reduction (because k is a proper fraction).

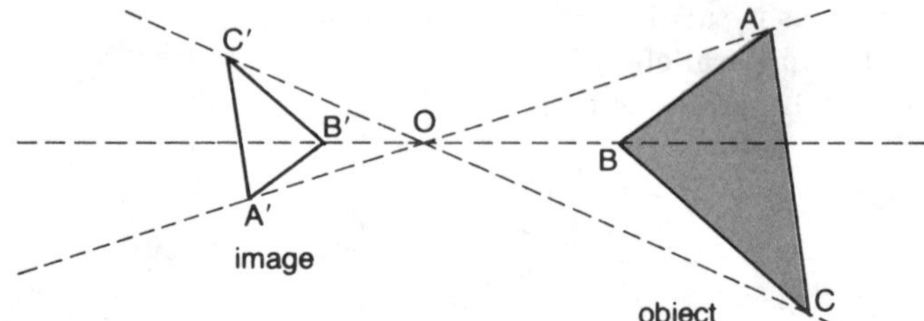

In the diagram above, the scale factor is $-\frac{1}{2}$.

FINDING SCALE FACTORS

To **find the scale factor** of an enlargement, either compare *matching* lengths on the object and image, or compare the distances of *matching* object and image points from the centre of enlargement O.
The lengths compared must be in the *same* unit.

$$\text{scale factor} = \frac{\text{image length}}{\text{matching object length}}$$

$$\text{or } \frac{\text{distance of image point from O}}{\text{distance of matching object point from O}}$$

Always check that your answer matches the image given.
A reduced image must have a proper fraction as its scale factor.
An inverted image must have a negative scale factor.

Question

In the following diagram, ABC has been enlarged to A′B′C′ using the centre of enlargement O. What is the scale factor of this enlargement?

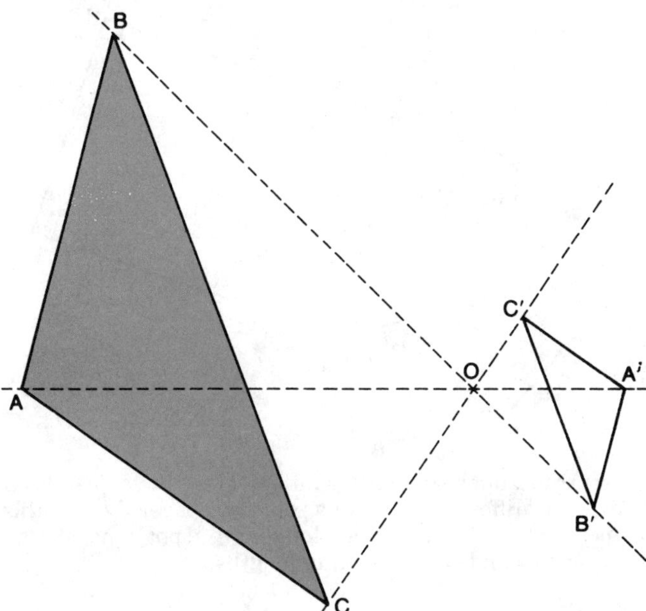

Answer

On this diagram, the distances from the centre are simpler lengths to work with, so use these to calculate the scale factor

From the diagram, OA = 6 cm, OA′ = −2 cm

opposite direction to OA

$$\text{scale factor} = \frac{OA'}{OA} = \frac{-2\text{ cm}}{6\text{ cm}} = -\frac{1}{3}$$

FINDING A CENTRE OF ENLARGEMENT

To find the **centre of an enlargement**, join *matching* image and object points with straight lines. The *point of intersection* of these lines is the *centre of the enlargement.*

Question

In the diagram below X′Y′Z′ is an enlargement of XYZ. Find the position of the centre of enlargement O.

Answer

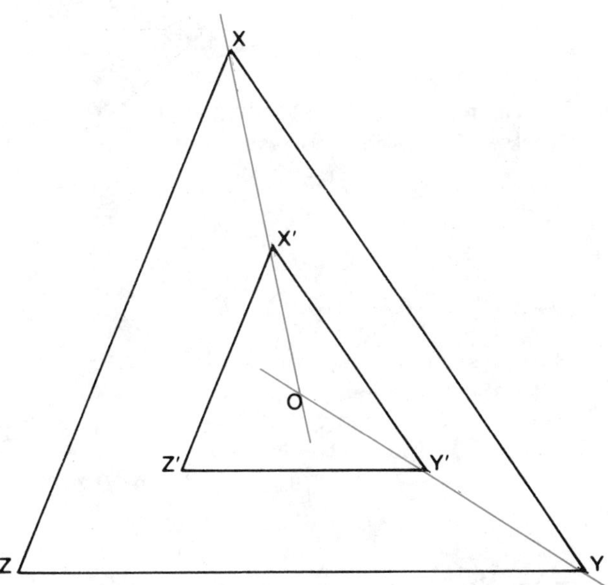

Draw straight lines joining XX′ and YY′ – the point of intersection O is the centre of enlargement

AREA AND VOLUME OF ENLARGEMENTS

When a shape is enlarged by a scale factor k, its **area** is enlarged by a factor k^2, (the area factor).

area of enlargement = k^2 × area of object

Question

In the diagram below, ABCD and WXYZ are squares, WX = 3AB.

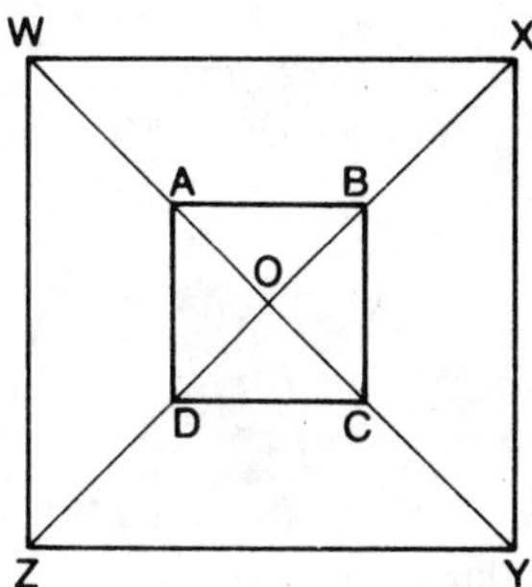

(a) How many times greater is the perimeter of WXYZ than the perimeter of ABCD?

(b) How many times greater is the area of WXYZ than the area of ABCD?

(c) If the area of triangle AOB is 4.2 cm², what is the area of triangle WOX?

Answer

WXYZ is an enlargement of ABCD.
Since WX = 3AB, the scale factor of the enlargement is 3.

(a) Perimeter is a length.
So perimeter of WXYZ = 3 × perimeter of ABCD.

(b) Area of WXYZ = 3^2 × area of ABCD
= 9 × area of ABCD

(c) Triangle WOX is an enlargement of triangle AOB, scale factor 3.
So area of triangle WOX = 3^2 × area of triangle AOB
= 9 × 4.2 cm²
= 37.8 cm²

When a **solid** is enlarged by a scale factor k, its **volume** is enlarged by a factor k^3 (the volume factor).

volume of enlargement = k^3 × volume of object

The surface area of the solid is enlarged by the area factor k^2.

surface area of enlargement = k^2 × surface area of object

Question

Cuboid A is an enlargement of cuboid X.

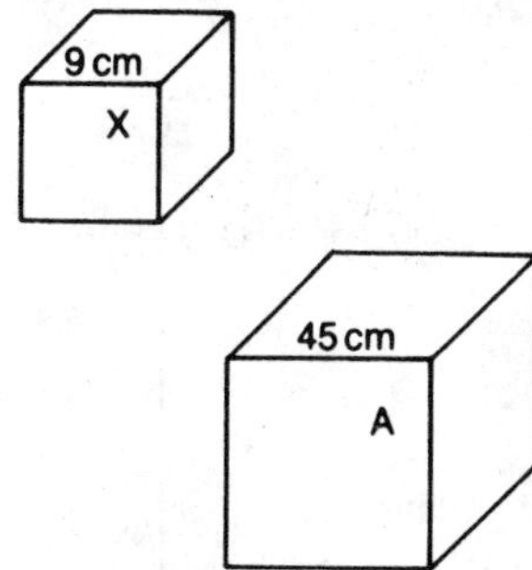

If the volume of cuboid X is 73 cm³, what is the volume of cuboid A?

Answer

From the diagram,

$$\text{scale factor } k = \frac{\text{image length}}{\text{matching object length}} = \frac{45\text{ cm}}{9\text{ cm}} = 5$$

Volume of cuboid A = k^3 × volume of cuboid X
= 5^3 × 73 cm³
= 9125 cm³

3.4 Similar figures

Similar figures are the *same shape* but they may be different sizes. In a pair of similar figures, one is an enlargement of the other. For example, these are similar plane shapes ...

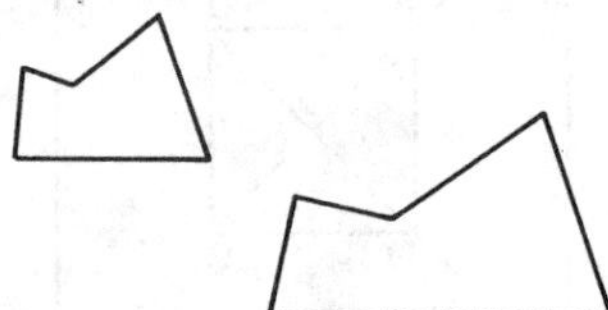

and these are similar solids.

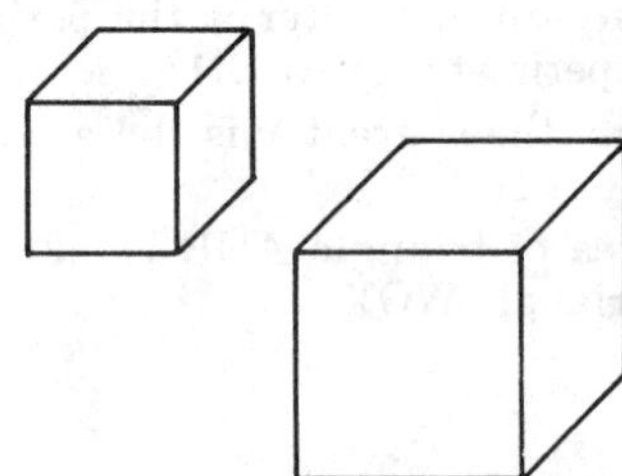

Similar figures are the basis of all real-life situations that depend on enlarging (or reducing) something. For example, a *scale model* of a car is similar to the real car, a *map* of a country is similar to the shape of the actual country, a *scale drawing* of a plan is similar to the full-size plan.

In similar figures

(**a**) corresponding angles are equal, *and*

(**b**) corresponding lengths are in the same ratio.

Always name similar figures with their letters in corresponding order. This makes it easier to work out corresponding angles and lengths. For example, these two trapeziums, ABCD and PQRS are similar.

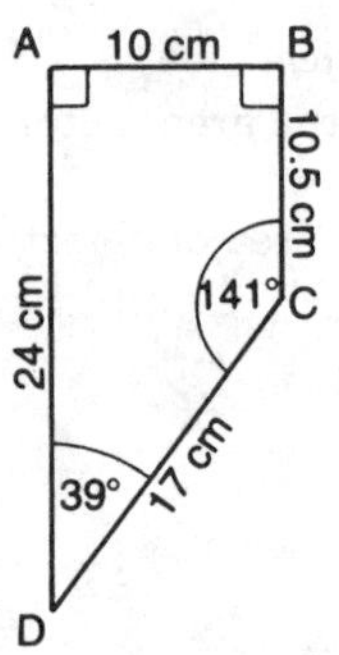

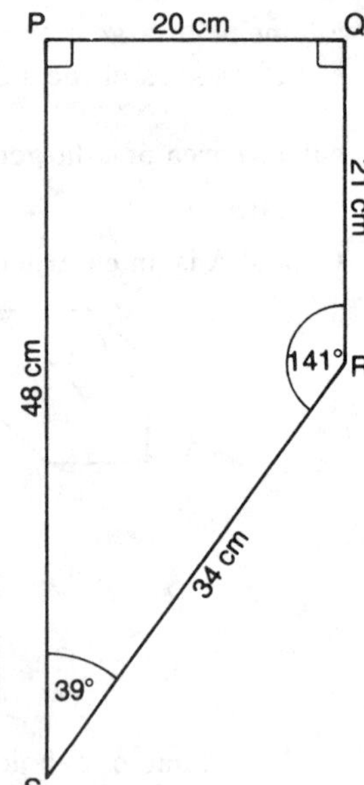

Corresponding letters are

A↔P, B↔Q, C↔R, D↔S.

Equal matching angles are

angle A = angle P = 90°
angle B = angle Q = 90°
angle C = angle R = 141°
angle D = angle S = 39°

The equal ratios of corresponding lengths are:

$$\frac{AB}{PQ}=\frac{BC}{QR}=\frac{CD}{RS}=\frac{DA}{SP}$$

$$\text{i.e. } \frac{10}{20}=\frac{10.5}{21}=\frac{17}{34}=\frac{24}{48}\left(\text{all equal to }\frac{1}{2}\right)$$

Similar figures are *not* always drawn the 'same way up' on the page. For example, here are the two similar trapeziums ABCD and PQRS again.

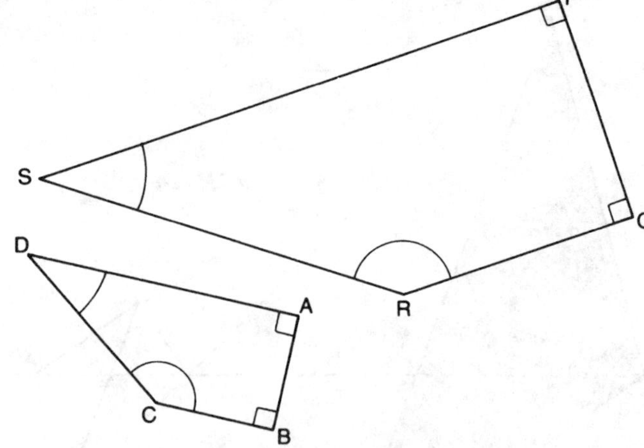

These trapeziums are still similar. They have just been drawn in different positions on the page. When this happens it may take you longer to spot and match equal angles and corresponding lengths.

Question

These quadrilaterals are similar.

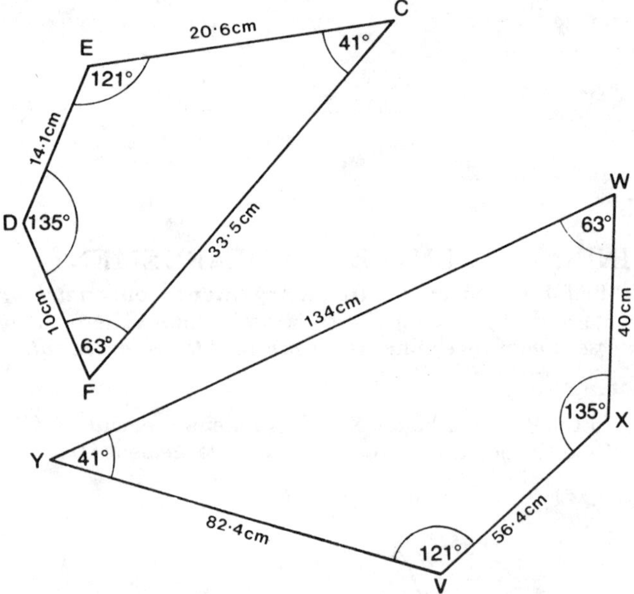

(a) Which angles are corresponding angles?

(b) Work out the ratio of corresponding lengths.

Answer

(a) From the diagram:
angle D = 135° = angle X
angle F = 63° = angle W
angle C = 41° = angle Y
angle E = 121° = angle V

So corresponding angles are:
∠D and ∠X, ∠F and ∠W,
∠C and ∠Y, ∠E and ∠V.

Naming the quadrilaterals with letters 'in the same order' gives quadrilaterals DFCE and XWYV.

(b) The ratio of corresponding lengths is:

$$\frac{DF}{XW}=\frac{FC}{WY}=\frac{CE}{YV}=\frac{ED}{VX}$$

The simplest lengths are for the ratio $\frac{DF}{XW}$, *so use these*

$$\frac{DF}{XW}=\frac{10}{40}=\frac{1}{4}$$

So the ratio of corresponding lengths is $\frac{1}{4}$.

Figures with corresponding angles equal do *not* have to be similar. For example, these rectangles have corresponding angles equal (=90°) but they are not similar. The ratios of corresponding sides are different.

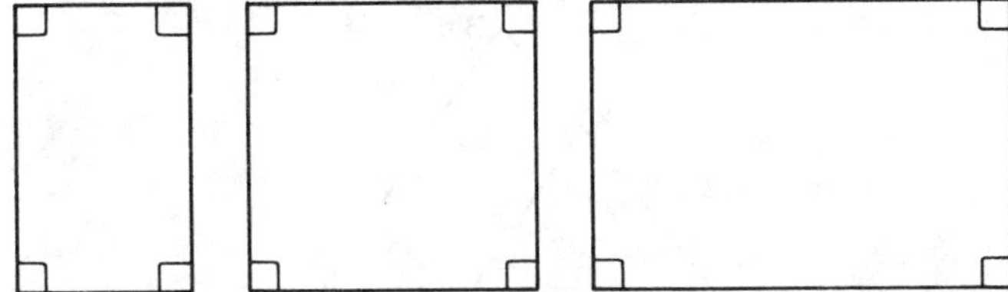

Triangles are an exception to this.

SIMILAR TRIANGLES

If two triangles are similar, then

(**a**) they have 3 pairs of corresponding equal angles, and

(**b**) the 3 ratios of corresponding sides are equal.

For example, triangles ABC and XYZ are similar.

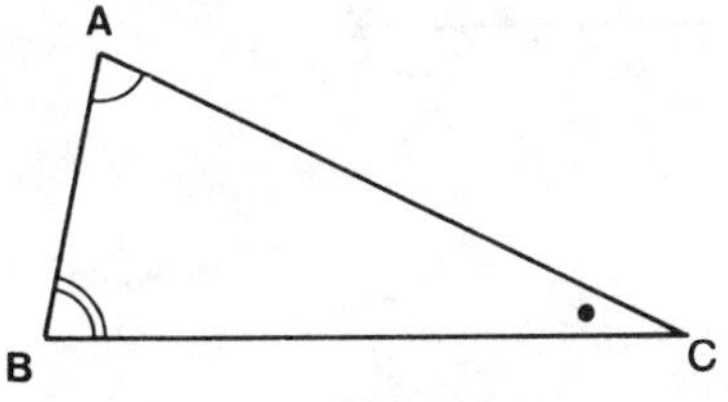

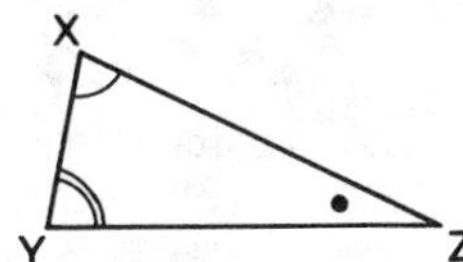

So ∠A = ∠X, ∠B = ∠Y, ∠C = ∠Z

and $\frac{AB}{XY} = \frac{BC}{YZ} = \frac{CA}{ZX}$

Similar triangles are *special* similar figures. You do not have to know the sizes of all the angles and sides of two triangles to decide whether they are similar or not. If you can show that *one* of the following conditions is true for two triangles, then the two triangles are similar.

1 The angles of one triangle are equal to the corresponding angles of the other triangle.

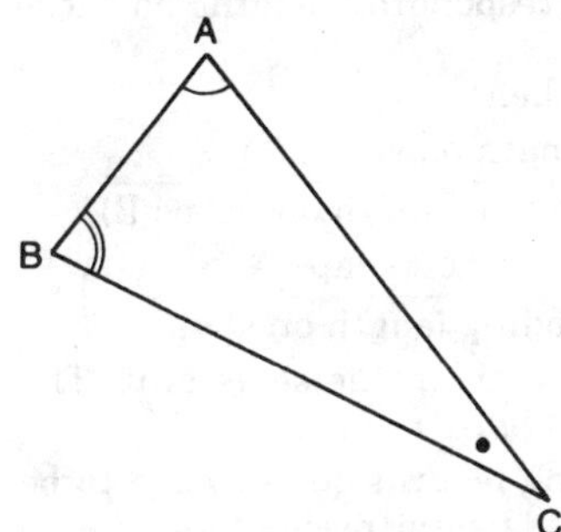

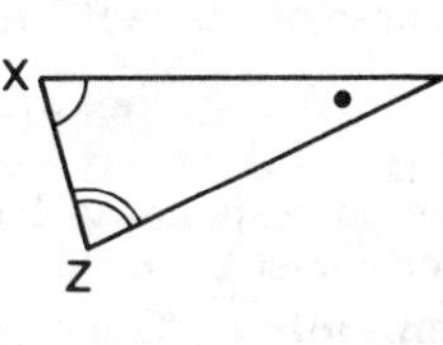

Triangle ABC is similar to triangle XZY, because:

∠A = ∠X, ∠B = ∠Z, ∠C = ∠Y

(In fact, if *two* pairs of corresponding angles are equal, then the third pair must be equal because of the angle sum of a triangle.
So, if, for example, ∠A = ∠X and ∠B = ∠Z, then it follows that ∠C = ∠Y.)

2 The ratios of corresponding sides are equal.

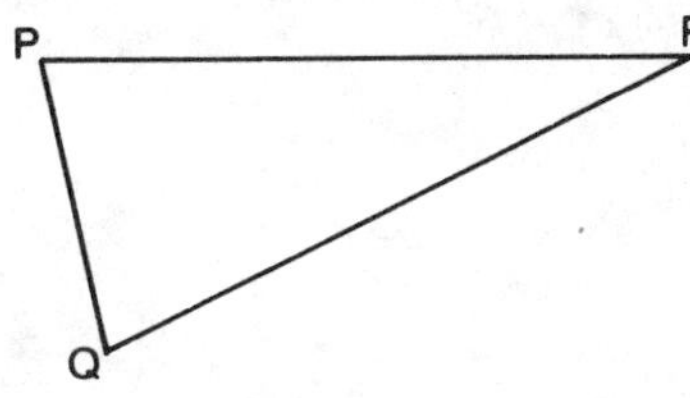

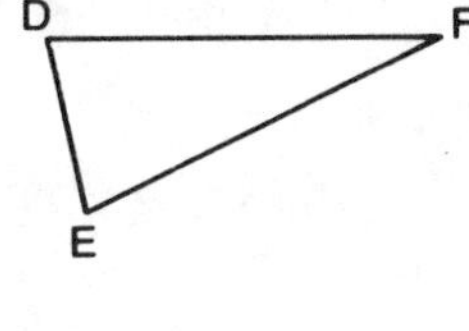

Triangle PQR is similar to triangle DEF, if

$\frac{PQ}{DE} = \frac{QR}{EF} = \frac{RP}{FD}$

3 The ratios of two corresponding sides are equal and the angles included between them are equal.

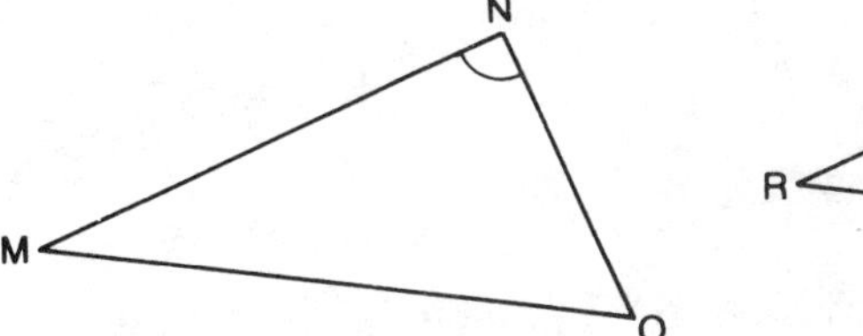

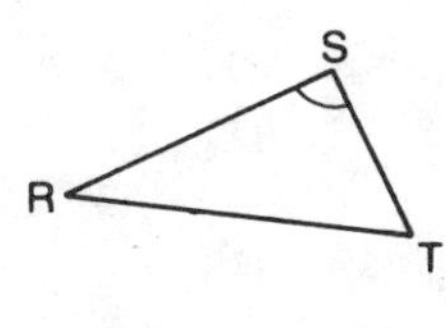

Triangle MNO is similar to triangle RST, if, for example,

∠N = ∠S and $\frac{MN}{RS} = \frac{NO}{ST}$

Question

Identify the pair of similar triangles in each of these groups of triangles. Give reasons for your answers.

Note: The triangles are not drawn accurately. They may look similar even when they are not.

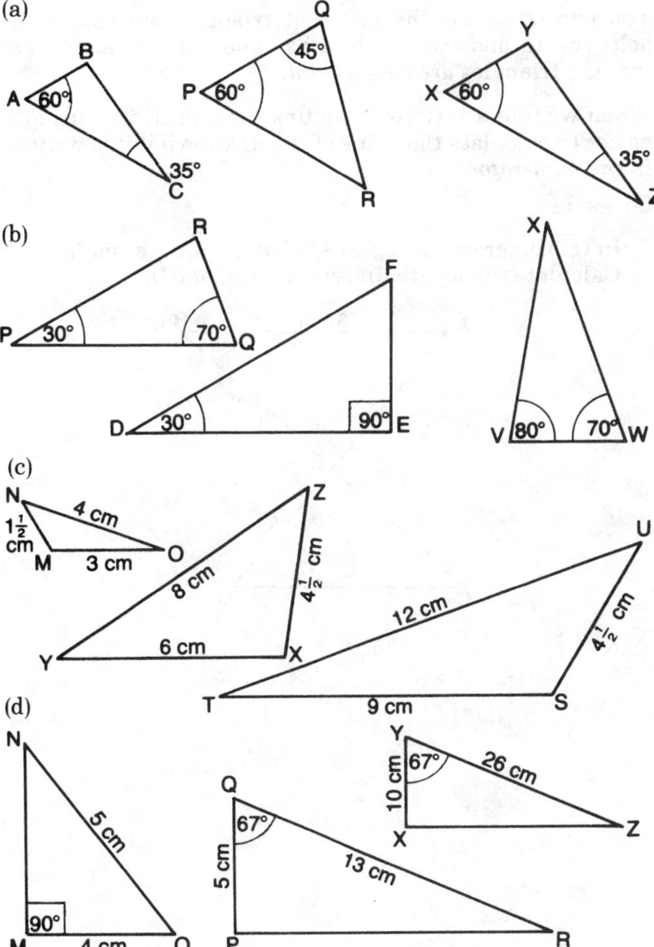

Answer

(a) Triangles ABC and XYZ are similar, because:

∠A = 60° = ∠X

∠C = 35° = ∠Z

and ∠B = ∠Y (Angle sum of a triangle)

So the angles of triangle ABC are equal to the angles of triangle XYZ.

(b) The angle sum of a triangle is 180°, so:

in triangle PQR, ∠P = 30°, ∠Q = 70°, ∠R = 80°

in triangle DEF, ∠D = 30°, ∠E = 90°, ∠F = 60°

in triangle VWX, ∠V = 80°, ∠W = 70°, ∠X = 30°

So triangles PQR and XWV are similar because their angles are equal.

(c) Triangles MON and STU are similar because

$\frac{MO}{ST}=\frac{3}{9}=\frac{1}{3}$

$\frac{ON}{TU}=\frac{4}{12}=\frac{1}{3}$

$\frac{NM}{US}=\frac{1\frac{1}{2}}{4\frac{1}{2}}=\frac{1}{3}$

i.e. $\frac{MO}{ST}=\frac{ON}{TU}=\frac{NM}{US}\left(=\frac{1}{3}\right)$

So the ratios of corresponding sides are equal.

(d) Triangles PQR and XYZ are similar because:

$\angle Q=67°=\angle Y$ (Included angle)

$\left.\begin{array}{l}\frac{PQ}{XY}=\frac{5}{10}=\frac{1}{2}\\ \frac{QR}{YZ}=\frac{13}{26}=\frac{1}{2}\end{array}\right\}$ Same ratio

The ratios of two corresponding sides are equal and the included angles are equal.

You can often use the fact that triangles are similar to help you to find missing lengths. You may have to *show* that the triangles are similar *first*.

When writing a ratio with an unknown in it, it is usually easier to calculate the value of the unknown if it is written in the *numerator*.

Question

In this diagram, triangles ABE and CDE are similar. Calculate the length, in centimetres, of CD.

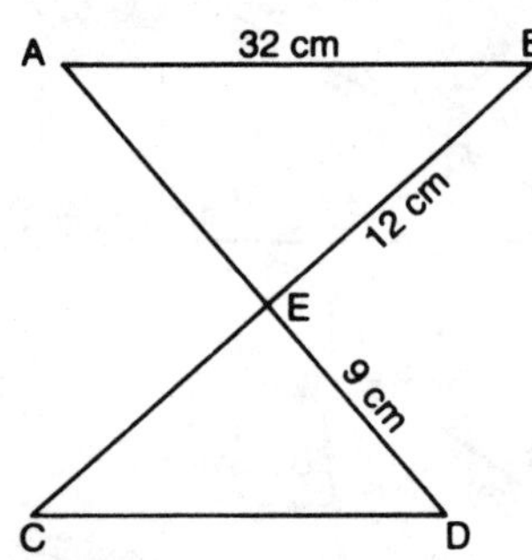

Answer

Since triangles ABE and CDE are similar, the ratios of corresponding sides are equal.

$\frac{CD}{AB}=\frac{DE}{BE}=\frac{EC}{EA}$ *Write CD 'on top' because it is unknown*

$\frac{CD}{32}=\frac{DE}{BE}=\frac{9}{12}$

Use these to find CD

So $\frac{CD}{32}=\frac{9}{12}$

$CD=\frac{9}{12}\times 32\text{ cm}$

$=\frac{\overset{3}{\cancel{9}}}{\underset{\underset{1}{\cancel{4}}}{\cancel{12}}}\times \overset{8}{\cancel{32}}\text{ cm}$

$=24\text{ cm}$

So CD is 24 cm long.

When a line is drawn across a triangle parallel to one of its sides, a similar triangle is formed. You can show that this is true without knowing the actual sizes of the triangles.

Question

In triangle ABC, the line XY is drawn parallel to the side BC.
Show that triangle AXY is similar to triangle ABC.

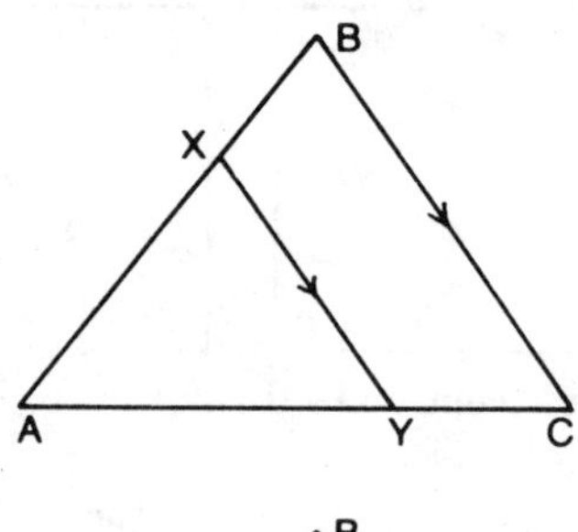

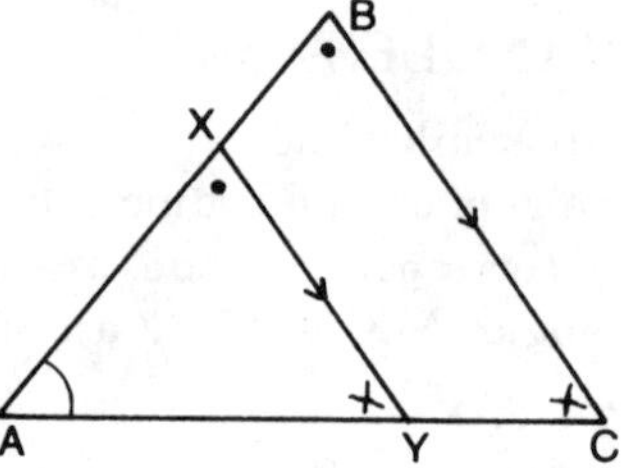

Answer

In triangles AXY and ABC,

$\angle A$ is common to both triangles,

$\left.\begin{array}{l}\angle X=\angle B\\ \angle Y=\angle C\end{array}\right\}$ (Corresponding angles between parallel lines XY and BC)

So triangles AXY and ABC are similar because their angles are equal.

You may often have to show that triangles are similar without knowing the actual measurements. Usually you will have to use angle properties you know to do this.

AREAS OF SIMILAR FIGURES

The **ratio of the areas** of two similar figures is equal to the ratio of the **squares** of corresponding lengths on these figures.

If shapes A and B are similar, then:

$$\frac{\text{area of shape A}}{\text{area of shape B}}=\frac{(\text{length on shape A})^2}{(\text{corresponding length on shape B})^2}$$

$$\text{or}\left(\frac{\text{length on shape A}}{\text{corresponding length on shape B}}\right)^2$$

The corresponding lengths must be in the *same* unit. The areas must be in the matching *square units*.

Remember The corresponding lengths do not have to be 'sides' of shapes. They can be diagonals, perimeters, ...

Question

The perimeters of two similar shapes X and Y are 60 cm and 90 cm. The area of shape Y is 45 cm². What is the area of shape X?

Answer

$\frac{\text{area of shape X}}{\text{area of shape Y}}=\left(\frac{\text{perimeter of X}}{\text{perimeter of Y}}\right)^2$

$\frac{\text{area of shape X}}{45}=\left(\frac{60}{90}\right)^2$

$\text{area of shape X}=\left(\frac{{}^{2}\cancel{60}}{\cancel{90}_{3}}\right)^2\times 45\text{ cm}^2$

$=\frac{4}{\underset{1}{\cancel{9}}}\times \overset{5}{\cancel{45}}\text{ cm}^2$

$=20\text{ cm}^2$

The ratio of the **surface areas** of two similar solids is equal to the ratio of the squares of corresponding lengths on these solids. For example, if these two cones X and Y are similar, then:

$$\frac{\text{surface area of X}}{\text{surface area of Y}} = \frac{H^2}{h^2} \text{ or } \frac{D^2}{d^2} \text{ or } \ldots$$

VOLUMES OF SIMILAR SOLIDS

The **ratio of the volumes** of two similar solids is equal to the ratio of the **cubes** of corresponding lengths on these solids. If solids P and Q are similar, then

$$\frac{\text{volume of solid P}}{\text{volume of solid Q}} = \frac{(\text{length on solid P})^3}{(\text{corresponding length on solid Q})^3}$$

$$\text{or } \left(\frac{\text{length on solid P}}{\text{corresponding length on solid Q}}\right)^3$$

The corresponding lengths must be in the *same* unit. The volumes must be in the matching *cubic units*.

Question

These two cylinders C and D are similar.
The volume of cylinder C is 73.5 cm^3.
What is the volume of cylinder D?

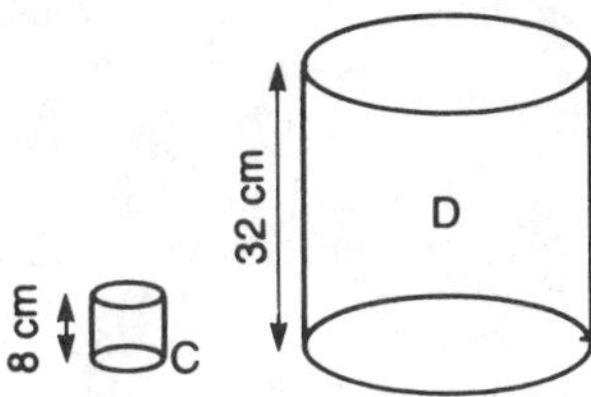

Answer

$$\frac{\text{volume of cylinder D}}{\text{volume of cylinder C}} = \left(\frac{\text{height of D}}{\text{height of C}}\right)^3$$

$$\frac{\text{volume of cylinder D}}{73.5} = \left(\frac{32}{8}\right)^3$$

$$\text{volume of cylinder D} = \left(\frac{{}^4\cancel{32}}{\cancel{8}_1}\right)^3 \times 73.5 \text{ cm}^3$$

$$= \frac{64}{1} \times 73.5 \text{ cm}^3$$

$$= 4704 \text{ cm}^3$$

When a plane cuts across a pyramid or cone *parallel* to its base, a similar pyramid or cone is formed. The rest of the solid is called a **frustum**.

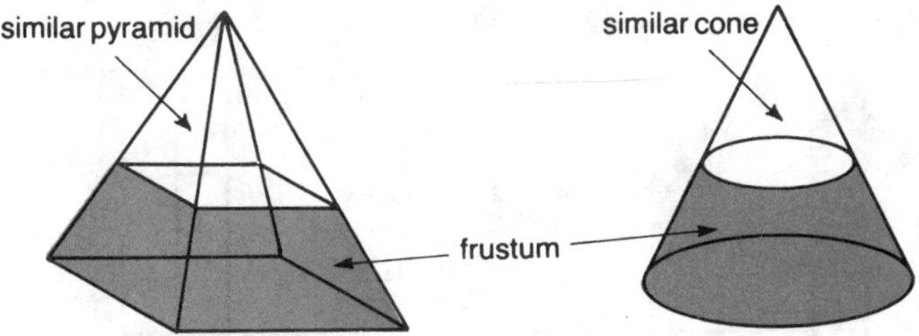

If you know the volume of the original pyramid or cone, then you can often find the volume of the similar pyramid or cone.

volume of frustum
= volume of original pyramid or cone
− volume of similar pyramid or cone

3.5 Combinations of transformations

When an object has been *transformed*, i.e. changed, its image can then be transformed again to form a new image. This is called **combining the transformations**. For example, on the grid below,

triangle A has been transformed to triangle B, then triangle B has been transformed to triangle C.

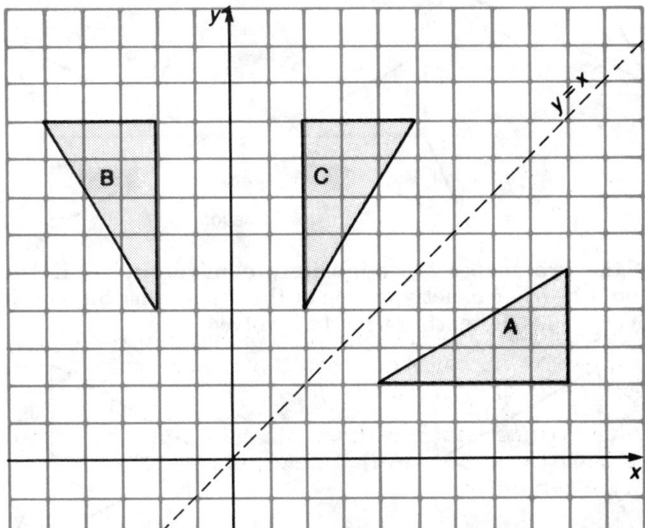

After a combination of transformations, the change from the original object to the final image can usually be described by a *single* transformation. For example, on the grid above, the single transformation which would move triangle A (the original object) to triangle C (the final image) is **reflection in the line** $y = x$.

The transformations which may be combined at this level are translations, rotations, reflections (see unit 2.19) and enlargements (see unit 2.18).

FINDING A TRANSFORMATION

You can find the single transformation equivalent to the combined transformations by drawing. Start with a simple object (this may be given) and draw the effect of one transformation on that object, followed by the effect of the other transformation on the image. The *order* in which the transformations are combined is *important*.

By comparing the original object with the final image you can decide what single transformation would produce the same effect. The shape of the final image gives some clues to help you.

If the original object and final image are **congruent**, then the single transformation can be a **translation**, **rotation** or **reflection**. This is because these transformations are called **isometries**. (An isometry is a transformation in which the object and image are *congruent*.)

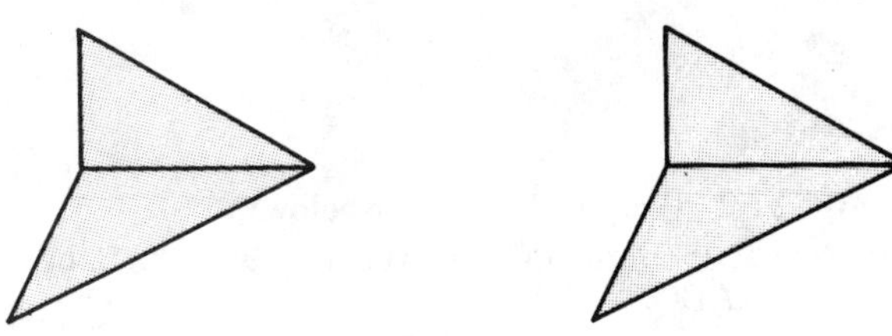

directly congruent shapes

If the two shapes are **directly congruent**, i.e. if one could be fitted exactly on top of the other, without 'flipping it over', then the transformation must be a **translation** or **rotation**.

For example,

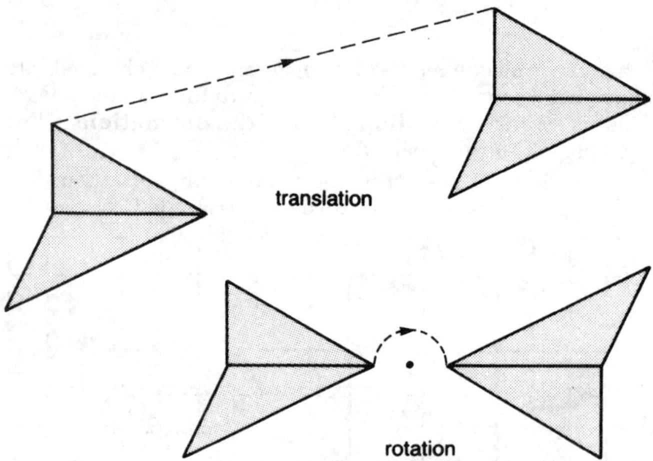

If the two shapes are **oppositely congruent**, i.e. if one could be fitted exactly on top of the other, *after* flipping it over, then a **reflection** must be involved.

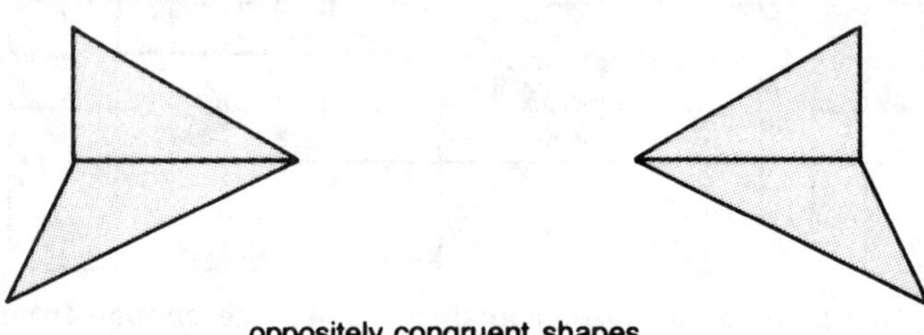

oppositely congruent shapes

If the original object and final image are **similar**, but not congruent, then the transformation must involve an **enlargement**. Enlargement is not an isometry, so object and image are not always congruent.

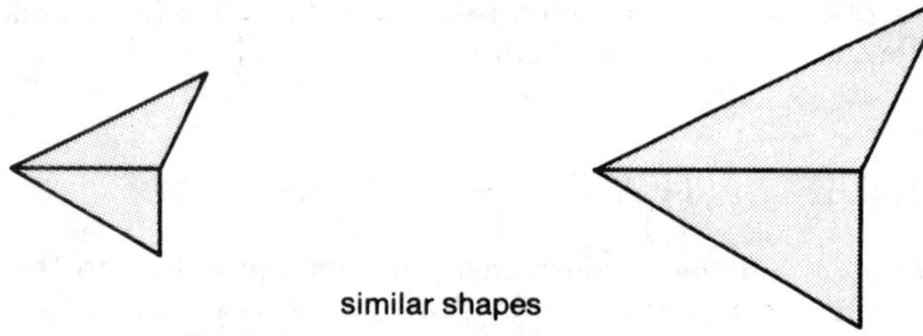

similar shapes

After deciding on what type of transformation you have, you can give a full description of the transformation.

For translation→distance and direction (see Unit 2.19)
or column vector (see Unit 3.30)

For rotation→centre, angle and direction of rotation
(see Unit 2.19)

For reflection→position of mirror line (see Unit 2.19)

For enlargement→scale factor and centre of enlargement
(see Units 2.18 and 3.3)

You can work out the single transformation for any number of combined transformations from a drawing in this way.

Question

On the grid given in the answer below:

(a) Reflect triangle PQR in the line $x=-3$. Label the image ABC.

(b) Translate triangle ABC $\begin{pmatrix}10\\2\end{pmatrix}$. Label the image DEF.

(c) Reflect triangle DEF in the line $y=1$. Label the image XYZ.

Which single transformation would have mapped triangle PQR on to triangle XYZ?

Answer

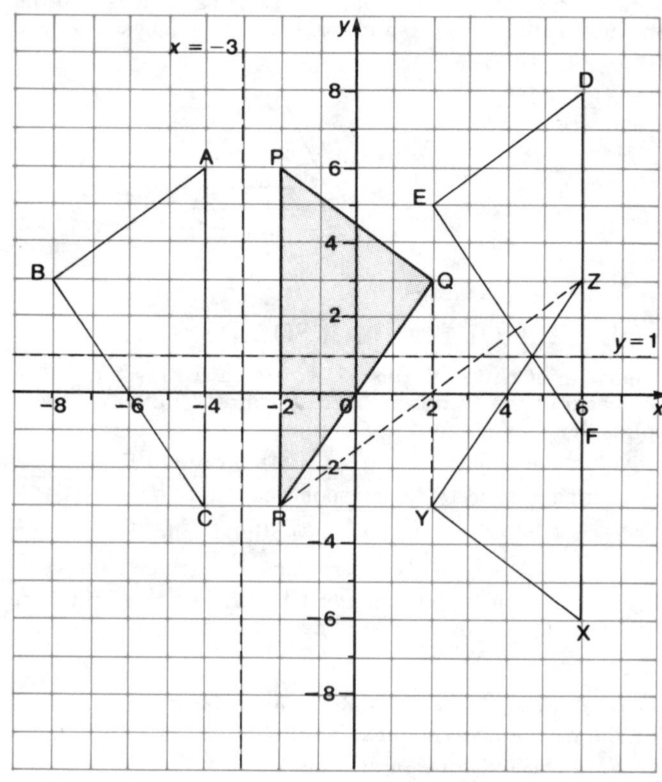

From the drawing you can see that triangles PQR and XYZ are directly congruent. So the transformation is a translation or rotation. Clearly it is not a translation, it is a rotation.

To find the centre of rotation,
join matching points, Q↔Y and R↔Z, on the diagram.
Their point of intersection is (2, 0), *i.e. the centre.*
The angle of rotation is $\frac{1}{2}$ *turn* (180°).

The transformation is a rotation of 180° ($\frac{1}{2}$ turn) about the point (2, 0).

COMBINING TRANSFORMATIONS OF THE SAME TYPE

Two transformations of the *same type* are often combined, for example, two translations, two rotations, ... The single transformation for each combination can be worked out from a drawing as before. This section shows some of the results you would expect to obtain.

Two translations

A **translation followed by a translation** is equivalent to a **single translation**. To describe this translation you must give the distance and direction of the translation or a column vector. For example, the diagram below shows an L-shape which has been translated from P to Q and then from Q to R.

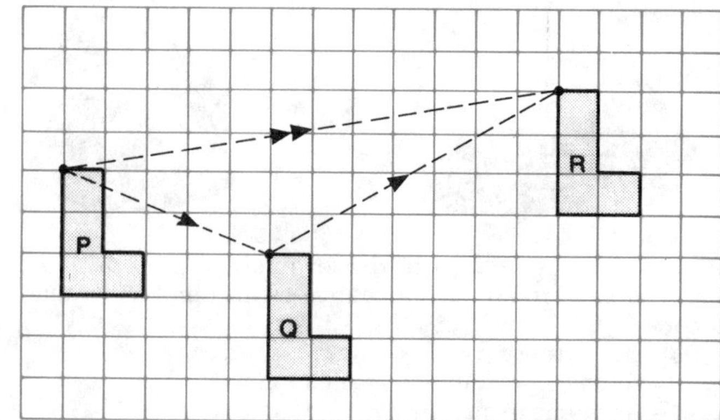

Clearly the L-shape could have been translated from P directly to R.
Translations described by column vectors can be easily combined by calculation.

Two rotations

In general, a **rotation followed by a rotation** is equivalent to a **single rotation**. To describe this rotation you must give the *angle of rotation* and the *centre of rotation* (see Unit 2.19).
The *angle of rotation* is the sum of the two angles of rotation.
For example, a rotation of $a°$
followed by a rotation of $b°$
is equivalent to a single rotation of $(a+b)°$.

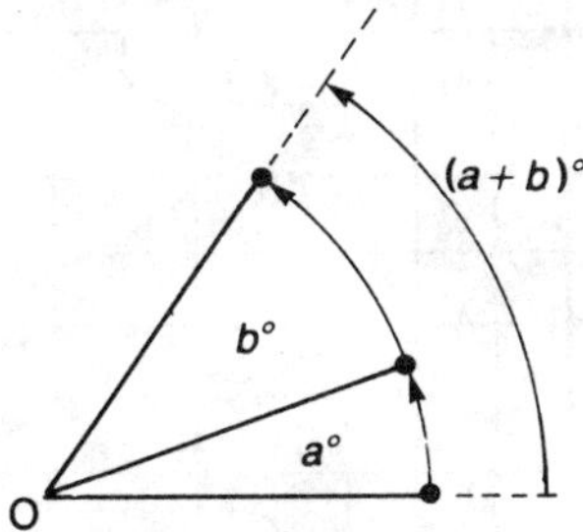

When the two rotations are about the *same* centre, the equivalent rotation is about the *same* centre.
When the two rotations are about *different* centres, the equivalent rotation is about a *third* centre. You will have to find this centre by drawing.

Question

A flag shape F is drawn on the grid in the answer below.
On the grid:

(a) Rotate the flag F about the point (1, 1) through an angle of +90°. Label the image G.

(b) Rotate the flag G about the point (0, 0) through an angle of +90°. Label the image H.

Which single transformation would map the flag F directly onto the flag H?

Answer

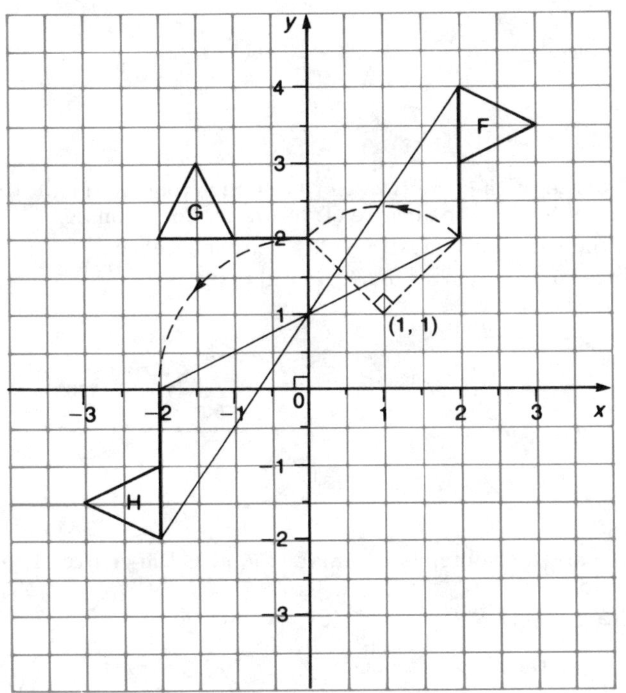

On the diagram, a rotation followed by a rotation is equivalent to a single rotation.
The angle of rotation = 90° + 90° = 180°
To find the centre of rotation, join matching points on F and H.
From the diagram, the centre of rotation is (0, 1).
The single transformation to map F to H is a rotation of 180° about (0, 1).

Rotations of half a turn (180°) give different results. When the two 180° rotations are about the same centre, the shape returns to its original position. For example, on the grid below, the L-shape has been rotated from X to Y and then from Y back to X.

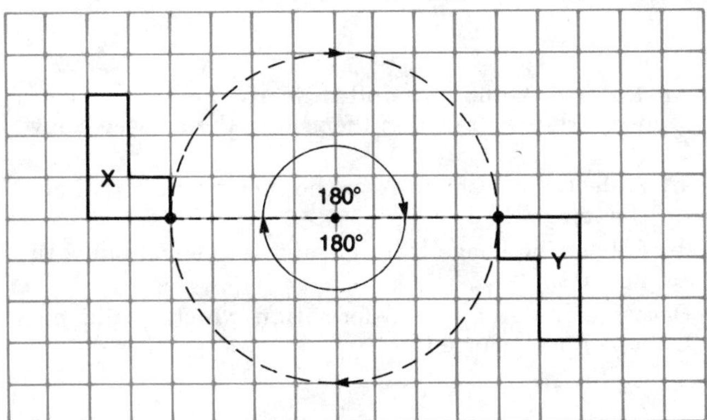

When the two 180° rotations are about different centres, the equivalent single transformation is a translation. For example, on the grid below, the L-shape X has rotated 180° about A and the image is Y. The image Y has rotated 180° about B and the image is Z.

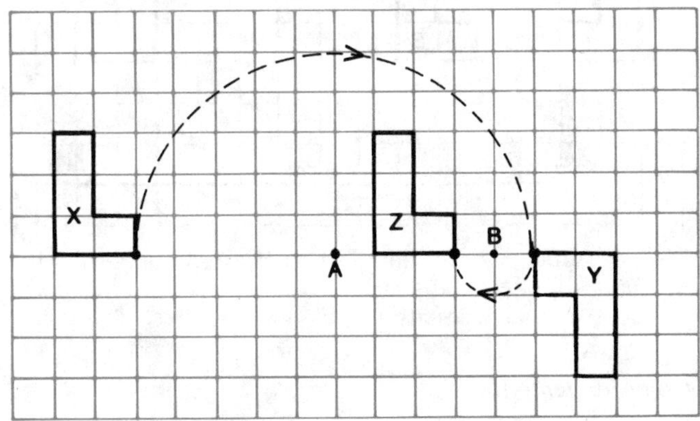

The transformation from X to Z is a translation.

Two reflections

When the **two mirror lines are at an angle** (i.e. *not parallel*), a reflection followed by a reflection is equivalent to a single rotation. To describe this rotation you must give the angle and centre of rotation.
The angle of this rotation is *twice* the angle between the two mirror lines. The centre of this rotation is the *point of intersection* of the two mirror lines. For example, the diagram below shows triangle A reflected in mirror line m_1 on to triangle B. Triangle B has then been reflected in mirror line m_2 onto triangle C.

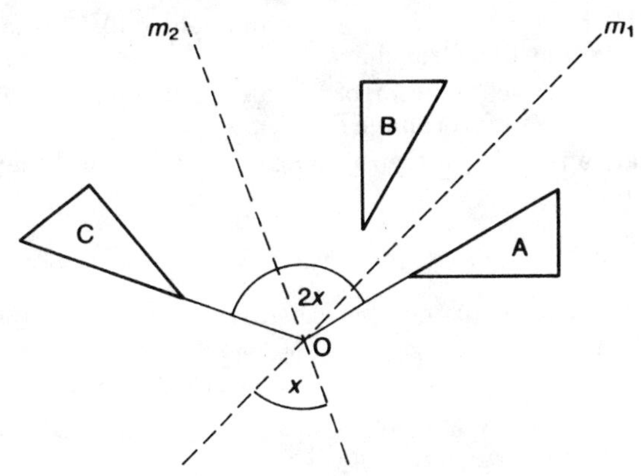

Triangle A can be mapped directly on to C by a rotation. The angle of rotation is $2x$, where x is the angle between the two mirror lines. The centre of rotation is O, the point of intersection of the lines m_1 and m_2.

When the **two mirror lines are parallel**, a reflection followed by a reflection is equivalent to a translation. The distance of the translation is twice the distance between the mirror lines. The direction of the translation is perpendicular to the mirror lines.

Question

An L-shape A and two dotted mirror lines m_1 and m_2 (3 cm apart) are drawn on the grid in the answer below. On the grid:

(a) Reflect the L-shape A in the mirror line m_1. Label the image B.

(b) Reflect the image B in the mirror line m_2. Label the image C.

Describe the single transformation which would map L-shape A to L-shape C.

Answer

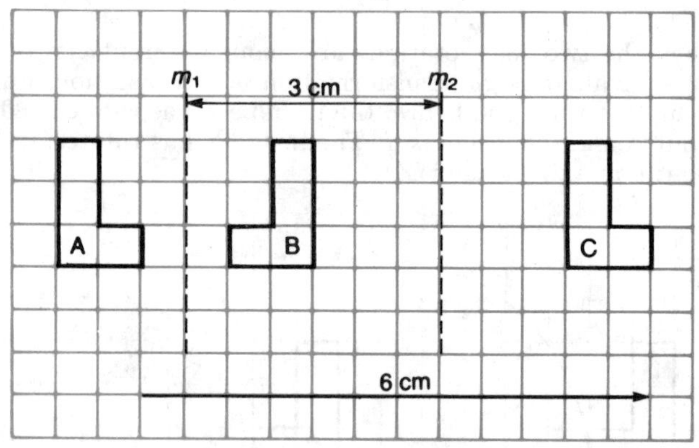

On the diagram, the single transformation A→C is a translation. The translation is for a distance of 6 cm, in a direction perpendicular to the mirror lines.

Two enlargements

An **enlargement followed by an enlargement** is equivalent to a single **enlargement**. To describe this enlargement you must give the scale factor and centre of enlargement. The scale factor of this single enlargement is equal to the product of the two scale factors used.

When the two enlargements are about the *same* centre, the equivalent enlargement is about the *same* centre.

When the two enlargements are about *different* centres, the equivalent enlargement is about a *third* centre. You will have to find this centre by drawing.

Question

On the following grid, draw triangle T whose vertices are (4, 4), (8, 4) and (4, 10).

(a) Using a scale factor of $-\frac{1}{2}$ and centre (0, 0) enlarge triangle T to form shape S.

(b) Using a scale factor of -1 and centre (0, 0) enlarge shape S to form shape R.

What is the single transformation which would map T on to R?

Answer

On the diagram at the top of the next column, the single transformation T→R is an enlargement.

The scale factor of the enlargement $=(-\frac{1}{2})(-1)$
$=+\frac{1}{2}$

The centre of the enlargement is (0, 0).

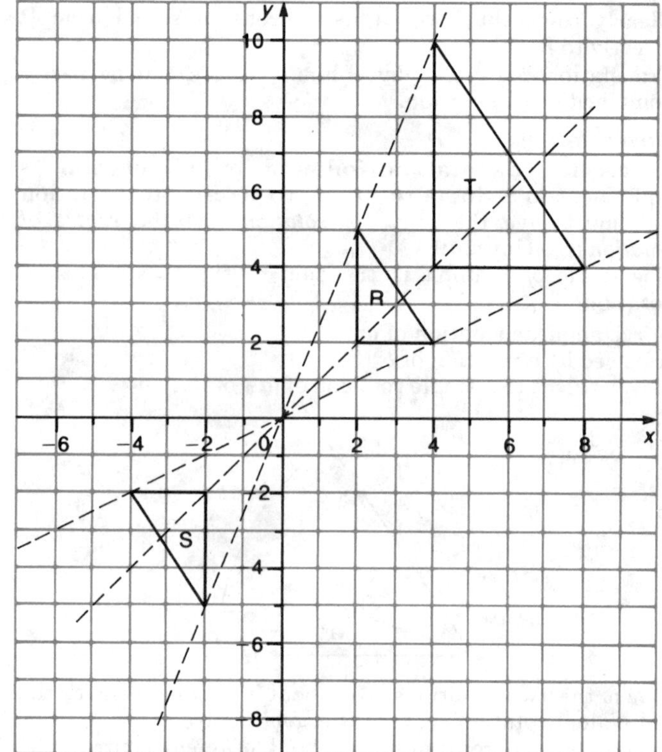

3.6 Circle measure

ARC LENGTH

An **arc** is part of a circle. So the length of an arc is a *fraction* of the circumference of a circle.

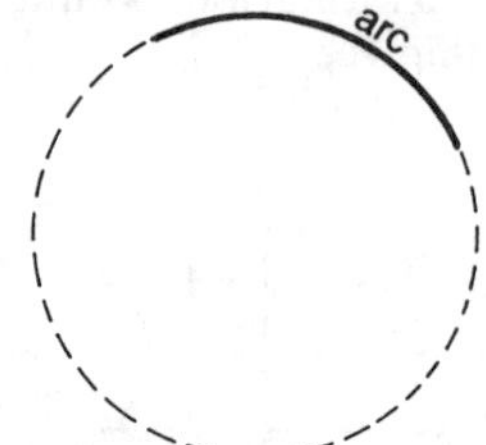

The size of this fraction can be found from the angle the arc subtends at the centre of the circle. For example,

the length of arc AB $=\frac{1}{4}$ of the circumference

since 90° is a quarter of 360° (a full turn) or

$$\frac{90°}{360°}=\frac{1}{4}$$

A
90°
O
B
360°

This arc XY subtends an angle of $\theta°$ at O the centre of the circle.

So arc length XY

$=\frac{\theta}{360}$ of the circumference.

The radius of the circle is r.

So the circumference $=2\pi r$

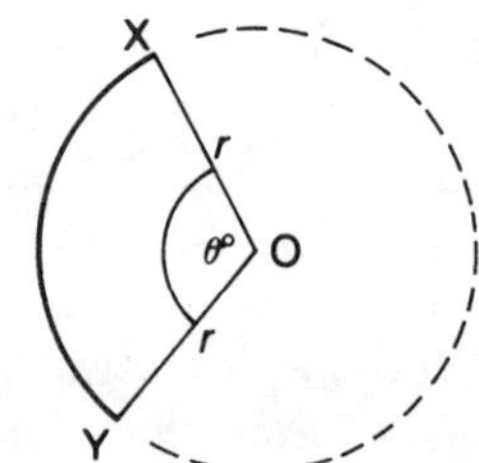

From this comes the general formula:

$$\text{arc length XY} = \frac{\theta}{360} \times \text{circumference}$$
$$= \frac{\theta}{360} \times 2\pi r$$

Question

The diagram shows a piece of wire used in the frame of a lampshade. It is made from the major arc AB of the circle centre O and the two radii OA and OB.
The marked angle AOB = 30° and the radius of the circle is 5 cm.

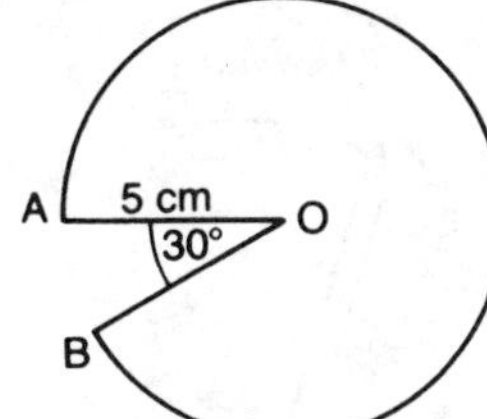

Calculate:

(a) the length of the major arc AB,

(b) the total length of the wire.

Give both answers correct to 3 significant figures. Take $\pi = 3.14$.

Answer

(a) The major arc AB subtends an angle of
(360° − 30°) = 330°

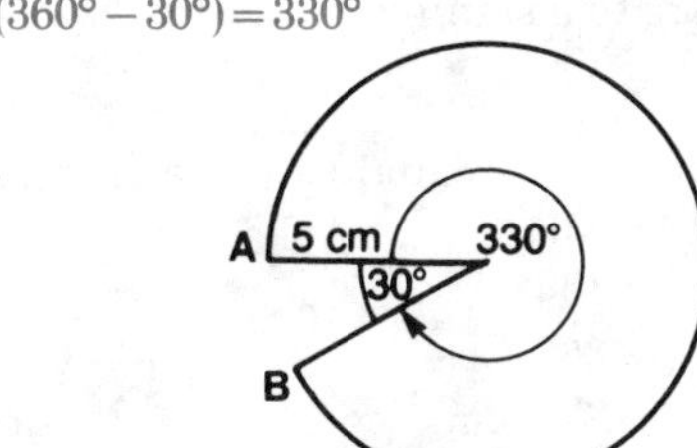

$$\text{Major arc length AB} = \frac{330}{360} \text{ of the circumference}$$
$$= \frac{330}{360} \times 2\pi r$$
$$= \frac{330}{360} \times 2 \times 3.14 \times 5 \text{ cm}$$

= 28.8 cm (to 3 s.f.)

Display: 28.78333333

(b) The wire is made up of the arc and the two radii.

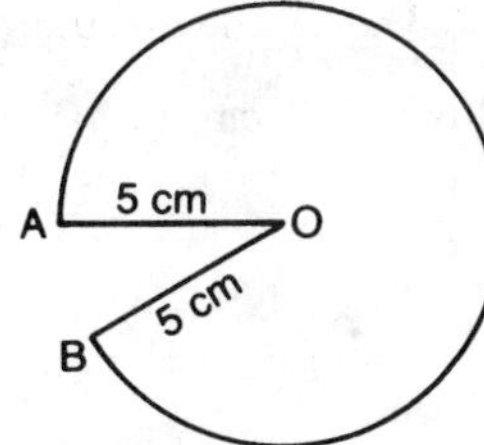

Total length of the wire
= major arc length AB + radius + radius
= 28.8 cm + 5 cm + 5 cm
= 38.8 cm (to 3 s.f.)

You can find the angle subtended at the centre by an arc if you know the length of the arc and either the radius or circumference of the circle. Start with the formula

$$\text{arc length} = \frac{\theta}{360} \times \text{circumference}$$

This can be arranged to give

$$\theta = \frac{\text{arc length}}{\text{circumference}} \times 360°$$

This shows that θ is a fraction of 360°. The fraction is given by

$$\frac{\text{arc length}}{\text{circumference}}$$

SECTOR AREA

A **sector** is an **area** inside a circle. The area of a sector is a fraction of the area inside a circle.

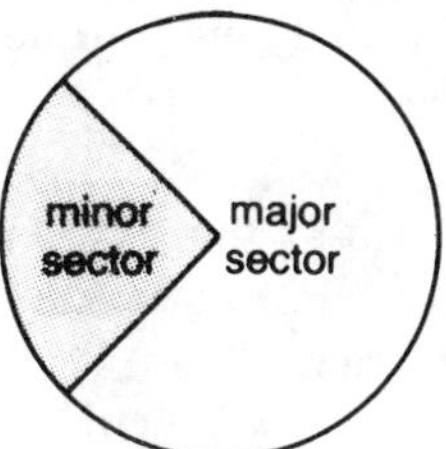

The size of this fraction depends on the size of the angle at the centre of the circle. For example, the area of shaded sector AOB
= $\frac{1}{2}$ of the area inside the circle since 180° is half of 360°
or

$$\frac{180°}{360°} = \frac{1}{2}$$

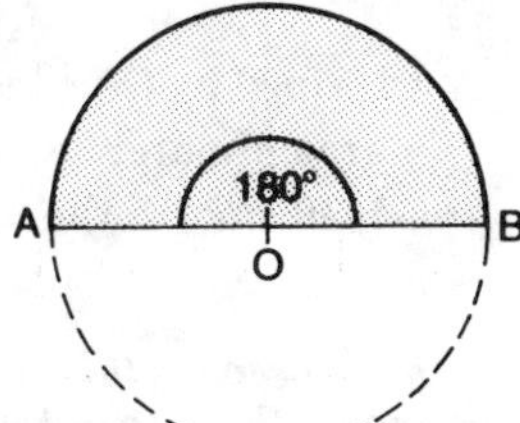

This shaded sector XOY has an angle θ at the centre.

So the sector area XOY $= \frac{\theta}{360}$ of the area inside the circle.

The radius of the circle is r.

So the area inside the circle $= \pi r^2$.

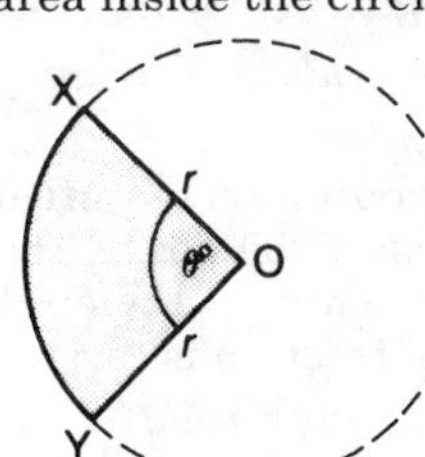

From this comes the general formula

$$\text{sector area XOY} = \frac{\theta}{360} \times \text{area inside circle}$$
$$= \frac{\theta}{360} \times \pi r^2$$

Question

The label for the lid of a box of Brie cheese is a sector of angle 40° and radius 15 cm as in the diagram.

Calculate the area of the label. (Take $\pi = 3.14$.)

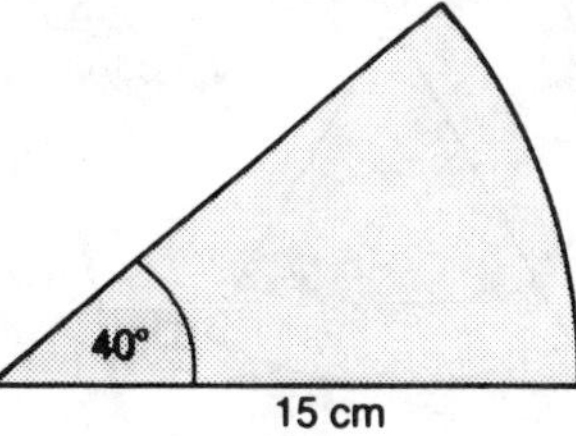

Answer

$$\text{Area of the sector} = \frac{40°}{360°} \text{ of the area inside the circle}$$
$$= \frac{40}{360} \times \pi r^2$$
$$= \frac{40}{360} \times 3.14 \times 15 \times 15 \text{ cm}^2$$
$$= 78.5 \text{ cm}^2$$

Question

A windscreen wiper has a rotating arm 40 cm long. The rubber blade is fixed to the outer 30 cm of the arm. The arm rotates through an angle of 110°.

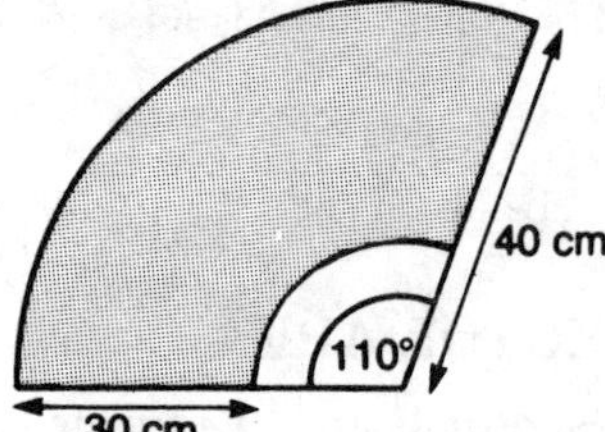

Find the area of the windscreen wiped by the rubber blade. Use $\pi = 3.142$ and give your answer to the nearest square centimetre.

Answer

The wanted area is the difference between two sector areas.

The radius of the inner sector = 40 cm − 30 cm = 10 cm

The area of the inner sector $= \frac{110}{360} \times 3.142 \times 10^2\ \text{cm}^2$ C

Display: 96.00555555

The area of the outer sector $= \frac{110}{360} \times 3.142 \times 40^2\ \text{cm}^2$ C

Display: 1536.088888

Area wiped by the blade
= area of outer sector − area of inner sector
$= 1440\ \text{cm}^2$ (to the nearest cm^2) C

Display: 1440.083333

**One way to do this on your calculator: calculate the area of the inner sector first and store it in the memory, then calculate the area of the outer sector and subtract the inner area (recalled from the memory). If your calculator has an* M− *key, then try to use it for this calculation*

If you know the area of a sector and either the radius or area of the circle, then you can find the sector angle θ at the centre of the circle. θ is a fraction of 360° (a full turn). The fraction is given by

$$\frac{\text{sector area}}{\text{area of circle}}$$

So $\theta = \dfrac{\text{sector area}}{\text{area of circle}} \times 360°$

You can also obtain this formula by rearranging the formula for the sector area.

CONES FROM SECTORS

The **sector** AOB can be made into a **cone**. Join OA to OB, edge to edge without overlapping.

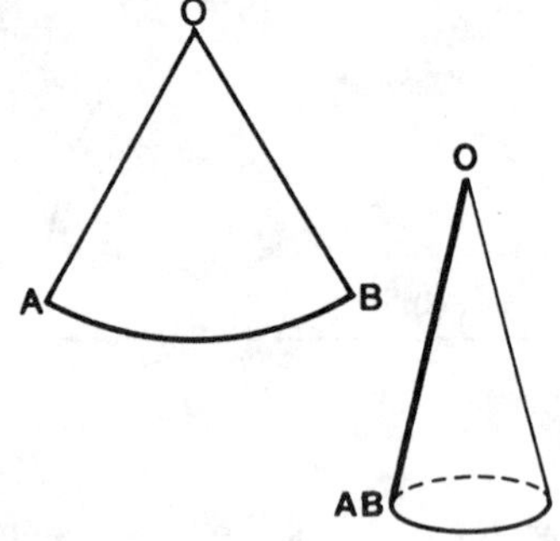

The **area** of the sector is the **area of the curved surface** of the cone.

The **radius** of the sector (OA = OB) is the **slant height** of the cone.

The **arc length** AB is the **circumference of the circular base** of the cone.

From these facts you can find the radius and perpendicular height of the cone.

Question

Toni makes a cone out of a circular piece of card of radius 10 cm. She cuts the minor sector XOY, with angle XOY = 135°, out of the card. Then she sticks the radii OX and OY of this sector edge to edge to make a conical surface.

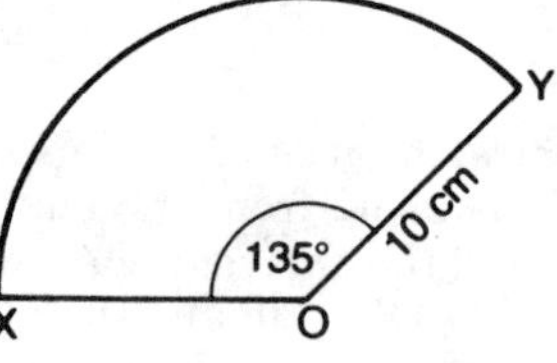

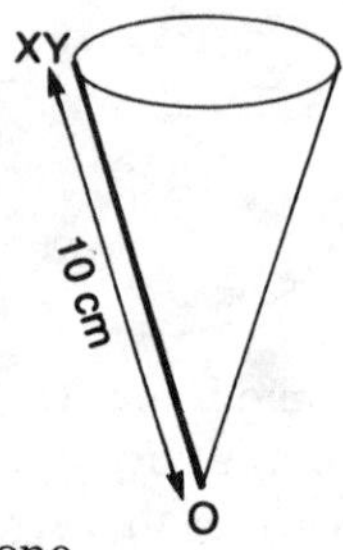

Calculate for the cone
(a) the circumference of its base in terms of π,
(b) the base radius,
(c) the perpendicular height.
Give your answers to 3 significant figures.

Answer

(a) The arc length XY is equal to the circumference of the base of the cone.

Arc length XY $= \frac{135}{360} \times 2 \times \pi \times 10$ cm C
$= 7.5\pi$ cm

So the circumference of the cone's base $= 7.5\pi$ cm (in terms of π).

(b) Let the radius of the cone's base be r cm.

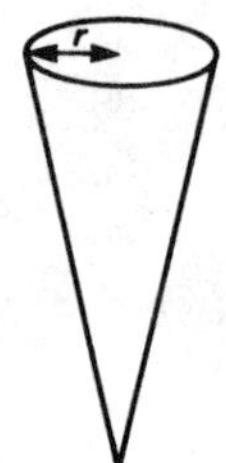

The circumference of the cone's base $= 2\pi r$.
But from (a) this is 7.5π cm.
So $2\pi r = 7.5\pi$ cm

Divide by 2π $\quad r = \frac{7.5\pi}{2\pi}$ cm C
$= 3.75$ cm

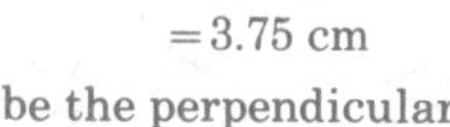

(c) Let h cm be the perpendicular height of the cone.

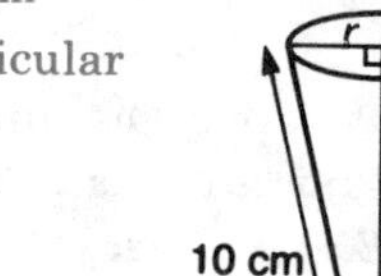

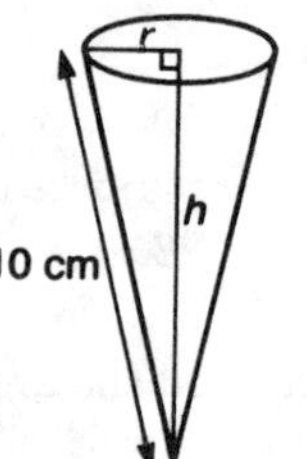

By Pythagoras' theorem:
$h^2 = 10^2 - 3.75^2$

Display: 85.9375

$h = \sqrt{h^2}$
$= 9.27$ cm (to 3 s.f.) **Display:** 9.270248108

SEGMENT AREA

The **area** of a **minor segment** can be found by working out the *difference* between the areas of a minor sector and an isosceles triangle.

Area of this shaded minor segment AB
= minor sector area AOB − triangle area AOB

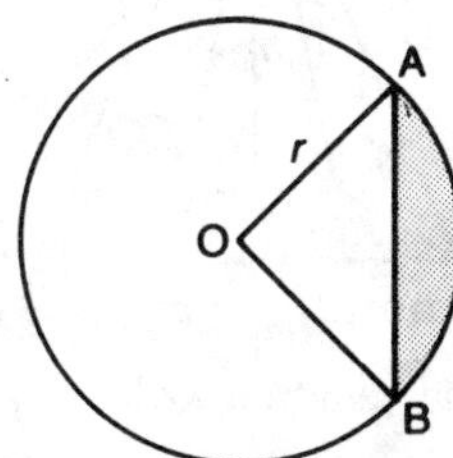

The **area** of a **major segment** can be found by working out the *sum* of the areas of a major sector and an isosceles triangle.

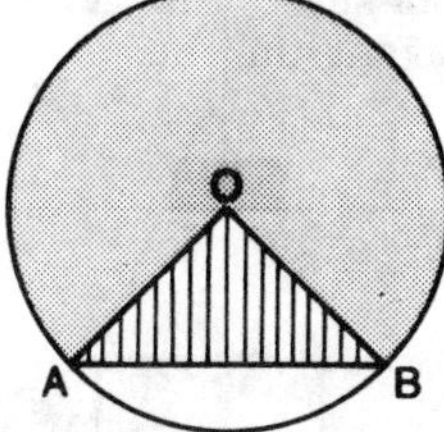

Area of this shaded **major** segment AB
= major sector area AOB + triangle area AOB

In segment area problems it is usually easier to use the formula $\frac{1}{2}ab \sin C$ for the area of the triangle (see Unit 3.27).

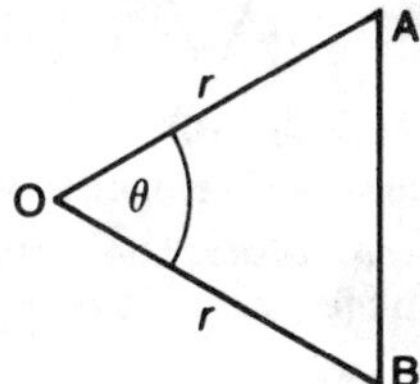

The a and b in this formula are both equal to r (the radius). The angle $C = \theta$.

So area of triangle AOB $= \frac{1}{2}r^2 \sin \theta$.

Question

In the diagram, O is the centre of a circle radius 8 cm. Find the area of the shaded segment XY, to 2 significant figures. (Take $\pi = 3.14$.)

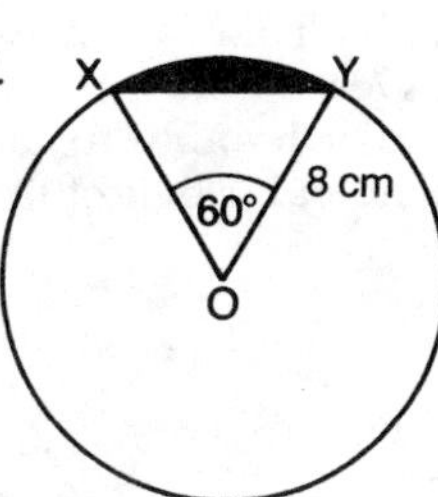

Answer

Area of sector XOY $= \frac{60}{360} \times$ area inside the circle

$= \frac{60}{360} \times \pi r^2$

$= \frac{60}{360} \times 3.14 \times 8 \times 8 \text{ cm}^2$ [C]

Display: 33.49333333

Area of triangle XOY $= \frac{1}{2}r^2 \sin \theta$ [C]

$= \frac{1}{2} \times 8 \times 8 \times \sin 60° \text{ cm}^2$

Display: 27.71281292

Area of minor segment XY
= area of minor sector XOY − area of triangle XOY [C]
$= 5.8 \text{ cm}^2$ (to 2 s.f.) **Display:** 5.78052041

**Here is one of the easiest ways to do this on your calculator: first calculate the area of the triangle and store it in the memory, then calculate the sector area and subtract the triangle area (recalled from the memory)*

3.7 Surface area and volume

The **surface area** and **volume** of some solids have been dealt with already in earlier units. They are

cuboid surface area (Unit 1.53), volume (Unit 1.54),
cylinder surface area (Unit 2.21), volume (Unit 2.22),
prism volume (Unit 2.22).

In this unit are the other surface areas and volumes you should know how to find.

Remember When calculating areas and volumes all the measurements must be in the same unit. Change any unit(s) first if you need to.

Always give the correct unit in your answer:

square units for area, e.g. mm², cm², m²,
cubic units for volume, e.g. mm³, cm³, m³.

Nets of most of the solids described in this unit are given. Use these nets to help you to understand how to find each surface area.

PRISM

A **prism** is a solid with uniform cross-section (see Unit 2.22). The net of a prism shows that its **surface** is made up of 2 equal 'ends' (the cross-section) and a rectangle.

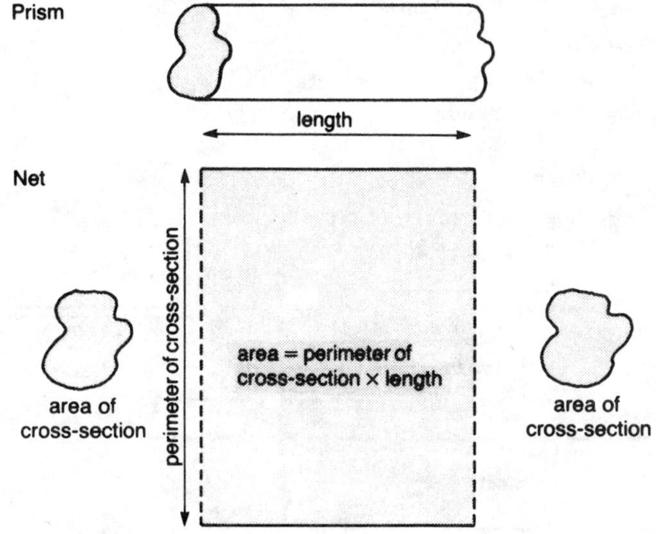

Surface area of a prism
= (2 × area of cross-section)
+ (perimeter of cross-section × length)

Question

A prism of length 15 cm has a cross-section of area 6 cm² and perimeter 12 cm. What is its surface area?

Answer

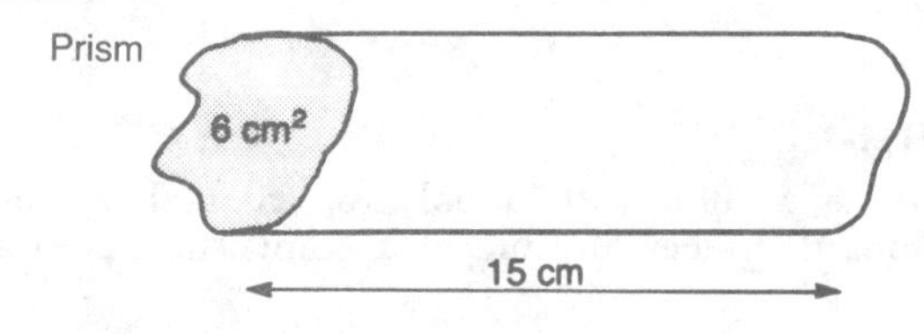

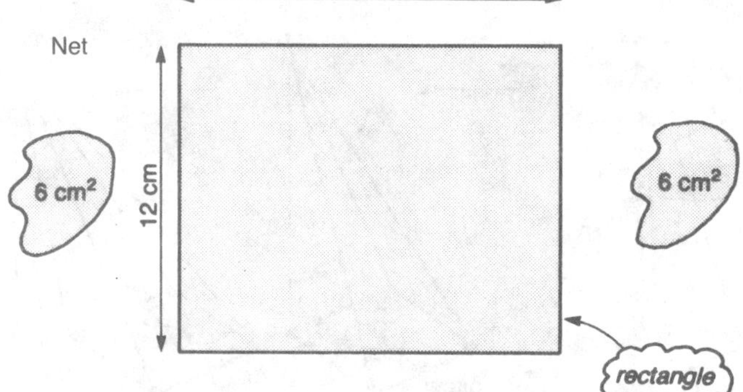

Surface area of prism
$=(2\times 6\text{ cm}^2)+(12\text{ cm}\times 15\text{ cm})$
$=\quad 12\text{ cm}^2 \quad + \quad 180\text{ cm}^2$
$=\ 192\text{ cm}^2$

The cross-section of the prism may be a shape whose area and perimeter you have to *calculate*. The easiest shapes to deal with are polygons, e.g. triangles, parallelograms, trapeziums. Their perimeters and areas are calculated in earlier units (see units 1.51 and 2.21).

Question

A wooden kerb ramp for a wheelchair is a triangular prism as shown in the diagram.
What is its surface area, in cm²?

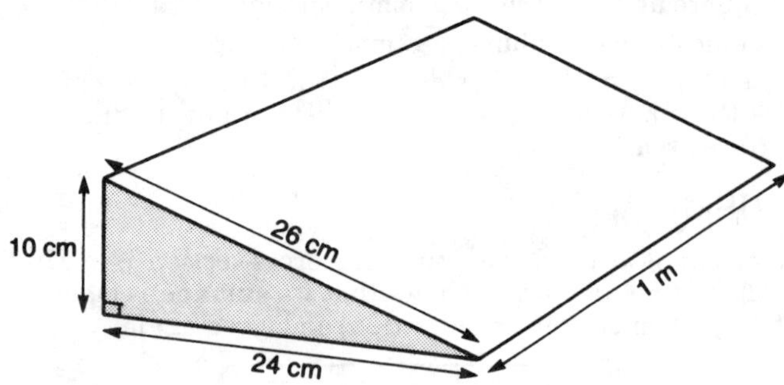

Answer

Area of triangular cross-section
$=\frac{1}{2}(\text{base}\times\text{height})$
$=\frac{1}{2}(24\text{ cm}\times 10\text{ cm})$
$=120\text{ cm}^2$

Perimeter of triangular cross-section
$=10\text{ cm}+24\text{ cm}+26\text{ cm}$
$=60\text{ cm}$
Length of prism $=1\text{ m}=100\text{ cm}$

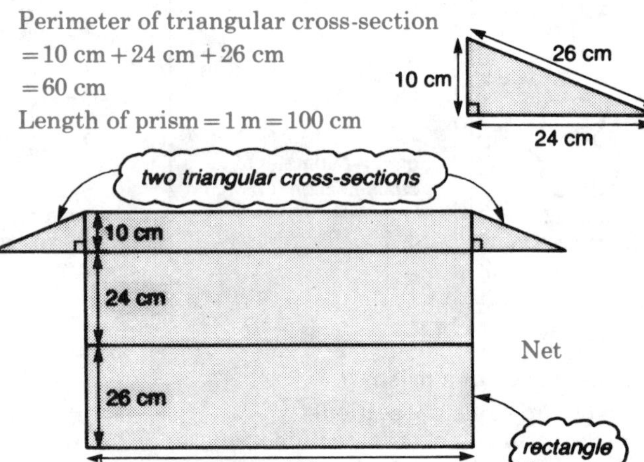

Surface area of triangular prism
$=(2\times 120\text{ cm}^2)+(60\text{ cm}\times 100\text{ cm})$
$=240\text{ cm}^2 \quad + \quad 6000\text{ cm}^2$
$=6240\text{ cm}^2$

PYRAMID

A **pyramid** is a solid with a polygon as its base and sloping triangular faces meeting at a point (the **apex**) at the top.

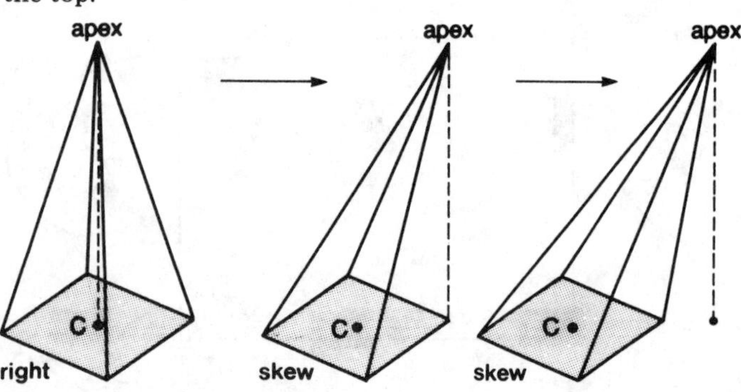

Pyramids can be **right** or **skew**. In a right pyramid, the apex (top) is *directly over the centre of the base*, in a skew pyramid it is not. Right pyramids are often just called pyramids.

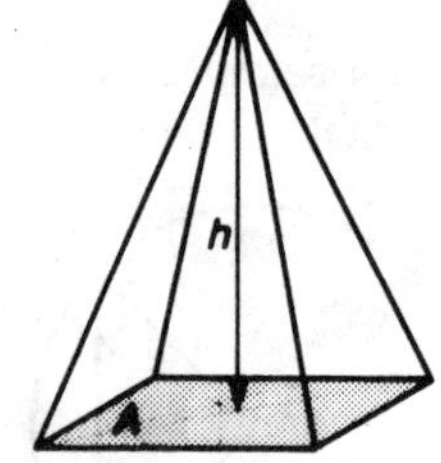

Volume of any pyramid
$=\frac{1}{3}\times(\text{base area})\times(\text{perpendicular height})$
$=\frac{1}{3}Ah$

The net of a pyramid shows that its surface is made up of a polygon base and triangular faces.

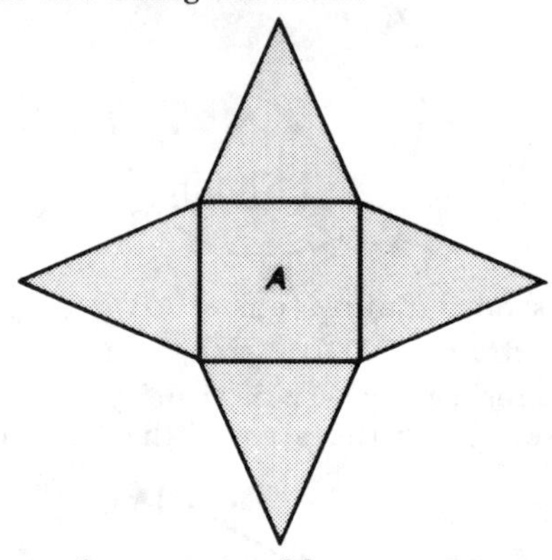

Surface area of any pyramid
=(area of polygon base)+(areas of triangular faces)

You may have to *calculate* the areas of the base and triangular faces. These calculations are easier to do for right pyramids.
In a right pyramid, all the sloping edges are equal in length. So each sloping triangular face is an isosceles triangle. This fact may help you to find the areas of the triangles.
You may be able to use Pythagoras' theorem to find the perpendicular height of each triangle.

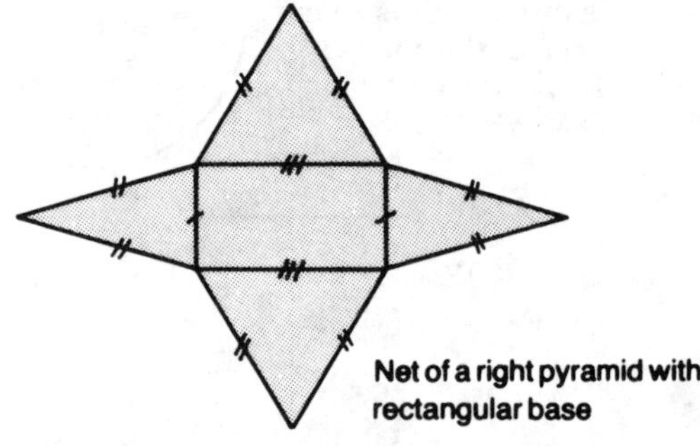
Net of a right pyramid with rectangular base

If the right pyramid has a regular polygon as its base, then all the sloping faces are **congruent isosceles triangles**. So they have the same area.

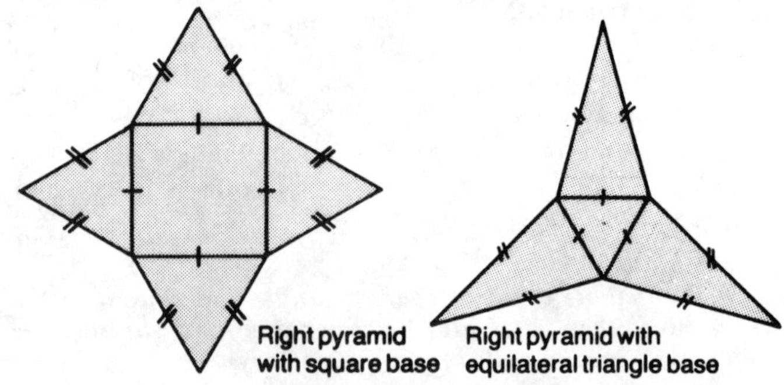
Right pyramid with square base

Right pyramid with equilateral triangle base

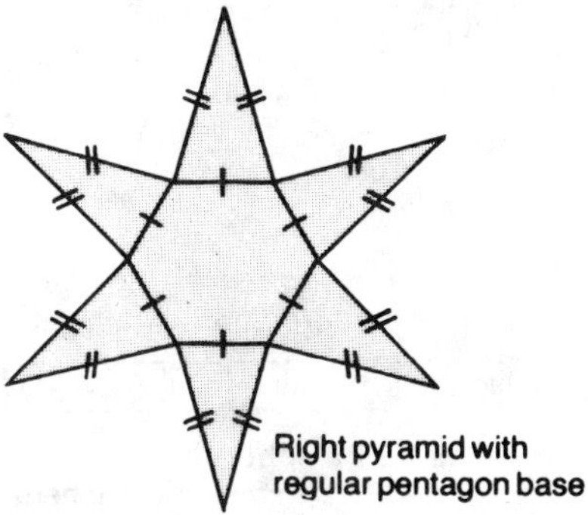

In a skew pyramid, only matching sloping edges are equal in length.

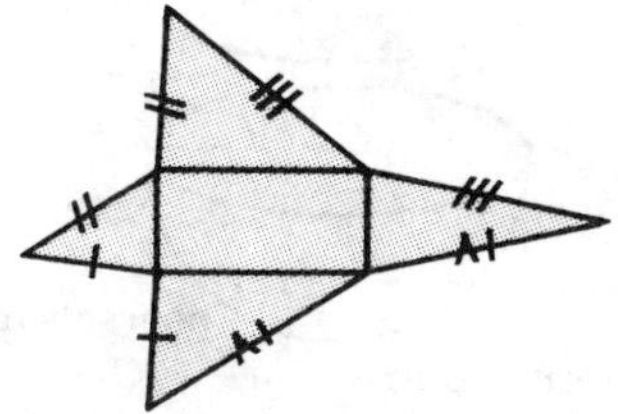

Question

Part of a plastic toy is a right square-based pyramid. It has the dimensions shown on the diagram.

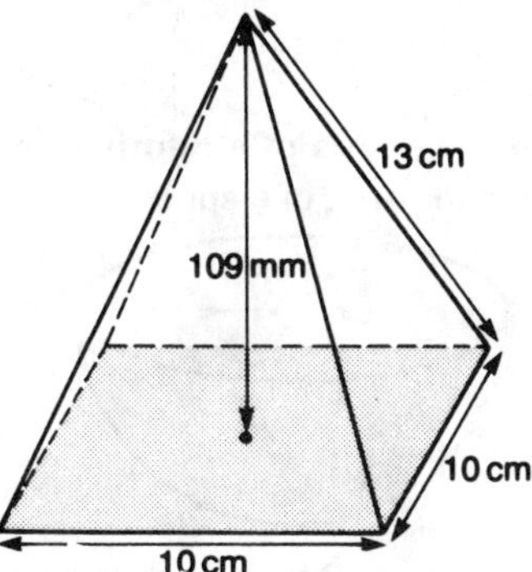

Calculate

(a) the volume of the pyramid (to the nearest cm^3),

(b) the surface area of the pyramid.

Answer

(a) The base is a square of side 10 cm.

Area of base square $= 10 \text{ cm} \times 10 \text{ cm}$
$= 100 \text{ cm}^2$

The perpendicular height $= 109 \text{ mm} = 10.9 \text{ cm}$

Volume of pyramid

$= \frac{1}{3} \times (\text{base area}) \times (\text{perpendicular height})$

$= \frac{1}{3} \times 100 \text{ cm}^2 \times 10.9 \text{ cm}$

$= 363 \text{ cm}^3$ (to nearest cm^3)

(b) Net of pyramid

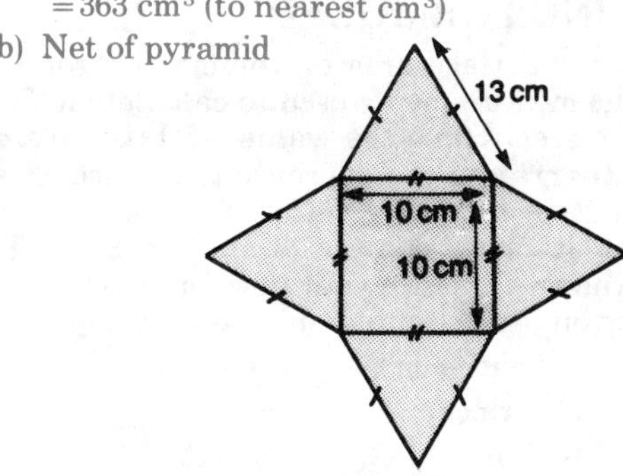

This net shows that the surface area is made up of a square base and four congruent isosceles triangles.

By Pythagoras' theorem (or Pythagorean triple: 5,12,13) the height of each triangle is 12 cm.

Area of triangular face

$= \frac{1}{2}(\text{base} \times \text{height})$

$= \frac{1}{2}(10 \text{ cm} \times 12 \text{ cm})$

$= 60 \text{ cm}^2$

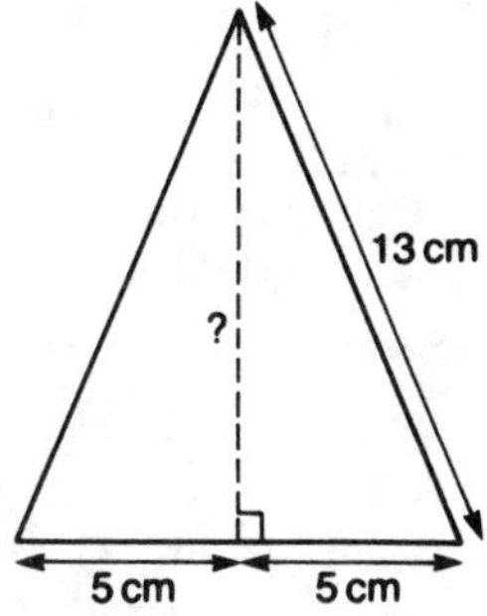

Surface area of right square-based pyramid

$= (\text{area of square base}) + (4 \times \text{area of triangular face})$

$= 100 \text{ cm}^2 + (4 \times 60) \text{ cm}^2$

$= 100 \text{ cm}^2 + 240 \text{ cm}^2$

$= 340 \text{ cm}^2$

CONE

A **circular cone** is a solid which has a circular base and tapers to a point (the **apex**) at the top. It is often thought of as a *special pyramid* with a circle at its base.

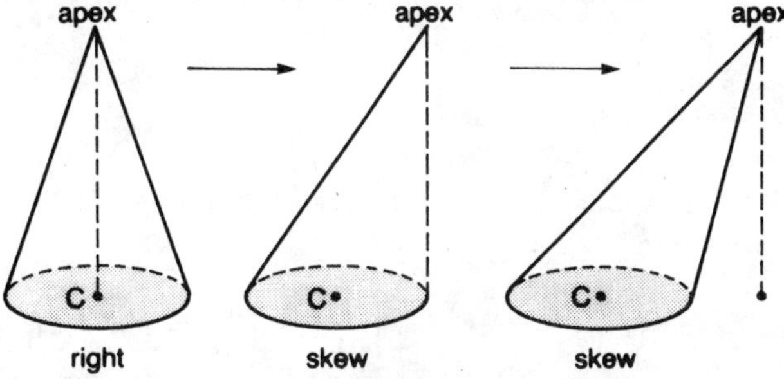

Like pyramids, cones can be **right** or **skew**. A right circular cone has its apex directly above the centre of the circle. Right circular cones are often just called cones.

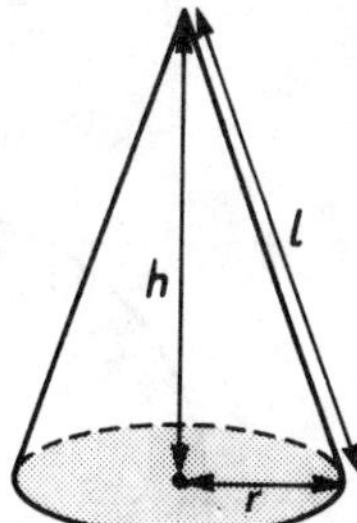

Volume of a cone

$= \frac{1}{3} \times (\text{area of circular base}) \times (\text{perpendicular height})$

$= \frac{1}{3}\pi r^2 h$

where r is the radius of the base and h is the perpendicular height.

The **surface** of a cone is made up of a circular base and the curved surface (a sector of a circle).

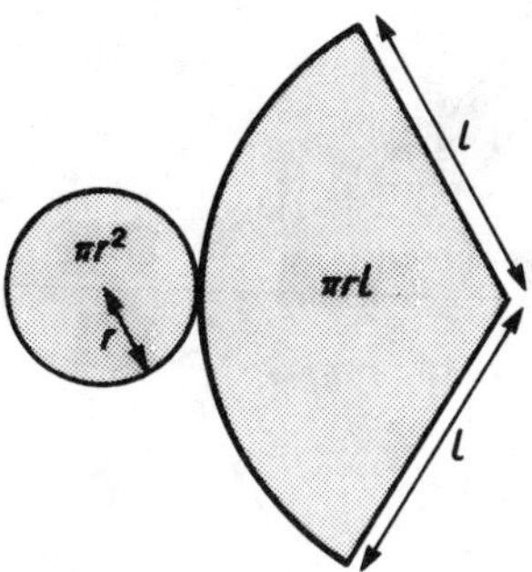

Surface area of a cone

$= (\text{area of circular base}) + (\text{area of curved surface})$

$= \pi r^2 + \pi r l$ where r is the radius of the base and l is the slant length or slant height.

Question

In a modern set of chess pieces each pawn is a cone of radius 7 mm, height 24 mm and slant height 2.5 cm. Calculate the volume and surface area of a pawn in this chess set. (Take π as $\frac{22}{7}$.)

Answer

radius $r = 7$ mm

height $h = 24$ mm

slant height $l = 2.5$ cm $= 25$ mm

Write all measurements in same unit

Volume of the cone

$$= \frac{1}{3} \times (\text{area of circular base}) \times \text{perpendicular height}$$

$$= \frac{1}{3}\pi r^2 h$$

$$= \frac{1}{3} \times \frac{22}{7} \times 7^2 \times 24 \text{ mm}^3$$

$$= \frac{1}{3} \times \frac{22}{7} \times 7 \times 7 \times 24 \text{ mm}^3$$

$$= 1232 \text{ mm}^3$$

Surface area of the cone

$$= (\text{area of circular base}) + (\text{area of curved surface})$$

$$= \pi r^2 + \pi r l$$

$$= \left(\frac{22}{7} \times 7^2 \text{ mm}^2\right) + \left(\frac{22}{7} \times 7 \times 25 \text{ mm}^2\right)$$

$$= \left(\frac{22}{7} \times 7 \times 7 \text{ mm}^2\right) + \left(\frac{22}{7} \times 7 \times 25 \text{ mm}^2\right)$$

$$= 154 \text{ mm}^2 + 550 \text{ mm}^2$$

$$= 704 \text{ mm}^2$$

SPHERE

Volume of a sphere

$$= \frac{4}{3} \times \pi \times (\text{radius})^3$$

$$= \frac{4}{3}\pi r^3$$

Surface area of a sphere

$$= 4 \times \pi \times (\text{radius})^2$$

$$= 4\pi r^2$$

Question

A snooker ball is a sphere with diameter 5.24 cm. Calculate its volume, in cm³, and surface area, in cm². Use $\pi = 3.14$ and give each answer correct to 2 decimal places.

Answer

Diameter of ball $= 5.24$ cm

Radius of ball $r = (5.24 \div 2)$ cm $= 2.62$ cm

Volume of snooker ball

$$= \frac{4}{3}\pi r^3$$

$$= \frac{4}{3} \times 3.14 \times 2.62^3 \text{ cm}^3$$

$$= 75.30 \text{ cm}^3 \text{ (to 2 d.p.)}$$

Display: 75.29606122

Here is one way to do this working on a calculator. Try it. Then find the best way to do it on your calculator

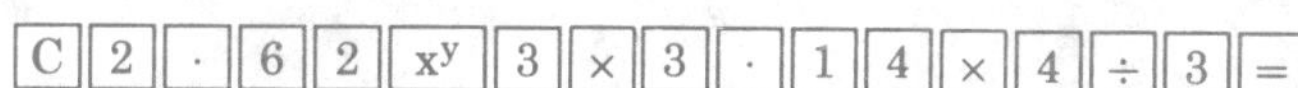

Surface area of snooker ball

$$= 4\pi r^2$$

$$= 4 \times 3.14 \times 2.62^2 \text{ cm}^2$$

$$= 86.22 \text{ cm}^2 \text{ (to 2 d.p.)}$$

Display: 86.216864

Try this way to do this working. Then find the best way to work it out on your calculator

C 4 × 3 . 1 4 × 2 . 6 2 x² =

A **hemisphere** is half a sphere.

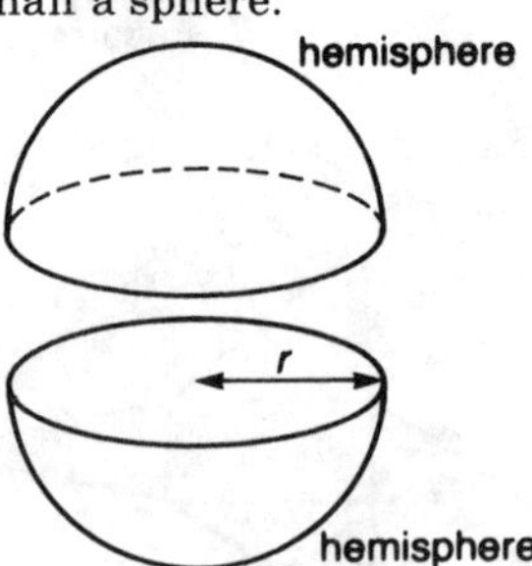

Volume of a hemisphere

$$= \tfrac{1}{2} \text{ of the volume of a sphere}$$

$$= \tfrac{1}{2} \times \frac{4}{3}\pi r^3$$

$$= \frac{2}{3}\pi r^3$$

The **curved surface area of a hemisphere**

$$= \tfrac{1}{2} \text{ of the surface area of a sphere}$$

$$= \tfrac{1}{2} \times 4\pi r^2$$

$$= 2\pi r^2$$

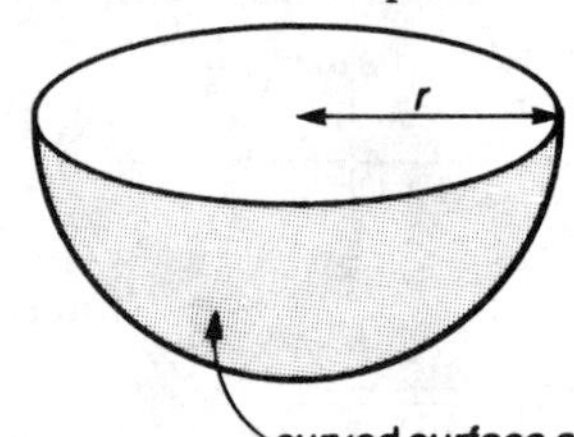

The surface of a *solid* hemisphere is made up of the curved surface of the hemisphere and the circular cross-section.

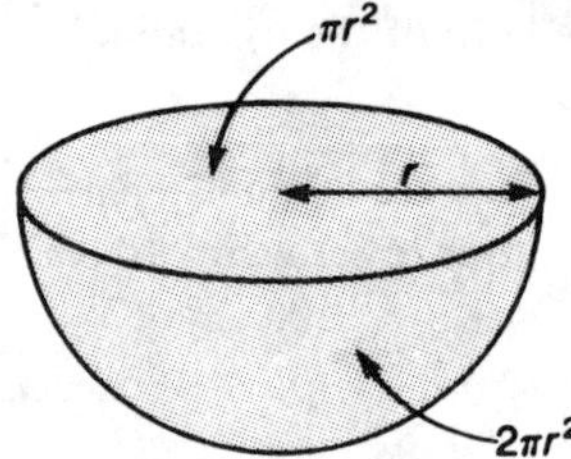

Surface area of a solid hemisphere

$$= \text{curved surface area} + \text{area of circle}$$

$$= 2\pi r^2 + \pi r^2$$

$$= 3\pi r^2$$

REARRANGING FORMULAE

You may know the surface area or volume of a solid and all but one of the measurements used to calculate it. When this happens you can find the value of this unknown measurement. **Rearrange** the appropriate surface area or volume formula so that the letter for the unknown measurement is its new subject (see Unit 3.13). Then substitute the known values in your new formula.

Make sure that you use matching units. For example,

use mm with mm² with mm³,

use cm with cm² with cm³,

use m with m² with m³,

and so on ...

If you are given the capacity of a solid, then remember the relationship between capacity and volume, e.g.

1 litre ≡ 1000 cm³

Question

A hollow sphere was completely filled with 1 litre of water. Calculate the internal radius of the sphere in centimetres. Give your answer to 2 significant figures. (Take π as 3.14.)

Answer

The formula for the volume V of a sphere with radius r is

$$V = \frac{4}{3}\pi r^3$$

Rearrange this formula so that r is the subject

$$V = \frac{4}{3}\pi r^3$$

Multiply by 3 $$3V = \overset{1}{\cancel{3}} \times \frac{4\pi r^3}{\underset{1}{\cancel{3}}}$$

Divide by 4π $$\frac{3V}{4\pi} = \frac{\overset{1}{\cancel{4\pi}} r^3}{\underset{1}{\cancel{4\pi}}}$$

Take the cube root $$\sqrt[3]{\frac{3V}{4\pi}} = \sqrt[3]{r^3}$$

$$\sqrt[3]{\frac{3V}{4\pi}} = r$$

Write with r on the LHS $$r = \sqrt[3]{\frac{3V}{4\pi}}$$

The capacity of the sphere $= 1$ litre
So the internal volume $V = 1000\ \text{cm}^3$ *(1 litre = 1000 cm³)*

Using $r = \sqrt[3]{\frac{3V}{4\pi}}$

$$= \sqrt[3]{\frac{3 \times 1000}{4 \times 3.14}}\ \text{cm}$$ *(cm because V is in cm³)* [C]

$= 6.2$ cm (to 2 s.f.) **Display:** [6.20455357]

So the internal radius of the sphere is 6.2 cm (to 2 s.f.).

Here is one way to do this calculation. Try it. Find the best way to do it on your calculator

Work out denominator [C] [4] [×] [3] [·] [1] [4] [=]

Put answer in memory [Min]

Work out numerator divided by answer from memory [3] [0] [0] [0] [÷] [MR] [=]

Find cube root [$x^{1/y}$] [3] [=]

Your root key may be different, e.g. [$\sqrt[x]{y}$]

It may be in the '2nd function' on your calculator. If it is, then you will have to press [2nd F] *or* [INV] *before the root key*

MORE COMPLICATED SOLIDS

Some complicated solids look like simple solids added together …

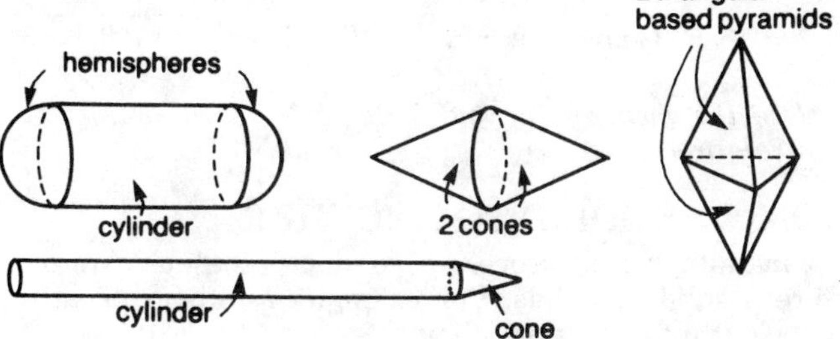

… or simple solids with hole(s) cut out of them.

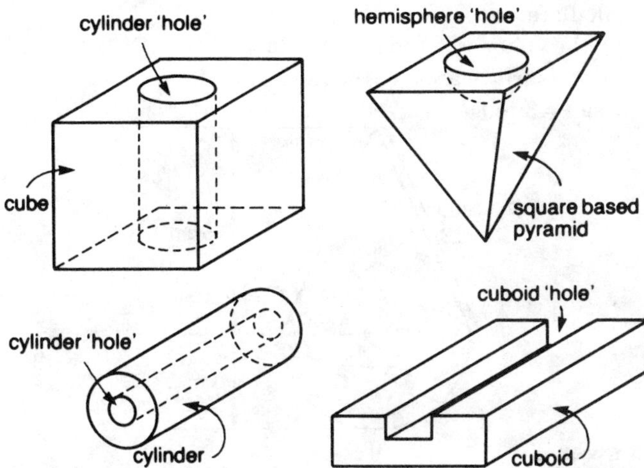

Splitting these complicated solids into simpler solids can help you to find their surface areas and volumes.
Always draw a sketch of the solid. Think carefully about how the surface and/or volume are made.
The volume is usually the *sum* or *difference* of the volumes of the simple solids. For example,
the volume of the material in this pipe
= volume of outer cylinder − volume of inner cylinder

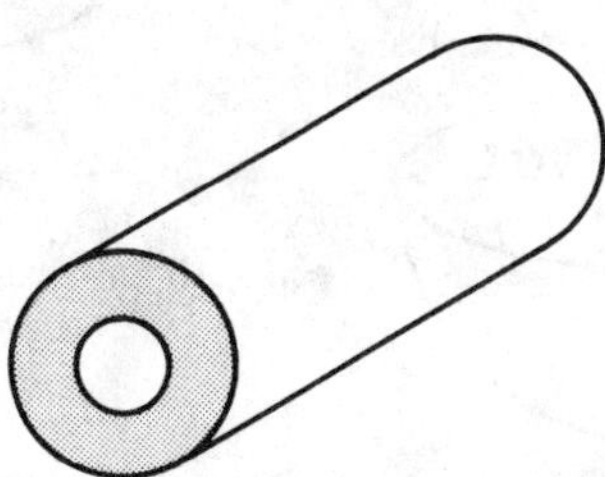

Surface area usually needs more working out. Look carefully for surfaces which are not part of the new surface area.

Some surfaces are 'stuck together'. For example, in this solid the base of the pyramid is stuck to one end face of the prism. So these surfaces are not on the outside of the new solid.

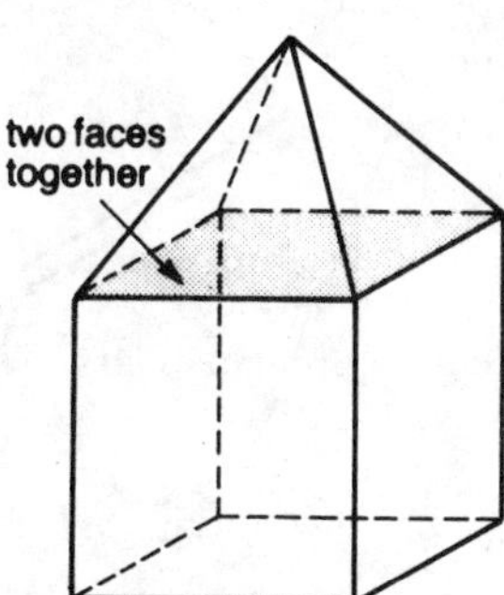

Sometimes a surface is replaced by another. For example, in this solid the base of the cone is replaced by the curved surface of a hemisphere.

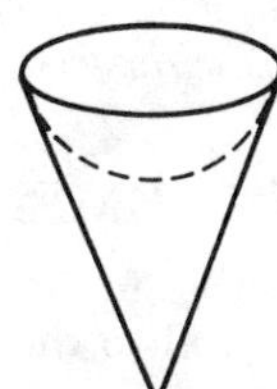

Question

The diagram shows a child's plastic toy. For this toy, calculate

(a) the volume (to the nearest cm^3)

(b) the surface area (to the nearest cm^2).

(Use $\pi = 3.14$.)

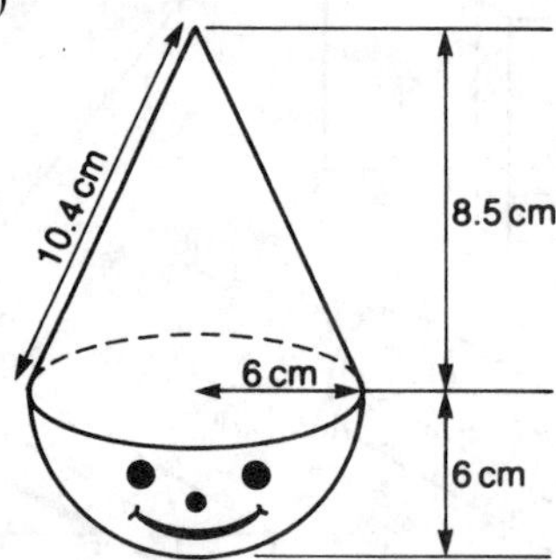

Answer

The toy is 'made of' a cone and a hemisphere.

(a) Volume of cone $= \frac{1}{3}\pi r^2 h$

$= \frac{1}{3} \times 3.14 \times 6^2 \times 8.5 \text{ cm}^3$

$= 320.28 \text{ cm}^3$

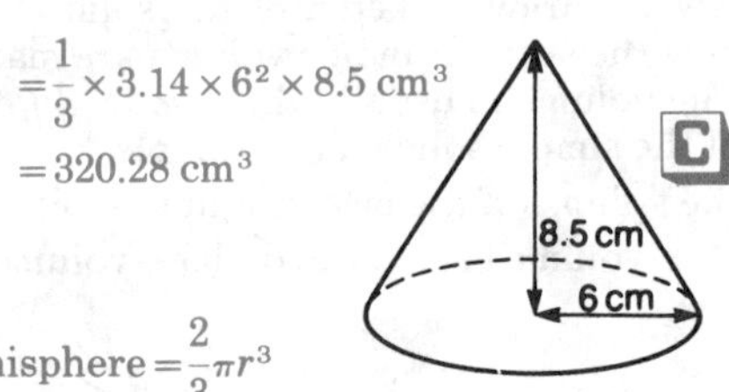

Volume of hemisphere $= \frac{2}{3}\pi r^3$

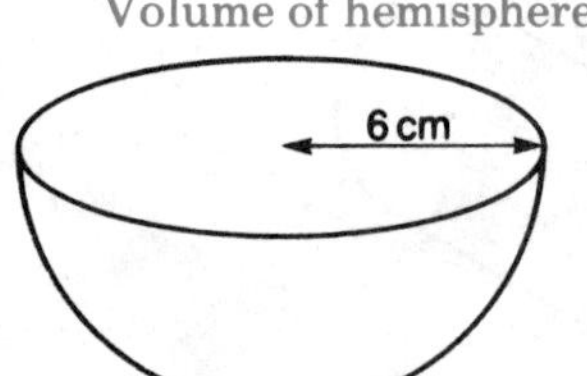

$= \frac{2}{3} \times 3.14 \times 6^3 \text{ cm}^3$

$= 452.16 \text{ cm}^3$

Volume of toy = volume of cone + volume of hemisphere

$= 320.28 \text{ cm}^3 + 452.16 \text{ cm}^3$

$= 772.44 \text{ cm}^3$

$= 772 \text{ cm}^3$ (to nearest cm^3)

(b) Curved surface area of cone

$= \pi r l$

$= 3.14 \times 6 \times 10.4 \text{ cm}^2$

$= 195.936 \text{ cm}^2$

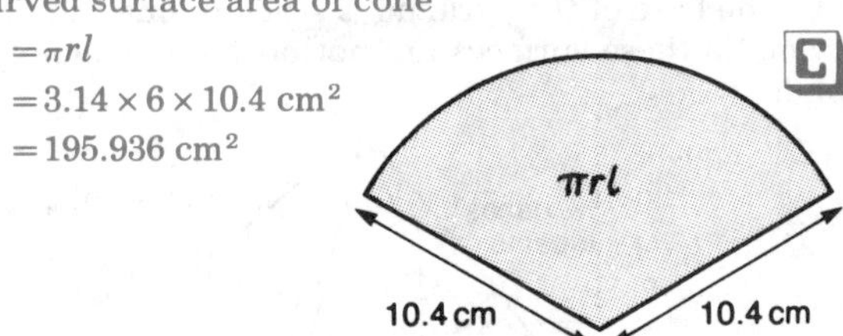

Curved surface area of hemisphere

$= 2\pi r^2$

$= 2 \times 3.14 \times 6^2 \text{ cm}^2$

$= 226.08 \text{ cm}^2$

Total surface area

= curved surface of cone + curved surface of hemisphere

$= 195.936 \text{ cm}^2 + 226.08 \text{ cm}^2$

$= 422.016 \text{ cm}^2$

$= 422 \text{ cm}^2$ (to nearest cm^2)

** Use the memory in your calculator to do these calculations*

VOLUME BY DISPLACEMENT

The volume of a solid can be found by immersing it in a container of water. It is equal to the volume of water that the solid 'lifts up' or displaces.

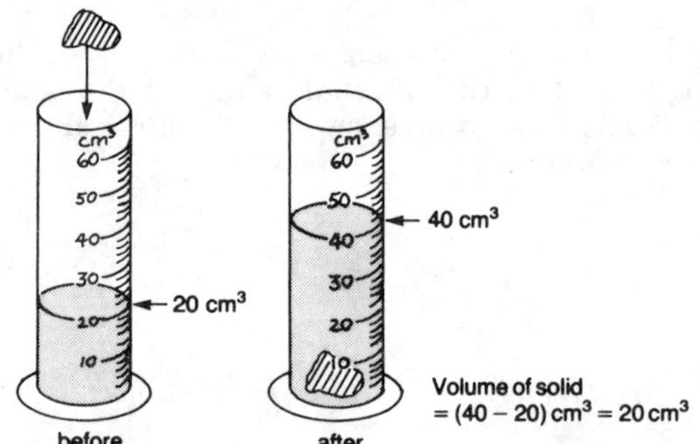

This method is often used in science to find the volume of an irregular solid.

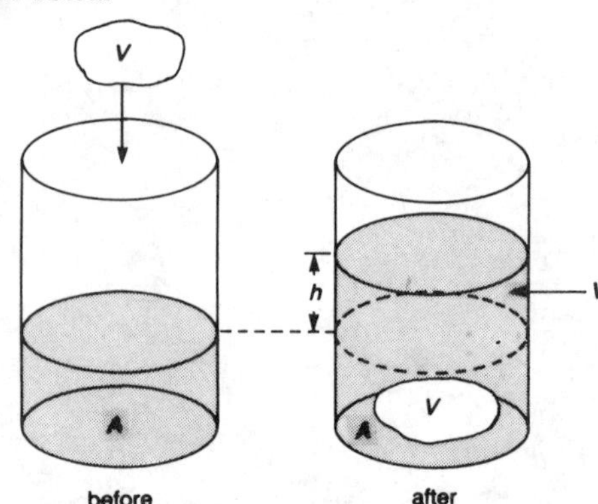

If the container has a uniform cross-section area A and h is the rise in liquid level, then the volume V of the solid is given by:

$V = Ah$

so $h = \frac{V}{A}$ or $V \div A$.

In science the container is usually a cylinder, so the cross-section is a circle.

Question

A cylindrical measuring jar with base radius 4 cm contained water to a depth of 5 cm. In a science experiment Kate gently lowered a metal sphere of radius 3.5 cm into the water. What is the rise in height (to the nearest mm) of the water level in the cylinder? (Take $\pi = 3.14$.)

Answer

Area of circular cross-section of jar

$A = \pi \times 4^2 \text{ cm}^2$

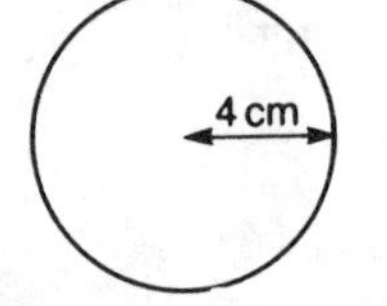

Volume of sphere

$V = \frac{4}{3} \times \pi \times 3.5^3 \text{ cm}^3$

The water rises up inside the jar to form an extra 'cylinder'.

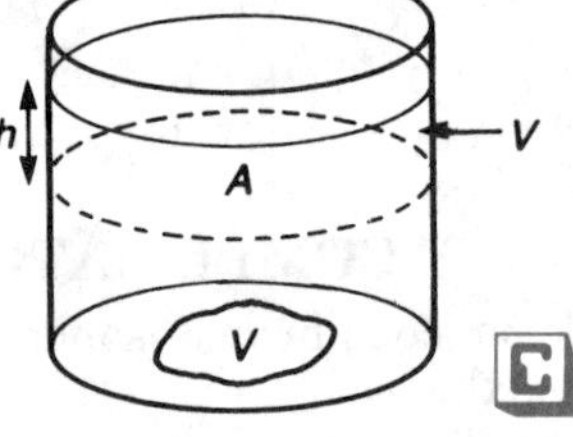

Volume of this 'cylinder' is given by

$V = Ah$

or $h = V \div A$

$= \left(\frac{4}{3} \times \pi \times 3.5^3\right) \div (\pi \times 4^2) \text{ cm}$

$= 3.6 \text{ cm}$ (to nearest mm) **Display:** 3.572916666

** Use the memory in your calculator when doing this calculation*

FROM ONE SOLID TO ANOTHER

In a manufacturing process a solid may be made into a different solid or solids. For example, a cuboid of wood may be cut into cubes or cuboids.

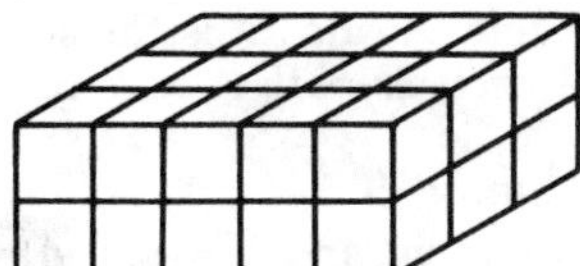

If there is no waste in the process, then the volume of the solids before and after processing is the same.

Question

An ingot of silver is a prism with a trapezium as its cross-section. A silversmith melts down the ingot and recasts the silver into small charms for bracelets. Each charm is a square-based pyramid.

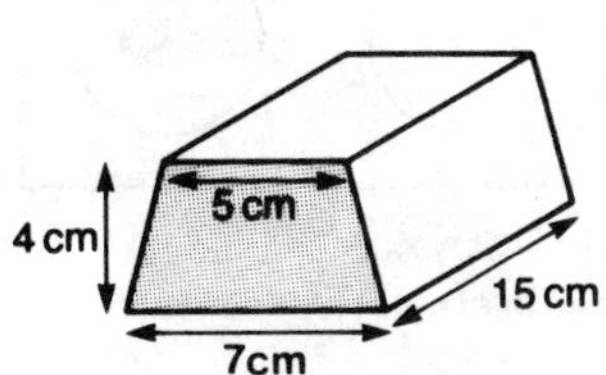

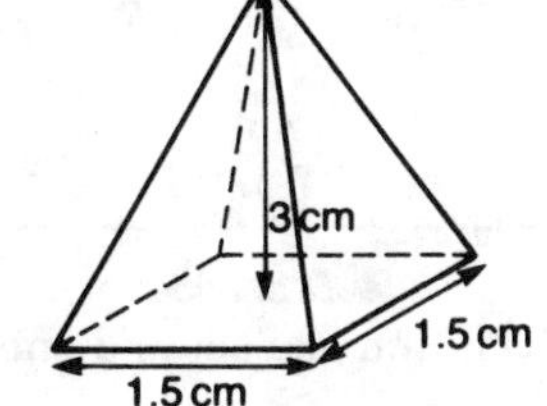

The dimensions of the ingot and charms are given in the diagram.
How many charms can the silversmith cast from the silver ingot?

Answer

Volume of the trapezium prism

$= \text{(area of trapezium cross-section)} \times \text{length}$

$= \left[\frac{1}{2} \times 4\text{ cm} \times (5+7)\text{ cm}\right] \times 15\text{ cm}$

$= \frac{1}{2} \times 4 \times 12 \times 15\text{ cm}^3$

$= 360\text{ cm}^3$

Volume of a square-based pyramid charm

$= \frac{1}{3} \times \text{(base area)} \times \text{(perpendicular height)}$

$= \frac{1}{3} \times (1.5\text{ cm} \times 1.5\text{ cm}) \times 3\text{ cm}$

$= \frac{1}{3} \times 1.5 \times 1.5 \times 3\text{ cm}^3$

$= 2.25\text{ cm}^3$

The number of charms cast

$= \text{volume of ingot} \div \text{volume of one charm}$

$= 360\text{ cm}^3 \div 2.25\text{ cm}^3$

$= 160$

3.8 Sets and symbols

The basic ideas of sets (see Unit 2.23) are given in set notation and illustrated using Venn diagrams in this unit. Problem-solving using sets is also extended to problems involving three sets.

A **set** is a collection of objects called **members** or **elements**. **Curly brackets** or braces { } stand for the words 'the set of'. For example,

$A = \{\text{letters of the alphabet}\}$

means A is the set of the letters of the alphabet.

A set can be **defined** by:

(a) a list of all its members. For example,

$X = \{1, 2, 3, 4, 5\}$.

The order of the members does not matter and each member is listed only once.

(b) a list of the first few members and indicating by three dots that the pattern shown continues. For example,

$N = \{0, 1, 2, 3, 4, \ldots\}$

(c) a description or rule in words which would give the members. For example,

$Z = \{\text{integers}\}$

(d) an algebraic expression (sometimes called 'set-builder' notation). For example,

$S = \{x : x^2 = 7\}$

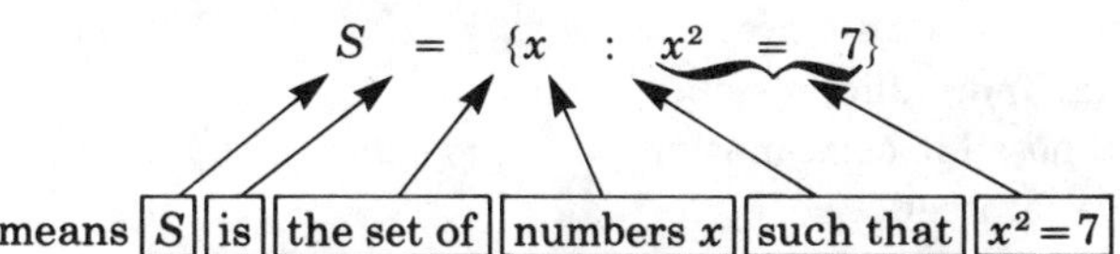

The colon (:) stands for 'such that'.

The symbol $\in$ means 'is a member or element of'

and $\notin$ means 'is *not* a member or element of'.

For example, for $Y = \{\text{even numbers}\}$

$2 \in Y$ i.e. '2 is a member of Y'

and $3 \notin Y$ i.e. '3 is not a member of Y'

The **number of members** in a set A is written as $n(A)$. This number is sometimes called the **cardinal number** or **order** of the set. For example,

for $A = \{\text{April, May, June}\}$

$n(A) = 3$

i.e. A has 3 members.

A **finite set** has a finite number of members. For example,

$F = \{1, 7\}$ is a finite set with two members.

A finite set can have a very large number of members, but the number can be counted and the members listed. For example,

$U = \{\text{states in the USA}\}$ is a finite set with 50 members,

$U = \{\text{Alabama, Arizona, Arkansas, \ldots, Washington}\}$

An **infinite set** has an infinite number of members. It goes on for ever and the members cannot be listed. For example,

$W = \{\text{whole numbers}\}$ is an infinite set.

The **empty** or **null set** has no members. Its symbol is $\varnothing$ or { }. For example,

$\{\text{quadrilaterals with five sides}\} = \varnothing$.

Note: {0} is *not* a null set. It has one member, i.e. 0.

Equal sets have exactly the same members. The order in which they are written does not matter. For example,

{a, b, c} = {b, c, a} = {c, a, b}

because each set has the same members a, b, c.

Equivalent sets have the same number of members. The symbol $\leftrightarrow$ means 'is equivalent to'. For example,

$\{1, 2, 3\} \leftrightarrow \{a, b, c\}$

because each set has three members.

The **universal set** is the set that contains all the possible members being considered. Its symbol is $\mathscr{E}$. For example, in a problem about whole numbers, $\mathscr{E}$ could be {integers}.

On a Venn diagram, the universal set is shown by a rectangle.

In the diagram, the shaded area is $\mathscr{E}$.

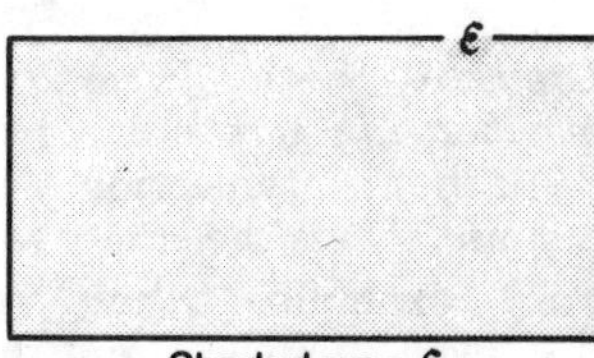

Shaded area ℰ

The **complement** of a set A is the set of members of $\mathscr{E}$ *not* in A. Its symbol is A' (read 'A dash'). For example,

for $\mathscr{E} = \{2, 4, 6, 8, 10\}$

and $A = \{2, 6, 8\}$

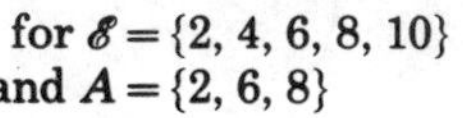

$A' = \{4, 10\}$

In the diagram, the shaded area is A'.

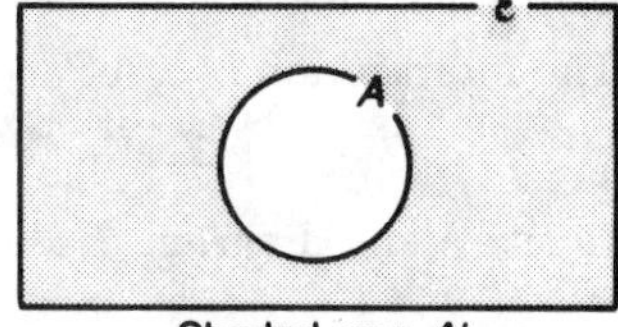

Shaded area A'

SUBSETS

A **subset** is a set whose members all belong to another set.
The symbol $\subset$ means 'is a subset of'.
So $B \subset A$ means 'B is a subset of A',
i.e. every member of set B is also a member of set A.

For example, if $S=\{a, b\}$ and $T=\{a, b, c\}$
then $S \subset T$.

The subsets of a set are:

(**a**) each individual member of the set,
(**b**) all possible combinations of the members,
(**c**) the set itself,
(**d**) the empty set $\varnothing$.

So every set has at least two subsets, the set itself and the empty set $\varnothing$.
The **proper subsets** of a set are all the subsets, *except* the set itself and the empty set $\varnothing$.

For example, the subsets of $X=\{1, 2, 3\}$ are:

$\{1\}, \{2\}, \{3\}$, (individual members)
$\{1, 2\}, \{2, 3\}, \{1, 3\}$, (combinations)
$\{1, 2, 3\}$ and $\varnothing$ (*S* and empty set)

All sets are subsets of a universal set $\mathscr{E}$.

So $A \subset \mathscr{E}$ is drawn as a closed curve *inside* $\mathscr{E}$ on a Venn diagram.

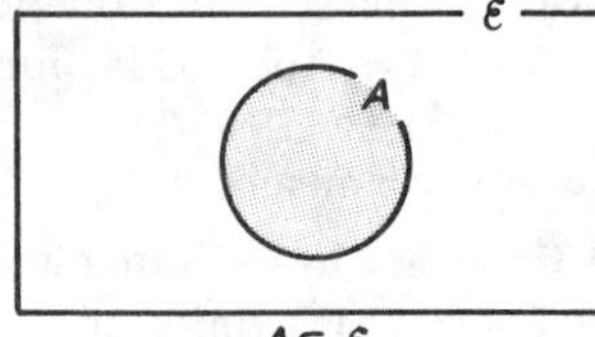

$A \subset \mathscr{E}$

If B is a subset of A, i.e. $B \subset A$, then B is drawn *inside* A on a Venn diagram.

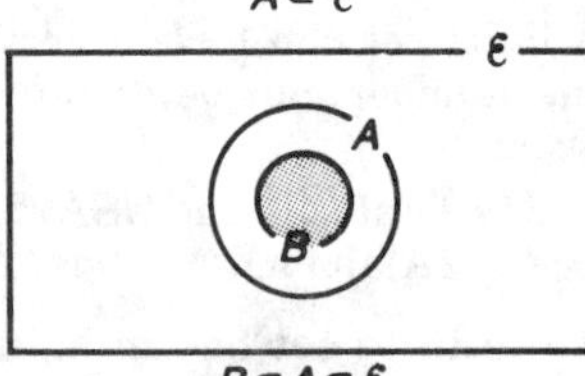

$B \subset A \subset \mathscr{E}$

COMBINATIONS OF SETS

Sets can be combined by the operations **intersection** and **union**. The result is another set.
The **intersection** of two sets, A and B, is the set whose members are *common to both A and B*. The symbol $\cap$ is used for intersection.
For $A \cap B$, read 'A intersect B' or 'A intersection B'.

For example, for $P=\{a, c, f\}$ and $Q=\{b, c, d, f\}$
$P \cap Q=\{c, f\}$

On a Venn diagram, intersecting sets overlap.
The shaded area on this diagram is $A \cap B$.

Intersecting sets

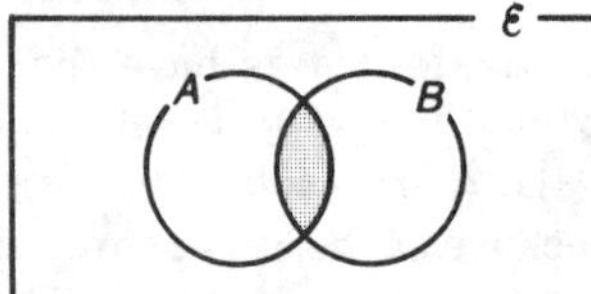

Disjoint sets have *no members in common*.
So the intersection of disjoint sets is the empty set.
For example, the set $A=\{\text{even numbers}\}$ and the set $B=\{\text{odd numbers}\}$ are disjoint sets.

i.e. $A \cap B=\varnothing$

Disjoint sets do not overlap on a Venn diagram.

Disjoint sets

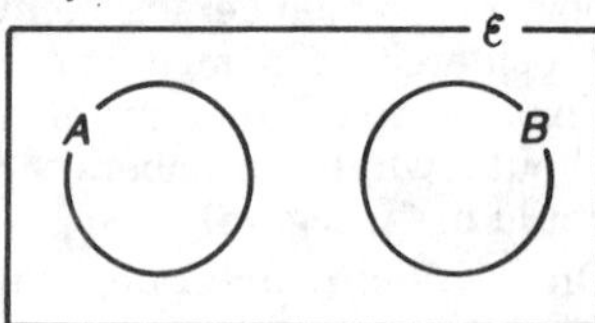

$A \cap B=\varnothing$

The intersection of a set and one of its subsets is the subset itself.
In this Venn diagram, B is a subset of A,

$B \subset A$
and $A \cap B=B$

Subsets

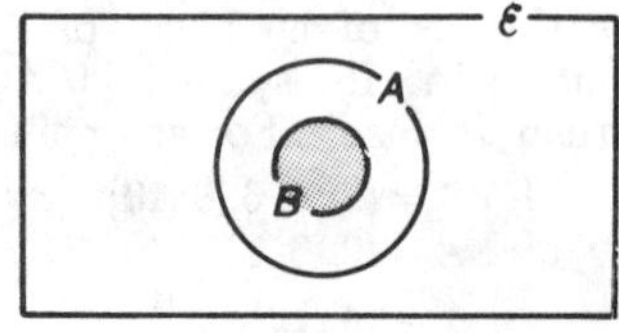

$B \subset A$ so $A \cap B=B$

The **union** of two sets, A and B, is the set whose members belong to *either A or B or both A and B*. The symbol $\cup$ is used for union.
For $A \cup B$ read 'A union B'.

For example, for $X=\{a, b\}$ and $Y=\{b, c, d\}$
$X \cup Y=\{a, b, c, d\}$

Note: b is a member of both X and Y but it appears *only once* in $X \cup Y$.

The shaded area on each Venn diagram below shows $A \cup B$.

Intersecting sets $A \cup B$ Disjoint sets $A \cup B$

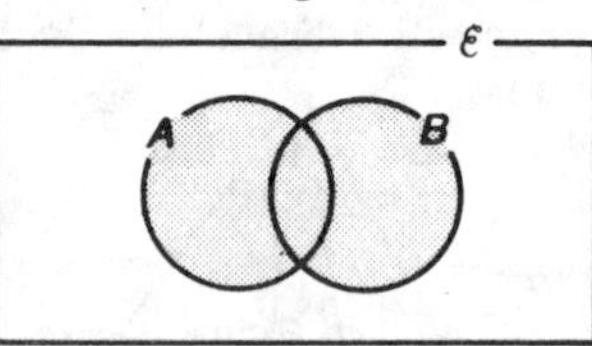

$A \cup B$ shaded $A \cup B$ shaded

The union of a set and one of its subsets is the set itself.

In this Venn diagram,
B is a subset of A.
i.e. $B \subset A$
and $A \cup B=A$

Subsets

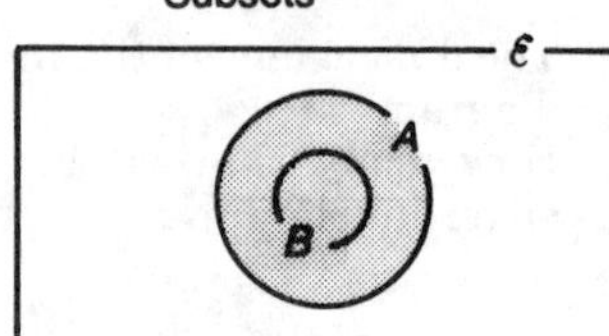

$A \cup B=A$ shaded

Sets and their complements can also be combined using intersection and union.
When you know the members of the sets, you must list the members of their complements before you can combine them.

Question

Given $\mathscr{E}=\{a, b, c, d, e, f, g, h, i\}$, $A=\{a, c, e, g\}$ and $B=\{a, h, i\}$, list the members of

(a) $A \cup B'$ (b) $A \cap B'$ (c) $A' \cup B$ (d) $A' \cap B$
(e) $A' \cup B'$ (f) $A' \cap B'$ (g) $(A \cup B)'$ (h) $(A \cap B)'$

Answer

$A=\{a, c, e, g\}$ $B=\{a, h, i\}$
So $A'=\{b, d, f, h, i\}$ and $B'=\{b, c, d, e, f, g\}$
(a) $A \cup B'=\{a, b, c, d, e, f, g\}$
(b) $A \cap B'=\{c, e, g\}$
(c) $A' \cup B=\{a, b, d, f, h, i\}$
(d) $A' \cap B=\{h, i\}$
(e) $A' \cup B'=\{b, c, d, e, f, g, h, i\}$
(f) $A' \cap B'=\{b, d, f\}$
(g) $A \cup B=\{a, c, e, g, h, i\}$
$(A \cup B)'=\{b, d, f\}$
(h) $A \cap B=\{a\}$
$(A \cap B)'=\{b, c, d, e, f, g, h, i\}$

When you do not know the actual members of the sets to be combined, you can still show their intersection and union on **Venn diagrams**. Shade the areas for the sets in the intersection or union on the same diagram. Use different shading or colours for each set to make them easier to see. Work out the 'area' needed for the combined set and show it on a separate diagram.

Question

A and B are subsets of $\mathscr{E}$ as shown on this Venn diagram.

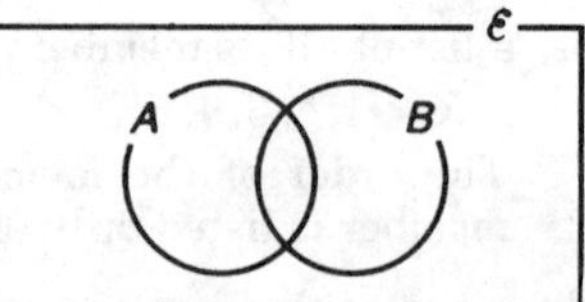

On separate Venn diagrams shade in

(a) A (b) A'
(c) B (d) B'
(e) $A' \cap B$ (f) $A' \cup B$
(g) $A' \cap B'$ (h) $A' \cup B'$
(i) $(A \cap B)'$ (j) $(A \cup B)'$

Answer

(a) A shaded

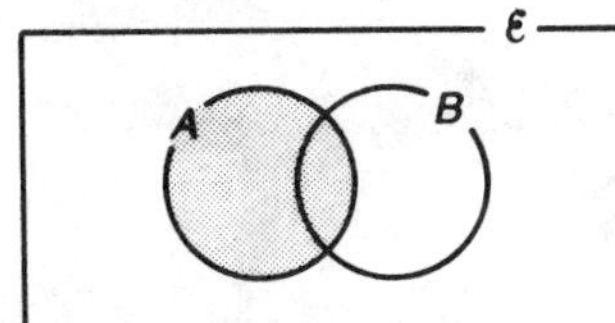

(b) A' shaded

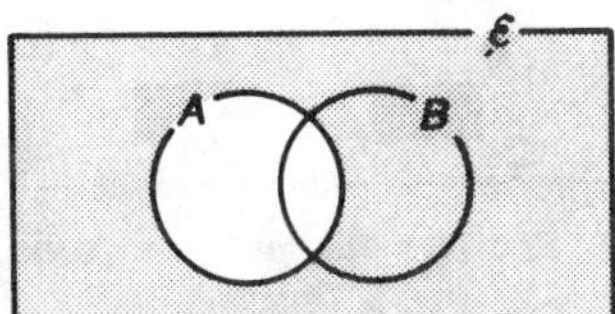

(c) B shaded

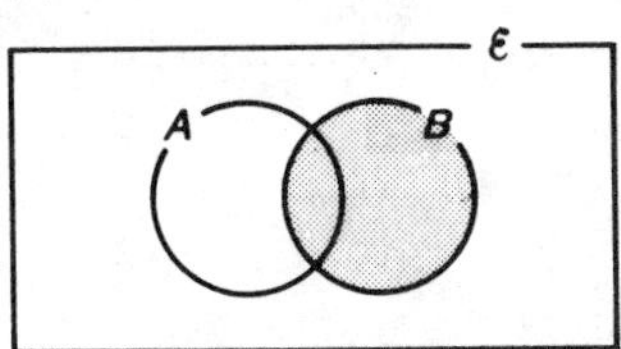

(d) B' shaded

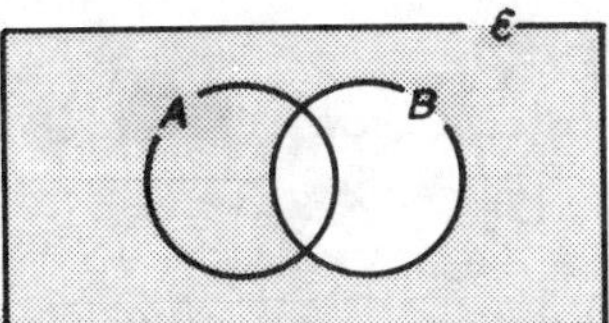

(e) $A' \cap B$ and
(f) $A' \cup B$

Shade A′ first, then B on the same diagram

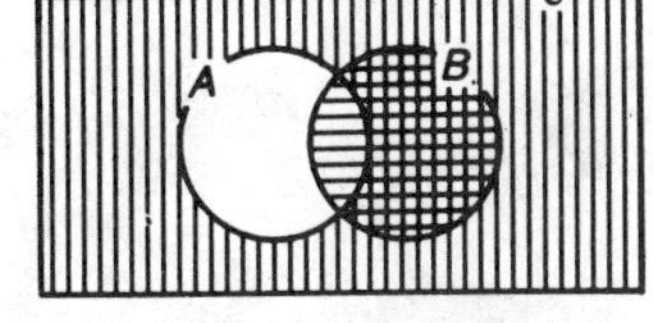

A' shaded |||||
B shaded ≡
$A' \cap B$ shaded #
$A' \cup B$ is the total shaded area.

(e) $A' \cap B$ shaded below

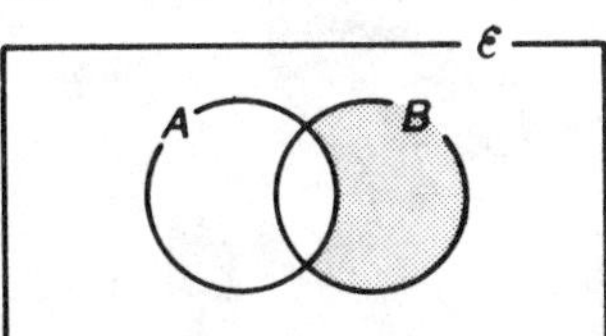

(f) $A' \cup B$ shaded below

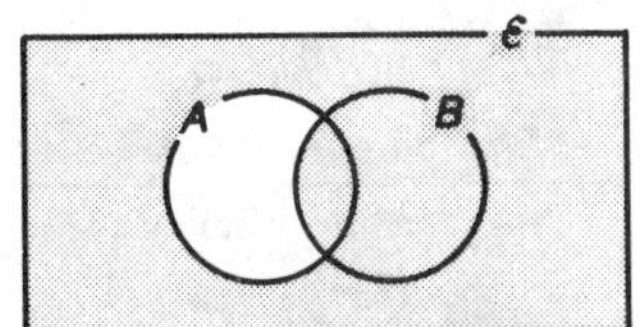

(g) $A' \cap B'$ and
(h) $A' \cup B'$

Shade A′ first, then B′ on the same diagram.

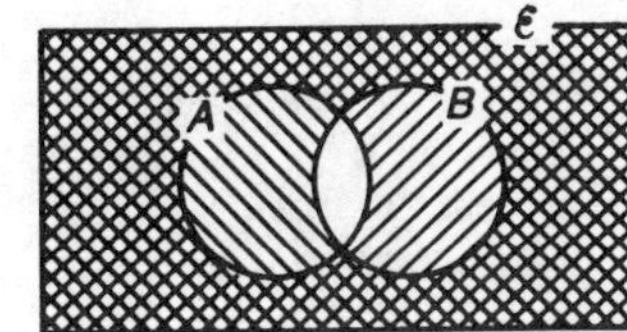

A' shaded ////
B' shaded \\\\
$A' \cap B'$ shaded ✕✕✕
$A' \cup B'$ is the total shaded area.

(g) $A' \cap B'$ shaded below

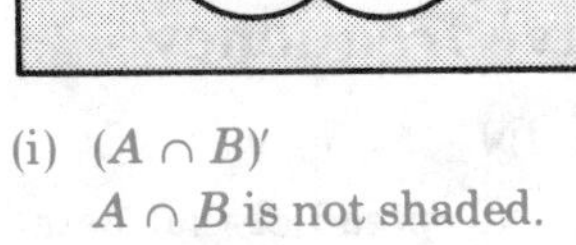

(h) $A' \cup B'$ shaded below

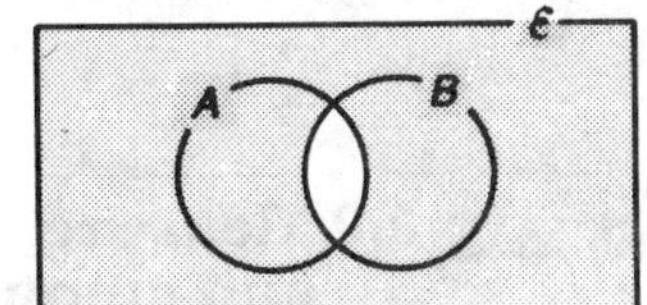

(i) $(A \cap B)'$
$A \cap B$ is not shaded.
$(A \cap B)'$ is shaded.

(j) $(A \cup B)'$
$A \cup B$ is not shaded.
$(A \cup B)'$ is shaded.

(A∩B)′ shaded

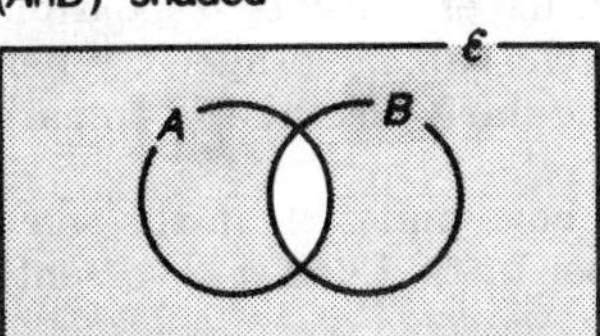

(A∪B)′ shaded

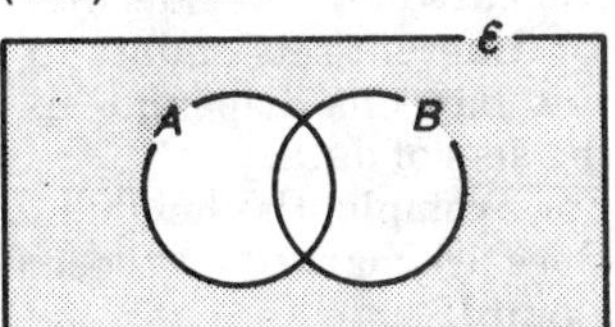

More than two sets can also be combined by union and intersection. At this level only two or three sets are combined. For example,

$A \cap B \cap C$ is the set of members common to A, B and C.

The Venn diagrams below show some combined sets. Check that you can work out how to obtain each shaded area. You may need to build up the shading step by step on a diagram as shown in the answer just given.

A∩B∩C shaded

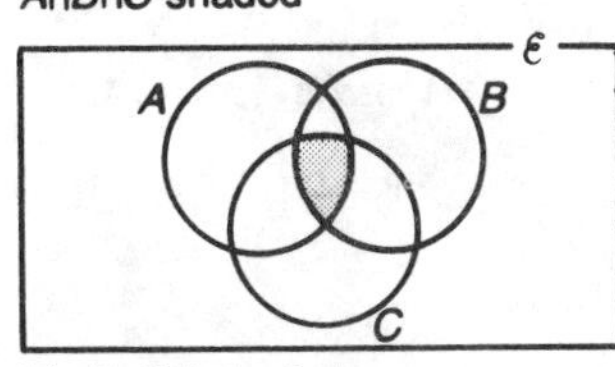

A∪B∪C shaded

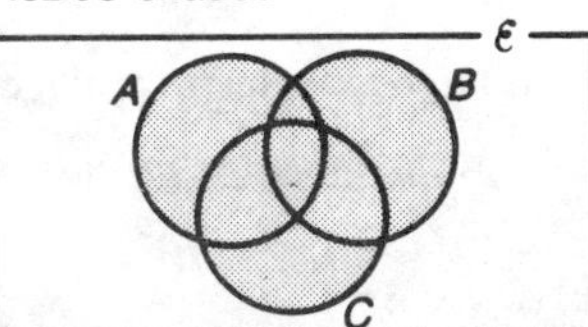

(A∩B∩C)′ shaded

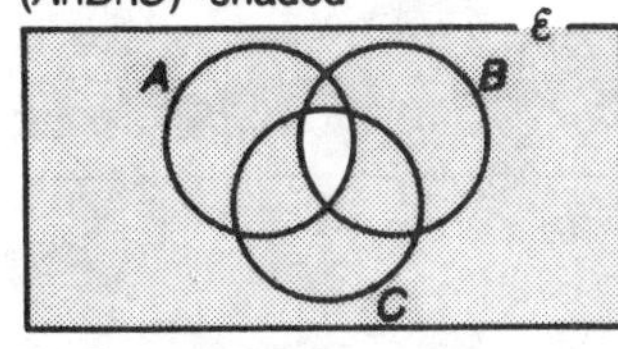

(A∪B∪C)′ shaded

B∩C shaded

(A∪B)∩C shaded

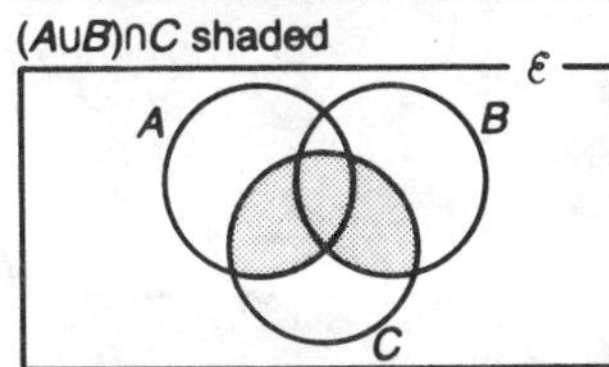

(A′∪B′)∩C shaded

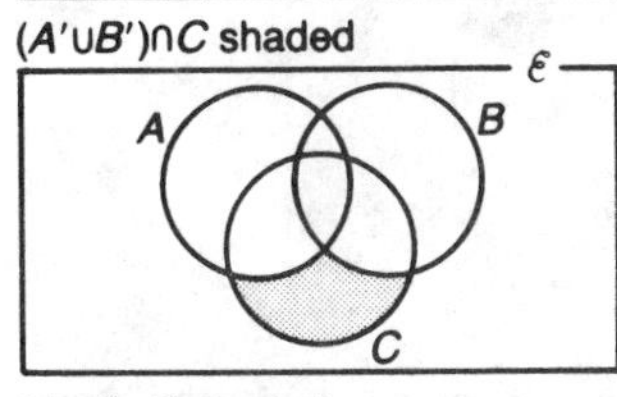

(A∩C)∩B′ shaded

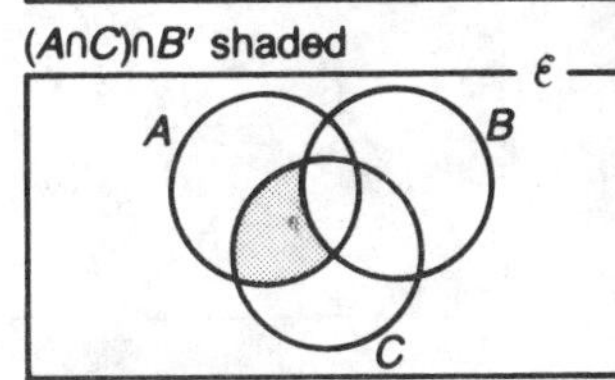

(A∩B)∪C shaded

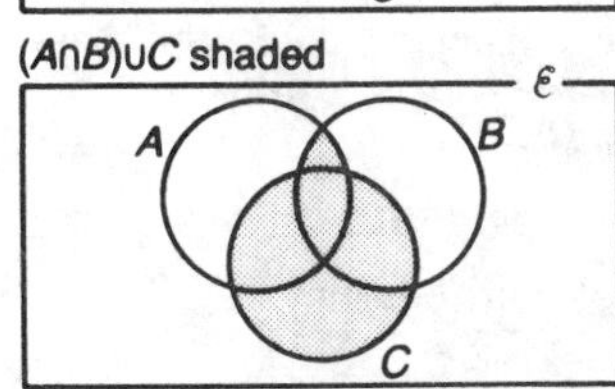

A′∩(B∪C) shaded

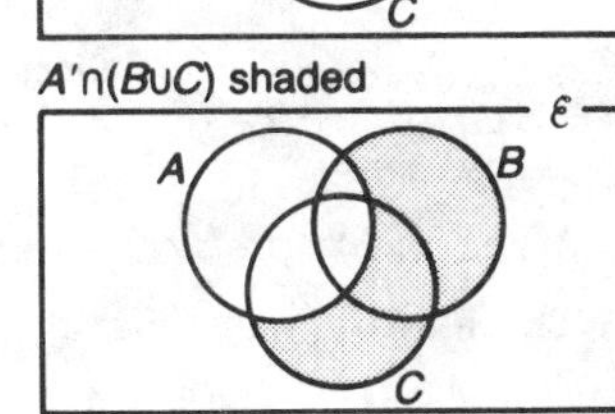

Knowing these areas can be useful when using Venn diagrams to solve problems.

PROBLEM SOLVING

Venn diagrams are useful in solving certain problems. Here are some steps to help you to solve such a problem.

1. Label each of the sets in the problem with a letter.
2. Draw a large Venn diagram to show how these sets are related. Look for intersecting sets, disjoint sets and subsets in the information. If you are not sure about how the sets are related, then show all the sets intersecting.
3. List the given information in terms of the sets.
4. Use the information to help you to write the number of members in each region of the Venn diagram. Start at the region of 'maximum overlap' and work 'outwards'. Express unknown number(s) in terms of letters. Use one letter only if possible.
5. Write equations relating the unknown(s) and numbers from the given information. Solve these equations and solve the problem.

Simple problems involving **two sets** are solved in Unit 2.23. Here is a more difficult 'two set problem'.

Question

In a sports club of 30 members, 17 play soccer, 19 play rugby and 2 do not play either.

How many members play

(a) both soccer and rugby, (b) soccer only,

(c) rugby only?

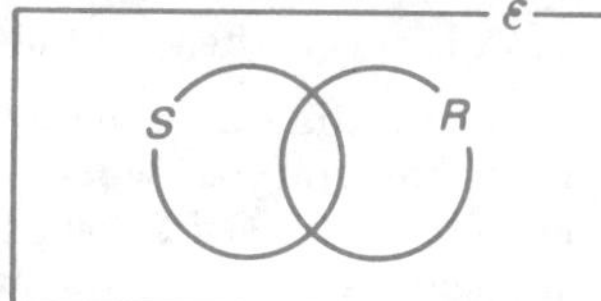

Answer

Let $\mathscr{E}$ = {sports club members}
S = {soccer players} and
R = {rugby players}

Draw two intersecting sets S and R on a Venn diagram

List the given information

$n(\mathscr{E}) = 30$

$n(S) = 17$

$n(R) = 19$

2 play neither game, so $n(S \cup R)' = 2$

On the Venn diagram, fill in the number of members who play each game.
Start at the centre and work 'outwards'

Let $n(S \cap R) = x$

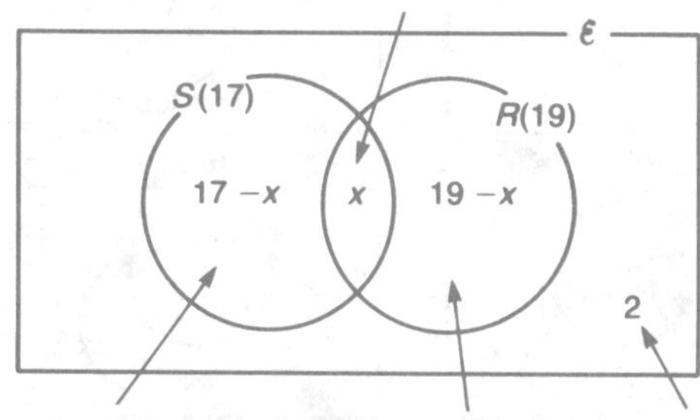

Make an equation relating the information

There are 30 members in the club altogether.

So $(17-x)+x+(19-x)+2=30$
$38-x=30$
$x=8$

(a) 8 members play both soccer and rugby.

(b) $(17-x)=(17-8)=9$ members play soccer only.

(c) $(19-x)=(19-8)=11$ members play rugby only.

Problems involving **three sets** can be solved in a similar way. Sometimes a separate universal set is not needed because the sets themselves make the universal set.

Question

In the sixth form of a school a pupil who studies science does one or more of the subjects Physics, Chemistry, Biology. In a group of science pupils, 32 do Biology, 16 do Biology only, 2 do Chemistry only, 7 do Physics only, 15 do Biology and Chemistry, 11 do Biology and Physics and 13 do Physics and Chemistry.

How many of these science pupils

(a) do all three subjects,

(b) do Chemistry,

(c) do Physics?

How many science pupils are there altogether in the group?

Answer

Let $\mathscr{E}$ = {group of science pupils}
P = {these science pupils who do Physics}
C = {these science pupils who do Chemistry}
B = {these science pupils who do Biology}

Draw three intersecting sets P, C and B on a Venn diagram

List the given information

$n(B) = 32$,
16 do Biology only,
2 do Chemistry only,
7 do Physics only.
$n(B \cap C) = 15$
$n(B \cap P) = 11$
$n(P \cap C) = 13$

On the Venn diagram, fill in the number of science pupils who study each subject.
Start at the centre and work 'outwards'

Let $n(P \cap C \cap B) = x$

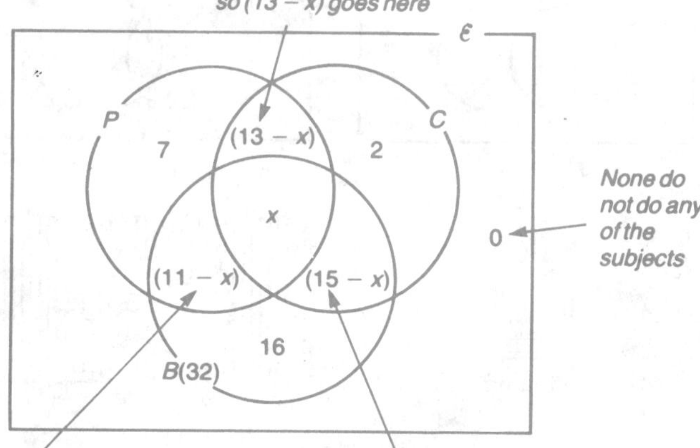

Make an equation relating the information

The total number of pupils who do Biology is 32.

So $16+(11-x)+x+(15-x)=32$
$42-x=32$
$x=10$

(a) So 10 pupils study all three subjects.

Fill in the unknown values on a Venn diagram to answer the other questions

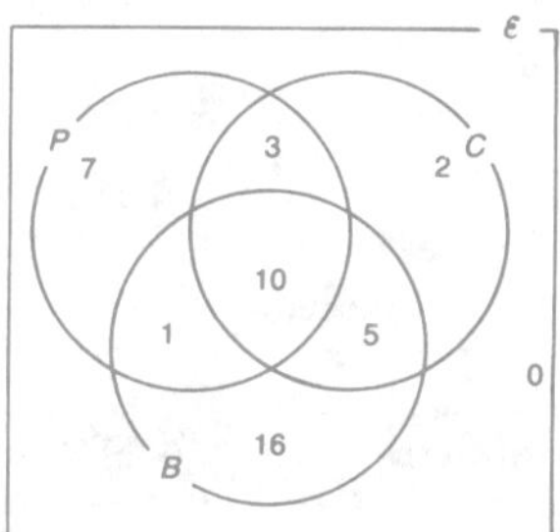

(b) $n(C) = 3+10+5+2 = 20$
So 20 pupils do Chemistry.

(c) $n(P) = 7+3+10+1 = 21$
So 21 pupils do Physics.

The total number of pupils in the group $= 7+3+2+1+10+5+16$
$= 44$

3.9 Measures of dispersion and cumulative frequency

MEASURES OF DISPERSION

The **dispersion** of a set of data is the spread of that data. Sets of data are often compared by comparing their averages, e.g. *mean*, *median*, *mode*. They can also be compared by considering their dispersions. It is possible for different sets of data to have the same average(s). When this happens dispersion is particularly useful to compare the sets of data.

For example, the heights of the boys and girls in the same class are marked on these number lines. Each ● represents a pupil.

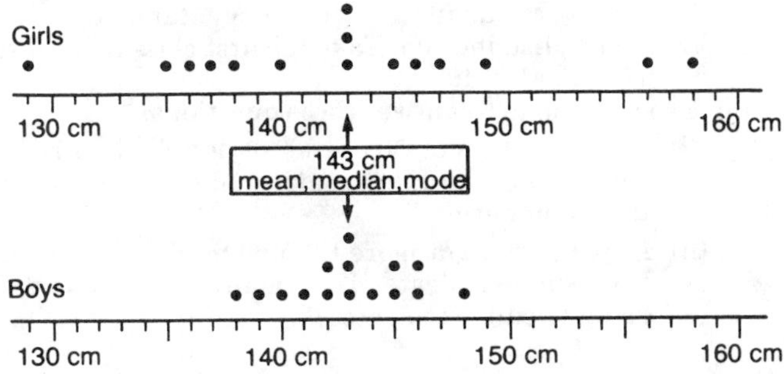

It is easy to see from these diagrams that, although the boys and girls have the same average height (143 cm), the heights of the girls are more spread out. So the dispersion of the girls' heights is greater than that of the boys.
The simplest **measures of dispersion** in statistics are the *range, interquartile range* and the *semi-interquartile range.* These are the only measures of dispersion studied at this level.

Range

The **range** of a set of data is the difference between the greatest and least values in that data.

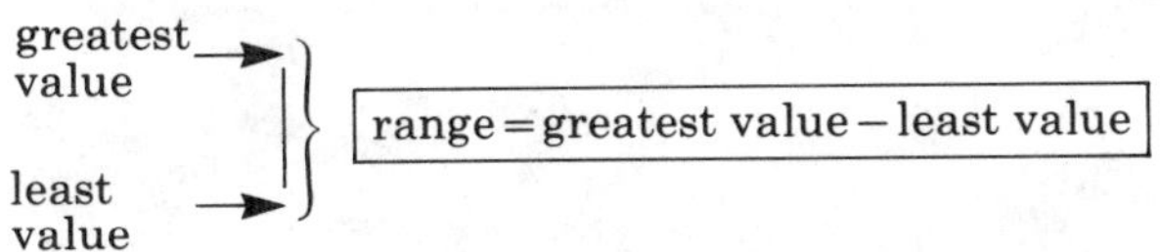

For example, for the height data in the diagrams above

range for girls' heights = 158 cm − 129 cm = 29 cm

range for boys' heights = 148 cm − 138 cm = 10 cm

The range is *not* a very good measure of dispersion. It depends on the two 'extreme values' which may be exceptional.
For example, in the diagram above, the greatest value (158 cm) and least value (129 cm) in the girls' heights can be seen to be exceptional heights. They are much greater and smaller than most of the other values.

INTERQUARTILE RANGE AND SEMI-INTERQUARTILE RANGE

The **interquartile range** and **semi-interquartile range** are slightly better measures of dispersion than the range. They are not affected by extreme values because they are based on the 'middle-half' of the data, i.e. between the upper and lower quartiles.
If a set of data is arranged in order of size, the **quartiles** divide the data into four equal parts. The positions of the quartiles are always measured *from the lower end* of the distribution.

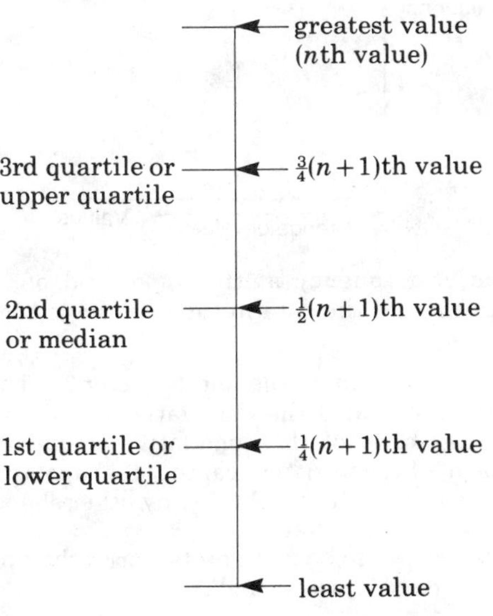

If there are n values in a distribution, then:

the **1st quartile** or **lower quartile** is the $\frac{1}{4}(n+1)$th value from the lower end

the **2nd quartile** or **median** is the $\frac{1}{2}(n+1)$th value from the lower end

the **3rd quartile** or **upper quartile** is the $\frac{3}{4}(n+1)$th value from the lower end.

The **interquartile range** is the difference between the upper quartile and lower quartile.

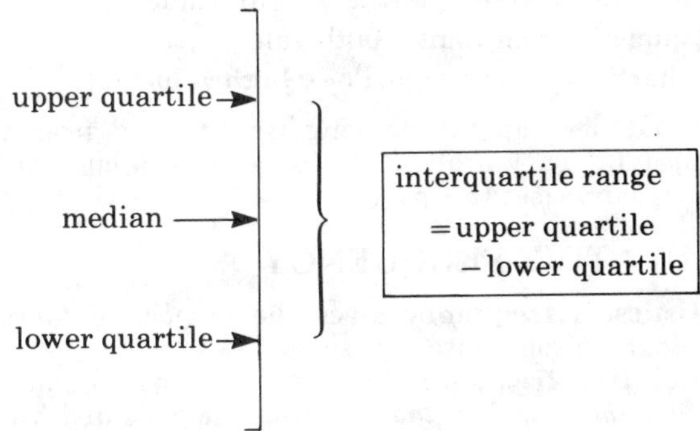

The **semi-interquartile** range is half of the interquartile range.

semi-interquartile range $= \frac{1}{2}$(upper quartile − lower quartile)

Question

The heights of 15 girls, measured to the nearest cm, are given below.

156 cm, 149 cm, 129 cm, 140 cm, 143 cm,
135 cm, 137 cm, 145 cm, 146 cm, 158 cm,
147 cm, 136 cm, 143 cm, 143 cm, 138 cm

For these data, find

(a) the quartiles, (b) the interquartile range.

Answer

Put the data in order of size first.
There are 15 values, so:

the lower quartile is the $\frac{1}{4}(15+1)$*th value, i.e. the 4th value;*

the median is the $\frac{1}{2}(15+1)$*th value, i.e. the 8th value;*

the upper quartile is the $\frac{3}{4}(15+1)$*th value, i.e. the 12th value*

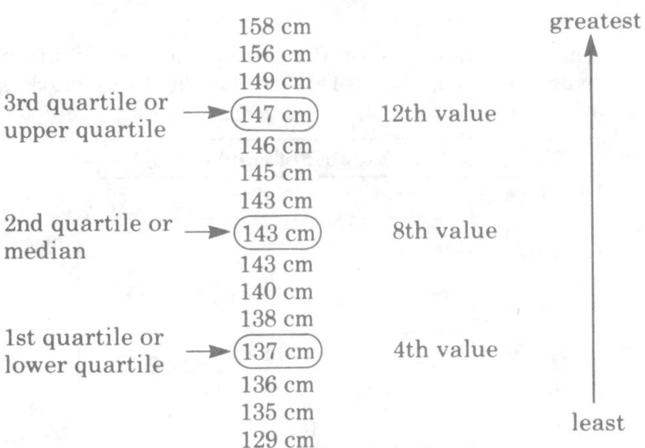

(a) The first quartile or lower quartile is 137 cm.
The second quartile or median is 143 cm.
The third quartile or upper quartile is 147 cm.

(b) Interquartile range = upper quartile − lower quartile
= 147 cm − 137 cm
= 10 cm

This question uses the height data from the beginning of the unit.
Check that you can show that the interquartile range for the boys' heights is 4 cm

For **a large amount of data**, i.e. when n is large, approximations for the positions of the quartiles are used.

1st quartile or lower quartile↔($\frac{1}{4}n$)th value.
2nd quartile or median↔($\frac{1}{2}n$)th value.
3rd quartile or upper quartile↔($\frac{3}{4}n$)th value.

These quartiles can take a long time to find from the original data. They are usually found from a cumulative frequency curve (see this page).

CUMULATIVE FREQUENCY

In statistics, a **frequency** gives the *number of times* a value occurs in some data.
A **cumulative frequency** gives the number of times a value *less than* or *less than or equal to* a stated value occurs in some data.

Cumulative frequency tables

A **cumulative frequency table** can be made from a frequency table. The cumulative frequency for any class is the sum of the frequencies of that class and all the lower classes. The easiest way to work this out is to add successive frequencies to give a 'running total'. Cumulative frequency tables are usually written in vertical columns like these.

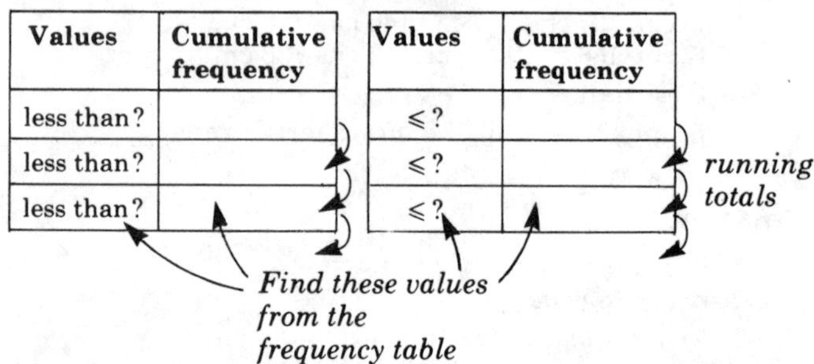

The last cumulative frequency in the table should give the total number of values in the data. This is a useful check of your addition!
A cumulative frequency table can be used to answer *some* questions about the data.

Question

The table below shows the frequency distribution of examination marks for 120 students. Each mark is a whole number.

Marks	Number of candidates
1–10	0
11–20	2
21–30	6
31–40	7
41–50	14
51–60	20
61–70	35
71–80	29
81–90	6
91–100	1

(a) Construct a cumulative frequency table for this frequency distribution. Take the first class to be 'less than or equal to 10'.
(b) Use your table to answer these questions.
(i) Anyone who got 50 marks or less had to resit the examination. How many students had to resit the examination?
(ii) Anyone who got more than 60 marks was given a Credit certificate. How many students were given Credit certificates?

Answer

(a) Cumulative frequency table

Marks	Cumulative frequency				
≤ 10					0
≤ 20	2	+	0	=	2
≤ 30	6	+	2	=	8
≤ 40	7	+	8	=	15
≤ 50	14	+	15	=	29
≤ 60	20	+	29	=	49
≤ 70	35	+	49	=	84
≤ 80	29	+	84	=	113
≤ 90	6	+	113	=	119
≤100	1	+	119	=	120

Check: *Total number of candidates is 120* ✓

(b) (i) From the table:
29 students obtained 50 marks or less.
So 29 students had to resit the examination.

(ii) *Students with 'more than 60 marks' gain a credit. But the table shows 'less than or equal to 60 marks'. So relate 'more than 60' to '60 or less'*
To gain a credit a student must have 'more than 60 marks'. So students with '60 marks or less' do *not* gain a credit.
From the table: 49 students obtained 60 marks or less. So (120 − 49) = 71 students obtained 'more than 60 marks', i.e. 71 students were given Credit certificates.

Cumulative frequency curve

A **cumulative frequency curve** can be drawn from a cumulative frequency table. On the graph, the *range of values* is always along the *horizontal axis* and the *cumulative frequency* is up the *vertical axis.*

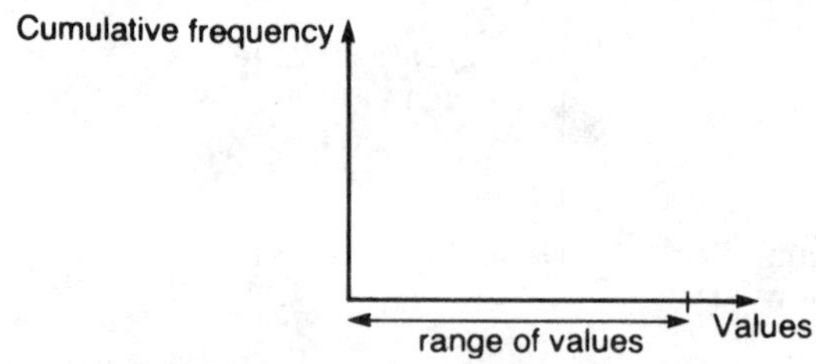

Plot each cumulative frequency at the upper end of its class. This ensures that all the data in the class have been included.

Draw a smooth curve through the plotted points. The curve you should get is called the cumulative frequency curve or **ogive**. The shape of the cumulative frequency curve or ogive is a characteristic leaning S-shape (see diagram at top of next page). If you obtain any other shape, then you may have made a mistake.
Check that you have plotted your points correctly and that the axes are the 'correct way round'.

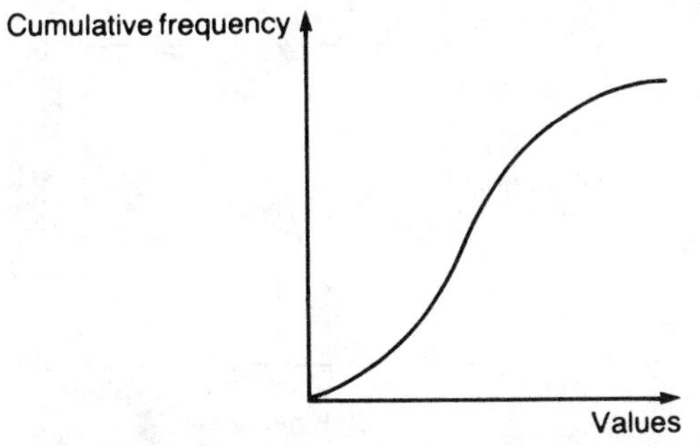

An ogive can be used to **estimate values** for the data. Always draw lines on your graph to show how you obtain your answers.

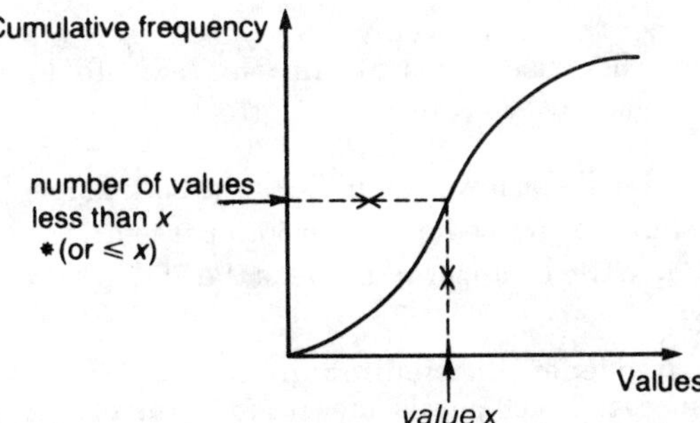

Given a value, you can estimate number of values *less than* (or *less than or equal to*)* that value and vice versa. You can also estimate the number of values *greater than* (or *greater than or equal to*)* that value and vice versa. To make this estimate you must relate the given *greater than* statement to a *less than* statement. For example,

greater than x is related to *less than or equal to x*,

$>x$ is related to $\leqslant x$,

and *greater than or equal to x* is related to *less than x*,

$\geqslant x$ is related to $<x$.

* This depends on your cumulative frequency table.

Question

(a) Draw the cumulative frequency curve for the frequency distribution of examination marks in the previous question.

(b) Estimate from your curve

(i) the number of students who got 25 marks or less,

(ii) the number of students who got more than 65 marks.

(c) If 20 students must fail the examination, estimate what the pass mark should be.

(d) If the top 20 students must be given distinction certificates, estimate the marks they must obtain.

Answer

(a) Cumulative frequency table

Marks	Cumulative frequency	Points to plot
$\leqslant$ 10	0	(10, 0)
$\leqslant$ 20	2	(20, 2)
$\leqslant$ 30	8	(30, 8)
$\leqslant$ 40	15	(40, 15)
$\leqslant$ 50	29	(50, 29)
$\leqslant$ 60	49	(60, 49)
$\leqslant$ 70	84	(70, 84)
$\leqslant$ 80	113	(80, 113)
$\leqslant$ 90	119	(90, 119)
$\leqslant$100	120	(100, 120)

Cumulative frequency curve for this distribution

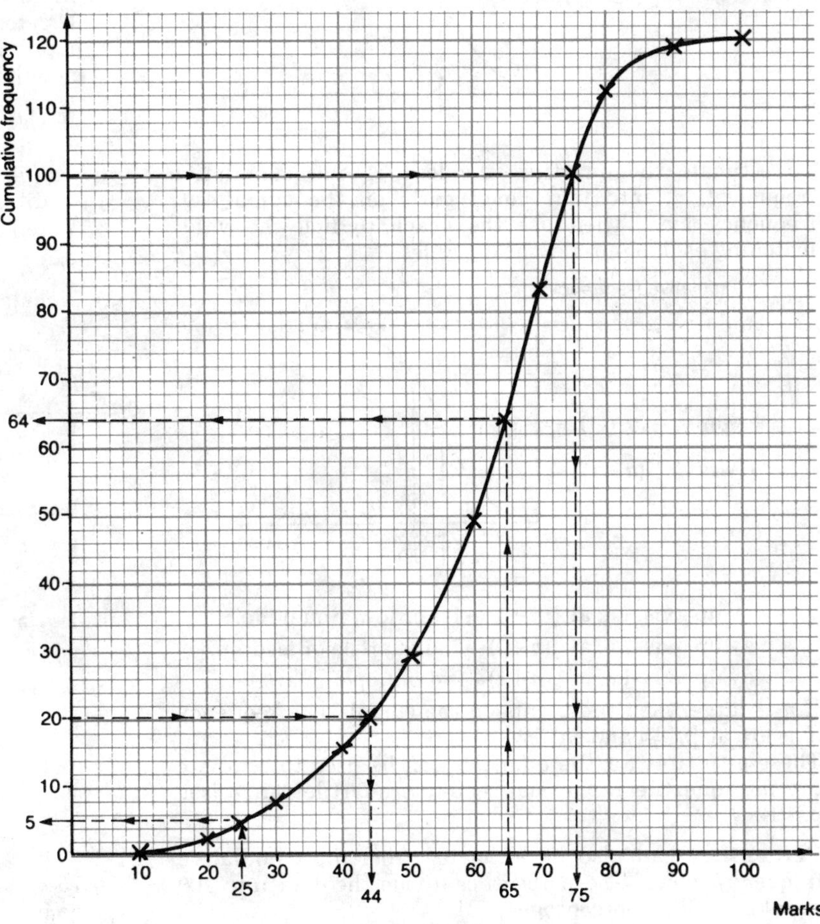

(b) (i) From the curve

25 marks or less↔5 students

So 5 students got 25 marks or less.

(ii) *'More than 65 marks' is related to '65 marks or less'*

From the curve

65 marks or less↔64 students

So $(120-64)=56$ students got more than 65 marks.

(c) From the curve

20 students↔44 marks or less

i.e. the students who fail got 44 marks or less.

So the students who pass got more than 44 marks.

The pass mark must be 45.

(d) If the top 20 must be given distinctions, then $(120-20)=100$ will not get distinctions.

From the curve

100 students↔75 marks or less

i.e. students with 75 marks or less do not get distinctions.

So students with more thar 75 marks are given distinctions.

A cumulative frequency curve can be used to **estimate** the **median** and **quartiles** (see pp.45 and 101).

To estimate the median, mark the $\frac{1}{2}$-*way point* on the cumulative frequency axis.

For n values, this point is at a cumulative frequency of $\frac{1}{2}(n+1)$ or $\frac{1}{2}n$, if n is large.

Then use the graph to find the value which matches this point, i.e. the **median**.

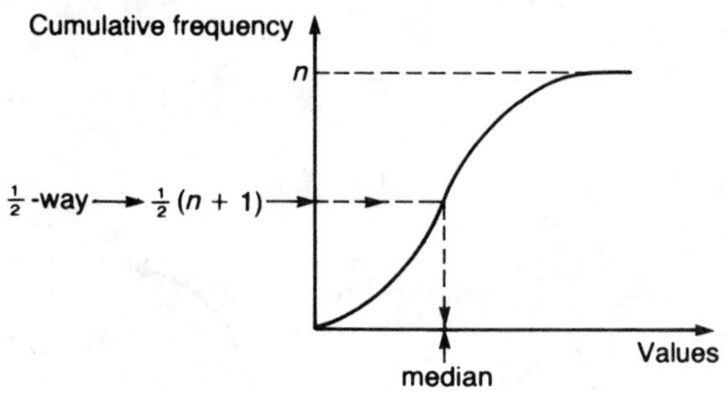

To estimate the quartiles, divide the total cumulative frequency, n, into four equal parts on the cumulative frequency axis. Then use the graph to find the value matching each point, i.e. the quartiles.

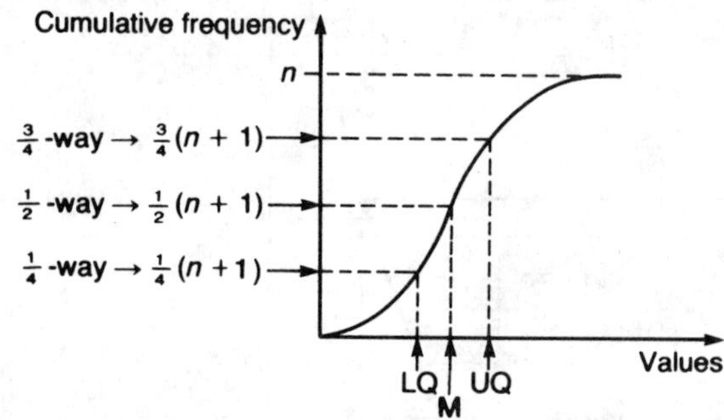

$\frac{1}{4}$ way up axis, i.e. at $\frac{1}{4}(n+1)$↔1st or lower quartile.

$\frac{1}{2}$ way up axis, i.e. at $\frac{1}{2}(n+1)$↔2nd quartile or median.

$\frac{3}{4}$ way up axis, i.e. at $\frac{3}{4}(n+1)$↔3rd or upper quartile.

If n is large, then the points on the cumulative frequency axis are at $\frac{1}{4}n$, $\frac{1}{2}n$ and $\frac{3}{4}n$.

These estimates for the quartiles can be used to estimate the interquartile range and semi-interquartile range (see p.101).

Percentiles can also be estimated from the cumulative frequency curve. The percentiles divide the data into 100 equal parts (like percentages).

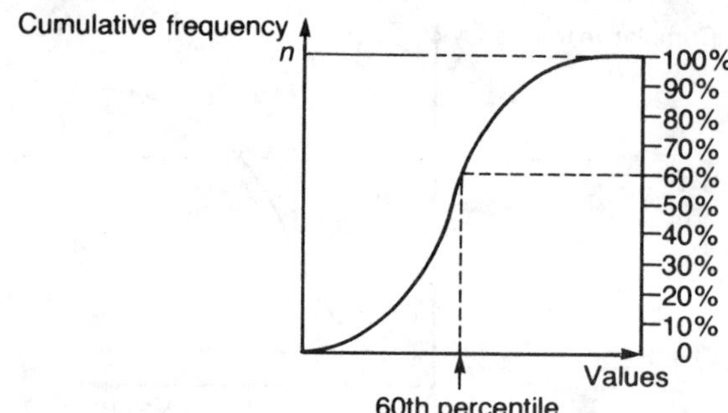

To estimate percentiles it helps to draw an extra axis on the right-hand side of the curve, marked 0–100, with

0↔cumulative frequency 0 and

100↔total frequency n

and number this scale evenly.

You can then use the scale on this axis to locate the required percentile(s).

Note

The 1st quartile or lower quartile is the 25th percentile,

the 2nd quartile or median is the 50th percentile,

the 3rd quartile or upper quartile is the 75th percentile.

Question

The frequency distribution in the table below gives the masses of 400 pupils, measured to the nearest kg.

(a) Construct a cumulative frequency table for the frequency distribution. Take the first value as 'less than 35.5 kg'.

(b) Draw the cumulative frequency curve (ogive) from your completed cumulative frequency table. (Use a scale of 2 cm to represent 10 kg on the mass axis, and 2 cm to represent 100 pupils on the cumulative frequency axis.)

Mass (to nearest kg)	Number of pupils
31–35	0
36–40	15
41–45	42
46–50	65
51–55	92
56–60	75
61–65	67
66–70	37
71–75	7

(c) Use your cumulative frequency curve to estimate
(i) the median mass,
(ii) the lower and upper quartiles,
(iii) the interquartile range,
(iv) the 95th percentile.

Answer

(a) Cumulative frequency table

Mass	Cumulative frequency	Points to plot
less than 35.5 kg	0	(35.5, 0)
less than 40.5 kg	15 + 0 = 15	(40.5, 15)
less than 45.5 kg	42 + 15 = 57	(45.5, 57)
less than 50.5 kg	65 + 57 = 122	(50.5, 122)
less than 55.5 kg	92 + 122 = 214	(55.5, 214)
less than 60.5 kg	75 + 214 = 289	(60.5, 289)
less than 65.5 kg	67 + 289 = 356	(65.5, 356)
less than 70.5 kg	37 + 356 = 393	(70.5, 393)
less than 75.5 kg	7 + 393 = 400	(75.5, 400)

These values are chosen because the masses were measured 'to the nearest kg'

Check
Total number of pupils is 400

e.g. 75 kg must be 'less than 75.5 kg' because 75.5 kg = 76 kg (to the nearest kg).

(b) Cumulative frequency curve for this distribution

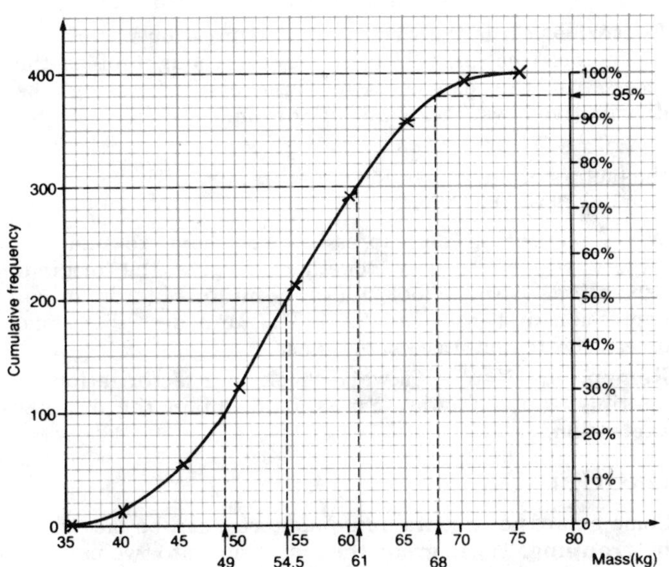

(c) Since there are 400 pupils, i.e. n is large,
the median
$\leftrightarrow$cumulative frequency of $(\frac{1}{2}\times 400)=200$
the lower quartile
$\leftrightarrow$cumulative frequency of $(\frac{1}{4}\times 400)=100$
the upper quartile
$\leftrightarrow$cumulative frequency of $(\frac{3}{4}\times 400)=300$.

(i) From the curve,
the median $(M)\approx 54.5$ kg

(ii) From the curve,
the lower quartile (LQ) ≈ 49 kg
the upper quartile (UQ) ≈ 61 kg

(iii) Interquartile range
= upper quartile − lower quartile
$\approx$ 61 kg − 49 kg
= 12 kg

(iv) From the curve,
95th percentile ≈ 68 kg

3.10 Indices

The basic ideas and rules of indices are given in Unit 2.28 for integer indices. In this unit these ideas are extended to indices which are fractions.

FRACTIONAL INDICES

A number with a **fractional index** is a way to write a root of the number.

A number 'to the power $\frac{1}{2}$' is a square root. For example,

$$7^{\frac{1}{2}}=\sqrt{7}$$

A number 'to the power $\frac{1}{3}$' is a cube root. For example,

$$5^{\frac{1}{3}}=\sqrt[3]{5}$$

In general, a number 'to the power $\frac{1}{n}$', is an nth root.

$$a^{\frac{1}{n}}=\sqrt[n]{a}$$

The value of a number with a fractional index can be found by changing it to a root. The root can be worked out in your head or on a *calculator*.

To find a root on your calculator, use the *inverse* of the power key 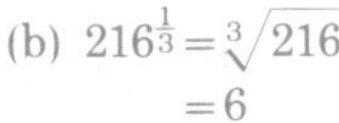 x^y or y^x .

Question

Work out the value of (a) $32^{\frac{1}{5}}$ (b) $216^{\frac{1}{3}}$

Answer

(a) $32^{\frac{1}{5}}=\sqrt[5]{32}=\sqrt[5]{2\times 2\times 2\times 2\times 2}=2$

(b) $216^{\frac{1}{3}}=\sqrt[3]{216}$
$=6$

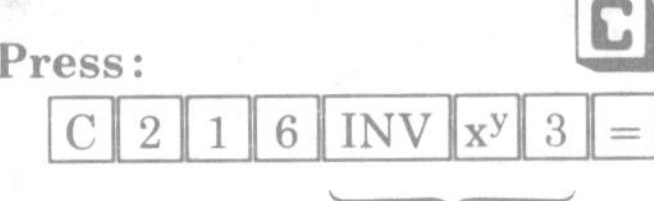

Press: C 2 1 6 INV x^y 3 =

gives cube root

To find the nth root of a power, divide the index by n.

In general, $\sqrt[n]{a^m}=a^{m/n}$

For example, $\sqrt[3]{a^6}=a^{\frac{6}{3}}=a^2$

since $\sqrt[3]{a^6}=\sqrt[3]{(a\times a)\times(a\times a)\times(a\times a)}=a\times a=a^2$

BASIC RULES OF INDICES

All numbers written with indices obey the *same* rules. The indices can be integer, fractional, positive, negative or zero. Here is a **summary** of these **basic rules**.

1 To multiply numbers written with the same base, add the indices.

$$a^m\times a^n=a^{m+n}$$

For example, $a^2\times a^3=a^{2+3}=a^5$

since $a^2\times a^3=(a\times a)\times(a\times a\times a)=a^5$

2 To divide numbers written with the same base, subtract the indices.

$$a^m\div a^n=a^{m-n}$$

For example, $a^6\div a^2=a^{6-2}=a^4$

since $a^6\div a^2=\dfrac{\not{a}\times\not{a}\times a\times a\times a\times a}{\not{a}\times\not{a}}=a^4$

3 Any base raised to the power 0 is 1.
For example, $a^0=1$

4 A negative index gives a reciprocal.

$$a^{-n}=\frac{1}{a^n}$$

For example, $a^{-2}=\dfrac{1}{a^2}$

5 To raise a power to a power, multiply the indices.

$$(a^m)^n=a^{m\times n}=a^{mn}$$

For example, $(a^2)^3=a^{2\times 3}=a^6$

since $(a^2)^3=a^2\times a^2\times a^2=a^6$

These rules can be used to simplify expressions.

Question

Simplify the following expressions.

(a) $a^{\frac{1}{4}}\times a^{-\frac{1}{4}}$ (b) $y^{\frac{1}{2}}\times y^{\frac{1}{3}}$ (c) $x^{\frac{3}{4}}\div x^{\frac{1}{2}}$

(d) $y^{-\frac{1}{2}}\div y^{-\frac{1}{4}}$ (e) $(27a^2)^{\frac{1}{3}}$ (f) $(2x^{-\frac{1}{4}})^4$

Answer

(a) $a^{-\frac{1}{4}}\times a^{-\frac{1}{4}}=a^{\frac{1}{4}+(-\frac{1}{4})}$ ← $\frac{1}{4}+(-\frac{1}{4})=\frac{1}{4}-\frac{1}{4}=0$
$=a^0$
$=1$

(b) $y^{\frac{1}{2}}\times y^{\frac{1}{3}}=y^{\frac{1}{2}+\frac{1}{3}}$ ← $\frac{1}{2}+\frac{1}{3}=\frac{3}{6}+\frac{2}{6}=\frac{5}{6}$
$=y^{\frac{5}{6}}$

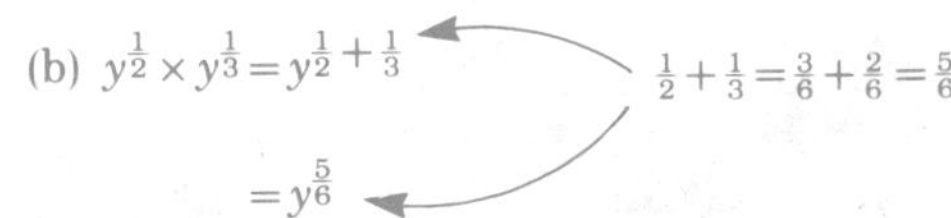

(c) $x^{\frac{3}{4}} \div x^{\frac{1}{2}} = x^{\frac{3}{4}-\frac{1}{2}}$ $\qquad \frac{3}{4}-\frac{1}{2}=\frac{3}{4}-\frac{2}{4}$

$= x^{\frac{1}{4}}$ $\qquad =\frac{1}{4}$

(d) $y^{-\frac{1}{2}} \div y^{-\frac{1}{4}} = y^{-\frac{1}{2}-(-\frac{1}{4})}$ $\qquad -\frac{1}{2}-(-\frac{1}{4}) = -\frac{1}{2}+\frac{1}{4}$

$\qquad = -\frac{2}{4}+\frac{1}{4}$

$= y^{-\frac{1}{4}}$ $\qquad = -\frac{1}{4}$

(e) $(27a^2)^{\frac{1}{3}} = 27^{\frac{1}{3}}a^{\frac{2}{3}} = \sqrt[3]{27}\,a^{\frac{2}{3}}$ $\qquad 27 = 3\times3\times3$

$= 3a^{\frac{2}{3}}$ $\qquad \sqrt[3]{27}=3$

(f) $(2x^{-\frac{1}{4}})^4 = 2^4x^{-\frac{4}{4}} = 16x^{-1}$

3.11 Expansion of brackets

This unit extends the work on brackets started in Unit 2.29. The methods used are the same but the examples are more difficult.

Question

Expand (a) $(2x+3y)(3x+5y)$
(b) $(3x-2y)(7x-5y)$

Answer

(a) $(2x+3y)(3x+5y)$

Rewrite the multiplication $= 2x(3x+5y)+3y(3x+5y)$

Remove brackets $= 6x^2+10xy+9yx+15y^2$

Collect like terms $= 6x^2 + 19xy + 15y^2$

(b) $(3x-2y)(7x-5y)$

Rewrite the multiplication $= 3x(7x-5y)-2y(7x-5y)$

Remove brackets $= 21x^2-15xy-14yx+10y^2$
Take care with signs!

Collect like terms $= 21x^2 - 29xy + 10y^2$

The square of a bracket is another common expansion. To work this out, write the square as the product of two brackets, then multiply the brackets as before.

Question

Expand (a) $(3x+5y)^2$ (b) $(2x-3y)^2$

Answer

(a) $(3x+5y)^2$

Rewrite as a product $= (3x+5y)(3x+5y)$

Rewrite the multiplication $= 3x(3x+5y)+5y(3x+5y)$

Remove brackets $= 9x^2+15xy+15yx+25y^2$

Collect like terms $= 9x^2 + 30xy + 25y^2$

(b) $(2x-3y)^2$

Rewrite as a product $= (2x-3y)(2x-3y)$

Rewrite the multiplication $= 2x(2x-3y)-3y(2x-3y)$

Remove brackets $= 4x^2-6xy-6yx+9y^2$
Take care with signs!

Collect like terms $= 4x^2 - 12xy + 9y^2$

3.12 Factorization

Factorization is the writing of an expression in terms of its factors (see Unit 2.29). It may be thought of as the *reverse* of the expansion of brackets, i.e. using the distributive laws 'backwards'. For example, since

$2x(3x-5) = 6x^2-10x$

the factors of the expression $6x^2-10x$ are

$2x$ and $(3x-5)$.

When factorizing an expression you have to find the factors which multiply together to give the original expression. Always look for a **common factor** in an expression first (see Unit 2.29). This unit describes some *other* ways to factorize expressions.

Remember You can always check your factorization by multiplying the factors. You should obtain the original expression.

GROUPING

Some expressions containing *four* terms can be factorized by **grouping**. Try to group the four terms into two pairs so that each pair has a common factor. If you can do this, then you can remove the common factor from each pair. For example,

$ac+ad+bc+bd$

$= (ac+ad)+(bc+bd)$ *Group the terms in two pairs. a is the common factor of the first pair*

$= a(c+d)+b(c+d)$ *b is the common factor of the second pair*

$= (c+d)(a+b)$ *(c+d) is the common factor of each pair*

You may have to rearrange the terms in the expression. Make sure that you do not change its meaning. Take care with the signs when grouping the terms.
It is useful to remember that:

$-a-b = -(a+b)$
$a-b = -(-a+b) = -(b-a)$

Question

Factorize

(a) $ax+bx-ay-by$ (b) $3a+4bx-3b-4ax$
(c) $3ab^2-c^2d+3ad-b^2c^2$

Answer

(a) $ax+bx-ay-by$
Group into pairs $= x(a+b)-y(a+b)$
Take out the common factor $= (a+b)(x-y)$

(b) $3a+4bx-3b-4ax$
Rearrange $= 3a-3b+4bx-4ax$
Group into pairs $= 3(a-b)+4x(b-a)$
Use $(b-a) = -(a-b)$ $= 3(a-b)-4x(a-b)$
Take out the common factor $= (a-b)(3-4x)$

(c) $3ab^2-c^2d+3ad-b^2c^2$
Rearrange $= 3ab^2+3ad-c^2d-b^2c^2$
Group into pairs $= 3a(b^2+d)-c^2(d+b^2)$
Use $(d+b^2) = (b^2+d)$ $= 3a(b^2+d)-c^2(b^2+d)$
Common factor $= (b^2+d)(3a-c^2)$

DIFFERENCE BETWEEN TWO PERFECT SQUARES

An expression such as a^2-b^2 is called the **difference between two perfect squares** (for obvious reasons). It is useful to be able to recognize this type of expression. For example,

$16y^2-49$

is the difference between two perfect squares, i.e. $(4y)^2-7^2$, since

$16y^2 = 4y \times 4y = (4y)^2$

and $49 = 7 \times 7 = 7^2$

Remember 1 is a perfect square, i.e. $1 = 1^2$.
Some other numbers that are perfect squares are

4, 9, 16, 25, 36, 49, 64, 81, 100, ...

An even power, such as x^2, x^4, x^6, x^8, ..., is always a perfect square,

$x^4 = (x^2)^2$, $x^6 = (x^3)^2$, $x^8 = (x^4)^2$, ...

These can help you to spot perfect squares. For example,

$1 - x^8$ is the difference between two squares, i.e. $1^2 - (x^4)^2$.

Factorizing the difference between two squares

The expansion of $(a+b)(a-b) = a^2 - b^2$
Reversing this gives $a^2 - b^2 = (a+b)(a-b)$
So the factors of $a^2 - b^2$ are the sum and difference of the square roots of each square. You can use this to factorize any expression that can be written as the difference between two squares. Each term must be written as a perfect square to find the factors.

Question

Factorize
(a) $9x^2 - 4y^2$ (b) $1 - 25a^4$ (c) $a^2 - (b-c)^2$

Answer

(a) $9x^2 - 4y^2 = (3x)^2 - (2y)^2$
$= (3x+2y)(3x-2y)$

(b) $1 - 25a^4 = (1)^2 - (5a^2)^2$
$= (1+5a^2)(1-5a^2)$

(c) $a^2 - (b-c)^2 = [a + (b-c)][a - (b-c)]$
$= (a+b-c)(a-b+c)$

This factorization can often be used to simplify some calculations without a calculator.

Question

Evaluate (a) $1001^2 - 999^2$ (b) $5.175^2 - 4.825^2$

Answer

(a) $1001^2 - 999^2 = (1001+999)(1001-999)$
$= (2000)(2)$
$= 4000$

(b) $5.175^2 - 4.825^2 = (5.175+4.825)(5.175-4.825)$
$= (10)(0.35)$
$= 3.5$

This technique can be useful when solving problems using Pythagoras' theorem (see Unit 2.36) and finding the area of a ring (see Unit 2.21). For example,

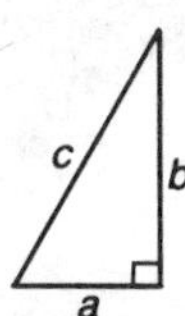

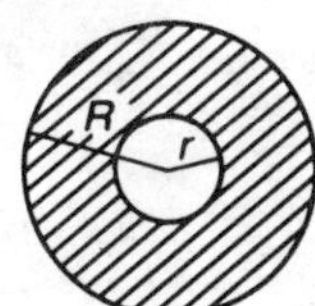

By Pythagoras' theorem
$c^2 = a^2 + b^2$
So $a^2 = c^2 - b^2$
and $b^2 = c^2 - a^2$

Area of shaded ring
$= \pi R^2 - \pi r^2$
$= \pi(R^2 - r^2)$

QUADRATIC TRINOMIALS

A **trinomial** is an expression containing *three* terms. For example,

$a+b-c$, $x^2+7x+20$, $x^4y - 3xy + 5x^2y^2$

are all trinomials.
A **quadratic** expression has a *square* as the *highest* power of the unknown. For example,

x^2+2, $3xy+7x^2+4$, $a^2-2ab+b^2$

are all quadratic expressions.

An expression such as ax^2+bx+c (where a, b and c are constants, not zero) is called a **quadratic trinomial** in x. It has three terms. They are an x^2 term, an x term and a constant term. For example,

x^2+2x+1, $3x^2+4x-7$, $2x^2-5x-1$

are all quadratic trinomials in x.

Factorizing quadratic trinomials

Many quadratic trinomials can be factorized. They can be written as the *product* of two brackets. For example,

$x^2+7x+6 = (x+6)(x+1)$
$2x^2-5x+3 = (2x-3)(x-1)$

There are several ways to work out the factors of quadratic trinomials. This unit shows one way. If you know and understand another way, then **continue to use that way**. You can work through the questions 'your way'. Always check your factors by expanding the brackets.

You can **factorize** a quadratic trinomial such as x^2+bx+c by changing the *three* terms into *four* – by splitting up the middle term. Then the four factors can be factorized by grouping. To split up the middle term of x^2+bx+c, find the factors of c which add up to b.

Question

Factorize x^2+3x+2

Answer

Look for the factors of 2 *which add up to* 3
They are +1 *and* +2

$x^2 + \underbrace{3x}\ +2$ *Factors of* +2
+1 and +2→+3 ✓

Split up middle term $= x^2 + 1x + 2x + 2$
Use grouping $= x(x+1) + 2(x+1)$
Factorize $= (x+1)(x+2)$

Check this yourself by expanding the brackets

You must be careful with the signs when finding factors. The + or − sign goes with the term that follows it.
It often helps to write out all the possible factors of the constant term c. With practice you will learn to spot the 'most likely' factors to try first.

Remember
(+)×(+)→(+)
(−)×(−)→(+)
(+)×(−)→(−)
(−)×(+)→(−)

Question

Factorize $x^2+2x-15$

Answer

Look for the factors of −15 *which add up to* +2
They are −3 *and* +5

$x^2 + \overbrace{2x} - 15$

Split up middle term $= x^2 - 3x + 5x - 15$
Use grouping $= x(x-3) + 5(x-3)$
Factorize $= (x-3)(x+5)$
Check by expanding the brackets

Factors of −15
+1 and −15→14
−1 and +15→14
+3 and −5→−2
−3 and +5→+2

To **factorize** a quadratic trinomial such as ax^2+bx+c, you need to find the factors of ac which add up to b.

Question

Factorize $3x^2-17x+10$

Answer

Look for factors of $3 \times 10 = 30$ *which add up to* -17
Try $(-)$ *factors first because you want* -17
Factors of $3 \times 10 = 30$*:*
-1 *and* $-30 = -31$
-2 *and* $-15 = -17$ ✓
They are -2 *and* -15

$$3x^2 - \underbrace{17x}+10$$

Split up the middle term $= 3x^2 \underbrace{-2x - 15x} + 10$
Use grouping $= x(3x-2) - 5(3x-2)$
Factorize $= (3x-2)(x-5)$
Check by expanding brackets

HARDER FACTORIZATION

To factorize some expressions you may need to use more than one type of factorization and/or repeated use of the same type. Do not try to do too much in each step.

Question

Factorize (a) $\pi R^2h - \pi r^2h$ (b) $24x^4 + 18x^3 + 3x^2$

Answer

(a) $\pi R^2h - \pi r^2h$
Common factor $= \pi h(R^2 - r^2)$
Difference between two squares $= \pi h(R+r)(R-r)$ **Check!**

(b) $24x^4 + 18x^3 + 3x^2$
Common factor $= 3x^2(8x^2 + \underbrace{6x} + 1)$
Quadratic trinomial $= 3x^2[8x^2 + 2x + 4x + 1]$
$= 3x^2[2x(4x+1) + 1(4x+1)]$
$= 3x^2[(4x+1)(2x+1)]$
$= 3x^2(4x+1)(2x+1)$ **Check!**

3.13 Transformation of formulae

Transforming a formula means rearranging it so that another letter in the formula becomes its subject. In the formulae transformed in Unit 2.31 the new subject letter appeared *only once*. At this level the new subject letter can appear *more than once* before the formula is transformed.

Here is a strategy to help you to transform formulae at this level. This strategy is an extension of the strategy given in Unit 2.31.

1 Clear roots, fractions and brackets first if there are any. If the new subject letter is under a square root sign, square each side of the equation to clear the root.
Remember $(\sqrt{a})^2 = a$.
Clear fractions by multiplying by the lowest common multiple (LCM) of the denominators.
Clear brackets by multiplying them out.

2 Collect together all the terms containing the new subject letter on the same side of the equation. Collect together all the other terms on the other side.

3 Factorize the terms on each side of the equation. The new subject letter will be a common factor on its side of the equation. This letter now appears once only.

4 Isolate the new subject letter on its side of the equation. This is usually done by dividing by the 'other factor' in the term. If the result is the square of the new subject letter, then take the square root of both sides to obtain a single letter.
Remember: $\sqrt{a^2} = a$

5 Write the formula with the new subject on the left hand side.

You may not need all of these steps to transform a formula. However, working through them in order acts as a useful checklist. Omit those steps not necessary for the formula you are transforming.

In the following question the new subject letter appears only once. It is, however, a more difficult transformation than those given in Unit 2.31.

Question

In physics, this formula is used for lenses or mirrors.

$$\frac{1}{f} = \frac{1}{u} + \frac{1}{v}$$

Make v the subject of the formula.

Answer

$$\frac{1}{f} = \frac{1}{u} + \frac{1}{v}$$

Multiply by fuv *the LCM of the denominators to clear fractions*
$$\frac{fuv}{f} = \frac{fuv}{u} + \frac{fuv}{v}$$
$$uv = fv + fu$$
Collect terms in v *on one side of the equation*
$$uv - fv = fu$$
Factorize
$$v(u-f) = fu$$
Divide by the factor $(u-f)$
$$\frac{v(u-f)}{(u-f)} = \frac{fu}{(u-f)}$$
$$v = \frac{fu}{(u-f)}$$

The transformation of the formula in the following question uses all the steps in the above strategy. The new subject letter appears twice in the formula.

Question

If $P = \sqrt{\left(\frac{nQ}{na+b}\right)}$ find n in terms of P, Q, a and b.

Answer

$$P = \sqrt{\left(\frac{nQ}{na+b}\right)}$$

Square each side to clear square root
$$P^2 = \left(\frac{nQ}{na+b}\right)$$
Multiply by $(na+b)$ *to clear fraction*
$$P^2(na+b) = \left(\frac{nQ}{na+b}\right)(na+b)$$
$$P^2(na+b) = nQ$$
Clear brackets
$$P^2na + P^2b = nQ$$
Collect together terms in n
$$P^2b = nQ - P^2na$$
Factorize
$$P^2b = n(Q - P^2a)$$
Divide by the factor $(Q - P^2a)$
$$\frac{P^2b}{(Q-P^2a)} = \frac{n(Q-P^2a)}{(Q-P^2a)}$$
$$\frac{P^2b}{(Q-P^2a)} = n$$
Write with n *on LHS*
$$n = \frac{P^2b}{(Q-P^2a)}$$

3.14 Linear equations

The **basic methods** for solving linear equations are given in Unit 2.30. This unit deals with some more difficult examples but the basic methods used are the same. *All* the steps taken are shown in the answers in this unit. With practice you may be able to do several steps at the same time. Take care if you do this! Checks are shown *in full* too. You may be able to do some of these in your head.

EQUATIONS WITH BRACKETS

To solve equations with brackets, follow the same steps as before (see Unit 2.30). At this level you may have several terms involving the unknown and several brackets to remove. The numbers may be more difficult than in Unit 2.30. Often they will test your knowledge of directed numbers (see Unit 2.2).

Question

Solve $2(x-1)-3(2x-1)=x+6$

Answer

$$2(x-1)-3(2x-1)=x+6$$

Remove brackets
Remember: $-3\times -1=+3$

$$2x-2-6x+3=x+6$$

Group 'x terms' on RHS
Subtract 2x from each side
Add 6x to each side

$$2x-2x-2-6x+6x+3=x-2x+6x+6$$

$$-2+3=5x+6$$

Group numbers on LHS
Subtract 6 from each side

$$-2+3-6=5x+6-6$$

$$-5=5x$$

Divide each side by 5

$$\frac{-5}{5}=\frac{5x}{5}$$

$$-1=x$$

Check LHS: $2(x-1)-3(2x-1)$
$=2(-1-1)-$
$=2(-2)-3(-2-1)$
$=-4-3(-3)$
$=-4+9$
$=+5$

RHS: $x+6$
$=-1+6$
$=5$

LHS = RHS ✓

EQUATIONS INVOLVING FRACTIONS

You may have more than one fraction in an equation at this level. To clear these fractions multiply *every* term in the equation by the *lowest common multiple* (LCM) of the denominators (see Unit 2.1 for LCM).

Question

Solve the equation $\frac{x}{4}+\frac{(x-3)}{3}=6$

Answer

$$\frac{x}{4}+\frac{(x-3)}{3}=6$$

The LCM of 4 and 3 is 12
Multiply each term by 12

$$12\frac{x}{4}+12\frac{(x-3)}{3}=12\times 6$$

$$3x+4(x-3)=72$$

Remove brackets $3x+4x-12=72$

Collect like terms $7x\quad -12=72$

Add 12 to each side $7x-12+12=72+12$

$$7x=84$$

Divide each side by 7

$$\frac{7x}{7}=\frac{84}{7}$$

$$x=12$$

Check LHS: $\frac{x}{4}+\frac{(x-3)}{3}=\frac{12}{4}+\frac{(12-3)}{3}=3+\frac{9}{3}=3+3=6$

RHS: 6

LHS = RHS ✓

Sometimes the denominator of a fraction is an *algebraic expression*. You can clear this fraction by multiplying every term by the algebraic denominator.

Question

Solve the equation $\frac{5}{x}=2$

Answer

$$\frac{5}{x}=2$$

Multiply each term by x $x\times\frac{5}{x}=2x$

$$5=2x$$

Divide each side by 2

$$\frac{5}{2}=\frac{2x}{2}$$

$$2.5=x$$

Check LHS: $\frac{5}{2.5}=2$

RHS: 2

LHS = RHS ✓

When the algebraic denominator has more than one term, then it is safer to put brackets around it first. This can help you to avoid mistakes when multiplying each term by the denominator.

Question

Solve the equation $2=\frac{6}{x-2}$

Answer

Put brackets around x − 2 $2=\frac{6}{(x-2)}$

Multiply each term by (x − 2) $2(x-2)=\frac{6}{(x-2)}(x-2)$

$$2(x-2)=6$$

Remove brackets $2x-4=6$

Add 4 to each side $2x-4+4=6+4$

$$2x=10$$

Divide each side by 2

$$\frac{2x}{2}=\frac{10}{2}$$

$$x=5$$

Check LHS: 2

RHS: $\frac{6}{(x-2)}=\frac{6}{(5-2)}=\frac{6}{3}=2$

LHS = RHS ✓

PROBLEM SOLVING

Linear equations are often formed when trying to solve 'word problems'. A strategy for solving problems is outlined in Unit 2.30. The equations formed are likely to be more difficult at this level.

Question

Two rival companies import ceramic tiles. Today company A imports twice as many tons of tiles as company B. Two years ago they each imported 5 tons fewer than today, but company A imported three times as many tons as company B. How many tons of ceramic tiles does each company import today?

Answer

Imports today

Suppose that B imports x tons of tiles today.
A imports twice as many tons as B.
So A imports $2x$ tons of tiles today.

Imports two years ago

A and B each imported 5 tons fewer than today.

So B imported $(x-5)$ tons of tiles.
A imported $(2x-5)$ tons of tiles.

But A imported 3 times as many tons as B.

$$(2x-5)=3(x-5)$$

Solve this equation to find x

Remove brackets $2x-5=3x-15$

Subtract 2x from each side $2x-2x-5=3x-2x-15$

$$-5=x\quad -15$$

Add 15 to each side $-5+15=x-15+15$

$10=x$

So, today company B imports 10 tons of tiles and company A imports 2×10 tons $=20$ tons of tiles.

Check Two years ago,
B imported $(10-5)$ tons $=5$ tons
A imported $(20-5)$ tons $=15$ tons
A imported 3 times as many tons as B.
15 tons $=3\times 5$ tons ✓

3.15 Simultaneous equations

Simultaneous equations are equations which are true at the same time, i.e. *simultaneously*. At this level only pairs of simultaneous equations in two unknowns are solved. For example, the solutions of

$x+y=6$
and $2x-3y=2$

are $x=4$ and $y=2$

Pairs of simultaneous equations can be solved algebraically and graphically.
Graphical methods are given in Unit 2.34 (for two linear equations) and in Unit 3.19 (for a linear and a quadratic equation). This unit gives an algebraic method.

TWO LINEAR EQUATIONS

Two linear simultaneous equations are usually solved by the **elimination** (i.e. 'getting rid') of one of the unknowns. This can be done by using *equal coefficients* or by *substitution*. Always **check** your solutions by substituting the values in both equations. This can often be done in your head.

Equal coefficients

One unknown may have **equal coefficients** in both equations. For example, in the equations

$2x-3y=7$
and $x+3y=4$

the unknown y has *equal coefficients*, i.e. 3, but *different* signs.
To solve equations with equal coefficients:

1. Eliminate the unknown with equal coefficients by adding or subtracting the equations.
   When the equal terms have *different* signs, *add* the equations to eliminate them.
   When the equal terms have the *same* sign, *subtract* the equations to eliminate them.
   (Numbering the equations makes them easier to describe in your answer.)
2. Solve the resulting equation to find the remaining unknown.
3. Substitute this value in one of the original equations to find the other unknown. Always check the equation which looks easier.
4. Check your solutions in both equations.

Question

Solve these simultaneous equations

(a) $2x-y=4$, $x+y=5$ (b) $2x-5y=8$, $x-5y=4$

Answer

(a) *Number each equation* $2x-y=4$ ......(1)
$x+y=5$ ......(2)

Add equations (1) and (2) to eliminate y $3x=9$
Divide both sides by 3 $x=3$
Substitute $x=3$ in (2) $3+y=5$
Subtract 3 from both sides $y=5-3=2$
So the solution of the equations is $x=3$, $y=2$
Check *Substitute $x=3$, $y=2$ into (1) and (2)*

(b) *Number each equation* $2x-5y=8$ ......(1)
$x-5y=4$ ......(2)

Subtract (2) from (1) $x=4$
Substitute $x=4$ in (2) $4-5y=4$
Subtract 4 from both sides $-5y=0$
So $y=0$
The solution of the equations is $x=4$, $y=0$
Check *Substitute $x=4$, $y=0$ into (1) and (2)*

This method can be used to solve equations without equal coefficients too. You can make one of the unknowns have *equal coefficients* by multiplying all the terms in *either* one *or* both equations by appropriate numbers. Comparing the coefficients of the equations will help you to choose the numbers to multiply by. Whenever possible, choose numbers so that adding the equations eliminates the unknown, i.e. make *equal terms* with *opposite* signs, ... it's easier. Then the equations can be solved as before.

Question

Solve this pair of simultaneous equations.
$2x-y=10$
$x+3y=5$

Answer

Number each equation $2x-y=10$ ......(1)
$x+3y=5$ ......(2)

Multiply (1) *by 3 to make the y terms 'equal'* $6x-3y=30$
(2) *remains the same.* $x+3y=5$
Add equations to eliminate y $7x=35$
Divide both sides by 7 $x=5$
Substitute $x=5$ in (1) $(2\times 5)-y=10$
$10-y=10$
$y=0$

So the solution of the equations is $x=5$, $y=0$.
Check *Substitute $x=5$, $y=0$ into (1) and (2)*

Sometimes the simultaneous equations are 'mixed up'. You need to rearrange them before trying to solve them. Put the two unknowns in the same order on the same side of each equation, and the constants on the other side.

Question

Solve the equations $7y=2x-9$ and $3x=2y+5$ simultaneously.

Answer

Rearrange the equations and number them
$-2x+7y=-9$ ......(1)
$3x-2y=5$ ......(2)

Multiply (1) by 3 (the coefficient of x in (2)) $-6x+21y=-27$
Multiply (2) by 2 $6x-4y=10$
Add the equations to eliminate x $17y=-17$
$y=-1$
Substitute $y=-1$ in (2) $3x-2(-1)=5$
$3x+2=5$
$x=1$

So the solution of the equations is $x=1$, $y=-1$.
Check *Substitute $x=1$, $y=-1$ in the given equations $7y=2x-9$ and $3x=2y+5$*

Substitution

To solve simultaneous equations by substitution:

1. Make one of the unknowns the subject of one equation (see Unit 2.31).

2 Substitute this expression for the unknown in the other equation.

3 Solve the resulting equation to find one unknown.

4 Find the other unknown by substituting your solution in the original equation.

5 Check your solutions.

This method is easiest to use when one of the coefficients of an unknown is 1 or -1.

Question

Solve the equations $-2x+3y=19$ and $2x+y=1$ simultaneously.

Answer

Number the equations $\quad -2x+3y=19 \quad \ldots\ldots(1)$

$2x+y=1 \quad \ldots\ldots(2)$

Make y the subject of (2) $\quad$ (2) gives $y=1-2x$

Substitute $(1-2x)$ *for y in equation* (1)

Equation (1) $\quad -2x+3y=19$

becomes $\quad -2x+3(1-2x)=19$

Remove brackets $\quad -2x+3-6x=19$

Collect like terms $\quad -8x+3=19$

Subtract 3 from both sides $\quad -8x=16$

Divide both sides by -8 $\quad x=-2$

Substitute $x=-2$ in (2) $\quad 2(-2)+y=1$

$-4+y=1$

$y=5$

So the solution of the equations is $x=-2$, $y=5$

Check *Substitute* $x=-2$, $y=5$ *in the original equations*

A LINEAR AND A QUADRATIC EQUATION

A simultaneous linear and quadratic equation is usually solved by **substitution**.

In this case it is easier to make one unknown the subject of the *linear* equation, then *substitute* the expression into the *quadratic* equation. This gives a quadratic equation in one unknown, which can be solved (see Unit 3.16). Usually there are two different solutions for the unknown. Substitute each of the solutions in turn into the linear equation to find the values of the other unknown. Make it clear in your answer which value of x goes with which value of y.

Question

Solve the equations $3x^2-4y+1=0$ and $2x-y=1$ simultaneously.

Answer

$3x^2-4y+1=0 \quad \ldots\ldots(1)$

$2x-y=1 \quad \ldots\ldots(2)$

From the linear equation (2) $\quad y=2x-1$

Substitute $(2x-1)$ *for y in* (1)

Equation (1) $\quad 3x^2-4y+1=0$

becomes $\quad 3x^2-4(2x-1)+1=0$

Remove brackets $\quad 3x^2-8x+4+1=0$

Collect like terms $\quad 3x^2-8x+5=0$

Factorize quadratic $\quad (3x-5)(x-1)=0$

Solve equation $\quad$ Either $(3x-5)=0$ or $(x-1)=0$

Either $\quad x=\frac{5}{3}$ or $\quad x=1$

Substitute each of these values of x into (2) *in turn*

When $x=\frac{5}{3}$, (2) gives $\quad 2\left(\frac{5}{3}\right)-y=1$

$\frac{10}{3}-y=\frac{3}{3}$

$y=\frac{10}{3}-\frac{3}{3}=\frac{7}{3}$

When $x=1$, (2) gives $\quad 2(1)-y=1$

$2-y=1$

$y=2-1=1$

So the two solutions are:

when $x=\frac{5}{3}$, $y=\frac{7}{3}$

and when $x=1$, $y=1$

Check *Substitute these solutions in the original equations*

PROBLEM SOLVING

Problems often involve two unknowns. To solve these you must first form two separate equations in the two unknowns from the given data. These simultaneous equations can then be solved using a method given in this unit.

Hints on solving problems using algebra are given in Unit 2.30.

Question

Mr Brown and Mr Green run a small business assembling two types of product. The cost of components and the labour needed for each product are shown in this table.

	Cost of component £	Labour man-hours
Type A	36	16
Type B	24	24

The business has £156 available to buy components each week. The total labour available each week is 96 man-hours. How many products of each type can they assemble each week to maintain maximum production?

Answer

Suppose each week Mr Brown and Mr Green make x of type A product and y of type B product.

Consider the cost of components:

x components of type A cost £$36x$

y components of type B cost £$24y$

The total possible cost of components is £156.

So $\quad 36x+24y=156 \quad \ldots\ldots(1)$

Consider the man-hours available:

x components of type A take $16x$ man-hours

y components of type B take $24y$ man-hours

The total possible man-hours is 96.

So $\quad 16x+24y=96 \quad \ldots\ldots(2)$

The simultaneous equations are

$36x+24y=156 \quad \ldots\ldots(1)$

$16x+24y=96 \quad \ldots\ldots(2)$

Subtract (2) from (1) $\quad 20x=60$

$x=3$

Substitute $x=3$ in equation (2).

$16(3)+24y=96$

$48+24y=96$

$24y=48$

$y=2$

So the solution of the equations is $x=3$, $y=2$.

This means that they should assemble 3 of type A and 2 of type B each week.

3.16 Quadratic equations

In a **quadratic equation** in x, the highest power of x is x^2, i.e. x to the power 2. For example,

$$x^2+2x-3=0, \quad 3x^2=2, \quad x=3x^2+1, \quad 2x^2=1$$

are all quadratic equations in x. (The unknown can be

represented by any letter. In this unit x will be used for the unknown.)
The general form of a quadratic equation in x is

$$ax^2+bx+c=0$$

where a, b and c are real numbers but a is not equal to zero. Any quadratic equation can be written in this form.
In general a quadratic equation has **two solutions**, i.e. it is *satisfied* by *two values* of x. When these two values are equal, the equation is said to have **two equal solutions** or **roots**. The solutions of an equation are also called its roots.
At this level only equations which have real roots, i.e. solutions which are *real numbers*, are studied.
Quadratic equations can be solved in several different ways. The four common methods used at this level are by **factorization**, by **formula**, by **calculator** and by **graph**. Graphical solution is described in Unit 3.19. The other methods are given in this unit.
Always **check** by substituting your solutions in the *original* equation. You can often do this check mentally or on your calculator.

BY FACTORIZATION

If the product of two real numbers is zero, then one or the other or both of the numbers must be zero. For example, if a and b are both real numbers and $ab=0$, then either $a=0$ or $b=0$ or both $a=0$ and $b=0$.
This fact about real numbers is used to solve some quadratic equations.
The quadratic equation must be written as

'quadratic expression' $=0$

The quadratic expression may be given as the product of two factors as in this question.

Question

Solve $x(x+4)=0$

Answer

Product is zero,	$x(x+4)=0$
so one or other or both	Either $x=0$ or $(x+4)=0$
must be zero	i.e. either $x=0$ or $x=-4$

Check *the answers mentally*

The quadratic equation may be given in the general form $ax^2+bx+c=0$. You have to rewrite the quadratic expression ax^2+bx+c as the product of two factors yourself. Use the methods given in Unit 3.12 to factorize the quadratic. Then you can solve the equation as shown above.

Question

Find the roots of $x^2-5x+6=0$

Answer

The factors of +6 which add up to −5 are −3 and −2

	$x^2-5x+6=0$
Split up the middle term	$x^2-3x-2x+6=0$
Use grouping	$x(x-3)-2(x-3)=0$
Factorize	$(x-3)(x-2)=0$
Solve the equation	Either $(x-3)=0$ or $(x-2)=0$
	i.e. either $x=3$ or $x=2$

Check *Substitute values for x in x^2-5x+6*

If $x=3$, $(3)^2-5(3)+6=9-15+6=0$

If $x=2$, $(2)^2-5(2)+6=4-10+6=0$

Sometimes the quadratic equation is not given in the general form $ax^2+bx+c=0$.
You must rewrite it in this form before you can find the factors of ax^2+bx+c.

Question

Solve the quadratic equation $2x^2=9x+5$

Answer

Rearrange into the form	$2x^2=9x+5$
$ax^2+bx+c=0$	$2x^2-9x-5=0$

The factors of $2\times-5=-10$ which add up to -9 are $+1$ and -10

	$2x^2-9x-5=0$
Split up the middle term	$2x^2+1x-10x-5=0$
Use grouping	$x(2x+1)-5(2x+1)=0$
Factorize	$(2x+1)(x-5)=0$
Solve the equation	Either $(2x+1)=0$ or $(x-5)=0$
	i.e. either $2x=-1$ or $x=5$
	So either $x=-\frac{1}{2}$ or $x=5$

Check *by substituting $x=-\frac{1}{2}$ and $x=5$ into $2x^2=9x+5$*
Do not use $2x^2-9x-5=0$ in case you have made a mistake rearranging it
Check

If $x=-\frac{1}{2}$, LHS: $2(-\frac{1}{2})^2=+\frac{1}{2}$; RHS: $9(-\frac{1}{2})+5=-4\frac{1}{2}+5=+\frac{1}{2}$ } LHS = RHS ✓

If $x=5$, LHS: $2(5)^2=50$; RHS: $9(5)+5=45+5=50$ } LHS = RHS ✓

When the equation is in the form $ax^2-c=0$, i.e. $b=0$, use the *difference between two squares* to factorize ax^2-c (see Unit 3.12).

Remember $a^2-b^2=(a+b)(a-b)$
(difference between two squares)

Question

Solve the equation $x^2=3$

Answer

	$x^2=3$
Rearrange the equation	$x^2-3=0$
Factorize by the difference between two squares	$(x+\sqrt{3})(x-\sqrt{3})=0$
Solve the equation	Either $(x+\sqrt{3})=0$ or $(x-\sqrt{3})=0$
	i.e. either $x=-\sqrt{3}$ or $x=+\sqrt{3}$

BY FORMULA

A quadratic equation in the general form $ax^2+bx+c=0$ may be solved using the formula

$$x=\frac{-b\pm\sqrt{(b^2-4ac)}}{2a}$$

This formula gives two roots because $\pm$ means + or −. It is a shorthand way to write

$$x=\frac{-b+\sqrt{(b^2-4ac)}}{2a} \quad \textbf{or} \quad x=\frac{-b-\sqrt{(b^2-4ac)}}{2a}$$

This formula is used when the quadratic expression ax^2+bx+c has no factors or if you are unable to find them. When using this formula, rearrange the quadratic equation in the general form $ax^2+bx+c=0$ first. This makes it easier for you to compare the equation with the general form to find values of a, b and c. Take care to put the correct sign with each number and remember that 'x^2' means '$1x^2$' and 'x' means '$1x$'. For example, in $x^2-2x+6=0$, $a=1$, $b=-2$ and $c=+6$. Substitute the values for a, b and c in the formula and do the necessary arithmetic. Use a calculator if you wish. Do not try to do too many steps at once.
Questions involving the formula often ask for a specific degree of accuracy in the answer, e.g. 'correct to three significant figures'. **Check** that you have given your answer to the required accuracy.

Question

Solve the equation $3x^2-2x=3$. Give your answer correct to two decimal places.

Answer $3x^2-2x=3$

Rearrange the equation $3x^2-2x-3=0$

Compare with general form $ax^2+bx+c=0$

This gives: $a=3$, $b=-2$, $c=-3$

Write the formula $x=\dfrac{-b\pm\sqrt{(b^2-4ac)}}{2a}$

Substitute the values for a, b and c $x=\dfrac{-(-2)\pm\sqrt{[(-2)^2-4(3)(-3)]}}{2(3)}$

$=\dfrac{+2\pm\sqrt{(+4+36)}}{6}$

$=\dfrac{+2\pm\sqrt{40}}{6}$

Write two solutions separately $=\dfrac{+2+\sqrt{40}}{6}$ or $\dfrac{+2-\sqrt{40}}{6}$ **C**

$x=1.39$ or -0.72 (to 2 d.p.)

BY CALCULATOR

One way to solve an equation is to try values in the equation until you find the solutions, i.e. those values which make the equation true. Doing this *in your head* or *on paper* can take a long time but a calculator enables you to test many values quickly and easily.

It is important that you do not just pick values at random to test. You must start with a sensible estimate for a solution first. Your knowledge of the graph of a quadratic equation (see Unit 3.19) can help you to make your first estimate for each root.

The graph of $y=ax^2+bx+c$ is a parabola. If the equation $ax^2+bx+c=0$ has two different roots, then it cuts the x-axis (the line $y=0$) at two points.

The x-coordinates of these points give the two roots of the equation.

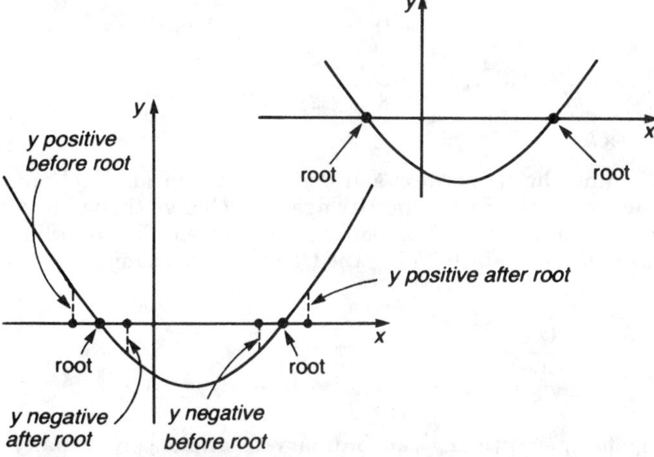

On this sketch graph, you can see that on either side of a root, the sign of y is different. On one side of the root, y is positive, on the other side, y is negative. You can use this to give you a clue as to where the roots can be found.

Make a table of results using some simple values of x and calculate the matching values of y. From the table you can find where the values of y change sign. These x-values give you estimates for the roots of the equation.

Question

The roots of $3x^2-x-5=0$ lie between -3 and $+3$. Find the two integer values each root lies between.

Answer **C**

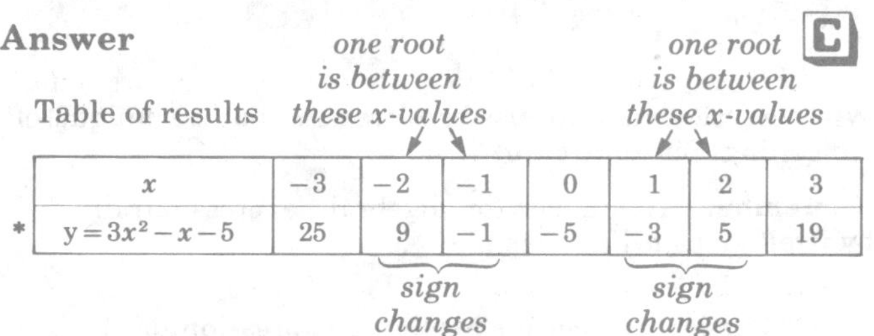

Table of results — *one root is between these x-values* (−2 and −1); *one root is between these x-values* (1 and 2)

x	−3	−2	−1	0	1	2	3
* $y=3x^2-x-5$	25	9	−1	−5	−3	5	19

sign changes (between −2 and −1); *sign changes* (between 1 and 2)

From this table of results

one root lies between $x=-2$ and $x=-1$

one root lies between $x=1$ and $x=2$.

**Here is one way to work out $y=3x^2-x-5$ for each value of x on a calculator*

Try this way first

Then find the best way on your calculator

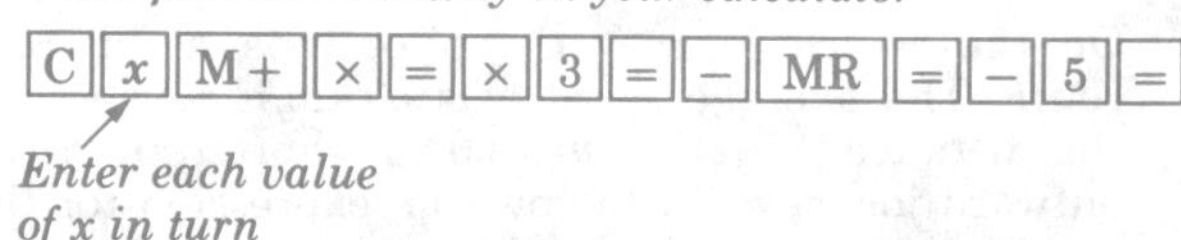

Your first estimates to each root help you to choose the next estimates to test. Continue testing values of x, looking for changes of sign of y to show when you are getting closer to the root. The following example shows you how to do this.

Since this method usually gives only approximate values for the roots, you must give your solution to the degree of accuracy stated in the problem. For example, if you need a solution to 2 decimal places, then you must calculate it to 3 decimal places and then correct it to 2 decimal places.

Question

One root of $3x^2-x-5=0$ lies between -2 and -1 (see previous answer). Use your calculator to help you to find the value of the root correct to 2 decimal places.

Answer

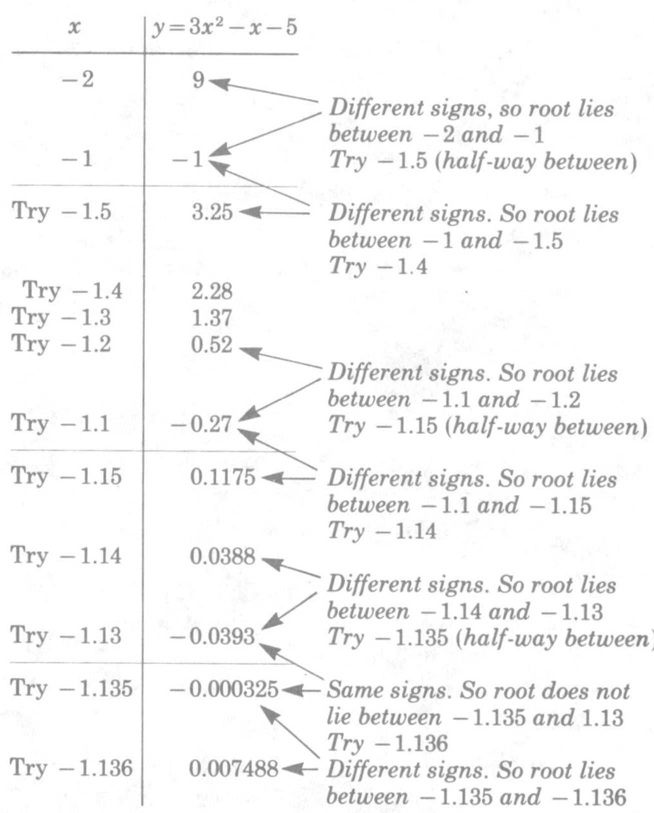

x	$y=3x^2-x-5$	
−2	9	*Different signs, so root lies between −2 and −1 Try −1.5 (half-way between)*
−1	−1	
Try −1.5	3.25	*Different signs. So root lies between −1 and −1.5 Try −1.4*
Try −1.4	2.28	
Try −1.3	1.37	
Try −1.2	0.52	*Different signs. So root lies between −1.1 and −1.2 Try −1.15 (half-way between)*
Try −1.1	−0.27	
Try −1.15	0.1175	*Different signs. So root lies between −1.1 and −1.15 Try −1.14*
Try −1.14	0.0388	*Different signs. So root lies between −1.14 and −1.13 Try −1.135 (half-way between)*
Try −1.13	−0.0393	
Try −1.135	−0.000325	*Same signs. So root does not lie between −1.135 and 1.13 Try −1.136*
Try −1.136	0.007488	*Different signs. So root lies between −1.135 and −1.136*

So one root of the equation lies between -1.135 and -1.136.

This gives one root as $x=-1.14$ (to 2 d.p.).

SOLVING PROBLEMS

When solving a problem using algebra you may obtain a quadratic equation. Solve this equation using the most appropriate and easiest method. If a question specifies the method to use, make sure that you use that method.

Sometimes one of the solutions of the quadratic equation does not make sense for the problem you are solving. Always explain why you are rejecting one solution to the equation.

(General hints on solving problems using algebra are given in Unit 2.27.)

Question

(a) An aeroplane travelled a distance of 660 km at an average speed of x km/h. Write down an expression for the number of hours taken.

(b) On the return journey the pilot took a different route. The average speed was 50 km/h slower and the distance travelled was 60 km shorter than the outward journey. Write down an expression for the number of hours taken for the return journey.

(c) Given that the outward journey took 12 minutes less than the return journey, form an equation in x. Show that it reduces to

$$x^2+250x-165\,000=0$$

(d) Given that $x^2+250x-165\,000=0$ can be expressed as $(x+550)(x-k)$, find the value of k. Hence find the time taken for the outward and return journeys.

Answer

(a) Outward journey

$$\text{time taken}=\frac{\text{distance travelled}}{\text{speed}}$$

$$=\frac{660}{x}\text{ hours}$$

(b) Return journey

Distance travelled is 60 km shorter than outward journey

$$=660\text{ km}-60\text{ km}=600\text{ km}$$

Speed is 50 km/h slower than outward journey

$$=(x-50)\text{ km/h}$$

$$\text{Time taken}=\frac{600}{(x-50)}\text{ hours}$$

(c) The outward journey was 12 minutes quicker than the return journey.

$$12\text{ minutes}=\frac{12}{60}\text{ hours}=\frac{1}{5}\text{ hour}$$

$$\text{Outward journey time}+\frac{1}{5}\text{ hour}=\text{return journey time}$$

$$\frac{660}{x}+\frac{1}{5}=\frac{600}{(x-50)}\text{ hours}$$

Multiplying by the common denominator $5x(x-50)$ gives

$$5(x-50)660+x(x-50)=5x\,.\,600$$

$$3300x-165\,000+x^2-50x=3000x$$

$$x^2+250x-165\,000=0$$

(d) Since $x^2+250x-165\,000=(x+550)(x-k)$

$$-550k=-165\,000$$

$$k=\frac{-165\,000}{-550}=300$$

So $(x+550)(x-300)=0$

Either $(x+550)=0$ or $(x-300)=0$

i.e. either $x=-550$ or $x=300$.

Since x is the speed in km/h, a negative value does not make sense.

So $x=300$ km/h

This gives the time for the outward journey

$$=\frac{660}{300}\text{ hours}$$

$=132$ minutes

$=2$ hours 12 minutes

The time for the return journey $=2$ h 12 min $+$ 12 min

$=2$ h 24 min

3.17 Algebraic fractions

In arithmetic, $5\div 9$ can be written as the fraction $\frac{5}{9}$.

In algebra, $a\div b$ can be written as the fraction $\frac{a}{b}$.

In the simplest algebraic fractions the denominators are numbers. For example,

$$\frac{a}{2},\quad \frac{7x}{5},\quad \frac{xy}{5},\quad \frac{b^2c^3}{7},\quad \frac{(x+2)}{3}$$

The denominators can be algebraic terms or expressions. For example,

$$\frac{3}{y},\quad \frac{2}{pq^3},\quad \frac{3xy}{z^2},\quad \frac{1}{(a+3)},\quad \frac{2x}{(x^2+5)}$$

Since the letters in algebraic fractions stand for numbers, fractions in algebra behave in the same way as fractions in arithmetic. Calculations with algebraic fractions use the same basic rules as for ordinary fractions (see units 1.9, 1.10 and 2.5).

EQUIVALENT FRACTIONS

The value of an algebraic fraction (like an ordinary fraction) is not changed when both the numerator and denominator are multiplied by the same quantity. The quantity you multiply by can be a number or an algebraic expression. The result is an **equivalent fraction**. For example,

$$\frac{x}{5}=\frac{3x}{15}\ (\times 3)\qquad \frac{7}{y}=\frac{7y}{y^2}\ (\times y)$$

$$\frac{a}{b}=\frac{ka}{kb}\ (\times k)\qquad \frac{4x}{3y}=\frac{4x(x+2)}{3y(x+2)}\ (\times (x+2))$$

Dividing the numerator and denominator of an algebraic fraction by the *same* quantity does not change the value of the fraction. It makes an equivalent fraction. This is called **cancelling** or **simplifying** the fraction. For example,

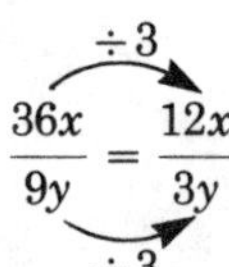

$$\frac{36x}{9y}=\frac{12x}{3y}\ (\div 3)$$

Algebraic fractions, like ordinary fractions, are usually written in their **simplest form**. A fraction in its simplest form cannot be cancelled. 1 will be the only number that divides exactly into both top and bottom. For example,

$$\frac{10a}{8}=\frac{5a}{4}\ (\div 2)\quad \text{or}\quad \frac{\overset{5}{\cancel{10}}a}{\underset{4}{\cancel{8}}}=\frac{5a}{4}$$

$$\frac{ka}{kb}=\frac{a}{b}\ (\div k)\quad \text{or}\quad \frac{\overset{1}{\cancel{k}}a}{\underset{1}{\cancel{k}}b}=\frac{a}{b}$$

With practice you can use the 'crossing out' technique of cancelling. But take care!

Remember A number (or algebraic expression) divided by itself gives 1. For example,

$$k\div k=1$$

Multiplying a number (or algebraic expression) by 1 gives

the same number (or algebraic expression). For example,

$1 \times a = a$

The basic rules of indices are often used when simplifying fractions. For example,

$x^4 \div x^3 = x^{4-3} = x^1$

Look for factors common to both numerator and denominator to cancel (divide by).

Question

Simplify (a) $\frac{9lm}{6l^2m}$ (b) $\frac{5c^2d^5}{25c^2d^2}$

Answer

(a) $\frac{9lm}{6l^2m}$ Common factors are $3lm$

$$\frac{9lm}{6l^2m} = \frac{3}{2l} \quad (\div 3lm)$$

or $\frac{\overset{3\,1\,1}{9lm}}{\underset{2\,l\,1}{6l^2m}} = \frac{3}{2l}$ ← $l^2 \div l = l^{2-1} = l$

(b) $\frac{5c^2d^5}{25c^2d^2}$ Common factors are $5c^2d^2$

$$\frac{5c^2d^5}{25c^2d^2} = \frac{d^3}{5} \quad (\div 5c^2d^2)$$

or $\frac{\overset{1\,1\,d^3}{5c^2d^5}}{\underset{5\,1\,1}{25c^2d^2}} = \frac{d^3}{5}$ ← $d^5 \div d^2 = d^{5-2} = d^3$

You may have to factorize the numerator and/or denominator before you can cancel any factors (see Unit 3.12). The factors can be expressions inside brackets.

Question

Simplify (a) $\frac{2a^2+6ab}{2a^3}$ (b) $\frac{5(x^2-y^2)}{2(x-y)}$

Answer

(a) $\frac{2a^2+6ab}{2a^3}$

Factorize $= \frac{2a(a+3b)}{2a^3}$

Cancel by $2a$ $= \frac{\overset{1\,1}{2a}(a+3b)}{\underset{1\,a^2}{2a^3}}$

$= \frac{(a+3b)}{a^2}$

(b) $\frac{5(x^2-y^2)}{2(x-y)}$

Factorize $= \frac{5(x+y)(x-y)}{2(x-y)}$

Cancel $(x-y)$ $= \frac{5(x+y)\overset{1}{(x-y)}}{2\underset{1}{(x-y)}}$

$= \frac{5(x+y)}{2}$

MULTIPLICATION AND DIVISION

To **multiply** algebraic fractions, multiply the numerators and denominators *separately*. For example,

$\frac{a}{b} \times \frac{x}{y} = \frac{ax}{by}$

Before multiplying, cancel any factors common to the numerators and denominators. This makes the multiplication easier.

Question

Evaluate (a) $\frac{12xy}{7} \times \frac{14x}{20}$ (b) $\frac{3ab}{5c^2d^3} \times \frac{10d^4}{9a^2}$

Answer

(a) $\frac{12xy}{7} \times \frac{14x}{20}$

Cancel by 4 and 7 $= \frac{\overset{3}{12}xy}{\underset{1}{7}} \times \frac{\overset{2}{14}x}{\underset{5}{20}}$

Multiply $= \frac{6x^2y}{5}$

(b) $\frac{3ab}{5c^2d^3} \times \frac{10d^4}{9a^2}$

Cancel by $3a$ and $5d^3$ $= \frac{\overset{1\,1}{3a}b}{\underset{1\;1}{5c^2d^3}} \times \frac{\overset{2\;d}{10d^4}}{\underset{3\;a}{9a^2}}$

Multiply $= \frac{2bd}{3ac^2}$

Always **check** that your answer is in its simplest form. If it is not, then you have not cancelled *all* the factors before multiplying. You must cancel them at the end. For example,

$\frac{3x}{4y} \times \frac{y^3}{x} = \frac{3xy^3}{4xy}$ *Not simplest form*

$= \frac{3\overset{y^2}{xy^3}}{4\underset{1}{xy}}$ *Cancel by xy*

$= \frac{3y^2}{4}$ *Simplest form*

When you have an algebraic expression in the numerator and/or denominator, always try to factorize it first. Then cancel if you can.

Question

Simplify $\frac{6x^2+2xy}{5z} \times \frac{15z^2}{3x+y}$

Answer

$\frac{6x^2+2xy}{5z} \times \frac{15z^2}{3x+y}$

Factorize $= \frac{2x(3x+y)}{5z} \times \frac{15z^2}{(3x+y)}$

Cancel by $(3x+y)$ and $5z$ $= \frac{2x\overset{1}{(3x+y)}}{\underset{1\,1}{5z}} \times \frac{\overset{3\;z}{15z^2}}{\underset{1}{(3x+y)}}$

Multiply $= \frac{6xz}{1}$

$= 6xz$

To **divide** by an algebraic fraction, multiply by its inverse. For example,

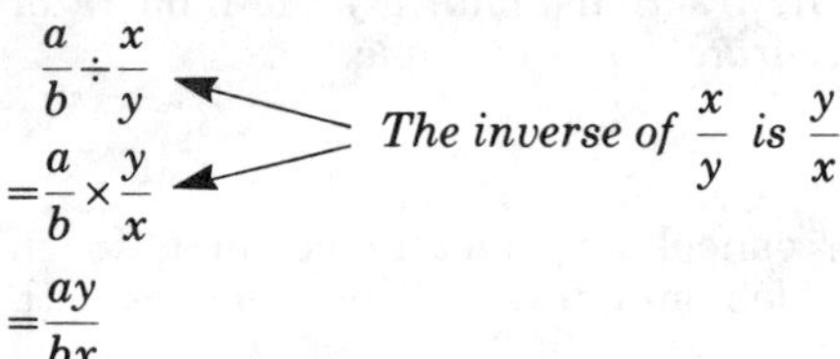

Question

Evaluate (a) $\frac{4x^2y}{5p}\div\frac{12xy^2}{20p^2}$ (b) $\frac{4a^2+8ab}{3}\div\frac{5ab+10b^2}{9}$

Answer

(a) $\frac{4x^2y}{5p}\div\frac{12xy^2}{20p^2}$

Change to multiplication $=\frac{4x^2y}{5p}\times\frac{20p^2}{12xy^2}$

Cancel by 4xy and 5p $=\frac{\overset{1\,x\,1}{\cancel{4}\cancel{x^2}\cancel{y}}}{\underset{1\,1}{\cancel{5p}}}\times\frac{\overset{4\,p}{\cancel{20}\cancel{p^2}}}{\underset{3\,1\,y}{\cancel{12}\cancel{x}\cancel{y^2}}}$

Multiply $=\frac{4px}{3y}$

(b) $\frac{4a^2+8ab}{3}\div\frac{5ab+10b^2}{9}$

Change to multiplication $=\frac{4a^2+8ab}{3}\times\frac{9}{5ab+10b^2}$

Factorize $=\frac{4a(a+2b)}{3}\times\frac{9}{5b(a+2b)}$

Cancel by (a+2b) and 3 $=\frac{4a\overset{1}{\cancel{(a+2b)}}}{\underset{1}{\cancel{3}}}\times\frac{\overset{3}{\cancel{9}}}{5b\underset{1}{\cancel{(a+2b)}}}$

Multiply $=\frac{12a}{5b}$

ADDITION AND SUBTRACTION

As in arithmetic, fractions with the **same denominator** can be added or subtracted to give a single fraction. Always simplify this fraction if you can.

Question

Calculate (a) $\frac{x}{8}+\frac{5x}{8}$ (b) $\frac{2y}{x^2}+\frac{3z}{x^2}$

(c) $\frac{2a}{5}-\frac{8b}{5}$ (d) $\frac{6x}{(x+y)}-\frac{4x}{(x+y)}$

Answer

(a) $\frac{x}{8}+\frac{5x}{8}=\frac{x+5x}{8}=\frac{6x}{8}=\frac{3x}{4}$

(b) $\frac{2y}{x^2}+\frac{3z}{x^2}=\frac{2y+3z}{x^2}$

(c) $\frac{2a}{5}-\frac{8b}{5}=\frac{2a-8b}{5}=\frac{2(a-4b)}{5}$

(d) $\frac{6x}{(x+y)}-\frac{4x}{(x+y)}=\frac{6x-4x}{(x+y)}=\frac{2x}{(x+y)}$

To add or subtract fractions with **different denominators**, use the same basic method as for arithmetic fractions. Find the lowest common multiple (LCM) of the denominator first. Then rewrite each fraction with this LCM as the denominator. (To do this, multiply the numerator and denominator of each fraction by the appropriate quantity.) When the fractions have the same denominator, you can add or subtract them as before.
The simplest algebraic fractions have just numbers in the denominators.

Question

Calculate (a) $\frac{x}{3}+\frac{y}{2}$ (b) $\frac{5a}{12}-\frac{a}{9}$

Answer

(a) $\frac{x}{3}+\frac{y}{2}$

The LCM of 3 and 2 is 6
Write each fraction with denominator 6

$\frac{x}{3}=\frac{2x}{6}$ (×2) $\frac{y}{2}=\frac{3y}{6}$ (×3)

So $\frac{x}{3}+\frac{y}{2}=\frac{2x}{6}+\frac{3y}{6}$

$=\frac{2x+3y}{6}$

(b) $\frac{5a}{12}-\frac{a}{9}$

The LCM of 12 and 9 is 36
Write each fraction with denominator 36

$\frac{5a}{12}=\frac{15a}{36}$ (×3) $\frac{a}{9}=\frac{4a}{36}$ (×4)

So $\frac{5a}{12}-\frac{a}{9}=\frac{15a}{36}-\frac{4a}{36}$

$=\frac{15a-4a}{36}$

$=\frac{11a}{36}$

If you do not find the *lowest* common multiple of the denominators, then you will be able to cancel the answer. Always **check** that your answer is in its simplest form. For example,

$\frac{5a}{12}-\frac{a}{9}=\frac{45a}{108}-\frac{12a}{108}$

$=\frac{33a}{108}$ *Cancel by 3*

$=\frac{11a}{36}$

The denominators in the fractions to be added (or subtracted) may be letters or algebraic terms. But the method used to add or subtract the fractions is basically the same.

Question

Express each of these as a single fraction

(a) $\frac{a}{b}+\frac{c}{d}$ (b) $\frac{4a}{3b}-\frac{5b}{2a}$ (c) $\frac{2x}{p^2}-\frac{x}{3pq}$

Answer

(a) $\frac{a}{b}+\frac{c}{d}$

The LCM of b and d is bd
Write each fraction with denominator bd

$$\frac{a}{b} = \frac{ad}{bd} \quad (\times d) \qquad \frac{c}{d} = \frac{bc}{bd} \quad (\times b)$$

$$\text{So} \quad \frac{a}{b} + \frac{c}{d} = \frac{ad}{bd} + \frac{bc}{bd} = \frac{ad+bc}{bd}$$

(b) $\dfrac{4a}{3b} - \dfrac{5b}{2a}$

The LCM of 3b and 2a is 6ab
Write each fraction with denominator 6ab

$$\frac{4a}{3b} = \frac{8a^2}{6ab} \quad (\times 2a) \qquad \frac{5b}{2a} = \frac{15b^2}{6ab} \quad (\times 3b)$$

$$\text{So} \quad \frac{4a}{3b} - \frac{5b}{2a} = \frac{8a^2}{6ab} - \frac{15b^2}{6ab} = \frac{8a^2 - 15b^2}{6ab}$$

(c) $\dfrac{2x}{p^2} - \dfrac{x}{3pq}$

The LCM of p^2 and 3pq is $3p^2q$
Write each fraction with denominator $3p^2q$

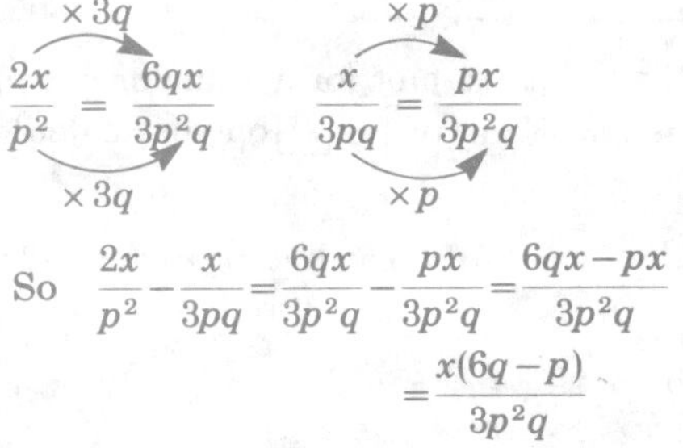

$$\frac{2x}{p^2} = \frac{6qx}{3p^2q} \quad (\times 3q) \qquad \frac{x}{3pq} = \frac{px}{3p^2q} \quad (\times p)$$

$$\text{So} \quad \frac{2x}{p^2} - \frac{x}{3pq} = \frac{6qx}{3p^2q} - \frac{px}{3p^2q} = \frac{6qx - px}{3p^2q} = \frac{x(6q-p)}{3p^2q}$$

The denominators may be expressions of the type $ax+b$. It is usually easier to put brackets around the expression $(ax+b)$ and then treat it as a single term.

Question

Write as a single fraction $\dfrac{2}{x+1} + \dfrac{3}{x-2}$

Answer

Use brackets	$\dfrac{2}{(x+1)} + \dfrac{3}{(x-2)}$
Use LCM $(x+1)(x-2)$	$= \dfrac{2(x-2)}{(x+1)(x-2)} + \dfrac{3(x+1)}{(x+1)(x-2)}$
Write with a common denominator	$= \dfrac{2(x-2)+3(x+1)}{(x+1)(x-2)}$
Remove brackets in numerator	$= \dfrac{2x-4+3x+3}{(x+1)(x-2)}$
Collect like terms	$= \dfrac{5x-1}{(x+1)(x-2)}$

3.18 Algebraic graphs

RECOGNIZING COMMON GRAPHS

Recognizing the shape of a graph from its equation is a useful skill. The shapes of the graphs of some of the more common functions (linear, quadratic, rectangular hyperbola) are described in Unit 2.33. This section deals with the shapes of the other graphs you may meet at this level.

Cubic

In a **cubic** function in x the highest power of x is x^3, i.e. 'x-cubed' or 'x to the power of 3'. For example,

$$y=x^3, \quad y=3x^3-4x, \quad y=2x^3-4x^2+3x+7,$$
$$y=x^3-5, \quad y=(x-2)(2x+1)(3x-4)$$

are all cubic functions in x.

Any cubic function can be written in the form

$$y=ax^3+bx^2+cx+d$$

where a, b, c, d are constants but $a \neq 0$.

The **graph of a cubic function** has a characteristic shape which is illustrated below. The sign of the coefficient a tells you which way round the curve is drawn.

Some cubic functions do not have such pronounced turning points or bends as these curves. A cubic function of the form $y=ax^3$ passes through the origin (0, 0) as shown below.

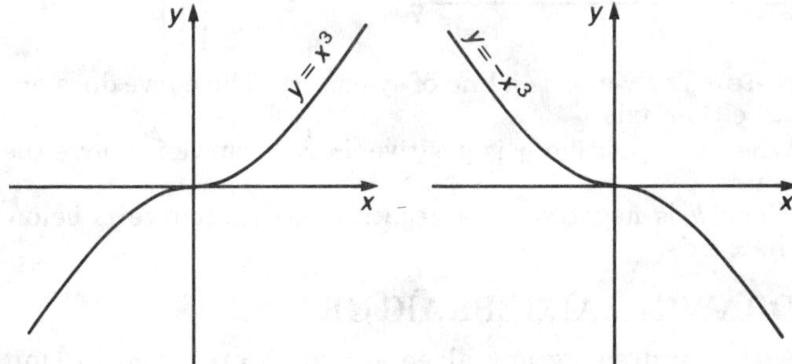

Exponential

Any equation of the form $y=a^x$ (where a is a positive constant) is called an **exponential function** in x. For example,

$$y=2^x, \quad y=(3.5)^x \quad \text{and} \quad y=10^x$$

are all exponential functions in x.

The *graph of* $y=a^x$ is a smooth curve with the basic shape shown below. It is sometimes called the **power curve**.

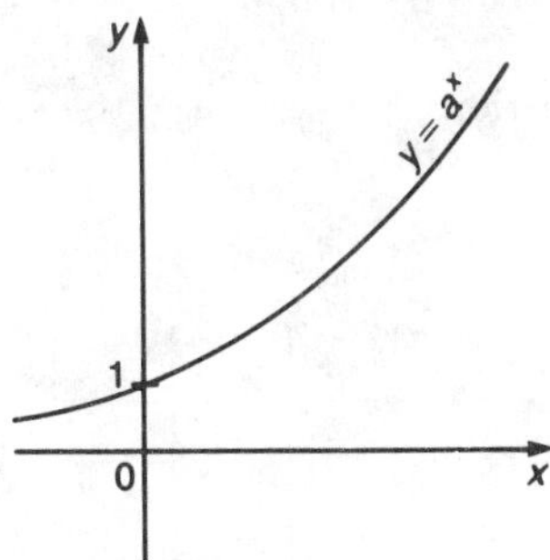

Note The curve is always above the x-axis. So y is always positive. The curve always passes through the point (0, 1) because, when $x=0$, $y=a^x=a^0=1$.

The exponential or power curve occurs in many practical situations. Musical instruments such as grand pianos and pipe organs are made in the shape of an exponential curve. The curve also shows the rate of growth of many biological phenomena and populations.

The basic shape of the associated curve $y=a^{-x}$ (where a is a positive constant) is shown overleaf.

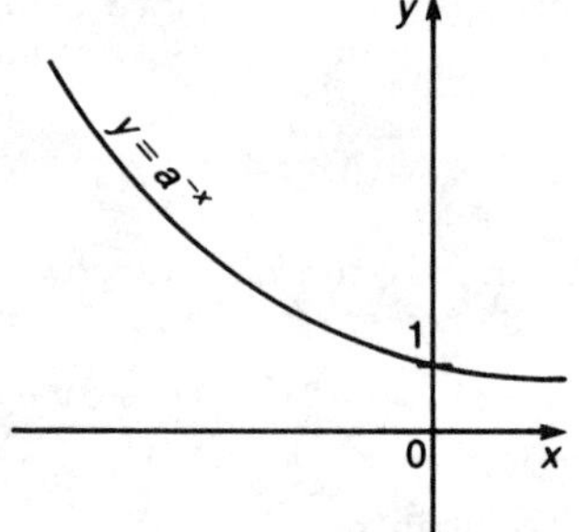

This curve often describes a rate of decay, e.g. the decay of radioactivity.

$y=\frac{k}{x^2}$

The curve of any function of the form $y=\frac{k}{x^2}$ (where k is a constant) is one of the basic shapes shown below.

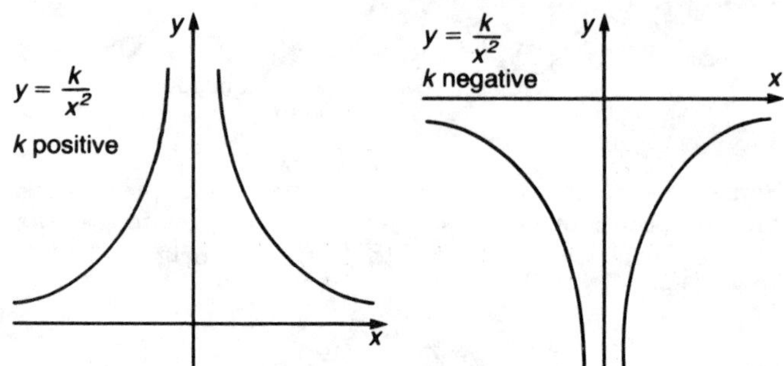

Note The y-axis is a line of symmetry. The curve does not cut either axis.
When k is positive, y is positive, i.e. the curve is above the x-axis.
When k is negative, y is negative, i.e. the curve is below the x-axis.

DRAWING ALGEBRAIC GRAPHS

Notes on drawing any algebraic graph are given in Unit 2.33. In that unit the graphs considered are of linear equations, quadratic equations such as $y=ax^2$ and $y=x^2+bx+c$ and rectangular hyperbolae such as $xy=k$. This unit considers other graphs you may have to plot at this level.
The graph of any quadratic $y=ax^2+bx+c$ is a parabola. To draw it follow the same procedure outlined on p.66.

Question

Draw the graph of $y=1-2x-3x^2$ for $-4\leqslant x\leqslant 3$.

Answer

From the equation $y=1-2x-3x^2$, the expected graph is a $\cap$-shaped parabola.

Table of values

C

x	-4	-3	-2	-1	0	1	2	3	Extra point -0.5
1	1	1	1	1	1	1	1	1	1
$-2x$	$+8$	$+6$	$+4$	$+2$	0	-2	-4	-6	$+1$
$-3x^2$	-48	-27	-12	-3	0	-3	-12	-27	-0.75
y	-39	-20	-7	0	1	-4	-15	-32	1.25

This extra point is needed because the graph turns between $x=-1$ and $x=0$

The points to be plotted are
$(-4, -39)$, $(-3, -20)$, $(-2, -7)$, $(-1, 0)$, $(0, 1)$, $(1, -4)$, $(2, -15)$, $(3, -32)$.
The extra point is $(-0.5, 1.25)$.

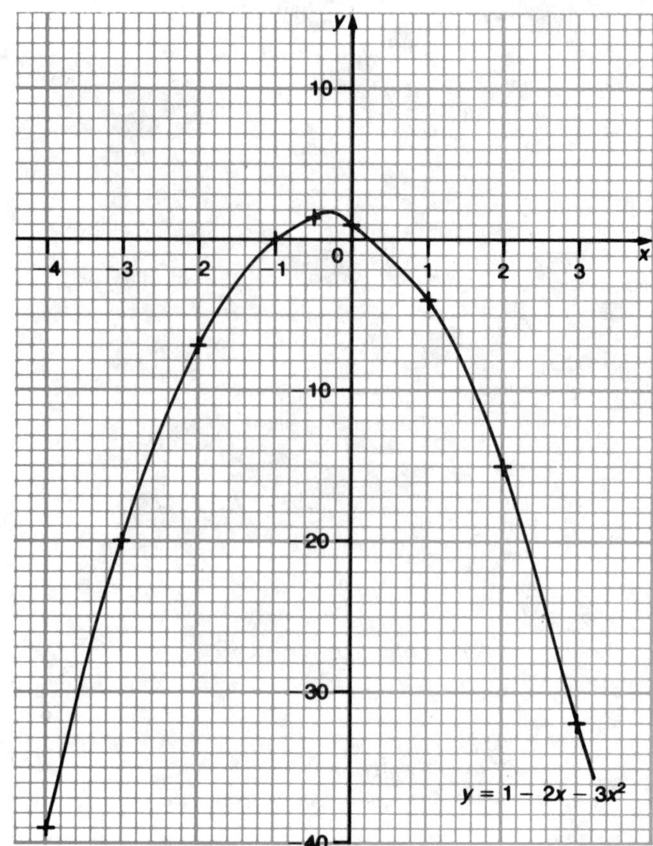

When finding the points to plot for a cubic or exponential function, use the power key y^x or x^y on your calculator.

Question

Draw a graph of $y=(1.5)^x$ for values of x from -2 to 4.

Answer

From the equation $y=(1.5)^x$, the expected curve is an exponential curve.

Table of values:

C

x	-2	-1	0	1	2	3	4
1.5^x	$0.\dot{4}$	$0.\dot{6}$	1	1.5	2.25	3.375	5.0625

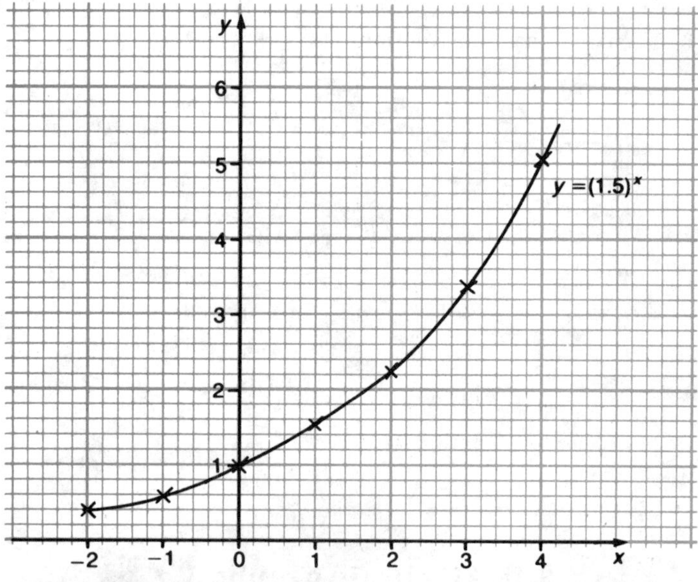

SKETCHING GRAPHS

In a **sketch** of a graph you simply show its basic shape and some of its special features. It is not intended to be an accurate drawing of the curve.
The equation of the function tells you what shape the curve should be. For example,

$y = mx + c \rightarrow$ straight line

$y = ax^2 + bx + c \rightarrow$ parabola

The equation can also tell you some special features of the curve. For example, in

$y = mx + c,$

m is the gradient and c the y-intercept.

Details about the basic shapes and some features of the curves you may have to sketch are in the sections on recognizing graphs on p.65 and p.117.

If the curve cuts the axes, then these points are often easy to find. They should be included in a sketch because they help to fix the position of the curve on the axes.

To find where the curve cuts the y-axis (i.e. the line $x=0$), put $x=0$ in the equation and find the corresponding value(s) of y. (This is usually very easy to work out.)

To find where the curve cuts the x-axis (i.e. the line $y=0$), put $y=0$ in the equation and find the corresponding value(s) of x. (To do this you usually have to solve an equation.)

Question

Draw a sketch of the curve of $y = x^2 + x - 12$.

Answer

$y = x^2 + x - 12$ is a ⋃-shaped parabola.

When $x=0$, $y=-12$.

So the curve cuts the y-axis at $y=-12$.

When $y=0$, $x^2 + x - 12 = 0$

$(x+4)(x-3) = 0$

So $x=-4$ or $x=3$.

The curve cuts the x-axis at $x=-4$ and $x=3$.

The line of symmetry of the parabola is parallel to the y-axis. It must cut the x-axis half-way between $x=-4$ and $x=3$, i.e. at $x=-\frac{1}{2}$. The minimum point of the curve must be on this line of symmetry.

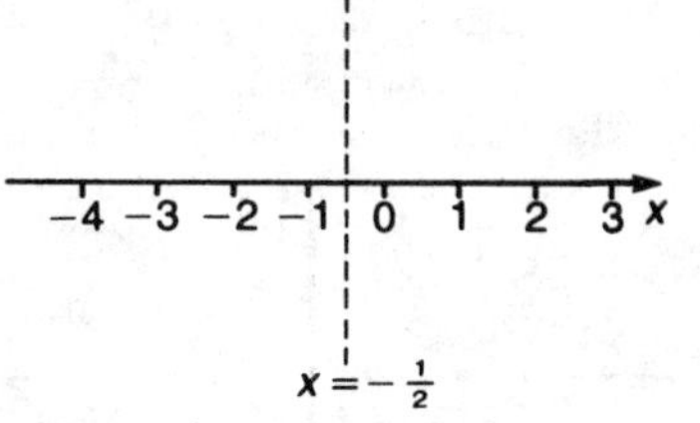

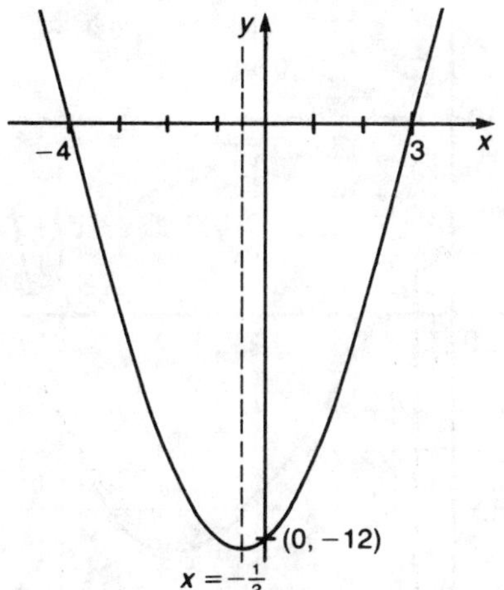

3.19 Graphical solution of equations

An algebraic equation may be solved by **drawing a graph**. However, solutions obtained graphically are only *approximate*: they depend upon the accuracy of the graph and the scale used. So a graphical method is often not the best way to find the solutions to an equation.

Examination questions sometimes specify the method to be used to solve a problem. When this happens, you usually gain *no* marks if you use a different method. **Make sure** that you use a graphical method if the question tells you to do so. If you have a choice, then use the easiest method for the given problem.

Linear and simple quadratic equations can always be easily solved algebraically (see units 2.30 and 3.15). This is not so for higher powers. In these cases solution by algebra can be more complicated and not necessarily more accurate than solution by graph.

Notes about drawing algebraic graphs are given in units 2.33 and 3.18.

INTERSECTION WITH THE x-AXIS

The graph of a function in x can be used to find the real solutions to the equation produced when the function is made equal to zero. For example, the graph of $y = 2x - 5$ can be used to solve the equation $2x - 5 = 0$.

The x-coordinate of any point where the curve cuts or touches the x-axis (i.e. where the function is zero) gives a real solution to the equation. For example, from this graph the solution to the equation $2x - 5 = 0$ is $x = 2.5$.

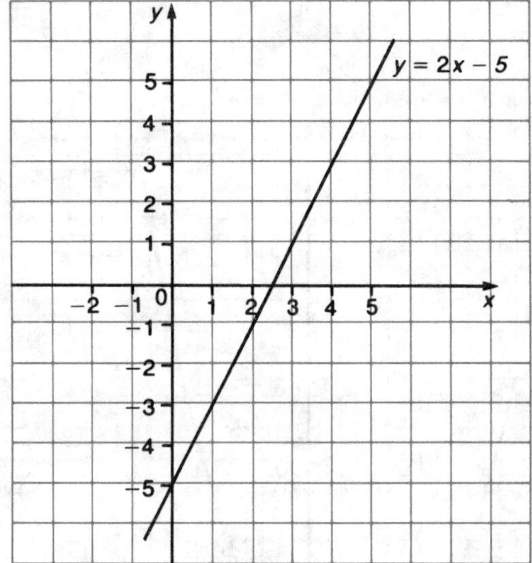

Solving linear equations in this way is described in Unit 2.34. In this unit graphical methods are used to solve higher order equations such as quadratics and cubics.

Quadratic equations

The graph of any **quadratic function** $y = ax^2 + bx + c$ is a parabola. This parabola can be used to solve the **quadratic equation** $ax^2 + bx + c = 0$ when $b^2 \geqslant 4ac$. (When $b^2 < 4ac$ the solutions are not real.) For example, the graph of $y = x^2 + 3x - 4$ can be used to solve the equation $x^2 + 3x - 4 = 0$.

If $b^2 > 4ac$, then the parabola cuts the x-axis in two different points. The x-coordinates of these two points are the roots or solutions of the quadratic equation $ax^2 + bx + c = 0$.

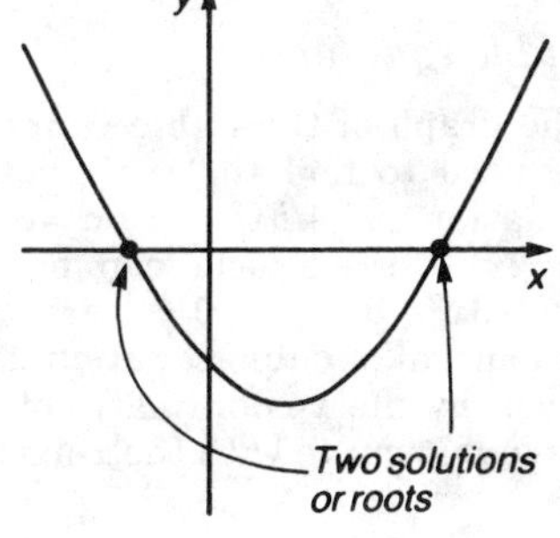

If $b^2 = 4ac$, then the parabola touches the x-axis at one point. The two roots of the equation are said to be equal. The x-coordinate of this point gives these two equal roots or solutions.

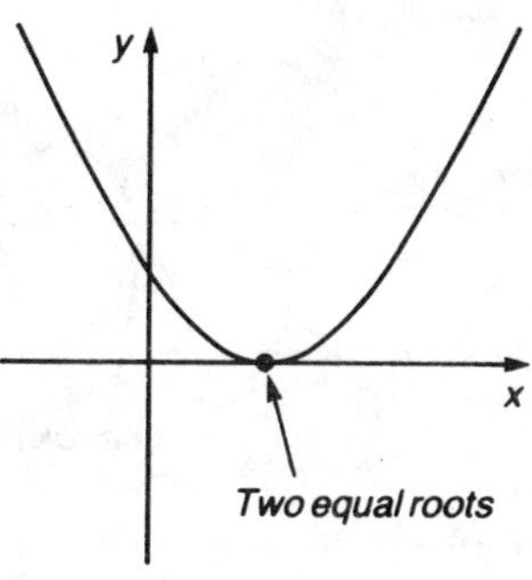

Question

Draw the graph of $y=x^2+x-1$ from $x=-3$ to $x=2$.
Use your graph to find the approximate solutions of the equation $x^2+x-1=0$.

Answer

From the equation $y=x^2+x-1$, the expected graph is a ⋃-shaped parabola.

Table of values:

x	-3	-2	-1	0	1	2	Extra point -0.5
x^2	9	4	1	0	1	4	0.25
$+x$	-3	-2	-1	0	1	2	-0.5
-1	-1	-1	-1	-1	-1	-1	-1
y	5	1	-1	-1	1	5	-1.25

The points to be plotted are
$(-3, 5)$, $(-2, 1)$, $(-1, -1)$, $(0, -1)$, $(1, 1)$, $(2, 5)$
Extra point: $(-0.5, -1.25)$.

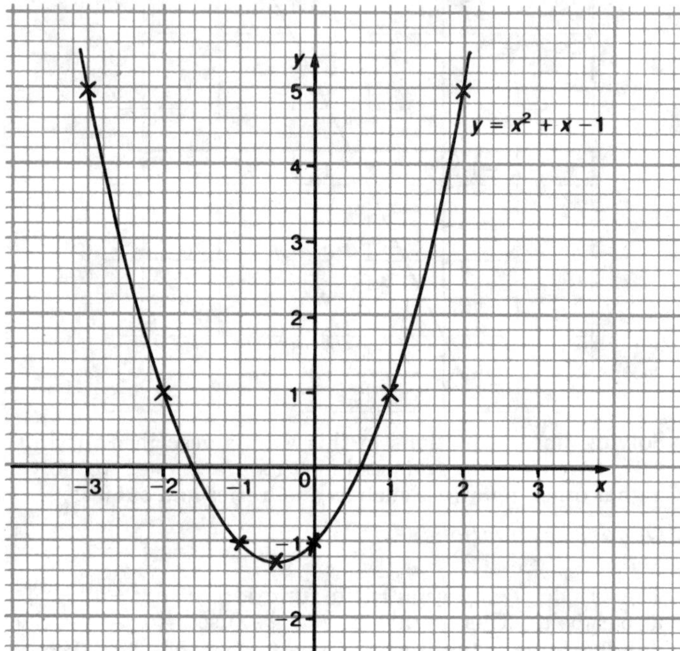

From the graph, the parabola cuts the x-axis where $x \approx -1.6$ and $x \approx 0.6$. These values are the approximate solutions to the equation $x^2+x-1=0$.

Cubic equations

The graph of the **cubic function** $y=ax^3+bx^2+cx+d$ can be used to find the real roots or solutions to the cubic equation $ax^3+bx^2+cx+d=0$. For example, the graph of $y=2x^3-3x^2-8x+12$ can be used to solve the equation $2x^3-3x^2-8x+12=0$.
In general, a cubic equation has *three* solutions. These are given by the x-coordinates of the points of intersection of the cubic curve with the x-axis.

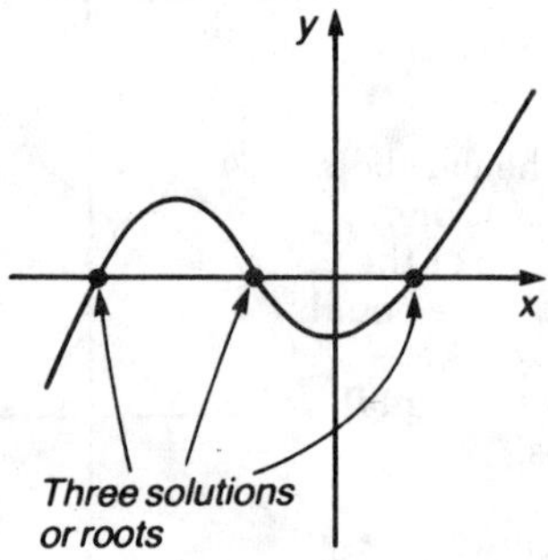

If a solution is not a real number, then it cannot be found from the cubic curve. When this happens in a question you will usually be told that only one or two solutions can be found from the graph.

Question

Draw the graph of the equation $y=x^3-4x^2-2x+3$ for $-2 \leqslant x \leqslant 5$.
Use your graph to estimate the solutions of the equation $x^3-4x^2-2x+3=0$.

Answer

From the equation, the expected graph is a cubic curve.

Table of values:

x	-2	-1	0	1	2	3	4	5
x^3	-8	-1	0	1	8	27	64	125
$-4x^2$	-16	-4	0	-4	-16	-36	-64	-100
$-2x$	$+4$	$+2$	0	-2	-4	-6	-8	-10
$+3$	$+3$	$+3$	$+3$	$+3$	$+3$	$+3$	$+3$	$+3$
y	-17	0	3	-2	-9	-12	-5	18

The graph crosses the x-axis between $x=0$ and $x=1$ and between $x=4$ and $x=5$ (the value of y changes sign)
So calculate extra points at $x=0.5$ and $x=4.5$

Extra points:

x	0.5	4.5
x^3	0.125	91.125
$-4x^2$	-1	-81
$-2x$	-1	-9
$+3$	$+3$	$+3$
y	1.25	4.125

Plot extra points (0.5, 1.25) and (4.5, 4.125).

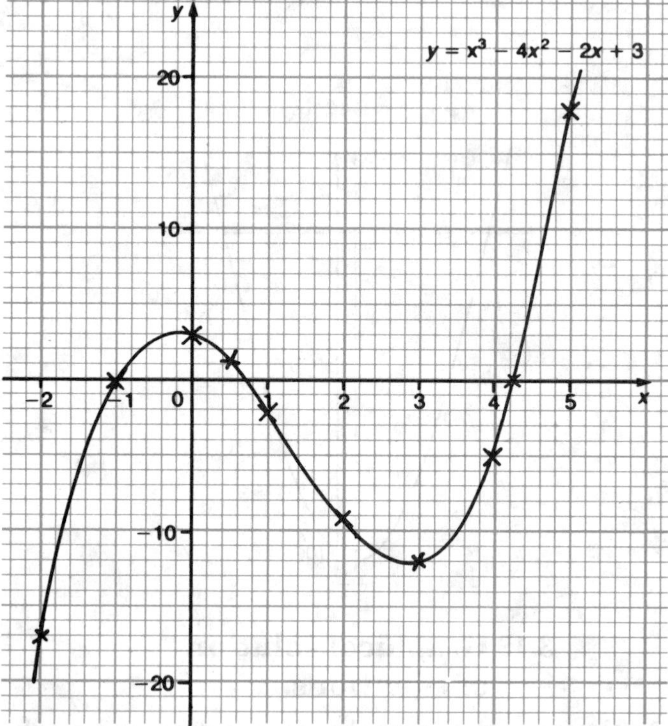

From the graph it can be seen that the curve cuts the x-axis in three places, i.e. where $x=-1$, $x=0.7$ and $x=4.3$. So estimates for the solutions of $x^3-4x^2-2x+3=0$ are $x=-1$, $x \approx 0.7$ and $x \approx 4.3$.

INTERSECTING GRAPHS

Equations can also be solved by using **two intersecting graphs**. The x-coordinate of each point of intersection gives a solution to an equation.

At this level the intersecting graphs will be a *straight line* and a *curve*. The curve can be any of the curves you have studied, for example, parabola, cubic, rectangular hyperbola, exponential, trigonometrical, ...

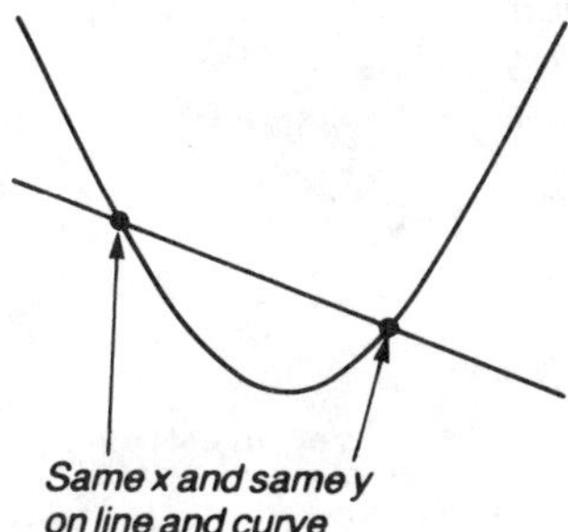

At a point of intersection of two graphs, the value of y is the same on each curve. You use this fact to find the equation which can be solved by the intersecting graphs. Write an expression for y using each equation and put these expressions equal to each other. This gives you the required equation. The equation is often rearranged so that it is in its simplest form, i.e. in the form:

'simple expression in x' $=0$

The simplest straight line used as one of the graphs is a line parallel to the x-axis, i.e. $y=k$. For example, the intersecting graphs of

a parabola: $y=ax^2+bx+c$, and
a line: $y=k$

can be used to solve the equation

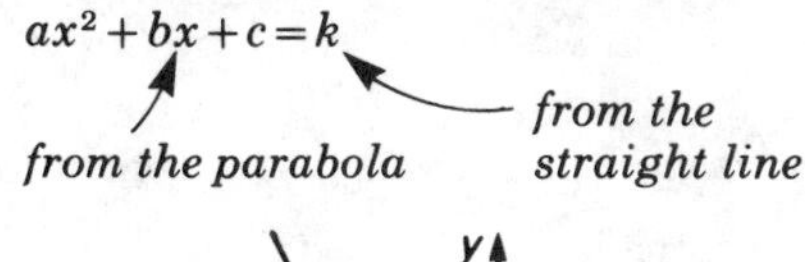

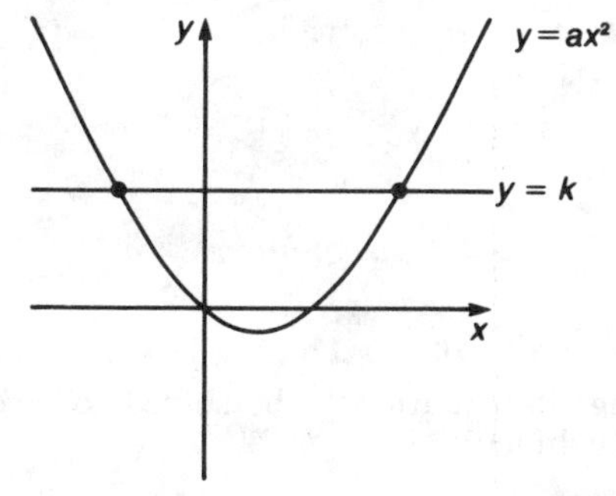

Any straight line, such as $y=mx+c$, can be used as one of the graphs. For example, the intersecting graphs of

the rectangular hyperbola: $y=\frac{k}{x}$ and

the straight line: $y=mx+c$

can be used to solve the equation:

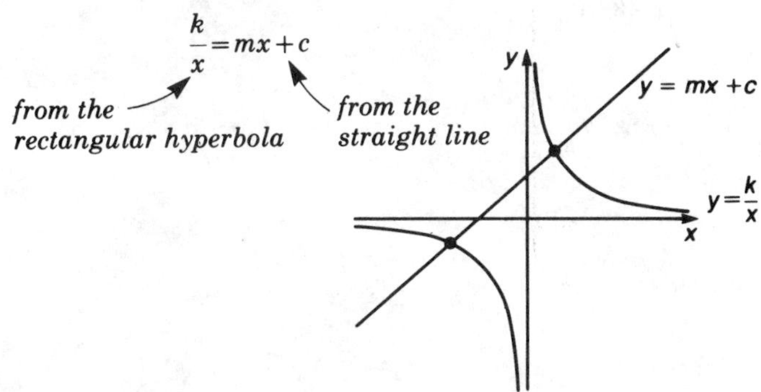

This method can be used to find the equation solved by any intersecting line and curve.

Question

Write in its simplest form the equation in x which can be solved by the intersection of each pair of graphs.

(a) $y=x^3-3x^2+2,\quad y=2$
(b) $y=2x^2-8x+1,\quad y=5x+6$
(c) $y=\frac{10}{x},\quad y=x+3$

Answer

(a) $\left.\begin{array}{l} y=x^3-3x^2+2 \\ y=2 \end{array}\right\}$ intersecting graphs

Equation solved at the intersection is

$x^3-3x^2+2=2$

This can be rearranged.

Subtract 2 *from both sides* $\quad x^3-3x^2=0$

(b) $\left.\begin{array}{l} y=2x^2-8x+1 \\ y=5x+6 \end{array}\right\}$ intersecting graphs

Equation solved at the intersection is

$2x^2-8x+1=5x+6$

This can be rearranged.

Subtract 5*x and* 6 *from both sides* $\quad 2x^2-8x-5x+1-6=0$

Collect like terms $\quad 2x^2-13x-5=0$

(c) $\left.\begin{array}{l} y=\frac{10}{x} \\ y=x+3 \end{array}\right\}$ intersecting graphs

Equation solved at the intersection is

$\frac{10}{x}=x+3$

This can be rearranged.

Multiply by x $\quad x\times\frac{10}{x}=x(x+3)$

$10=x(x+3)$

Remove brackets $\quad 10=x^2+3x$

Subtract 10 *from both sides* $\quad 0=x^2+3x-10$

or $\quad x^2+3x-10=0$

The x-coordinate of each point of intersection gives a solution to the equation formed. Always mark the points clearly on the graph you have drawn.

Question

(a) Draw the graph of $y=x^2-x-2$ for $-2\leqslant x\leqslant 4$. On the same axes draw the straight line $y=x+3$.
(b) Write down and simplify an equation which is satisfied by the values of x where the two graphs intersect.
(c) From your graph find the approximate value (correct to 1 decimal place) of the roots of this equation.

Answer

(a) Table of values for the ∪-shaped parabola $y=x^2-x-2$: **C**

x	-2	-1	0	1	2	3	4	Extra point 0.5
x^2	4	1	0	1	4	9	16	0.25
$-x$	2	1	0	-1	-2	-3	-4	-0.5
-2	-2	-2	-2	-2	-2	-2	-2	-2
y	4	0	-2	-2	0	4	10	-2.25

The points to be plotted for the parabola are: $(-2, 4)$, $(-1, 0)$, $(0, -2)$, $(1, -2)$, $(2, 0)$, $(3, 4)$, $(4, 10)$, $(0.5, -2.25)$

Extra point where parabola 'turns'

Table of values for $y=x+3$:

x	-2	0	2
y	1	3	5

The points to be plotted for the straight line are: $(-2, 1), (0, 3), (2, 5)$.

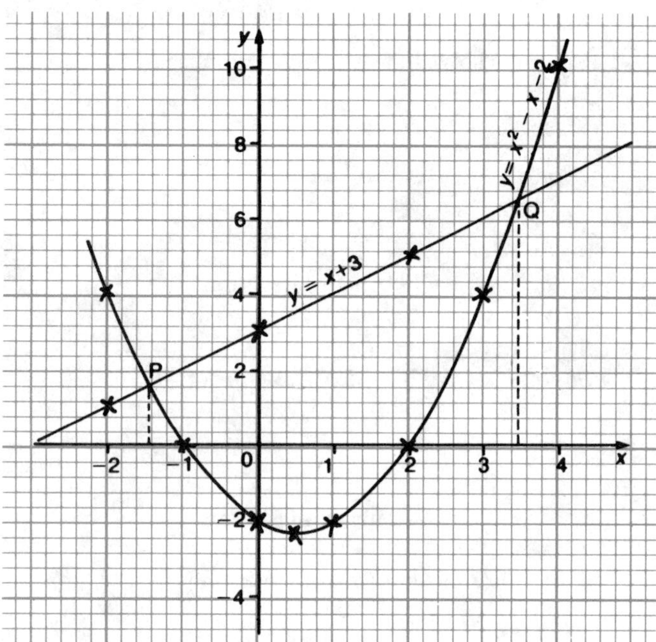

(b) At the points of intersection of the two graphs, the values of y are the same.

$$\left.\begin{array}{l} y=x^2-x-2 \\ y=x+3 \end{array}\right\}\text{intersecting graphs}$$

So the equation solved at the intersections is

$$x^2-x-2=x+3$$

This equation can be simplified.

Subtract x and 3 from both sides $\quad x^2-x-x-2-3=x-x+3-3$

$$x^2-2x-5=0$$

So the required equation is $x^2-2x-5=0$.

(c) The solutions of the equation $x^2-2x-5=0$ are the x-coordinates of the points of intersection (marked P and Q on the graph).
From the graph the roots are

$$x=-1.5 \text{ or } x=3.5 \text{ (correct to 1 d.p.).}$$

Sometimes you are given, or have already drawn, the graph of a curve. You may have to find the equation of the straight line you need to draw to solve another equation. To do this you must relate the equation to be solved to the equation of the curve already drawn. This is easiest to do if the 'expression in x' from the equation of the curve is on one side (usually the left) of the equation and all the other terms are on the other. You may have to rearrange the equation to be solved in this form,

'expression in x from graph equation' = 'other terms'

Writing these 'other terms' equal to y gives the equation of the line to be drawn.

Question

Given the graph of $y=x^2-4x+3$, which straight lines have to be drawn on the same axes to solve these equations?

(a) $x^2-4x+3=7$ (b) $x^2-4x+3=x-4$
(c) $x^2-4x+9=0$ (d) $x^2-7x-2=0$

Answer

(a) $x^2-4x+3=7$

expression in x from graph equation — *for line equation*

The equation of the required line is $y=7$.

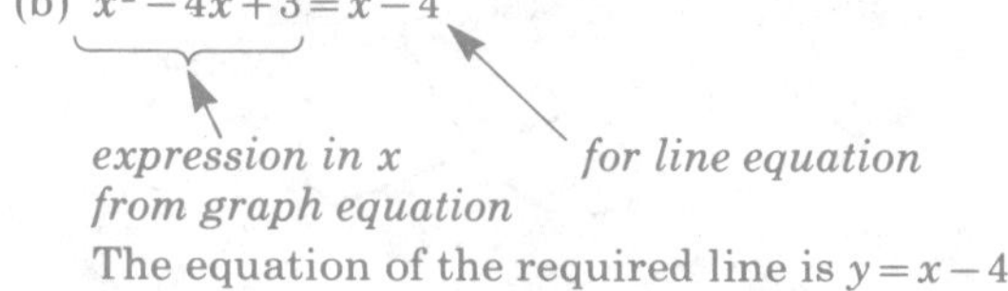

(b) $x^2-4x+3=x-4$

expression in x from graph equation — *for line equation*

The equation of the required line is $y=x-4$.

(c) *Compare 'graph expression':* $\quad x^2-4x+3$
with given 'expression': $\quad x^2-4x+9$
Difference: $\quad -6$

So rearrange equation by subtracting 6 from both sides

Given equation to solve: $\quad x^2-4x+9=0$

Subtract 6 from both sides $\quad x^2-4x+9-6=-6$

$$x^2-4x+3=-6$$

expression in x from graph equation — *for line equation*

The equation of the required line is $y=-6$.

(d) *Compare 'graph expression in x':* $\quad x^2-4x+3$
with given 'expression in x': $\quad x^2-7x-2$
Difference: $\quad 3x+5$

So rearrange equation by adding $(3x+5)$ to both sides

Given equation to solve $\quad x^2-7x-2=0$

Add $3x+5$ to both sides $\quad x^2-7x+3x-2+5=3x+5$

$$x^2-4x+3=3x+5$$

from graph equation — *for line equation*

The equation of the required line is $y=3x+5$.

Rearranging the equation to be solved to give a fraction may be more difficult.

Question

If the graph of $y=\dfrac{3}{x}$ is drawn, find the equation of the straight line which has to be drawn on the same axes in order to find the approximate solutions of the equation $x^2+x-3=0$.

Answer

Rearrange the equation to be solved so that a $\dfrac{3}{x}$ term appears

Given equation: $\quad x^2+x-3=0$

Add 3 to both sides $\quad x^2+x=3$

Divide by x $\quad \dfrac{x^2+x}{x}=\dfrac{3}{x}$ when $x\neq 0$

$$x+1=\frac{3}{x}$$

for line equation — *from graph equation*

The line which must be drawn on the same axes is $y=x+1$.

3.20 Inequalities

This unit extends the basic ideas about inequalities given in Unit 2.35.

NOTATION

In a simple inequation the 'unknown' is usually written on the left hand side. For example,

$x>5$

In an answer an inequality may end up written the other way round. It is usual to rewrite this with the unknown first. For example, $3<x$ is rewritten as $x>3$.

Remember If $a>b$, then $b<a$ and vice versa.
For example, $5>3$ and $3<5$ are equivalent.

An unknown value sometimes obeys more than one inequality. These inequalities may be combined and written as one statement. For example, if you have a number x where

$x<4$ and $x\geqslant -2$,

then you can write the combined inequalities as

$-2\leqslant x<4$.

To combine two inequalities like these:

		For example
1	Put the numbers in order of size, smallest first.	$-2 \quad 4$
2	Write the expression with the unknown in between the numbers.	$-2 \quad x \quad 4$
3	Place the signs in the correct directions and places.	$-2\leqslant x<4$

Inequalities may be given using **set notation** (see Unit 3.8). For example, the set of numbers less than 5 may be written as $\{x : x<5\}$

This set notation means

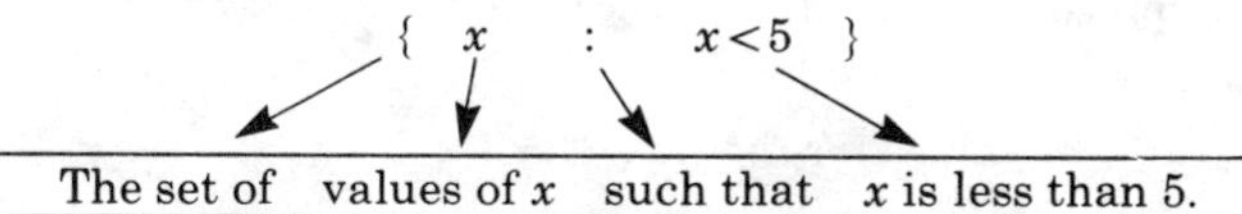

When an inequality is given in set notation, it is usual to give its solution set in set notation too.

USING A NUMBER LINE

The **solution** of an inequation is a **range** (or ranges) of values which satisfy the inequation. It may be impossible to list all the solutions of an inequation. But they can be represented on a **number line**.

Here are some points to help you to show an inequality on a number line.

1 Mark the endpoint(s) of the inequality first. Use
  - ○ an open circle to show that the endpoint is *not* included (i.e. the sign is $>$ or $<$),
  - ● a filled-in circle to show that the endpoint is included (i.e. the sign is $\geqslant$ or $\leqslant$).

2 Decide whether the values are to the right or left of the endpoint.
  greater than $>$ to the right
  less than $<$ to the left

3 If the solution set is infinite, then a region of the line represents the inequality. Draw
  —— a line to show the range of the values,
  ⟶ an arrowed line to show that the values go
  ⟵ on for ever in the direction of the arrow.

Question

On separate number lines show the solutions to:
(a) $x\geqslant 5$ (b) $x<-2$.

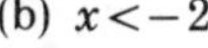

Answer

(a) $x \geqslant 5$

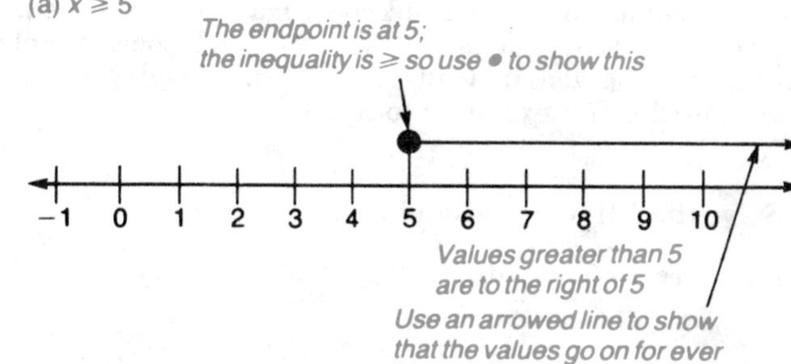

(b) $x<-2$

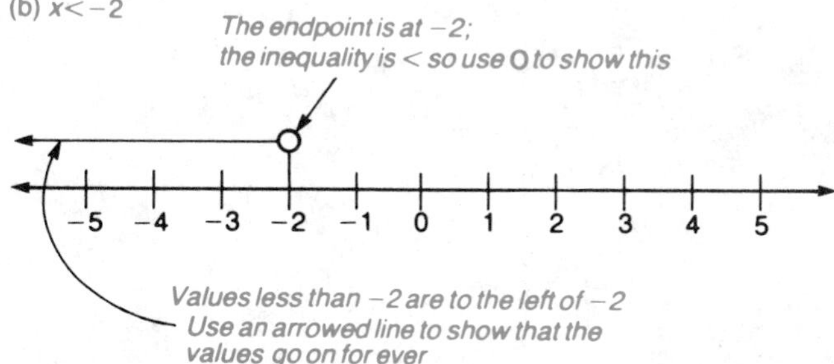

More than one inequality may be true at the same time (simultaneously). To solve these **simultaneous inequations**, you can draw each inequation separately on a number line. Where they overlap gives the solution.
For example, to solve $-3\leqslant x<2$, draw this.

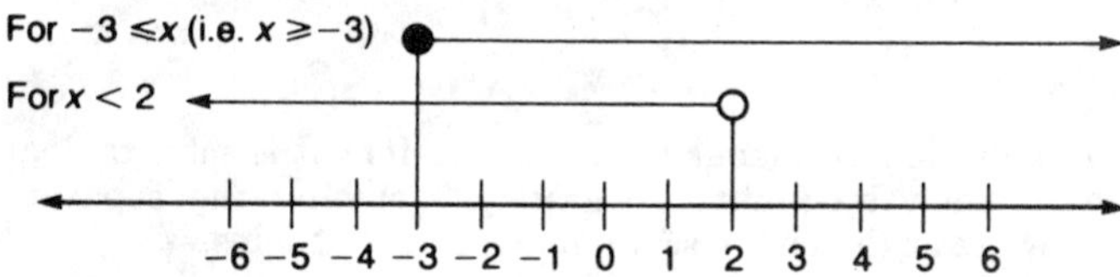

The 'overlap' gives the solution:

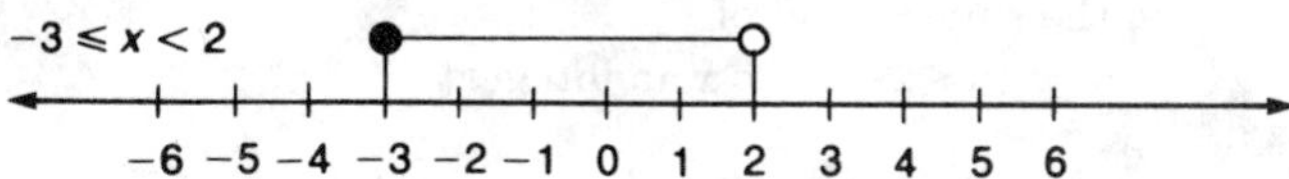

You can also work out what the inequality means. Then draw the solution on a number line. For example,

$-3\leqslant x<2$ means that

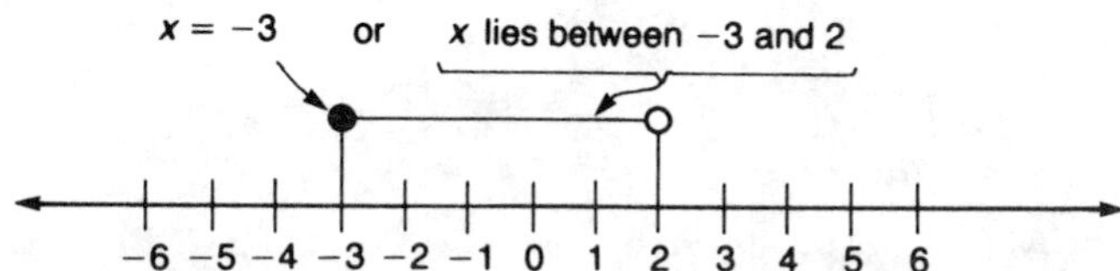

The solutions in the examples above are infinite. However not all sets of points on a number line are infinite. Sometimes the actual points can be marked on the line. As before, mark the endpoints of the inequality first. Then mark the other points on the line that belong to the solution.

Question

Find the solution set for

$S=\{x : 0\leqslant x<5, x \text{ an integer}\}$

on a number line. List the members of S.

Answer

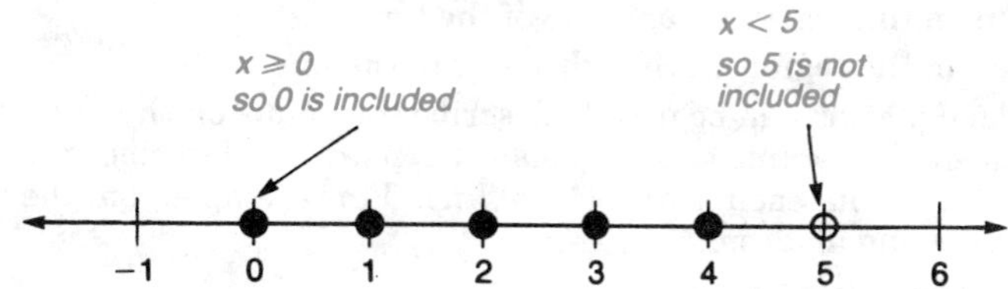

The integers from 0 to 4 belong to the solution too.

So $S=\{0, 1, 2, 3, 4\}$

USING THE RULES OF INEQUALITIES

Linear inequations in one unknown may be solved using the rules of inequalities. These rules and some simple examples are given in Unit 2.35. At this level you may have more difficult examples to solve.

Question

Solve the following inequalities.

(a) $5-2x>-3$ (b) $\frac{x}{3}-7\leqslant-2$

Answer

(a) $5-2x>-3$

Subtract 5 from both sides $-2x>-3-5$

$-2x>-8$

Divide both sides by −2 $\frac{-2x}{-2}<\frac{-8}{-2}$

Reverse the inequality

So $x<4$

(b) $\frac{x}{3}-7\leqslant-2$

Add 7 to both sides $\frac{x}{3}\leqslant-2+7$

$\frac{x}{3}\leqslant5$

Multiply both sides by 3 $3\times\frac{x}{3}\leqslant3\times5$

$x\leqslant15$

To solve simultaneous linear inequations it is safer to deal with each inequality separately. Combine the separate answers at the end. Use a number line if it helps.

Question

Find the solution set of

$S=\{x : 1\leqslant2-x<4,\ x \text{ an integer}\}$

Answer

Deal with each inequality separately

	LHS	RHS
	$1\leqslant2-x$	$2-x<4$
Subtract 2	$1-2\leqslant-x$	$-x<4-2$
	$-1\leqslant-x$	$-x<2$
Divide by −1 *Reverse the inequalities*	$1\geqslant x$	$x>-2$

Combine the two inequalities $1\geqslant x>-2$

Rewrite with smaller number first $-2<x\leqslant1$

x is an integer.

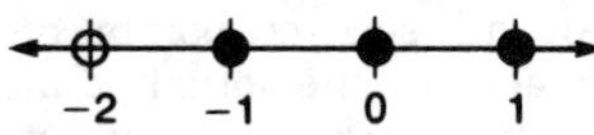

So the solution set is marked on this number line.

The solution set $S=\{-1, 0, 1\}$

GRAPHS OF INEQUALITIES

A straight line divides the plane into three sets of points. They are:

(a) on the line,

(b) in the region on one side of the line,

(c) in the region on the other side of the line.

An equation can be used to describe the points *on* the line. Inequalities (inequations) can be used to describe the regions on each side of the line. For example, on the following diagram,

the line is $y=x-3$,

the shaded region is $y>x-3$,

the unshaded region is $y<x-3$.

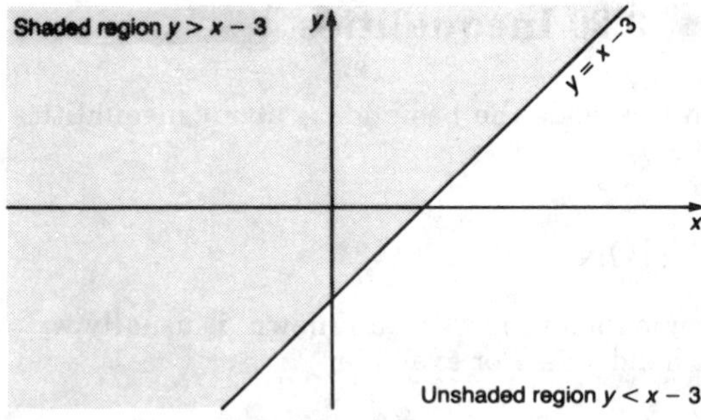

Some problems involving inequalities may be solved using graphs. Use these notes to help you to draw graphs of inequalities.

1 Draw the boundary line of the inequality. (The corresponding equation gives this line.)
If the inequality is ⩾ or ⩽, then the line is included in the region.
Show this by drawing a continuous line ———
If the inequality is > or <, the line is *not* included.
Show this by drawing a dotted line - - - - -.

2 Work out which side of the line is the region you want for the inequality. To do this, choose an easy point on one side of the line. Find out whether its coordinates obey the inequality or not.

3 Shade in the region you do *not* want, i.e. the region where the inequality is *not* obeyed. The unshaded region is the one you want.
(Some people do the opposite and shade in the wanted region. This can lead to confusion because the part of the graph you want to use can become covered with messy shading.) **Always** make it clear in your answer which region you are shading.

Question

Indicate on a diagram the region of the plane which represents $y>x+3$.

Answer

Table of values for the line $y=x+3$:

x	−3	0	3
y	0	3	6

Plot the points (−3, 0), (0, 3), (3, 6) to draw the line.

The boundary line is $y=x+3$
The inequality is >, so use a dotted line

O is in the unwanted region. See the working below. So shade in this region

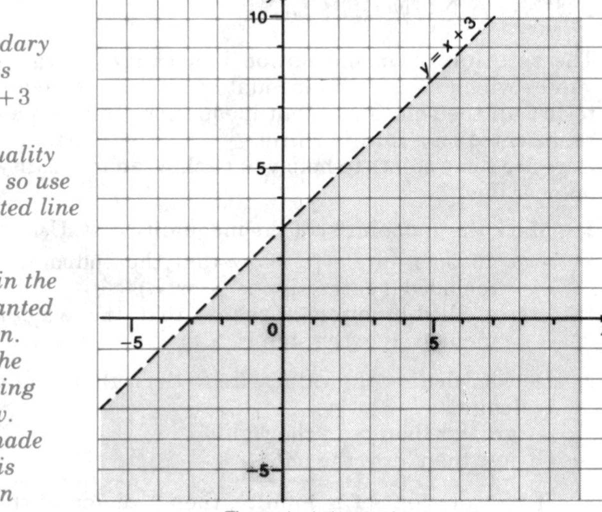

The unshaded region is $y > x + 3$

At the origin O, $x=0$, $y=0$.
For $y=x+3$, $x=0\Rightarrow y=3$
But $0<3$, so at the origin O, $y<x+3$
The region wanted is $y>x+3$. So O is in the unwanted region.

The solution of simultaneous inequations can be shown on a graph too. Sometimes the solution set is an infinite region.

Question

Indicate on a diagram the region of the plane which represents $-2<y\leqslant 3$.

Answer

The inequation $-2<y\leqslant 3$ can be split into $y\leqslant 3$ and $y>-2$.

For $y\leqslant 3$,
The boundary line is $y=3$
The inequality is $\leqslant$, so use a continuous line
All points less than 3, i.e. $y<3$ are below the line
So shade in above the line

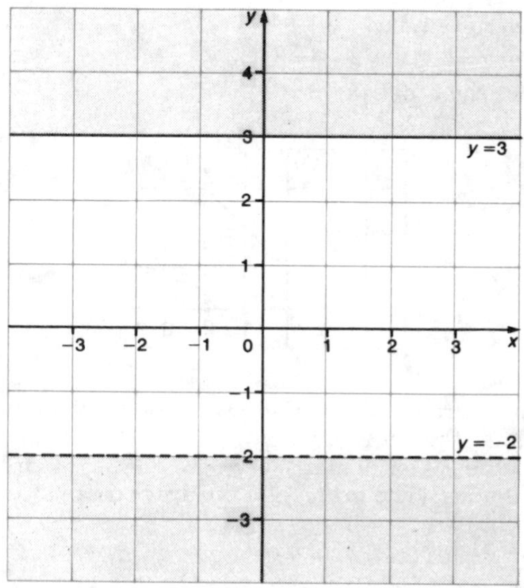

For $y>-2$
The boundary line is $y=-2$
The inequation is $>$, so use a dotted line
All points greater than -2, i.e. $y>-2$, are above the line
So shade in below the line
The unshaded region represents $-2<y\leqslant 3$.

The solution set may be a finite region or even a finite set of points.

Question

Find graphically $S=\{(x, y): x<3, y\leqslant 4, x+y>2\}$ where x and y are integers.

Answer

Show the regions $x<3$, $y\leqslant 4$, and $x+y>2$ on the same diagram

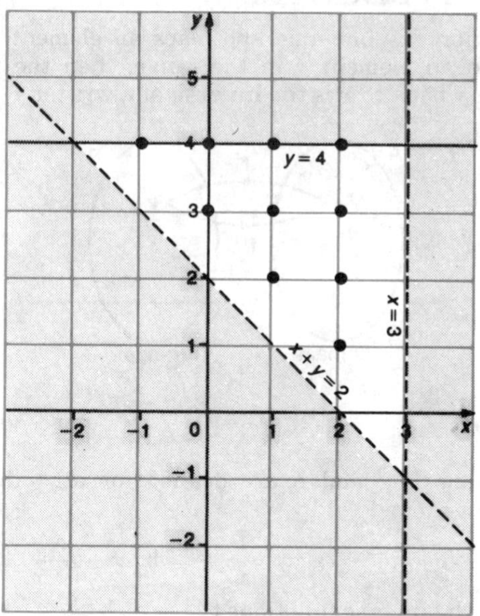

The solution set S is in the unshaded region.
In the set S, x and y are integers.
All the points in S with integer coordinates are marked by large dots.
So $S=\{(-1, 4), (0, 4), (1, 4), (2, 4), (0, 3), (1, 3), (2, 3), (1, 2), (2, 2), (2, 1)\}$.

3.21 Relations and functions

RELATIONS

A **relation** is a connection between two sets. In the statement 'John is the brother of Ann', the relation is 'is the brother of' and John $\in$ {boys} and Ann $\in$ {girls}. In Mathematics the quantities connected by relations are often numbers.

Below are four arrow diagrams illustrating the four different types of relations. Above each is written the type of relation and below each is written the meaning of the arrow.

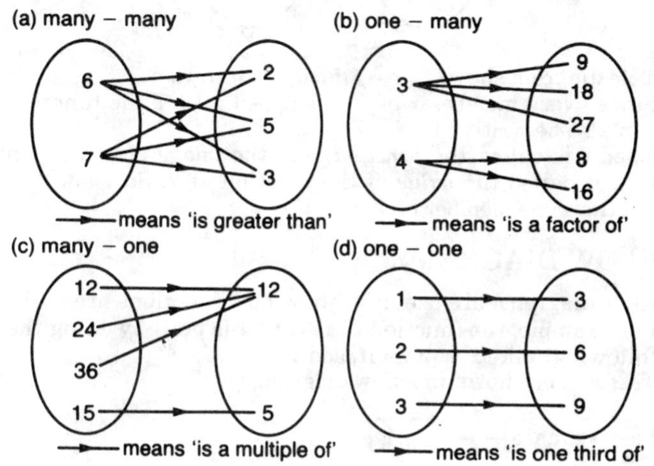

FUNCTIONS

A **function** or **mapping**

(a) is a *many–one* or *one–one* relation between two sets X and Y,

(b) relates every member of X to *one and only one* member of Y.

The **domain** of the function is X.
The **range** of the function is that subset of Y (the **image set**) which consists of all possible images of members of X.
Sometimes Y may contain members which are not images of members of X.

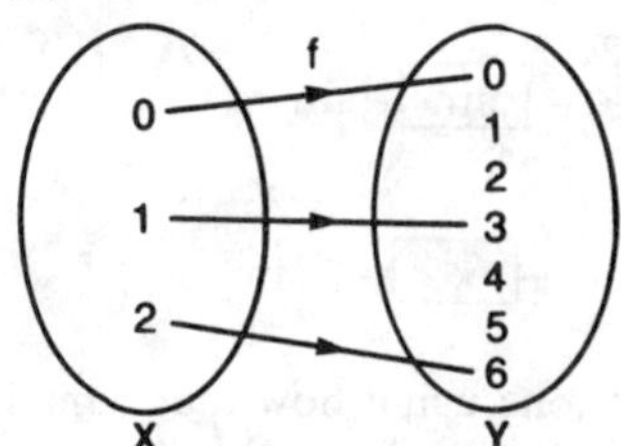

For example, for the mapping f and the two sets X and Y shown, the domain is {0, 1, 2} and the range is {0, 3, 6}.
There are various ways of describing a function. The most usual ones are:

(a) mapping diagrams, e.g.

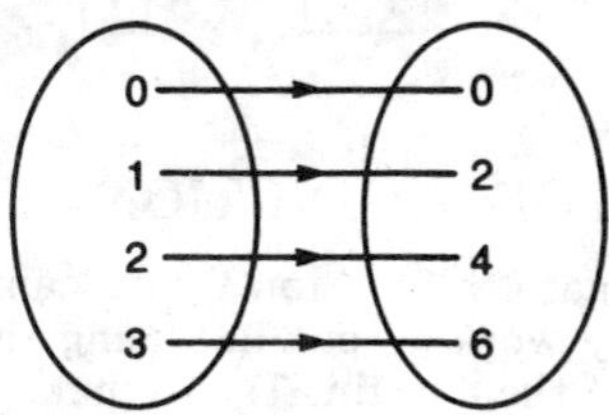

(b) sets of ordered pairs, e.g.
{(0, 0), (1, 2), (2, 4), (3, 6)},

(**c**) algebraic relations, e.g.
$y=2x$

(**d**) graphs (see Unit 2.33).

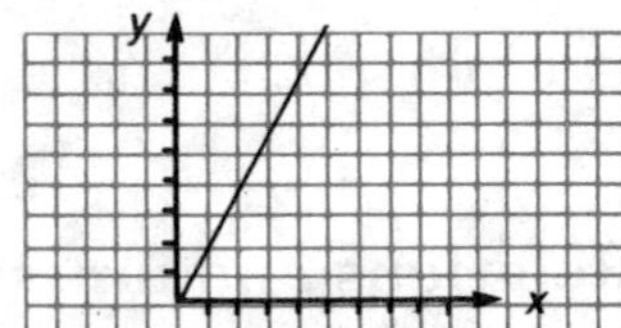

These all represent the same function written, $f: x \mapsto 2x$. This is read as 'f maps x into $2x$'.

In general, a function f relating two sets X and Y can be illustrated by a mapping diagram.

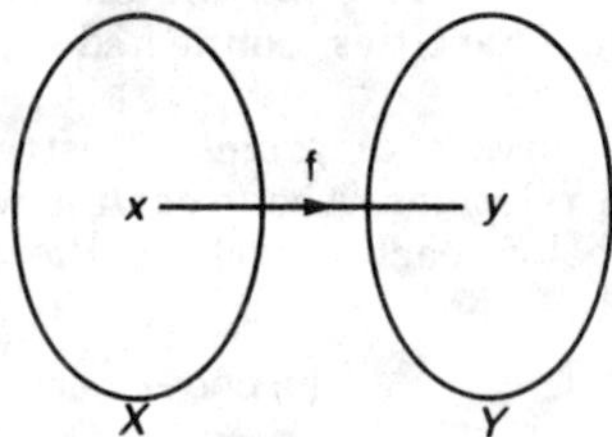

This diagram shows $f: x \mapsto y$ (f maps x into y).

Since every member x of X is mapped into Y the function can also be written $f: X \mapsto Y$.

Then f is called the *function*, and the *image* of x, written $f(x)$, is called the *value* of the function at x. So y and $f(x)$ are the same member of Y.

FLOW DIAGRAMS

Flow diagrams are useful to show how functions are built. For example, the function $f: x \mapsto x^2+1$ is built by doing the following: take x, square it, add 1.

This can be shown in a flow diagram as:

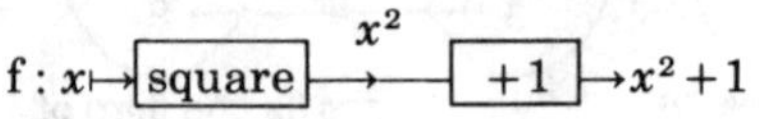

Question

Illustrate the function $h: x \mapsto 3+2\sin x$ with a flow diagram.

Answer

h : $x \mapsto$ [sin] —$\sin x$→ [×2] —$2\sin x$→ [+3] → $3+2\sin x$

Building up functions in this way helps to avoid making mistakes. For example, the functions $f: x \mapsto \sin 2x$ and $g: x \mapsto 2\sin x$ are different. The flow diagram helps you to see this.

f : $x \mapsto$ [×2] —$2x$→ [sin] → $\sin 2x$

g : $x \mapsto$ [sin] —$\sin x$→ [×2] → $2\sin x$

Building up functions using flow diagrams is very helpful when you need to work out actual values with a calculator. For example, to work out h(30) for the above function $h: x \mapsto 3+2\sin x$:

Press: [3] [0] [sin] [×] [2] [=] [+] [3] [=]

Display: [0.5] [1] [4]

So, $h(30)=4$.

THE RANGE OF A FUNCTION

To find the range of a function f, you cannot necessarily find it by simply working out $f(x)$ using the smallest and largest values of the domain. Try to make a sketch graph of the function over the given domain. This will help you to see how the function behaves.

Question

Functions f and g are defined by

$f: x \mapsto x+1$, for $-1 \leqslant x \leqslant 2$,

$g: x \mapsto 2x^2$, for $-2 \leqslant x \leqslant 2$.

Calculate the ranges of the functions f and g.

Answer

The endpoints of the domain do not necessarily give the endpoints of the range. Therefore, it is safer to draw a sketch of the graph of each function over its domain

Over the given domain, $-1 \leqslant x \leqslant 2$, f is linear and continuous (i.e. a straight line without gaps).

When $x=-1$, $f(x)=-1+1=0$.

When $x=2$, $f(x)=2+1=3$.

Hence the range of f is $0 \leqslant y \leqslant 3$.

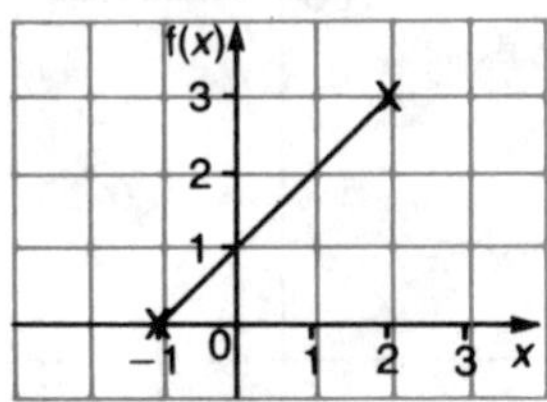

This diagram shows the graph of f over the given domain.

Over the given domain, $-2 \leqslant x \leqslant 2$, g is quadratic and continuous. (The graph of a quadratic is a parabola, see Unit 2.33).

When $x=0$, $g(x)=2\,.\,0^2=0$.

When $x=-2$, $g(x)=2\,.\,(-2)^2=8$.

When $x=2$, $g(x)=2\,.\,(2)^2=8$.

Hence the range of g is $0 \leqslant y \leqslant 8$.

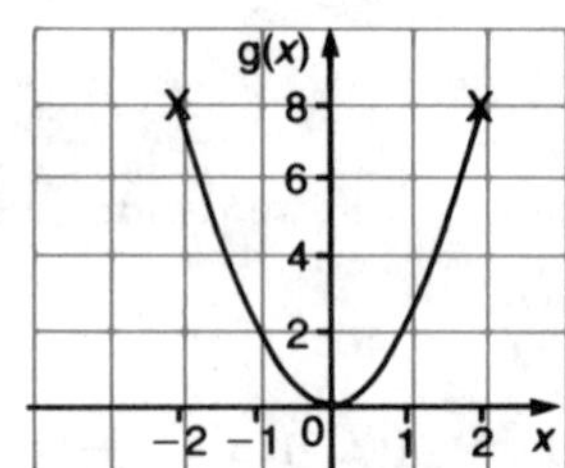

This diagram shows the graph of g over the given domain.

INVERSE FUNCTIONS

If a function f is one–one and maps an element x in the domain to an element y in the range, then the function that maps y back to x is the **inverse** of f, written f^{-1}.

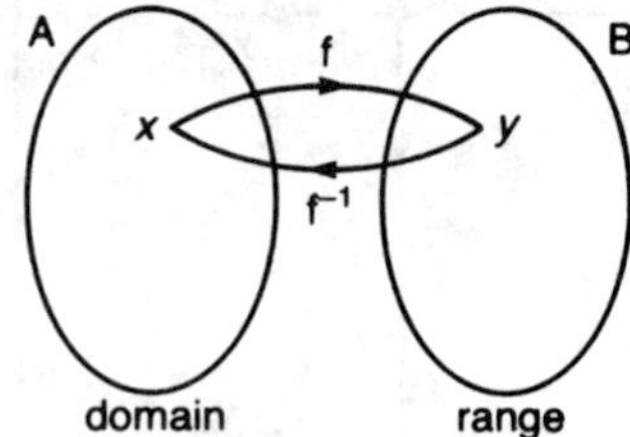

Question

Functions f, g and h are defined for all values of x except $x=0$ and -1 by

$f: x \mapsto 1+x$, $\quad g: x \mapsto \dfrac{1}{x}$, $\quad h: x \mapsto \dfrac{x}{1+x}$.

Define the inverse functions f^{-1}, g^{-1}, h^{-1}.

Answer

To find the inverse function f^{-1} *we write* $y=f(x)$ *and transform the equation to make* x *the subject (see Unit 2.31). Similarly for* g *and* h

$f: x \mapsto 1+x$ can be written $y=1+x \Rightarrow x=y-1$.

Hence $f^{-1}: x \mapsto x-1$ is the inverse of f.

$g: x \mapsto \frac{1}{x}$ can be written $y=\frac{1}{x} \Rightarrow x=\frac{1}{y}$.

Hence $g^{-1}: x \mapsto \frac{1}{x}$ is the inverse of g. (*Notice that* g *is its own inverse*)

$h: x \mapsto \frac{x}{1+x}$ can be written $y=\frac{x}{1+x} \Rightarrow x=\frac{y}{1-y}$.

Hence $h^{-1}: x \mapsto \frac{x}{1-x}$ is the inverse of h.

COMPOSITE FUNCTIONS

To find the composite function fg of two functions, f and g, acting on suitable sets

(a) find the image of x under the function g, i.e. $g(x)$,

(b) find the image of $g(x)$ under the function f, i.e. $f[g(x)]$

An alternative notation for $f[g(x)]$ is $fg(x)$.

Note: the order of the two functions is important.

A flow diagram helps when finding composite functions.

Question

If $f(x)=x+1$ and $g(x)=x^2$ find (a) $fg(x)$ (b) $gf(x)$

Answer

function	*flow diagram*
$f: x \mapsto x+1$ as flow diagram	$f: x \rightarrow$ [+1] $\rightarrow x+1$
$g: x \mapsto x^2$ as flow diagram	$g: x \rightarrow$ [square] $\rightarrow x^2$

fg : $x \rightarrow$ [square] $\xrightarrow{x^2}$ [+1] $\rightarrow x^2+1$
(g first, then f)

gf : $x \rightarrow$ [+1] $\xrightarrow{x+1}$ [square] $\rightarrow (x+1)^2$
(f first, then g)

So (a) $fg(x)=x^2+1$ (b) $gf(x)=(x+1)^2$

3.22 Variation

DIRECT VARIATION

If a car is travelling along a straight road at constant speed, the distance travelled is directly proportional to the time for which it travels. We say that the distance, d, travelled **varies directly** as the time, t, for which it travels. We write this in symbols as:

$d \propto t$.

This means that if the time, t, is doubled, the distance, d, will also be doubled. If t is halved, d will also be halved and so on. If a graph of d against t is drawn the result will be a straight line passing through the origin. The gradient of the graph will be constant and equal to $\frac{d}{t}$.

i.e. $\frac{d}{t}=k$ where k is a **constant of proportionality** equal to the gradient.

Any situation in which one variable varies directly as another can be described by such an equation involving a constant of proportionality.

Question

The extension, e, produced in a stretched spring varies directly as the tension, T, in the spring. If a tension of six units produces an extension of 2 cm, what will be the extension produced by a tension of 15 units?

Answer

$e \propto T \Rightarrow \frac{e}{T}=k$ the constant of proportionality

i.e. $e=kT$.

Given, $e=2$ cm when $T=6$

$2=k \times 6$

so $k=\frac{1}{3}$

The equation connecting e and T is, therefore,

$e=\frac{1}{3}T$.

So, when $T=15$ units,

$e=\frac{1}{3} \times 15$ cm

$=5$ cm

Sometimes a variable varies directly as a power of another. For example, the area, A, of a circle varies directly as the square of its radius, r. In this case the constant of proportionality will be π, since $A=\pi r^2$.

Question

If y varies directly as the cube of x and $y=24$ when $x=2$, find the value of y when $x=\frac{1}{2}$.

Answer

$y \propto x^3 \Rightarrow \frac{y}{x^3}=k$ the constant of proportionality

i.e. $y=kx^3$.

Given $y=24$ when $x=2$

$24=k \times 2^3$

$=k \times 8$

so $k=3$

The equation connecting y and x is

$y=3x^3$.

So, when $x=\frac{1}{2}$

$y=3 \times \left(\frac{1}{2}\right)^3$

$=\frac{3}{8}$

INVERSE VARIATION

If y **varies inversely** as x then $y \propto \frac{1}{x}$. In this case the equation connecting y and x is $y=\frac{k}{x}$, where k is the constant of proportionality.

Question

The illumination, I, of a bulb varies inversely as the square of the distance, d. If the illumination is five units at a distance of 3 m, what is the illumination at a distance of 2 m?

Answer

$I \propto \frac{1}{d^2} \Rightarrow I=\frac{k}{d^2}$.

Given $I=5$ when $d=3$

$5=\frac{k}{9}$

so $k=45$

Therefore, $I=\frac{45}{d^2}$

So, when $d=2$

$I=\frac{45}{4}$ units

$=11\frac{1}{4}$ units

3.23 Equation of a straight line

The **equation of a straight line** is the relationship satisfied by the coordinates of all the points on the line. For example, the equation of the line below is $y=2x$.

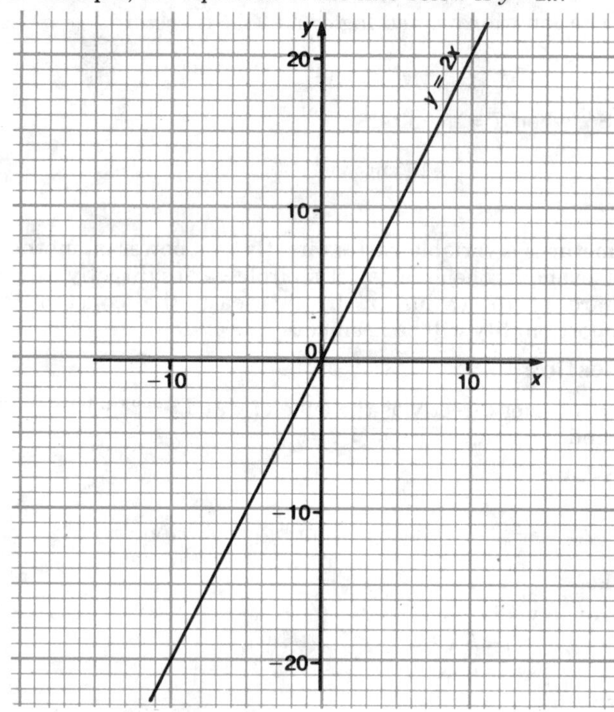

So for all points on this line,

y-coordinate $=2\times x$-coordinate

$y=mx+c$

The **equation** of any **straight line** can be written in the form

$y=mx+c$

where m and c are constants (see Unit 2.33).

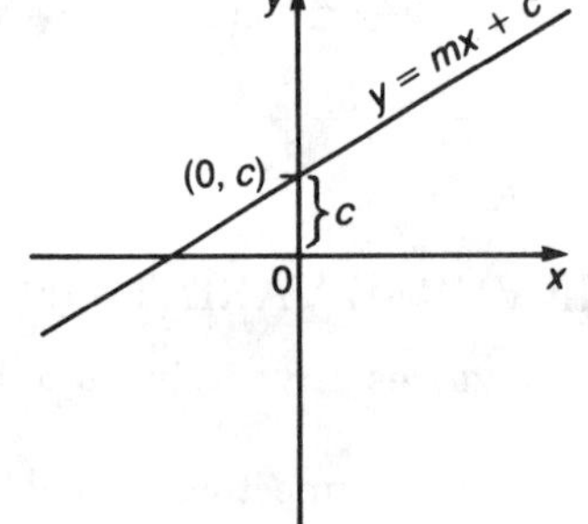

m gives the **gradient** (or slope) of the line

c gives the y-**intercept** – i.e. the line passes through the point $(0, c)$ on the y-axis.

Any equation of the form

$y=mx$

is a straight line with gradient m and passes through the origin $(0, 0)$.

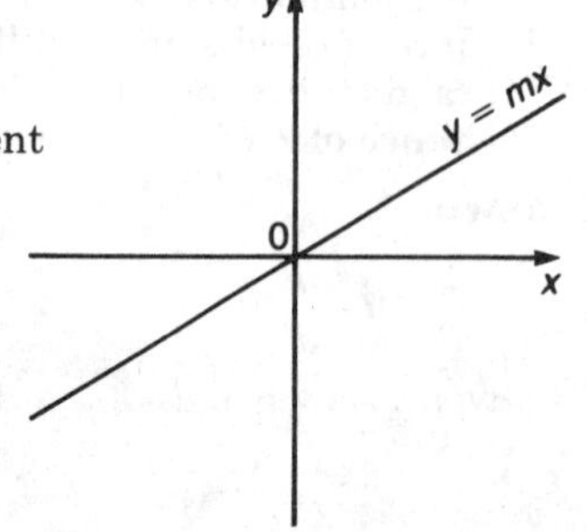

The gradient and intercept of any straight line can be obtained from its equation. For example,

compare $y=3x-4$
with $y=mx+c$

This gives $m=3$ and $c=-4$.

So the gradient of the line $y=3x-4$ is 3. Its y-intercept is -4, i.e. the line cuts the y-axis at $(0, -4)$.

The equation of the line may not always be given in the form $y=mx+c$. It is usually easy to rearrange it into this form.

Question

Find the gradients and y-intercepts of these straight lines.

(a) $x+y=5$ (b) $3y=6x-2$

Answer

(a) The equation $x+y=5$
can be rewritten as $y=-x+5$
Compare with $y=mx+c$
This gives the gradient $(m)=-1$
and the y-intercept $(c)=5$

(b) The equation $3y=6x-2$
can be rewritten as $y=2x-\frac{2}{3}$
Compare with $y=mx+c$
This gives the gradient $(m)=2$
and the y-intercept $(c)=-\frac{2}{3}$

PARALLEL LINES

Parallel lines have the same gradient or slope. The equations of parallel lines (written in the form $y=mx+c$) have the same value of m.

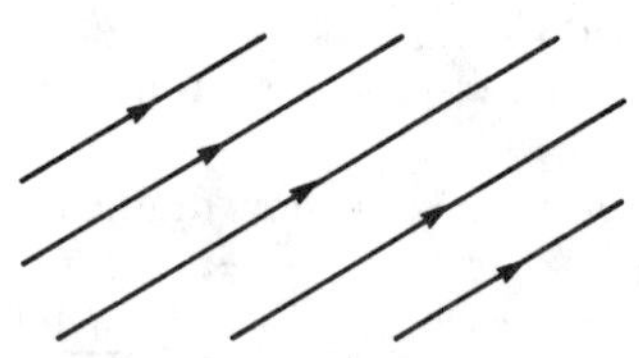

For example, the lines on the graph below are parallel to each other.

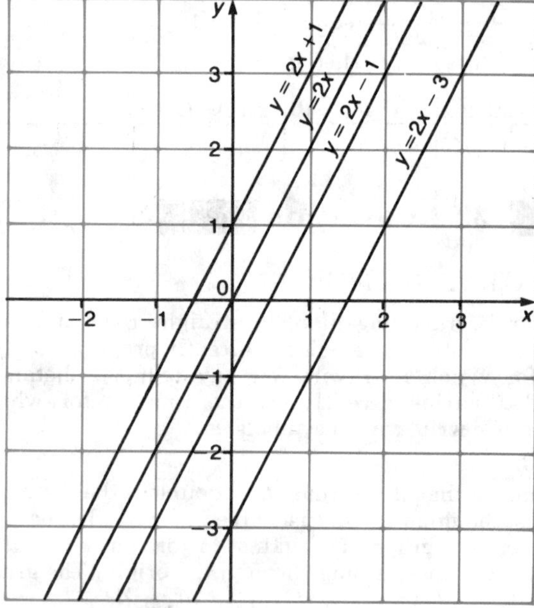

Each line has gradient 2.

So the equation of each line is of the form:

$y=2x+c$

$y=2x+1$ cuts the y-axis at $(0, 1)$.
$y=2x$ cuts the y-axis at $(0, 0)$.
$y=2x-1$ cuts the y-axis at $(0, -1)$.
$y=2x-3$ cuts the y-axis at $(0, -3)$.

Question

Show that the straight lines $2y+3x=7$ and $12x=16-8y$ are parallel.

Answer

Rewrite each equation in the form $y=mx+c$

$$2y+3x=7$$

$-3x$ from both sides $\quad 2y=-3x+7$

Divide by 2 $\quad y=-\frac{3}{2}x+\frac{7}{2}$

The gradient is $-\frac{3}{2}$

$$12x=16-8y$$

$+8y$ to both sides $\quad 8y+12x=16$

$-12x$ from both sides $\quad 8y=-12x+16$

Divide by 8 $\quad y=\frac{-12x}{8}+2$

The gradient is $-\frac{12}{8}=-\frac{3}{2}$.

The gradient of each line is $-\frac{3}{2}$. So the lines are parallel.

PERPENDICULAR LINES

The product of the gradients of two perpendicular lines is -1. For example, the lines $4y=3x$ and $3y+4x=12$ on the graph below are perpendicular.

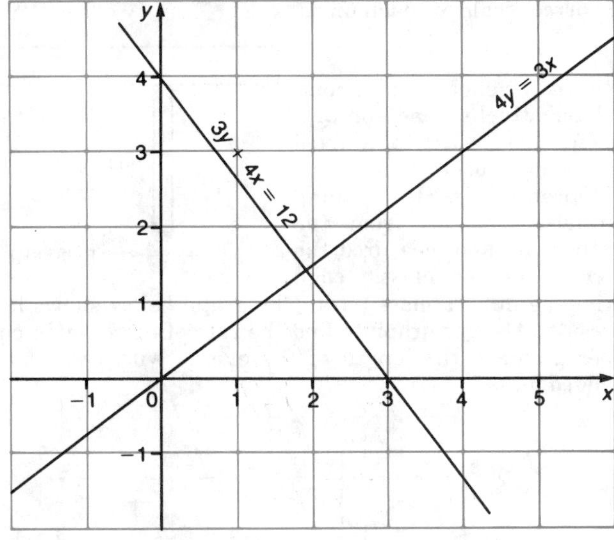

$4y=3x \Rightarrow y=\frac{3}{4}x$, i.e. a line with gradient $\frac{3}{4}$.

$3y+4x=12 \Rightarrow y=-\frac{4}{3}x+4$, i.e. a line with gradient $-\frac{4}{3}$.

Multiplying the two gradients gives

$$\frac{3}{4}\times-\frac{4}{3}=-1$$

i.e. the product of the gradients is -1.

FINDING THE EQUATION OF A STRAIGHT LINE

If you know the gradient of a straight line and a point on the line, then you can find the equation of the line.
The gradient gives the value of m in the equation $y=mx+c$. The value for c can be found by substituting the coordinates of the given point in the equation. These x and y values must satisfy the equation.

Question

Find the equation of the straight line that passes through the point $(-1, 2)$ and has a gradient of 5.

Answer

The gradient of the line is 5.
So the equation of the line is of the form

$$y=5x+c$$

The line passes through $(-1, 2)$.
Substitute $x=-1$ and $y=2$ in the equation $y=5x+c$

$$2=5(-1)+c$$
$$2=-5+c$$

so $7=c$

The required equation is $y=5x+7$.

The gradient of the line is often not given. However, if you know two points on the line, then you can use them to find the gradient (see Unit 2.32).
The gradient (m) is given by

$$m=\frac{\text{difference in } y\text{-values}}{\text{difference in } x\text{-values}}$$

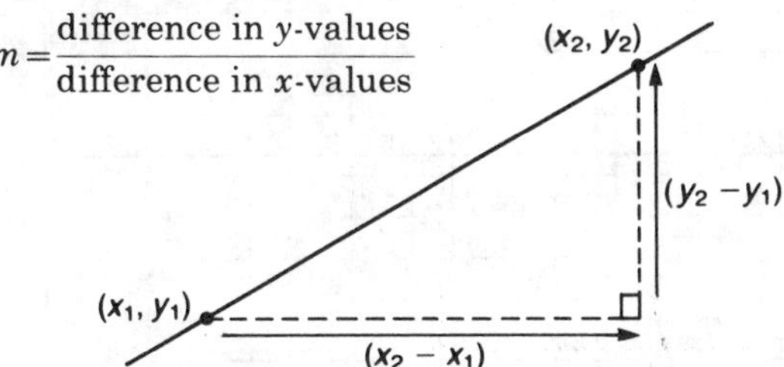

Use one of the points to find the value of c in $y=mx+c$ as before. Then check the equation by substituting the coordinates of the other point in it.

Question

Find the equation of the straight line passing through (5, 3) and (3, 7).

Answer

The gradient of the line

$$=\frac{\text{difference in } y\text{-values}}{\text{difference in } x\text{-values}}$$

$$=\frac{7-3}{3-5}$$

$$=\frac{4}{-2}=-2$$

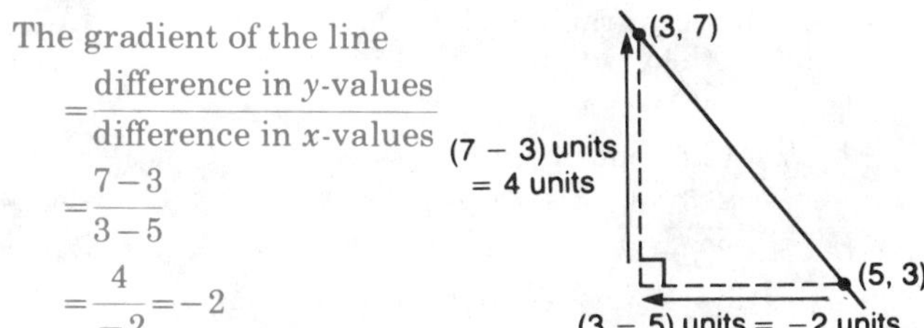

So the equation of the line is of the form

$$y=-2x+c$$

The line passes through (5, 3).
Substitute $x=5$ and $y=3$ in the equation

$$3=-2(5)+c$$
$$3=-10+c$$

so $13=c$

The required equation is $y=-2x+13$.

Check At (3, 7):
LHS: $y=7$
RHS: $-2x+13=-2(3)+13=-6+13=7$

A straight line graph may be obtained after plotting the results from an experiment in mathematics or science. You can find the equation of the line using the above method. Choose two points on the line as far apart as possible to help you to obtain the best possible equation. This equation gives a relationship between the two quantities being investigated in the experiment.

Question

Mark did an experiment in science. He hung different weights on the end of a spring and recorded the length of the spring for each weight he attached. These are the results he got.

Weight (N) W	25	50	75	100	125	150	175	200
Length (cm) L	8.2	8.8	10.1	11.3	11.9	12.8	14.0	15.1

(a) Plot these results on a graph and draw in the line of best fit.

(b) Find the equation of the line of best fit in the form $y=mx+c$.

Answer

(a)

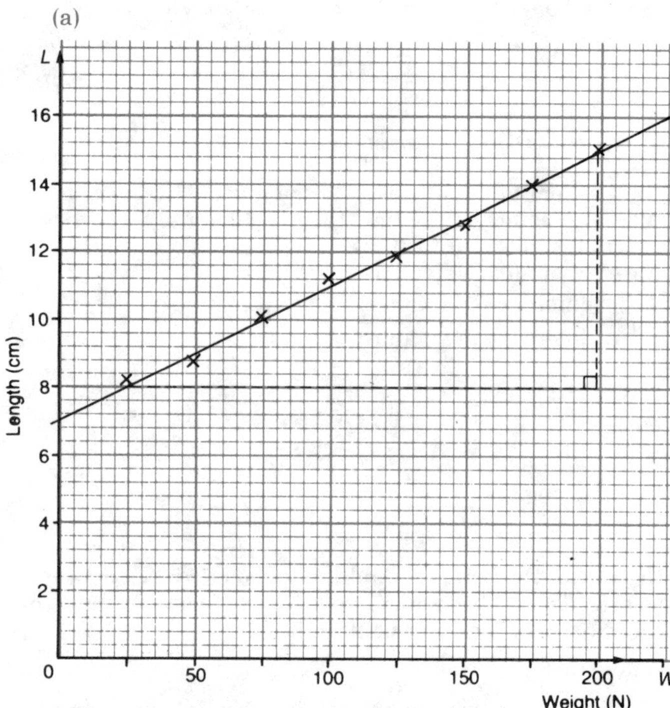

(b) *Mark two points on the line. Use them to find the gradient of the line*

From the graph and the two points (200, 15) and (25, 8) the gradient of the line

$$=\frac{\text{difference in } y\text{-values}}{\text{difference in } x\text{-values}}$$

$$=\frac{15-8}{200-25}$$

$$=\frac{7}{175}$$

$$=0.04$$

So the equation of the line is of the form

$L=0.04W+c$

The line cuts the length axis where $c=7$.
So the equation of the line is

$L=0.04W+7$

3.24 Gradient and area from graphs

GRADIENT

Gradient of a straight line

The basic idea of **gradient** as the slope of a straight line is described in Unit 2.32.

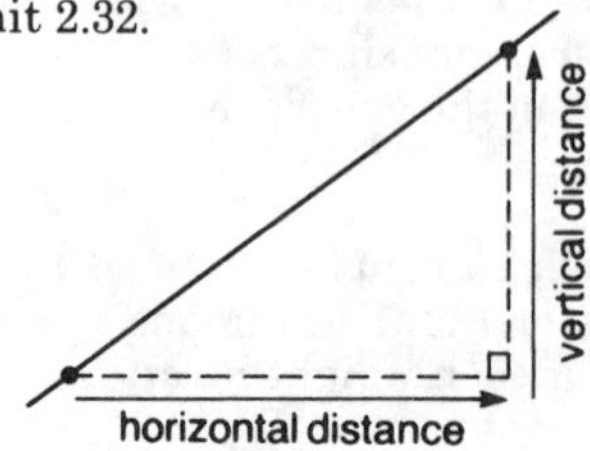

The gradient of the line is given by

$$\frac{\text{vertical distance}}{\text{horizontal distance}}$$

From the right-angled triangle formed by the line and the dotted vertical and horizontal lines, you can write

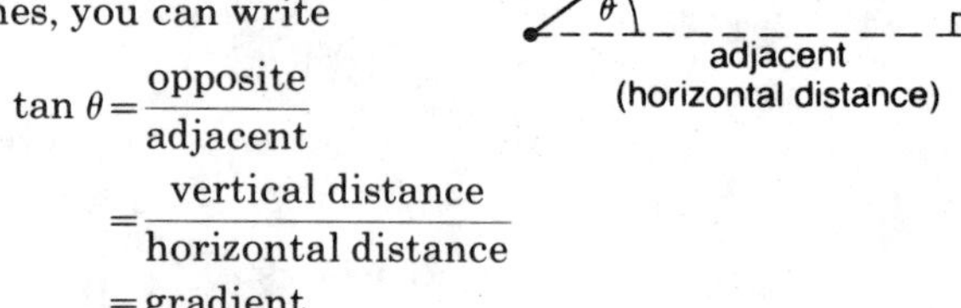

$$\tan\theta=\frac{\text{opposite}}{\text{adjacent}}$$

$$=\frac{\text{vertical distance}}{\text{horizontal distance}}$$

$$=\text{gradient}$$

So the value of the gradient is the same as the tangent of the angle θ that the line makes with the horizontal.
The gradient of a line also gives the size of the **rate of change** of one variable with respect to another. This value is often very useful in science and mathematics. For example,

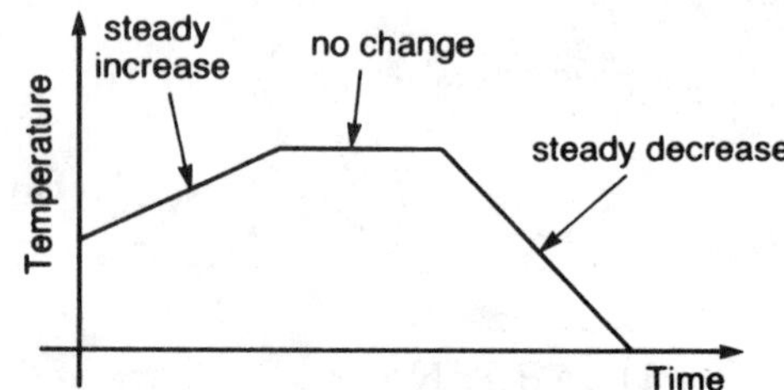

A gradient *itself* has no units but a rate of change *must* have its units clearly stated. You must work them out from the units given on the axes of the graph. The axes may be marked with different scales, so make sure that you use the correct scale for each unit.

Question

In a science experiment, Peter attached one end of a piece of elastic to a fixed wooden beam in the laboratory. He hung different masses from the other end and measured the length of the elastic each time he hung a mass on it. The graph below shows his results. Use his graph to find the rate of increase, in cm per gram, of the length of the elastic with respect to added mass.

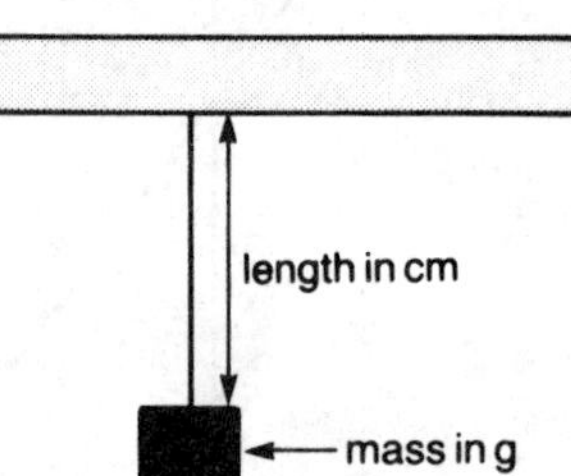

Answer

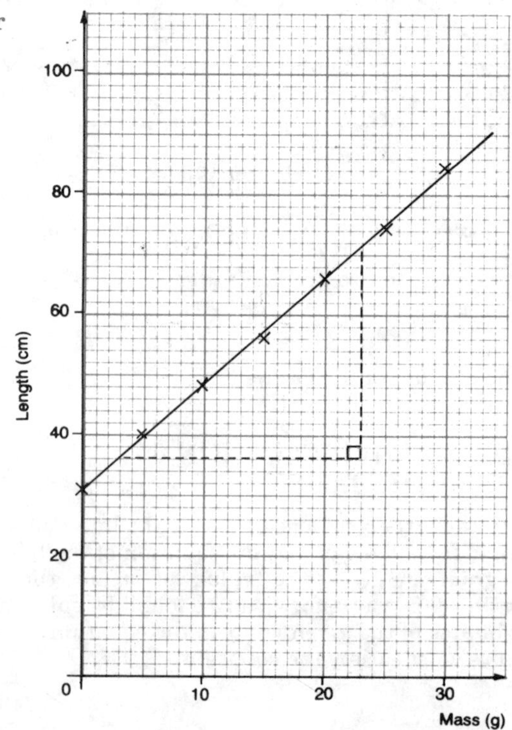

Mark two points on the line
Draw dotted lines (horizontal and vertical) from the points to make a right-angled triangle
Work out vertical and horizontal 'distances' with their units

From the graph:

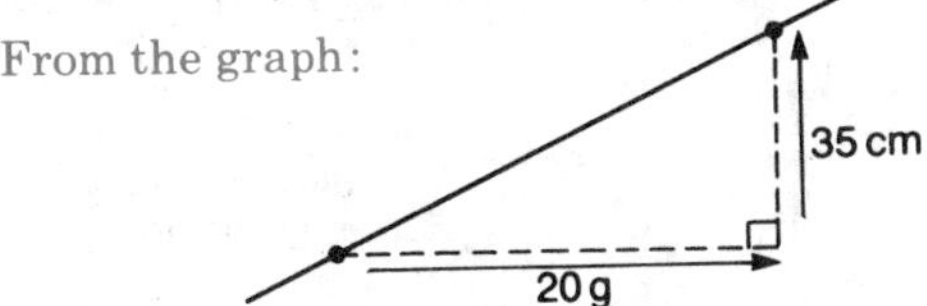

$$\text{rate of change} = \frac{35\text{ cm}}{20\text{ g}} = 1.75\text{ cm per gram}$$

So the rate of increase of the length of the elastic with respect to added mass is 1.75 cm per gram.

Gradient of a curve

The **gradient of a curve** varies from point to point on that curve. So you can only find the gradient of the curve *at particular points*.
The gradient of a curve at a point is given by the **gradient of the tangent** to the curve at that point.

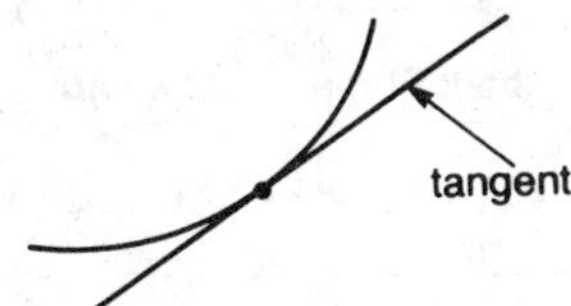

(A tangent is a straight line that touches a curve at one point only. It must never cut the curve.)
So to find the gradient at a point P, you must draw the tangent at P first, then find the gradient of the tangent (a straight line).

Gradient of curve at P

$$= \frac{BC}{AC}$$

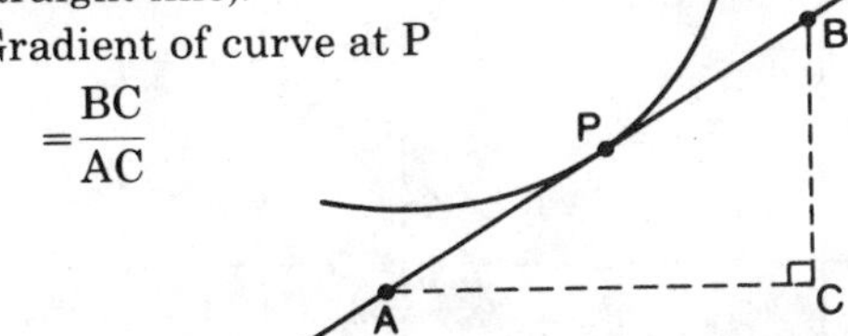

The value you obtain for the gradient will be only approximate. Its accuracy depends on the accuracy of the drawing of the curve itself and your drawing of the tangent to it.
You will need to practise drawing tangents to curves. Always use a sharp pencil and a good straight edge (ruler). Compare your drawings with the ones given here.

Question

Find the gradient of the curve below at the points P(3, −2) and Q(−2, 3).

Answer

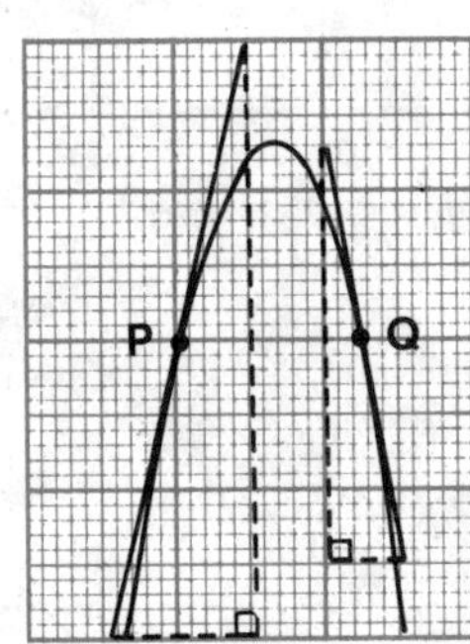

Draw tangents to the curve at P and Q
On each tangent
(*a*) *mark two points on the line,*
(*b*) *draw dotted lines (horizontal and vertical) from the points to make a right-angled triangle,*
(*c*) *work out horizontal and vertical distances*

From the graph:
Gradient of curve at P(3, −2)

$$= \frac{16}{4}$$
$$= 4$$

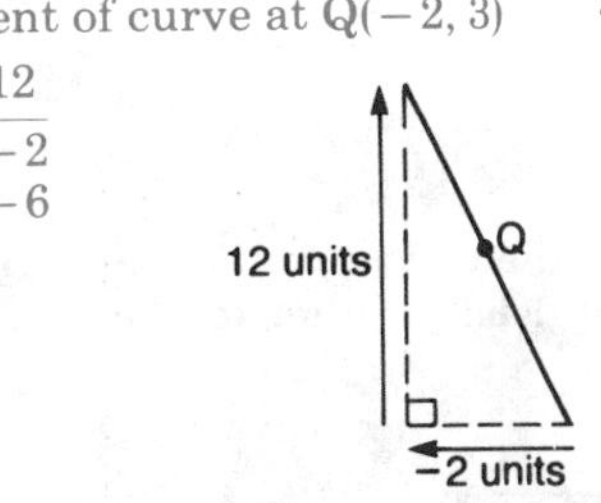

Gradient of curve at Q(−2, 3)

$$= \frac{12}{-2}$$
$$= -6$$

The gradient of a curve at a point also gives the rate of change of one of the variables with respect to the other at that point. Always state clearly the units used.

Question

The graph below shows the height of a growing tree (h in metres) plotted against the tree's age (t in years).

(a) Use the graph to estimate the tree's rate of increase in height in metres per year when the tree was 4 years old.

(b) How old and how high was the tree when it stopped growing?
Explain how you found the answer to this question.

Answer

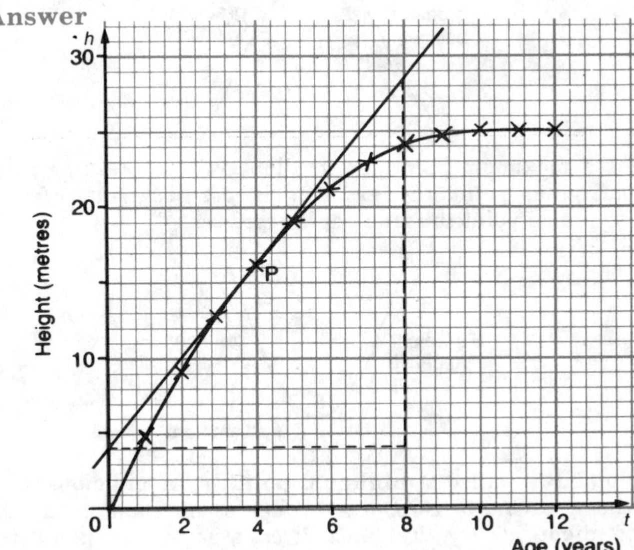

(a) *Draw the tangent to the curve at P, where t = 4*
Find the rate of increase from the gradient of this tangent

From the graph:
Rate of increase at P

$$= \frac{(28-4)\text{ metres}}{(8-0)\text{ years}}$$
$$= \frac{24\text{ metres}}{8\text{ years}}$$
$$= 3\text{ metres per year}$$

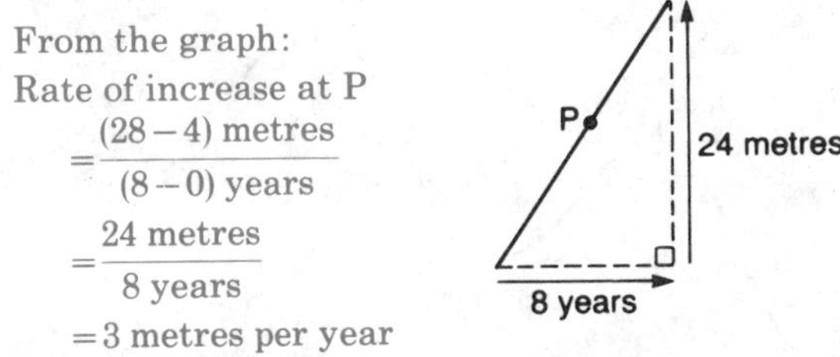

So at 4 years old the tree's rate of increase of height was 3 metres per year.

(b) The tree stopped growing when it was 10 years old and 25 metres high.
At this point on the graph, the gradient became zero, i.e. the rate of increase of height was zero.

Zero gradient

A line with **zero gradient** is *horizontal*.

horizontal gradient 0

On a graph a line with zero gradient is *parallel to the x-axis* i.e. horizontal. It has the equation $y=k$ where k is a constant.

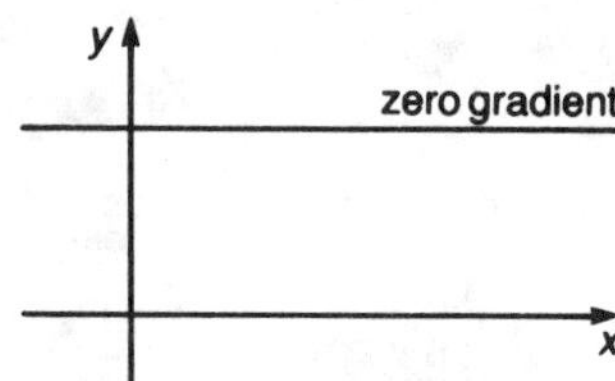

A curve can have zero gradient *at a point*. The *tangent* to the curve at this point will be parallel to the x-axis, i.e. horizontal.

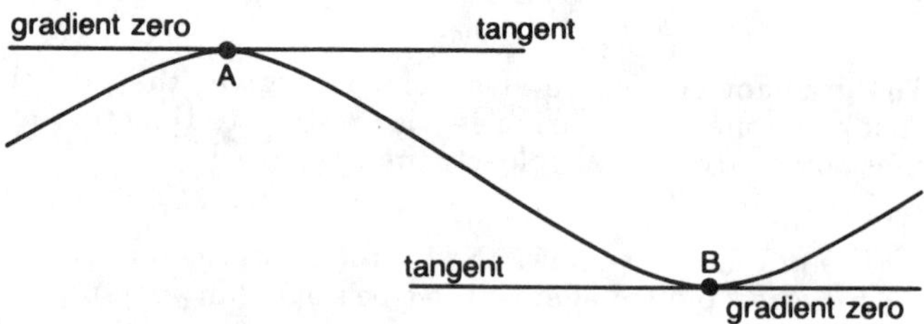

On the curve above, the gradient of the curve at points A and B is zero. These points are called **turning points**. Point A is called a **maximum point**.

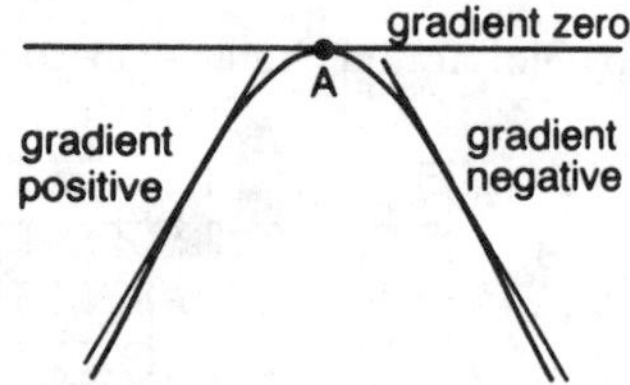

At a maximum point the gradient is zero. Just *before* a maximum point the gradient is *positive*. Just *after* a maximum point the gradient is *negative*.

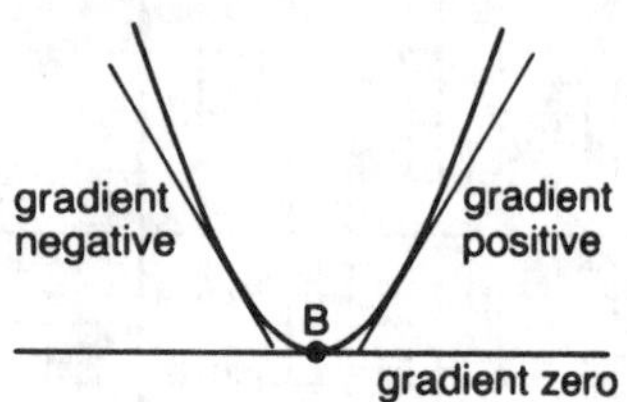

Point B is called a **minimum point**. At a minimum point the gradient is zero. Just *before* a minimum point the gradient is *negative*. Just *after* a minimum point the gradient is *positive*.

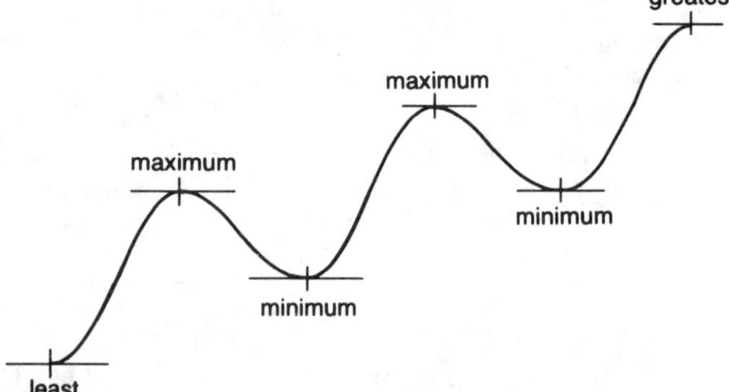

The value of y at a maximum point may not be the greatest value of y on the curve. Similarly the value of y at a minimum point may not be the least value of y on the curve.

AREA UNDER A CURVE

The **area under a curve** means the area between the curve and the x-axis. The curve can be linear or non-linear.

Linear graphs

Areas under straight line graphs are usually easy to find. They can be divided into polygons whose areas you know how to calculate (see units 1.52 and 2.21). For example, the area may be a right-angled triangle ...

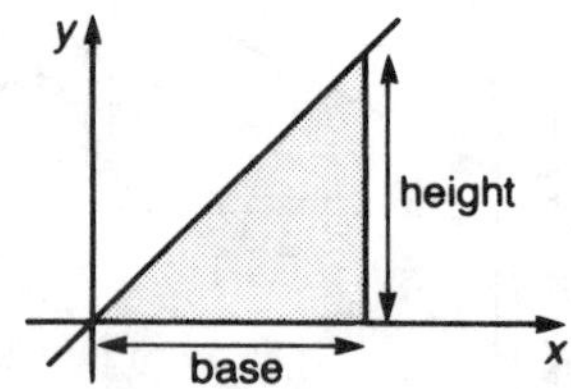

Shaded area $= \frac{1}{2}(\text{base} \times \text{height})$

... or a trapezium.

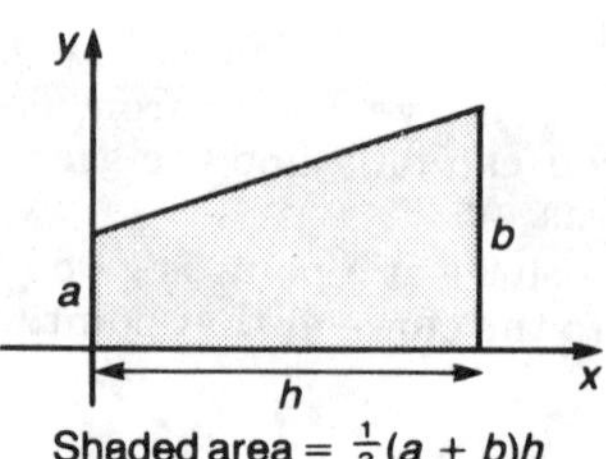

Shaded area $= \frac{1}{2}(a+b)h$

You can work out the lengths you need use in the calculations from the graph.

Remember to give the area in square units.

Question

Calculate the area shaded under this straight line $y=2x$ on the given graph.

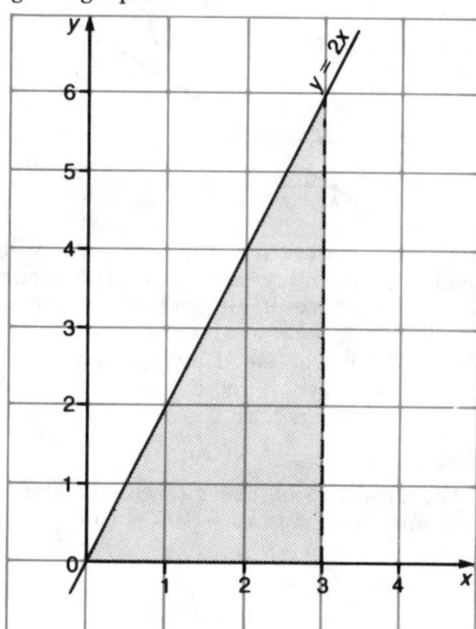

Answer

The shaded area is a right-angled triangle.
From the graph:
base = 3 units
height = 6 units

Shaded area $= \frac{1}{2}(\text{base} \times \text{height})$
$= \frac{1}{2}(3 \times 6)$ square units
$= 9$ square units

Non-linear graphs

The **area under a non-linear curve** is more difficult to find. Usually only an approximation to the area can be found.

A *rough estimate* to the area under a curve can be found by counting squares but a better approximation can be obtained by using the trapezium rule.

Trapezium rule

The area under this curve between A and B is approximately equal to the area of trapezium ABCD.

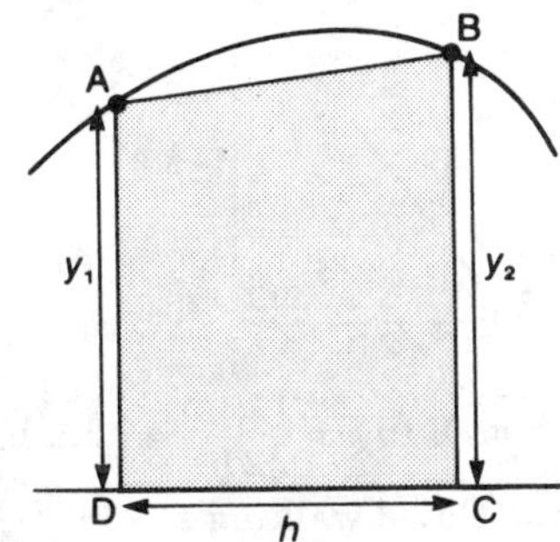

The area of ABCD
$=\frac{1}{2}(y_1+y_2)h$
where y_1 and y_2 are the y-coordinates of A and B, and h is the difference between their x-coordinates.

Drawing just one trapezium gives a very rough estimate to the area under the curve. Dividing the area into several trapeziums gives a better estimate. More trapeziums give an even better estimate. This idea is the basis of the trapezium rule.

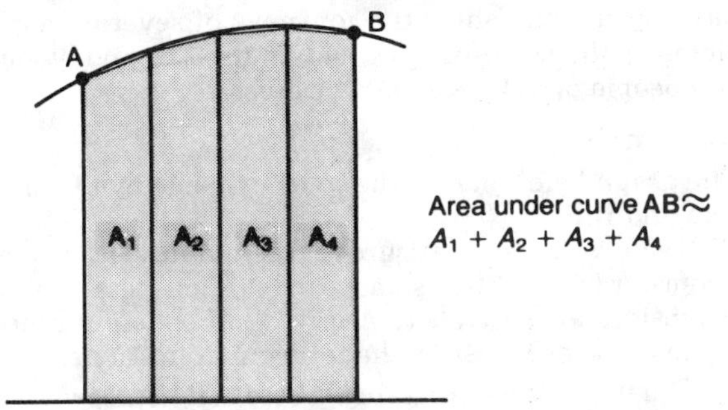

You can use the **trapezium rule** by following these steps.

1. Divide the area under the curve into trapeziums (strips) of equal 'width' h. Use an easy value for h if you can. (Questions often tell you the number of trapeziums or strips or how wide to make them.)
2. Calculate the area of each trapezium using
 $\frac{1}{2}$(sum of parallel sides) × width
3. Find the sum of the areas of these trapeziums to give an approximate area under the curve.

Question

Draw the graph of $y=x^3$ between $x=0$ and $x=3$.
Use the trapezium rule to estimate the area under your graph. Divide the area into three strips.

Answer

Table of values:

x	0	1	2	3
$y=x^3$	0	1	8	27

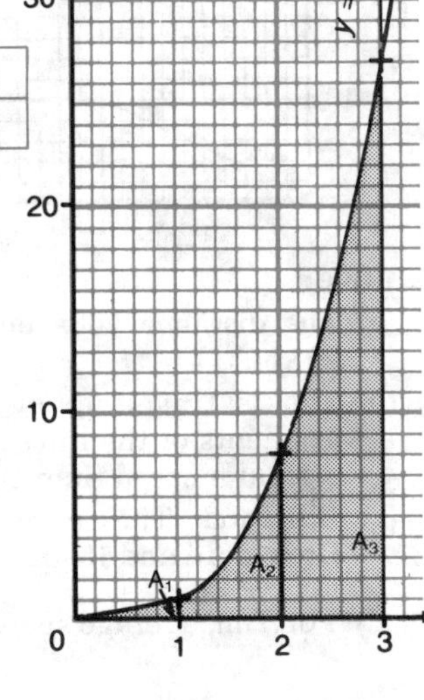

Divide area under curve into 3 trapeziums A_1, A_2 and A_3

From the graph

$$\text{area of } A_1 = \tfrac{1}{2}(0+1)1 \text{ square units} = \frac{1}{2} \text{ square unit}$$

$$\text{area of } A_2 = \tfrac{1}{2}(1+8)1 \text{ square units} = \frac{9}{2} \text{ square units}$$

$$\text{area of } A_3 = \tfrac{1}{2}(8+27)1 \text{ square units} = \frac{35}{2} \text{ square units}$$

Total area under graph = area of $(A_1+A_2+A_3)$

$$=\left(\frac{1}{2}+\frac{9}{2}+\frac{35}{2}\right)$$

$$=\frac{45}{2} \text{ square units}$$

$$=22\tfrac{1}{2} \text{ square units}$$

The trapezium rule can also be given as a formula.

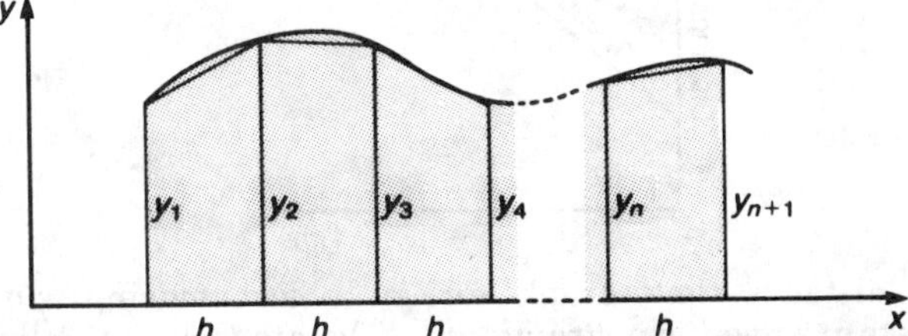

If the area under the curve is divided into n trapeziums, each of width h and $y_1, y_2, y_3, \ldots, y_{n+1}$ are the values of y at the 'edge' of each strip, then the area under the curve, A, is given by

$$A \approx [\tfrac{1}{2}(y_1+y_{n+1})+(y_2+y_3+\cdots+y_n)]h$$

In words, this formula tells you that to find the approximate area under the curve, add the average of the first and last values of y to the sum of all the other values of y, and then multiply by the width, h, of each trapezium.
The values of y can be found from a graph of the curve or from its equation.

Question

Use the trapezium rule to estimate the area under the graph $y=x^3$ between $x=0$ and $x=3$. Divide the area into six strips. Give your answer correct to three significant figures.

Answer

Divide the x-axis under the curve into 6 equal parts for 6 strips

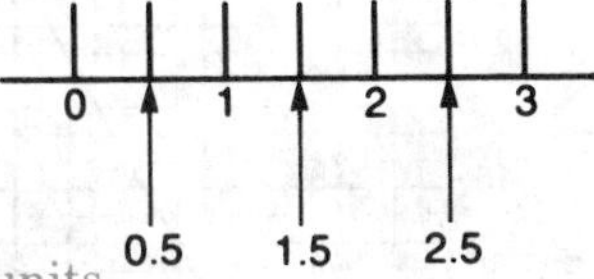

The width of each strip is 0.5 units.

Work out a table of values for y for the edge of each strip

Table of values:

x	0	0.5	1	1.5	2	2.5	3
$y=x^3$	0	0.125	1	3.375	8	15.625	27
	y_1	y_2	y_3	y_4	y_5	y_6	y_7

Using the trapezium rule

area under the curve

$$\approx [\tfrac{1}{2}(y_1+y_7)+(y_2+y_3+y_4+y_5+y_6)]h$$

$$=[\tfrac{1}{2}(0+27)+(0.125+1+3.375+8+15.625)]0.5$$

$$=20.8 \text{ square units (to 3 s.f.)}$$

Display: 20.8125

GRAPHS IN KINEMATICS

Kinematics is the mathematical study of moving objects. The *gradient* and *area* of graphs in kinematics usually have a special meaning. The methods used to find them are the same as described earlier in this unit.

Distance–time graphs

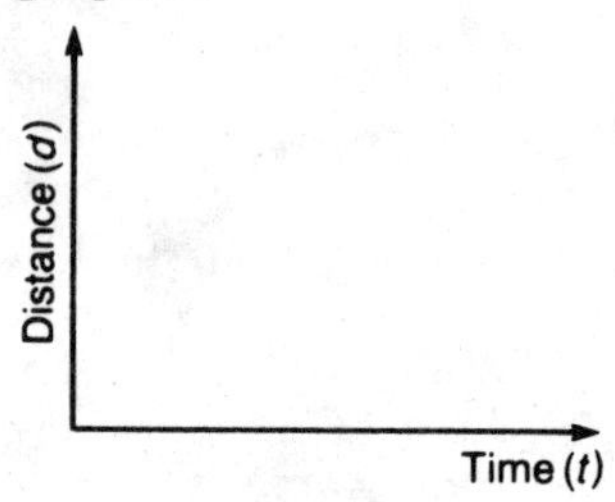

A **distance–time graph** illustrates the relationship between the distance travelled (d) by an object and the time (t) for which it travels.
It is usual to measure time along the horizontal axis ('time goes along') and distance on the vertical axis.

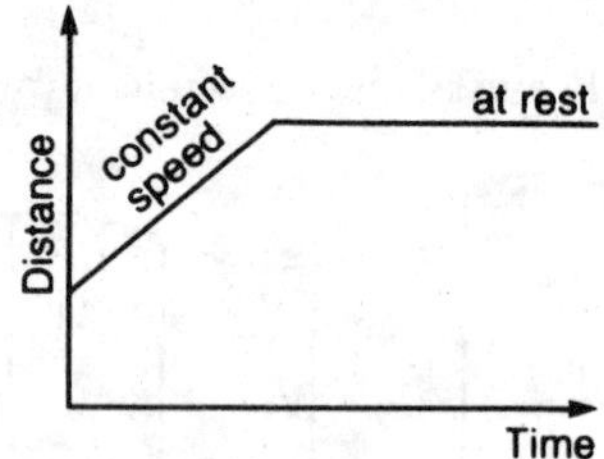

The distance–time graph for an object moving with **constant speed** is a *straight line*. The *gradient* of the line gives the *speed* of the object. Zero gradient means that the object is at rest, i.e. stationary.
Speed is the rate of change of distance with time. Always state its unit clearly. For example, distance in metres (m) and time in seconds (s) give speed in metres per second (m/s or m s^{-1}).
A **travel graph** is a special type of distance–time graph which describes a journey (see Unit 1.57).

Question

David went on a sponsored charity walk. He had trained so that he could walk at a steady speed. The graph below is about his journey.

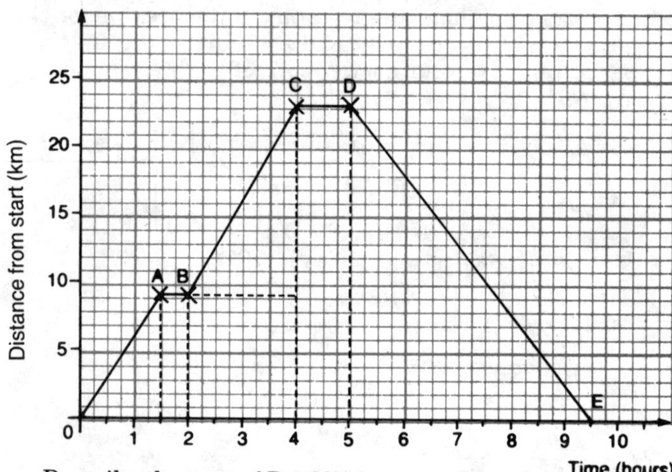

Describe the part of David's journey shown by
(a) OA (b) AB (c) BC (d) CD (e) DE.

Answer

(a) From the graph:

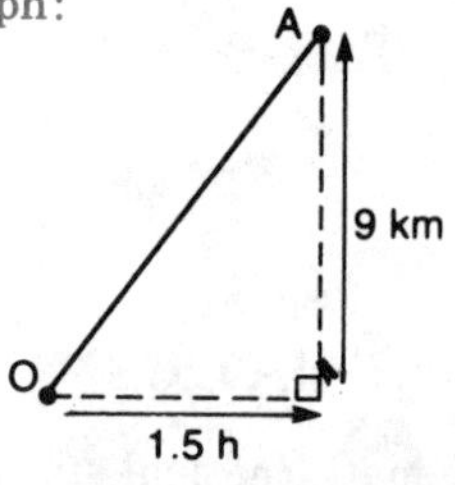

the speed from O to A $= \dfrac{9 \text{ km}}{1.5 \text{ h}} = 6$ km/h

So OA shows David walking at 6 km/h.

(b) Between A and B, the graph shows that David is resting (not walking) for $\frac{1}{2}$ hour.

(c) From the graph:

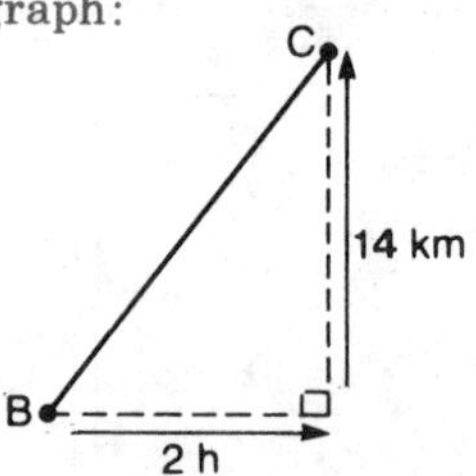

the speed from B to C $= \dfrac{14 \text{ km}}{2 \text{ h}} = 7$ km/h

So BC shows David walking at 7 km/h.

(d) CD shows David rests for 1 hour.

(e) From the graph:
the line DE is returning to the t-axis, so David is on the return journey.

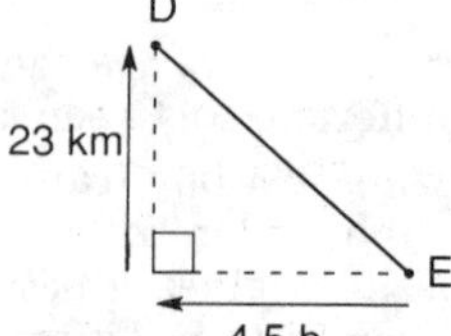

Speed $= \dfrac{23 \text{ km}}{4.5 \text{ h}} \approx 5$ km/h

A travel graph can show the journeys of several people or vehicles at the same time. It can be used to find when and where people or vehicles meet or cross.

Question

The graph below shows the journey made by two people, Tim and Bill.
Bill sets out from Ansgrove at mid-day to travel to Bromsford. At the same time, Tim sets off from Bromsford and travels to Ansgrove at constant speed.
From the graph answer the following questions.

(a) What is the distance between Ansgrove and Bromsford?
(b) Which traveller is travelling by car and which by cycle? How did you decide?
(c) At what time and where do they meet?
(d) What is Tim's average speed on the journey?

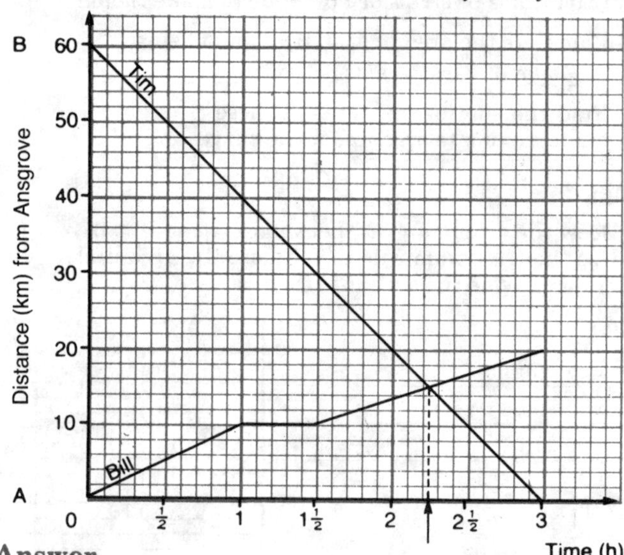

Answer

(a) The distance between Ansgrove and Bromsford is 60 km.
(b) Tim is travelling by car and Bill by cycle. The gradients of the lines show that Tim is travelling at a greater speed than Bill.
(c) Bill and Tim meet at 2.15 p.m., 45 km from Bromsford and 15 km from Ansgrove.
(d) For Tim, average speed $= \dfrac{60 \text{ km}}{3 \text{ h}} = 20$ km h^{-1}.

When an object travels at a **variable speed**, i.e. a speed that is not constant, its distance–time graph will be a curve, not a straight line.

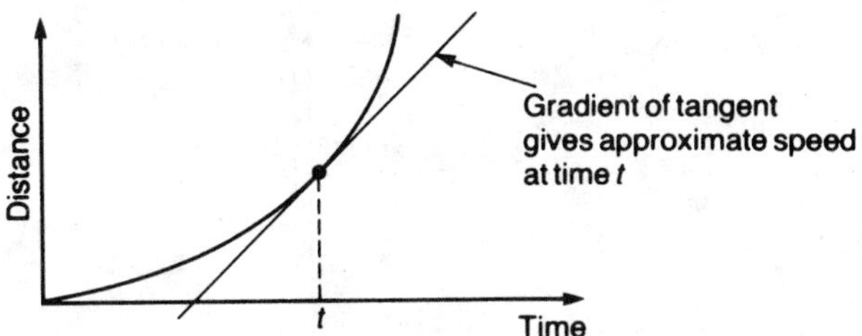

The speed of the object at any time may be estimated from the gradient of the tangent to the curve at that time.

Question

In this table for the motion of a car starting from rest, t stands for the time in seconds from the start and d the distance in metres travelled up to that time.

(a) Calculate the average speed for the first 5 seconds.

(b) Draw the distance–time graph for this table.

(c) Estimate the speed of the car when $t = 6$ seconds.

t	d
0	0
1	1
2	4
3	9
4	16
5	24
6	33
7	42
8	53
9	67
10	84

Answer

(a) For the first 5 seconds

$$\text{average speed} = \frac{\text{total distance}}{\text{total time}}$$

$$= \frac{24 \text{ metres}}{5 \text{ seconds}} \qquad \textit{From the table}$$

$$= 4.8 \text{ metres per second}$$

So the average speed for the first 5 seconds was 4.8 m s^{-1}.

(b) Distance–time graph

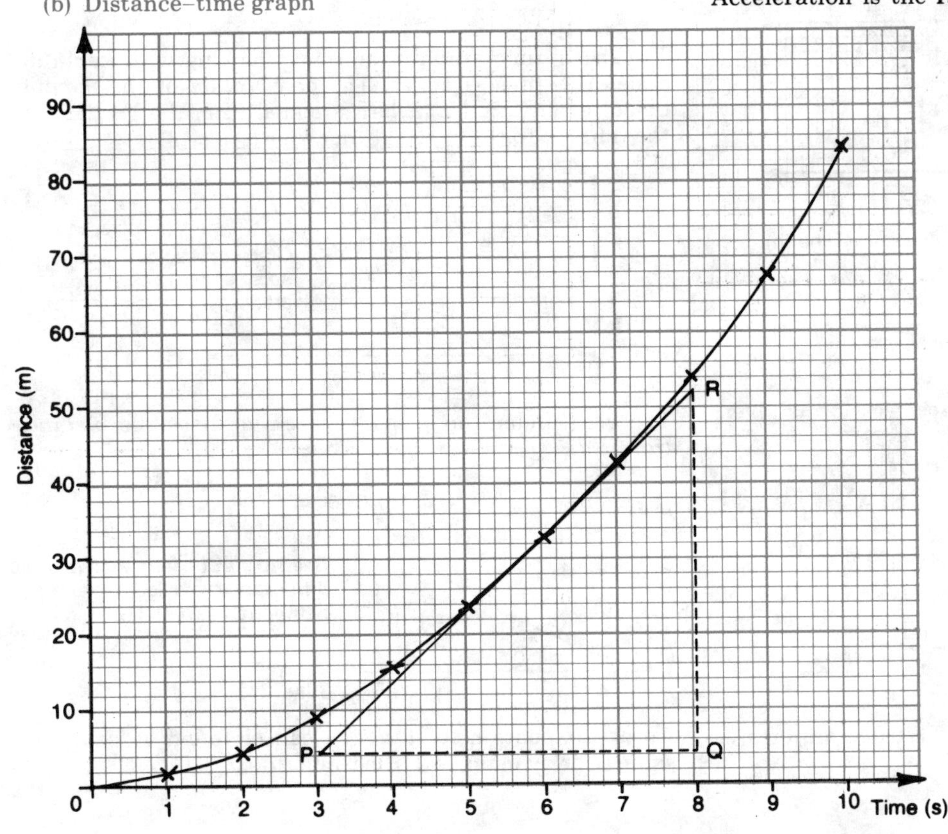

(c) *Draw the tangent to the curve at the point where $t = 6$ seconds*
Mark two points on the line, P and R
Draw dotted lines (horizontal and vertical) from the points to make the right-angled triangle PQR
Work out the horizontal and vertical distances PQ and QR

From the graph:

gradient of the curve where $t = 6$ s is

$$\frac{QR}{PQ} = \frac{(52-4) \text{ metres}}{(8-3) \text{ seconds}}$$

$$= \frac{48 \text{ metres}}{5 \text{ seconds}}$$

$$= 9.6 \text{ metres per second}$$

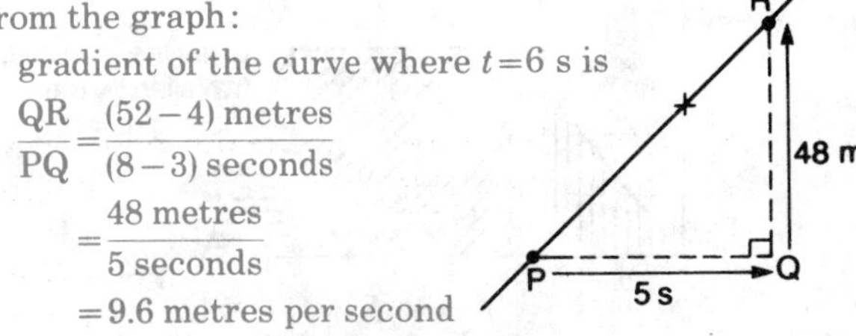

So the speed when $t = 6$ s is 9.6 m s^{-1}.

Speed–time (or velocity–time) graphs

When you know the speed (or velocity) of an object at certain times, you can draw a **speed–time** (or **velocity–time**) **graph** for the motion of the object.

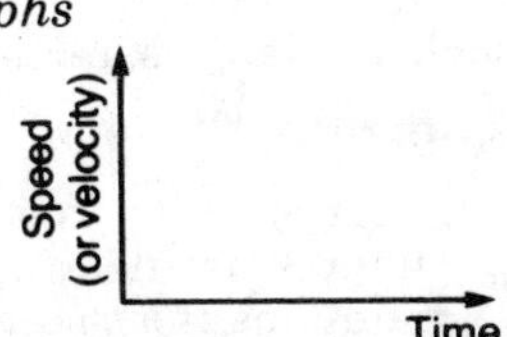

The speed–time (or velocity–time) graph for an object moving with **constant acceleration** is a straight line. The *gradient* of the line gives the *acceleration* of the object.

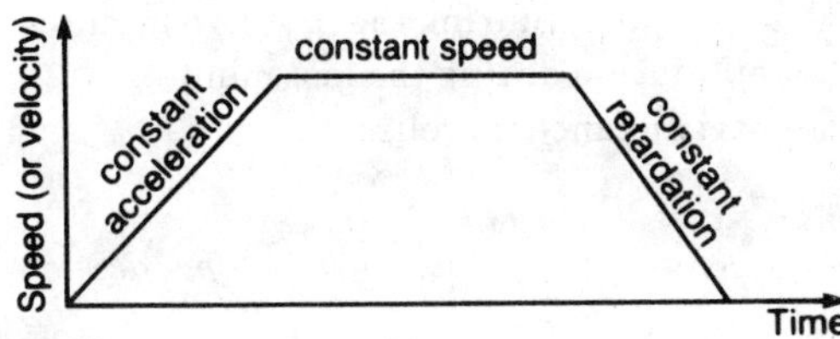

A *positive* gradient shows positive constant acceleration, i.e. a steady *increase* in speed.

A *negative* gradient shows negative constant acceleration, i.e. a steady *decrease* in speed. This is often called **deceleration** or **retardation**.

A *zero* gradient shows no acceleration, i.e. a *constant* speed.

Acceleration is the **rate of change of speed with time**.

Always state its unit clearly. For example, speed in kilometres per hour (km/h or km h^{-1}) and time in hours (h) give acceleration in kilometres per hour per hour (km/h^2 or km h^{-2}).

The **distance travelled** by a moving object is given by the area under its speed–time graph.

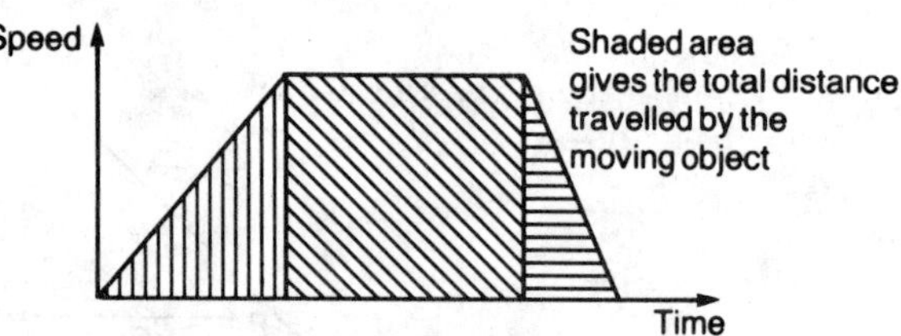

When the graph is made up of straight lines, then the area under the graph can be calculated.

Divide it up into easy shapes whose areas you can find, such as triangles, rectangles, trapeziums.

Question

A car starting from rest accelerates uniformly for two minutes until it reaches a speed of 40 km h^{-1}. It maintains this speed for three minutes, after which the brakes are applied, slowing it down uniformly until it stops after a further minute.

Draw the speed–time graph for the car and use it to calculate

(a) the acceleration during the first two minutes.

(b) the retardation during the last minute,

(c) the total distance travelled.

Answer

During each stage of the journey, the acceleration is uniform, i.e. constant

So the graph consists of three straight lines

Speed–time graph

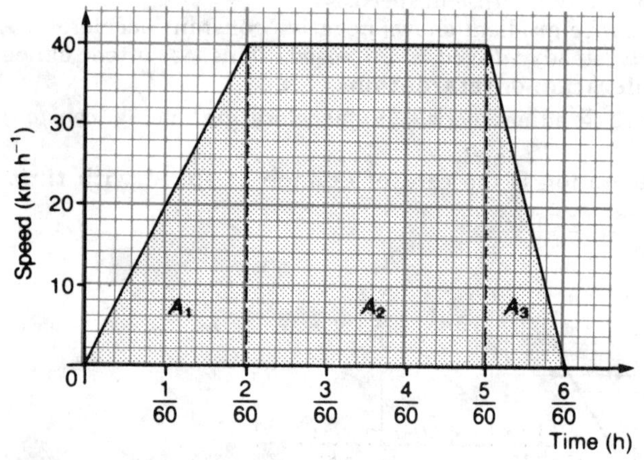

Note: *The times are given in hours, for example,* 2 *minutes* $=\frac{2}{60}$ *hour*

(a) From the graph:

For the first two minutes, the acceleration is given by

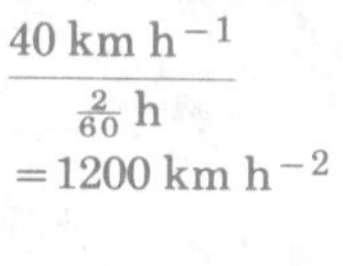

$$\frac{40 \text{ km h}^{-1}}{\frac{2}{60} \text{ h}}$$

$= 1200$ km h^{-2}

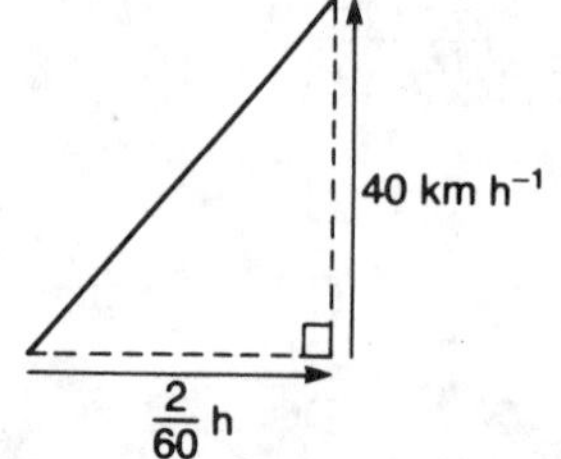

So the acceleration during the first two minutes is 1200 km h^{-2}.

(b) From the graph:

For the last minute, the retardation is given by

$$\frac{40 \text{ km h}^{-1}}{\frac{1}{60} \text{ h}}$$

$= 2400$ km h^{-2}

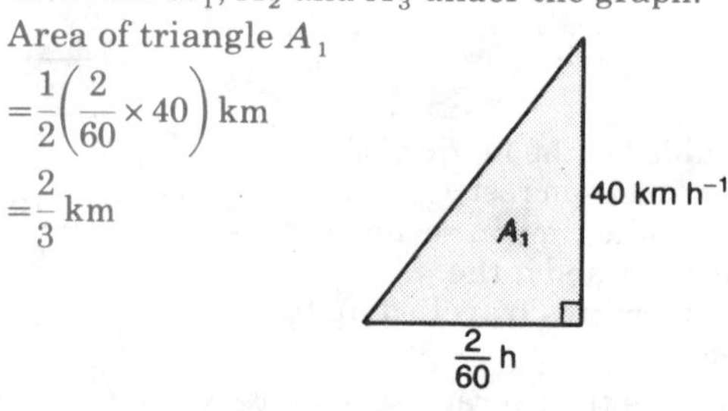

(c) The total distance travelled by the car is the sum of the areas A_1, A_2 and A_3 under the graph.

Area of triangle A_1

$=\frac{1}{2}\left(\frac{2}{60}\times 40\right)$ km

$=\frac{2}{3}$ km

Area of rectangle A_2

$=\frac{3}{60}\times 40$ km

$= 2$ km

Area of triangle A_3

$=\frac{1}{2}\left(\frac{1}{60}\times 40\right)$ km

$=\frac{1}{3}$ km

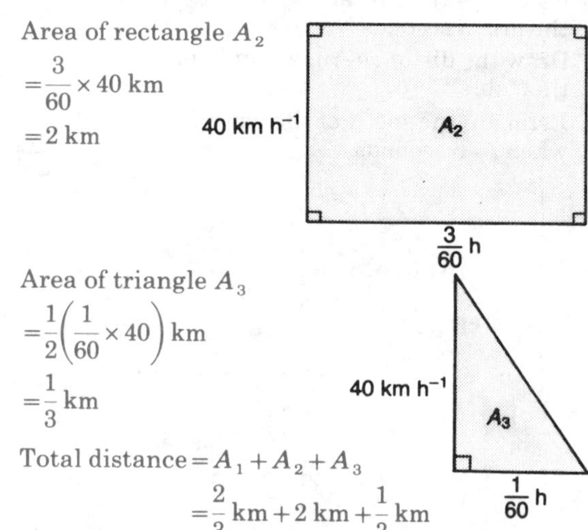

Total distance $= A_1 + A_2 + A_3$

$=\frac{2}{3}$ km $+ 2$ km $+\frac{1}{3}$ km

$= 3$ km

The speed–time graph of an object moving with **variable acceleration** is a curve. The *acceleration* of the moving object at any time can be estimated from the *gradient* of the tangent to the curve at that time (see p.131).

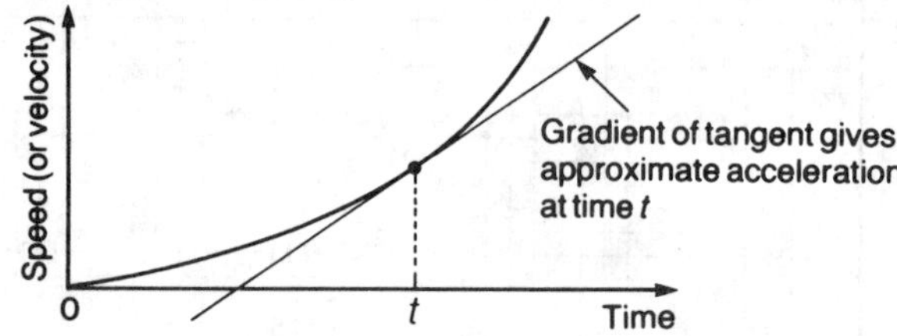

The *area* under the speed–time curve gives the *distance travelled.*

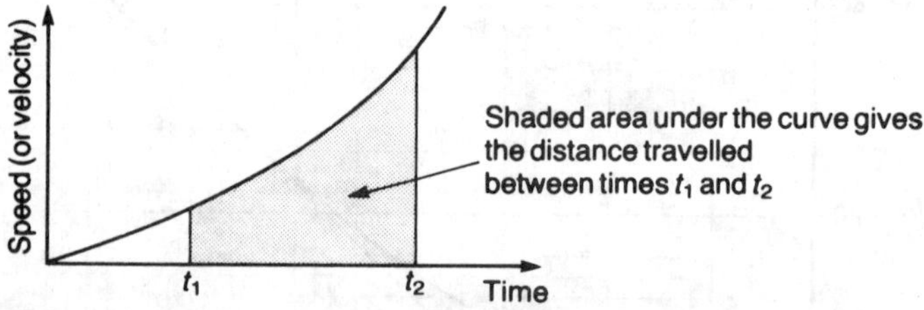

An approximation to this area can be found by counting squares or by using the trapezium rule.

Acceleration–time graph

When you know the acceleration of a moving object at certain times, you can draw an **acceleration–time graph** for the object.
The *speed* of the moving object can be found from the *area* under its acceleration-time graph.

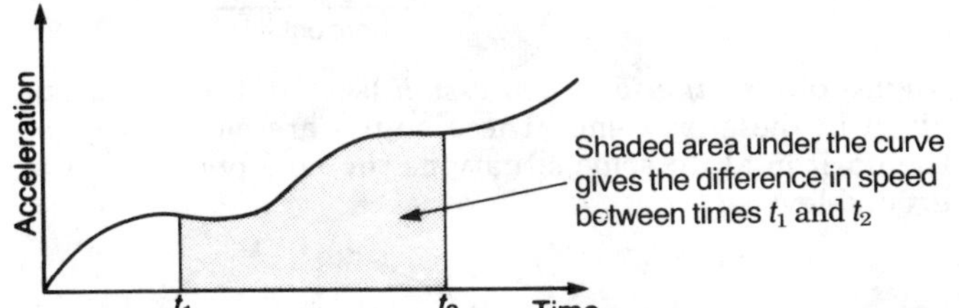

The area under the curve can be estimated by counting squares or, better still, by using the trapezium rule (see p.133).

Question

The graph below is the acceleration–time graph for a car during the first six seconds of its motion. Use the trapezium rule with intervals of 1 second to estimate the speed of the car after six seconds.

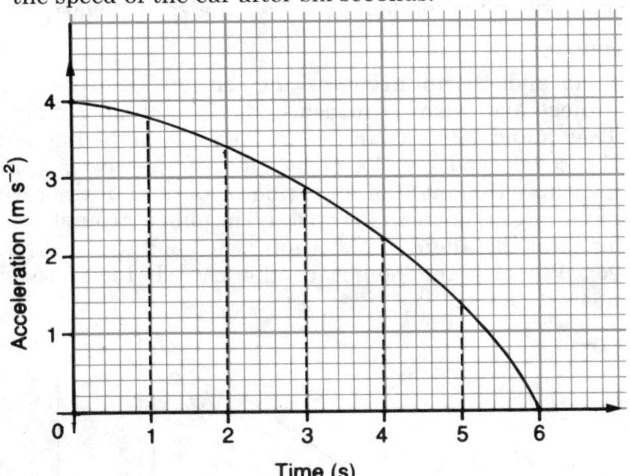

Answer

From the graph:

t(s)	0	1	2	3	4	5	6
a(m s^{-2})	4	3.8	3.4	2.8	2.2	1.4	0
	y_1	y_2	y_3	y_4	y_5	y_6	y_7

Using the trapezium rule with an interval of 1 second ($h=1$)

area under the curve

$\approx[\frac{1}{2}(4+0)+(3.8+3.4+2.8+2.2+1.4)]\times 1 \text{ m s}^{-1}$

$=15.6 \text{ m s}^{-1}$

So the speed of the car after 6 seconds is approximately 15.6 m s^{-1}.

3.25 Trigonometry and problems

To **solve problems** about unknown sides and angles in **right-angled triangles** you may need to use *both* Pythagoras' theorem (see Unit 2.36) and the trigonometrical ratios (see Unit 2.37).
It is important to draw a **good diagram** first. This diagram will help you to decide how to solve the problem. Mark your diagram with the given information. Then label each length and angle you have to find with a letter. Look for and mark angles that are right angles next. Use these to help you to spot the right-angled triangles that involve the 'given' and 'wanted' values. It usually helps to sketch each triangle separately and label them with these values. Jot down any trigonometrical ratios or Pythagoras' theorem relating the 'given' and 'wanted' values. Try to choose the easiest ones to use to solve the problem.

2D PROBLEMS

Problems in **two-dimensions** (2D) are often solved by using two right-angled triangles, one after the other. To be in 2D these triangles must be in the *same* plane, i.e. the same flat surface. The triangles you need to use may be all in the same horizontal plane, e.g. on a flat horizontal surface such as a floor or flat ground.

Practical problems may involve bearings or compass directions. These give you clues about where to mark some right angles on your diagram.

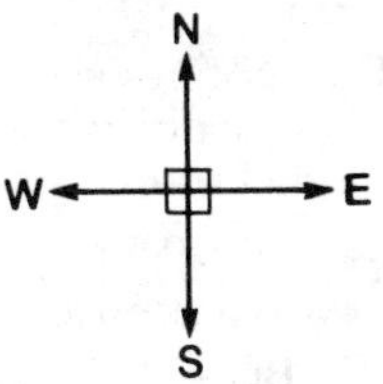

The shortest distance from a point to a straight line is perpendicular to the line. This can be used in many trigonometrical problems.

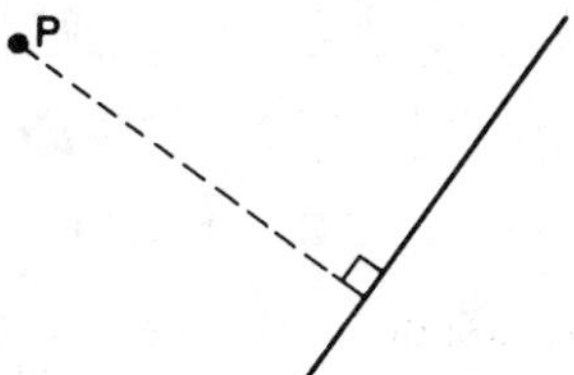

Question

Four towns Aymouth, Beeville, Ceeton and Deeside are on the same flat coastal plain. Aymouth, Beeville and Deeside are due north, due west and due east of Ceeton respectively. Beeville is 17 km from Aymouth and 20 km from Deeside. Deeside is 5 km from Ceeton.

(a) Calculate the distance of Ceeton from
(i) Beeville, (ii) Aymouth.

(b) Find the bearing (to the nearest degree) of Aymouth from
(i) Beeville, (ii) Deeside.

Answer

Let A represent Aymouth B represent Beeville
C represent Ceeton D represent Deeside

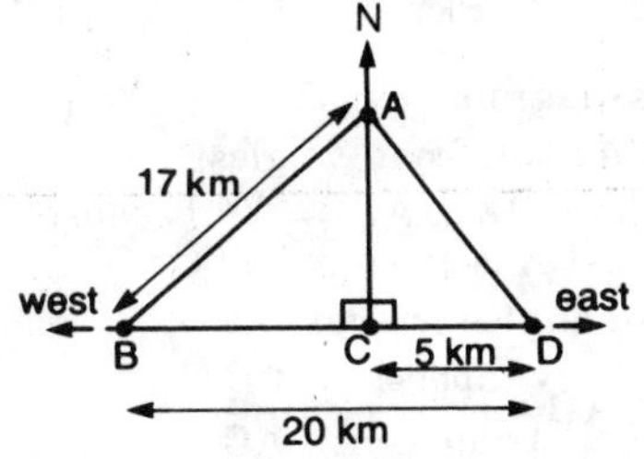

(a) (i) BC = BD − CD
$= 20 \text{ km} - 5 \text{ km} = 15 \text{ km}$
So Ceeton is 15 km from Beeville.

(ii) In triangle ABC, $\angle ACB = 90°$ because B is due west of C and A is due north of C.
By Pythagoras' theorem
$17^2 = b^2 + 15^2$
So $b^2 = 17^2 - 15^2$
$= 64$
$b = \sqrt{64} = 8$
So Ceeton is 8 km from Aymouth.

(b) (i) The bearing of A from B is given by angle θ.

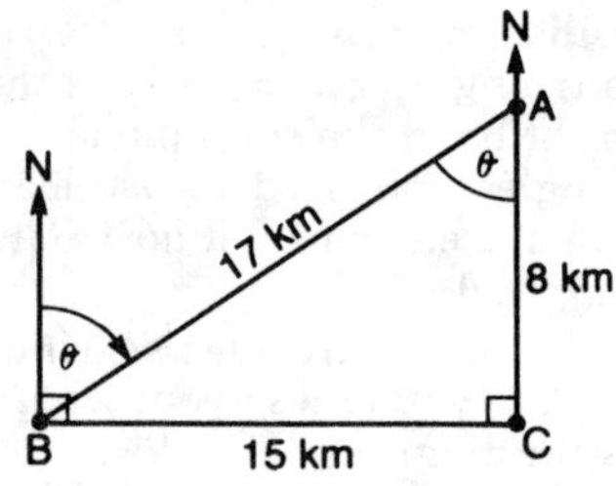

From the diagram

$\theta = \angle BAC$ (N-lines are parallel and these are alternate angles)

From right-angled triangle ABC

$$\sin \angle BAC = \frac{\text{opposite}}{\text{hypotenuse}} = \frac{BC}{AB} = \frac{15}{17}$$

Use these sides because AB is given and BC was easy to calculate

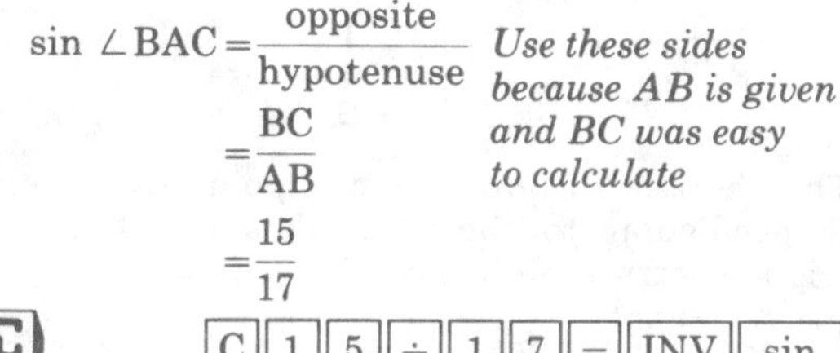

C | C | 1 | 5 | ÷ | 1 | 7 | = | INV | sin |

Display: 61.92751306

$\angle BAC = 62°$ (to the nearest degree)

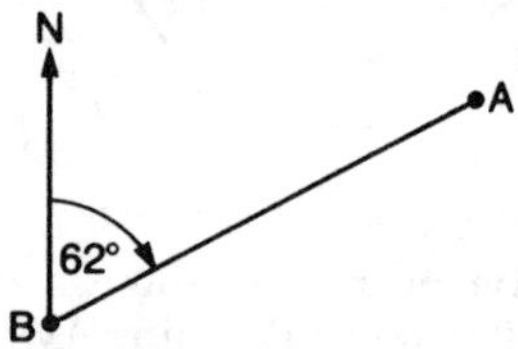

The bearing of Aymouth from Beeville is 062° (to the nearest degree).

(ii) The bearing of A from D is given by angle $(360° - x)$.

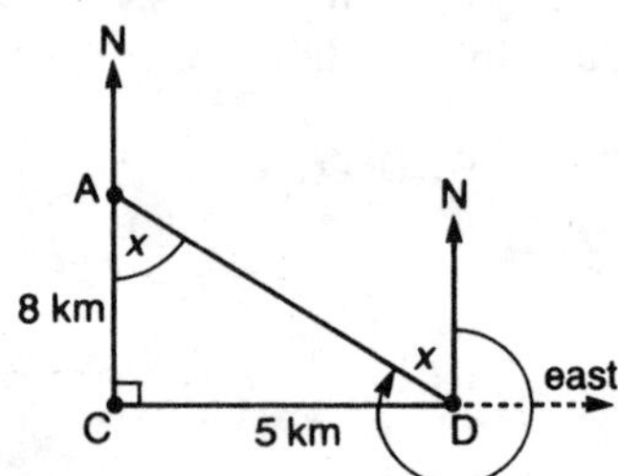

From this diagram

$x = \angle CAD$ (alternate angles)

In triangle ACD, $\angle ACD = 90°$ because D is due east of C and A is due north of C.

From right-angled triangle ACD

$$\tan \angle CAD = \frac{\text{opposite}}{\text{adjacent}} = \frac{CD}{AC} = \frac{5}{8}$$

C | C | 5 | ÷ | 8 | = | INV | tan |

Display: 32.00538321

$\angle CAD = 32°$ (to the nearest degree)

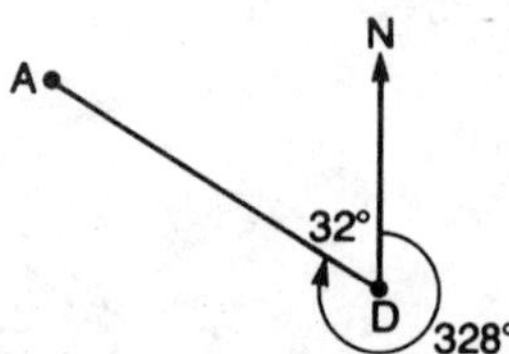

The bearing of Aymouth from Deeside is $(360° - 32°) = 328°$ (to the nearest degree)

The triangles you need to solve a problem may be all in the **same vertical plane**, e.g. on a flat vertical surface such as a wall.

In these problems you will often use the right angle between a *horizontal* line and a *vertical* line.

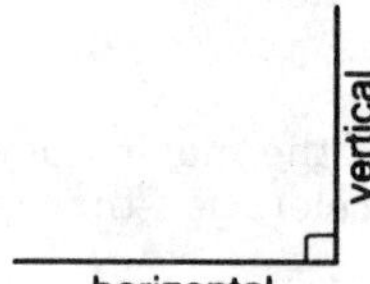

Angles of *elevation* and *depression* (see Unit 2.37) may be given in these problems. These angles are measured from the horizontal. In some situations the horizontal is not at ground-level.

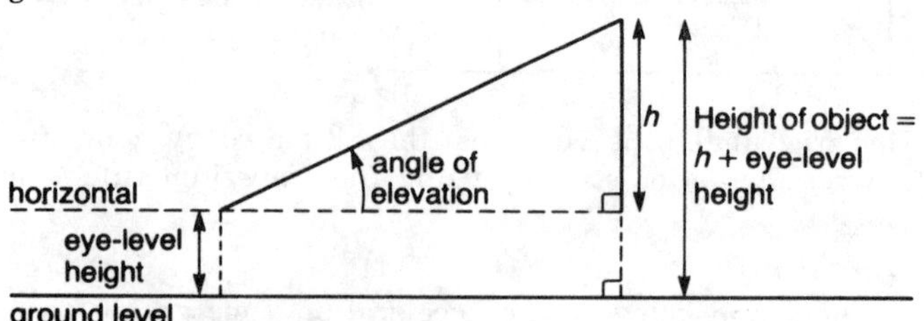

The measuring instrument may be mounted above ground-level, e.g. at 'eye-level'. You must take this into account when finding heights using angles of elevation.

Question

Paul and Sarah are working on an environmental project and wish to measure the height of a church. They stand 100 m apart on the same straight line with the tower and on the same side of the tower. Each measures the angle of elevation of the top of the tower using a clinometer mounted 1.5 m above ground level. To Paul the angle of elevation is 10° and to Sarah it is 20°. What is the height of the church tower to the nearest metre?

Answer

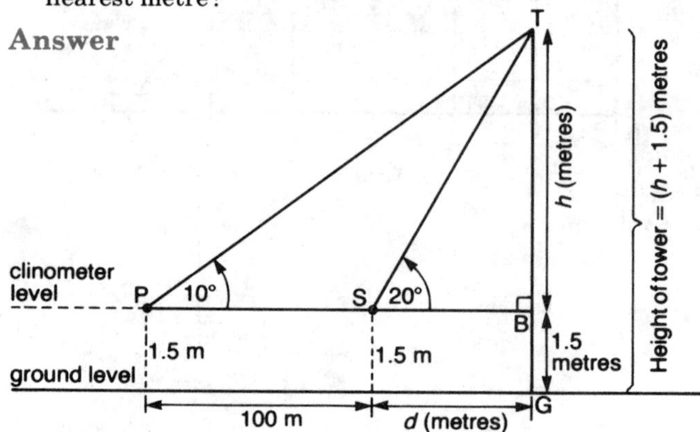

The diagram shows the positions of Paul (P), Sarah (S) and the tower TBG.

Let the height of the tower be $(h + 1.5)$ metres.

Let d metres be the distance of Sarah from the tower.

In triangle STB,

$$\tan 20° = \frac{h}{d}$$

So $$d = \frac{h}{\tan 20°} \quad \text{......(1)}$$

In triangle PTB,

$$\tan 10° = \frac{h}{(100 + d)}$$

So $$100 + d = \frac{h}{\tan 10°} \quad \text{......(2)}$$

Subtract equation (1) from equation (2) to eliminate d. This gives

$$100 = \frac{h}{\tan 10°} - \frac{h}{\tan 20°} = h\left(\frac{1}{\tan 10°} - \frac{1}{\tan 20°}\right)$$

So $h = 100 \div \left(\dfrac{1}{\tan 10°} - \dfrac{1}{\tan 20°}\right)$ **C**

Display: 34.20201425

Height of tower $= (h + 1.5)$ metres **C**

$= 36$ metres (to the nearest m)

Display: 35.70201425

So the height of the church tower is 36 metres (to the nearest metre).

* *Here is one way to do this calculation. Try it on your calculator*

Work out $\dfrac{1}{\tan 10°}$	C 1 0 tan 1/x
Subtract $\dfrac{1}{\tan 20°}$	− 2 0 tan 1/x =
Put the answer into memory	Min
Divide 100 by the answer recalled from memory	1 0 0 ÷ MR =
Add 1.5	+ 1 · 5 =

Find the best way to do this working on your calculator

3D PROBLEMS

Problems in **three-dimensions** (3D) are usually solved by using right-angled triangles in *different* planes.
A diagram to represent a 3D situation can sometimes be difficult to draw.

Drawing vertical lines up and down your page ...

... and drawing parallel lines parallel ...

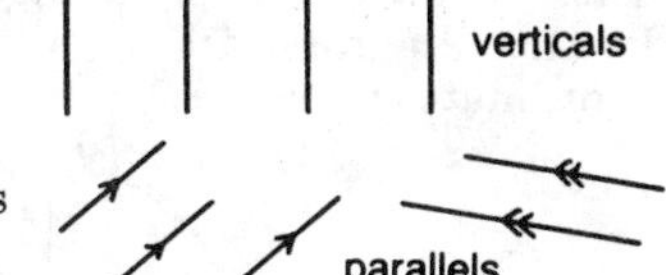

can help you to make diagrams that look reasonable.
For example, in this square based pyramid

OV is vertical,
AB and DC are parallel,
AD and BC are parallel.

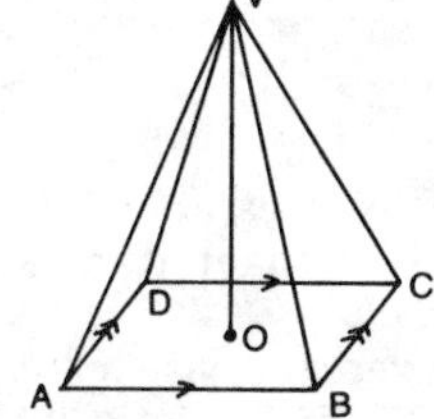

On a 3D diagram the right angles may not look like right angles. You must work out which angles *should be* right angles from the given information.
If a line is perpendicular to a plane, then it is perpendicular to every line in the plane.
For example, in this diagram, if AB is perpendicular to the shaded plane, then
$\angle XBA = \angle YBA = \angle ZBA = 90°$
You can often use this fact to spot right angles in a 3D diagram.

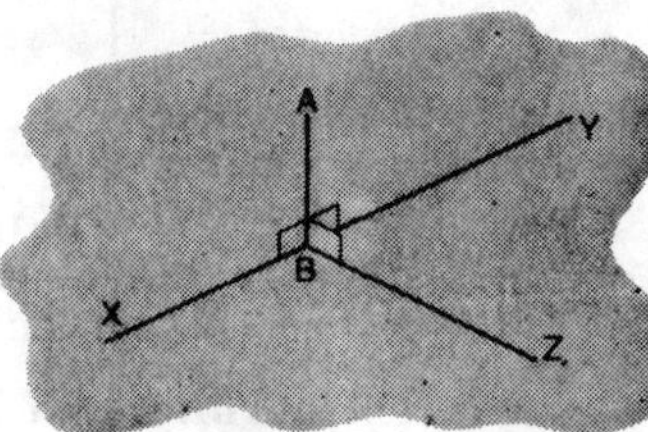

Question

The diagram represents a school hall. It is a cuboid 56 feet long, 42 feet wide and 24 feet high.

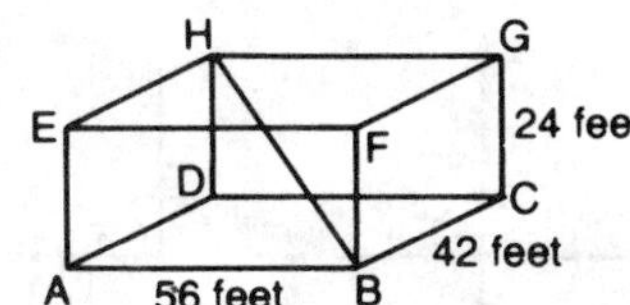

Calculate
(a) the diagonal length BH,
(b) the angle that BH makes with the floor. (Give your answer to the nearest degree.)

Answer

(a) *To find HB, look for a right-angled triangle with HB as a side*

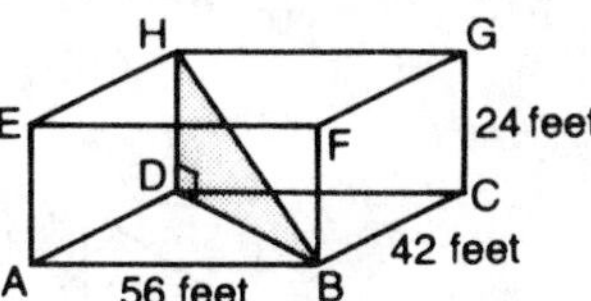

HD is perpendicular to the floor
DB is a line in the floor
So $\angle HDB = 90°$
HD = 24 feet (the hall's height)

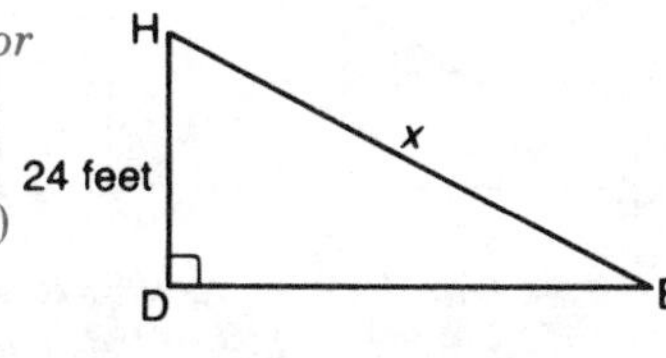

If you know DB, then you can find HB. Look for a right-angled triangle with DB as a side and the other sides known

In triangle DAB, $\angle DAB = 90°$ (a corner of the cuboid)

By Pythagoras' theorem
$BD^2 = 56^2 + 42^2$
$= 4900$
$BD = \sqrt{4900}$ **C**
$= 70$ feet

In triangle HDB, by Pythagoras' theorem
$BH^2 = 70^2 + 24^2$
$= 5476$
$BH = \sqrt{5476}$ **C**
$= 74$ feet

So the diagonal length BH is 74 feet.

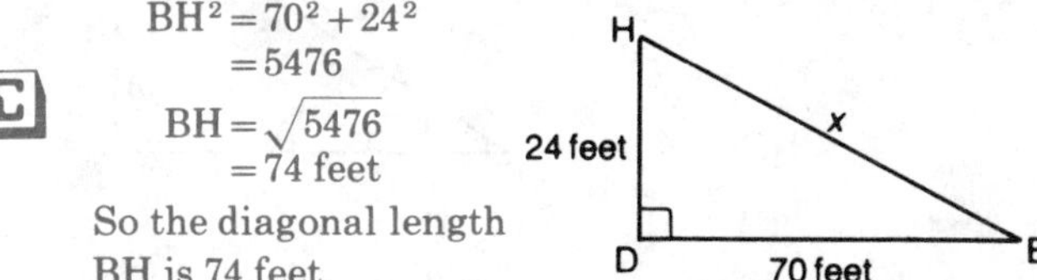

(b) The angle between BH and the floor is given by angle DBH.

$\tan \angle DBH = \dfrac{\text{opposite}}{\text{adjacent}} = \dfrac{HD}{DB}$
$= \dfrac{24}{70}$
$\angle DBH = 19°$ **C**
(to the nearest degree)

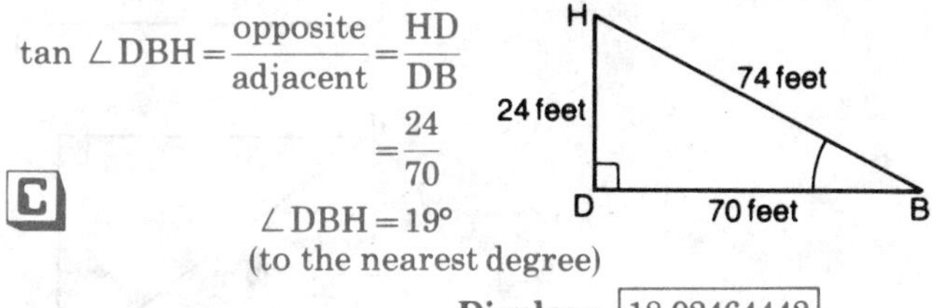

Display: 18.92464442

So the angle that BH makes with the floor is 19° (to the nearest degree).

Measuring angles of elevation or depression from different points can result in a 3D situation.

Question

From a point P on the ground due west of a perpendicular mast the angle of elevation of the top of the mast is 33° and from a point Q on the ground due south of the mast the angle of elevation of the top is 27°. If the distance PQ is 730 m, what is the height of the mast? Give your answer to the nearest metre.

Answer

Sketch of the 3D situation

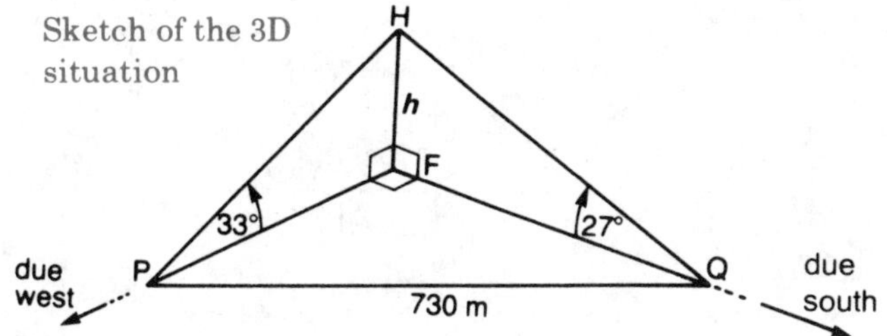

Let HF be the mast, height h.
The mast HF is perpendicular to the ground. So HF is perpendicular to PF and QF.
i.e. $\angle HFP = 90°$ and $\angle HFQ = 90°$
This gives two right-angled triangles involving h.

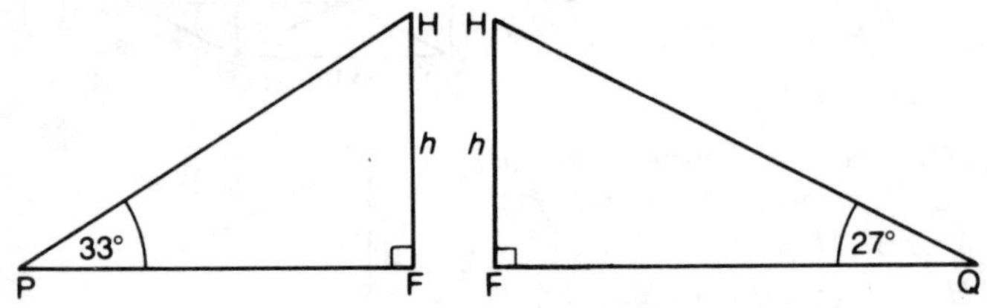

No lengths are given in these triangles. Look for a right-angled triangle that connects these triangles with the only known length PQ = 730 m

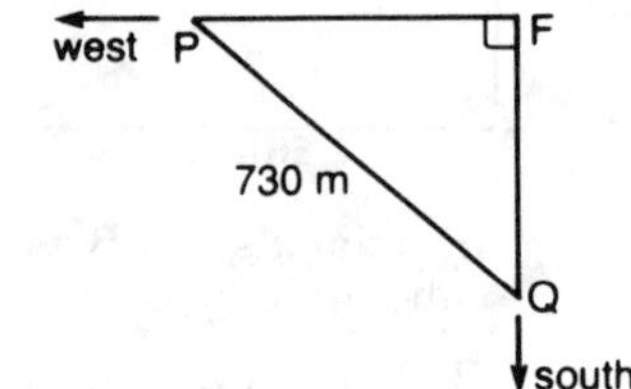

In triangle PFQ,
$\angle PFQ = 90°$
because P is due west of F and Q is due south of F.
Sides PF and FQ are sides of the other right-angled triangles.

In triangle PFH

$$\tan 33° = \frac{h}{PF}$$

So $$PF = \frac{h}{\tan 33°}$$

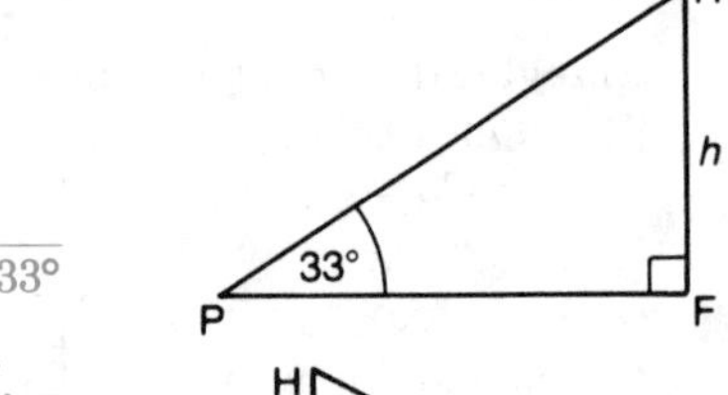

In triangle QFH,

$$\tan 27° = \frac{h}{FQ}$$

So $$FQ = \frac{h}{\tan 27°}$$

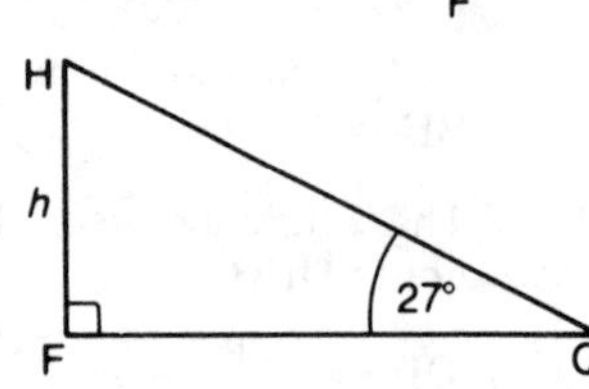

In triangle PFQ,
by Pythagoras' theorem

$$PQ^2 = PF^2 + FQ^2$$

$$730^2 = \left(\frac{h}{\tan 33°}\right)^2 + \left(\frac{h}{\tan 27°}\right)^2$$

$$730^2 = h^2\left[\left(\frac{1}{\tan 33°}\right)^2 + \left(\frac{1}{\tan 27°}\right)^2\right]$$

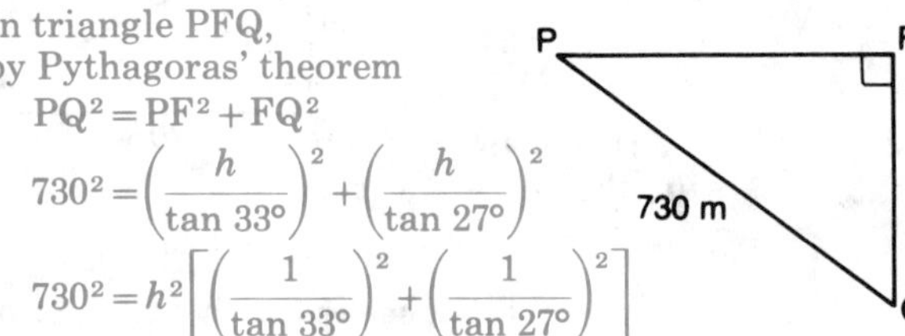

Rearranging this equation gives

$$h^2 = 730^2 \div \left[\left(\frac{1}{\tan 33°}\right)^2 + \left(\frac{1}{\tan 27°}\right)^2\right]$$

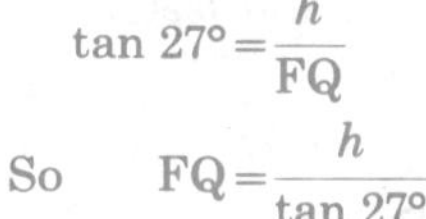

Display: 85633.60691

$$h = \sqrt{h^2}$$
$$= 293 \text{ metres (to the nearest metre)}$$

Display: 292.6322041

So the height of the mast is 293 m, to the nearest metre.

**Here is one way to do this calculation. Try it on your calculator*

Work out $\left(\frac{1}{\tan 33°}\right)^2$	C 3 3 tan 1/x x^2
Add $\left(\frac{1}{\tan 27°}\right)^2$	+ 2 7 tan 1/x x^2 =
Put the answer in memory	Min
Square 730 and divide by the answer recalled from memory	7 3 0 x^2 ÷ MR =
Find the square root	√

Find the best way to do this working on your calculator

3.26 Trigonometrical ratios and graphs

The trigonometrical ratios sine, cosine, and tangent are defined using the sides of a right-angled triangle in Unit 2.37. For example,

$$\sin A = \frac{\text{opposite}}{\text{hypotenuse}}$$

$$\cos A = \frac{\text{adjacent}}{\text{hypotenuse}}$$

$$\tan A = \frac{\text{opposite}}{\text{adjacent}}$$

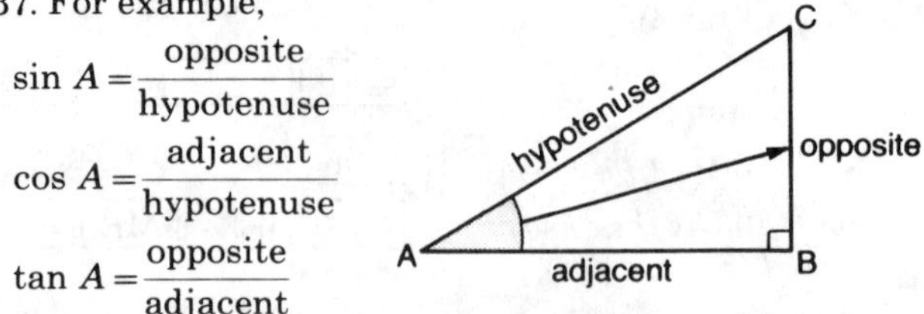

These definitions only apply to angles between 0° and 90°, i.e. **acute** angles. This is because the other two angles in a right-angled triangle must be acute.
This unit gives definitions for sine, cosine and tangent which apply to any angle.

SINE, COSINE AND TANGENT OF ANY ANGLE

Sine, cosine and tangent can be defined using coordinates. These definitions apply to **any size of angle**.
In this diagram, OP is a line 1 unit long and P has coordinates (x, y).

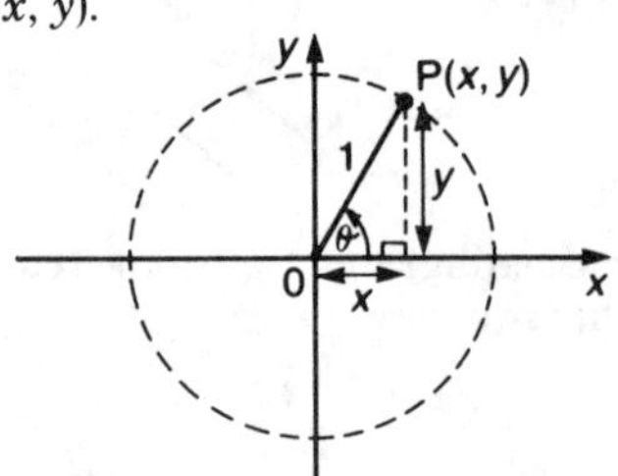

As OP rotates about the origin O in a positive direction (**anticlockwise**) it makes an angle θ with the *positive* x-axis.
Whatever the size of θ, the **coordinates** of P give the trigonometrical ratios of θ.

$\sin \theta = y$**-coordinate of P**
(shown in blue in each quadrant below)

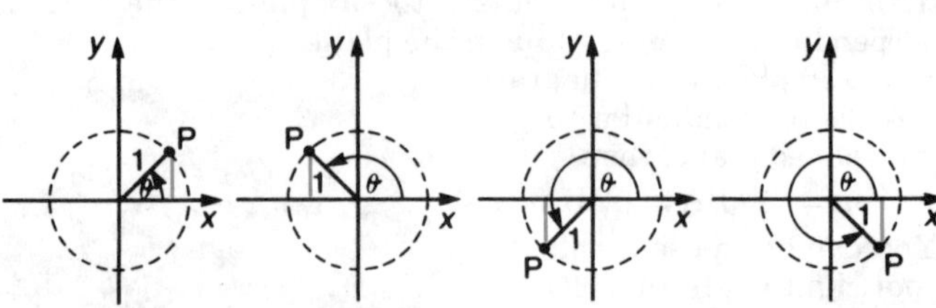

$\cos \theta = x$**-coordinate of P**
(shown in blue in each quadrant below)

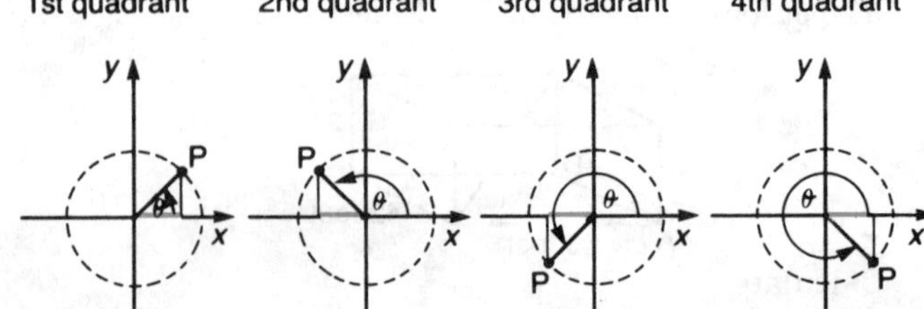

$$\tan\theta = \frac{y\text{-coordinate of P}}{x\text{-coordinate of P}}$$

(shown in blue in each quadrant below)

1st quadrant 2nd quadrant 3rd quadrant 4th quadrant

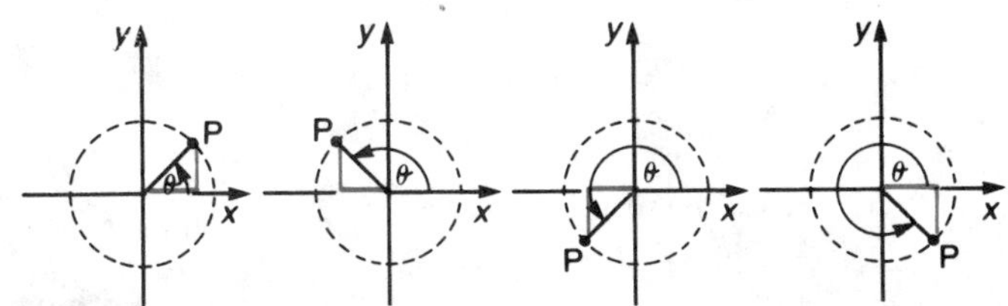

As the point P rotates, its coordinates are *positive* or *negative* depending upon which quadrant P is in. So the trigonometrical ratios of angle θ will be positive or negative depending upon which quadrant it is in.

y

2nd quadrant	1st quadrant
x −ve y +ve	x +ve y +ve
x −ve y − ve	x +ve y − ve
3rd quadrant	4th quadrant

x

The signs (+ or −) of the trigonometrical ratios are summarized in the diagram below. It reminds you which ratios are **positive** in each quadrant, i.e.

in the **first** quadrant, **all (A)**,
in the **second** quadrant, the **sines (S)**,
in the **third** quadrant, the **tangents (T)**,
in the **fourth** quadrant, the **cosines (C)**.

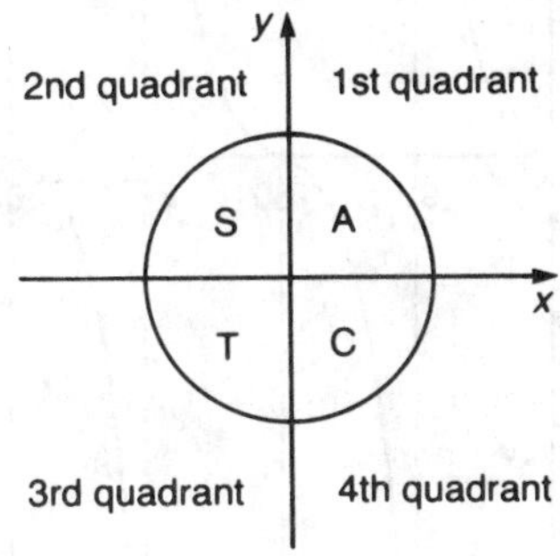

You can use your *calculator* to find the sine, cosine and tangent of any angle. Just use the same method as for acute angles (see Unit 2.37). The *calculator* will give you the sign of the ratio on its display. Make sure that you do not omit it.

For example, to find the ratios for 125° (an obtuse angle):

C

for sin 125°
Press: [C] [1] [2] [5] [sin] **Display:** [0.819152044]

for cos 125°
Press: [C] [1] [2] [5] [cos] **Display:** [−0.573576436]

for tan 125°
Press: [C] [1] [2] [5] [tan] **Display:** [−0.1428148007]

GRAPHS OF TRIGONOMETRICAL FUNCTIONS

You can use your *calculator* to help you to draw **graphs of trigonometrical functions**.

Find the trigonometrical ratio for a series of angles and plot the points they give.
Make sure that you **take care with the signs**.

Question

(a) Make a table of values of $\sin x$ and $\cos x$ for $x = 0°, 10°, 20°, 30°, \ldots, 180°$.
Give the values of $\sin x$ and $\cos x$ correct to 2 d.p.

(b) Use your table of values to draw graphs of $y = \sin x$ and $y = \cos x$ for $0° \leqslant x \leqslant 180°$.
Draw the graphs on separate axes.
Scale: on the x-axis, 1 large square represents 20°, on the y-axis, 5 large squares represent 1 unit.

(c) Use your graphs to find
(i) the angle whose sine is 0.6,
(ii) the angle whose cosine is −0.6.

Answer

(a)

Angle x	$\sin x$	$\cos x$
0°	0	1.00
10°	0.17	0.98
20°	0.34	0.94
30°	0.50	0.87
40°	0.64	0.77
50°	0.77	0.64
60°	0.87	0.50
70°	0.94	0.34
80°	0.98	0.17
90°	1.00	0
100°	0.98	−0.17
110°	0.94	−0.34
120°	0.87	−0.50
130°	0.77	−0.64
140°	0.64	−0.77
150°	0.50	−0.87
160°	0.34	−0.94
170°	0.17	−0.98
180°	0	−1.00

(b) **Graph of $y = \sin x$ for $0° \leqslant x \leqslant 180°$**

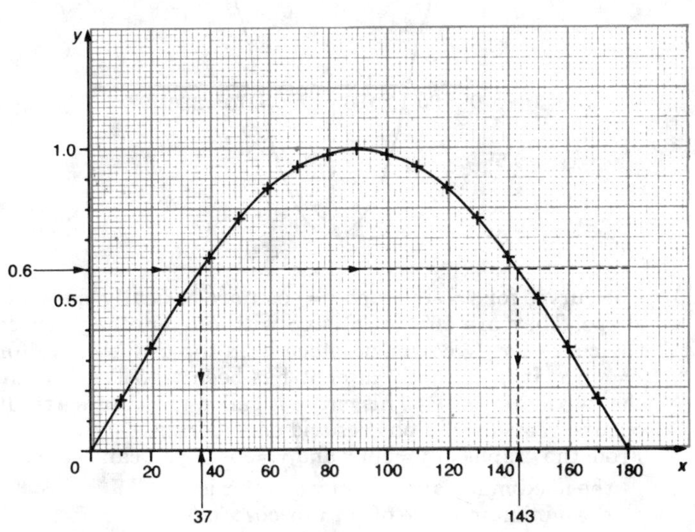

Graph of $y = \cos x$ for $0° \leqslant x \leqslant 180°$

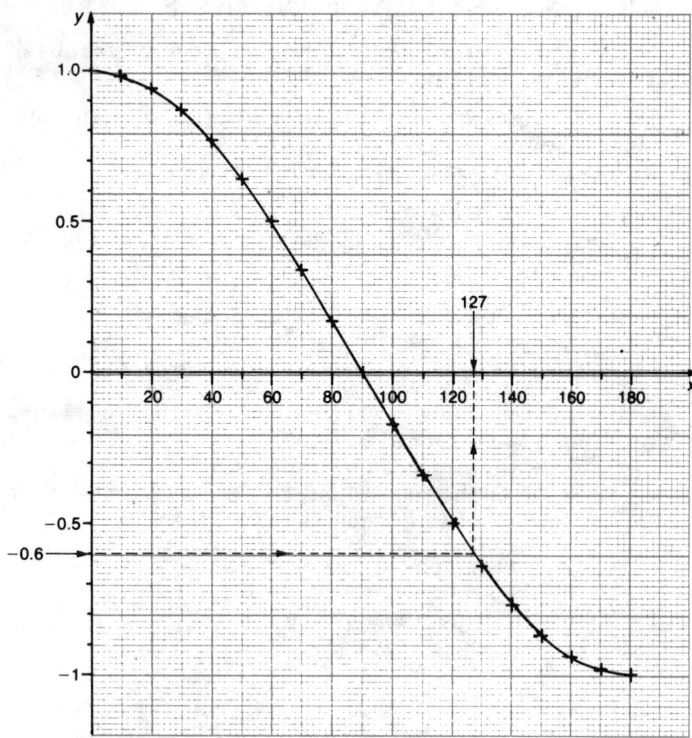

(c) (i) From the graph $y = \sin x$,
$0.6 \leftrightarrow 37°$ and $0.6 \leftrightarrow 143°$.
So two angles, 37° and 143°, on this graph have sine of 0.6.

(ii) From the graph $y = \cos x$,
$-0.6 \leftrightarrow 127°$.
So on this graph, $\cos 127° = -0.6$.

When you draw the graphs of $y = \sin x$ and $y = \cos x$ **for** $0° \leqslant x \leqslant 360°$, you should get the curves shown below. (Try plotting them on graph paper yourself.)

Graph of $y = \sin x$ $(0° \leqslant x \leqslant 360°)$

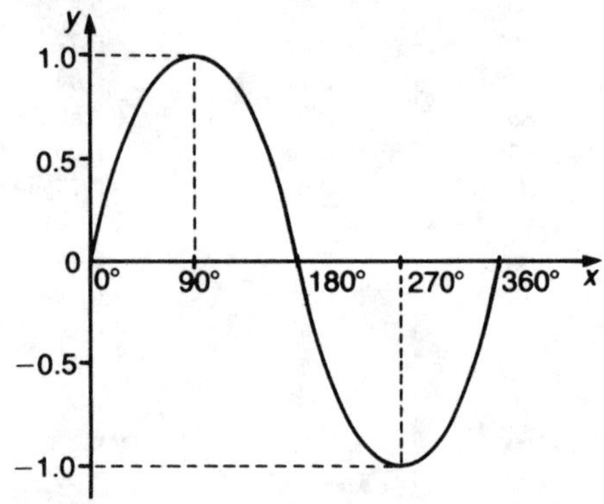

Graph of $y = \cos x$ $(0° \leqslant x \leqslant 360°)$

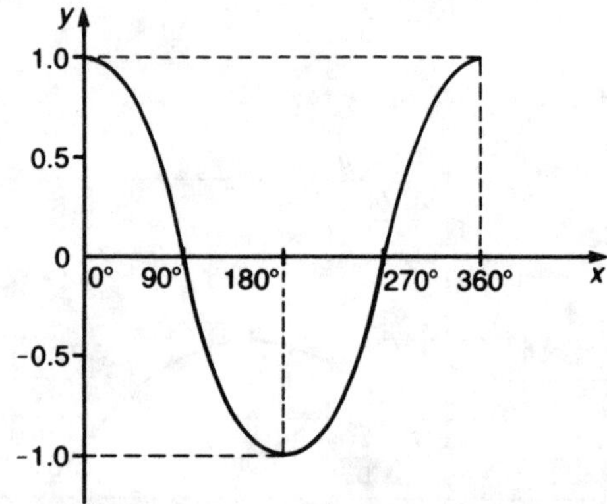

The curves for $y = \sin x$ and $y = \cos x$ are basically the same shape. They are 90° out of step with one another. (Trace the curve for $y = \cos x$ and place it on top of the curve for $y = \sin x$. It fits exactly after it has been translated along the x-axis to $x = 90°$.) This curve is called the **sine wave**. It occurs frequently in physics and engineering.

From the graphs of $y = \sin x$ and $y = \cos x$, you can see that

the maximum value of $\sin x$ or $\cos x$ is 1,
the minimum value of $\sin x$ or $\cos x$ is -1.

So all values of $\sin x$ and $\cos x$ must be between 1 and -1.

The shape of the curve for $y = \tan x$ **for** $0° \leqslant x \leqslant 360°$ is different. (Try plotting it on graph paper yourself.)

Graph of $y = \tan x$ $(0° \leqslant x \leqslant 360°)$

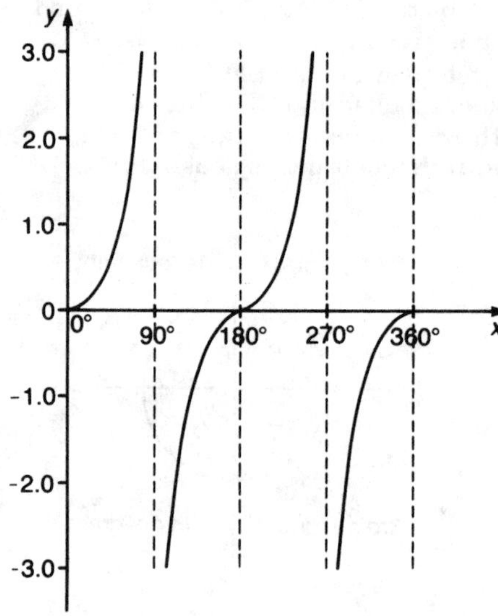

The dotted lines show where the graph goes to infinity. From the graph you can see that $\tan x$ can have any value (positive, negative or zero).

3.27 Sine and cosine rules

The **sine** and **cosine rules** are used to solve scalene triangles in which there are no right angles. Right-angled triangles and isosceles triangles are easier to solve using Pythagoras' theorem (see Unit 2.36) and/or the trigonometrical ratios sine, cosine and tangent (see Unit 2.37).

When trying to solve any triangle it is important to draw a clear diagram first. Label it carefully with the given information. Mark the value(s) you have to calculate. Using different colours for *given* and *wanted* values can help you to see them clearly on the diagram. This can also help you to decide which rule to use. Whenever possible use *given* values in the rule you choose. This is safer than using a value you have calculated ... just in case you have made a mistake!

SINE RULE

For any triangle ABC, the **sine rule** can be written as

$$\frac{a}{\sin A}=\frac{b}{\sin B}=\frac{c}{\sin C}$$

or

$$\frac{\sin A}{a}=\frac{\sin B}{b}=\frac{\sin C}{c}$$

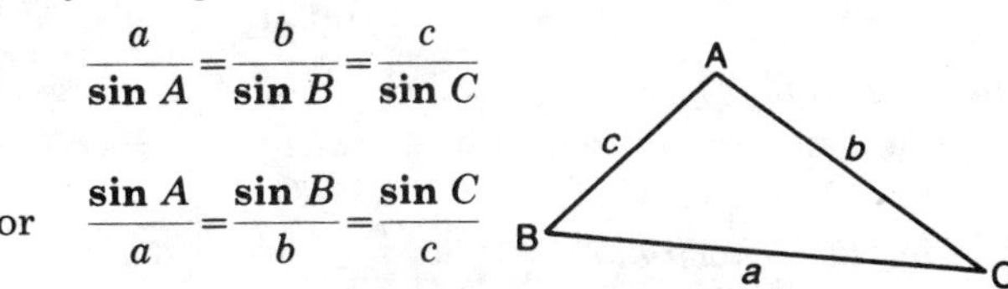

The sine rule relates each angle to the side opposite to it. So look for this relationship between the marked values on your diagram. This will give you a clue to use the sine rule.

To find the *length* of a side, use the sine rule in this form

$$\frac{a}{\sin A}=\frac{b}{\sin B}=\frac{c}{\sin C}$$

(It is easier this way because the unknown length is on top of the fraction.)

You need to know the length of another side and the size of any two angles (AAS).

You may have to find the size of the third angle before you can use the sine rule. Use the angle sum of a triangle, i.e. 180° to do this.

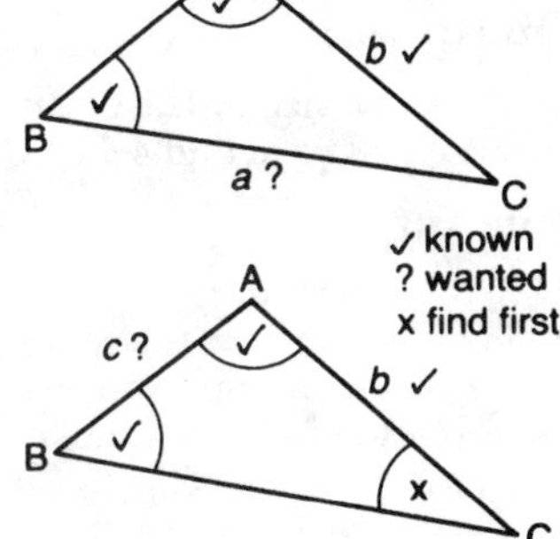

Question

In triangle ABC, angle B = 30°, angle C = 70° and AC = 12 cm.

Find the lengths (to 1 d.p.) of the sides

(a) AB (b) BC.

Answer

Use the sine rule in this form:

$$\frac{a}{\sin A}=\frac{b}{\sin B}=\frac{c}{\sin C}$$

Put in the given values.
Mark the wanted values

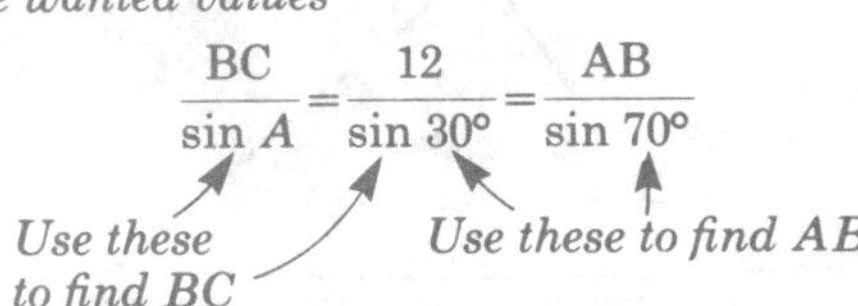

(a) $$\frac{AB}{\sin 70°}=\frac{12}{\sin 30°}$$

$$AB=\sin 70°\times\frac{12}{\sin 30°}$$

$$=22.6 \text{ cm (to 1 d.p.)}$$

C 7 0 sin × 1 2 = ÷ 3 0 sin =

Display: 22.55262289

(b) $$\frac{BC}{\sin A}=\frac{12}{\sin 30°}$$

By the angle sum of a triangle

$$A+30°+70°=180°$$

So $A=180°-(30°+70°)=180°-100°=80°$.

So $$\frac{BC}{\sin 80°}=\frac{12}{\sin 30°}$$

$$BC=\sin 80°\times\frac{12}{\sin 30°}$$

$$=23.6 \text{ cm (to 1 d.p.)}$$

Display: 23.63538607

To find the size of an *angle*, use the sine rule in this form

$$\frac{\sin A}{a}=\frac{\sin B}{b}=\frac{\sin C}{c}$$

(This way the unknown angle is on top of the fraction.)

You need to know the lengths of two sides and the size of an angle opposite to one of these sides (SSA).

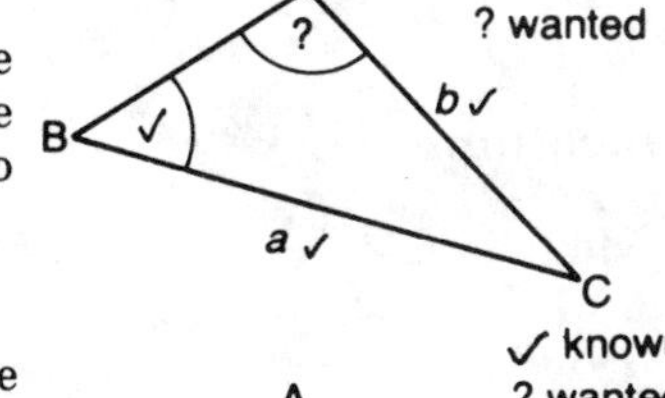

Sometimes you will not be able to find the angle you want directly. Use the sine rule to find the third angle, then use the angle sum of a triangle to find the angle you want.

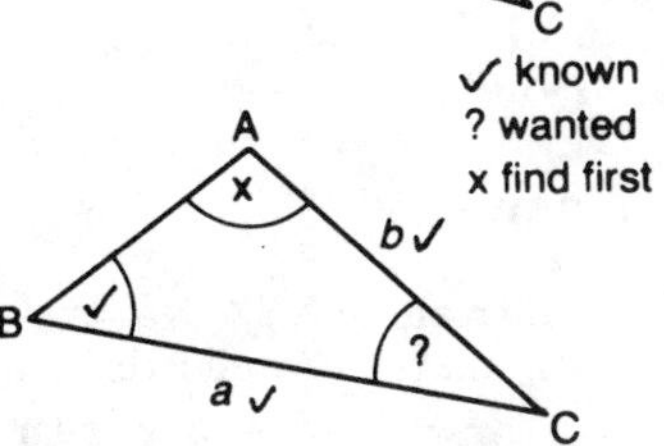

Question

In a triangle PQR, angle P = 56.5°, PQ = 6.4 cm and RQ = 7.6 cm.

Find the size (to 1 d.p.) of the other two angles.

Answer

Use the sine rule in this form:

$$\frac{\sin P}{p}=\frac{\sin Q}{q}=\frac{\sin R}{r}$$

Put in the given values.
Mark the wanted values

$$\frac{\sin 56.5°}{7.6}=\frac{\sin Q}{q}=\frac{\sin R}{6.4}$$

Use these to find R
Then find Q by the angle sum

$$\frac{\sin R}{6.4}=\frac{\sin 56.5°}{7.6}$$

$$\sin R=6.4\times\frac{\sin 56.5°}{7.6}$$

C 6 . 4 × 5 6 . 5 sin = ÷ 7 . 6 = INV sin

$\angle R=44.6°$ (to 1 d.p.) **Display:** 44.6053584

By the angle sum of a triangle

$$\angle Q=180°-(56.5°+44.6°)$$
$$=78.9° \text{ (to 1 d.p.)}$$

COSINE RULE

For any triangle ABC, the cosine rule can be written as

$$a^2=b^2+c^2-(2bc\cos A)$$

The brackets are not essential in this rule. They emphasize that you must work out $2bc\cos A$ before doing the subtraction. Not doing this is a common mistake.

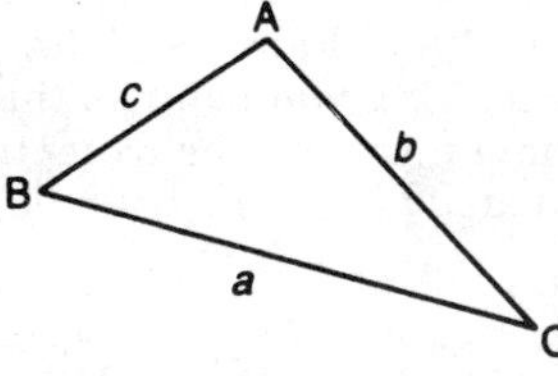

This formula can also be given with b or c as the subject.

$$b^2=a^2+c^2-(2ac\cos B)$$
$$c^2=a^2+b^2-(2ab\cos C)$$

When you know two sides and the angle between them (SAS), you can find the third *side* using this rule.

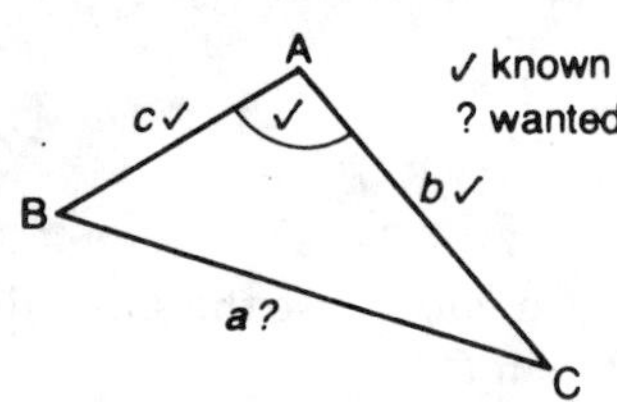

The given angle may be acute or obtuse.
If it is *obtuse*, then the *cosine* will be *negative* (see Unit 3.26). Your calculator will give you this automatically.

Question

In triangle XYZ, XY = 3.5 cm, YZ = 7.4 cm and angle Y = 30°.
Find XZ correct to 1 d.p.

Answer

In triangle XYZ, XZ = y.
Using the cosine rule

$$y^2 = x^2 + z^2 - (2xz \cos Y)$$
$$= 7.4^2 + 3.5^2 - (2 \times 7.4 \times 3.5 \times \cos 30°)$$

Display: 22.14988408

$$y = \sqrt{y^2}$$

Display: 4.706366335

So XZ = 4.7 cm (to 1 d.p.)

Here is one way to do this calculation on a calculator
Try it on your calculator

Work out the bracket first:	[C] [2] [×] [7] [.] [4] [×] [3] [.] [5] [×] [3] [0] [cos] [=]
Store the answer in memory:	[Min]
Square and add the other sides:	[7] [.] [4] [x²] [+] [3] [.] [5] [x²] [=]
Subtract the bracket, recalled from memory	[−] [MR] [=]
Find the square root	[√]

Find the best way to do this working on your calculator

The cosine rule

$$a^2 = b^2 + c^2 - (2bc \cos A)$$

can be written as

$$\cos A = \frac{b^2 + c^2 - a^2}{2bc}$$

Equivalent forms for cos B and cos C can be written too.

$$\cos B = \frac{a^2 + c^2 - b^2}{2ac}$$

$$\cos C = \frac{a^2 + b^2 - c^2}{2ab}$$

When you know all three sides (SSS), you can use this form of the cosine rule to find an *angle* in the triangle.

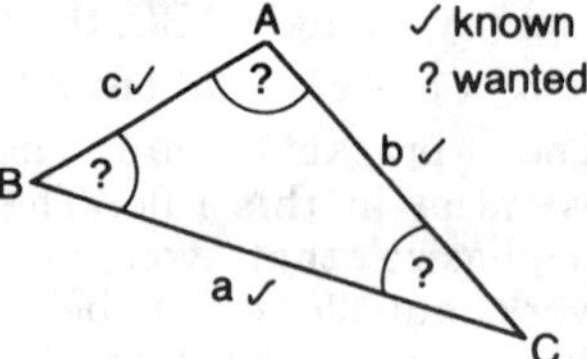

Question

In triangle ABC, AB = 6 cm, AC = 4 cm and BC = 3 cm.
Calculate the size of angle A correct to 1 d.p.

Answer

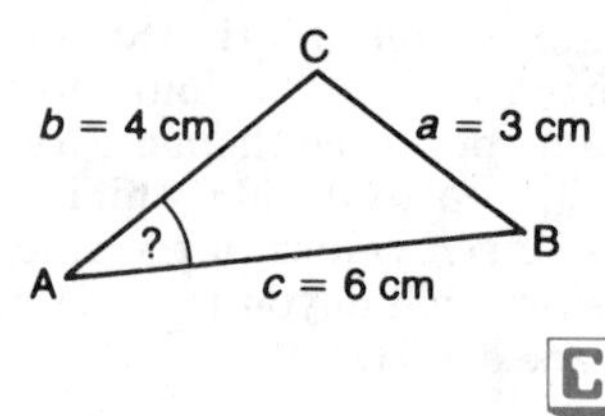

Use the cosine rule

$$\cos A = \frac{b^2 + c^2 - a^2}{2bc}$$
$$= \frac{4^2 + 6^2 - 3^2}{2 \times 4 \times 6}$$
$$= \frac{43}{48}$$

Display: 0.895833333

$\angle A = 26.4°$ (to 1 d.p.) **Display:** 26.38432976

All this working can be done on a calculator
Find the best way to do it on your calculator. Here is one way to try

Work out the denominator:	[C] [2] [×] [4] [×] [6] [=]
Store the answer in memory:	[Min]
Work out the numerator:	[4] [x²] [+] [6] [x²] [−] [3] [x²] [=]
Divide by the denominator: (recalled from memory)	[÷] [MR] [=]
Find the angle:	[INV] [cos]

If the cosine of the angle is *negative* then the angle will be *obtuse*. Your calculator will automatically give you the size of the obtuse angle.

Question

Find the size of the obtuse angle in a triangle with sides 2.4 cm, 3.6 cm and 4.7 cm.

Answer

The obtuse angle will be the largest angle in the triangle.
So it will be opposite to the longest side, i.e. 4.7 cm.
Let its value be θ.
By the cosine rule

$$\cos \theta = \frac{2.4^2 + 3.6^2 - 4.7^2}{2 \times 2.4 \times 3.6}$$
$$= \frac{-3.37}{17.28}$$

Display: −0.195023148

So $\theta = 101.2°$ (to 1 d.p.) **Display:** 101.2460758

Check this working on your own calculator

AREA OF A TRIANGLE

The basic formula for the area of a triangle is

area of a triangle = $\frac{1}{2}$ × base × height

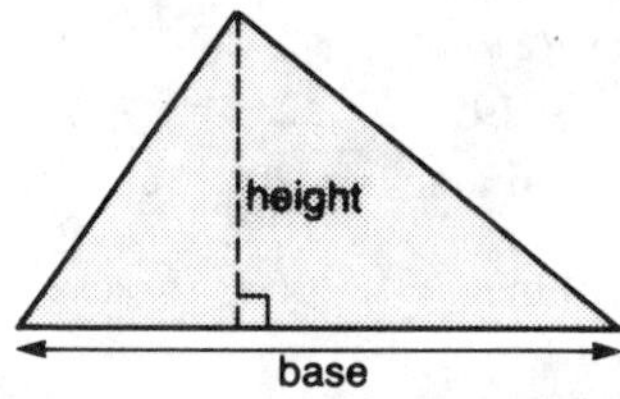

Often this basic formula cannot be used because you do not know the perpendicular height.
Here is a formula you can use if you know the lengths of two sides and the size of the angle between them (SAS).

Area of a triangle = $\frac{1}{2}$ × (product of two sides) × (sine of the included angle)

For any triangle ABC, this can be written as

Area of triangle ABC
= $\frac{1}{2}ab$ **sin** C
or $\frac{1}{2}ac$ **sin** B
or $\frac{1}{2}bc$ **sin** A

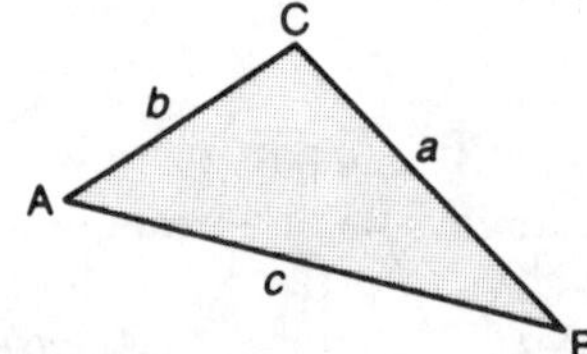

Question

Calculate the area of this triangle.
Give your answer in cm² correct to 1 decimal place.

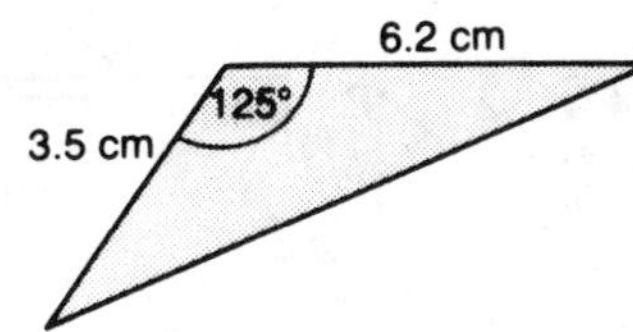

Answer

Area of triangle

$=\frac{1}{2}\times(3.5\times6.2)\times\sin 125°$

$=8.9\ \text{cm}^2$ (to 1 d.p.) **Display:** 8.88779968

PROBLEM SOLVING

Triangles occur in many practical and real life situations. Since these triangles are often *not* right-angled or isosceles, the sine and cosine rules are needed to solve these 'practical triangles'.

Question

The diagram shows a crane lifting a load.

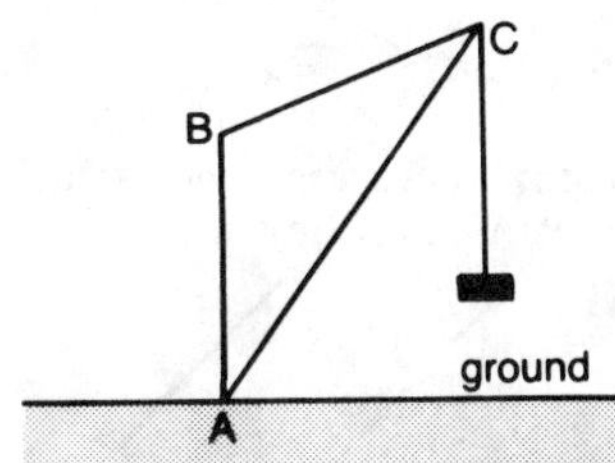

The lengths of the three girders forming the crane are AB = 7 m, BC = 8 m and AC = 13 m. If AB is vertical, calculate the angle between the jib AC and the vertical. Give your answer to the nearest degree.

Answer

In triangle ABC, angle BAC is the angle between the jib AC and the vertical AB.
By the cosine rule

a = 8 m, b = 13 m, c = 7 m

$$\cos A=\frac{b^2+c^2-a^2}{2bc}$$

$$=\frac{13^2+7^2-8^2}{2\times13\times7}$$

$$=\frac{154}{182}$$

Display: 0.846153846

Angle A = 32° (to the nearest degree)

Display: 32.20422751

So the angle between the jib and the vertical is 32° (to the nearest degree).

To solve some problems you need to use *both* the sine rule and cosine rule. You may have to calculate some angles before you can use these rules.

Question

The diagram shows two ports P and Q on the east coast of Scotland. Q is due south of P.
A ship S is on a bearing of 137° from P and on a bearing of 068° from Q. The distance of S from P is 4 km.

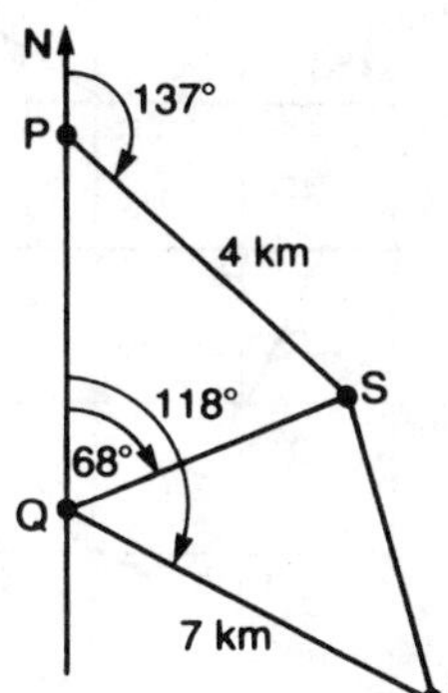

(a) Calculate the distance of S from the port Q. Give your answer to 1 d.p.

A lifeboat L is 7 km from Q on a bearing of 118°.

(b) Calculate the distance of L from S. Give your answer to 1 d.p.

Answer

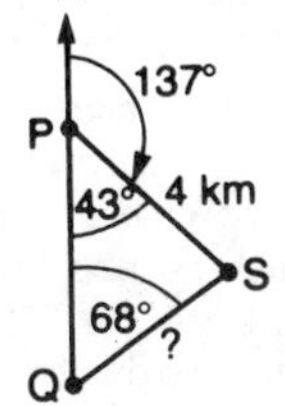

(a) In triangle PQS, SQ is the distance of S from Q.

NPQ is a straight angle, i.e. 180°.

So angle QPS = 180° − 137°
= 43°

Using the sine rule in triangle PQS

$$\frac{SQ}{\sin 43°}=\frac{4}{\sin 68°}$$

So $SQ=\sin 43°\times\frac{4}{\sin 68°}$

$=2.9$ km (to 1 d.p.) **Display:** 2.942235702

So the distance of S from the port Q is 2.9 km (to 1 d.p.).

(b) In triangle QSL, SL is the distance of L from S.

From the diagram

$\angle SQL+68°=118°$

$\angle SQL=118°-68°$

$=50°$

Using the cosine rule in triangle QLS

$SL^2=7^2+2.9^2-(2\times7\times2.9\times\cos 50°)$

Display: 31.31282304

$SL=\sqrt{SL^2}$ **Display:** 5.595786186

$=5.6$ km (to 1 d.p.)

So the distance of L from S is 5.6 km (to 1 d.p.).

3.28 Vectors

A **vector** is a quantity with both **magnitude** (or size) *and* **direction**. For example, a velocity of 20 km/h to the north has magnitude (20 km/h) and direction (north) and so is a vector.

N

20 km/h

Other examples of vectors are *displacement*, *acceleration*, *force* and *momentum*.

A **scalar** is a quantity with magnitude *only*. It has no direction. For example, a distance of 3 km has magnitude (3 km) only, no direction, and so is a scalar. Other examples of scalars are *time*, *temperature*, *speed*, *mass* and *area*.

Question

State whether the following are vector or scalar quantities.

(a) 25 sweets in a packet (b) 5 km due west
(c) body temperature 37°C (d) 7 pints of milk
(e) 30 m/s on a bearing 120°
(f) a pawn's move on a chessboard

Answer

(a) 25 sweets: magnitude only, so a scalar
(b) 5 km due west: magnitude and direction, so a vector
(c) body temperature 37°C: magnitude only, so a scalar
(d) 7 pints: magnitude only, so a scalar
(e) 30 m/s on a bearing 120°: magnitude and direction, so a vector
(f) a pawn's move: magnitude and direction, so a vector

REPRESENTATION

Vector quantities are often represented by arrowed lines on diagrams.

The *length* of the line represents the *magnitude* of the vector.

The *arrow* shows the *direction* of the vector.

A vector can be named using two capital letters and an arrow, e.g. $\overrightarrow{AB}$. The capital letters are the endpoints of the vector. The arrow gives the direction of the vector.

This is **important**. For example,
$\overrightarrow{AB}$ is a vector going from A to B,
$\overrightarrow{BA}$ is a vector going from B to A.

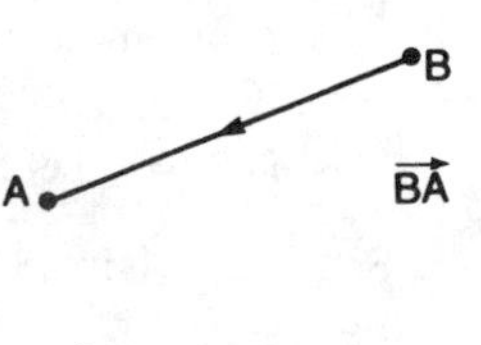

The magnitude (size) of the vector $\overrightarrow{AB}$ is shown as $|\overrightarrow{AB}|$ or AB (the length of the line AB).

A vector can also be named using a small letter.

In books the small letter is printed in bold type, e.g. **a**.

You cannot write in bold type. So in handwriting you can show that a small letter represents a vector by underlining it like this $\underline{a}$ or with a squiggle like this $\underset{\sim}{a}$.

The magnitude of a vector **a** is shown as either $|\mathbf{a}|$ or a.

Letters used for scalars are usually printed in books in italic type, e.g. a, or written in ordinary handwriting.

UNIT AND ZERO VECTORS

A **unit vector** is a vector with magnitude 1. For example, if **a** is a unit vector, then $|\mathbf{a}|=1$.

The **zero** or **null vector**, **0**, is any vector with zero magnitude. It follows that it has no direction.

DISPLACEMENT VECTORS

A **displacement vector** describes a change in position, i.e. a movement from one point to another.

For example, a journey from Exeter (E) to Norwich (N) can be described by the displacement vector $\overrightarrow{EN}$. The return journey from Norwich to Exeter can be described by $\overrightarrow{NE}$.

A displacement vector can be given as a **column vector**. This is often called the **component form** of the vector.

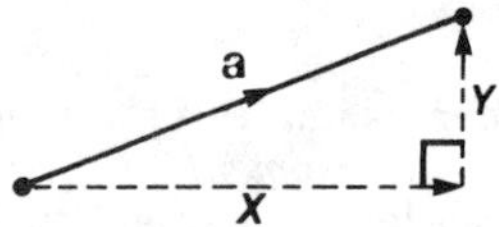

This displacement vector **a** can be represented by a column vector $\begin{pmatrix} X \\ Y \end{pmatrix}$.

X and Y are called the **components** of the vector **a**.

X gives the number of units moved *across*.

Y gives the number of units moved *up* or *down*.

Movements to the *right* are +, to the *left* are −.

Movements *up* are +, *down* are −.

The components X and Y are easy to work out if the displacement vector is drawn on a grid.

The **magnitude** of displacement vector **a** is given by

$$|\mathbf{a}|=\sqrt{(X^2+Y^2)}$$

This can be shown by Pythagoras' theorem.

$|\mathbf{a}|^2 = X^2 + Y^2$

A **position vector** is a special displacement vector.

It describes the movement from the origin O to a point P(x, y) on a coordinate grid system. It gives the position of P relative to the origin O.

The position vector of P is $\overrightarrow{OP}=\begin{pmatrix} x \\ y \end{pmatrix}$.

The magnitude of $\overrightarrow{OP}$ is $|\overrightarrow{OP}|=\sqrt{(x^2+y^2)}$

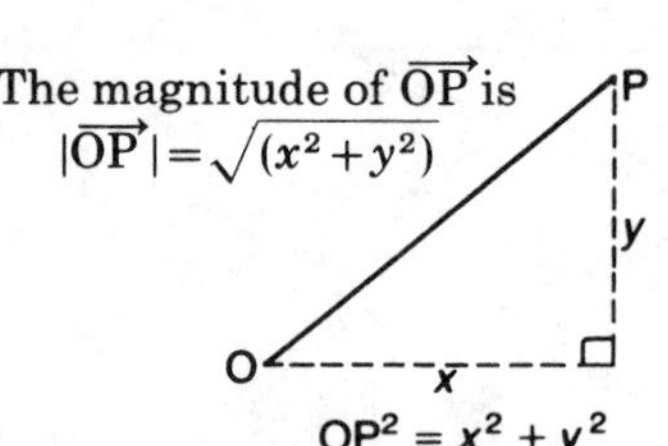

$OP^2 = x^2 + y^2$

The **inverse** of a vector **a** is −**a**. It is equal in magnitude to **a** but is in the opposite direction.

The inverse of a vector $\overrightarrow{AB}$ is $-\overrightarrow{AB}$ or $\overrightarrow{BA}$.

If $\mathbf{a}=\begin{pmatrix} X \\ Y \end{pmatrix}$, then its inverse $-\mathbf{a}=\begin{pmatrix} -X \\ -Y \end{pmatrix}$

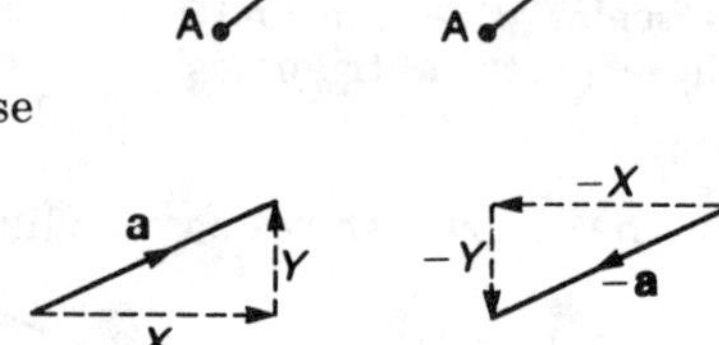

Equal or **equivalent** vectors are equal in magnitude and have the same direction, i.e. they are parallel.

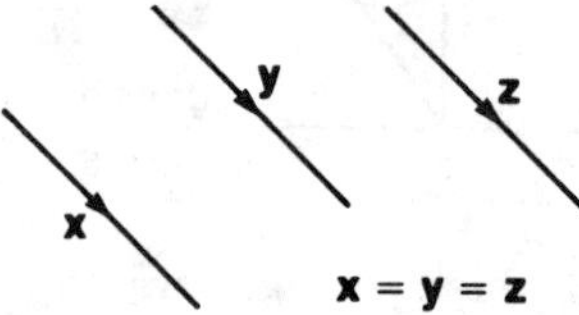

x = **y** = **z**

In terms of components, if $\mathbf{a}=\begin{pmatrix} X_1 \\ Y_1 \end{pmatrix}$, and $\mathbf{b}=\begin{pmatrix} X_2 \\ Y_2 \end{pmatrix}$ are equal vectors, then $X_1=X_2$ and $Y_1=Y_2$.

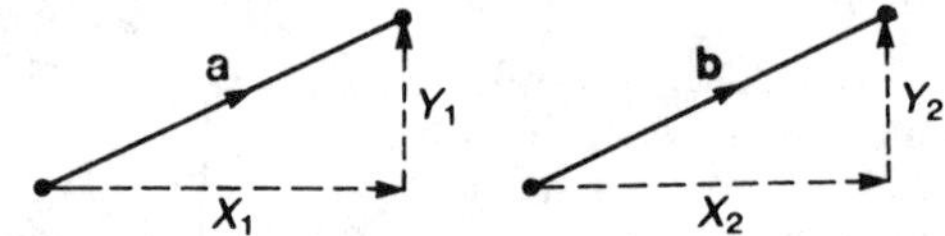

Question

The diagram below shows a set of eight displacement vectors.

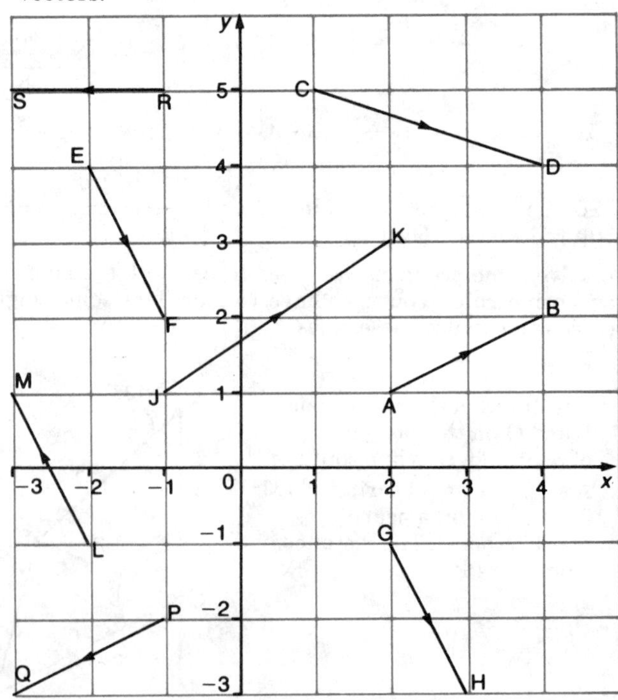

(a) Write the column vector for each of the displacement vectors:
$\overrightarrow{AB}, \overrightarrow{CD}, \overrightarrow{EF}, \overrightarrow{GH}, \overrightarrow{JK}, \overrightarrow{LM}, \overrightarrow{PQ}, \overrightarrow{RS}$.

(b) Which vector is equal to $\overrightarrow{EF}$?

(c) Which vector is the inverse of $\overrightarrow{AB}$?

(d) What is the magnitude of $\overrightarrow{JK}$? Leave your answer as a root.

(e) Write down the position vectors of the points A, H, Q and E.

Answer

(a) $\overrightarrow{AB}=\begin{pmatrix}2\\1\end{pmatrix}$ *2 right, 1 up* $\quad\overrightarrow{CD}=\begin{pmatrix}3\\-1\end{pmatrix}$ *3 right, 1 down*

$\overrightarrow{EF}=\begin{pmatrix}1\\-2\end{pmatrix}$ *1 right, 2 down* $\quad\overrightarrow{GH}=\begin{pmatrix}1\\-2\end{pmatrix}$ *1 right, 2 down*

$\overrightarrow{JK}=\begin{pmatrix}3\\2\end{pmatrix}$ *3 right, 2 up* $\quad\overrightarrow{LM}=\begin{pmatrix}-1\\2\end{pmatrix}$ *1 left, 2 up*

$\overrightarrow{PQ}=\begin{pmatrix}-2\\-1\end{pmatrix}$ *2 left, 1 down* $\quad\overrightarrow{RS}=\begin{pmatrix}-2\\0\end{pmatrix}$ *2 left, 0 up or down*

(b) $\overrightarrow{GH}=\overrightarrow{EF}=\begin{pmatrix}1\\-2\end{pmatrix}$

(c) $\overrightarrow{AB}=\begin{pmatrix}2\\1\end{pmatrix}$ Its inverse is $\begin{pmatrix}-2\\-1\end{pmatrix}=\overrightarrow{PQ}$

(d) $\overrightarrow{JK}=\begin{pmatrix}3\\2\end{pmatrix}$

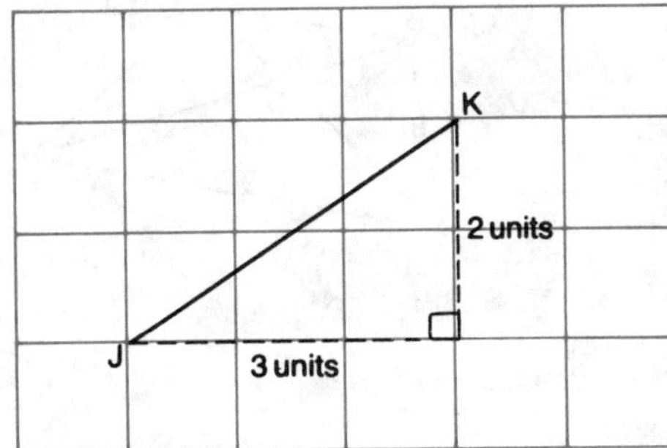

Magnitude of $\overrightarrow{JK}=|\overrightarrow{JK}|$
$=\sqrt{(3^2+2^2)}$
$=\sqrt{9+4}$
$=\sqrt{13}$

(e) The position vectors of A, H, Q and E are

$\overrightarrow{OA}=\begin{pmatrix}2\\1\end{pmatrix}$

$\overrightarrow{OH}=\begin{pmatrix}3\\-3\end{pmatrix}$

$\overrightarrow{OQ}=\begin{pmatrix}-3\\-3\end{pmatrix}$

$\overrightarrow{OE}=\begin{pmatrix}-2\\4\end{pmatrix}$

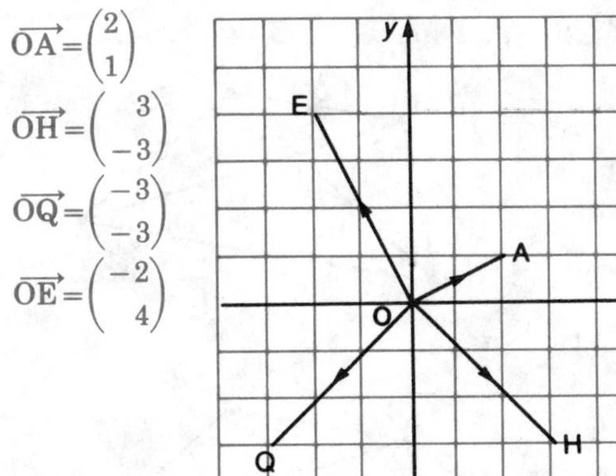

MULTIPLICATION BY A SCALAR (REAL NUMBER)

Multiplying a vector **a** by a **scalar** k, gives a vector k**a**. The vector k**a**

(a) has magnitude k times the magnitude of **a**, i.e. $|k\mathbf{a}|=k|\mathbf{a}|$,

(b) is parallel to the vector **a**.

If k is *positive*, then the new vector is in the *same* direction as **a**.

If k is *negative*, then the new vector is in the *opposite* direction to **a**.

For example, in this diagram:

3a is parallel to **a**, in the same direction as **a** and 3 times its length.

$\frac{1}{2}$**a** is parallel to **a**, in the same direction as **a** and $\frac{1}{2}$ its length.

-2**a** is parallel to **a**, in the opposite direction to **a** and 2 times its length.

To multiply a **column vector by a scalar**, simply multiply each part by the scalar.

If $\mathbf{a}=\begin{pmatrix}X\\Y\end{pmatrix}$, then $k\mathbf{a}=\begin{pmatrix}kX\\kY\end{pmatrix}$

For example, if $\mathbf{a}=\begin{pmatrix}3\\1\end{pmatrix}$, then $5\mathbf{a}=\begin{pmatrix}5\times 3\\5\times 1\end{pmatrix}=\begin{pmatrix}15\\5\end{pmatrix}$.

Question

Vector $\mathbf{a}=\begin{pmatrix}4\\2\end{pmatrix}$.

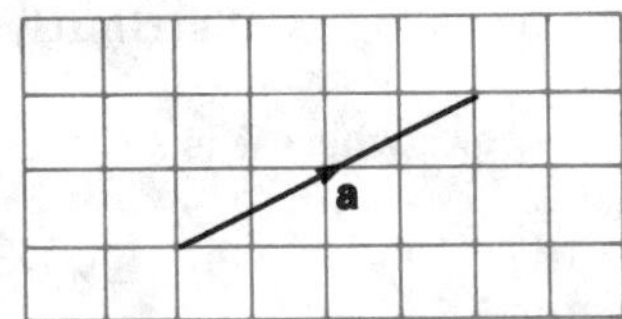

On the grid below draw the vectors

(a) 2**a** (b) $-$**a** (c) $-\frac{1}{2}$**a**

Calculate column vectors for each of these vectors.

Answer

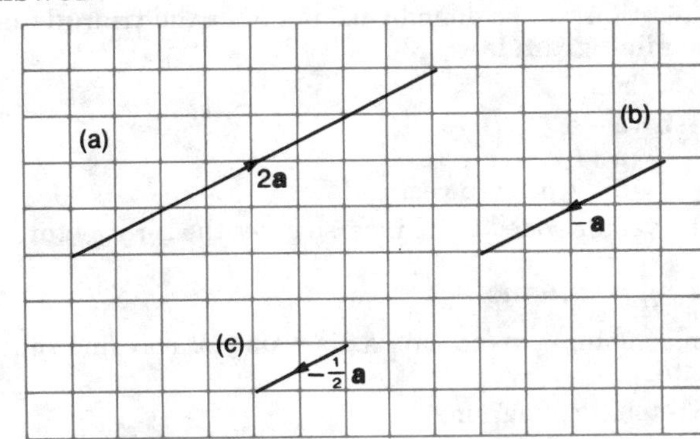

(a) $2\mathbf{a}=\begin{pmatrix}2\times 4\\2\times 2\end{pmatrix}=\begin{pmatrix}8\\4\end{pmatrix}$

(b) $-\mathbf{a}=\begin{pmatrix}-4\\-2\end{pmatrix}$

(c) $-\frac{1}{2}\mathbf{a}=\begin{pmatrix}-\frac{1}{2}\times 4\\-\frac{1}{2}\times 2\end{pmatrix}=\begin{pmatrix}-2\\-1\end{pmatrix}$

ADDITION AND SUBTRACTION

Vectors can be combined by **addition** and **subtraction**. The vector obtained as a result is called the **resultant.** On a diagram the resultant is usually marked with a double arrowhead 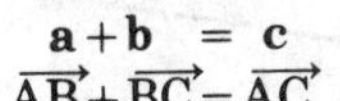.

Addition

The **triangle law** can be used to **add** vectors. In this diagram, by the triangle law,

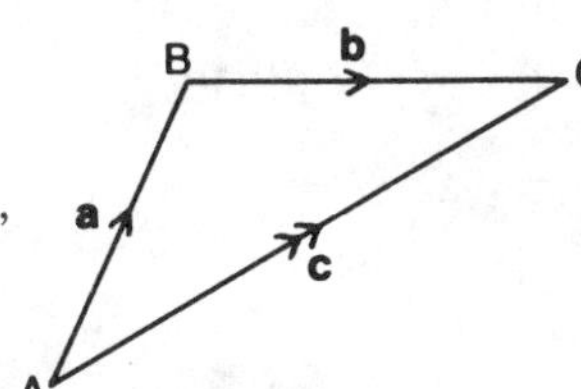

$\mathbf{a}+\mathbf{b}=\mathbf{c}$
$\overrightarrow{AB}+\overrightarrow{BC}=\overrightarrow{AC}$

This shows that 'from A to B' followed by 'from B to C', takes you to the same point as 'from A to C'.
Look at the relationship between the letters

$\overrightarrow{AB}+\overrightarrow{BC}=\overrightarrow{AC}$

The vector $\overrightarrow{AC}=\mathbf{c}$ is the **vector sum** or **resultant** of the other two vectors.
The **parallelogram law** can also be used to **add** vectors.

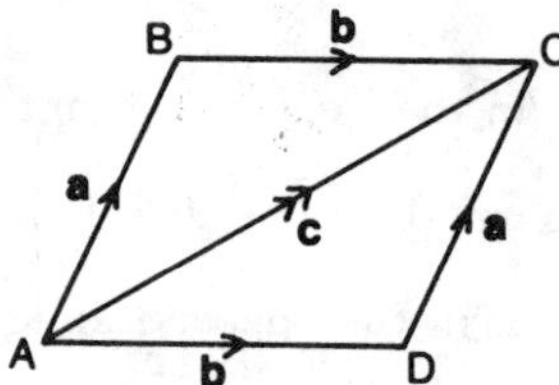

In this diagram, by the parallelogram law

$\mathbf{a}+\mathbf{b}=\mathbf{c}$ or $\mathbf{b}+\mathbf{a}=\mathbf{c}$

$\overrightarrow{AB}+\overrightarrow{BC}=\overrightarrow{AC}$ or $\overrightarrow{AD}+\overrightarrow{DC}=\overrightarrow{AC}$

This is equivalent to the triangle law. But it also shows that vector addition is **commutative**.

$\left.\begin{array}{r}\mathbf{a}+\mathbf{b}=\mathbf{c}\\ \text{and } \mathbf{b}+\mathbf{a}=\mathbf{c}\end{array}\right\}$ gives $\mathbf{a}+\mathbf{b}=\mathbf{b}+\mathbf{a}$, i.e. commutativity.

Vector addition is also **associative**,

i.e. $(\mathbf{a}+\mathbf{b})+\mathbf{c}=\mathbf{a}+(\mathbf{b}+\mathbf{c})$

Multiplication by a scalar is **distributive** over vector addition too,

i.e. $k(\mathbf{p}+\mathbf{q})=k\mathbf{p}+k\mathbf{q}$ where k is a scalar.

Subtraction

To **subtract** a vector, add its inverse.

$\mathbf{a}-\mathbf{b}=\mathbf{a}+(-\mathbf{b})$

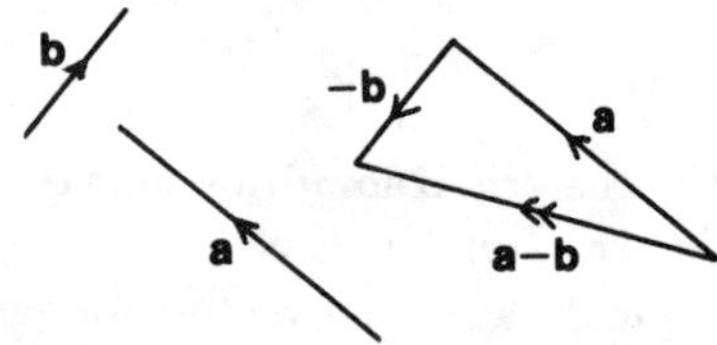

The addition can be done by using either the **triangle law** or **parallelogram law**.

If $\mathbf{a}=\mathbf{b}$, then

$$\begin{aligned}\mathbf{a}-\mathbf{b}&=\mathbf{a}-\mathbf{a}\\ &=\mathbf{a}+(-\mathbf{a})\\ &=\mathbf{0} \quad \text{(the zero vector)}\end{aligned}$$

since a vector added to its inverse gives the zero vector.

Finding resultants

When combining vectors on a diagram you may find that it helps to:

1 Sketch the diagram.
2 Mark the vectors to be combined, checking that the arrows are in the correct directions.
3 Work out the resultant and mark it with a double arrowhead.

Question

A quadrilateral PQRS has diagonals which cross at D.
Write a single vector to represent:

(a) $\overrightarrow{PQ}+\overrightarrow{QR}$ (b) $\overrightarrow{PD}+\overrightarrow{DS}$
(c) $\overrightarrow{QD}+\overrightarrow{DS}$ (d) $\overrightarrow{PD}-\overrightarrow{PS}$
(e) $\overrightarrow{RS}-\overrightarrow{PS}$ (f) $\overrightarrow{QD}-\overrightarrow{RD}$
(g) $\overrightarrow{RS}+\overrightarrow{SP}+\overrightarrow{PQ}$ (h) $\overrightarrow{PD}+\overrightarrow{DS}+\overrightarrow{SP}$

Answer

(a) $\overrightarrow{PQ}+\overrightarrow{QR}=\overrightarrow{PR}$

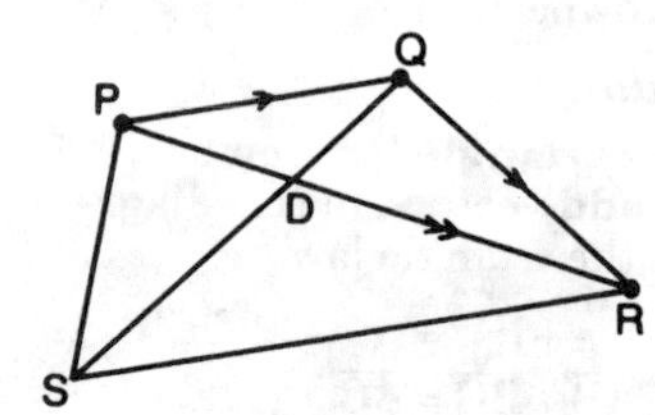

(b) $\overrightarrow{PD}+\overrightarrow{DS}=\overrightarrow{PS}$

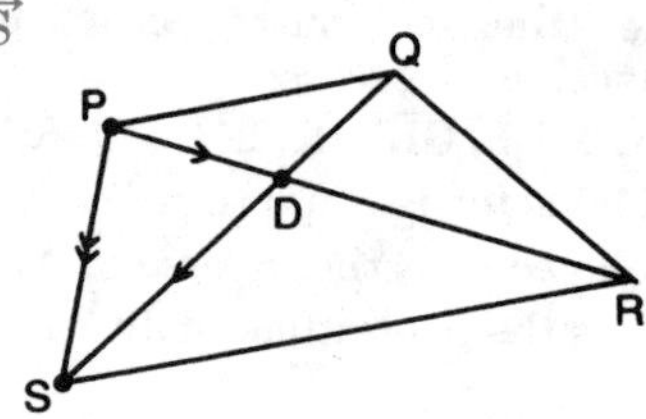

(c) $\overrightarrow{QD}+\overrightarrow{DS}=\overrightarrow{QS}$

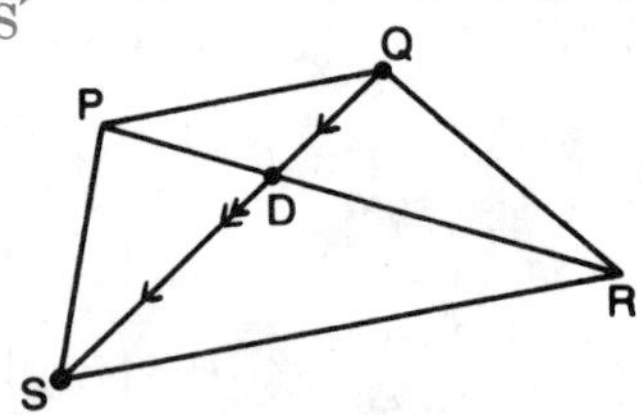

(d) $\overrightarrow{PD}-\overrightarrow{PS}=\overrightarrow{PD}+\overrightarrow{SP}=\overrightarrow{SD}$

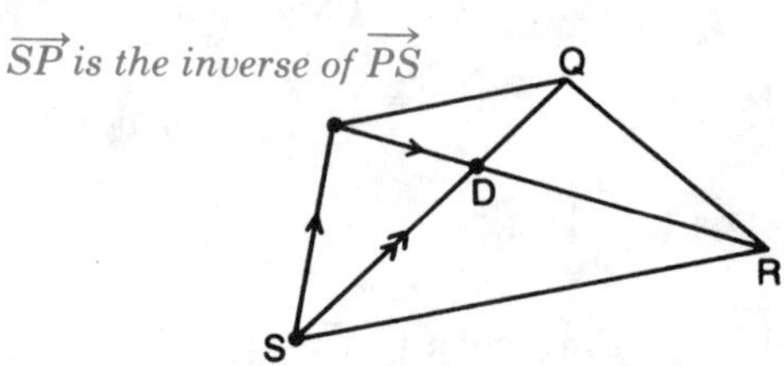
$\overrightarrow{SP}$ is the inverse of $\overrightarrow{PS}$

(e) $\overrightarrow{RS}-\overrightarrow{PS}=\overrightarrow{RS}+\overrightarrow{SP}=\overrightarrow{RP}$

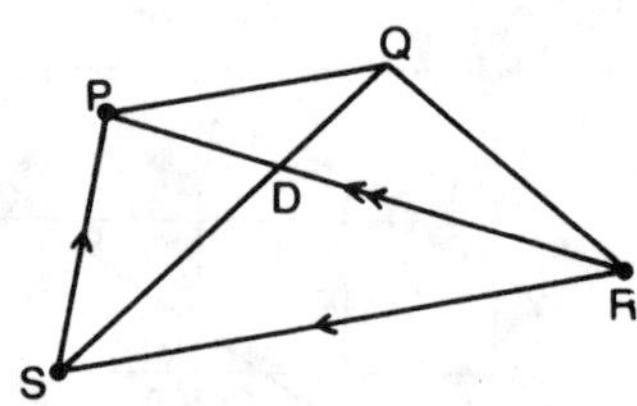

(f) $\overrightarrow{QD}-\overrightarrow{RD}=\overrightarrow{QD}+\overrightarrow{DR}=\overrightarrow{QR}$

$\overrightarrow{DR}$ is the inverse of $\overrightarrow{RD}$

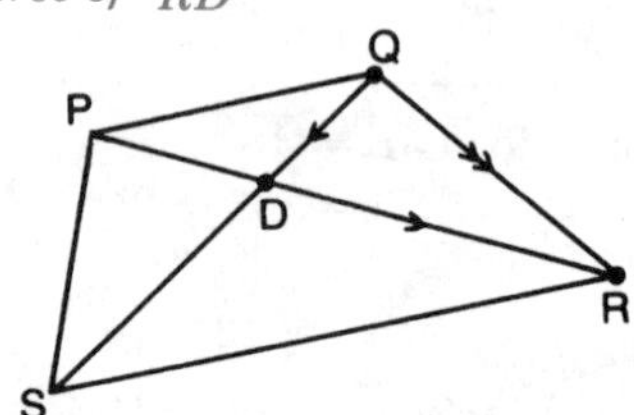

(g) $\overrightarrow{RS}+\overrightarrow{SP}+\overrightarrow{PQ}=\overrightarrow{RQ}$

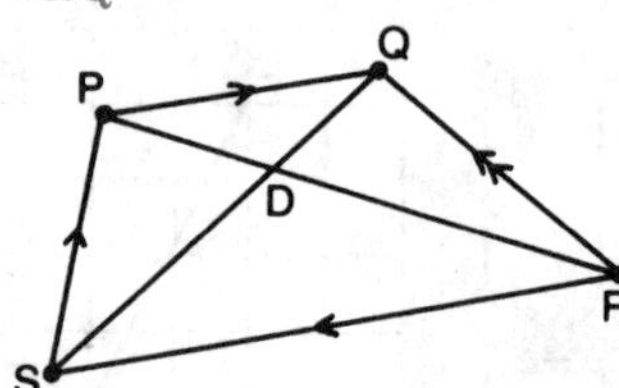

(h) $\overrightarrow{PD}+\overrightarrow{DS}+\overrightarrow{SP}=\mathbf{0}$

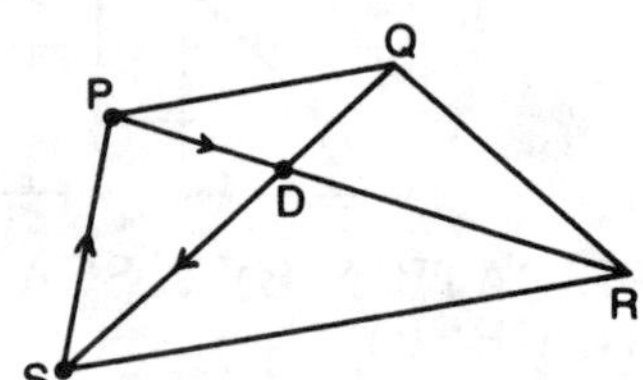

You return to the starting point

ADDITION AND SUBTRACTION OF COLUMN VECTORS

To **add** (or **subtract**) **column vectors**, add (or subtract) corresponding components.

If $\mathbf{a}=\begin{pmatrix}X_1\\Y_1\end{pmatrix}$ and $\mathbf{b}=\begin{pmatrix}X_2\\Y_2\end{pmatrix}$

then $\quad \mathbf{a}+\mathbf{b}=\begin{pmatrix}X_1+X_2\\Y_1+Y_2\end{pmatrix}$

and $\quad \mathbf{a}-\mathbf{b}=\begin{pmatrix}X_1-X_2\\Y_1-Y_2\end{pmatrix}$

Take care with the signs!

Question

Given $\mathbf{p}=\begin{pmatrix}3\\-2\end{pmatrix}$ and $\mathbf{q}=\begin{pmatrix}-4\\1\end{pmatrix}$, find

(a) $\mathbf{p}+\mathbf{q}$ (b) $\mathbf{p}-\mathbf{q}$ (c) $-3\mathbf{p}$
(d) $2\mathbf{p}+3\mathbf{q}$ (e) $2\mathbf{q}-\mathbf{p}$

Answer

(a) $\mathbf{p}+\mathbf{q}=\begin{pmatrix}3\\-2\end{pmatrix}+\begin{pmatrix}-4\\1\end{pmatrix}=\begin{pmatrix}3-4\\-2+1\end{pmatrix}=\begin{pmatrix}-1\\-1\end{pmatrix}$

(b) $\mathbf{p}-\mathbf{q}=\begin{pmatrix}3\\-2\end{pmatrix}-\begin{pmatrix}-4\\1\end{pmatrix}=\begin{pmatrix}3+4\\-2-1\end{pmatrix}=\begin{pmatrix}7\\-3\end{pmatrix}$

(c) $-3\mathbf{p}=-3\begin{pmatrix}3\\-2\end{pmatrix}=\begin{pmatrix}-3\times 3\\-3\times -2\end{pmatrix}=\begin{pmatrix}-9\\+6\end{pmatrix}$

(d) $2\mathbf{p}+3\mathbf{q}=\begin{pmatrix}6\\-4\end{pmatrix}+\begin{pmatrix}-12\\3\end{pmatrix}=\begin{pmatrix}-6\\-1\end{pmatrix}$

(e) $2\mathbf{q}-\mathbf{p}=\begin{pmatrix}-8\\2\end{pmatrix}-\begin{pmatrix}3\\-2\end{pmatrix}=\begin{pmatrix}-11\\4\end{pmatrix}$

VECTORS AND GEOMETRY

Vectors can often be used to show **geometrical results**. When doing this you usually have to find an expression for a vector in terms of some other vectors. To find an expression for a vector, say $\overrightarrow{AB}$, you must find a path on the diagram to move from A to B using vectors you know or that are parallel to vectors you know. Drawing a sketch of the diagram, marking the vector you want —»— and labelling the vectors you know is useful. This may help you to work out the path you want. You will probably find that there are several possible paths to choose from. They *should* all give the same answer, so try to choose the easiest.

Question

The diagram shows a quadrilateral PQRS with ST = 2TQ, $\overrightarrow{PQ}=\mathbf{a}$, $\overrightarrow{SR}=2\mathbf{a}$ and $\overrightarrow{SP}=\mathbf{b}$.

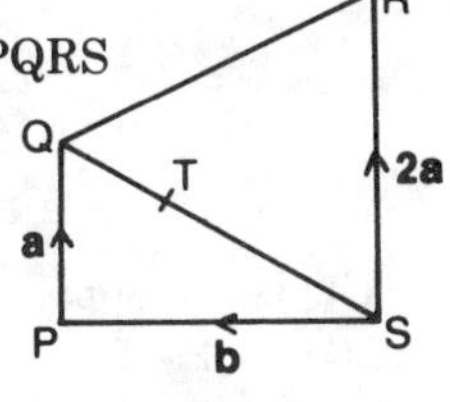

(a) Find, in terms of **a** and **b**
(i) $\overrightarrow{SQ}$ (ii) $\overrightarrow{TQ}$ (iii) $\overrightarrow{RQ}$ (iv) $\overrightarrow{PT}$ (v) $\overrightarrow{TR}$.

(b) What do your answers to (iv) and (v) tell you about the points P, T and R?

Answer

(a) (i) $\overrightarrow{SQ}=\overrightarrow{SP}+\overrightarrow{PQ}$
$=\mathbf{b}+\mathbf{a}$
(or $\mathbf{a}+\mathbf{b}$ by commutativity)

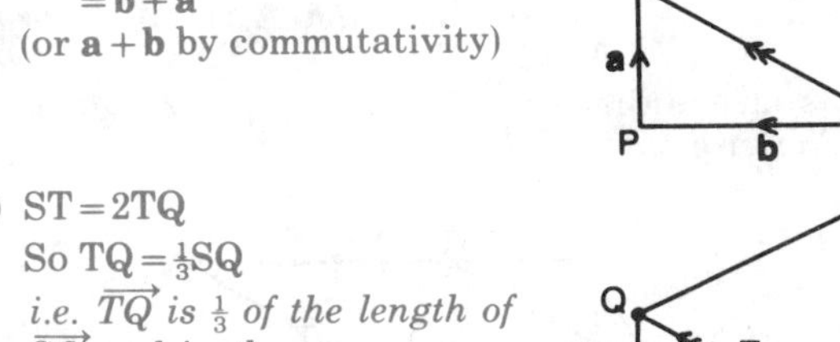

(ii) ST = 2TQ
So TQ = $\frac{1}{3}$SQ
i.e. $\overrightarrow{TQ}$ is $\frac{1}{3}$ of the length of $\overrightarrow{SQ}$ and in the same direction
So $\overrightarrow{TQ}=\frac{1}{3}\overrightarrow{SQ}=\frac{1}{3}(\mathbf{b}+\mathbf{a})$
or $\frac{1}{3}(\mathbf{a}+\mathbf{b})$

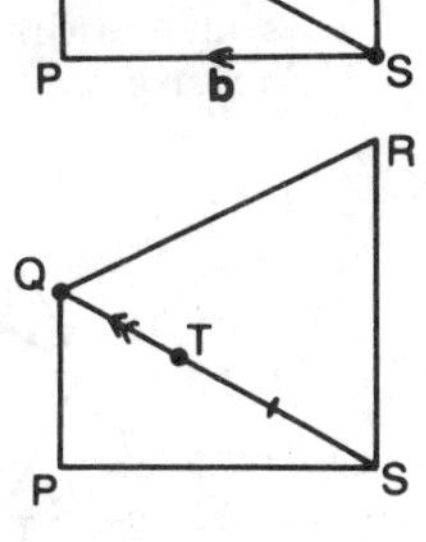

(iii) $\overrightarrow{RQ}=\overrightarrow{RS}+\overrightarrow{SQ}$ *You know $\overrightarrow{SR}$, so use $\overrightarrow{RS}=-\overrightarrow{SR}$*
$=-\overrightarrow{SR}+\overrightarrow{SQ}$
$=-2\mathbf{a}+(\mathbf{b}+\mathbf{a})$
$=-2\mathbf{a}+\mathbf{b}+\mathbf{a}$
$=\mathbf{b}-\mathbf{a}$

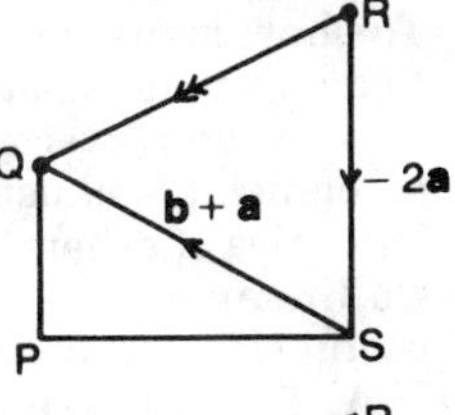

(iv) $\overrightarrow{PT}=\overrightarrow{PQ}+\overrightarrow{QT}$ *You know $\overrightarrow{TQ}$, so use $\overrightarrow{QT}=-\overrightarrow{TQ}$*
$=\overrightarrow{PQ}-\overrightarrow{TQ}$
$=\mathbf{a}-\frac{1}{3}(\mathbf{a}+\mathbf{b})$
$=\mathbf{a}-\frac{1}{3}\mathbf{a}-\frac{1}{3}\mathbf{b}$
$=\frac{2}{3}\mathbf{a}-\frac{1}{3}\mathbf{b}$
$=\frac{1}{3}(2\mathbf{a}-\mathbf{b})$

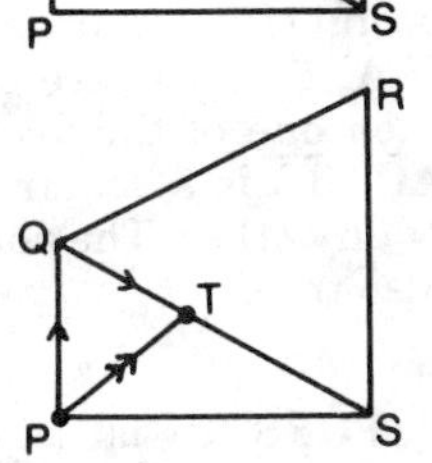

(v) $\overrightarrow{TR}=\overrightarrow{TQ}+\overrightarrow{QR}$ *You know $\overrightarrow{RQ}$, so use $\overrightarrow{QR}=-\overrightarrow{RQ}$*
$=\overrightarrow{TQ}-\overrightarrow{RQ}$
$=\frac{1}{3}(\mathbf{a}+\mathbf{b})-(\mathbf{b}-\mathbf{a})$
$=\frac{1}{3}\mathbf{a}+\frac{1}{3}\mathbf{b}-\mathbf{b}+\mathbf{a}$
$=\frac{4}{3}\mathbf{a}-\frac{2}{3}\mathbf{b}$
$=\frac{2}{3}(2\mathbf{a}-\mathbf{b})$

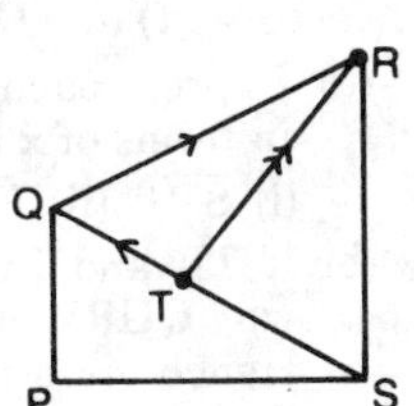

(b) $\overrightarrow{PT}=\frac{1}{3}(2\mathbf{a}-\mathbf{b})$
$\overrightarrow{TR}=\frac{2}{3}(2\mathbf{a}-\mathbf{b})$

So $\overrightarrow{PT}$ and $\overrightarrow{TR}$ are multiples of the same vector $(2\mathbf{a}-\mathbf{b})$.
This means that $\overrightarrow{PT}$ and $\overrightarrow{TR}$ are parallel vectors.
But T is on both vectors.
So T is common to both lines PT and TR and $\overrightarrow{PT}$ and $\overrightarrow{TR}$ are in the same direction.
This means that P, T and R lie on the same line, i.e. they are **collinear**.

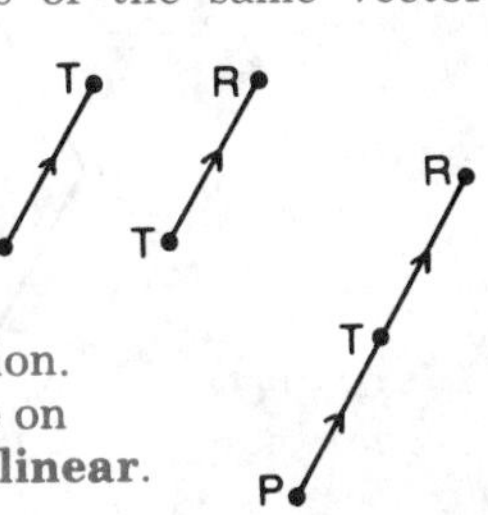

Many **geometrical theorems** can be proved using vectors. The midpoint theorem can be proved this way.

Question

In triangle ABC, X and Y are the midpoints of AB and AC respectively. Use vectors to prove that XY is parallel to BC and half the length of BC (i.e. prove the midpoint theorem).

Answer

Let $\overrightarrow{XA}=\mathbf{a}$ and $\overrightarrow{AY}=\mathbf{b}$
So $\overrightarrow{XY}=\overrightarrow{XA}+\overrightarrow{AY}$
$=\mathbf{a}+\mathbf{b}$

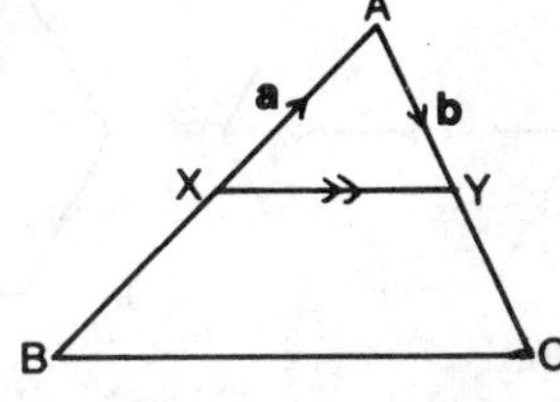

X is the midpoint of BA. So BA = 2XA and $\overrightarrow{BA}=2\overrightarrow{XA}=2\mathbf{a}$.
Y is the midpoint of AC. So AC = 2AY and $\overrightarrow{AC}=2\overrightarrow{AY}=2\mathbf{b}$.
So $\overrightarrow{BC}=\overrightarrow{BA}+\overrightarrow{AC}=2\mathbf{a}+2\mathbf{b}$
$=2(\mathbf{a}+\mathbf{b})$
But $\overrightarrow{XY}=(\mathbf{a}+\mathbf{b})$
So $\overrightarrow{BC}=2\overrightarrow{XY}$

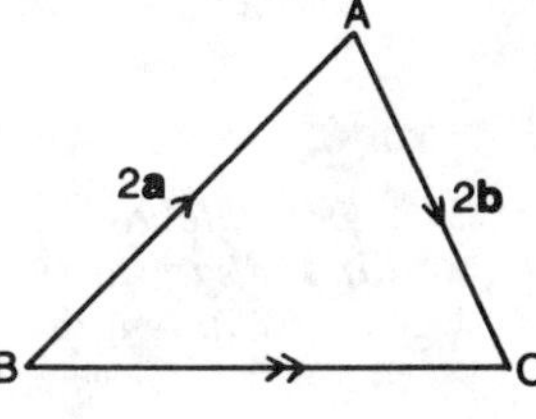

This means that BC and XY are parallel, since they are multiples of the same vector $(\mathbf{a}+\mathbf{b})$.
The magnitude of $\overrightarrow{BC}$ is 2 times the magnitude of $\overrightarrow{XY}$.
i.e. BC = 2XY
or XY = $\frac{1}{2}$BC.

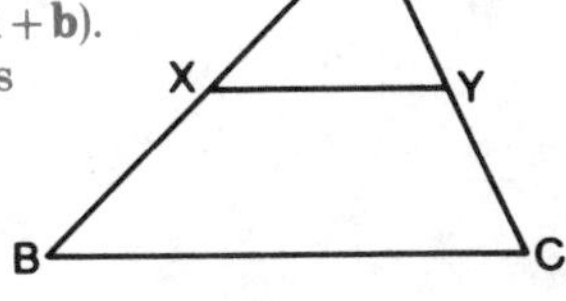

So XY is parallel to BC and half the length of BC.

To show many geometrical results using vectors you have to translate geometrical facts you know about the diagram into vector terms. Many problems are based on recognizing and using parallel vectors and vectors that are multiples of others.

Collinear points, i.e. points in the same straight line, are useful to recognize.

If A, B and C are collinear, then one of the vectors $\overrightarrow{AB}$, $\overrightarrow{AC}$, $\overrightarrow{BC}$ is a scalar multiple of any other. The converse is also true.

Question

PQRSTU is a regular hexagon. The displacement vectors $\overrightarrow{PQ}$ and $\overrightarrow{QR}$ are denoted by $\mathbf{x}$ and $\mathbf{y}$ respectively.

(a) Express each of the following displacement vectors in terms of $\mathbf{x}$ and $\mathbf{y}$ or both:

(i) $\overrightarrow{ST}$ (ii) $\overrightarrow{UR}$ (iii) $\overrightarrow{PU}$ (iv) $\overrightarrow{US}$ (v) $\overrightarrow{TR}$

(b) If TR and PQ are produced to meet at V, explain why QURV is a parallelogram.

Hence, or otherwise, express in terms of $\mathbf{x}$ or $\mathbf{y}$ or both

(i) $\overrightarrow{PV}$ (ii) $\overrightarrow{TV}$

Answer

PQRSTU is a regular hexagon. This tells you about equal lengths:

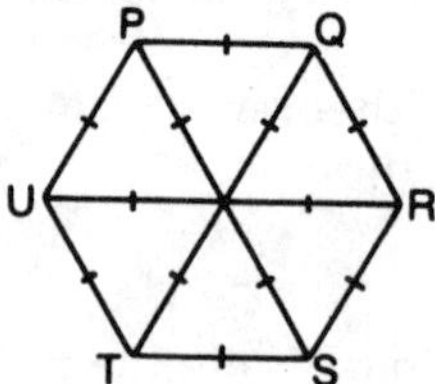

about parallel lines:

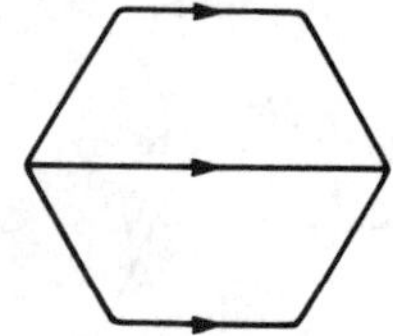

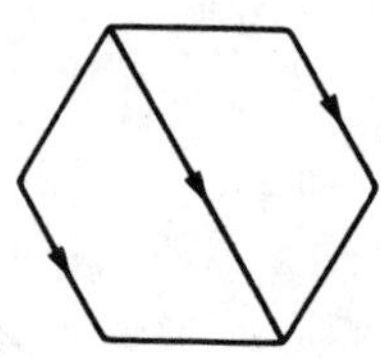

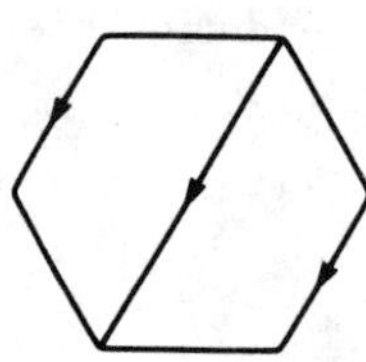

(a) (i) $\overrightarrow{ST} = -\mathbf{x}$

$\overrightarrow{ST}$ is parallel to $\overrightarrow{PQ}$ i.e. $\mathbf{x}$, but in the opposite direction ST = PQ in length

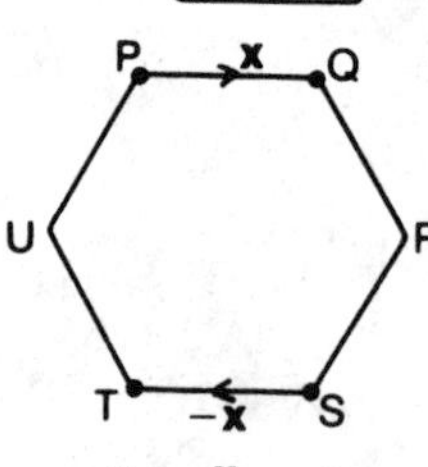

(ii) $\overrightarrow{UR} = 2\mathbf{x}$

$\overrightarrow{UR}$ is parallel to $\overrightarrow{PQ}$, i.e. $\mathbf{x}$, and in the same direction UR = 2PQ in length.

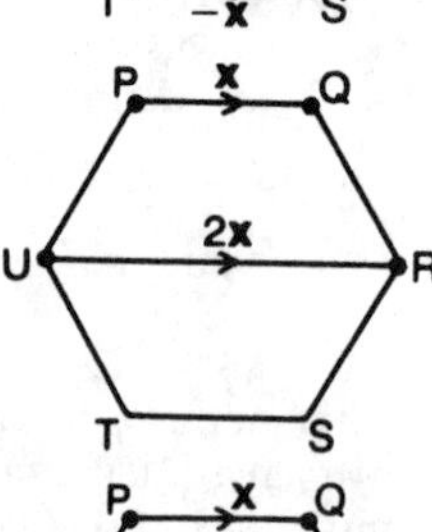

(iii) $\overrightarrow{PU} = \overrightarrow{PQ} + \overrightarrow{QR} + \overrightarrow{RU}$ *Use $\overrightarrow{RU}$ is $-\overrightarrow{UR}$*

$= \overrightarrow{PQ} + \overrightarrow{QR} - \overrightarrow{UR}$

$= \mathbf{x} + \mathbf{y} - 2\mathbf{x}$

$= \mathbf{y} - \mathbf{x}$

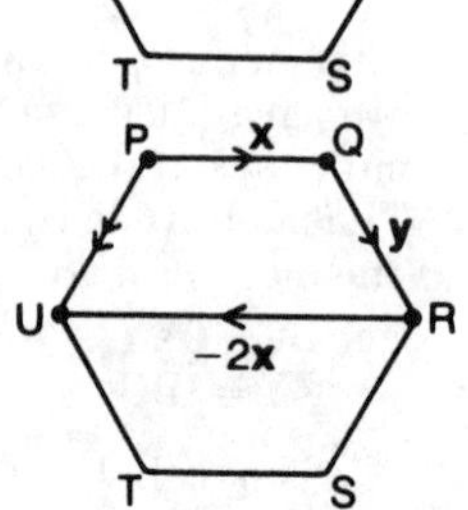

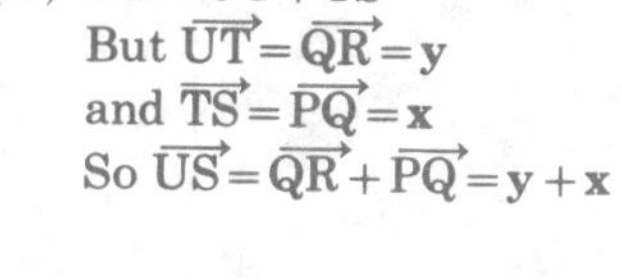

(iv) $\overrightarrow{US} = \overrightarrow{UT} + \overrightarrow{TS}$

But $\overrightarrow{UT} = \overrightarrow{QR} = \mathbf{y}$

and $\overrightarrow{TS} = \overrightarrow{PQ} = \mathbf{x}$

So $\overrightarrow{US} = \overrightarrow{QR} + \overrightarrow{PQ} = \mathbf{y} + \mathbf{x}$

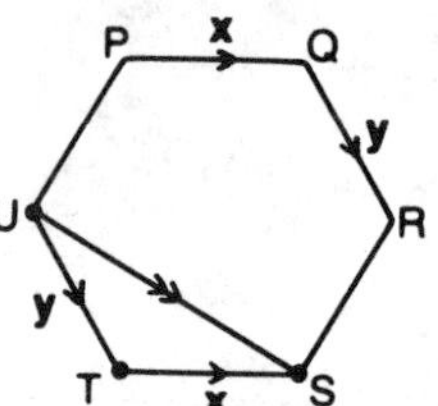

(v) $\overrightarrow{TR} = \overrightarrow{TS} + \overrightarrow{SR}$

But $\overrightarrow{TS} = \overrightarrow{PQ} = \mathbf{x}$

and $\overrightarrow{SR} = \overrightarrow{UP} = -\overrightarrow{PU}$

$= -(\mathbf{y} - \mathbf{x}) = -\mathbf{y} + \mathbf{x}$

So $\overrightarrow{TR} = \overrightarrow{TS} + \overrightarrow{SR} = \mathbf{x} + (-\mathbf{y} + \mathbf{x})$

$= 2\mathbf{x} - \mathbf{y}$

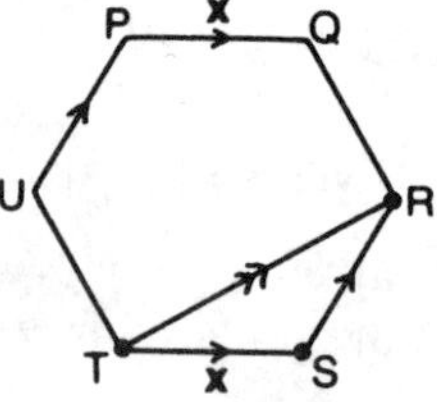

(b)

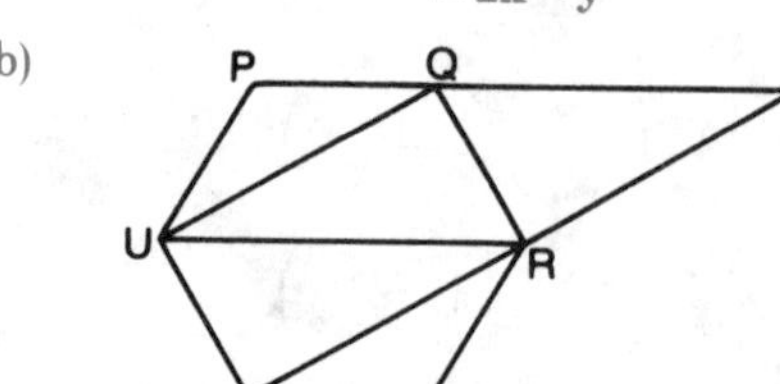

To prove that UQVR is a parallelogram, try to prove that opposite sides are parallel

PQ is produced to V.

So PQV is a straight line, i.e. P, Q and V are collinear.

This means that $\overrightarrow{QV}$ will be a scalar multiple of $\overrightarrow{PQ}$.

Let $\overrightarrow{QV} = k\overrightarrow{PQ}$ where k is a scalar.

$= k\mathbf{x}$

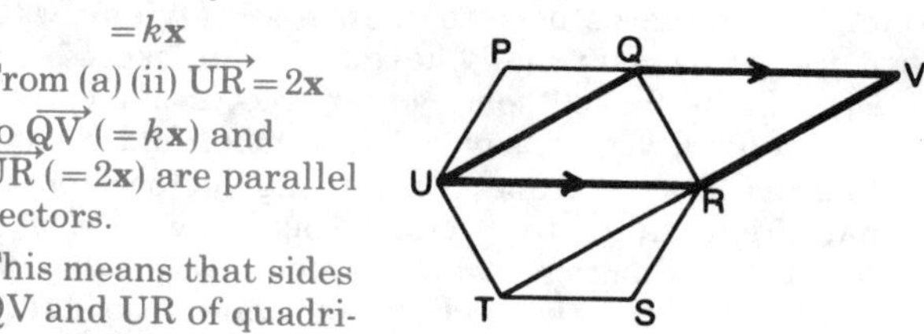

From (a) (ii) $\overrightarrow{UR} = 2\mathbf{x}$

so $\overrightarrow{QV}$ $(= k\mathbf{x})$ and $\overrightarrow{UR}$ $(= 2\mathbf{x})$ are parallel vectors.

This means that sides QV and UR of quadrilateral UQVR are parallel.

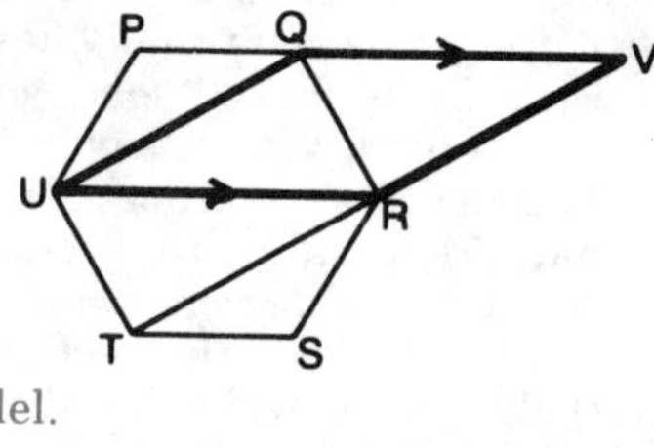

Similarly, since T, R and V are collinear,

$\overrightarrow{RV} = a\overrightarrow{TR}$ where a is a scalar.

$= a(2\mathbf{x} - \mathbf{y})$

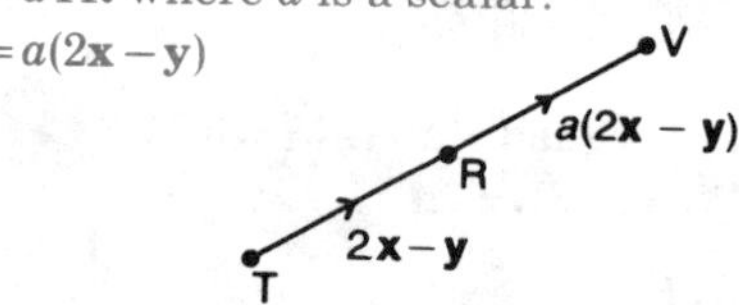

UQ is the opposite side to RV in UQVR.

$\overrightarrow{UQ} = \overrightarrow{UP} + \overrightarrow{PQ}$

$= -\overrightarrow{PU} + \overrightarrow{PQ}$

$= -(\mathbf{y} - \mathbf{x}) + \mathbf{x}$

$= -\mathbf{y} + \mathbf{x} + \mathbf{x}$

$= 2\mathbf{x} - \mathbf{y}$

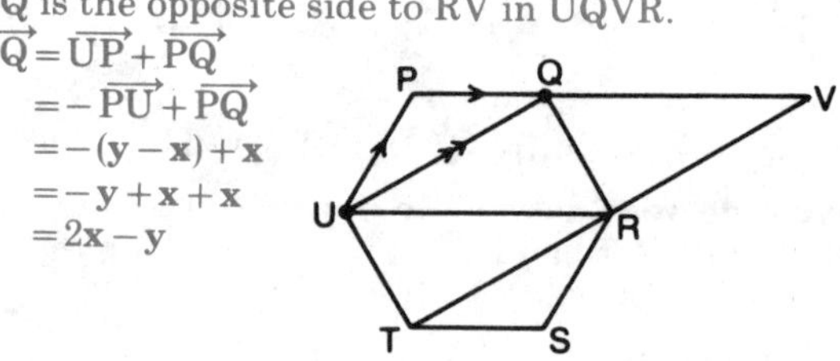

So $\overrightarrow{RV} = a(2\mathbf{x} - \mathbf{y})$ and $\overrightarrow{UQ} = (2\mathbf{x} - \mathbf{y})$ } i.e. RV and UQ are parallel vectors.

This means that sides RV and UQ of quadrilateral UQVR are parallel.

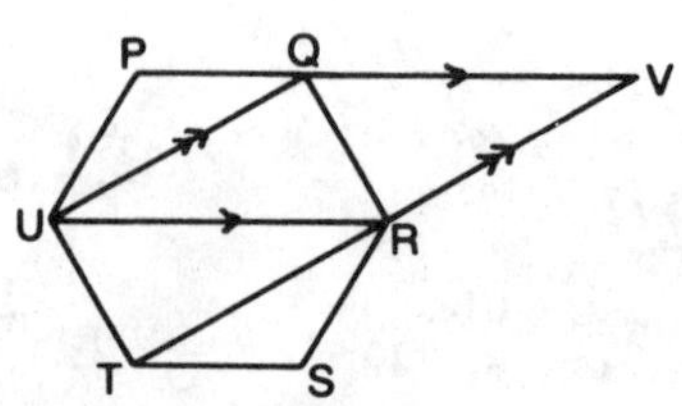

A quadrilateral with opposite sides parallel is a parallelogram. So UQVR is a parallelogram.

(i) $\vec{PV}=\vec{PQ}+\vec{QV}$

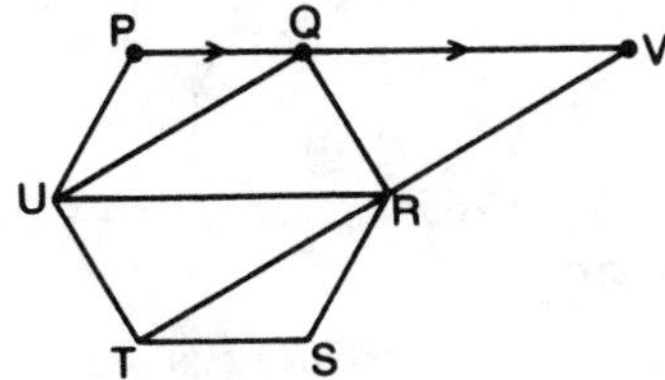

QV and UR are opposite sides of parallelogram UQVR.
So QV and UR are parallel and QV=UR in length.
This gives $\vec{QV}=\vec{UR}=2\mathbf{x}$
So $\vec{PV}=\vec{PQ}+\vec{QV}$
$=\mathbf{x}+2\mathbf{x}$
$=3\mathbf{x}$

(ii) $\vec{TV}=\vec{TR}+\vec{RV}$
RV and UQ are opposite sides of parallelogram UQVR.

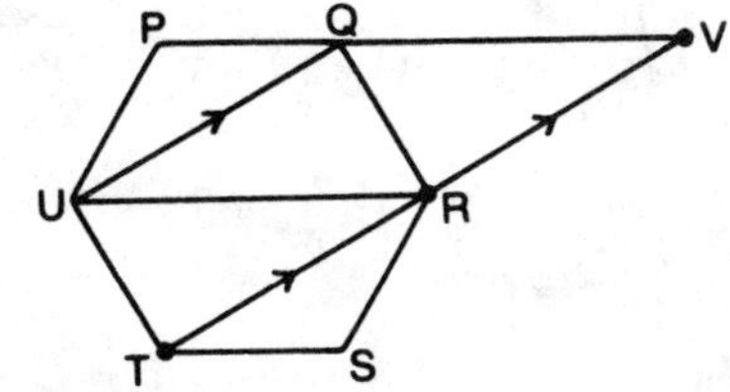

So RV and UQ are parallel and RV=UQ in length.
This gives $\vec{RV}=\vec{UQ}=2\mathbf{x}-\mathbf{y}$
So $\vec{TV}=\vec{TR}+\vec{RV}$
$=(2\mathbf{x}-\mathbf{y})+(2\mathbf{x}-\mathbf{y})$
$=2(2\mathbf{x}-\mathbf{y})$

3.29 Matrices

A **matrix** can be thought of as a store of information. The plural of matrix is **matrices**. In a matrix the information, usually numbers, is arranged in a rectangular pattern (**array**) of rows and columns and enclosed in brackets. It is usual to name a matrix using a capital letter.
For example, these are all matrices:

$$\mathbf{A}=\begin{pmatrix}1\\2\\4\end{pmatrix}\quad \mathbf{B}=\begin{pmatrix}3&7\\0&5\end{pmatrix}\quad \mathbf{C}=\begin{pmatrix}6&0\\4&1\\-1&\frac{2}{3}\end{pmatrix}$$

$$\mathbf{D}=\begin{pmatrix}5&0&1&-3\\-1&0&0&2\\1&4&6&3\end{pmatrix}$$

Note: Commas are not used in matrices. Gaps are left between the columns.
Tables of information are easy to write as matrices. This makes the information compact and easy to store. Information is often stored this way in computers.
For example, the information in this football league table:

	Won	Lost	Drawn
Liverpool	4	0	1
Manchester United	2	1	2
Nottingham Forest	3	0	2
Everton	1	3	1

can be written as this matrix:
$$\begin{pmatrix}4&0&1\\2&1&2\\3&0&2\\1&3&1\end{pmatrix}$$

Units of measurement are not written inside a matrix. All the information must be written with the same unit before putting it into the matrix.

For example, the prices in this table must be written either all in pence or all in pounds before writing them in a matrix.

	Prices	
	Tea	**Coffee**
Shop A	50p	£1.00
Shop B	53p	£1.03
Shop C	49p	£1.12

Here are the two matrices they give.

Pence matrix
$$\begin{pmatrix}50&100\\53&103\\49&112\end{pmatrix}$$

Pounds matrix
$$\begin{pmatrix}0.50&1.00\\0.53&1.03\\0.49&1.12\end{pmatrix}$$

Each item of information in a matrix is called an **entry** or **element**. For example,
the football league matrix given has 12 elements,
the price matrix above has 6 elements.
The **order** of a matrix gives the number of rows and columns it has.
A matrix with m rows and n columns has order $(m \times n)$. We say 'm by n'. The football league matrix has 4 rows and 3 columns, so its order is (4×3). We say 'four by three'.

TYPES OF MATRICES

A **row matrix** has only one row of elements. Its order is of the form $(1 \times n)$. These are all row matrices:

(7)	$(5\ \ 3)$	$(7\ \ -1\ \ 2)$	$(6\ \ 0\ \ 0\ \ 5)$
order (1×1)	order (1×2)	order (1×3)	order (1×4)

A **column matrix** has only one column of elements. Its order is of the form $(m \times 1)$. For example, these are all column matrices:

(7)	$\begin{pmatrix}2\\4\end{pmatrix}$	$\begin{pmatrix}8\\5\\0\end{pmatrix}$	$\begin{pmatrix}-1\\2\\7\\0\end{pmatrix}$
order (1×1)	order (2×1)	order (3×1)	order (4×1)

A **square matrix** has the same number of rows and columns, so its order is of the form $(n \times n)$. These are all square matrices:

(7)	$\begin{pmatrix}3&5\\0&-1\end{pmatrix}$	$\begin{pmatrix}6&7&0\\-1&3&-4\\8&9&2\end{pmatrix}$	$\begin{pmatrix}5&0&0&1\\0&3&2&6\\5&0&7&3\\6&1&0&0\end{pmatrix}$
order (1×1)	order (2×2)	order (3×3)	order (4×4)

EQUAL MATRICES

Equal matrices are identical. They have the *same* order and their *corresponding elements* are *equal*. For example,

$$\begin{pmatrix}1&2\\3&4\end{pmatrix}=\begin{pmatrix}1&2\\3&4\end{pmatrix}$$

but
$$\begin{pmatrix}1&2\\3&4\end{pmatrix}\neq\begin{pmatrix}1&4\\2&3\end{pmatrix}$$

$$\begin{pmatrix}1&2\\3&4\end{pmatrix}\neq(1\ \ 2\ \ 3\ \ 4)$$

and so on ...
If two matrices are equal, then their corresponding elements must be equal. For example,

if $\begin{pmatrix}a&b\\c&d\end{pmatrix}=\begin{pmatrix}3&5\\0&7\end{pmatrix}$

then $a=3$ $\quad b=5$
$c=0$ $\quad d=7$

ADDITION AND SUBTRACTION

Matrices can only be **added** (or **subtracted**) if they are of the *same* order. For example,

$$\begin{pmatrix} 0 & 1 & 2 \\ 6 & 5 & 3 \end{pmatrix} \text{ can be added to } \begin{pmatrix} -1 & 7 & 9 \\ 0 & 2 & -6 \end{pmatrix}$$

order (2 × 3) ← *same order* → order (2 × 3)

but $\begin{pmatrix} 3 & 0 \\ 7 & 2 \end{pmatrix}$ cannot be added to $\begin{pmatrix} 5 \\ 3 \end{pmatrix}$

order (2 × 2) ← *different orders* → order (2 × 1)

To **add** (or **subtract**) matrices, simply add (or subtract) corresponding elements. This gives a matrix of the *same* order. For example, for these 2 × 2 matrices:

$$\begin{pmatrix} a & b \\ c & d \end{pmatrix} + \begin{pmatrix} e & f \\ g & h \end{pmatrix} = \begin{pmatrix} a+e & b+f \\ c+g & d+h \end{pmatrix}$$

$$\begin{pmatrix} a & b \\ c & d \end{pmatrix} - \begin{pmatrix} e & f \\ g & h \end{pmatrix} = \begin{pmatrix} a-e & b-f \\ c-g & d-h \end{pmatrix}$$

Take care with the signs when adding (or subtracting) the numbers.

Question

For $\mathbf{A} = \begin{pmatrix} 2 & 4 \\ -1 & 3 \\ 0 & -2 \end{pmatrix}$ and $\mathbf{B} = \begin{pmatrix} 0 & 1 \\ 8 & 7 \\ -3 & 2 \end{pmatrix}$

find (a) **A** + **B** (b) **A** − **B**

Answer

(a) $\mathbf{A}+\mathbf{B} = \begin{pmatrix} 2 & 4 \\ -1 & 3 \\ 0 & -2 \end{pmatrix} + \begin{pmatrix} 0 & 1 \\ 8 & 7 \\ -3 & 2 \end{pmatrix}$

$= \begin{pmatrix} 2+0 & 4+1 \\ -1+8 & 3+7 \\ 0-3 & -2+2 \end{pmatrix} = \begin{pmatrix} 2 & 5 \\ 7 & 10 \\ -3 & 0 \end{pmatrix}$

(b) $\mathbf{A}-\mathbf{B} = \begin{pmatrix} 2 & 4 \\ -1 & 3 \\ 0 & -2 \end{pmatrix} - \begin{pmatrix} 0 & 1 \\ 8 & 7 \\ -3 & 2 \end{pmatrix}$

$= \begin{pmatrix} 2-0 & 4-1 \\ -1-8 & 3-7 \\ 0-(-3) & -2-2 \end{pmatrix} = \begin{pmatrix} 2 & 3 \\ -9 & -4 \\ 3 & -4 \end{pmatrix}$

The **addition** of matrices is **commutative**, but the subtraction of matrices is **not** commutative. For example, if **A** and **B** are matrices of the same order, then:

A + **B** = **B** + **A** (commutative)
A − **B** ≠ **B** − **A** (*not* commutative)

Matrix **addition** is **associative**. But matrix subtraction is **not** associative. For example, if **A**, **B** and **C** are matrices of the same order, then:

(**A** + **B**) + **C** = **A** + (**B** + **C**) (associative)
(**A** − **B**) − **C** ≠ **A** − (**B** − **C**) (*not* associative)

Simple **matrix equations** involving addition and subtraction can be solved like an ordinary algebraic equation. You want to isolate the unknown matrix on one side of the equation. To do this you must do the same to both sides of the equation.

Question

Solve these equations for the matrices **X** and **Y**.

(a) $\mathbf{X} + \begin{pmatrix} 3 & 2 \\ 0 & 1 \end{pmatrix} = \begin{pmatrix} 7 & 4 \\ 3 & 0 \end{pmatrix}$

(b) $\mathbf{Y} - \begin{pmatrix} -4 & 0 \\ 0 & 1 \end{pmatrix} = \begin{pmatrix} -4 & 2 \\ 0 & 6 \end{pmatrix}$

Answer

(a) $\mathbf{X} + \begin{pmatrix} 3 & 2 \\ 0 & 1 \end{pmatrix} = \begin{pmatrix} 7 & 4 \\ 3 & 0 \end{pmatrix}$

Subtract the same matrix from both sides $\mathbf{X} = \begin{pmatrix} 7 & 4 \\ 3 & 0 \end{pmatrix} - \begin{pmatrix} 3 & 2 \\ 0 & 1 \end{pmatrix}$

$= \begin{pmatrix} 4 & 2 \\ 3 & -1 \end{pmatrix}$

(b) $\mathbf{Y} - \begin{pmatrix} -4 & 0 \\ 0 & 1 \end{pmatrix} = \begin{pmatrix} -4 & 2 \\ 0 & 6 \end{pmatrix}$

Add the same matrix to both sides $\mathbf{Y} = \begin{pmatrix} -4 & 2 \\ 0 & 6 \end{pmatrix} + \begin{pmatrix} -4 & 0 \\ 0 & 1 \end{pmatrix}$

$= \begin{pmatrix} -8 & 2 \\ 0 & 7 \end{pmatrix}$

MULTIPLICATION BY A NUMBER (A SCALAR)

To multiply a matrix by a number (a scalar), multiply each element of the matrix by the number. For example, for 2 × 2 matrices:

$$k\begin{pmatrix} a & b \\ c & d \end{pmatrix} = \begin{pmatrix} ka & kb \\ kc & kd \end{pmatrix}$$

Question

For $\mathbf{A} = \begin{pmatrix} 3 & 6 \\ -1 & 5 \\ 0 & 2 \end{pmatrix}$ find (a) 3**A** (b) −2**A** (c) $\frac{1}{4}$**A**

Answer

(a) $3\mathbf{A} = 3\begin{pmatrix} 3 & 6 \\ -1 & 5 \\ 0 & 2 \end{pmatrix} = \begin{pmatrix} 3\times 3 & 3\times 6 \\ 3\times -1 & 3\times 5 \\ 3\times 0 & 3\times 2 \end{pmatrix} = \begin{pmatrix} 9 & 18 \\ -3 & 15 \\ 0 & 6 \end{pmatrix}$

(b) $-2\mathbf{A} = -2\begin{pmatrix} 3 & 6 \\ -1 & 5 \\ 0 & 2 \end{pmatrix} = \begin{pmatrix} -2\times 3 & -2\times 6 \\ -2\times -1 & -2\times 5 \\ -2\times 0 & -2\times 2 \end{pmatrix}$

$= \begin{pmatrix} -6 & -12 \\ 2 & -10 \\ 0 & -4 \end{pmatrix}$

(c) $\frac{1}{4}\mathbf{A} = \frac{1}{4}\begin{pmatrix} 3 & 6 \\ -1 & 5 \\ 0 & 2 \end{pmatrix} = \begin{pmatrix} \frac{1}{4}\times 3 & \frac{1}{4}\times 6 \\ \frac{1}{4}\times -1 & \frac{1}{4}\times 5 \\ \frac{1}{4}\times 0 & \frac{1}{4}\times 2 \end{pmatrix} = \begin{pmatrix} \frac{3}{4} & \frac{6}{4} \\ -\frac{1}{4} & \frac{5}{4} \\ 0 & \frac{2}{4} \end{pmatrix}$

MULTIPLICATION OF TWO MATRICES

Two matrices can **only** be multiplied if the number of columns in the first matrix **equals** the number of rows in the second. When this happens, the two matrices are said to be **compatible**.

To see if two matrices are compatible, write down the orders of the matrices to be multiplied (in the order of multiplication).

If the two middle numbers are the same, then they *are* compatible. For example, matrices of order

($p \times q$) and ($q \times r$)
equal (the two q's)

are compatible if multiplied in this order.

The orders of the matrices also give you the order of the resulting matrix. For example, matrices of order

($p \times q$) and ($q \times r$)
→ ($p \times r$) ←

give a matrix of order ($p \times r$) if multiplied in this order.

Question

Given $\mathbf{A} = \begin{pmatrix} 3 & 0 & 1 \\ -1 & 1 & 0 \end{pmatrix}$ $\mathbf{B} = \begin{pmatrix} 2 \\ 1 \\ -2 \end{pmatrix}$ $\mathbf{C} = \begin{pmatrix} 1 & 0 \\ 0 & 3 \end{pmatrix}$

which of these pairs of matrices are compatible when multiplied in this order?

(a) **AB** (b) **BA** (c) **BC** (d) **CA**

For the compatible matrices, give the order of the resulting matrix.

Answer

(a) Matrices: **A** **B**
Orders: (2 × 3) (3 × 1)
equal
→(2 × 1)← So **AB** is compatible.

The order of the resulting matrix is (2 × 1).

(b) Matrices: **B** **A**
Orders: (3 × 1) (2 × 3)
not equal So **BA** is not compatible.

(c) Matrices: $\mathbf{B}$ (3×1), $\mathbf{C}$ (2×2)
Orders: (3×1) (2×2) — not equal. So **BC** is not compatible.

(d) Matrices: $\mathbf{C}$, $\mathbf{A}$
Orders: (2×2) (2×3) — equal → (2×3). So **CA** is compatible.

The order of the resulting matrix is (2×3).

The multiplication of a **row matrix** and **column matrix** is the simplest multiplication of two matrices. Multiply each element of the row by the corresponding element in the column and add the answers. For example,

$$\begin{pmatrix} a & b & c \end{pmatrix}\begin{pmatrix} x \\ y \\ z \end{pmatrix} = \begin{pmatrix} ax+by+cz \end{pmatrix}$$

Check orders: (1×3) $(3\times 1) \longrightarrow (1\times 1)$ — equal → (1×1). Compatible. Resulting order is (1×1). ✓

Question

Calculate the product $\begin{pmatrix} 3 & 2 \end{pmatrix}\begin{pmatrix} 4 \\ 1 \end{pmatrix}$

Answer

$$\begin{pmatrix} 3 & 2 \end{pmatrix}\begin{pmatrix} 4 \\ 1 \end{pmatrix} = (3\times 4 + 2\times 1) = (12+2)$$
$$= (14)$$

Check orders: (1×2) $(2\times 1) \longrightarrow (1\times 1)$ — equal → (1×1). Compatible. Resulting order is (1×1). ✓

To find the **product of two matrices**, multiply every row of the first matrix by every column of the second. Do each multiplication just like multiplying a row matrix by a column matrix. Each element of the product comes from a row in the first matrix and a column in the second.

For example, multiplying the *2nd* row of the first matrix by the *3rd column* of the second matrix gives the element in the *2nd row* and *3rd column* of the answer.

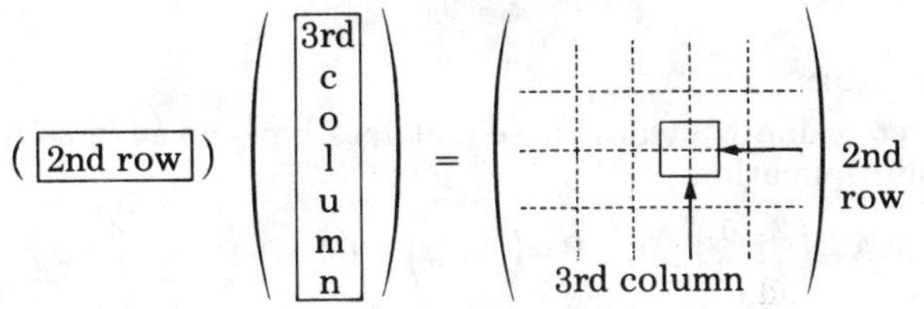

Before multiplying matrices it helps if you:

(a) label the rows of the first matrix and the columns of the second,

(b) work out the order of the answer.

In the following answer each stage of the working is written out in full. You would not be expected to do this in an examination.

Question

Calculate the matrix product

$$\begin{pmatrix} 1 & 3 & -2 \\ 5 & 0 & 1 \end{pmatrix}\begin{pmatrix} 4 & 0 \\ 1 & 2 \\ -3 & -2 \end{pmatrix}$$

Answer

$$\begin{matrix} R_1 \\ R_2 \end{matrix}\begin{pmatrix} 1 & 3 & -2 \\ 5 & 0 & 1 \end{pmatrix}\overset{\begin{matrix} C_1 & C_2 \end{matrix}}{\begin{pmatrix} 4 & 0 \\ 1 & 2 \\ -3 & -2 \end{pmatrix}} = \begin{matrix} R_1 \\ R_2 \end{matrix}\overset{\begin{matrix} C_1 & C_2 \end{matrix}}{\begin{pmatrix} 13 & 10 \\ 17 & -2 \end{pmatrix}}$$

Orders: (2×3) (3×2) — equal → (2×2). Compatible. Answer is order (2×2).

Multiply 1st row R_1 by 1st column C_1:

$$\begin{matrix} R_1 \\ R_2 \end{matrix}\begin{pmatrix} \boxed{1 \quad 3 \quad -2} \\ 5 \quad 0 \quad 1 \end{pmatrix}\begin{pmatrix} \boxed{\begin{matrix} 4 \\ 1 \\ -3 \end{matrix}} & \begin{matrix} 0 \\ 2 \\ -2 \end{matrix} \end{pmatrix} = R_1\begin{pmatrix} \boxed{13} & \square \\ \square & \square \end{pmatrix}$$

$(1\times 4)+(3\times 1)+(-2\times -3)$
$=4+3+6$
$=13$

Multiply 1st row R_1 by 2nd column C_2:

$$\begin{matrix} R_1 \\ R_2 \end{matrix}\begin{pmatrix} \boxed{1 \quad 3 \quad -2} \\ 5 \quad 0 \quad 1 \end{pmatrix}\begin{pmatrix} \begin{matrix} 4 \\ 1 \\ -3 \end{matrix} & \boxed{\begin{matrix} 0 \\ 2 \\ -2 \end{matrix}} \end{pmatrix} = R_1\begin{pmatrix} 13 & \boxed{10} \\ \square & \square \end{pmatrix}$$

$(1\times 0)+(3\times 2)+(-2\times -2)$
$=0+6+4$
$=10$

Multiply 2nd row R_2 by 1st column C_1:

$$\begin{matrix} R_1 \\ R_2 \end{matrix}\begin{pmatrix} 1 \quad 3 \quad -2 \\ \boxed{5 \quad 0 \quad 1} \end{pmatrix}\begin{pmatrix} \boxed{\begin{matrix} 4 \\ 1 \\ -3 \end{matrix}} & \begin{matrix} 0 \\ 2 \\ -2 \end{matrix} \end{pmatrix} = R_2\begin{pmatrix} 13 & 10 \\ \boxed{17} & \square \end{pmatrix}$$

$(5\times 4)+(0\times 1)+(1\times -3)$
$=20+0-3$
$=17$

Multiply 2nd row R_2 by 2nd column C_2:

$$\begin{matrix} R_1 \\ R_2 \end{matrix}\begin{pmatrix} 1 \quad 3 \quad -2 \\ \boxed{5 \quad 0 \quad 1} \end{pmatrix}\begin{pmatrix} \begin{matrix} 4 \\ 1 \\ -3 \end{matrix} & \boxed{\begin{matrix} 0 \\ 2 \\ -2 \end{matrix}} \end{pmatrix} = R_2\begin{pmatrix} 13 & 10 \\ 17 & \boxed{-2} \end{pmatrix}$$

$(5\times 0)+(0\times 2)+(1\times -2)$
$=0+0-2$
$=-2$

It is not possible at this level to give a general rule for matrix multiplication since the compatible matrices can be of different orders. However two common types of matrix multiplications are:

(a) $$\begin{pmatrix} a & b \\ c & d \end{pmatrix}\begin{pmatrix} x \\ y \end{pmatrix} = \begin{pmatrix} ax+by \\ cx+dy \end{pmatrix}$$

Orders: (2×2) $(2\times 1) \longrightarrow (2\times 1)$

(b) $$\begin{pmatrix} a & b \\ c & d \end{pmatrix}\begin{pmatrix} w & x \\ y & z \end{pmatrix} = \begin{pmatrix} aw+by & ax+bz \\ cw+dy & cx+dz \end{pmatrix}$$

Orders: (2×2) $(2\times 2) \longrightarrow (2\times 2)$

In the matrix product **AB**,

B is said to be **pre-multiplied** by **A**,
A is said to be **post-multiplied** by **B**.

The order in which matrix multiplication is done matters. In general, matrix multiplication is *not* commutative, i.e. $\mathbf{AB} \neq \mathbf{BA}$. However it is associative, i.e. $(\mathbf{AB})\mathbf{C} = \mathbf{A}(\mathbf{BC})$.

Remember: the square of **A**, i.e. $\mathbf{A}^2 = \mathbf{AA}$
the cube of **A**, i.e. $\mathbf{A}^3 = \mathbf{AAA}$ or $\mathbf{AA}^2$

and so on ...

Question

Given $\mathbf{X} = \begin{pmatrix} 2 & 0 \\ 1 & -1 \end{pmatrix}$ and $\mathbf{Y} = \begin{pmatrix} 0 & 1 \\ 2 & -3 \end{pmatrix}$

calculate these products: (a) **XY** (b) **YX** (c) $\mathbf{X}^2$

What do your answers to (a) and (b) show you about matrix multiplication?

Answer

$$\text{(a) } \mathbf{XY} = \begin{matrix} R_1 \\ R_2 \end{matrix}\begin{pmatrix} 2 & 0 \\ 1 & -1 \end{pmatrix}\overset{\begin{matrix} C_1 & C_2 \end{matrix}}{\begin{pmatrix} 0 & 1 \\ 2 & -3 \end{pmatrix}} = \begin{pmatrix} 0 & 2 \\ -2 & 4 \end{pmatrix}$$

(b) $\mathbf{YX}=\begin{matrix} \\ R_1 \\ R_2\end{matrix}\begin{matrix} C_1 & C_2 \\ \begin{pmatrix}0 & 1\\2 & -3\end{pmatrix} & \end{matrix}\begin{pmatrix}2 & 0\\1 & -1\end{pmatrix}=\begin{pmatrix}1 & -1\\1 & 3\end{pmatrix}$

From these answers, $\mathbf{XY}\neq\mathbf{YX}$. So matrix multiplication is not commutative.

(c) $\mathbf{X}^2=\mathbf{XX}=\begin{matrix} R_1 \\ R_2\end{matrix}\begin{pmatrix}2 & 0\\1 & -1\end{pmatrix}\begin{matrix} C_1 \; C_2 \\ \end{matrix}\begin{pmatrix}2 & 0\\1 & -1\end{pmatrix}=\begin{pmatrix}4 & 0\\1 & 1\end{pmatrix}$

IDENTITY MATRICES

An **identity matrix** combined with another matrix leaves this other matrix unchanged. There are different types of identity matrices for addition and for multiplication.

For addition

The **identities for addition** are called **zero** or **null** matrices. In a **zero** or **null matrix** every element is zero (0). It is denoted by **O**. For example,

for 2 × 2 matrices, $\mathbf{O}_{2\times 2}=\begin{pmatrix}0 & 0\\0 & 0\end{pmatrix}$

for 1 × 3 matrices, $\mathbf{O}_{1\times 3}=(0 \quad 0 \quad 0)$

Adding a matrix to its zero or null matrix simply gives the original matrix.
If **M** is a matrix and **O** is its null matrix, then

$\mathbf{M}+\mathbf{O}=\mathbf{O}+\mathbf{M}=\mathbf{M}$

For example, for this 2 × 2 matrix

$$\begin{pmatrix}2 & -1\\3 & 0\end{pmatrix}+\begin{pmatrix}0 & 0\\0 & 0\end{pmatrix}=\begin{pmatrix}2 & -1\\3 & 0\end{pmatrix}$$

$$\begin{pmatrix}0 & 0\\0 & 0\end{pmatrix}+\begin{pmatrix}2 & -1\\3 & 0\end{pmatrix}=\begin{pmatrix}2 & -1\\3 & 0\end{pmatrix}$$

For multiplication

The **identities for multiplication** are called **unit** matrices. They are also often called the **identity matrices**. A unit matrix is a square matrix in which each element in the leading diagonal is 1 and every other element is zero. (The **leading diagonal** is the diagonal line of elements from the top left to the bottom right.) It is denoted by **I**. For example

the 2 × 2 identity/unit matrix $\mathbf{I}_2=\begin{pmatrix}1 & 0\\0 & 1\end{pmatrix}$ ← leading diagonal

the 3 × 3 identity/unit matrix $\mathbf{I}_3=\begin{pmatrix}1 & 0 & 0\\0 & 1 & 0\\0 & 0 & 1\end{pmatrix}$ ← leading diagonal

Multiplying a matrix by its unit matrix gives the original matrix.
If **M** is a matrix and **I** is its unit matrix, then

$\mathbf{IM}=\mathbf{MI}=\mathbf{M}$

Although matrix multiplication is, in general, not commutative, pre- or post-multiplying by a unit matrix gives the same answer. For example,

$$\begin{pmatrix}1 & 0\\0 & 1\end{pmatrix}\begin{pmatrix}2 & -1\\3 & 0\end{pmatrix}=\begin{pmatrix}2 & -1\\3 & 0\end{pmatrix}\begin{pmatrix}1 & 0\\0 & 1\end{pmatrix}=\begin{pmatrix}2 & -1\\3 & 0\end{pmatrix}$$

INVERSE MATRICES

An **inverse matrix** combined with another matrix gives the identity matrix. The inverse depends on whether the matrices are combined by addition or multiplication.

For addition

Adding a matrix and its additive inverse gives its zero matrix.

If **M** is a matrix and **O** is its zero matrix, then the inverse of **M** for addition is $-\mathbf{M}$ and

$\mathbf{M}+(-\mathbf{M})=(-\mathbf{M})+\mathbf{M}=\mathbf{O}$

To find the additive inverse of a matrix, change the sign of each element. For example,

the additive inverse of $\begin{pmatrix}-2 & 1\\3 & -1\end{pmatrix}$

is $-\begin{pmatrix}-2 & 1\\3 & -1\end{pmatrix}$ or $\begin{pmatrix}2 & -1\\-3 & 1\end{pmatrix}$

since $\begin{pmatrix}-2 & 1\\3 & -1\end{pmatrix}+\begin{pmatrix}2 & -1\\-3 & 1\end{pmatrix}=\begin{pmatrix}0 & 0\\0 & 0\end{pmatrix}$

For multiplication

Not all matrices have inverses for multiplication. It is only possible to calculate inverses for multiplication for square matrices. At this level only the inverses of 2 × 2 matrices are studied.
If a square matrix **M** has an inverse $\mathbf{M}^{-1}$ for multiplication, then

$\mathbf{MM}^{-1}=\mathbf{M}^{-1}\mathbf{M}=\mathbf{I}$

i.e. multiplying **M** and its inverse gives their unit matrix. The order does not matter.
For example, for the 2 × 2 matrices in these multiplications:

$$\begin{pmatrix}7 & 4\\5 & 3\end{pmatrix}\begin{pmatrix}3 & -4\\-5 & 7\end{pmatrix}=\begin{pmatrix}3 & -4\\-5 & 7\end{pmatrix}\begin{pmatrix}7 & 4\\5 & 3\end{pmatrix}=\begin{pmatrix}1 & 0\\0 & 1\end{pmatrix}$$

$\begin{pmatrix}3 & -4\\-5 & 7\end{pmatrix}$ is the inverse of $\begin{pmatrix}7 & 4\\5 & 3\end{pmatrix}$

and $\begin{pmatrix}7 & 4\\5 & 3\end{pmatrix}$ is the inverse of $\begin{pmatrix}3 & -4\\-5 & 7\end{pmatrix}$

The **determinant** of a square matrix *determines* (and so tells you) whether the matrix has an inverse or not.
The determinant of a 2 × 2 matrix $\mathbf{A}=\begin{pmatrix}a & b\\c & d\end{pmatrix}$ is the number $ad-bc$. It is usually written as det **A** or $|\mathbf{A}|$.

If the determinant of a matrix is zero, then the matrix does *not* have an inverse. It is called a **singular matrix**.
If the determinant of a matrix is *not* zero, then the matrix has an inverse. The matrix is called a **non-singular matrix**.

Question

Determine which of these matrices have an inverse for multiplication.

(a) $\mathbf{A}=\begin{pmatrix}2 & 1\\4 & 3\end{pmatrix}$ (b) $\mathbf{B}=\begin{pmatrix}6 & 3\\4 & 2\end{pmatrix}$ (c) $\mathbf{C}=\begin{pmatrix}-1 & 4\\2 & 3\end{pmatrix}$

Answer

(a) For $\mathbf{A}=\begin{pmatrix}2 & 1\\4 & 3\end{pmatrix}$ det $\mathbf{A}=(2\times 3)-(1\times 4)$

$=6-4=2$

So **A** has an inverse (since det $\mathbf{A}\neq 0$).

(b) For $\mathbf{B}=\begin{pmatrix}6 & 3\\4 & 2\end{pmatrix}$ det $\mathbf{B}=(6\times 2)-(3\times 4)$

$=12-12=0$

So **B** does not have an inverse (since det $\mathbf{B}=0$).

(c) For $\mathbf{C}=\begin{pmatrix}-1 & 4\\2 & 3\end{pmatrix}$ det $\mathbf{C}=(-1\times 3)-(4\times 2)$

$=-3-8=-11$

So **C** has an inverse (since det $\mathbf{C}\neq 0$).

The multiplicative inverse of a non-singular 2 × 2 matrix

$\mathbf{A}=\begin{pmatrix}a & b\\c & d\end{pmatrix}$

is given by:

$$\mathbf{A}^{-1}=\frac{1}{\det\mathbf{A}}\begin{pmatrix}d & -b\\-c & a\end{pmatrix}=\frac{1}{ad-bc}\begin{pmatrix}d & -b\\-c & a\end{pmatrix}$$

From this you can see that if det $\mathbf{A}=0$, then the inverse $\mathbf{A}^{-1}$ does not exist because $\frac{1}{0}$ does not exist. This is why det $\mathbf{A}$ determines whether $\mathbf{A}$ has an inverse or not.

So to find the inverse of $\mathbf{A}=\begin{pmatrix} a & b \\ c & d \end{pmatrix}$

1 Exchange the elements in the leading diagonal. $\begin{pmatrix} d & b \\ c & a \end{pmatrix}$

2 Change the signs of the elements on the other diagonal. $\begin{pmatrix} d & -b \\ -c & a \end{pmatrix}$

3 Multiply by $\frac{1}{\det \mathbf{A}}$ $\qquad \frac{1}{\det \mathbf{A}}\begin{pmatrix} d & -b \\ -c & a \end{pmatrix}$

i.e. $\frac{1}{ad-bc}$ or $\frac{1}{ad-bc}\begin{pmatrix} d & -b \\ -c & a \end{pmatrix}$

Always **check** that your inverse is correct. Multiply the matrix by your inverse and check that it gives

$$\mathbf{I}=\begin{pmatrix} 1 & 0 \\ 0 & 1 \end{pmatrix}$$

Question

For $\mathbf{A}=\begin{pmatrix} 3 & 2 \\ -5 & 4 \end{pmatrix}$ find its multiplicative inverse $\mathbf{A}^{-1}$.

Show that $\mathbf{AA}^{-1}=\mathbf{I}$.

Answer

For $\mathbf{A}=\begin{pmatrix} 3 & 2 \\ -5 & 4 \end{pmatrix}$ det $\mathbf{A}=(3\times 4)-(2\times -5)$

$=12-(-10)=22$

$$\text{So } \mathbf{A}^{-1}=\frac{1}{22}\begin{pmatrix} 4 & -2 \\ 5 & 3 \end{pmatrix}$$

$$=\begin{pmatrix} \frac{4}{22} & -\frac{2}{22} \\ \frac{5}{22} & \frac{3}{22} \end{pmatrix}$$

$$\mathbf{AA}^{-1}=\begin{pmatrix} 3 & 2 \\ -5 & 4 \end{pmatrix}\begin{pmatrix} \frac{4}{22} & -\frac{2}{22} \\ \frac{5}{22} & \frac{3}{22} \end{pmatrix}$$

$$=\begin{pmatrix} \frac{22}{22} & 0 \\ 0 & \frac{22}{22} \end{pmatrix}$$

$$=\begin{pmatrix} 1 & 0 \\ 0 & 1 \end{pmatrix}=\mathbf{I}$$

NETWORKS AND ROUTE MATRICES

A **network** is a diagram of connected lines.
The lines are called **arcs**.

The points at which the lines meet are called **nodes**.

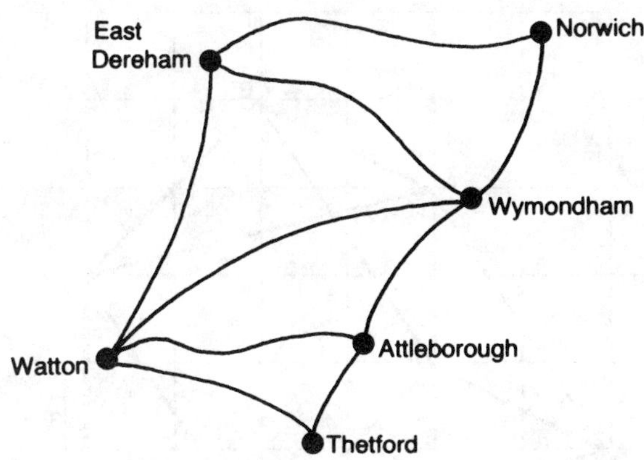

For example, this simple road map is a network.
The lines for the roads are the arcs.
The points for the towns are the nodes.

A **route matrix** represents the routes on a network. Each element of the matrix gives the number of different routes between two nodes along arcs. The numbers can be worked out from the network.

For a route matrix the shape or length of a route does not matter. Where it starts and finishes is important. For example,

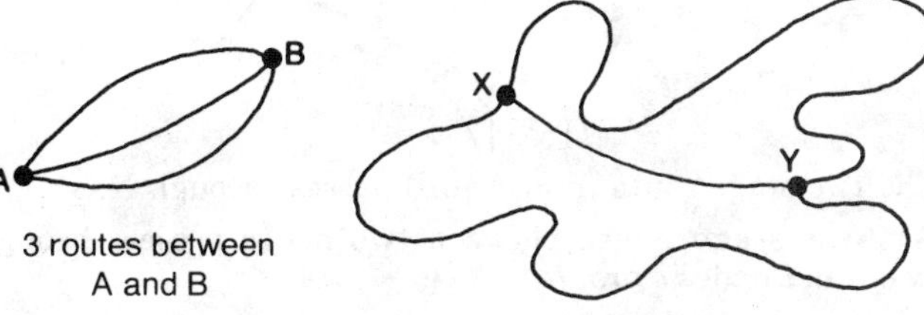

3 routes between A and B

3 routes between X and Y

A route can be either 'two-way' or 'one-way' (just like roads). A line (arc) *without* an arrowhead shows a *two-way* route.

For example, on this network there is
a route from C to D and
a route from D to C.

An arrowhead on the line (arc) shows the *direction* of the route.

For example, on this network there is only one route from X to Y (like a one-way street).

One-stage routes

A **one-stage** or **direct route** connects two nodes directly. The route must not pass through any other node *en route*.

For example,

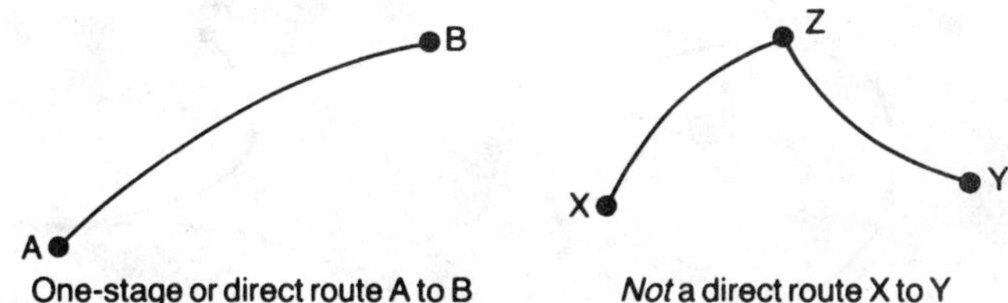

One-stage or direct route A to B

Not a direct route X to Y

A **loop route** is a special 'one-stage' route. It goes from a node and back again without passing through any other place.

Loop route from A to A

The one-stage route matrix is often just called *the* route matrix.

Question

This map shows four towns connected by roads.

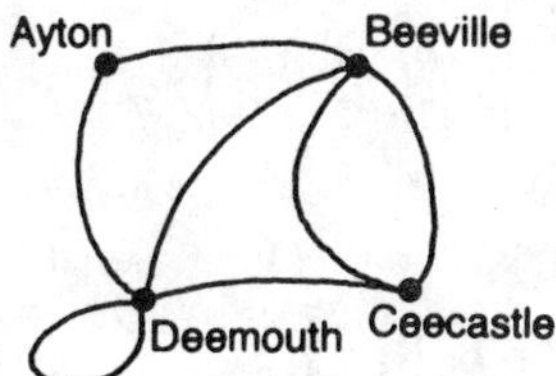

Work out the one-stage route matrix $\mathbf{R}_1$ for this road system.

Answer

One-stage route matrix $\mathbf{R}_1$

		To			
		Ayton	Beeville	Ceecastle	Deemouth
From	Ayton	0	1	0	1
	Beeville	1	0	2	1
	Ceecastle	0	2	0	1
	Deemouth	1	1	1	2

Multi-stage routes

Routes can have more than one stage.
A **two-stage route** between two nodes passes through only one other node *en route*.

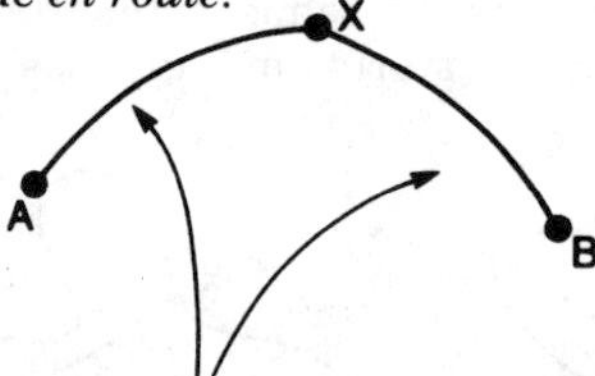

The two-stage route from A to B passes through X.
A **three-stage route** between two nodes passes through two other nodes *en route*.

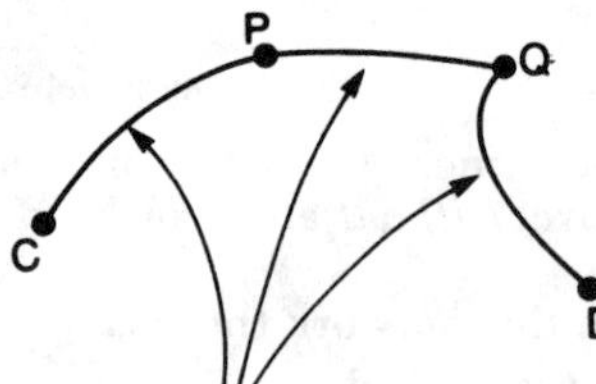

The three-stage route from C to D passes through P and Q.

Question

From the road map on the previous page
(a) sketch all the two-stage routes from Beeville to Deemouth,
(b) work out the two-stage route matrix $\mathbf{R}_2$,
(c) calculate the square of $\mathbf{R}_1$, the one-stage matrix. Comment on your result.

Answer

(a)

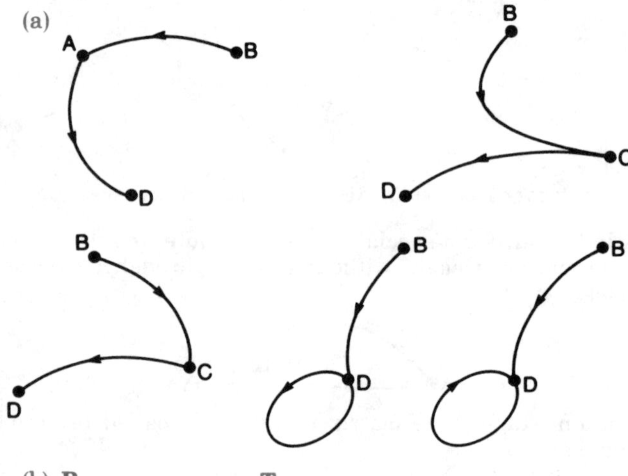

(b) $\mathbf{R}_2$

		To			
		A	B	C	D
From	A	2	1	3	3
	B	1	6	1	5
	C	3	1	5	4
	D	3	5	4	7

(c) $\mathbf{R}_1{}^2$

$$\mathbf{R}_1{}^2=\mathbf{R}_1\mathbf{R}_1=\begin{pmatrix}0&1&0&1\\1&0&2&1\\0&2&0&1\\1&1&1&2\end{pmatrix}\begin{pmatrix}0&1&0&1\\1&0&2&1\\0&2&0&1\\1&1&1&2\end{pmatrix}$$

$$=\begin{pmatrix}2&1&3&3\\1&6&1&5\\3&1&5&4\\3&5&4&7\end{pmatrix}$$

The square of $\mathbf{R}_1$, the one-stage route matrix, equals $\mathbf{R}_2$ the two-stage route matrix.

For any network the one-stage route matrix can be used to give the two-stage, three-stage, ... route matrices.

The *square* of the one-stage route matrix gives the *two*-stage route matrix.
The *cube* of the one-stage route matrix gives the *three*-stage route matrix.
So if $\mathbf{R}_1$, $\mathbf{R}_2$, $\mathbf{R}_3$, ... are the one-stage, two-stage, three-stage, ... route matrices for a network, then:

$\mathbf{R}_1{}^2=\mathbf{R}_2$
$\mathbf{R}_1{}^3=\mathbf{R}_3$
$\mathbf{R}_1{}^4=\mathbf{R}_4$

and so on ...

3.30 Matrix transformations

Many simple geometrical transformations can be described using matrices. Some transformations are easier to describe using matrices than words.
A transformation maps an object point P(*x*, *y*) to an image point P′(*x*′, *y*′). The matrix for that transformation changes the position vector $\begin{pmatrix}x\\y\end{pmatrix}$ of the object point P into the position vector $\begin{pmatrix}x'\\y'\end{pmatrix}$ of the image point P′.

A column vector (or 2×1 matrix) can describe a translation.
A 2×2 matrix can describe other transformations such as reflections, rotations and enlargements.

TRANSLATIONS BY VECTOR (OR 2×1 MATRIX)

The **column vector** $\begin{pmatrix}a\\b\end{pmatrix}$ describes a translation of
a units in the *x*-direction,
b units in the *y*-direction.

Different directions have different signs.
In the *x*-direction:
to the right → is +,
to the left ← is −
In the *y*-direction:
up ↑ is +,
down ↓ is −

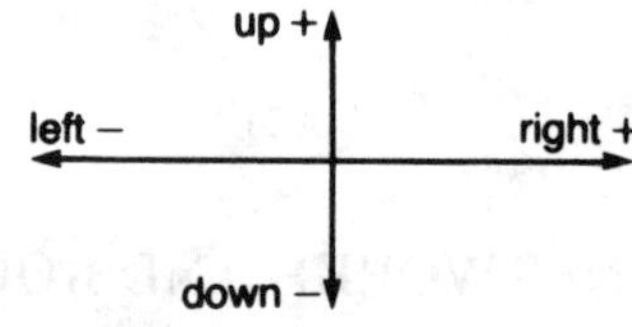

In a translation, every point on a shape moves the same amount in the same direction.
For example, triangle ABC has been translated to triangle A′B′C′.

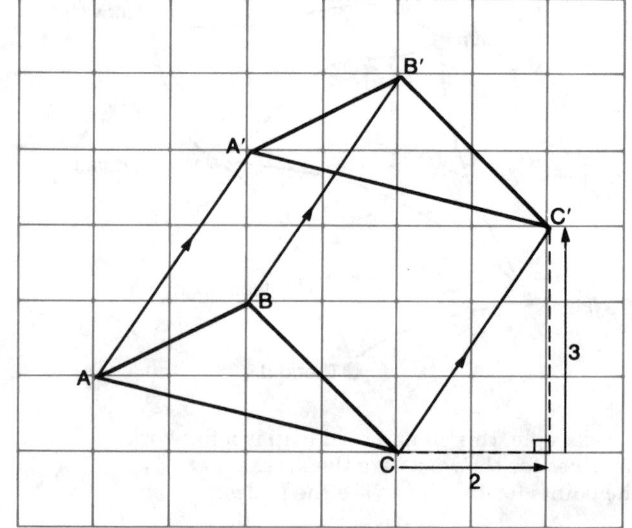

The lines AA′, BB′, CC′ are all parallel and equal in length. So the vectors

$$\overrightarrow{AA'}=\overrightarrow{BB'}=\overrightarrow{CC'}=\begin{pmatrix}2\\3\end{pmatrix}$$

The vector $\begin{pmatrix}2\\3\end{pmatrix}$ completely describes the translation.

To find the vector for a translation, you only need to work out the movement of one translated point.

Question

Find the column vector which translates shape A to (a) shape B, (b) shape C.

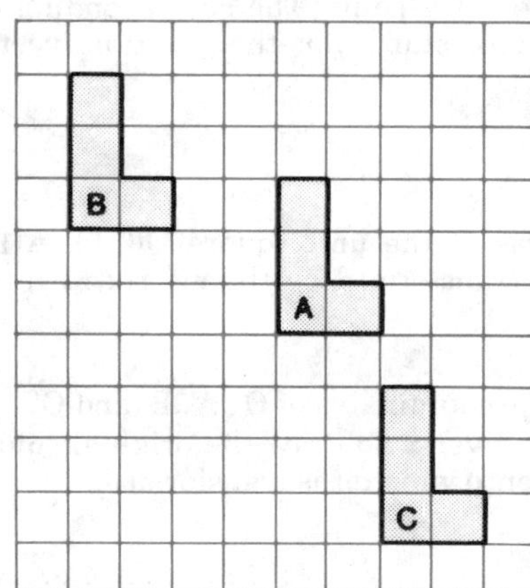

Answer

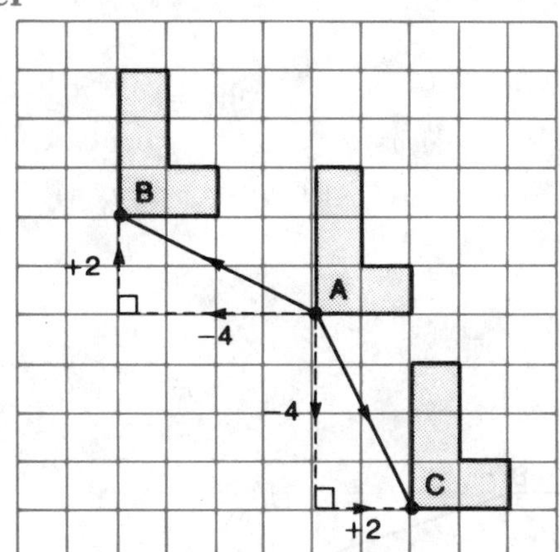

From the diagram, the column vector

(a) for A→B is $\begin{pmatrix}-4\\2\end{pmatrix}$ *4 to the left* *2 up*

(b) for A→C is $\begin{pmatrix}2\\-4\end{pmatrix}$ *2 to the right* *4 down*

The image of any point P(x, y) after a translation can be found by **vector addition**.

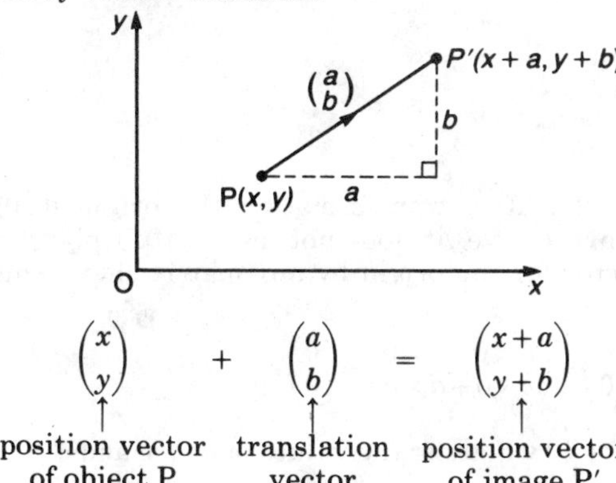

$$\begin{pmatrix}x\\y\end{pmatrix}+\begin{pmatrix}a\\b\end{pmatrix}=\begin{pmatrix}x+a\\y+b\end{pmatrix}$$

position vector of object P — translation vector — position vector of image P′

Question

Point P(3, 4) is translated to points Q, R, S and T by the column vectors $\begin{pmatrix}4\\0\end{pmatrix}$, $\begin{pmatrix}0\\-6\end{pmatrix}$, $\begin{pmatrix}2\\-3\end{pmatrix}$ and $\begin{pmatrix}-5\\-7\end{pmatrix}$ respectively.

Work out the coordinates of each of these image points. On the given grid plot the point P and each of its image points.

Answer

The position vector of P is $\begin{pmatrix}3\\4\end{pmatrix}$.

The position vector of Q is given by

$$\begin{pmatrix}3\\4\end{pmatrix}+\begin{pmatrix}4\\0\end{pmatrix}=\begin{pmatrix}7\\4\end{pmatrix}$$

So the coordinates of Q are (7, 4).
The position vector of R is given by

$$\begin{pmatrix}3\\4\end{pmatrix}+\begin{pmatrix}0\\-6\end{pmatrix}=\begin{pmatrix}3\\-2\end{pmatrix}$$

So the coordinates of R are (3, −2).
The position vector of S is given by

$$\begin{pmatrix}3\\4\end{pmatrix}+\begin{pmatrix}2\\-3\end{pmatrix}=\begin{pmatrix}5\\1\end{pmatrix}$$

So the coordinates of S are (5, 1).
The position vector of T is given by

$$\begin{pmatrix}3\\4\end{pmatrix}+\begin{pmatrix}-5\\-7\end{pmatrix}=\begin{pmatrix}-2\\-3\end{pmatrix}$$

So the coordinates of T are (−2, −3).

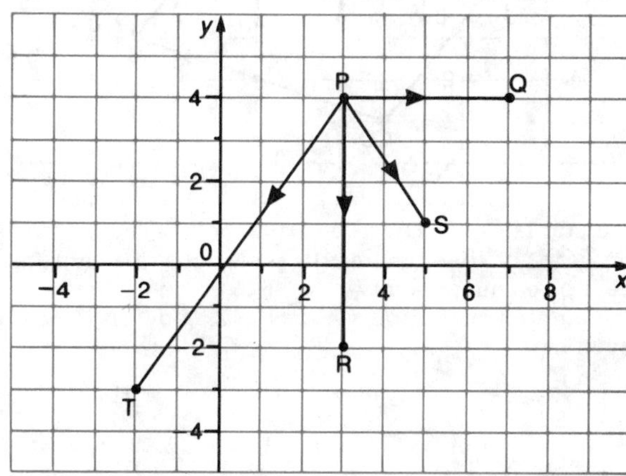

The **identity** translation leaves all points unchanged. It is represented by the zero vector $\begin{pmatrix}0\\0\end{pmatrix}$.

The **inverse** of a transformation moves a point *back* to its original position.

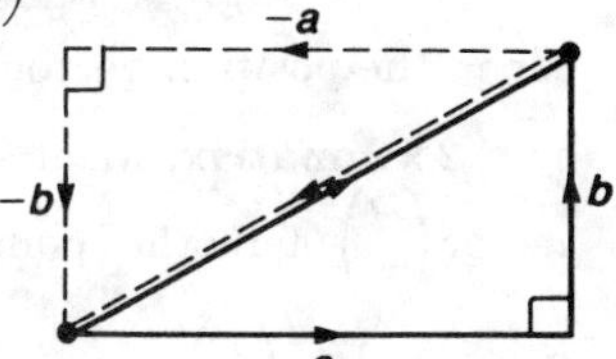

The inverse of the translation $\begin{pmatrix}a\\b\end{pmatrix}$ is $\begin{pmatrix}-a\\-b\end{pmatrix}$.

COMBINED TRANSLATIONS

A translation followed by a translation is equivalent to a single translation. The vector for this single translation can be found by drawing or calculation.
To calculate the single vector for combined translations, add the vectors representing them.

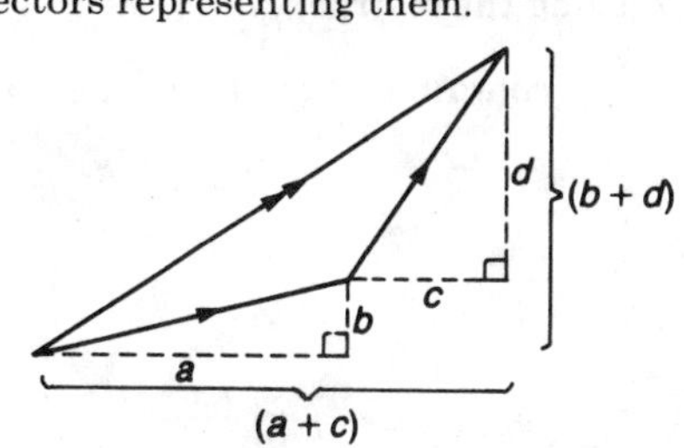

A translation $\begin{pmatrix} a \\ b \end{pmatrix}$ followed by a translation $\begin{pmatrix} c \\ d \end{pmatrix}$ is equivalent to the single translation $\begin{pmatrix} a+c \\ b+d \end{pmatrix}$.

Question

On the given grid plot the point P(3, 4). Plot the image of P

(a) after translation $\mathbf{X}=\begin{pmatrix} -6 \\ -2 \end{pmatrix}$ (call it A)

(b) after translation $\mathbf{Y}=\begin{pmatrix} 4 \\ -5 \end{pmatrix}$ (call it B)

(c) after translation **X** followed by **Y** (call it C)

(d) after translation **Y** followed by **X** (call it D)

What do you notice about the points for (c) and (d)? Calculate the single translation vector which is equivalent to **X** combined with **Y**.

Answer

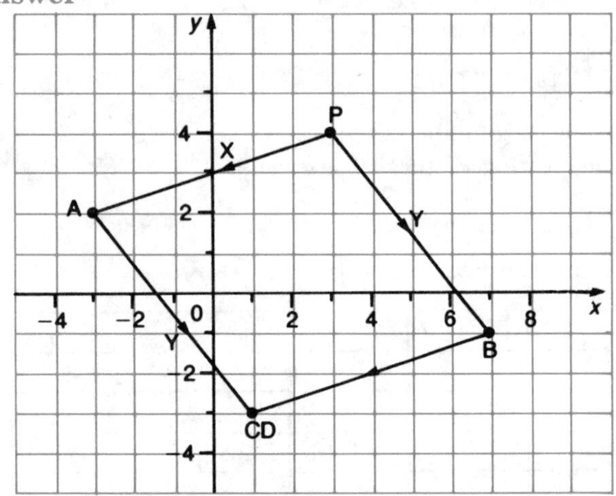

The points C and D are the same point. This shows that the order of the combined translations does not matter (i.e. it is commutative).

The single translation vector for **X** combined with **Y** is given by

$$\begin{pmatrix} -6 \\ -2 \end{pmatrix}+\begin{pmatrix} 4 \\ -5 \end{pmatrix} = \begin{pmatrix} -2 \\ -7 \end{pmatrix}$$

↑ *vector for X* ↑ *vector for Y* ↑ *vector for X combined with Y*

TRANSFORMATIONS BY 2 × 2 MATRICES

When the position vector $\begin{pmatrix} x \\ y \end{pmatrix}$ of a point is pre-multiplied by a **2 × 2 matrix**, **M**, it is transformed into the position vector $\begin{pmatrix} x' \\ y' \end{pmatrix}$ of another point.

So $\mathbf{M}\begin{pmatrix} x \\ y \end{pmatrix}=\begin{pmatrix} x' \\ y' \end{pmatrix}$

In general, the matrix $\mathbf{M}=\begin{pmatrix} a & b \\ c & d \end{pmatrix}$ transforms $\begin{pmatrix} x \\ y \end{pmatrix}$ like this.

$$\begin{pmatrix} a & b \\ c & d \end{pmatrix}\begin{pmatrix} x \\ y \end{pmatrix}=\begin{pmatrix} ax+by \\ cx+dy \end{pmatrix}$$

Question

Transform the vertices of the triangle A(3, 1), B(−2, −1) and C(−4, 2) using the matrix $\begin{pmatrix} 2 & 0 \\ 0 & 1 \end{pmatrix}$.

Write down the coordinates of the image points A′, B′ and C′.

Answer

For A(3, 1)

$$\begin{pmatrix} 2 & 0 \\ 0 & 1 \end{pmatrix}\begin{pmatrix} 3 \\ 1 \end{pmatrix}=\begin{pmatrix} 6 \\ 1 \end{pmatrix}$$

So A′ is (6, 1).

For B(−2, −1)

$$\begin{pmatrix} 2 & 0 \\ 0 & 1 \end{pmatrix}\begin{pmatrix} -2 \\ -1 \end{pmatrix}=\begin{pmatrix} -4 \\ -1 \end{pmatrix}$$

So B′ is (−4, −1).

For C(−4, 2)

$$\begin{pmatrix} 2 & 0 \\ 0 & 1 \end{pmatrix}\begin{pmatrix} -4 \\ 2 \end{pmatrix}=\begin{pmatrix} -8 \\ 2 \end{pmatrix}$$

So C′ is (−8, 2).

When transforming a set of points, e.g. the vertices of a polygon, by a 2 × 2 matrix you can represent the points by a single matrix. Each column in the matrix stands for the position vector of a point. The corresponding columns in the final matrix stand for the position vectors of the images of the points.

Question

The vertices of the unit square O(0, 0), A(1, 0), B(1, 1), C(0, 1) are transformed by the matrix **M** into O′A′B′C′.

$\mathbf{M}=\begin{pmatrix} 3 & 1 \\ -1 & 1 \end{pmatrix}$

(a) Find the coordinates of O′, A′, B′ and C′.

(b) On the given grid draw the original square and the shape onto which it is transformed.

Answer

(a)

$$\underset{\text{matrix M}}{\begin{pmatrix} 3 & 1 \\ -1 & 1 \end{pmatrix}}\ \underset{\text{object}}{\overset{\text{O A B C}}{\begin{pmatrix} 0 & 1 & 1 & 0 \\ 0 & 0 & 1 & 1 \end{pmatrix}}}=\underset{\text{image}}{\overset{\text{O′ A′ B′ C′}}{\begin{pmatrix} 0 & 3 & 4 & 1 \\ 0 & -1 & 0 & 1 \end{pmatrix}}}$$

The coordinates are: O′(0, 0), A′(3, −1), B′(4, 0) and C′(1, 1).

(b)

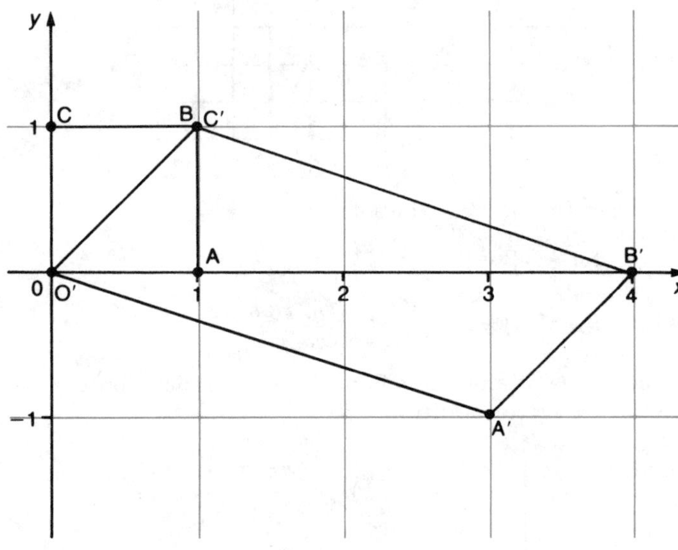

Under a 2 × 2 matrix transformation the origin (0, 0) is always **invariant**, i.e. it does not move. Multiplying the position vector for the origin by any matrix shows this is true.

$$\begin{pmatrix} a & b \\ c & d \end{pmatrix}\begin{pmatrix} 0 \\ 0 \end{pmatrix}=\begin{pmatrix} a\times 0+b\times 0 \\ c\times 0+d\times 0 \end{pmatrix}=\begin{pmatrix} 0 \\ 0 \end{pmatrix}$$

The result is $\begin{pmatrix} 0 \\ 0 \end{pmatrix}$ whatever the values of a, b, c and d.

This means that 2 × 2 matrices can only represent transformations in which the origin is invariant, for example rotations about the origin and reflections in a mirror line through the origin.

SOME SIMPLE TRANSFORMATIONS AND THEIR MATRICES

A summary of some simple transformations and the matrices that produce them is given below.

Reflections

(a) Reflection in the x-axis

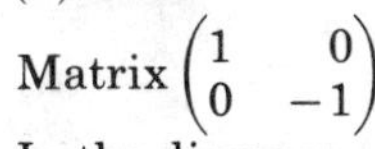

Matrix $\begin{pmatrix}1 & 0\\ 0 & -1\end{pmatrix}$

In the diagram

$P(x, y) \rightarrow P'(x, -y)$

Using the matrix

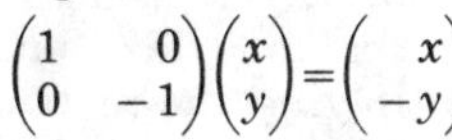

$$\begin{pmatrix}1 & 0\\ 0 & -1\end{pmatrix}\begin{pmatrix}x\\ y\end{pmatrix}=\begin{pmatrix}x\\ -y\end{pmatrix}$$

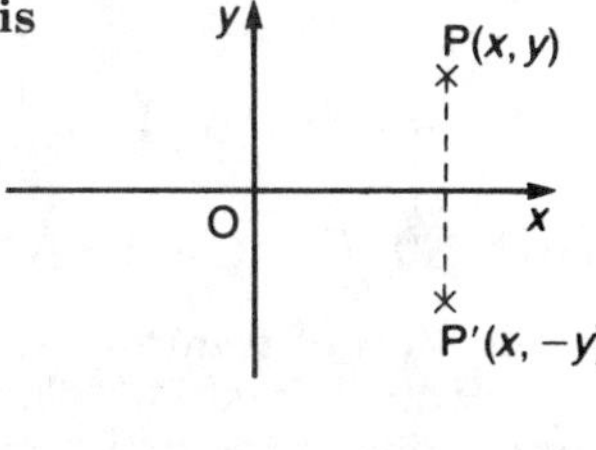

(b) Reflection in the y-axis

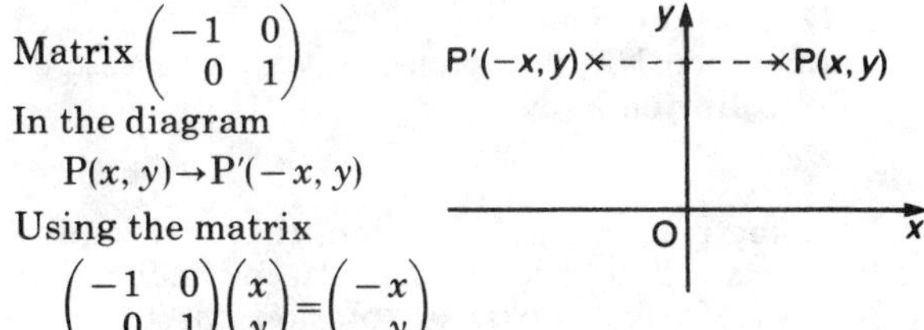

Matrix $\begin{pmatrix}-1 & 0\\ 0 & 1\end{pmatrix}$

In the diagram

$P(x, y) \rightarrow P'(-x, y)$

Using the matrix

$$\begin{pmatrix}-1 & 0\\ 0 & 1\end{pmatrix}\begin{pmatrix}x\\ y\end{pmatrix}=\begin{pmatrix}-x\\ y\end{pmatrix}$$

(c) Reflection in the line $y=x$

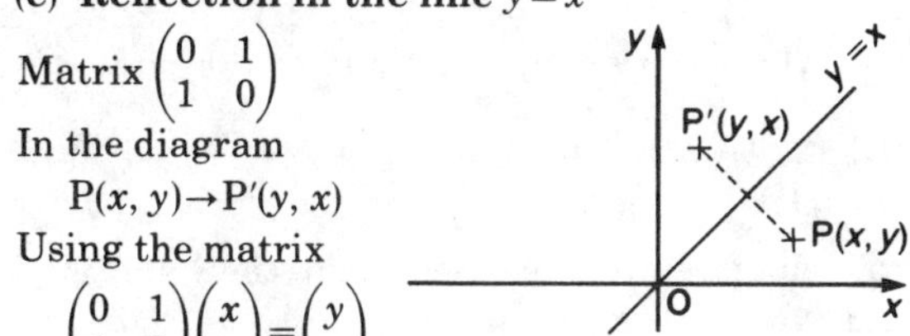

Matrix $\begin{pmatrix}0 & 1\\ 1 & 0\end{pmatrix}$

In the diagram

$P(x, y) \rightarrow P'(y, x)$

Using the matrix

$$\begin{pmatrix}0 & 1\\ 1 & 0\end{pmatrix}\begin{pmatrix}x\\ y\end{pmatrix}=\begin{pmatrix}y\\ x\end{pmatrix}$$

(d) Reflection in the line $y=-x$

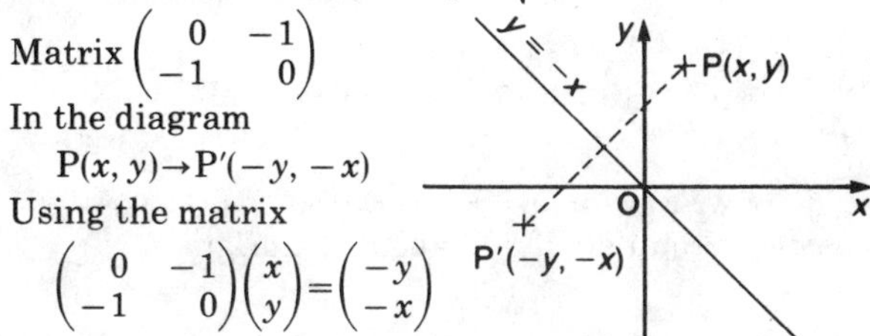

Matrix $\begin{pmatrix}0 & -1\\ -1 & 0\end{pmatrix}$

In the diagram

$P(x, y) \rightarrow P'(-y, -x)$

Using the matrix

$$\begin{pmatrix}0 & -1\\ -1 & 0\end{pmatrix}\begin{pmatrix}x\\ y\end{pmatrix}=\begin{pmatrix}-y\\ -x\end{pmatrix}$$

Rotations about origin O

(a) Rotation of $+90°$ (or $-270°$)

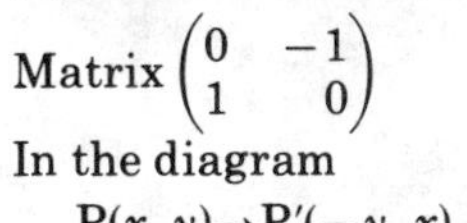

Matrix $\begin{pmatrix}0 & -1\\ 1 & 0\end{pmatrix}$

In the diagram

$P(x, y) \rightarrow P'(-y, x)$

Using the matrix

$$\begin{pmatrix}0 & -1\\ 1 & 0\end{pmatrix}\begin{pmatrix}x\\ y\end{pmatrix}=\begin{pmatrix}-y\\ x\end{pmatrix}$$

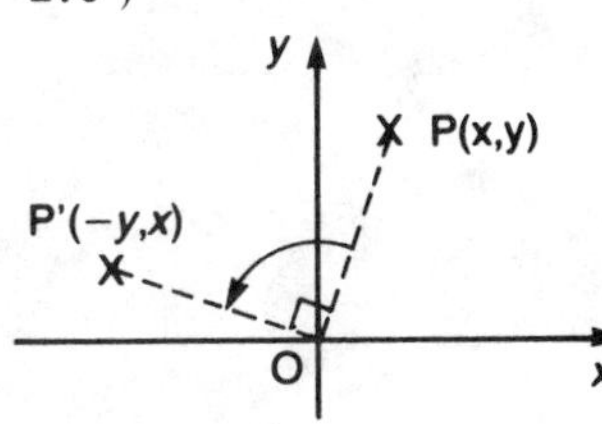

(b) Rotation of $+180°$ (or $-180°$)

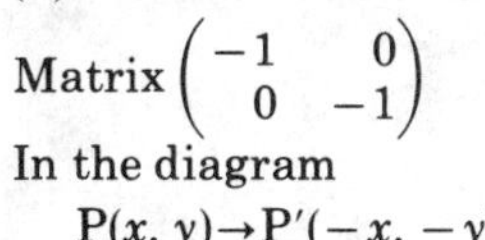

Matrix $\begin{pmatrix}-1 & 0\\ 0 & -1\end{pmatrix}$

In the diagram

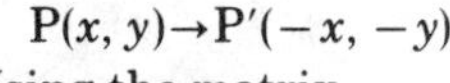

$P(x, y) \rightarrow P'(-x, -y)$

Using the matrix

$$\begin{pmatrix}-1 & 0\\ 0 & -1\end{pmatrix}\begin{pmatrix}x\\ y\end{pmatrix}=\begin{pmatrix}-x\\ -y\end{pmatrix}$$

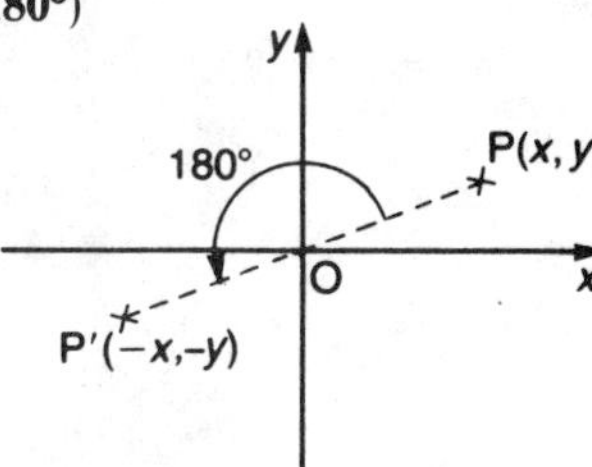

(c) Rotation of $+270°$ (or $-90°$)

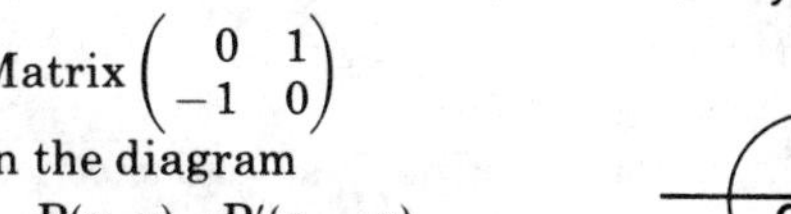

Matrix $\begin{pmatrix}0 & 1\\ -1 & 0\end{pmatrix}$

In the diagram

$P(x, y) \rightarrow P'(y, -x)$

Using the matrix

$$\begin{pmatrix}0 & 1\\ -1 & 0\end{pmatrix}\begin{pmatrix}x\\ y\end{pmatrix}=\begin{pmatrix}y\\ -x\end{pmatrix}$$

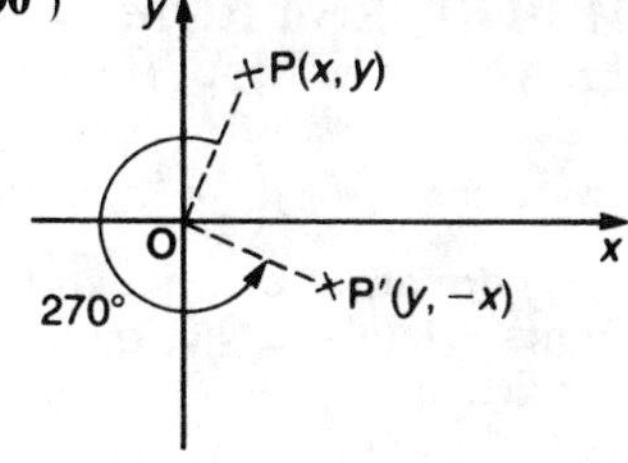

Enlargements

The matrix $\begin{pmatrix}k & 0\\ 0 & k\end{pmatrix}$ represents an enlargement of scale factor k, with centre the origin O.

In the diagram

$P(x, y) \rightarrow P'(kx, ky)$

Using the matrix

$$\begin{pmatrix}k & 0\\ 0 & k\end{pmatrix}\begin{pmatrix}x\\ y\end{pmatrix}=\begin{pmatrix}kx\\ ky\end{pmatrix}$$

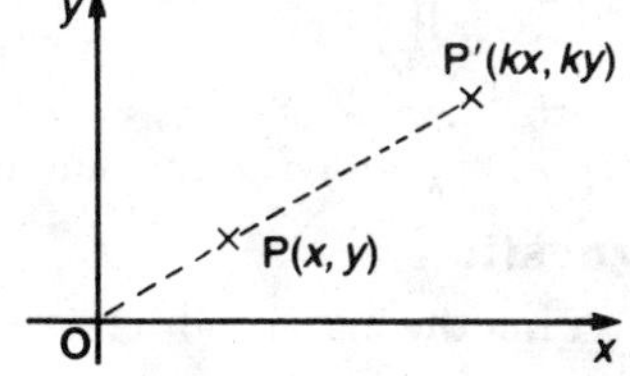

The determinant of the matrix, k^2, is the **area factor** of the enlargement.

IDENTITY AND INVERSE TRANSFORMATIONS

The **identity** transformation leaves a point unchanged. It is represented by the 2×2 identity matrix $\begin{pmatrix}1 & 0\\ 0 & 1\end{pmatrix}$.

The **inverse** of a transformation moves a point back to its original position. It is represented by the inverse of its transformation matrix.

If $\mathbf{M}=\begin{pmatrix}a & b\\ c & d\end{pmatrix}$ is the matrix of a transformation and $|\mathbf{M}| \neq 0$, then the inverse matrix of $\mathbf{M}$,

$$\mathbf{M}^{-1}=\frac{1}{ad-bc}\begin{pmatrix}d & -b\\ -c & a\end{pmatrix}$$

is the matrix of the inverse transformation.

Question

A point P(7, 3) is transformed to P′ by the matrix $\mathbf{M}=\begin{pmatrix}0 & 2\\ 1 & 0\end{pmatrix}$.

(a) Find the coordinates of P′.

(b) Find the inverse of **M** and show that it returns the point P′ to its original position P.

Answer

(a) The coordinates of P′ are given by

$$\begin{pmatrix}0 & 2\\ 1 & 0\end{pmatrix}\overset{P}{\begin{pmatrix}7\\ 3\end{pmatrix}}=\overset{P'}{\begin{pmatrix}6\\ 7\end{pmatrix}}$$

i.e. P′ is (6, 7).

(b) The inverse of $\begin{pmatrix}0 & 2\\ 1 & 0\end{pmatrix}$ is given by

$$\frac{1}{-2}\begin{pmatrix}0 & -2\\ -1 & 0\end{pmatrix}=\begin{pmatrix}0 & 1\\ \frac{1}{2} & 0\end{pmatrix}$$

Applying this matrix to the position vector of P′ gives

$$\begin{pmatrix}0 & 1\\ \frac{1}{2} & 0\end{pmatrix}\overset{P'}{\begin{pmatrix}6\\ 7\end{pmatrix}}=\begin{pmatrix}7\\ 3\end{pmatrix}$$

This is the position vector of P(7, 3). So P′ has been mapped back to P.

MATRICES FROM TRANSFORMATIONS

The matrix $\begin{pmatrix} a & b \\ c & d \end{pmatrix}$ representing a geometrical transformation can be worked out from the images of the points P(1, 0) and Q(0, 1).
For P(1, 0)

$$\begin{pmatrix} a & b \\ c & d \end{pmatrix}\begin{pmatrix} 1 \\ 0 \end{pmatrix}=\begin{pmatrix} a \\ c \end{pmatrix}$$

So the image of P is (a, c). These coordinates give the values of a and c in the matrix.
For Q(0, 1)

$$\begin{pmatrix} a & b \\ c & d \end{pmatrix}\begin{pmatrix} 0 \\ 1 \end{pmatrix}=\begin{pmatrix} b \\ d \end{pmatrix}$$

So the image of Q is (b, d). These coordinates give the values of b and d in the matrix.

Question

Find the matrix which represents reflection in $y=-x$.

Answer

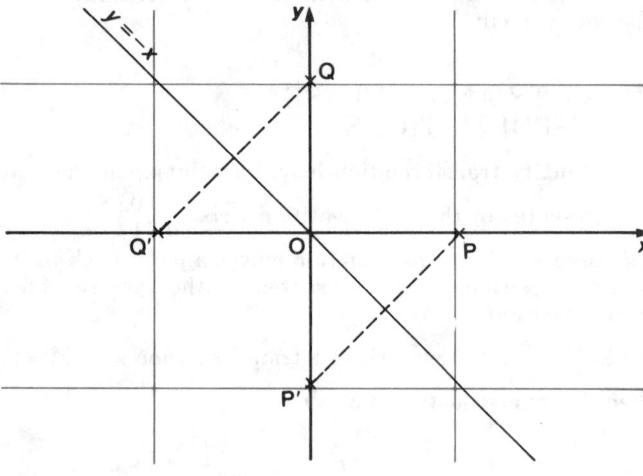

From the diagram,

P(1, 0)→P′(0, −1)

Q(0, 1)→Q′(−1, 0)

If $\begin{pmatrix} a & b \\ c & d \end{pmatrix}$ is the matrix for this transformation, then

$$\overset{}{\begin{pmatrix} a & b \\ c & d \end{pmatrix}}\overset{P\ \ Q}{\begin{pmatrix} 1 & 0 \\ 0 & 1 \end{pmatrix}}=\overset{P'\ \ \ Q'}{\begin{pmatrix} 0 & -1 \\ -1 & 0 \end{pmatrix}}$$

object *image*

Multiplying this gives

$a=0, \quad b=-1$
$c=-1, \quad d=0$

So the matrix is $\begin{pmatrix} 0 & -1 \\ -1 & 0 \end{pmatrix}$

COMBINATION OF TRANSFORMATIONS

A **combination** of transformations can be represented by a **single** transformation. The matrix for this single transformation can be found by multiplying the matrices of the combined transformations. The order in which the multiplication is written **is** important. (Matrix multiplication is *not* commutative.)
If **M** and **N** are the matrices of the two combined transformations, then **NM** is the matrix which represents the result of **M followed by N**.

Question

Show, by using matrix multiplication, that a reflection in the line $y=x$ followed by a reflection in the y-axis is equivalent to an anticlockwise rotation through 90° about the origin.

Answer

The matrix which represents reflection in the line $y=x$ is

$$\mathbf{M}=\begin{pmatrix} 0 & 1 \\ 1 & 0 \end{pmatrix}$$

The matrix which represents reflection in the y-axis is

$$\mathbf{N}=\begin{pmatrix} -1 & 0 \\ 0 & 1 \end{pmatrix}$$

The matrix for **M** followed by **N** is given by

first **M**

$$\mathbf{NM}=\begin{pmatrix} -1 & 0 \\ 0 & 1 \end{pmatrix}\begin{pmatrix} 0 & 1 \\ 1 & 0 \end{pmatrix}=\begin{pmatrix} 0 & -1 \\ 1 & 0 \end{pmatrix}$$

then **N**

This matrix represents a rotation of +90°, i.e. *anticlockwise* rotation of 90°, about the origin.

WRITTEN EXAMINATIONS

Although other forms of assessment may be used for your GCSE or SCE examination, timed written examinations still provide a large percentage (between 50% and 75%) of the total marks available to you. So it is important that you can give good answers to examination questions. The following self-test section contains a selection of questions from *specimen* and *actual* GCSE and SCE examination papers. You can use These questions both to test your understanding of the units in your syllabus and to practise answering written examination questions. Also, at the end of this section (p. 209), there are two sample aural tests, at different levels, to give you some practice.

Hints on answering written questions

Read the *whole* question carefully. Misreading or misinterpreting a question is a common mistake.

- Jot down points relating to the question, e.g. formulae you will need.
- Draw a sketch, if it helps, labelling it with the information given.
- Check that you have copied the given information correctly.
- Always draw a sketch before doing a construction or scale drawing.

When answering a question:

- Make sure that your writing is legible. It's no use if the examiner cannot read your answer.
- Write your answer neatly and carefully. Make it easy for the examiner to give you marks.
- Show all your working unless the question says otherwise. Most marks are usually given for legible working, not just 'right answers'. Often 'no working' can mean 'no marks'.
- State any formulae used. Make sure you remember or copy them from a given list correctly.
- Try to explain your reasons for using a formula or stating a result.
- Do not do things you are not asked for, e.g. do not use a scale drawing if the question tells you to 'calculate' an answer.
- Make sure that you answer the question the examiner has actually asked.
- Use and state the correct units, e.g. cm^2, kg, h, …
- Always do a rough estimate of any calculation. Use it to check that your answer is sensible.
- Show clearly any calculation that you have done on a calculator (if it has one).
- Do not use approximations until the end of your working unless the question says otherwise. In questions involving π, if a value is given for π then you must use that value, otherwise use the π button on your calculator (if it has one).
- Given your final answer to the required degree of accuracy, e.g. a given number of decimal places or significant figures. If you are not given a degree of accuracy, make sure that you give your 'calculator' answer clearly then round it off sensibly for your final answer. Draw graphs, scale drawings, etc as carefully as possible using the correct equipment and paper. Graph paper will be provided in the examination.
- Leave all construction lines on the completed drawing in a construction or scale drawing.

If you get 'stuck', reread the question carefully. Check that you have not missed any important information or hints given in the question itself. If necessary leave that question for the moment, then return to it later. A fresh look at a question often helps.

After answering a question:

- Check that you have answered all parts in the question.
- Check that your answer(s) make sense!

The questions

The questions given in the following self-test section have been divided into three sections, covering List 1, 2 and 3 topics.

List 1 questions contain work only from List 1 topics. List 2 and 3 questions may contain work from topics in the previous list(s).

Above each question is a reference to the topic(s) in this book which are relevant to that question. If you have difficulty answering a question you can refresh your memory by working through the appropriate topic(s) again. then you have answered a question first check your answer with that given in the Answers section on page 213. Then look back to the relevant topic(s) to check that your method was correct too. In most examinations marks are given for legible, correct working, not just the 'right' answers.

Below most questions is a reference to the Examining Group which set the question. (Specimen questions are marked with an asterisk, *.) Try to answer *all* questions on the topics you have studied, whether they were set by your Examining Group or not. A list of the names and abbreviations used for each group are given on p. xviii.

Formulae

Some formulae you should know by heart, for example:

Area of a rectangle = length × breadth

Some formulae may be given to you in the examination, for example in a formula checklist like the one below.

Different Examining Groups provide different formulae for each paper and in different ways. Ask your teacher which formulae will be given on your papers and where to find them. The formulae may be given inside the front cover of the question paper, in the question itself or in a separate leaflet.

It will help you to either make your own formulae lists for each of your papers or mark the relevant formulae on the list below. Use them when you answer the examination questions in the Self-Test Unit. This is good practice for using them in the examination itself: being familiar with them will give you confidence.

MENSURATION

Area of triangle

$= \frac{\text{base} \times \text{height}}{2}$

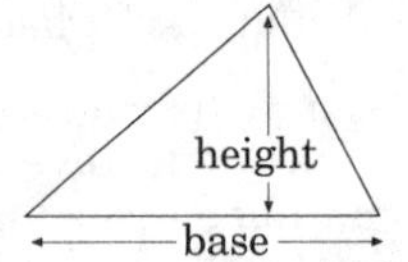

Area of parallelogram

= base x height

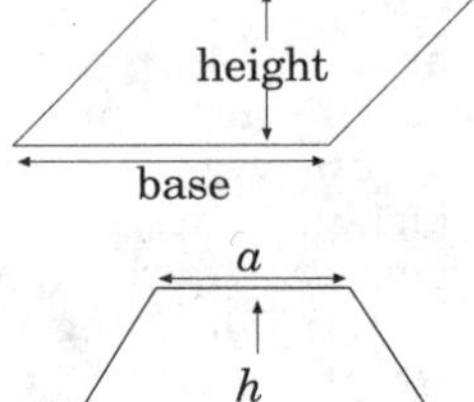

Area of trapezium

$= \frac{1}{2}(a + b)h$

$= \frac{1}{2}$(sum of parallel sides × distance between)

Circumference of circle

$= \pi d$

$= 2\pi r$

Area of circle $= \pi r 2$

$= 2\pi r$

$\pi = 3.14$ to 2 decimal places

Volume of cuboid

= length × width × height

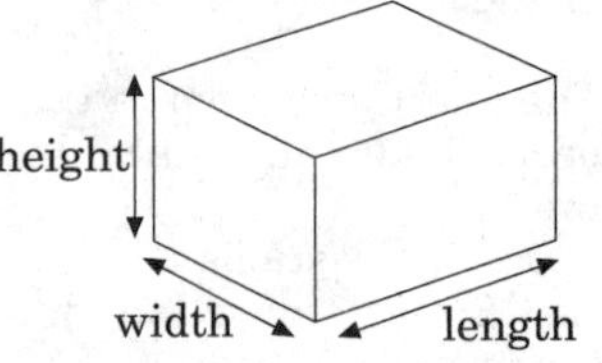

1 litre = 1000cm³

Volume of prism

= area of cross-section × length

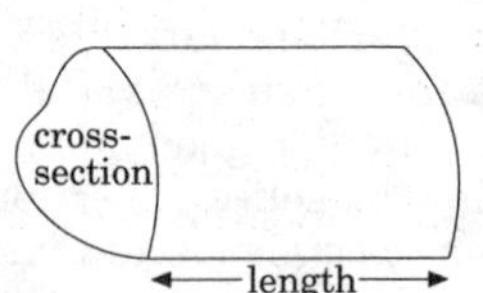

Volume of cylinder $= \pi r^2 h$

Area of curved surface of cylinder

$= 2\pi rh$

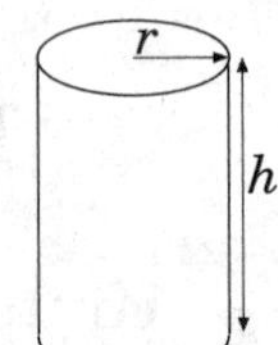

Volume of sphere $= \frac{4}{3}\pi r^3$

Surface area of sphere $= 4\pi r^2$

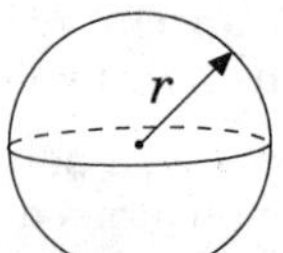

Volume of pyramid

$= \frac{1}{3} \times$ area of base × height

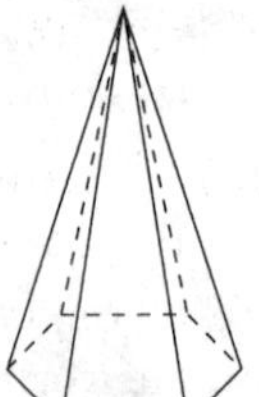

Volume of circular cone

$= \frac{1}{3}\pi r^2 h$

Area of curved surface $= \pi r l$

where l = slant height $= \sqrt{h^2 + r^2}$

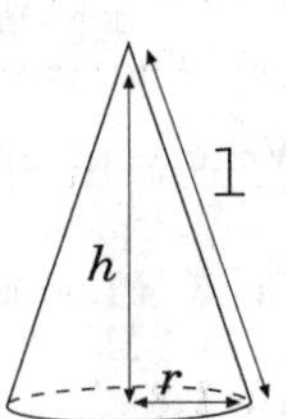

TRIGONOMETRY

Right-angled triangle

adj = hyp × cos θ

opp = hyp × sinθ

opp = adj × tan θ

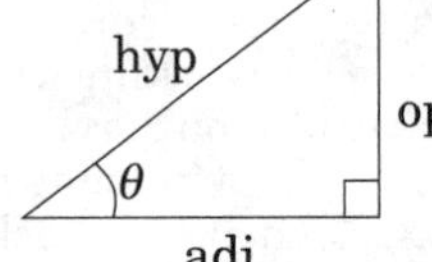

or cost $\theta = \frac{\text{adj}}{\text{hyp}}$ sin $\theta = \frac{\text{opp}}{\text{hyp}}$ tan $\theta = \frac{\text{opp}}{\text{adj}}$

Any triangle

Sine rule:

$\frac{a}{\sin A} = \frac{b}{\sin B} = \frac{c}{\sin C}$

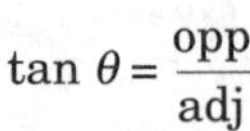

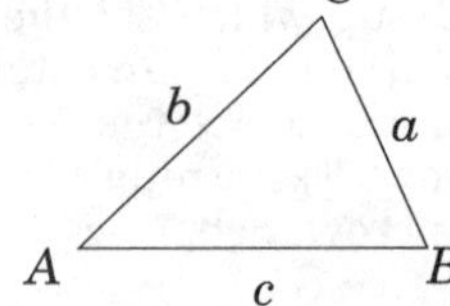

Cosine rule:

$a^2 = b^2 + c^2 - 2bc\cos A$ or $\cos A = \frac{b^2 + c^2 - a^2}{2bc}$

Area of triangle $ABC = \frac{1}{2}ab \sin C$ etc.

PYTHAGORAS' THEOREM

Right-angled triangle

$a^2 + b^2 = c^2$

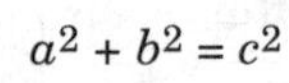

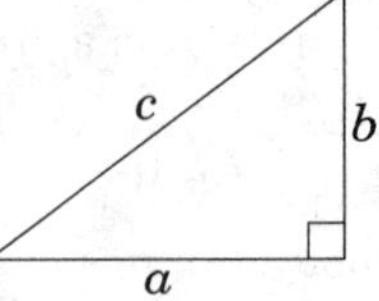

STANDARD FORM

a × 10^n, where $1 \le a < 10$ and n is an integer.

QUADRATIC EQUATIONS

The solutions of

$ax^2 + bx + c = 0$

where $a \neq 0$, are given by

$$x = \frac{-b \pm \sqrt{(b^2 - 4ac)}}{2a}$$

SELF-TEST UNITS

GCSE QUESTIONS

List 1

Unit 1.1

1 David enters a number into a calculator and then performs the following operations.

÷ 2 + 3 =

(i) David enters the number 4.
What is the answer obtained after doing the above operations?

(ii) David enters the number 3.214.
What is the answer obtained after doing the above operations?

(iii) What number would have to be entered to obtain the answer 8? (*WJEC**)

2 Simon used a calculator to work out the value of 3.12×4.36. He wrote down the answer as 136.032.

(a) What **simple check** could Simon have used, **without using his calculator**, to show that this answer is incorrect?

(b) Write down the correct answer. (*WJEC*)

Unit 1.2

3 There were forty thousand, eight hundred and four spectators at a football match. Write down in figures the number of spectators at the match. (*NEA**)

4 What is the next whole number after 3099? (*LEAG**)

Units 1.2 and 1.3

5 Add two hundred and four to five thousand three hundred and seven and give your answer in figures. (*LEAG*, 1988)

6 Of the total land areas of Belgium, 1.4 million hectares is cultivated and six hundred thousand hectares is forest.

(a) Write both these numbers in figures.

(b) The total land area of Belgium is 3 million hectares. What area of land is neither cultivated nor forest? (*MEG*, 1988)

Unit 1.3

7

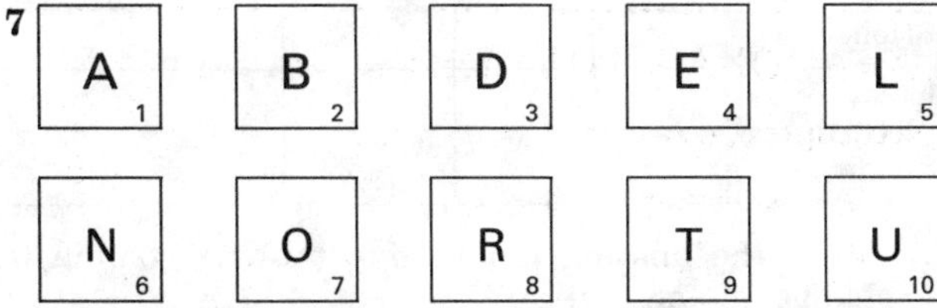

The ten tiles shown above are used in a game to make words and the scores shown on the tiles are added together. For example, BONE scores
$2 + 7 + 6 + 4 = 19$.

(a) Calculate the score for DOUBT.

(b) A player makes a five-letter word and scores a total of 17. Four of the letters in the word are A, B, E, O. What is the fifth letter?

(c) Another player makes a five-letter word using the letters L, N, O and two others. The score for the word is 23. What could the other two letters be?

(d) What is the highest possible score for four letters which are all different?

(e) A player makes a four-letter word with a score of 33. All the letters in the word are different. What are the four letters? (*MEG**)

8 A train stopped in Sheffield where 86 passengers got off and 145 passengers boarded the train. When the train left Sheffield it had 329 passengers. How many passengers were on the train when it arrived in Sheffield? (*NEA*, 1988)

9 A bakery delivers bread to a number of shops.
The bread is packed in trays and there are 48 loaves in each tray.
A van holds 30 trays.

(a) Work out the number of loaves in the van.

All the bread in the van is delivered to 9 shops and each shop gets the same number of loaves.

(b) Work out the number of loaves deliverd to each shop. (*LEAG*, 1988)

10 Mark's computer can do 50 000 calculations each second. How long will it take to do 4 million calculations? (*NEA**)

Unit 1.4

11 **BIRTHS**

> HUTTON – On June 14 at Kings Hospital, to Kate and Gary, a son Rhys Andrew, weight 3467.

(a) Write Rhys's weight correct to the nearest hundred units.

(b) The units of weight were left out of the announcement. Write down the most likely unit for the baby's birth weight. (*LEAG*, 1988)

12 Thirteen thousand two hundred and eighteen spectators watched a football match at Wimbledon.

(a) Write that number in figures.

(b) Give the number correct to the nearest thousand. (*LEAG*, 1988)

Units 1.5 and 1.7

13 2, 3, 4, 5, 6, 7, 8, 9, 10, 11, 12

From this list write down all the numbers that are

(a) even,

(b) factors of 45,

(c) multiples of both 2 and 3,

(d) prime numbers,

(e) square numbers. (*LEAG*, 1988)

14 The first eight square numbers are

1, 4, 9, 16, 25, 36, 49, 64

(a) Which of these eight square numbers
(i) are multiples of 3?
(ii) are factors of 64?

(b) Which two of these numbers have a difference of nine?

(c) What is the next number in the sequence?

(d) What is the square root of 49? (*SEG*, 1988)

Unit 1.6

15 Write down the next two numbers in the following patterns:

(a) 1, 4, 7, 10, 13, ...

(b) 3, 6, 12, 24, 48, ...

(c) 1, 4, 9, 16, 25, ...

(d) 160, 80, 40, 20, 10, ... (*MEG**)

16

'stairs' with one level　'stairs' with two levels　'stairs' with three levels

A child is building sets of 'stairs' with some bricks. The diagram shows the view of the 'stairs' that the child has built for 1, 2 and 3 levels.

(a) Draw the view for the 'stairs' with 4 levels.
(b) Complete the table:

Number of levels	*Number of bricks*
1	1
2	4
3	
4	

(c) How many bricks are needed to build a set of 'stairs' with 10 levels? (*LEAG*, 1988)

17 The table shows John's weekly pocket money, in pence, at certain ages.

Age (years)	5	6	7	8	9	10
Pocket money (p)	25	26	28	32	40	56

He receives an increase on each birthday. The increase on his 6th birthday was 1p, the increase on his 7th birthday was 2p and the increase on his 8th birthday was 4p.

(a) What was the increase on his
  (i) 9th birthday? (ii) 10th birthday?
(b) The increases follow a pattern.
  Using this pattern, find the increase on his
  (i) 11th birthday. (ii) 12th birthday.
(c) What was his weekly pocket money when his age was
  (i) 11 years? (ii) 12 years?
(d) How old will he be when his pocket money is £5.36?
(e) Will his pocket money ever become an odd number of pence after he is 11? Explain your answer.
(f) Jenny's increases in pocket money also follow a pattern. Complete the table for Jenny's pocket money.

Age (years)	5	6	7	8	9	10	11
Pocket money (p)	23	24	27	36	63		

(*SEG*, 1988)

Unit 1.7

18 (a) Work out $5^2 + 12^2$.
(b) Work out $(5 + 12)^2$. (*MEG*, 1988)

19 The picture is in a square of area 25 cm^2. Calculate
(a) the length of a side of the square,
(b) the perimeter of the square.
(*NEA*, 1988)

Unit 1.8

20 A local record store lists the top five recording artists in the charts like this.

1 (+1) Nick Berry
2 (+1) Madonna
3 (+2) Five Star
4 (−3) Status Quo
5 (−1) Cliff Richard

The figures in brackets show the number of places that the artist has moved up or down in the charts since the previous week. For example, Nick Berry has moved up one place since last week.

(a) What position in the charts was Five Star the previous week?
(b) Who in the above chart was number one before Nick Berry?

During the following week, these changes occurred.

Madonna dropped two places.
Five Star moved up a place.
Status Quo stayed in the top five but did not move up.
Cliff Richard fell three places.
Paul Young was the only new entry, at number three.

(c) Prepare the new top five list. (*NEA*, 1988)

21 The time in Sydney is 10 hours ahead of the time in London. The time in New York is 5 hours behind the time in London. Give all of your answers using the 24 hour clock.
(a) When it is midday in London, what time is it in Sydney?
(b) When it is 03 00 in New York, what time is it in London?
(c) When it is midnight in New York, what time is it in Sydney? (*LEAG*, 1988)

22 On January 13th the following lunchtime temperatures were recorded.

Athens	17°C
Brussels	−10°C
Cairo	22°C
London	0°C
Moscow	−15°C
Vienna	−9°C

(a) Which place was the warmest?
(b) Which place was the coldest?
(c) By how many degrees was Cairo warmer than Vienna? (*LEAG*, 1988)

23 Here are the temperatures in some cities around the world on two consecutive days.

City	*Yesterday's temp. °F*	*Today's temp. °F*	*Change in temp. +/− °F*
Paris	30	34	+4
Colombo	84	80	−4
Melbourne	66	71	
St Helier	37	35	
Moscow	−2	−11	
Warsaw	−1	2	

Fill in the missing numbers in the last column (the change in temperature).

(*MEG*, 1988)

Unit 1.9

24 Zenka wants to buy her father a packet of electric drill bits for his birthday.
(a) In the first packet that she looks at, there are four different drills and their sizes are marked in inches.

The sizes are $\frac{3}{8}$, $\frac{1}{4}$, $\frac{1}{2}$, and $\frac{1}{8}$.

(i) Which is the larger size drill bit, $\frac{3}{8}$, or $\frac{1}{4}$?

(ii) Write the four sizes in order, starting with the smallest.

(b) Zenka looks at a second packet which contains seven drill bits, each increasing in size by $\frac{1}{16}$ of an inch. If the smallest drill bit in the packet is marked $\frac{1}{8}$, write down the sizes of the other six bits. (You should give the sizes in their simplest form.) *(NEA, 1988)*

25 Write $\frac{7}{4}$ as (a) a mixed number, (b) a decimal. *(MEG, 1988)*

26 Some of the nutritional contents of 100 grams of Bran Cereal are as follows:

Fat	5.0 grams
Protein	11.6 grams
Fibre	21.5 grams

(a) What fraction of Bran Cereal is fat?

(b) A normal helping of Bran Cereal is 40 grams.

(i) Express 40 grams as a fraction of 100 grams. Give the fraction in its simplest form.

(ii) How many grams of fibre does a normal helping of Bran Cereal contain? *(MEG, 1988)*

27 Three fifths of the pupils in a school stay to lunch. There are 600 pupils in the school. How many do not stay to lunch? *(SEG*)*

Units 1.9 and 1.56

28 Mr Dane leaves his home near Sheffield to travel to Birmingham by car. Before he sets off he looks at his petrol gauge and milometer.

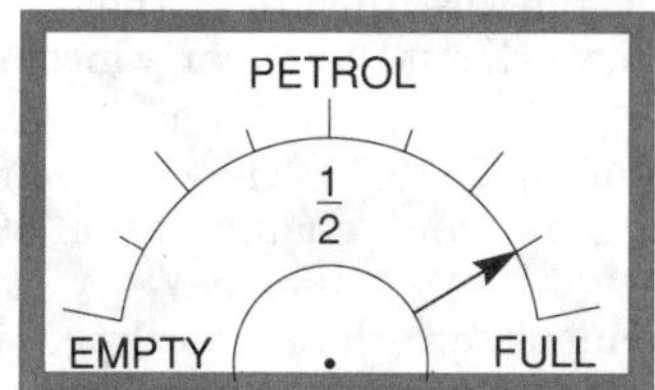

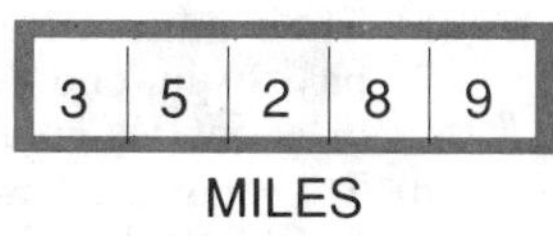

(a) What fraction of a full tank of petrol is shown by the petrol gauge?

(b) Write your answer to part (a) as a decimal.

Later that day Mr Dane arrives back in Sheffield and notices that his petrol tank is now one-quarter full and his mileometer reads 35468.

(c) How many miles has Mr Dane travelled?

(d) What fraction of a full tank of petrol has been used?

(e) Mr Dane spent 4 hours travelling. Calculate his average speed for the journey. Give your answer to the nearest mile per hour. *(NEA, 1988)*

Unit 1.10

29 The sweets in a box are classed as creams, caramels or toffees. In a box of Keely's Choice, $\frac{3}{8}$ of the contents are creams, $\frac{1}{4}$ of them are caramels and the remainder are toffees.

(a) Work out the fraction of the sweets in the box that are either creams or caramels.

(b) What fraction of the sweets in the box are toffees?

(c) There are 24 sweets in the box. Work out the number of caramels in the box. *(LEAG, 1988)*

30 As part of her daily keep fit training programme, Ann runs around the gymnasium 15 times. After doing $5\frac{1}{2}$ laps of the gymnasium, Ann stops to do some press-ups. She then runs another $6\frac{1}{4}$ laps before doing some more press-ups.
How many laps has she got left to do? *(WJEC*)*

Unit 1.11

31 Write down the reading given by the pointer on the scale.

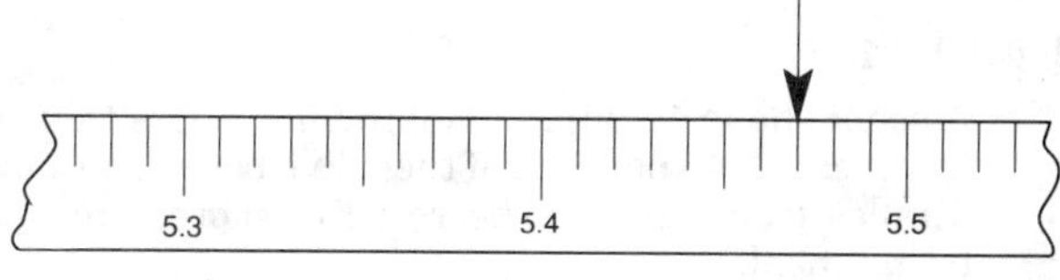

(MEG, 1988)

32 Write these numbers in order of size, smallest first.
0.66 0.625 0.088 0.667 *(NEA*)*

Units 1.11, 1.12 and 1.68

33 In an international 2000 metres race consisting of 5 laps of 400 metres, five athletes have the following lap times in seconds:

	John Bingham	Trevor Jones	Mark Adams	Christopher Stewart	James Logan
1st lap	47.3	47.1	48.3	47.0	46.2
2nd lap	45.8	46.0	47.2	45.8	46.3
3rd lap	46.1	45.9	46.1	45.9	46.1
4th lap	45.8	45.8	45.8	46.4	46.0
5th lap	45.9	46.3	45.3	46.3	46.1
Total					

(a) Calculate the total time for each athlete (answer in the spaces provided in the table).

(b) Which athlete won the race?

(c) What was the final finishing order?

(d) What was the average (mean) lap time of the winner? *(NISEC, 1988)*

Unit 1.12

34 An extension ladder consists of two ladders, each 4.55 m long.

When the extension ladder is fully extended, there is an overlap of 0.75 m.

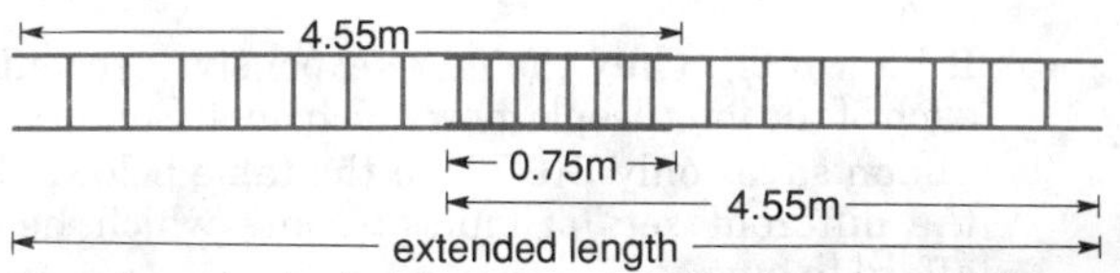

How long is the ladder when it is fully extended? *(WJEC, 1988)*

35

A saline drip in a hospital releases 0.1 ml every 3 seconds. How long does it take to empty a 500 ml bag? *(WJEC, 1988)*

Unit 1.13

36

EASTMINSTER	BARNLY	TOPLAND
Rate of Interest	Rate of Interest	Rate of Interest
9.7%	$9\frac{3}{4}$%	$9\frac{5}{8}$%

Which bank pays the highest rate of interest? *(LEAG*)*

Units 1.13 and 1.14

37 (a) Sharon got 9 out of 10 in a Mathematics test. A month later, in a longer Mathematics test, she got 49 marks out of a total of 56.

(i) Write $\frac{9}{10}$ as a decimal.

(ii) Write $\frac{49}{56}$ as a decimal.
(iii) In which test did Sharon do best? Why?
(b) Write $\frac{17}{20}$ as a percentage. (*MEG**)

Unit 1.14

38 A school has 840 pupils. $\frac{3}{10}$ of them live less than 1 mile from school. 45 per cent of them live between 1 mile and 3 miles from school. The rest live more than 3 miles from school.

What percentage of the pupils live more than 3 miles from school? (*LEAG*, 1988)

Unit 1.15

39 During the first few weeks of its life, an octopus increases its body weight by 5% each day. An octopus was born with a body weight of 150 grams.

How much will it weigh after
(a) 1 day? (b) 3 days? (*NEA*, 1988)

Units 1.15, 1.16 and 1.68

40 Each member of Melchester Diners' Club has to pay an annual subscription of £45 and a fee of £5.50 at each meeting attended. The Club has 42 meetings each year.

(a) Find the total cost of a year's membership for a member who attends all 42 meetings.
(b) To retain membership, a member must attend at least 60% of the year's meetings. Find the minimum number of meetings that a member can attend in a year and still retain membership.
(c) Calculate, to the nearest penny, the average cost per meeting for a member who attends 32 meetings in the year. (*MEG*, 1988)

Unit 1.16

41 Simon is saving money to buy a Christmas present for each member of his family as follows:

Mum:	perfume	£6.99	or gloves	£5.50
Dad:	book	£4.95	or tie	£3.15
Sister:	record	£3.49	or tights	£2.99
Gran:	scarf	£4.90	or hankies	£4.50

(a) What is the least amount of money Simon must save?
(b) If he wants to buy the more expensive present for each of the four people, how much must Simon save?
(c) Simon saves only £16.70. In the table below, show the different sets of four presents which he can afford to buy.

Mum	*Dad*	*Sister*	*Gran*

(*MEG*, 1988)

42 A school bought 60 copies of a French textbook for £168. Calculate the cost per book. (*LEAG*, 1988)

43 Fill in the missing amounts in this bill.

14lbs of potatoes @ 11p per lb	£_____
3 cauliflowers @ _____ each	£1.35
2 dozen oranges @ 6p each	£_____
_____lb of grapes @ 90 per lb	£1.35
Total	£_____

(*NISEC*, 1988)

44 Chris travels to work five days a week from Runcorn to Liverpool. A peak hour return ticket costs £2.80. A 13-week season ticket costs £145.20.

(a) How much does she save if she buys a 13-week season ticket instead of a peak hour return ticket each day?
(b) In one 13-week period Chris had a fortnight's holiday, and was at home sick for 3 days. Her friend, Alan, said that her season ticket had been a waste of money. Was Alan right? Show how you worked out your answer. (*NEA*, 1988)

Units 1.9, 1.16 and 1.17

45 A theatre has the following seats available for a concert:

700 seats at £4 each,
600 seats at £5 each,
300 seats at £6 each.

(a) How many people can the theatre seat altogether?
(b) If all the seats were sold, what would be the total money from the ticket sales?
(c) On the actual day of the concert all the £4 seats, one half of the £5 seats and two-thirds of the £6 seats were sold.
 (i) How many seats were sold altogether?
 (ii) What fraction, in its lowest terms, of the total number of seats remained unsold?
(d) The theatre gave a discount of 10 per cent off all its prices for parties of more than twenty people. Find how much a Youth Club had to pay when it bought thirty-five £5 seats. (*MEG*)

Units 1.16 and 1.17

46 A young married couple living in Enniskillen want to buy some kitchen units, but are unsure if they can afford them. They have to work out their yearly income and expenditure.

(a) Their annual Rates bill is £316.80. They decide to pay it in one lump sum and qualify for a 5% discount. Calculate what they actually pay.
(b) The monthly repayment on their mortgage is £152.64. Calculate the total repayments in one year.
(c) If they spend on average £50 a month on the electricity and heating and £106 a month on food, calculate the total yearly cost of food, electricity and heating.
(d) They have a quarterly telephone bill which averages £36.45. Calculate how much the telephone costs per year.
(e) The couple's nett income is £641.25 per month. Calculate how much they have left from their yearly income after deducting the total yearly expenditure in (a), (b), (c) and (d).

(*NISEC*, 1988)

Unit 1.17

47 New cars lose about 20% of their value in the first year.

About how much will this car be worth when it is one year old? (*NEA**)

48 At the beginning of 1987 a house was valued at £49 500. During 1987 the prices of houses in the area went up by 13%. What was the house worth at the end of 1987? (*NEA*, 1988)

Unit 1.18

49 Abdul Hassan's standard working week is 40 hours from Monday to Friday. Overtime worked in the evenings is paid for at time and a quarter, and all work on Saturday is paid at double time.
His normal rate is £3.60 per hour. Last week he worked 56 hours, 12 of which were in the evening and 4 on Saturday morning.

(a) (i) How much is Abdul paid for a standard working week?
(ii) What is the evening overtime rate?
(iii) What is the Saturday morning overtime rate?
(iv) How much did Abdul earn last week?

(b) Abdul pays $7\frac{1}{2}$% of his wages into the firm's pension fund. How much did he pay into the pension fund last week? (*NEA*, 1988)

50 Here are three Job Centre advertisements.

SALES ASSISTANT
(LARGE DEPARTMENT STORE) £4300 per year

TRAINEE
(ENGINEERING COMPANY) £85 per week

CLERK
(SOLICITORS OFFICE) GOOD PROSPECTS STARTING SALARY £350 per month

(i) How much will the clerk earn in a year?
(ii) How much will the trainee earn in a year if he is paid £85 for each of 52 weeks?
(iii) Nassim got the job of clerk. After one year, her salary increased by 7%. How much is her new salary per month? (*NEA**)

Units 1.18 and 1.68

51 Vivek assembles circuits boards. The table shows his production for a week.

Day	*Hours worked*	*Boards assembled*
Mon	7	220
Tue	$7\frac{1}{2}$	240
Wed	8	270
Thu	8	260
Fri	$7\frac{1}{2}$	225
TOTAL		

(a) Vivek is paid £1.80 per hour and 6p per board assembled. Complete the table and calculate his earnings for the week.
(b) What is the mean number of boards produced per hour? (*NEA*, 1988)

Unit 1.19

52 Income tax, at the rate of 30%, is deducted from an examiner's fee of £30 for setting a question paper. How much does the examiner receive? (*SEG**)

53 Mr Hopkin earns an annual wage of £10 500. His total tax allowances are £3240.
(i) Calculate his taxable income.
(ii) Calculate the income tax paid by him during a year, given that the rate of tax is 29% of the taxable income. (*WJEC**)

54 VAT at 15% is added to the basic price of an article. Calculate
(a) the VAT payable on a diary costing £2 without VAT,
(b) the basic price of a diary selling for £4.60. (*LEAG*, 1988)

Unit 1.20

55 The readings on Mr Power's electricity meter were as follows:

Beginning of first quarter

0	2	3	4	7

End of first quarter (beginning of second)

0	2	8	2	6

(a) How many units of electricity did Mr Power use during the first quarter?
(b) Mr Power uses 435 units of electricity during the second quarter. What is the reading of Mr Power's meter at the end of the second quarter?
(c) Complete Mr Power's electricity bill for the second quarter.

	£
435 units at 5.2p per unit	....
Quarterly standing charge	8.15
Total	

(*WJEC*, 1988)

56 British Telecom send out domestic telephone accounts quarterly. For the first quarter of 1985, the charge was made up of a rental of £19.15 plus 4.7p for each dialled unit. Value Added Tax at 15% was then added to the total. In this quarter Mr and Mrs Thomson used 882 dialled units. Calculate, correct to the nearest penny, the amount of their quarterly account. (*MEG**)

Unit 1.21

57 Sally put £250 into a savings account which paid interest at the rate of 8% per annum.
(a) Find the amount in the account at the end of one year.
She leaves this amount of money in the account for another year. During this year, the rate of interest is 9.75% per annum for the whole year.
(b) Find, to the nearest penny, the amount in the account at the end of the second year. (*LEAG*, 1988)

58 John has taken out a Personal Loan of £1500 from his bank for a period of two years at an annual interest rate of 12%.
(a) Use the formula below to calculate the total interest which he will have to pay on this loan.

$$\text{Interest} = \frac{\text{principal} \times \text{rate} \times \text{years}}{100}$$

(b) What is the total amount which John will have to repay to his bank? (*NISEC**)

Unit 1.22

59 A set of encyclopaedias costs £84.95 cash. The set can also be bought by paying 9 monthly instalments of £9.68 each. How much more does it cost to buy by instalments than for cash?

(*LEAG*, 1988)

60 The cash price for a car was £5530. Miss Russell decided to buy the car on hire purchase.

(a) She paid a deposit of 20% of the cash price. Calculate the amount of the deposit.

(b) She also made 36 monthly payments of £165.90 each. Calculate the total of the 36 monthly payments.

(c) Calculate the total amount paid by Miss Russell for the car. (*MEG**)

61 Rachel is to buy a new stereo system, costing £240, on an interest free credit scheme.

(a) She must pay a 25% deposit. How much is this?

(b) How much is left to pay after she has paid the deposit?

(c) How much are her monthly payments, if she pays the remainder in six equal monthly payments?

(*LEAG*, 1988)

Unit 1.23

62 A garden centre buys a tray of 24 plants for £15 and sells each plant for 90p. Calculate the profit made on the sale of a tray of plants.

(*LEAG*, 1988)

63 A school decides to have a disco from 8 p.m. to midnight. The price of the tickets will be 20p. The costs are as follows:

Disco and D.J., £25
Hire of hall, £5 an hour

200 cans of soft drinks at 15p each
200 packets of crisps at 10p each
Printing of tickets, £5

(i) What is the total cost of putting on the disco?

(ii) How many tickets must be sold to cover the cost?

(iii) If 400 tickets are sold, all the drinks are sold at 20p each and all the packets of crisps at 12p each, calculate the profit or loss the school finally makes.

(*NEA**)

64 Errol bought an old bike for £20. He cleaned it up and sold it for £32.50.

(a) What was his profit?

(b) What is this as a percentage of the cost price?

(*MEG*, 1988)

Unit 1.25

65 Travel Protector Insurance issued the following table of premiums for holiday insurance in 1985.

Premiums
per injured person

Period of Travel	**Area 'A'** UK†	**Area 'B'** Europe	**Area 'C'** Worldwide
1– 4 days	£3.60	£5.40	£16.90
5– 8 days	£4.50	£7.80	£16.90
9–17 days	£5.40	£9.95	£21.45
18–23 days	£6.30	£12.30	£27.95
24–31 days	£7.20	£15.25	£32.50
32–62 days	–	£24.10	£44.20
63–90 days	–	£34.50	£53.95

†Excluding Channel Islands

Winter Sports
Cover is available at 3 times these premium rates.

Discount for Children
Under 14 years at date of Application – **20 per cent reduction**

Under 3 years at date of Application – **Free of charge**

(Source: *Travel Protector Insurance,* published by National Westminster Bank PLC.)

Find the premiums paid by

(i) Mr Jones holidaying in Blackpool with his wife and three children, aged 2, 9 and 15, from 2 August to 16 August.

(ii) Carole Smith going to Switzerland to ski from 19 December to 8 January. (*NEA**)

Unit 1.26

66

Basic holiday price in £'s per person – Gatwick departures

Departures between	26 March 27 April		28 April 18 May		19 May 15 June		16 June 13 July		14 July 31 Aug.		1 Sep. 28 Oct.	
Number of nights	7	14	7	14	7	14	7	14	7	14	7	14
Hotel Esplanade	218	353	222	360	226	367	231	374	235	380	200	320
Hotel Cervantes	152	223	159	236	168	253	174	260	178	291	140	210
Hotel Calypso	139	195	150	206	153	219	156	226	162	233	120	181

Addition for Heathrow departure £24 per person.
Addition for balcony and sea view £1.50 per person per night.
Addition for insurance cover £3.75 per person.

Mr and Mrs Mathews and their two children reserved a 14 night holiday at the Hotel Cervantes, for the period from 21 July to 4 August. They wish to fly from Heathrow Airport and have accommodation with balcony and sea view. Insurance cover was required for each person.

(i) Write down the basic cost, per person, of the holiday.

(ii) Calculate the additional cost, per person, for the Heathrow departure and Insurance cover.

(iii) Calculate the additional cost for the holiday, per person, for a balcony and sea view.

(iv) Calculate the total cost of the holiday for the family. (*WJEC**)

67

		Mondays to Saturdays			
Norwich	*d*	06 40	07 42	07 50	08 40
Wymondham	*d*	06 56		08 05	08 56
Spooner Row	*d*			08 09	
Attleborough	*d*	07 03		08 14	09 03
Eccles Road	*d*			08 20	
Harling Road	*d*			08 25	09 13
Thetford	*a*	07 21	08 16	08 35	09 24

d means depart; *a* means arrive

The above shows part of the timetable of trains travelling from Norwich to Thetford.

(i) If you live in Norwich, which is the first train you can catch after 7 a.m. which will take you to your work in Harling Road?

(ii) On another occasion you have to meet an important visitor on Thetford Station at 08.30. Which train should you catch in Norwich to be there in reasonable time to meet him? (*LEAG**)

Unit 1.28

68 The hour hand of the clock turns through 60°.

(a) How much time has elapsed?

(b) How many degrees has the minute hand turned through in this time? (*MEG*, 1988)

Units 1.29 and 1.34

69 This is a framework of a gate. *ABCD* is a rectangle. Calculate the values of *x* and *y*. (*MEG*, 1988)

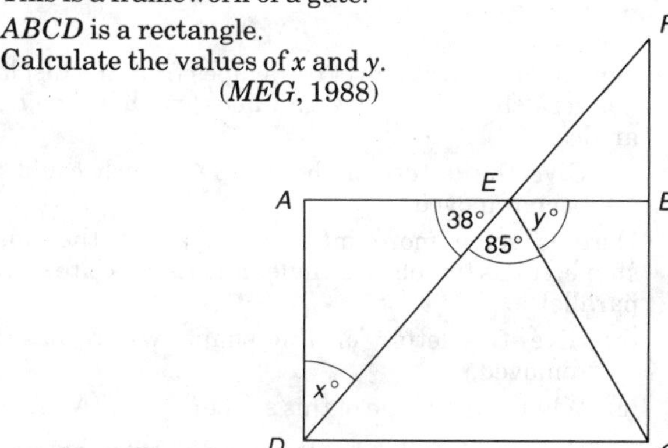

70 This is a framework for a roof. $AC = CD$ and $AB = BC$. *BCD* is a straight line and angle $ACD = 130°$. Calculate the values of *x*, *y* and *z*. (*MEG*, 1988)

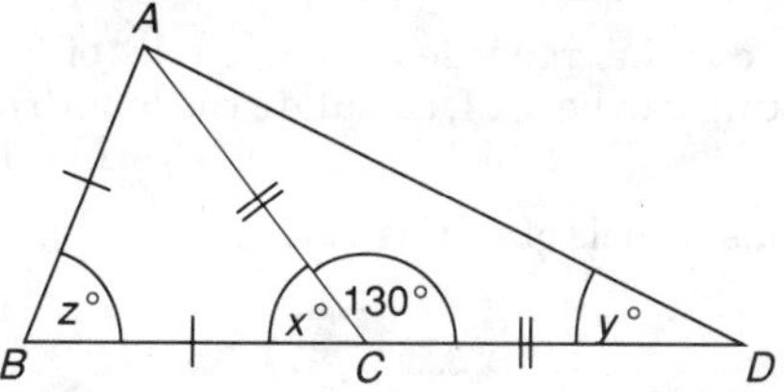

Unit 1.31

71 This diagram shows the wings of a model aircraft.

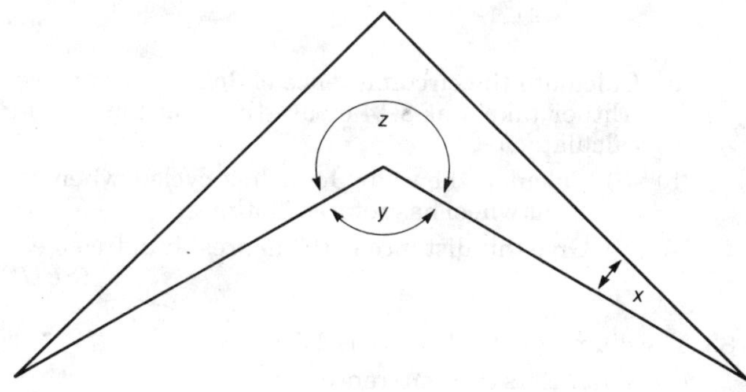

(a) Use your protractor to measure angle *x*.

(b) Use your protractor to measure angle *y*.

(c) Calculate the size of angle *z*. (*SEG**)

Unit 1.32

72

In Pembrokeshire, Fishguard is due north of Haverfordwest, Whitland is due east of Haverfordwest and Broad Haven is on a bearing of 260° from Haverfordwest. The diagram is a **sketch** of their relative positions. Find the values of *x*, *y* and *z*. (*LEAG*, 1988)

Units 1.31 and 1.32

73 The scale diagram shows the position of Norwich (*N*) and two towns on the coast of East Anglia, Sheringham (*S*) and Lowestoft (*L*).

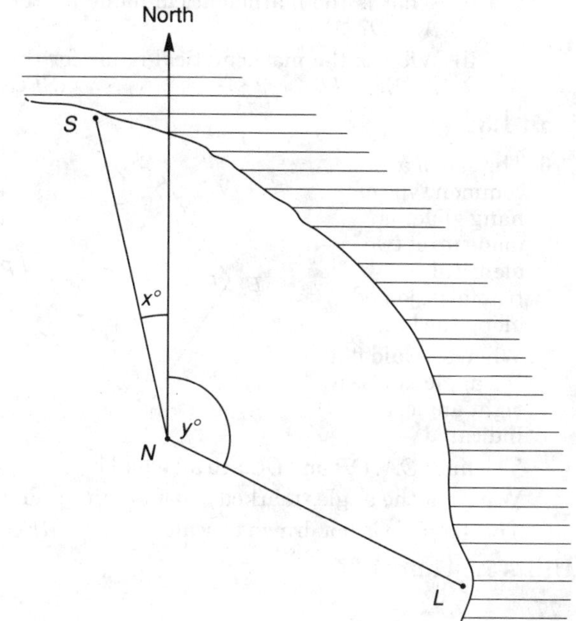

(a) Measure and write down the values of
(i) *x* (ii) *y*.

(b) What is the bearing of Sheringham from Norwich? (*MEG*, 1988)

74 Part of the South Down coastline

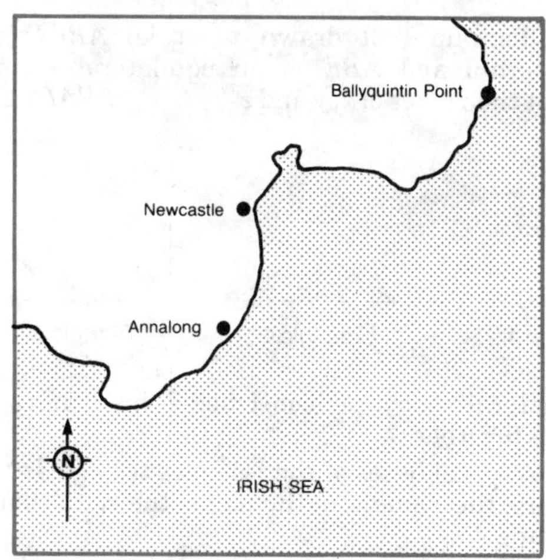

Alan calculates that his boat is at a bearing of 080° from Annalong and 210° from Ballyquintin Point.

(a) Draw (i) a bearing line of 080° fron Annalong;
(ii) a bearing line of 210° from Ballyquintin Point.

(b) Mark the position of Alan's boat. (*NISEC**)

Unit 1.33

75

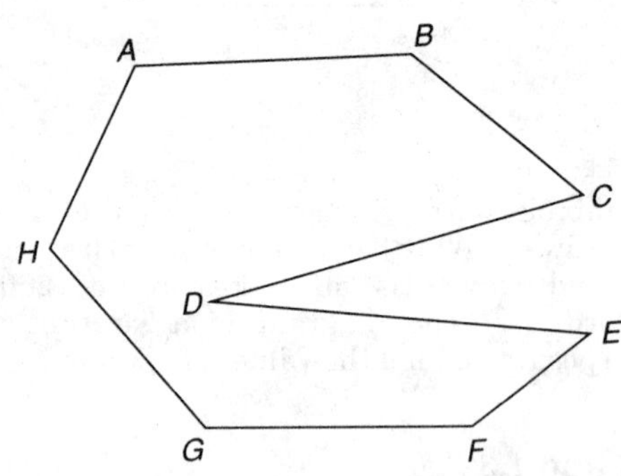

(a) What is the mathematical name for the shape *ABCDEFGH*?

(b) Join *AD*.
(i) What is the mathematical name for the shape *ABCD*?
(ii) What is the mathematical name for the shape *ADEFGH*? (*SEG*, 1988)

Unit 1.34

76 The sail of a common type of hang glider is made up of two identical triangles, joined along the keel.

When it is laid flat the angle at *O* is a right angle, as indicated.

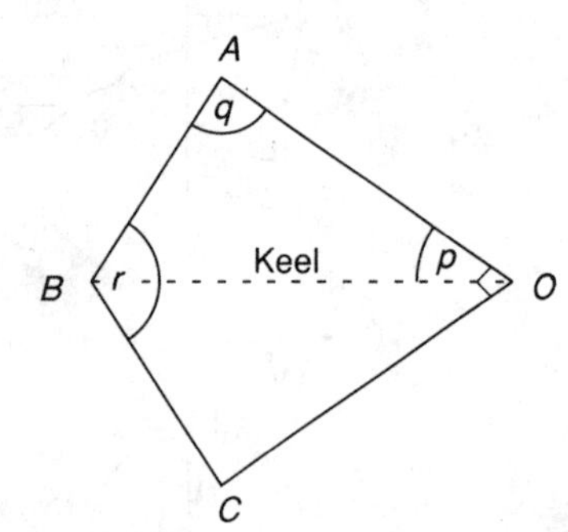

The lines *OA*, *OB* and *OC* are all equal i

Work out the angles marked *p*, *q* and *r* in the diagram.

The diagram is not drawn to scale. (*MEG*, 1988)

Units 1.34 and 1.35

77

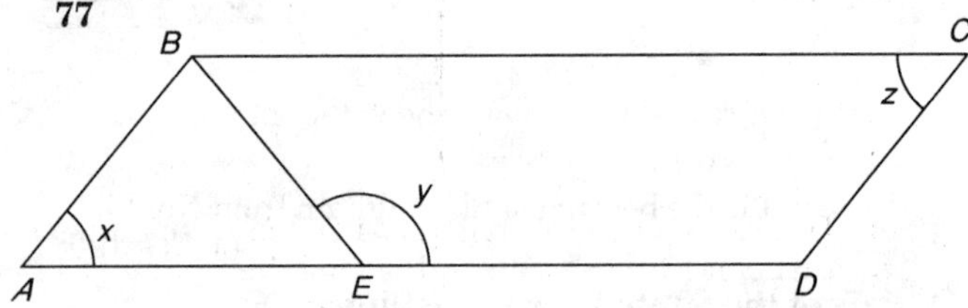

In the diagram (not drawn to scale) *ABCD* is a parallelogram and *ABE* is an equilateral triangle. Work out the values of *x*, *y* and *z*. (*LEAG*, 1988)

78

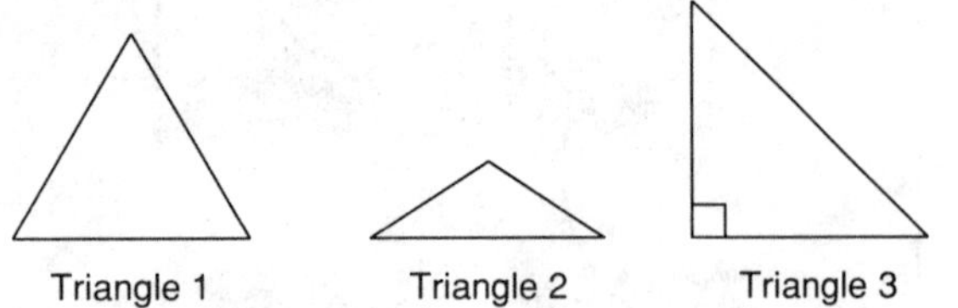

Quadrilaterals may be constructed by joining two triangles together.

If the horizontal bases of the isosceles triangles shown above are the same length, name the quadrilateral formed by

(a) joining two of **triangle 1** base to base.

(b) joining a **triangle 1** and a **triangle 2** base to base.

(c) joining two of **triangle 3** longest side to longest side.

(d) Sketch how you would join two of **triangle 3** together to form a parallelogram where the four sides are not all equal. (*NISEC*, 1988)

Unit 1.35

79 These shapes are displayed on a mathematics classroom wall.

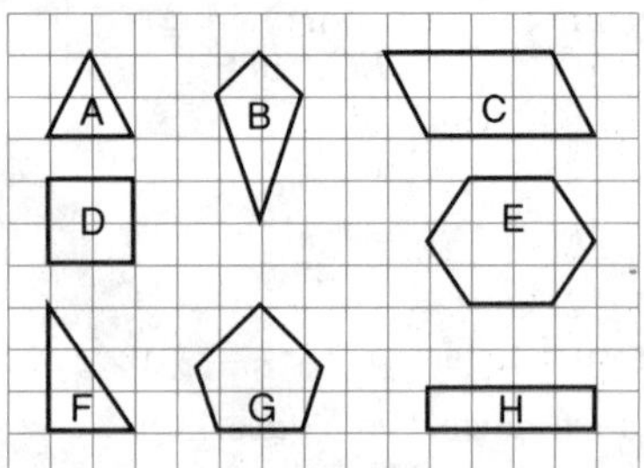

Someone removes one of the shapes from the display. It has less than five sides and does not have any right angles.

(a) Give the letters of the **shapes** which could have been removed.

Here is some more information about the missing shape. It has two obtuse angles and its opposite sides are parallel.

(b) Give the letter of the shape which has been removed.

(c) What is the name of this shape? (*NEA*, 1988)

80 Three of the interior angles of a quadrilateral are 49°, 121° and 127°. What is the size of the fourth angle? (*SEG**)

Unit 1.36

81 The equator can be regarded as a circle of radius 6370 km. Taking π to be 3.14, calculate the length of the equator. (*MEG*, 1988)

82 John's cycle has wheels of radius 1 ft.

(a) Calculate the circumference of John's front wheel. (Either take π as 3.14 or use the π button on your calculator.)

(b) (i) Calculate how far John has cycled when the front wheel has rotated 70 times.
(ii) Give this distance to the nearest hundred feet. (*SEG**)

83 The diameter of a 2p piece is 2.5 cm.

(a) What is its circumference? (π may be taken as 3.14)

(b) How many complete turns does it make in rolling 78.5 cm across a table?

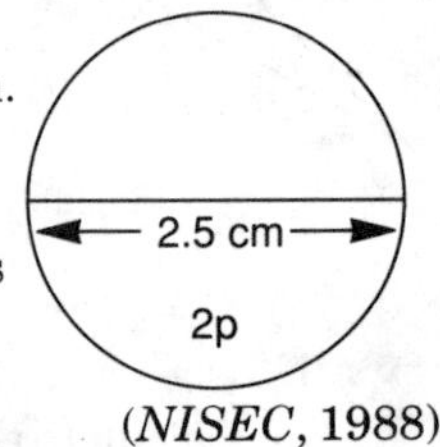

(*NISEC*, 1988)

84

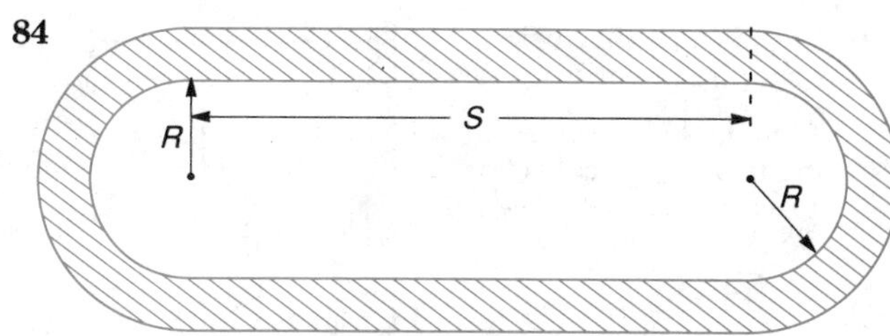

The diagram shows a school running track, which consists of two straight sections of length S metres and two semi-circular bends of inside radius R metres.

The distance around the inside of the track is 400 m, and $R = 35$ m.

Calculate the value of S. (*NEA*, 1988)

Unit 1.37

85 (a) Line AB below is the base of an equilateral triangle ABC. Use any drawing instruments you wish to complete accurately the triangle ABC.

A B

(b) (i) Line DE below is the base of an isosceles triangle DEF. The height of point F above DE is 4 cm. Use any drawing instruments you wish to complete accurately the triangle DEF.

D E

(ii) Measure and write down the size of angle F. (*LEAG*, 1988)

Unit 1.38

86 A tessellation is to be constructed on the grid below, using more tiles of this shape. Show, by drawing in at least six more tiles, how such a regular pattern may be built up.

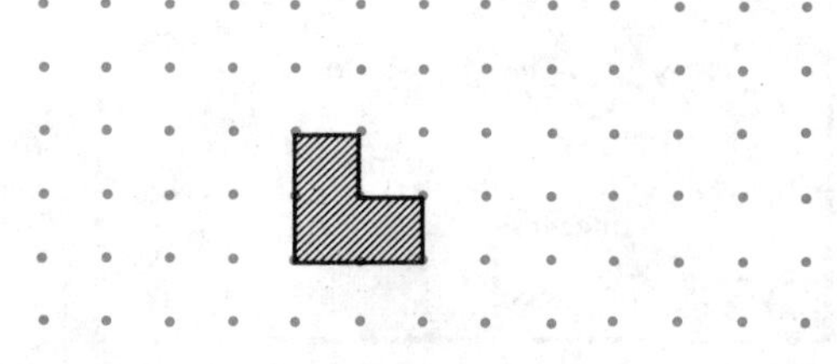

(*MEG**)

Unit 1.39

87 When my digital watch shows the time 15 : 21 the left-hand digits are a reflection of the right-hand digits. State **two** other times at which this happens. (*NEA*, 1988)

88

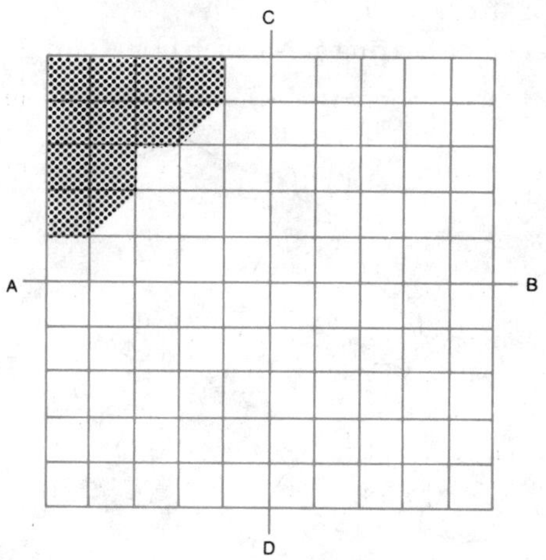

The figure shows a bathroom wall tile with part of the pattern shaded. Complete the figure so that it is symmetrical about AB and CD, shading where appropriate.

What fraction of the tile is shaded? (*WJEC**)

89 In **each** diagram below, shade **six** sectors so that they have the order of rotational symmetry indicated.

(a) order 3 (b) order 2 (c) order 1

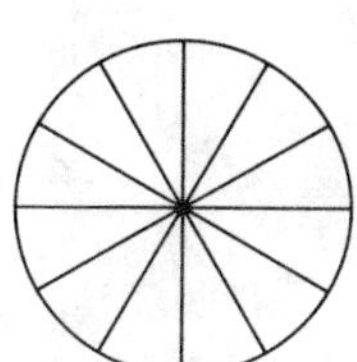

(*NEA*, 1988)

Unit 1.40

90

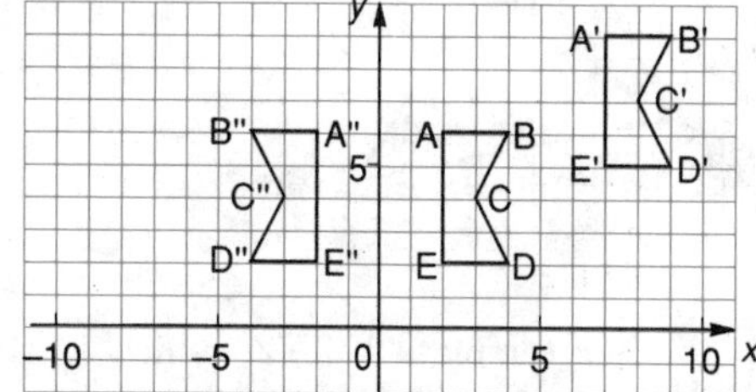

Describe, fully, the single transformation that maps
(a) ABCDE to A′B′C′D′E′,
(b) ABCDE to A″B″C″D″E″.

(*LEAG*, 1988)

91

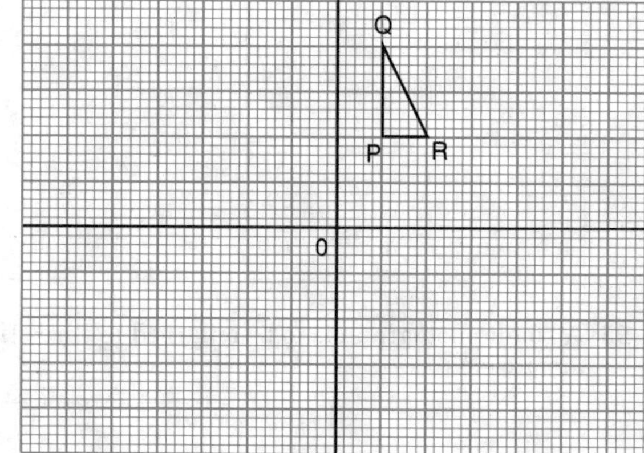

(a) Draw the image of triangle PQR after a quarter turn, anticlockwise about P. Label this image **A**.
(b) Draw the image of triangle PQR after a quarter turn, clockwise about O. Label this image **B**.

(*LEAG*, 1988)

92

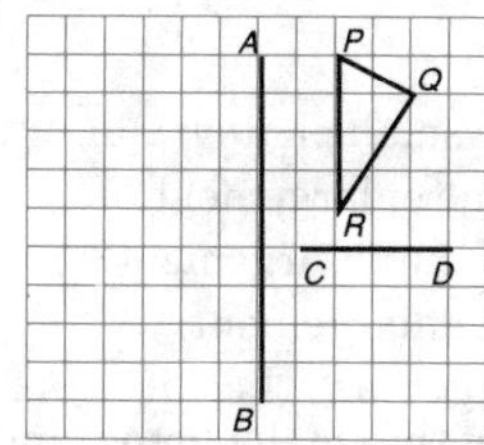

On the grid above, draw the triangle which is produced when triangle PQR is
(a) reflected in the line AB,
(b) reflected in the line CD. (*NEA*, 1988)

93 The diagram (overleaf) shows a shape and a mirror line. Draw the reflection of the shape.

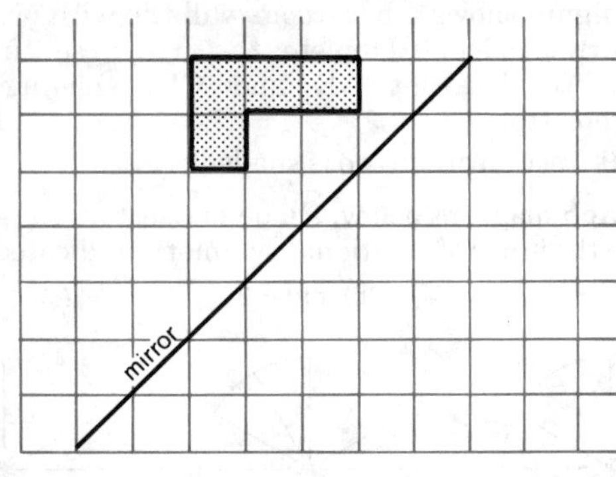

(*NEA**)

Unit 1.41

94 A machinist makes a template ABCD for use in the design of wallpaper patterns. The size and shape of ABCD is shown on the grid below.

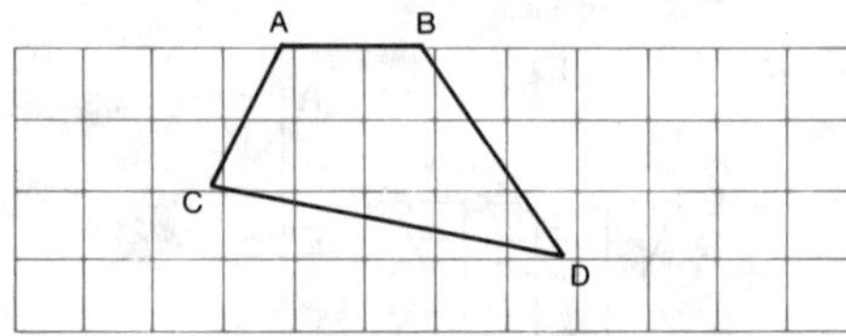

Draw another template WXYZ, which is **similar** to ABCD, but has a perimeter which is twice as big as ABCD. One side has been drawn for you.(*SEG**)

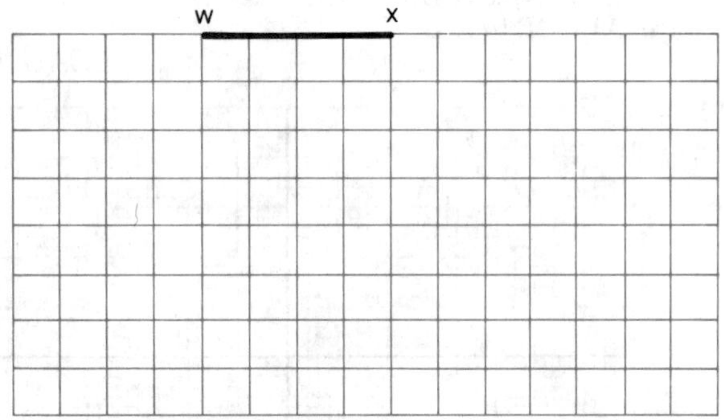

95 A small photograph is to be enlarged to three times its dimensions.

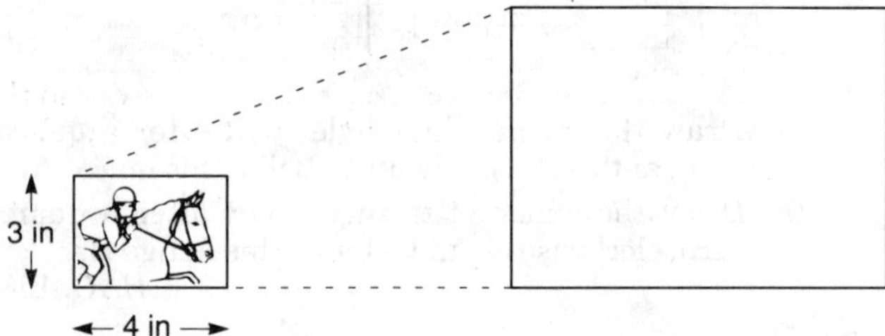

(a) Calculate the area of the small photograph.
(b) Give the dimensions of the enlargement.
(c) What is the perimeter of the enlargement?
(d) Calculate the area of the enlargement.
(e) How many times bigger is the area of the enlargement than that of the small photograph?

(*NEA*, 1988)

Unit 1.42

96 A model of a tank is 6.5 cm long. The scale of the model is 1 to 72. Calculate the length of the tank in metres.

(*MEG**)

97 The sketch of a clock tower is shown.

A model of the tower is made using a scale of 1 to 20.

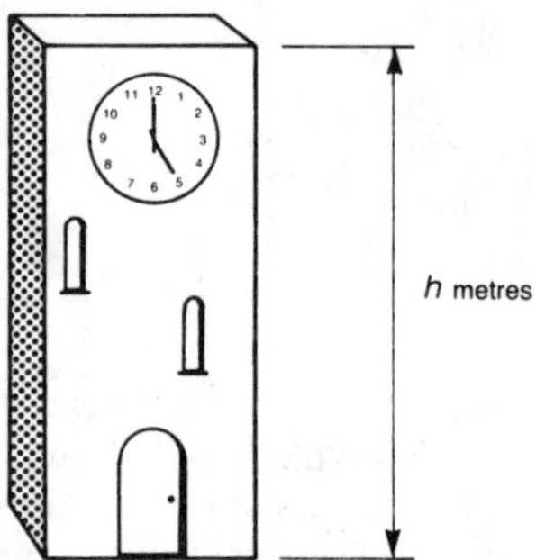

(a) The minute hand on the tower clock is 40 cm long. What is the length of the minute hand on the model?
(b) The height of the model is 40 cm. What is the height (h), in metres, of the clock tower?

(*SEG**)

Unit 1.43

98

The map shows some of the towns in England, Scotland and Wales. It is drawn on a scale of 1 cm to 100 km. The direction of North is shown. Use your ruler and/or protractor to answer the following questions.

(a) Which town marked is approximately due East of Oxford?
(b) What is the distance between Liverpool and Brighton?
(c) Which town is approximately 360 km on a bearing of 132° from Carlisle?
(d) What is the bearing of Norwich from Cardiff?

(*MEG**)

99

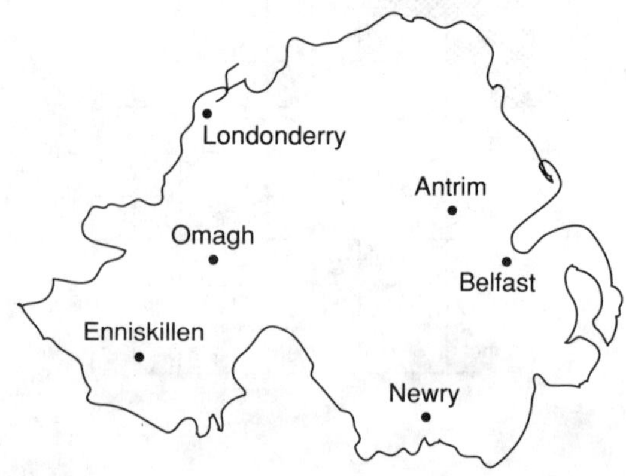

There is a fairly direct road from Belfast to Newry.

(a) (i) Measure the distance between Belfast and Newry, correct to the nearest centimetre, on the map.

(ii) Taking the direct distance of Belfast from Newry to be 56 km, give the scale of the map.

(b) (i) There is also a fairly direct road from Londonderry to Antrim. Measure the distance on the map, correct to one decimal place.

(ii) Find, correct to one decimal place, the approximate distance by road from Londonderry to Antrim.

(*NISEC*, 1988)

Unit 1.44

100 This sketch shows three posts A, B and C on a building site. It also shows some lengths and some bearings.

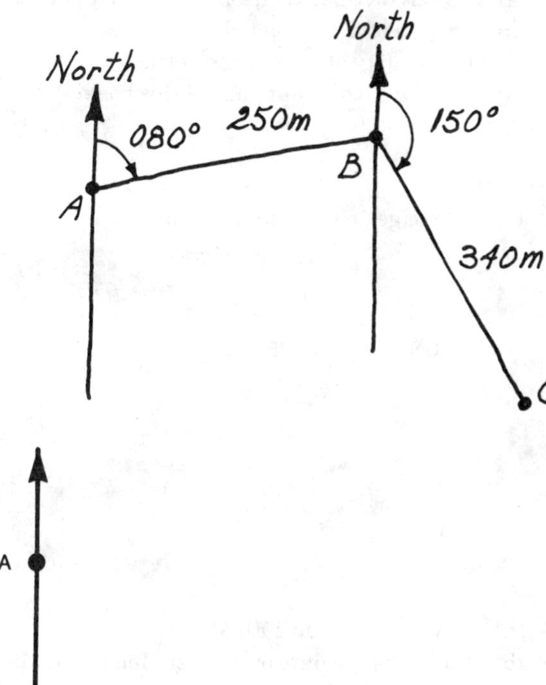

(a) Using the distances and bearings shown on the diagram make a scale drawing to show the positions of A, B and C. Use a scale of 1 cm to represent 50 m.

(b) (i) Join AC and measure its length to the nearest millimetre.

(ii) What is the distance, on the building site, between the two posts A and C?

(c) (i) Measure and write down the size of angle BAC.

(ii) What is the bearing of C from A?

(iii) What is the bearing of A from C?

(d) By drawing further lines on your scale drawing, find how far the post C is East of the post A.

(*SEG**)

101 A group of children measured the school playing field. As a result of their survey they produced the following diagram.

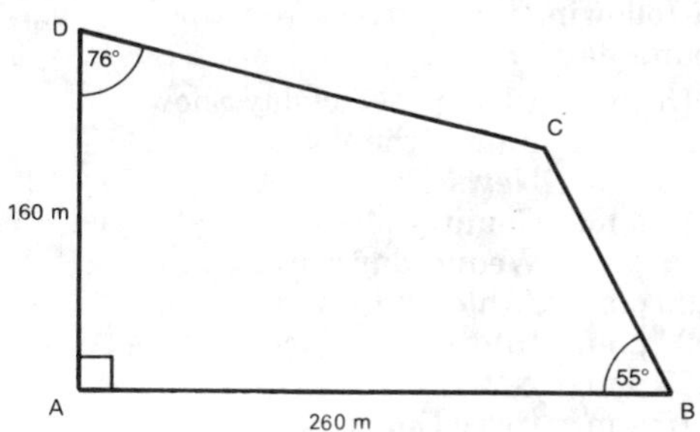

Using the scale of 1 cm to represent 20 m, make a scale drawing of the field.

(*WJEC**)

Unit 1.45

102 The picture shows a pyramid. The dotted lines show hidden edges.

(i) How many faces has the pyramid got?

(ii) How many edges has the pyramid got?

This picture shows a cuboid. (The hidden edges are not shown.)

(iii) How many edges does the cuboid have?

(iv) How many faces does the cuboid have?

This picture shows the pyramid fitting exactly on top of the cuboid making a single solid.

(v) How many faces has it got?

(vi) How many edges has it got?

(vii) How many corners has it got?

(viii) Explain why it is not correct to add together the number of faces of the pyramid and the number of faces of the cuboid to get the number of faces of the combined shape.

(*NEA**)

103

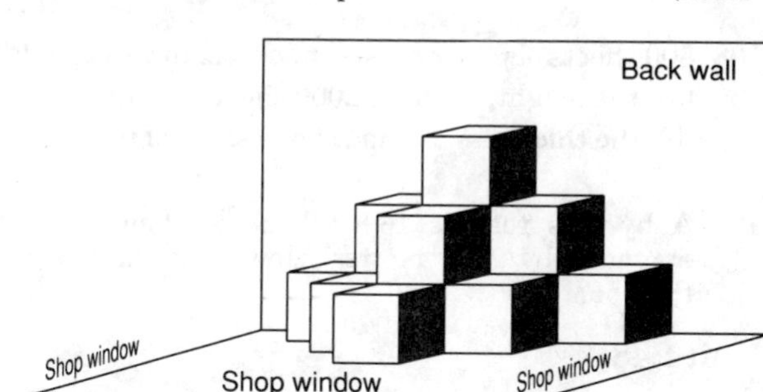

Jill Baker has been given the job of creating a shop display. She wants to use a number of identical cubical boxes stacked against the back wall of the shop window as shown. It is around this that she wants to create her display.

(a) How many boxes are there in the stack?

(b) If all the surfaces of the boxes that are visible in the window are to be painted yellow, how many faces need painting?

(c) Each edge of each box is 0.4 metres long. What is the total area that Jill must paint, to the nearest square metre?

(*NEA*, 1988)

Unit 1.46

104

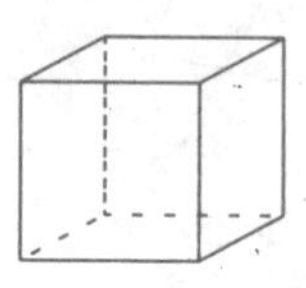

The front and back faces of this cube are to be coloured yellow, the left and right faces green, the top and bottom faces black. The nets below are to be coloured and made into cubes the same as this one. Mark on the nets B for black, Y for yellow, G for green.

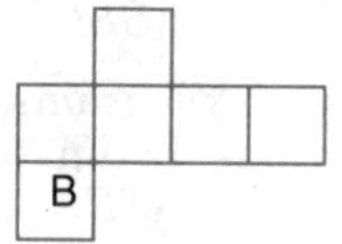

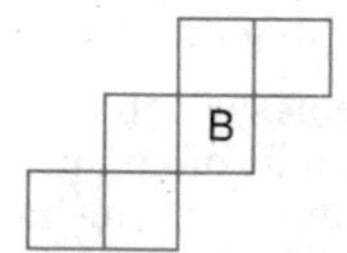

(*NISEC*, 1988)

105 The figure shows a net consisting of 2 squares and 4 rectangles. It is cut out and folded to make a solid figure.

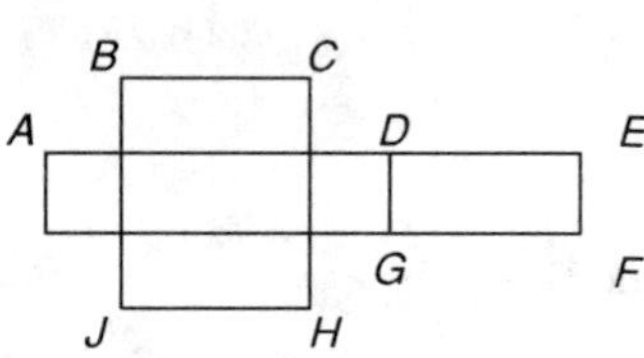

(a) What type of solid is formed?
(b) Which points of the net meet at B?
(*SEG*, 1988)

106 The diagram shows the net of a three dimensional solid.
(i) Write down the name of the solid.
(ii) How many corners does the solid have?
(iii) How many edges does the solid have?

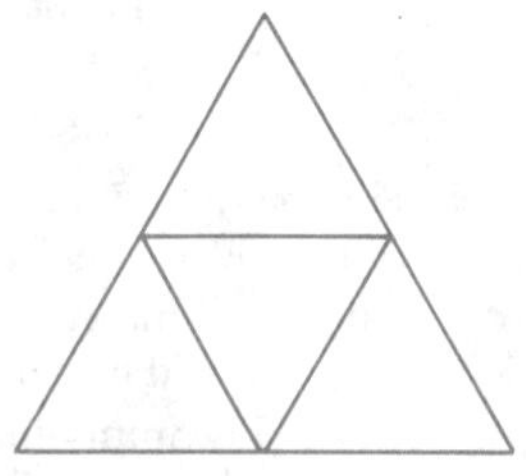

(*WJEC**)

Unit 1.47

107 You have a piece of ribbon 3 m long. You cut off 2.8 m. How long is the piece you have left? Give your answer in cm.

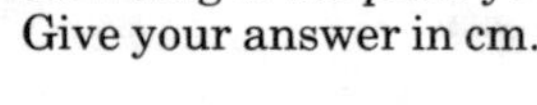

(*LEAG**)

108 500 sheets of paper make a pile 6 cm high. Calculate
(a) the height, in cm, of 2000 sheets of paper,
(b) the thickness, in mm, of one sheet of paper.
(*LEAG*, 1988)

109 A by-pass road is 16.8 kilometres long. It is to be extended by 2780 metres. How long will the by-pass then be? (*LEAG*, 1988)

Unit 1.48

110 A recipe for Rice Cake lists the following ingredients:

butter	200 g
castor sugar	385 g
5 eggs	
ground rice	380 g

If the mass of one egg is 55 g, find the total mass of the ingredients, expressing your answer in kilograms.
(*MEG**)

111 Roger weighs some rice. The diagram shows the weight in kilograms.

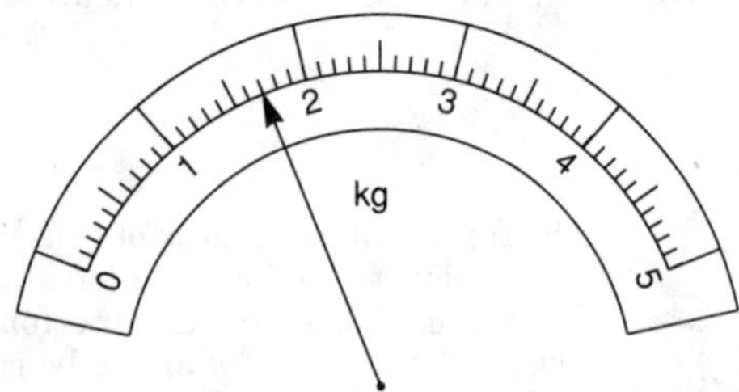

(a) What is the weight of the rice in kilograms?
(b) What is the weight of the rice in grams?
(c) Taking 1 kg to be 2.2 pounds, calculate the weight of the rice in pounds. (*SEG*, 1988)

112 A bag of apples weighs approximately 2 kilograms. The average weight of an apple is 205 grams. Estimate the number of apples in the bag. (*SEG*, 1988)

Unit 1.49

113 At a cafe, cola is sold in 250 cm^3 glasses. How many glasses could be completely filled from a 3 litre bottle?
(*LEAG*, 1988)

Units 1.47, 1.48 and 1.49

114 Complete each of the following
(a) 125 mm = __________ cm
(b) 2.2 kg = 2 kg __________ g
(c) 750 ml = __________ l (*MEG*, 1988)

Units 1.47, 1.49 and 1.52

115 Write down the most appropriate **metric** unit for measuring
(a) the distance between Birmingham and Cambridge,
(b) the area of a playing field,
(c) the capacity of a medicine bottle,
(d) the area of the front page of this book.
(*MEG*, 1988)

Unit 1.50

116 Part of a page of a calendar was found.

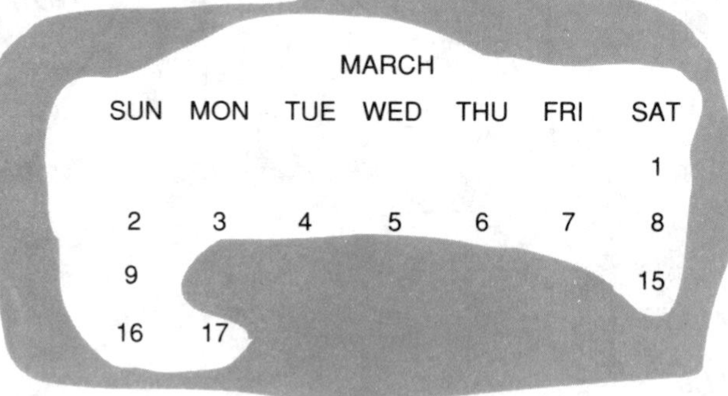

(a) On what day was 29th March?
(b) What was the date of the last Monday in March?
(c) How many Wednesdays were there in March that year?
(d) On what day was 21st April in the same year?
(e) On what day was 11th June in the same year?
(f) Could the 27th February have been on a Wednesday?
(g) Explain your answer to part (f).
(*NISEC*, 1988)

117 A liner left Southampton on 25 March for a Mediterranean cruise. The liner returned to Southampton nineteen days later. What was the date of return to Southampton? (*NEA*, 1988)

118 About three babies are born every second somewhere in the world. How many is this in a year, to the nearest million? (*MEG*, 1988)

119 Sivayogi took 3 hours 10 minutes to run a marathon. The race began at 10.30 a.m. At what time did she finish the race? (*LEAG*, 1988)

120 The following is an extract from the TV programmes for Wednesday 19 June.

7.15 p.m.	Blackpool Holiday Show
8.20 p.m.	Film of the Week
10.05 p.m.	News
10.15 p.m.	Country Music (repeat of last Wednesday's programme)
11.00 p.m.	Athletics Championships
11.25 p.m.	International Ice-Skating
11.55 p.m.	News
12.15 a.m.	Close Down

(i) How long does the film last?
(ii) Which programme lasts just over an hour?
(iii) On what date was Country Music first shown?
(iv) If someone watches all the above programmes, how long will they have been watching? (*NEA**)

121 These are some of the television programmes on Sunday night.

6.40 Songs of Praise
7.15 Howard's Way
7.50 Crisis
9.45 Mastermind
10.15 News

I wish to record **'Crisis'** on my video machine. It has to be set using the 24-hour clock.
(a) Write down the starting time.
(b) The machine switches off at the start of **'Mastermind'**. How long will it have been on?
(c) I started the recording on a new 3-hour tape. How much recording time is left on the tape?
(*MEG*, 1988)

122 After a day on the beach at Barry Island, Sarah and Lisa catch the train back to Cardiff.
(a) The train leaves Barry at 17 45. Write down this time in the 12-hour system.
(b) The train arrives in Cardiff at 18 05. How long does the journey take? (*WJEC*, 1988)

123 An aeroplane from America is due to land at Heathrow at 14.15. Because of a strong tail wind it actually arrives 55 minutes early. What time does it arrive?
(*SEG**)

Units 1.51 and 1.45

124 A piece of wire is 60 cm long. It can be made into any one of the following shapes. No wire is wasted.
(a) Equilateral triangle. What is the length of each side?
(b) Square. What is the length of each side?
(c) Rectangle. The rectangle is 10 cm wide. What is its length?
(d) Cuboid.
The skeleton framework is shown in the diagram.
What is the height, h cm, of this cuboid?

h cm
5 cm
7 cm

(*MEG*, 1988)

Units 1.51 and 1.52

125 A racehorse trainer buys 28 fence panels.
(a) Use spotty paper to work out **all** the possible ways of arranging the fence panels to enclose a rectangle (one is drawn for you).

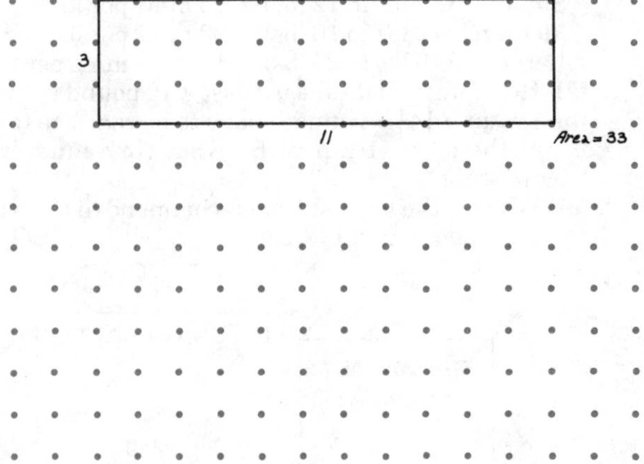

(b) (i) Which of the arrangements will give the trainer the largest paddock?
(ii) What is its area? (*LEAG**)

126

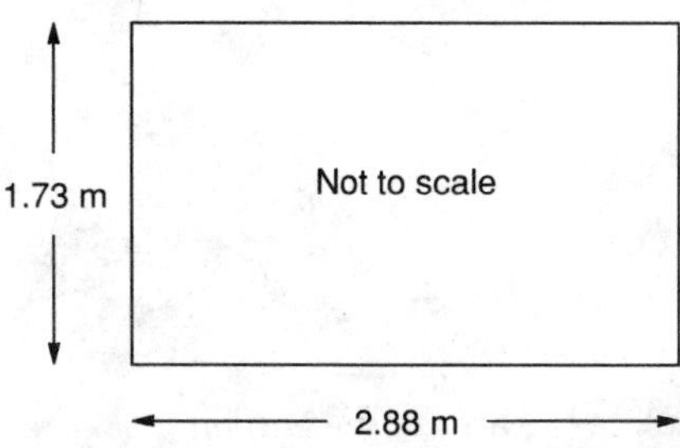

The diagram is of a sheet of glass which has been cut to fit a large rectangular window.
(a) Calculate the exact value of
(i) the perimeter of the glass,
(ii) the area of one side of the glass.
(b) Write down your answers to part (a) correct to the nearest whole number.
(*MEG*, 1988)

Unit 1.52

127 The diagram shows a shape drawn on a rectangular grid. Each square measures 1 cm by 1 cm.

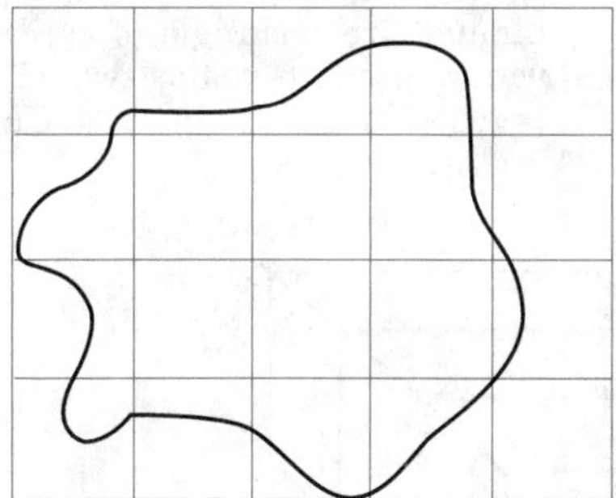

Estimate the area of the shape in cm^2. (*NEA*, 1988)

128

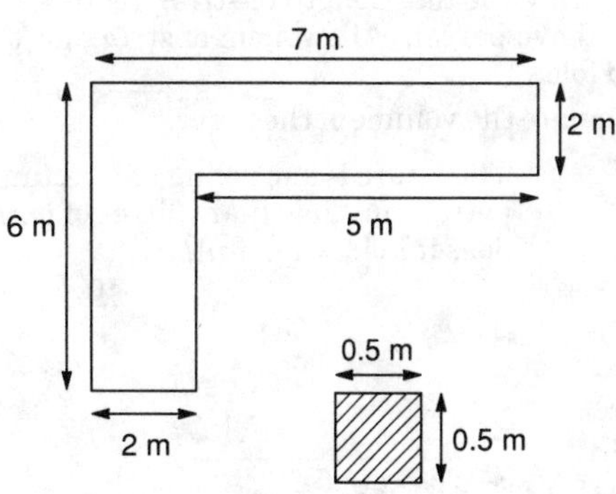

(a) The diagram shows a corridor 2 m wide.
Calculate the area of the floor of the corridor.
(b) The floor of this corridor is covered with square carpet tiles which have a side of 0.5 m as shown.
(i) How many carpet tiles are needed to cover 1 square metre?
(ii) How many tiles are needed to cover the corridor?
(*SEG*, 1988)

129 This is a sketch of Brian's garden. The measurements are in metres.

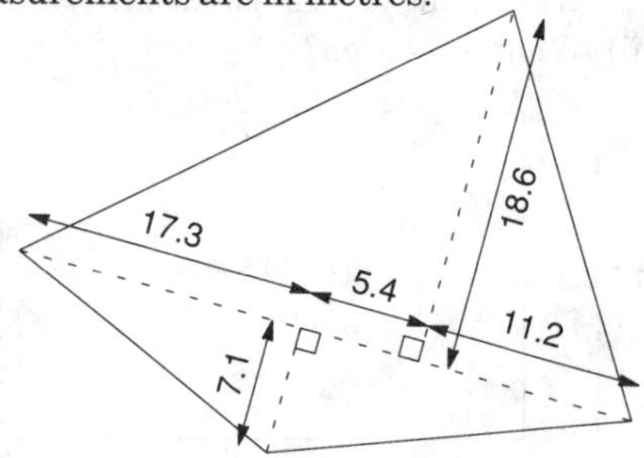

(a) Calculate the area of the garden.

(b) Brian is going to sow grass seed over the whole garden. He uses 45 g of seed for each square metre. He can buy seed in 2 kg bags. How many bags should he buy?

(*MEG*, 1988)

Unit 1.53 and 1.46

130

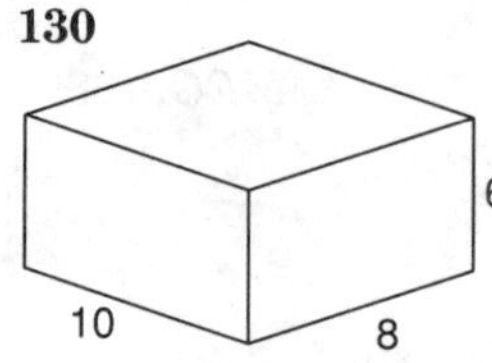

A cuboid measures 10 cm by 8 cm by 6 cm.

(a) On graph paper using a scale of 1 cm to represent 2 cm, draw an accurate net which could be folded to make the cuboid.

(b) (i) Find the area of the net **on your graph paper**.
(ii) Find the total surface area of the **cuboid**.

(c) What is the minimum size rectangle of card you would need if you wanted to make two of the cuboids?

(*SEG**)

Unit 1.54

131

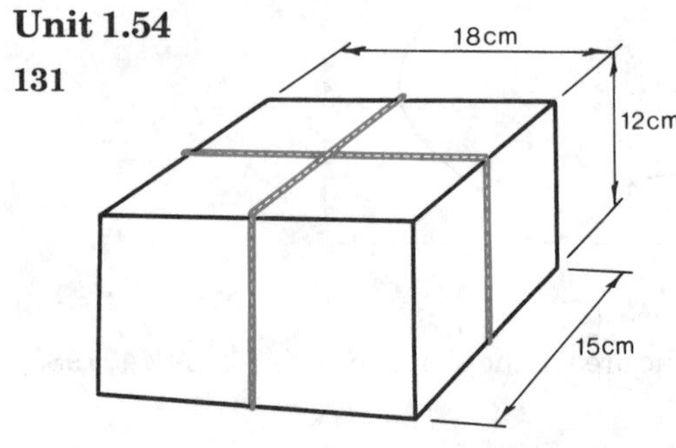

(i) Calculate the total length of string required to wrap the above parcel. (Allow 4 cm of string for the knot and folds.)

(ii) Calculate the volume of the parcel. (*WJEC**)

132 The figure is a drawing of a rectangular petrol can. How many litres of petrol does it hold when full?

(*LEAG*, 1988)

32 cm
25 cm
10 cm

133

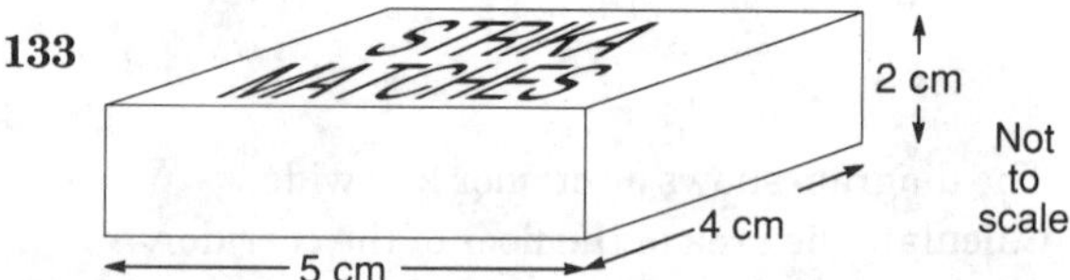

The diagram shows a matchbox measuring 5 cm by 4 cm by 2 cm.

(a) Calculate the volume of the matchbox.

12 similar matchboxes fill a carton with base dimensions of 10 cm by 8 cm. Calculate

(b) the volume of the carton,

(c) the height of the carton,

(d) the total number of matches in the carton, if each box contains 48 matches. (*MEG*, 1988)

134

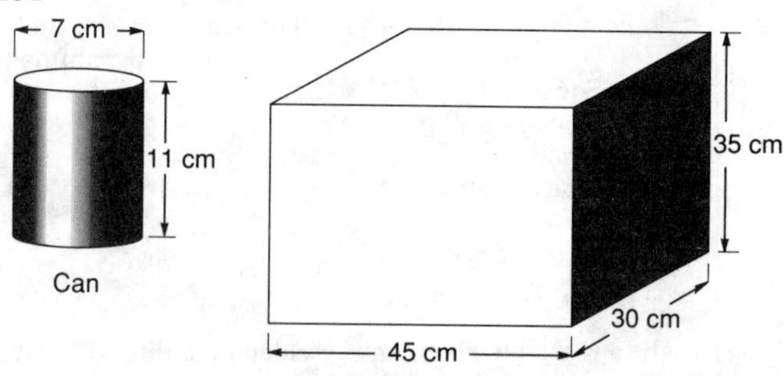

(a) John is responsible for packing these cans into boxes. He can pack the cans in more than one way. Describe **two** ways in which they could be packed, finding out for each method how many cans fit in the box and using diagrams if necessary.

(b) Calculate the volume of the box.

(c) The volume of each can is approximately 420 cm^3. Choosing **one** of your methods for packing the box, find how much empty space in left inside the box.

(*NEA*, 1988)

Unit 1.55

135 To hire a car, a customer has to pay a basic charge of £17. There is a further charge of 7p per mile for each mile travelled. Calculate the total cost of hiring a car to travel 150 miles. (*LEAG*, 1988)

136 A machine always works at the same rate. It produces 150 rods in 5 minutes. How long will it take to produce 375 rods? (*SEG*, 1988)

137 Margaret and David want to find out how much petrol their car uses in miles per gallon. They fill the car with petrol when the reading on the milometer is

0	2	8	3	4	0

After a few days they stop at a garage selling petrol at £1.70 per gallon. They fill the car up again and the cost of the petrol is £13.60. By this time the milometer reading is

0	2	8	6	2	0

How many miles per gallon does the car do over this period?

(*WJEC*, 1988)

138 My cookery book gives these times for roasting a turkey:

Small	(6 lbs to 12 lbs)	25 mins per lb
Medium	(12 lbs to 16 lbs)	20 mins per lb
Large	(16 lbs to 25 lbs)	15 to 18 mins per lb.

(a) How long will it take to roast a 10 pound turkey?

(b) I want a 14½- pound turkey to be ready to take out of the oven at 2 p.m. By what time must it start roasting?

(c) What is the longest time recommended for roasting a 22- pound turkey? (*MEG*, 1988)

139

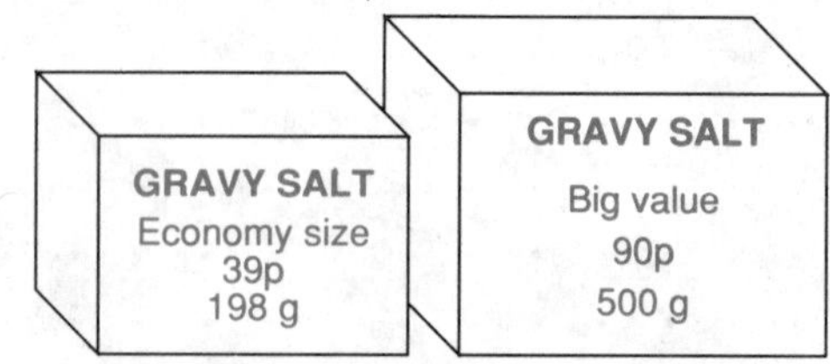

Gravy salt is sold in two different sized packets as shown.

(a) What is the weight of the gravy salt per penny
   (i) for the 'Economy' packet?
   (ii) for the 'Big value' packet?

(b) From your answer to part (a), which packet is the better value, and why? (*NEA*, 1988)

Unit 1.56

140 During the rush hour, it takes a telephonist 40 minutes to travel the 5 miles from home to work. Find the telephonist's average speed in miles per hour. (*LEAG*, 1988)

141 This chart shows the distances between six towns in miles.

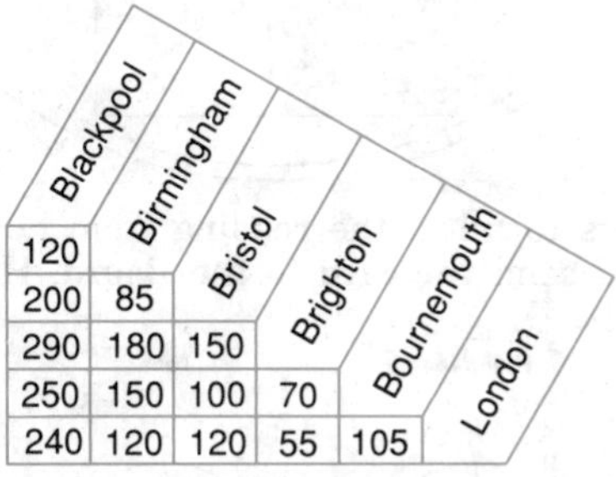

	Blackpool	Birmingham	Bristol	Brighton	Bournemouth
Birmingham	120				
Bristol	200	85			
Brighton	290	180	150		
Bournemouth	250	150	100	70	
London	240	120	120	55	105

A lorry driver travels from Birmingham to Bristol and then on to Brighton at an average speed of 45 mph. How long does her journey take? (Give your answer to the nearest hour.) (*SEG**)

142 A boy lives 2.4 miles from his school.

(a) Calculate the time, in minutes, that he takes to walk from his home to school, if he walks at an average speed of 3 mph.

(b) If he arrives at the school at 8.35 a.m., at what time did he leave home? (*MEG*, 1988)

Unit 1.57

143 The graph shows Mrs Parr's journey from her home in Winchester to Bournemouth, a distance of 60 km. Mrs Parr left home at 0900 and travelled towards Bournemouth for 40 km. She stopped at a garage to fill up with petrol before continuing her journey to Bournemouth.

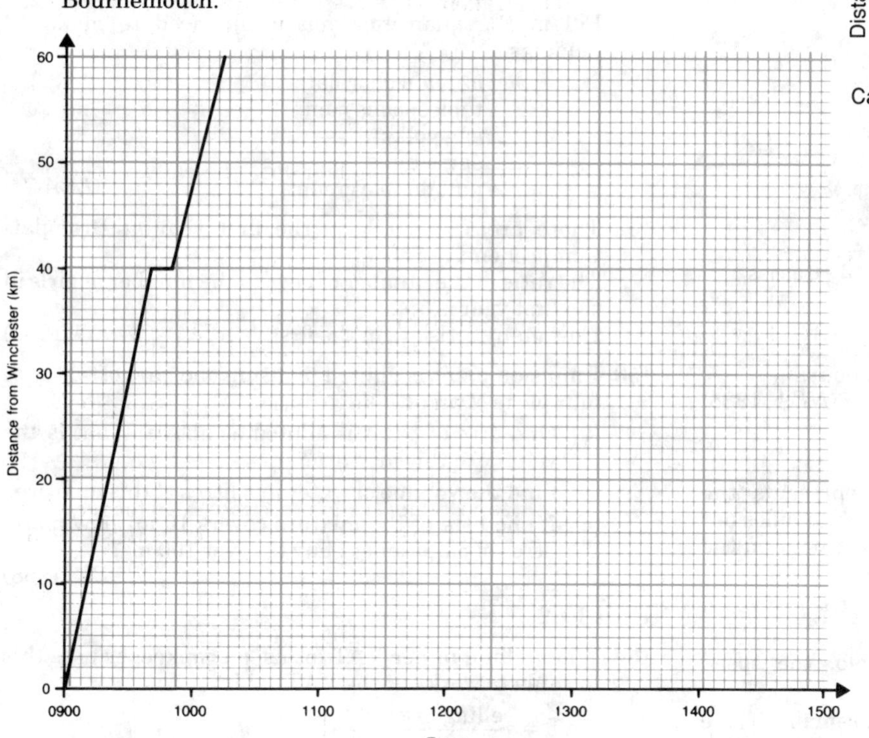

(a) What was the time when Mrs Parr stopped at the garage?

(b) How long did Mrs Parr stop at the garage?

(c) (i) After leaving the garage, how long did it take Mrs Parr to reach Bournemouth?
   (ii) What was Mrs Parr's speed, in kilometres per hour, during this stage of her journey?

Mrs Parr stayed in Bournemouth for 3 hours before starting her return journey to Winchester.

(d) (i) At what time did she leave Bournemouth?
   (ii) Draw a line on the travel graph to represent her stay in Bournemouth.

(e) Mrs Parr began driving home at an average speed of 60 kilometres per hour, but 15 minutes after starting her journey she punctured a tyre and had to stop. She took 18 minutes to change the wheel and then continued at the same average speed.
   (i) Complete the travel graph to show Mrs Parr's return journey.
   (ii) At what time did Mrs Parr arrive home?

(*SEG**)

144 A car leaves Carlisle and travels to Birmingham at a speed of 70 mph. At the same time a car leaves Birmingham and travels to Carlisle on the same route at a speed of 50 mph.

On the diagram, draw the travel graph for the first car. The travel graph for the second car is already printed on the diagram.

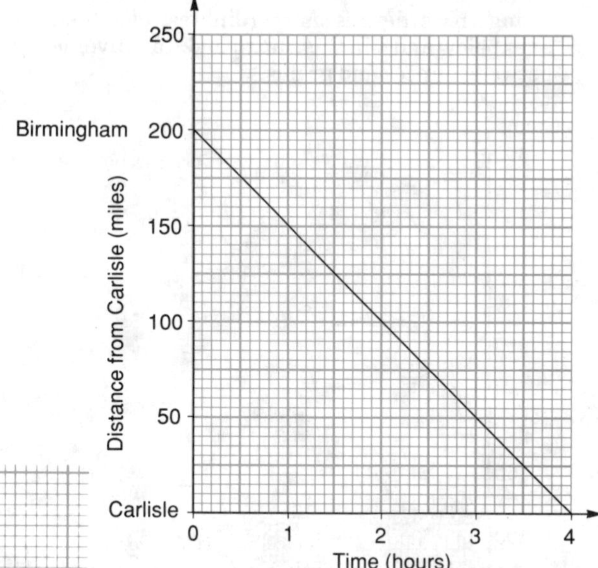

Clearly mark on your graph the point at which the two cars pass each other.

(a) At what distance from Carlisle does the diagram suggest that they will pass?

(b) How long have the cars been travelling when they pass each other? Give your answer in hours and minutes.

(*NEA*, 1988)

Unit 1.58

145 Jane is going on holiday to France and needs to buy some films for her camera. If she buys them in England before she goes, they will cost her £2.25 each. If she waits until she gets to France and buys them there, they will cost her 20.16 francs each.

If the exchange rate is £1 to 9.60 francs, find out how much, in English currency, she can save on each film by buying them in France. (*MEG*, 1988)

146 Express a speed of 15 metres per second as a speed in kilometres per hour. (*LEAG*, 1988)

147 Sanjeev is considering buying a new car. Of two similar models, one is claimed to do 45 miles per gallon, whilst the manufacturers of the other model claim that it uses 6 litres per 100 km.

Compare the petrol consumption of the two cars and state which car has the better claimed petrol consumption.

(One mile = 1.609 km; one gallon = 4.54 litres.)

(*NEA*, 1988)

Unit 1.59

148 Some packets and jars have both ounces and grams written on them.

Stuffing 12 ounces, 340 grams.
Gravy granules 6 ounces, 170 grams.
Peas 10 ounces, 280 grams.
Mustard 3 ounces, 85 grams.

Using these figures as coordinates, plot them on the axes below and join them up to make a conversion graph between ounces and grams.

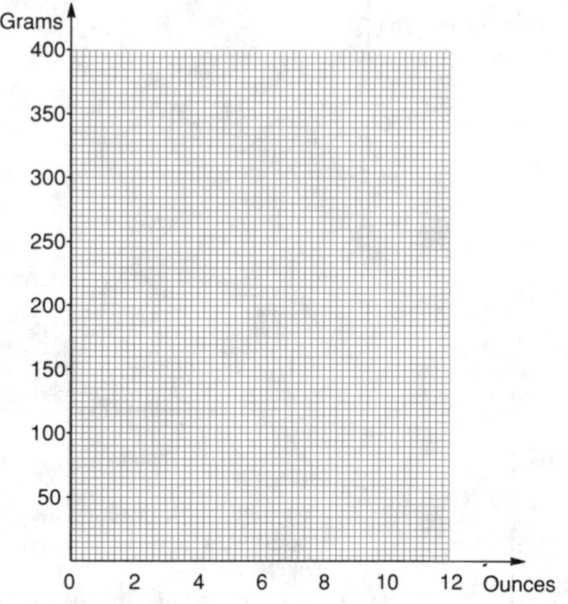

Use your graph to estimate

(a) the weight in grams of 4 ounces of salt,

(b) the weight in ounces of 265 grams of flour.

(*NEA*, 1988)

Unit 1.60

149 The diagram (top of next column) represents the speedometer of a car. The speeds are given in miles per hour on the outer scale and kilometres per hour on the inner scale. There is also a fuel gauge.

(a) Write down the speed, in m.p.h., that is shown on the dial.

(b) Estimate, as accurately as possible, the speed shown in km/h.

(c) What fraction, of a full tank of fuel, remains in the car? (*LEAG*, 1988)

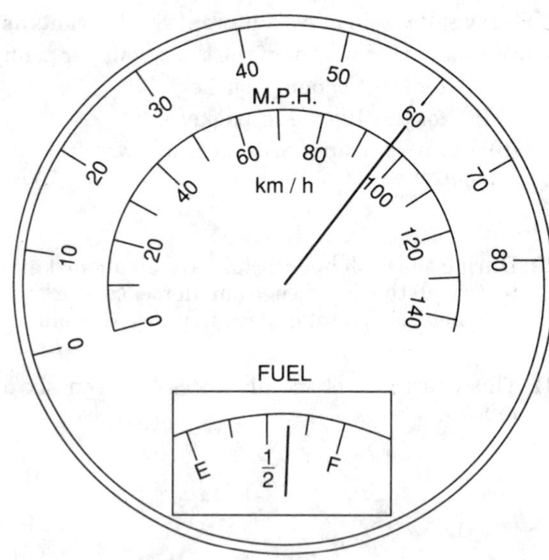

150 Mandy has to fill in the reading from her electricity meter and send the card to the Board. Here are the meter dials.

Thousands Hundreds Tens Units

Fill in the spaces on the card.

Meter reading	1000s	100s	Tens	Units

(*LEAG**)

Unit 1.61

151 This is a recipe for 4 helpings of a chocolate pudding.

4 oz plain chocolate
2 tablespoons rum
4 egg yolks
6 eggs whites
½ pint double cream

Fill in the quantities you would need to make 10 helpings.

_____ oz plain chocolate
_____ tablespoons rum
_____ egg yolks
_____ egg whites
_____ pint double cream (*LEAG**)

152 There are 180 pupils in the first year at Bronglais Comprehensive School.

The ratio of the number of boys to the number of girls in the first year is 5:4.

How many girls are in the first year? (*WJEC*, 1988)

153 Emulsion paint is diluted by using one part of water to four parts of paint.

(a) One litre of paint is diluted as above. What is the volume of this mixture?

(b) Find the volume of water in 5 litres of this mixture.

(c) If one litre of the mixture covers 10 m^2 how many litres of paint must I buy to cover 100 m^2?

(*NISEC*, 1988)

Unit 1.62

154 When filling in her VAT forms, a shopkeeper uses this formula to work out the VAT paid.

$$\text{VAT} = \frac{\text{selling price} \times 3}{23}$$

Work out the VAT on
(i) a jacket sold for £46.
(ii) a bookshelf sold for £39.95, giving your answer to the nearest penny. (*WJEC**)

155 The cooking time, T minutes, for a joint of meat is given by the formula

$$T = 15 + 20W,$$

where W pounds is the weight of the joint of meat.
(a) Find the value of T when $W = 4$.
(b) At what time of day should you start cooking a joint of meat of weight 3 pounds so that it is ready to eat at 13.00 hours? (*NEA*, 1988)

156 (a) Use the formula $d = s \times t$ to find d when $s = 5.5$ and $t = 4.3$.
(b) Use the formula $V = a^2h$ to find V when $a = 4$ and $h = 3$. (*MEG*, 1988)

Unit 1.63

157

$n \rightarrow$ [subtract 2] $\rightarrow (n-2) \rightarrow$ [multiply by 180] $\rightarrow 180(n-2)$

The flow diagram is used to find the number of degrees in the sum of the interior angles of polygon with n sides.
A hexagon has 6 sides.
(a) Using $n = 6$, find the sum of the interior angles of a hexagon.
The interior angles of a regular hexagon are all equal.
(b) Work out the size of one of the interior angles of a regular hexagon. (*LEAG*, 1988)

158

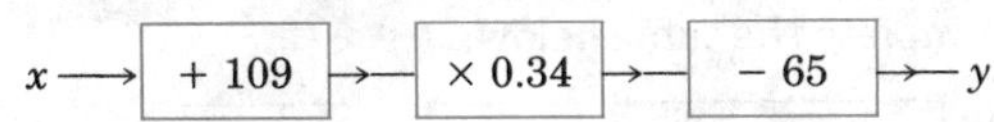

Calculate the exact value of y when $x = 213$. (*NEA*, 1988)

159 (a) Rachel thinks of a number. She doubles it, adds one, and gets twenty-three. What was her number?
(b) Jenny chooses a prime number between ten and twenty. She doubles it, adds five, and this gives her a number more than thirty-two. What numbers could Jenny have chosen? (*NEA*, 1988)

Unit 1.64

160

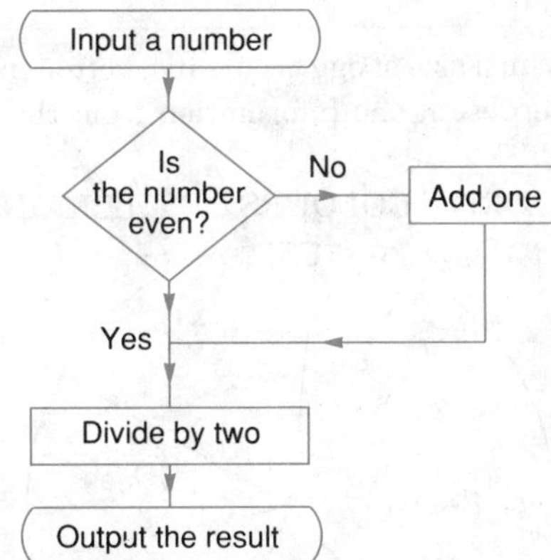

(a) What is the output when the input is 7?
(b) If the output is 3, what are the two possible inputs? (*SEG*, 1988)

Unit 1.65

161 Jan Kirby uses a code to send messages to her friends. Each letter is changed to a pair of numbers using the grid shown below.
For example, B is changed to (2, 4) and TEA is changed to (4, 3)(4, 4)(2, 5).

Second number					
5	J	A	N	K	I
4	R	B	Y	E	X
3	M	O	U	T	H
2	C	D	F	G	L
1	P	Q	S	V	W
	1	2	3	4	5

First number

(a) Put COSY into code.
(b) What word, written in code, is
(3, 5)(5, 5)(4, 2)(5, 3)(4, 3)?
(c) Suggest a code for the letter Z. (*MEG*, 1988)

Units 1.65, 1.35 and 1.52

162

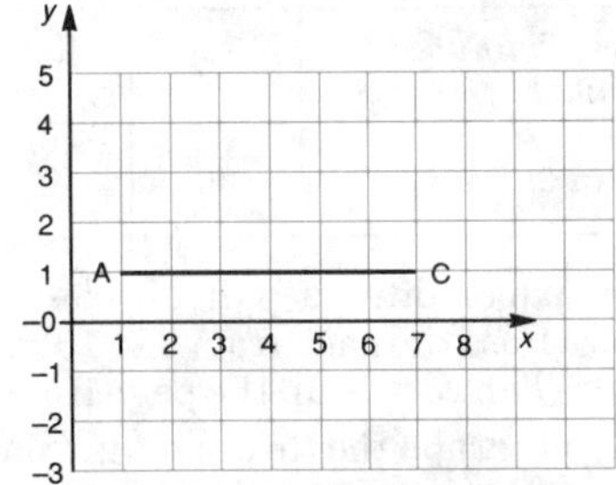

On the grid shown A is the point (1,1) and C is the point (7,1). AC is a line of symmetry of a kite.
(a) B is the point (3,4). Mark this on the grid and draw the kite ABCD.
(b) Write down the coordinates of D.
(c) ABED is a rhombus.
(i) Draw ABED on the grid.
(ii) Write down the coordinates of E.
(d) Find the area of shape BCDE. (*NISEC*, 1988)

Unit 1.66

163 Emily was seriously ill in hospital, and it was necessary to keep a constant watch on her temperature. She was therefore connected to a machine which measured her temperature and drew the following graph.

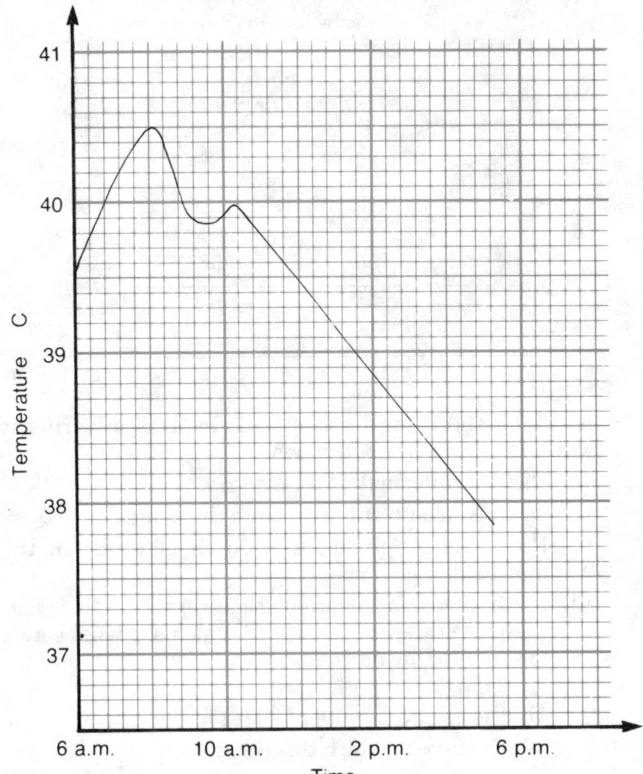

(i) At what time was her temperature highest?
(ii) What was this highest temperature?
(iii) At what time did her temperature start to go down steadily and not rise again?
(iv) Emily's normal temperature is 37°C. For how long was her temperature more than 2°C higher than this?
(v) Emily's temperature continues to fall at the same rate. At what time will it be back at normal?

(*LEAG**)

164 The total charge a computer firm makes for running a program is made up of two parts.

(i) A fixed basic fee and
(ii) a charge for each minute the program runs.

The total charges for three programs are shown in the following table:

Time (Number of minutes the program runs)	5	10	15
Total charge (in £)	35	45	75

(a) On graph paper draw a pair of axes. Mark your *Time* axis across the page from 0 to 16 minutes. Mark your *Charge* axis up the page from 0 to £90.
(b) Mark on your graph the three points from the table.
(c) Draw the straight line passing through the three plotted points.
(d) Use your graph to find
 (i) the total charge for a 12 minute program.
 (ii) the number of minutes a program runs when the total charge is £43.
 (iii) the fixed basic fee which the firm always charges.
(e) What would be the total charge for a 25 minute program?

(*MEG*, 1988)

165

Time	1 p.m.	2 p.m.	3 p.m.	4 p.m.	5 p.m.	6 p.m.	7 p.m.
Depth in metres	1.0	1.6	2.4	3.2	3.2	2.4	1.6

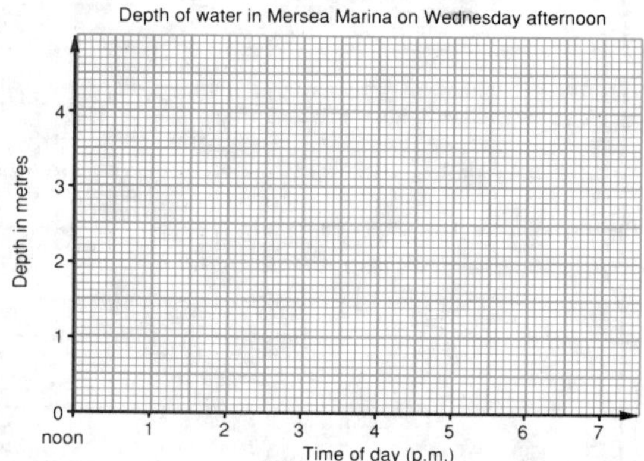

The table shows the depth of water in Mersea Marina at various times in the afternoon.

(a) Plot this information on the grid.
(b) Draw a smooth curve through the points.
(c) From the graph find the depth of water in the marina at 6.30 p.m.
(d) Amanda needs a depth of 2 metres to sail her boat. Estimate the earliest time at which she will be able to sail into the marina.
(e) Estimate
 (i) the greatest depth of water in the marina,
 (ii) the time at which this occurs.

(*LEAG*, 1988)

Unit 1.67

166

KEY  represents £1 million

Donations  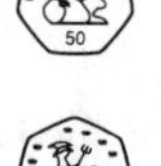   

Interest  

Legacies  

The pictogram represents the income received by a charity fund in 1984.

(a) Write, in figures, the amount the charity fund received from **legacies**.
(b) How much did the charity fund receive altogether?
(c) Give the ratio of the amount received from donations to the amount received from interest.
(d) In 1985, the amount received from donations increased by £2 million, the amount received from interest increased by £1 million and the amount received from legacies fell by £1½ million. Construct a pictogram for 1985, using the symbol □ to represent £2 million.

(*LEAG*, 1989)

167 Eggs are graded on a scale 1 to 6 according to size. Here are the grades of a batch of 30 eggs.

3 5 3 6 4 5 5 6 4 4
4 2 4 4 5 4 4 2 4 3
6 4 5 3 1 6 3 5 5 4

(a) Complete the table below.

Egg size	*Number of eggs*
1	1
2	2
3	5
4	
5	
6	

(b) Which size of egg occurs most often in this batch?
(c) Represent the information from the table in a bar chart.

(*NEA*, 1988)

168 FAVOURITE COLOURS OF THE RAINBOW

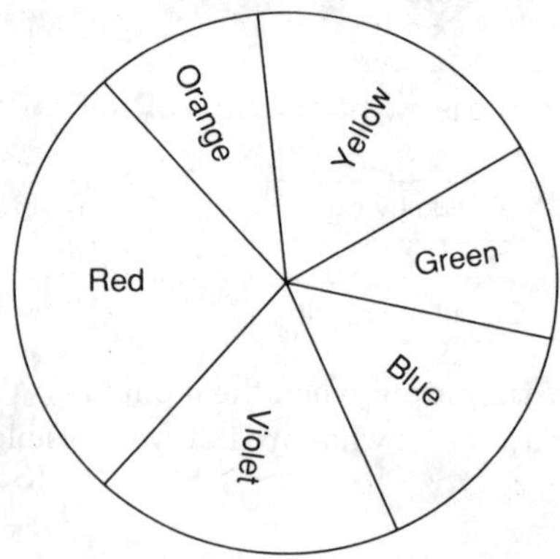

60 children were asked which was their favourite colour of the rainbow. The result is shown in the pie chart above.

Use your protractor to find

(a) which two colours were equally popular,

(b) how many children chose red as their favourite colour,
(c) how many more children chose blue than chose green,
(d) what percentage of the children chose orange.
(NISEC, 1988)

Unit 1.68

169 The attendance figures for the Ulster Motor Show are given below.

Monday	11 232
Tuesday	11 499
Wednesday	14 238
Thursday	13 168
Friday	13 403
Saturday	11 724

(a) What was the total attendance?
(b) What was the average (mean) daily attendance?
(NISEC, 1988)

170 The number of goals scored in each of the eleven First Division Football League matches one Saturday last season was

0, 0, 1, 1, 2, 2, 4, 5, 6, 6, 6

Find
(a) the mode, (b) the median, (c) the mean.
(MEG, 1988)

171 The midday temperature in London on ten consecutive days was recorded in degrees Fahrenheit as follows:
54, 53, 52, 49, 50, 54, 55, 54, 51, 53
(a) What is the range of temperatures over these ten days?
(b) What is the mean temperature? *(SEG, 1988)*

Unit 1.69

172 Jessica finds that it rains on 100 out of 300 days. Using this information,
(a) what is the probability that it will rain on her birthday?
(b) what is the probability that it will not rain on her birthday?
(c) how many days would you expect it to rain during a month of 30 days? *(LEAG, 1988)*

173 The diagram shows a fairground game. The pointer is spun and comes to rest pointing at the sum of money the player wins.

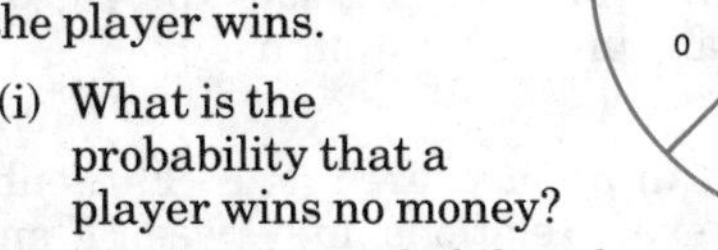

(i) What is the probability that a player wins no money?
(ii) What is the probability that a player wins 5p or more? *(NEA*)*

174 (a) A bag contains eight toffees and five chocolates. Andrew takes a sweet from the bag. Write down the probability that he picks a toffee.
(b) Andrew eats the toffee and Robert now takes a sweet from the same bag. What is the probability that Robert will pick a chocolate? *(WJEC, 1988)*

List 2

Unit 2.1

1 Insert brackets in the following statements to make them correct.
(a) 12 × 4 − 2 = 24
(b) 6 − 2 × 4 + 3 = 28 *(MEG*)*

2 (a) The factors of 10 are 1, 2, 5, 10.
(i) List all the factors of 20.
(ii) List all the factors of 24.
(iii) List the common factors of 20 and 24.
(iv) State the highest common factor of 20 and 24.
(b) The first six multiples of 10 are 10, 20, 30, 40, 50, 60.
(i) List the first six multiples 20.
(ii) List the first six multiples of 24.
(iii) List the first two common multiples of 20 and 24.
(iv) State the lowest common multiple of 20 and 24.
(c) Find the product of your answers to (a)(iv) and (b)(iv). Comment on the result. *(MEG, 1988)*

3 (a) List the set of factors of
(i) 48, (ii) 72.
(b) List the common factors of 48 and 72.
(c) (i) List the prime factors of 48.
(ii) Express 48 as a product of primes.
(NEA, 1988)

4 (a) Express as a product of its prime factors.
(i) 126
(ii) 420
(b) Find the smallest number of which 126 and 420 are factors. *(SEG, 1988)*

Unit 2.2

5 This table gives the temperature in Sheffield during one week in January 1987.

Day	Sun	Mon	Tues	Wed	Thurs	Fri	Sat
Noon	−3°C	−2°C	1°C	−3°C	2°C	3°C	−2°C
Midnight	−8°C	−8°C	−6°C	−10°C	−6°C	−3°C	−5°C

(a) What is the lowest temperature in the table?
(b) On which day was there the biggest drop in temperature between noon and midnight?
(c) How much was this drop?
(d) What was the least rise in temperature between midnight one day and noon the following day?
(e) On the next Sunday the temperature was 8° higher at noon than at midnight the previous night. What was the temperature at noon?
(MEG, 1988)

6 According to the Guinness Book of Records, the steepest temperature rise ever recorded occurred in South Dakota on 22 January 1943 when the temperature rose from −20°C at 7.30 a.m. to 7.2°C at 7.32 a.m.
(a) By how much did the temperature rise?
(b) What was the average rate at which the temperature was rising in °C/sec?
(NEA, 1988)

Unit 2.4

7 (a) Write down the next two numbers in the sequence
1, 5, 14, 30, 55, ____, ____.
(b) Explain how you obtained your answer to part (a).
(NEA, 1988)

8

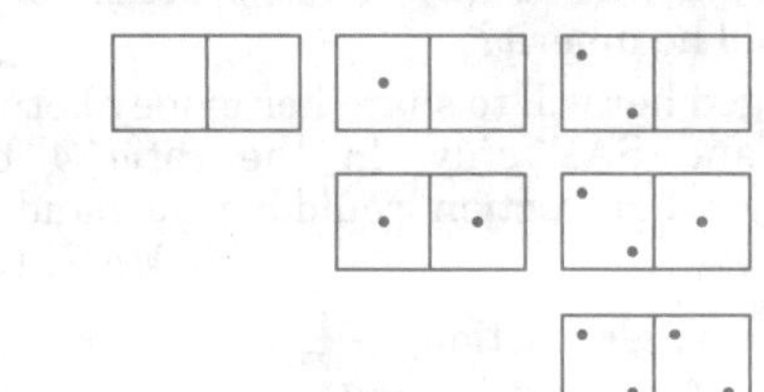

The diagram shows some dominoes arranged in a pattern.

(a) In the space to the right of the diagram, draw the next column of dominoes in the pattern.
(b) Write down the total number of spots in each of these four columns of dominoes.
(c) Divide each of these totals by 3 and write down the new sequence of numbers.
(d) Write down the next two numbers in the sequence you obtained in part (c).
(e) Using your previous answers, find the total number of spots in the column in which the double 6 domino appears.
(f) [domino]

In which row and which column of the pattern above would this domino appear? (*NEA*, 1988)

9 Four rods are used to make a square.

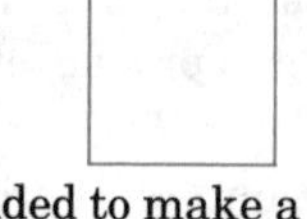

Rods are then added to make a row of 2 squares, then 3 squares and so on.

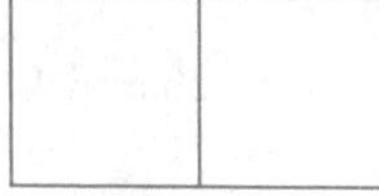

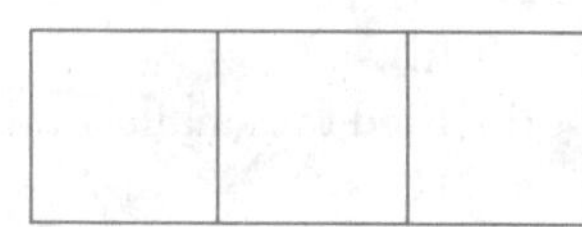

(a) How many rods are needed to make a row of
 (i) 5 squares,
 (ii) 6 squares,
 (iii) 15 squares?
(b) Find the formula which gives the number of rods, r, needed to make a row of s squares in the form: $r = \ldots$
(c) Use your formula to find how many squares could be made using 70 rods.
(d) Rearrange your formula in (b) into the form: $s = \ldots$
(e) What is the greatest number of squares you can make in a row with 120 rods? How many rods will you have left over? (*WJEC*, 1988)

10 The following seven points have a common pattern.
$(1, 12); (2, 6); (3, 4); (4, 3); (6, p); (8, q); (12, 1)$.
(a) State the values of p and q.
(b) Plot these points on graph paper. Join up the points with a smooth curve.
(c) Find the equation that is satisfied by these points and write it in the form $y = \ldots$
(d) (i) State the coordinates of three points which lie on the line

$$x + y = 12$$

 (ii) Draw this line on the same graph.
(e) State the values of x where the line cuts the curve.
(f) State the value of the gradient of the line $x + y = 12$. (*SEG*, 1988)

Unit 2.5

11 (a) In her will Mrs Hannah Pennypincher left half her money to the SMP, a third to the SDP, a tenth to the SNP, and the remainder to her husband, Simon Alan Pennypincher (SAP). What fraction of her money would he inherit?
(b) If she changed her will to share her money between the SMP and SAP only, in the ratio 4 to 1 respectively, what fraction would her husband now inherit? (*MEG*, 1988)

12 (a) Express as a single fraction $\frac{1}{4} - \frac{1}{5}$.
(b) Find the value of R such that $\frac{R}{100} = \frac{1}{4} - \frac{1}{5}$.
(*MEG**)

13 Jenny has $2\frac{1}{4}$ metres of material. She uses $\frac{1}{3}$ of this. What length of material is left? (*SEG*, 1988)

14 A tank was $\frac{3}{4}$ full of oil. 100 litres of oil were used. It was then $\frac{2}{3}$ full.
How much does the tank hold when full? (*NISEC*, 1988)

Unit 2.6

15 (a) Use your calculator to do the following calculations. In each case, write down the full calculator display.
(i) $240 \div 99$ (ii) $240 \div 999$ (iii) $240 \div 9999$
(b) What do you notice about your answers to part (a)? (*MEG*, 1988)

16 My calculator gives $\sqrt{7} = 2.645751311$.
Which of the numbers $\frac{127}{48}$, $2\frac{20}{31}$, 2.645, 2.646 is closest to this? (*MEG*, 1988)

17 A newspaper headline states that 35% of the population is aged under 21. What is this percentage as a fraction in its lowest terms? (*SEG*, 1988)

18 A hill whose gradient is 1 in 5 can be said to have a gradient of 20%. Express a gradient of 1 in 7 as a percentage correct to the nearest integer. (*NEA*, 1988)

Unit 2.7

19 (a) Calculate the reduction in the price of the camera.
(b) What is this reduction as a percentage of the normal price? (*NEA*, 1988)

SALE
35 mm Camera
was £39.95
Now £31.96

20 A car is sold for £4500 at a loss of 40% of the original purchase price. Calculate the original purchase price. (*MEG**)

21 The following information was given on two labels taken from a bottle of 'Blackvit', a blackcurrant drink.

BLACKVIT	CONTENTS
25 ml of this product provide 173% of the recommended daily intake of vitamin C.	Water Glucose Syrup Blackcurrant Juice Colours Vitamin C (52 mg per 100 ml) Preservatives

Calculate, from the information provided, the recommended daily intake of vitamin C. (*NEA*, 1988)

22 A temperature can be measured as F °Fahrenheit or C °Celsius. The exact relationship between F and C is given by

$$F = \frac{9}{5}C + 32.$$

(a) Find the value of C when $F = 14$.
(b) Find the value of C when $F = C$.
An approximate relationship between F and C is given by the following rule:
'To find F, add 15 to C and double your answer.'
(c) Write this relationship as a formula.
(d) Find, correct to three significant figures, the percentage error in using the approximate relationship when $C = 20$. (*MEG*, 1988)

Unit 2.8

23 The volume, V, of a piece of metal can be found using the formula

$$V = \pi h^2\left(r - \frac{h}{3}\right)$$

where $r = 6.87$ and $h = 2.96$.

(a) Using suitable whole number approximations for π, h and r, find an estimate for the value of V. (*To earn the marks you must show the stages of your working.*)

(b) Using the given values of h and r, find the value of V correct to 1 decimal place.

(*LEAG*, 1988)

24 Estimate the value of $17\frac{3}{4} \times 120$, correct to one significant figure. Show how you obtain your answer. (*LEAG*, 1988)

25 (a) The attendance at United's last match was 15 374. Write the attendance figure correct to three significant figures.

(b) The attendance at City's last match was given as 24 000, correct to the nearest 1000. Write down the lowest and highest possible attendances.

(*MEG**)

26 A wall is measured and is found to be 4.35 m long and 2.25 m high.

(a) Use these measurements to calculate the area of the wall, giving your answer correct to

(i) one decimal place,

(ii) three significant figures.

(b) Another wall is measured. To the nearest metre its length is 5 m and its height is 2 m. Calculate the upper and lower limits for the area of the wall.

(*NEA*, 1988)

Unit 2.9

27 The distance from the Sun to the Earth is 93 million miles. Express this distance in standard form.

(*NISEC**)

28 A pack of 52 playing cards is 1.5 cm thick. Write down, in standard form, the thickness, in cm, of one playing card. (*NEA*, 1988)

29 The area of England is 1.304×10^5 km^2 and the area of Wales is 2.077×10^4 km^2.

(a) Find the total area of England and Wales, giving your answer in standard form.

(b) Find the ratio of the area of England to the area of Wales, giving your answer in the form $n : 1$, with n correct to two significant figures. (*MEG*, 1988)

30 The distance light travels in one year is called a 'light year'. One light year equals 9.46×10^{12} km to three significant figures. The most distant object from Earth is 1.5×10^{10} light years away.

How far is this in kilometres? Give your answer in standard form to two significant figures.

(*MEG*, 1988)

31 $p = 3.6 \times 10^5$ $\quad q = 6.0 \times 10^{-4}$

(a) Give the value of the digit 6 in (i) p (ii) q

(b) Calculate $\frac{p}{q}$ giving the answer in standard form.

(*NISEC*, 1988)

32 The following table gives the distance of planets from the Sun.

Planet	*Distance in kilometres*
Earth	1.496×10^8
Jupiter	7.783×10^8
Mars	2.279×10^8
Mercury	5.791×10^7
Neptune	4.498×10^9
Pluto	5.900×10^9
Saturn	1.427×10^9
Uranus	2.869×10^9
Venus	1.082×10^8

(i) 'Planet **A** is roughly 100 times as far from the Sun as planet **B**.' Which planets do **A** and **B** represent?

(ii) How much further from the Sun is Neptune than Mars? Give your answer in standard index form.

(*WJEC*, 1988)

Unit 2.10

33 An investor can invest money either at 11 per cent simple interest per annum or 9 per cent compound interest per annum. If £6000 is to be invested for three years, calculate (a) which would be the more profitable investment, and (b) by how much. (*NISEC*, 1988)

34 Pauline and Karl each won £2000 in a competition. They looked in a Building Society's window and saw two posters.

Super Saver Bonds £1000 each	Flexi Savers Account
After 2 years can be cashed in to give £1250 (Cashed in before 2 years at face value of £1000 only)	5% interest added to balance every 6 months

(a) Pauline buys two Super Saver Bonds. What is the total amount she can cash them in for after two years?

(b) Karl put his £2000 in the Flexi Savers Account. How much will he have in the account after

(i) 6 months? (ii) 1 year? (iii) 2 years?

(c) State one advantage that the Flexi Savers Account has over buying Super Saver Bonds. (*NEA*, 1988)

35 The sediment in a lake causes a 15% reduction in light intensity for each 20 cm of water depth.

(a) Complete this table, which shows the light intensity as it varies with depth in the lake. Light intensity is measured as a percentage of its value at the surface.

Depth (in metres)	*Light intensity (% of intensity at surface)*
0	100
0.2	85
0.4	72.25
0.6	
0.8	
1.0	
1.2	
1.4	

(b) An underwater camera can only work in light intensities of more than 20% of the intensity at the surface. What is the greatest depth at which the camera can work in the lake? Give your answer to the nearest 0.2 m. (*MEG*, 1988)

Unit 2.11

36 Jill has 40 pence and Dave has 60 pence. They agree to spend all the money on sweets and to share them in the same ratio as their money. They buy 30 toffee-lumps. How many toffee-lumps should each have?

(*LEAG*, 1988)

37 A man left £6000 in his will to be divided amongst three people in the ratios 3 : 5 : 7. How much did each receive?

(*SEG*, 1988)

38 Alan, Brian and Charles stake £5 on the football pools each week. Alan pays £1, Brian £1.50 and Charles £2.50. They agree to share any winnings in proportion to their payments. One week they win £375. Find Brian's share of this. (*NEA**)

Unit 2.12

39

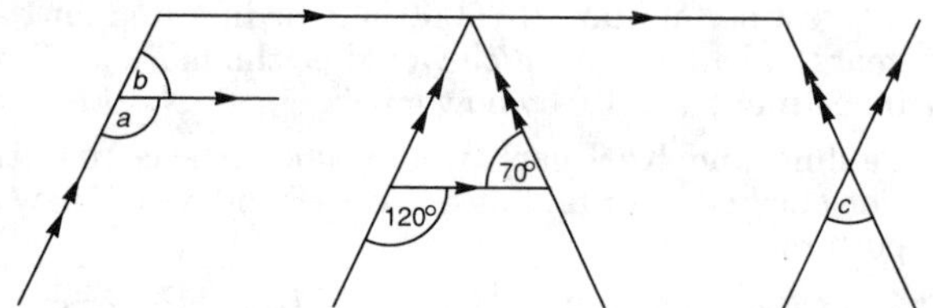

The diagram above (which is not to scale) represents three sets of parallel lines. State the size of

(a) angle a, (b) angle b, (c) angle c.

(*NEA*, 1988)

Units 2.12 and 2.13

40

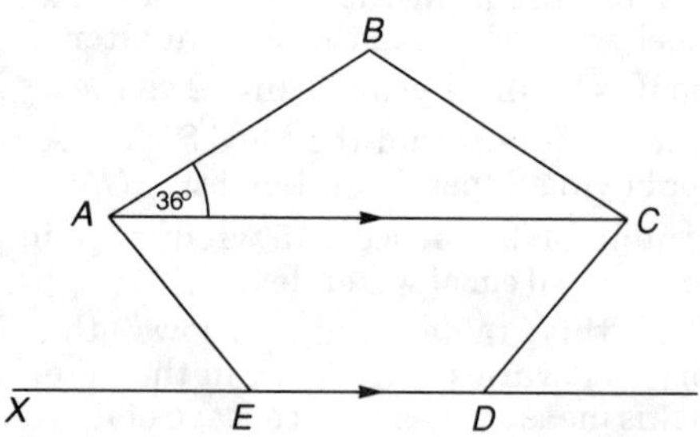

ABCDE represents a swimming pool with all its sides of equal length. A rope joins *A* to *C* and is parallel to *ED*. Given that $\angle BAC = 36°$ calculate:

(a) $\angle ABC$, (b) $\angle CAE$, (c) $\angle AEX$.

(*SEG*, 1988)

Units 2.12 and 2.14

41 (a) Calculate the size of each of the angles marked a, b, c. The diagram is not drawn to scale.

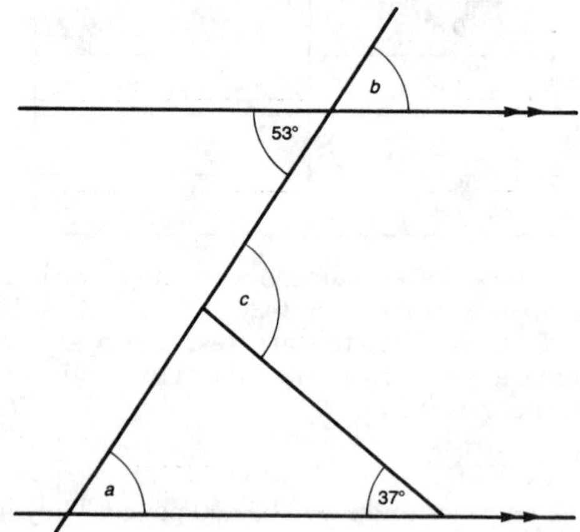

(b) The three points, E, F and G are on the circumference of the circle centre O and EG is a diameter. ET is the tangent to the circle at E. Write down the size of each of the angles marked a and b. The diagram is not drawn to scale.

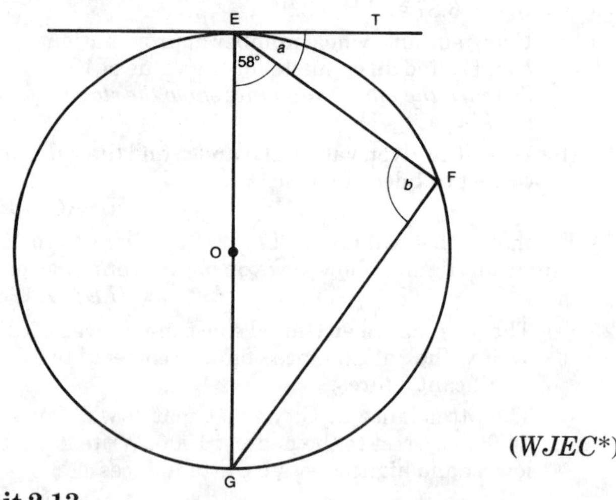

(*WJEC**)

Unit 2.13

42 The diagram shows a regular pentagon inscribed in a circle of centre *O*.

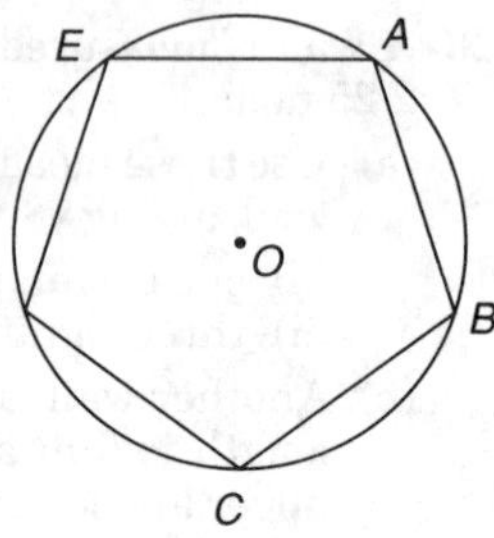

(a) Prove that the total of all the interior angles of the pentagon (at *A, B, C, D* and *E*) is 540°. Explain your reasoning.

(b) Calculate the size of angle *ADB*.

(*NEA*, 1988)

43

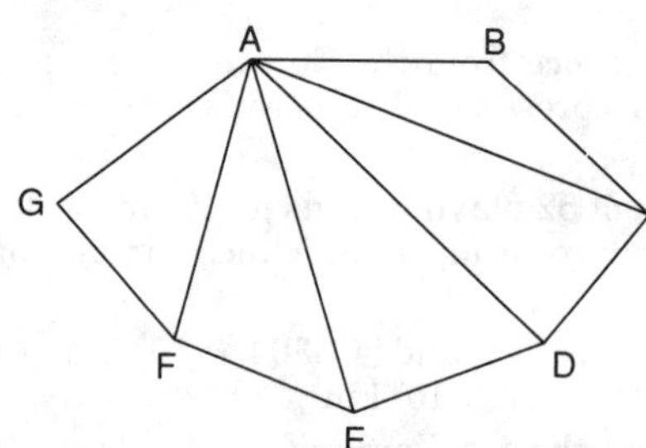

Fig. 1

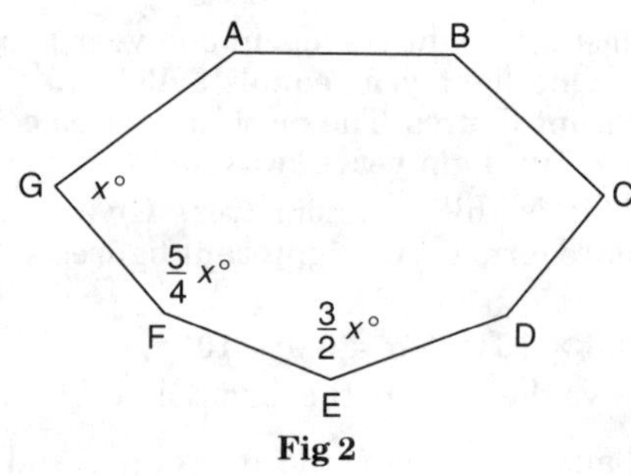

Fig 2

(a) Using Fig. 1, calculate the sum of the angles of the polygon ABCDEFG.

(b) If, in Fig. 2, angle GAB = angle ABC = angle DEF and angle FGA = angle BCD and angle EFG = angle CDE, calculate x. (*NISEC*, 1988)

44 The diagram represents part of a water wheel. The complete water wheel forms a regular polygon with each side extended as shown. The polygon has 20 sides. Calculate the angle *AOB*.

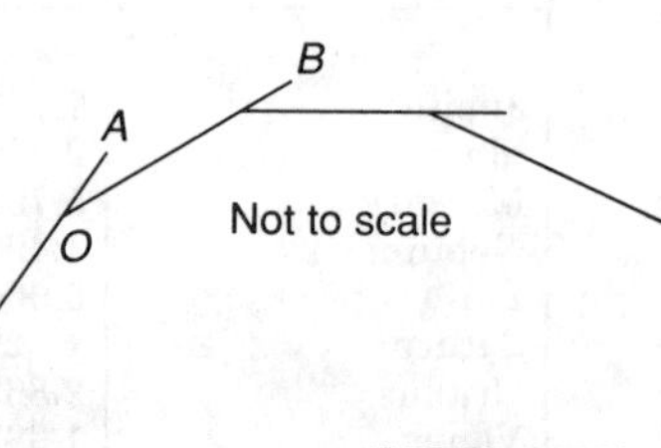

(*MEG*, 1988)

Unit 2.14

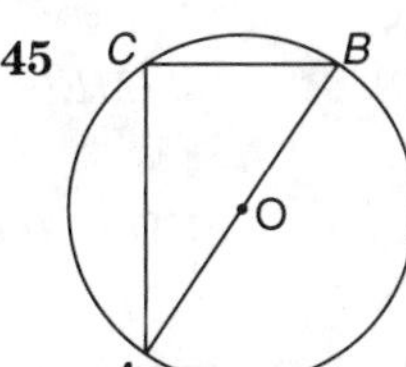

45 A circle has diameter AB. C is a point on its circumference. Angle $BAC = 32°$. Calculate the angle ABC, giving reasons for the steps you take. (*SEG*, 1988)

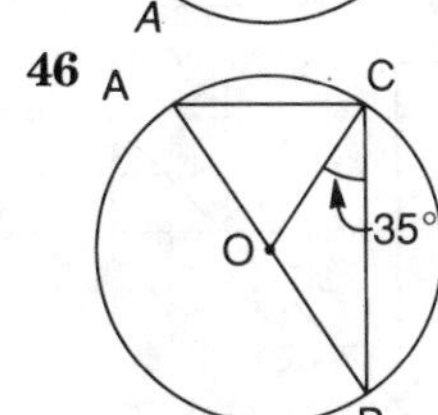

46 AB is a diameter of a circle, centre O. C is a point on the circumference, such that angle OCB = 35°. Find the size of
(a) angle OBC, (b) angle AOC,
(c) angle ACO.
(*LEAG*, 1988)

47

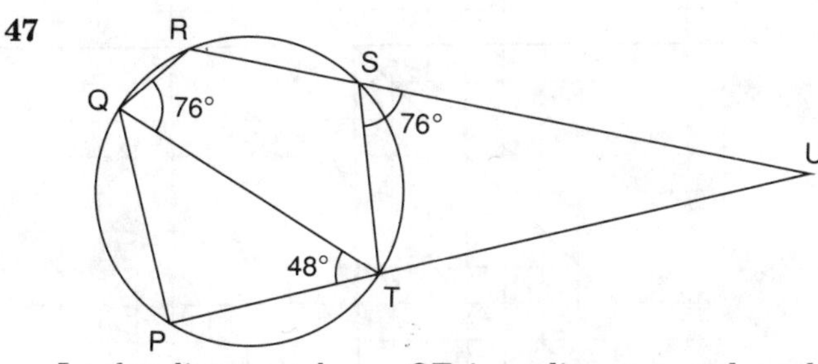

In the diagram above, QT is a diameter and angle SRT = 37°. Calculate the following angles:
(a) QRT (b) RTS, (c) SUT. (*NISEC*, 1988)

Unit 2.15

48 A field is in the shape of a quadrilateral ABCD with AB = 80 m, BC = 70 m and CD = 110 m. The angle ABC = 80° and the angle BCD = 120°.
Using a scale of 1 cm to represent 10 m make an accurate scale drawing of the field.
(i) Use your scale drawing to find the length of the side DA.
(ii) A tree is at the point of intersection of the bisector of the angle CDA and the perpendicular bisector of the side BC. Using only ruler and compasses construct and indicate the position of the tree.
(iii) Find the distance of the tree from the corner B of the field. (*NEA**)

Units 2.15 and 2.16

49 Using a scale of 1 centimetre to represent 2 metres, mark the positions of three boys so that each boy is 12 metres from the other two. (*MEG*, 1988)

50

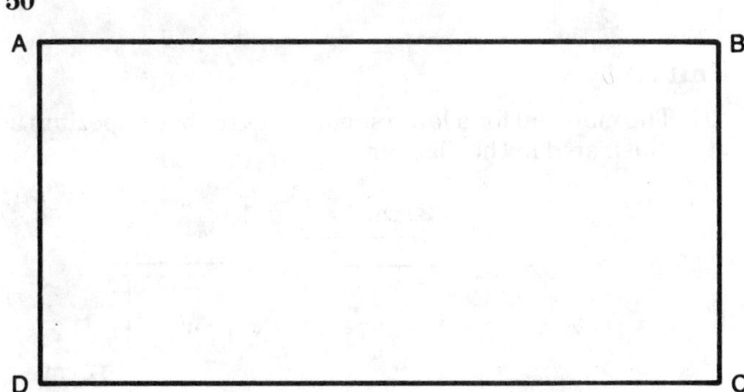

The diagram above shows a rectangular area of sea, ABCD, measuring 800 m by 400 m. It is drawn using a scale of 1 cm to represent 100 m. It is known that a submarine is inside the rectangle, more than 600 m from B and closer to AD than DC.
Indicate, clearly and accurately, the region in which the submarine must be. (*MEG**)

51

A yachtsman, out at sea, wishes to find his position, Y on a map. He can see two lighthouses, L and M, but does not know how far he is from either. He takes bearings on the lighthouses and finds that angle LYM is 90°.
(a) On the diagram draw the arc of the circle on which his position must lie.
(b) He knows that he is the same distance from L as he is from N. Mark his position in the diagram, and label it Y.
(*SEG*, 1988)

Unit 2.16

52

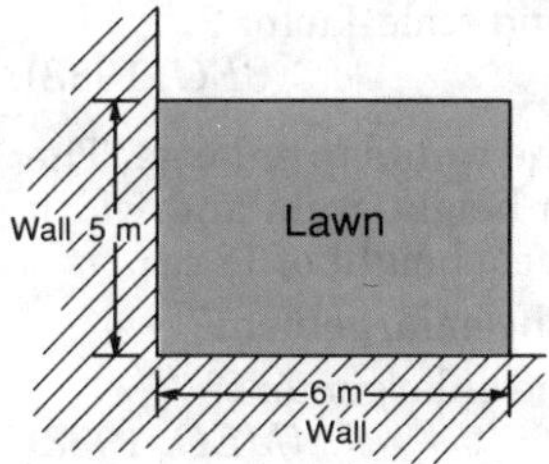

The drawing shows a lawn, surrounded on two sides by a wall. It is not drawn to scale.
(a) On the diagram, sketch a path around the non-walled boundary of the lawn so that the outer boundary of the path is always 1.5 m from the lawn.
(b) Calculate the area of the path.
(*NEA*, 1988)

Units 2.17 and 2.18

53

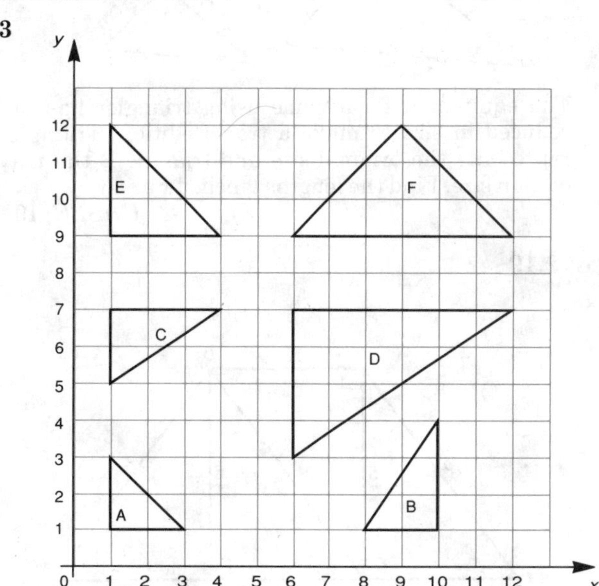

(a) Which triangle is congruent to triangle C?
(b) Which triangles are similar to triangle A?
(*LEAG*, 1988)

54 (a) Describe fully the transformation which maps shape A onto shape F. (Diagram overleaf)
(b) Which of the shapes are congruent to shape A?

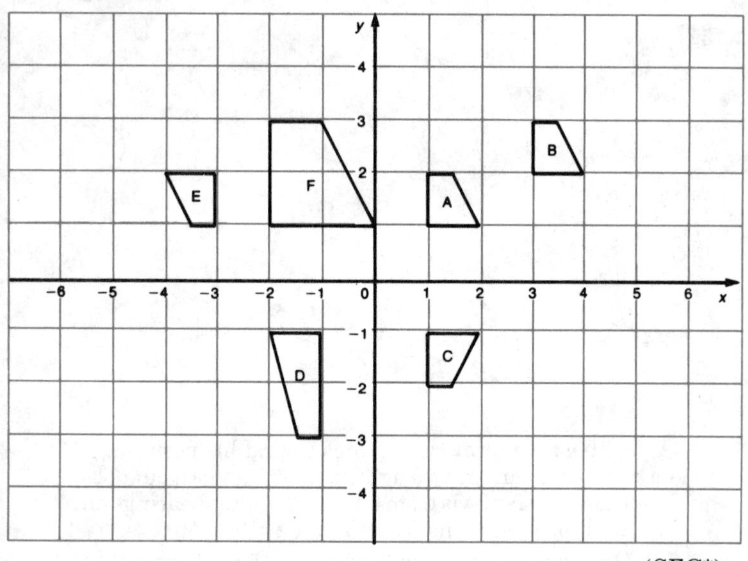

(*SEG**)

Unit 2.18

55 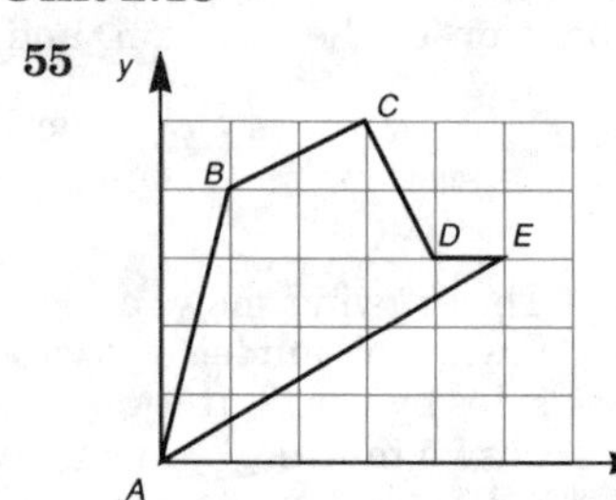

(a) What is the gradient of the line *AE*?

(b) Copy figure *ABCDE* on to graph paper with the point *C* near the top centre of the page.

(c) Draw the enlargement of *ABCDE* with centre *C* and scale-factor 2.

(*SEG*, 1988)

56 Peta has a photograph which she wants to enlarge. The photograph is a rectangle with height 8 cm and width 6 cm. The enlargement will have a height of 12 cm.

(a) What is the scale factor of the enlargement?

(b) What will be the width of the enlargement?

(*MEG*, 1988)

57 Triangle A Triangle B

14 cm, 9 cm, y; 5 cm, $4\frac{1}{2}$ cm, x

The equipment for a game using triangles has to be reduced in size to make a travel edition. Triangle A represents the original size and triangle B the travel edition size. Find the lengths labelled *x* and *y*.

(*NISEC*, 1988)

Unit 2.19

58

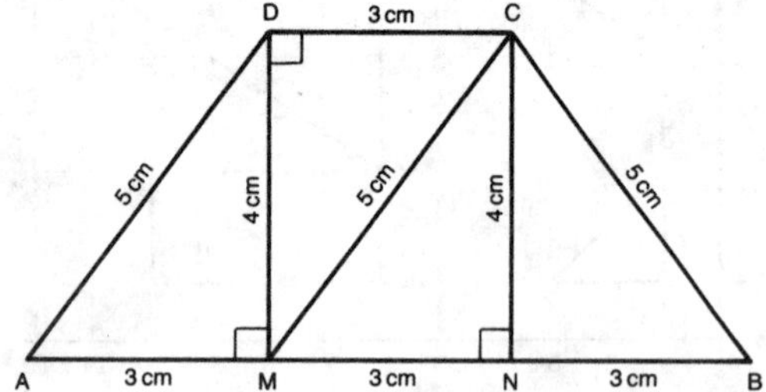

The diagram shows a trapezium ABCD in which AB is parallel to DC. The trapezium consists of four right-angled triangles ADM, CMD, MCN and BCN, each with sides of length 3 cm, 4 cm and 5 cm.

Describe fully the single transformation which will map:

(a) triangle ADM onto triangle MCN,

(b) triangle BCN onto triangle MCN,

(c) triangle CMD onto triangle MCN. (*MEG**)

59 On the diagram below,

(i) draw the reflection of the rectangle ABCD in the line $y = x$ and label it A′B′C′D′,

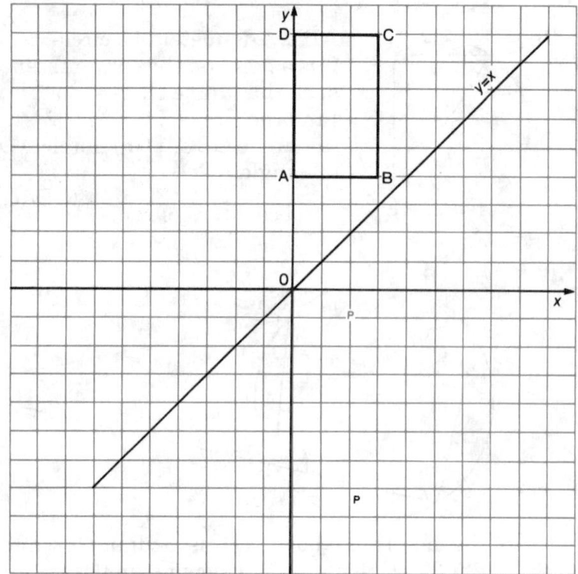

(ii) draw the image of A′B′C′D′ after a rotation through $\frac{1}{4}$ of a turn clockwise about the origin and label it A″B″C″D″,

(iii) describe the single transformation which will transform ABCD into A″B″C″D″. (*NEA**)

60 The four vertices of a square *S* are (1, 2), (3, 2), (3, 4) and (1, 4).

(a) Using a scale of 2 cm to 1 unit draw axes showing values of *x* from −4 to +4 and values of *y* from 0 to 6.

(b) Draw the square *S* on your diagram.

(c) The image of *S* under reflection in the *y*-axis is the square *S′*. Draw the image *S′* on your diagram.

(d) Describe the translation which maps *S* onto *S′*.

(e) There is a rotation with angle +90° which maps *S* onto *S′*. Give the coordinates of the centre of this rotation.

(f) Write down two other rotations each of which maps *S* onto *S′*. Describe them in full.

(*MEG*, 1988)

Unit 2.21

61 The material for a lamp shade is cut from a trapezium as illustrated in the diagram.

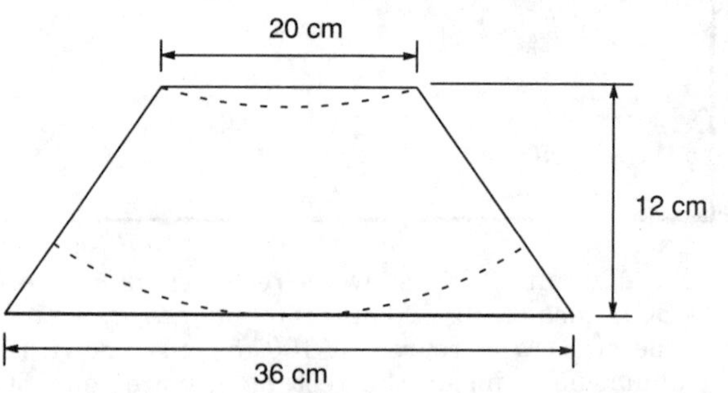

Calculate the area of the trapezium

(a) in cm^2, (b) in m^2. (*SEG*, 1988)

62

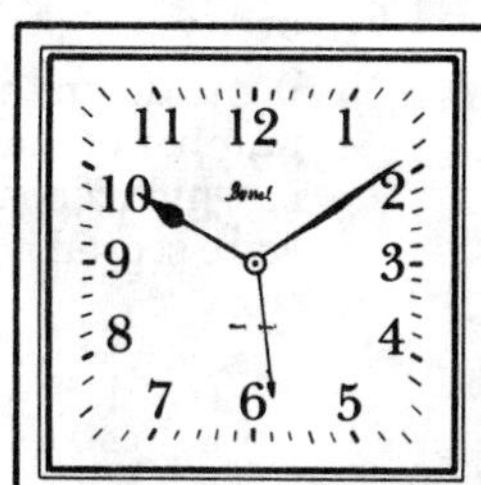

The faces of a round and a square clock are exactly the same area. The round clock has a radius of 10 cm. How wide is the square clock? (They are not drawn to scale.) *(SEG*)*

63 The diagram shows a metal plate with four quadrants of a circle cut away at the corners.

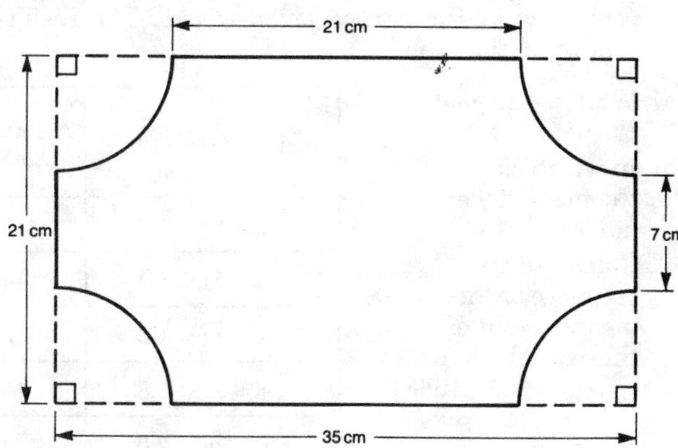

Calculate:

(i) the radius of the circle of which the quadrants are a part;

(ii) the total area cut away;

(iii) the area of metal plate remaining.
(Use $A = \pi r^2$ and take $\pi = 3.14$.) *(NISEC*)*

64 The diagram shows the plan of a concrete drive that Mr Fraser intends to lay in his garden. *ABC* and *CDE* are perpendicular straight lines and both *DEFG* and *ABHJ* are rectangles. The arc *HPG* is part of a circle, of radius 1 m, with centre at *O*.

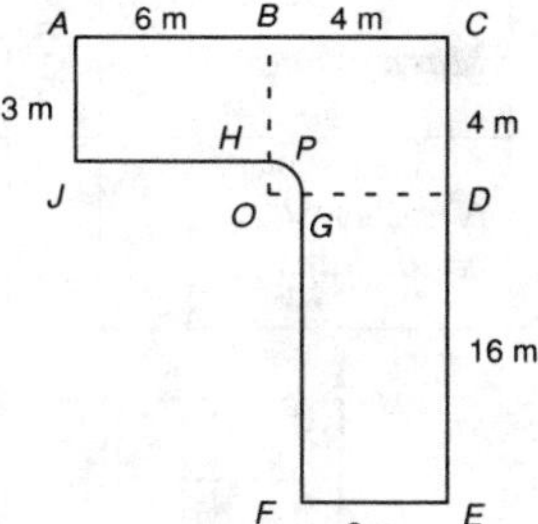

$AJ = EF = 3$ m
$AB = 6$ m
$BC = CD = 4$ m $DE = 16$ m
$OB = OD = 4$ m
NB The diagram is not to scale.
Taking π to be 3.14, find the total area of the drive, correct to the nearest square metre. *(MEG, 1988)*

Units 2.21 and 2.37

65

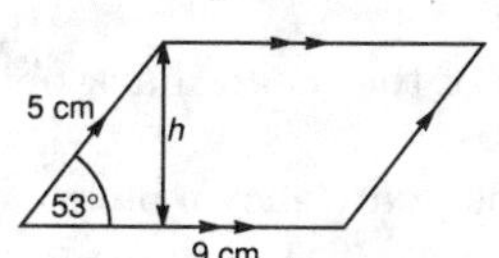

The diagram represents a parallelogram with a base of 9 cm.

(a) Calculate the height (h) of the parallelogram.

(b) Calculate the area of the parallelogram. *(NEA, 1988)*

Units 2.21 and 2.22

66

(a) Calculate the volume of a cylindrical can with diameter 7.4 cm and height 10.6 cm.

(b) Calculate the area of sheet metal used to make this can. *(NEA, 1988)*

67

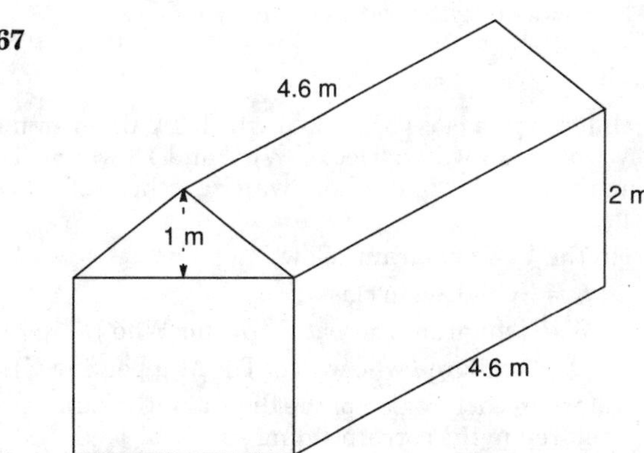

A greenhouse with the size and shape shown above can be thought of as a cuboid with a triangular prism on top. Mr Khan has built a greenhouse like this, and now wants a heater for it. To choose the right heater, he needs to know the volume of his greenhouse. Calculate the volume of the greenhouse. *(NEA, 1988)*

68 The diagram shows the uniform cross-section of a concrete breakwater which is 200 m long. It is made up of two shapes: a trapezium and a parallelogram. The measurements are as shown in the diagram.

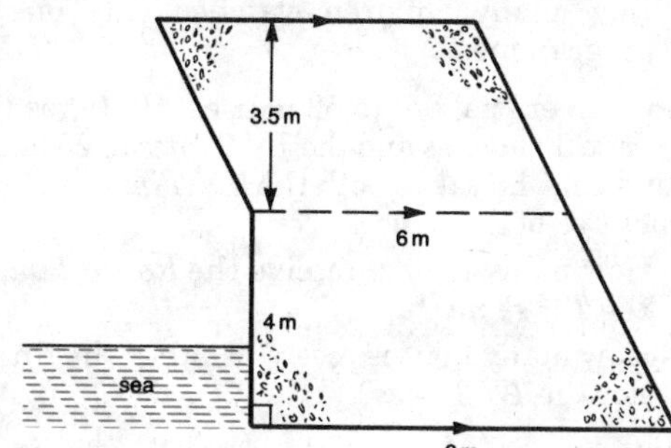

(a) Calculate:

(i) the area of the uniform cross-section,

(ii) the volume of concrete needed to build this breakwater.

(b) Ready mixed concrete is brought to the site of the breakwater in lorryloads of 245 m^3.
Calculate the number of lorryloads of concrete that would be needed for this work. *(WJEC*)*

Unit 2.22

69 In this question, take π to be 3.142 and give each answer correct to three significant figures.

(a) A firm sells 500 g packs of butter in the form of a circular cylinder with radius 3.9 cm and length 10.5 cm. Calculate the volume of the cylinder.

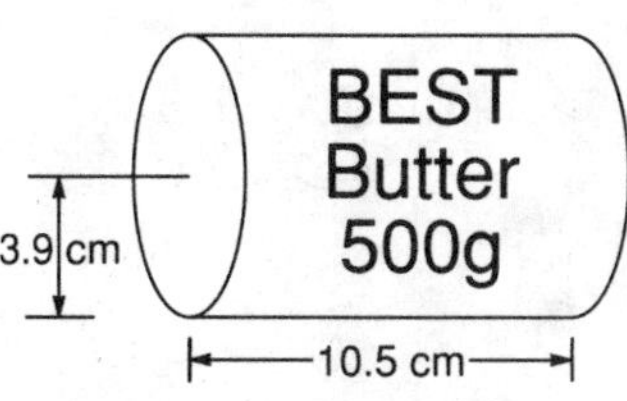

(b) The firm also sells 500 g packs of butter in the form of a rectangular block with a square cross-section of side 6.5 cm. Calculate the length of the rectangular block.

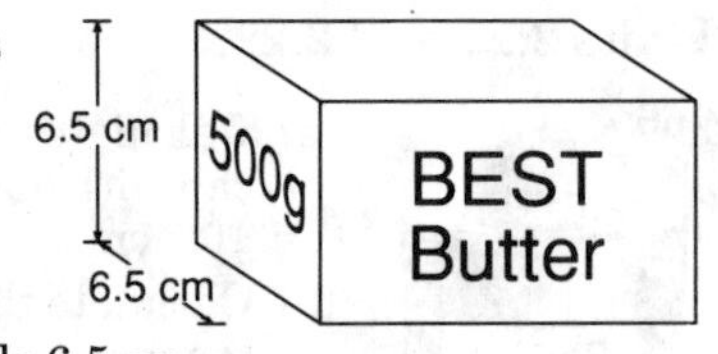

(c) The firm decides to sell 250 g packs of butter in the form of a circular cylinder.

(i) If the radius of the (250 g) cylinder is 3.9 cm, find the length of the cylinder.

(ii) If the length of the (250 g) cylinder is 10.5 cm, calculate the radius of the cylinder.

(*MEG*, 1988)

Unit 2.23

70 27 children in a class are asked which TV programmes they watch. 16 watch 'Doctor Who' and 13 watch 'The Muppet Show'. 2 do not watch either of these programmes.

(a) In the Venn diagram below,

$\mathscr{E}$ = {children in class},

W = {children who watch 'Doctor Who'}.

M = {children who watch 'The Muppet Show'}.

Show, in each region of the diagram, the number of children in the corresponding subset of $\mathscr{E}$.

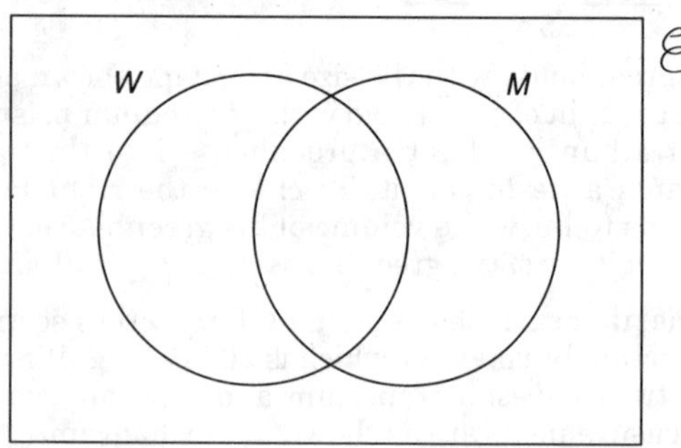

(b) How many children watched only one of these programmes? (*NEA*, 1988)

71 Sam delivers papers to 52 houses. He takes the *Radio Times* to 30 houses and the *TV Times* to 28 houses. Sam knows that he takes both the *TV Times* and the *Radio Times* to 8 of the houses.

(i) How many houses receive the *Radio Times* but not the *TV Times*?

(ii) How many houses receive neither the *Radio Times* nor the *TV Times*? (*NEA**)

Unit 2.24

72 Two dice were thrown together 125 times. The scores obtained are shown in this frequency table. Use this information to find

(a) the mode of the scores,

(b) the median score,

(c) the mean score.

Score	*Frequency*
2	4
3	7
4	9
5	11
6	7
7	5
8	17
9	19
10	24
11	12
12	10

(*NEA*, 1988)

73 This chart shows the goals scored per match in league hockey matches on a certain Saturday.

(i) Write down the number of matches in which 2 goals were scored.

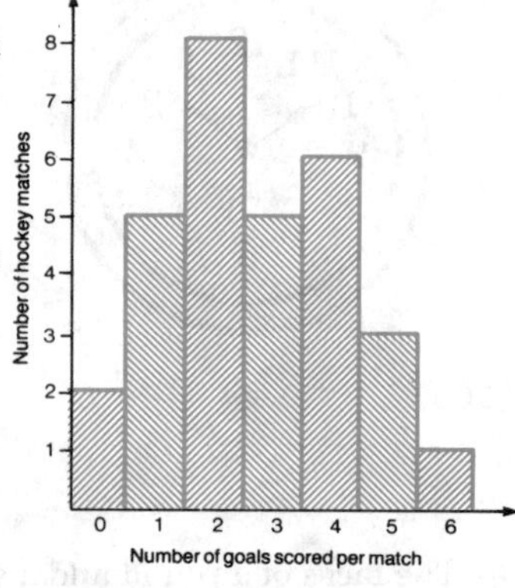

Calculate

(ii) the number of matches played,

(iii) the number of goals scored altogether,

(iv) the mean number of goals scored per match. (*WJEC**)

74 A poultry farmer recorded the weight (w kg) of 50 chickens at the age of seven weeks. The results are shown in the table.

(a) What is the modal class?

(b) In which class does the median weight lie?

(c) Calculate an estimate of the mean weight of these 50 chickens. (*MEG*, 1988)

Weight (w kg)	*Number of chickens*
$1 \leqslant w < 1.2$	12
$1.2 \leqslant w < 1.4$	14
$1.4 \leqslant w < 1.6$	5
$1.6 \leqslant w < 1.8$	15
$1.8 \leqslant w < 2.0$	4

Units 2.24 and 2.25

75 A school entered 50 candidates for GCSE mathematics. There are two papers, each marked out of a maximum of 50. The marks obtained in Paper 1 are shown in the table and illustrated by the frequency diagram.

Mark range	0–4	5–9	10–14	15–19	20–24	25–29	30–34	35–39	40–44	45–49
Number of candidates	0	0	1	1	2	8	19	14	4	1

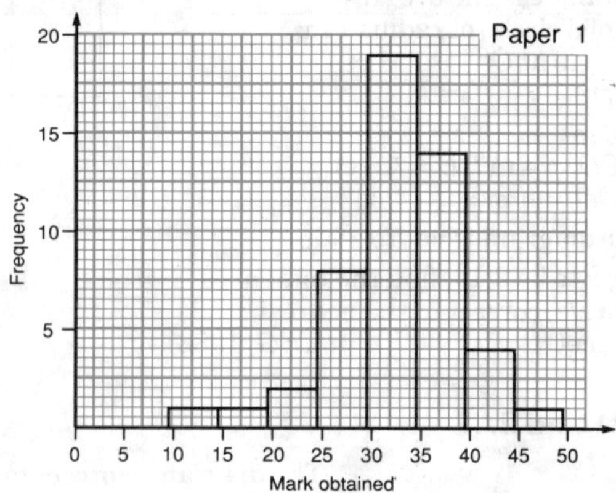

(a) Calculate an estimate of the mean mark obtained in Paper 1.

The marks obtained in Paper 2 are shown below.

27	18	31	12	16	37	24	42	15	23
27	27	42	21	3	12	27	24	34	13
9	29	19	32	24	26	33	15	24	25
24	30	23	13	17	6	39	19	18	38
12	18	18	26	31	24	49	12	23	29

(b) Compile a frequency table for the marks in Paper 2. Use the same classes 0–4, 5–9, etc. as for Paper 1.

(c) On your graph paper illustrate the data for Paper 2 using the same scales as the frequency diagram for Paper 1.

(d) Comment briefly on the differences between the candidates' performances in the two papers. (You may like to use the fact that the mean mark for Paper 2 is 23.6.) (*MEG*, 1988)

Unit 2.25

76

Type of crisp	*Tally*	*Frequency*	*Angle*
Plain	卌 ||||		
Salt and vinegar	卌 卌 卌 |		
Cheese and onion	卌 卌 |		
Beef	卌 |		
Crispy bacon	|||		
	Total	45	

The table shows the result of a survey taken on the sale of crisps one day in a school tuckshop.

(a) Complete the *Frequency* column in the table.

The information is to be shown on a pie chart.

(b) Calculate the size of the angle of each sector of this pie chart and complete the *Angle* column in the table.

(c) Draw an accurate pie chart to show this information on the circle given. Label the sectors clearly.

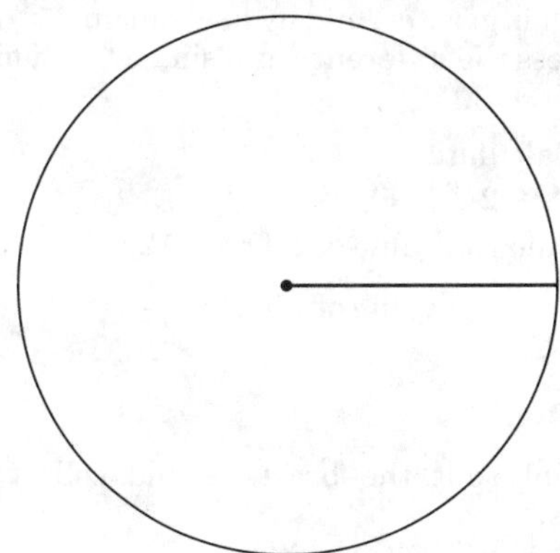

77 The table below shows the prices of some paperback novels and the number of pages in them.

Price	85p	£1.00	95p	£1.25	£1.50	£1.65	95p	£1.00	£1.35	65p	75p
Pages	224	254	170	236	330	380	210	190	320	136	150

continued

On graph paper construct a scatter diagram for this information. Use scales of 2 cm to represent 50 pages and 2 cm to represent 20p.

(i) Draw a line of best fit.

(ii) Use you line to estimate the cost of a book with 300 pages. (*NEA**)

Unit 2.26

78 The probability of a train arriving early at a station is $\frac{1}{10}$.

The probability of a train arriving late at a station is $\frac{2}{5}$.

(a) If 400 trains are expected at a station during the day, how many of them are likely to arrive at the correct time?

(b) What is the probability that both the trains arriving at the station from Exeter are late? (*SEG**)

79 Two unbiased dice (one red die, one blue die) are thrown. The set of possible outcomes is shown in this sample space diagram.

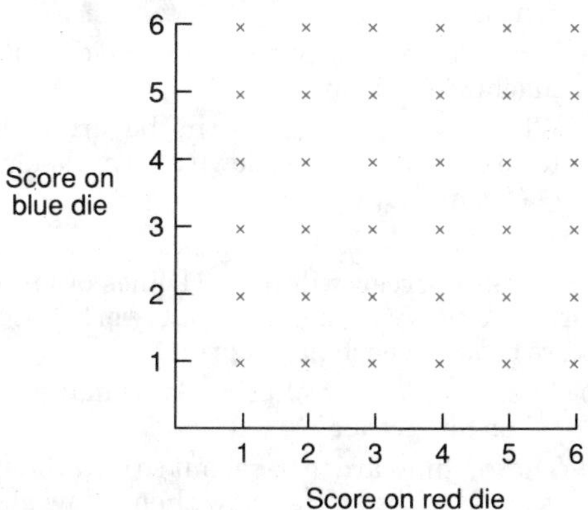

(a) On the diagram show the events A, B, C, where

A = {red die has score less than three},

B = {blue die has score three or more},

C = {both dice have same score}.

(b) Calculate the probability of

(i) the event A, (ii) the event B, (iii) the event C. (*NEA*, 1988)

80 John cycles to school on average 3 days out of 5. Otherwise he goes by bus.

Bill cycles to school on average 2 days out of 5. Otherwise he walks.

Find the probability that, on a certain school day

(a) they both will cycle to school,

(b) only one of them will cycle to school. (*LEAG*, 1988)

81 When a biased 6-sided dice is thrown, a score of 6 is twice as likely as a score of 5, a score of 5 is twice as likely as a score of 4 and scores of 1, 2, 3, 4 are equally likely.

(a) Calculate the probability of a score of 1.

(b) Calculate the probability of a score of 6.

(c) Calculate the probability of scoring an even number. (*NEA*, 1988)

82 A bag contains 5 red discs, 4 white discs and 1 blue disc. Two discs are to be chosen at random, without replacement.

(a) Copy and complete the probability tree diagram.

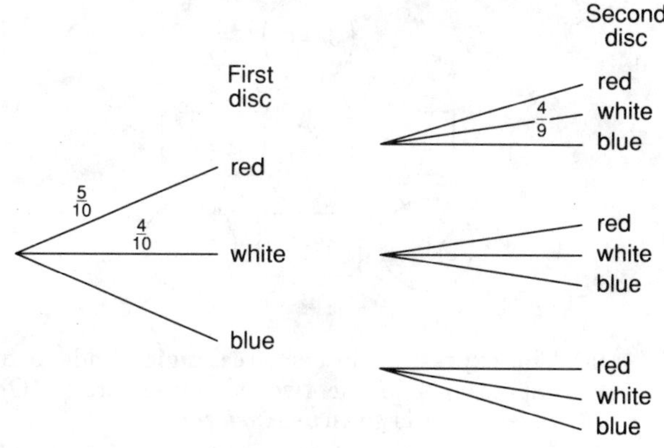

(b) Find the probability that

(i) both discs will be red,

(ii) both discs will be blue,

(iii) both discs will be the same colour,

(iv) the two discs will be different colours. (*LEAG*, 1988)

Unit 2.27

83 The cost of hiring a cleaning machine is a fixed charge of £C with an additional charge of £A for each day of the hire period.

(i) Write down an expression for the cost of hiring the machine for 3 days.

(ii) When the number of days in the hire period is n, the total cost is £T. Write down a formula for T in terms of C, n and A.

(*NEA**)

84 A computer screen will take 31 lines of either print or spaces. A programmer sets out work with a line of spaces between each line of print.

(a) There are 7 lines of print. How many lines will be taken altogether?

(b) These 7 lines are to be set out so that the space above is equal to the space below them. How many lines of spaces will be needed above them?

(c) There are n lines of print. Find an expression for the number of lines taken altogether.

(d) These n lines are to be set out so that the space above is equal to the space below. Find an expression for the number of lines of spaces needed above them. (*MEG*, 1988)

85 Calculate the exact value of $x^2 - 4x - 1$

(a) when $x = -1$, (b) when $x = 2.56$. (*NEA*, 1988)

86 Given that

$$a = \frac{v^2 - u^2}{2s},$$

evaluate a, when $u = 4.71$, $v = 6.95$, $s = 2.3$, giving your answer correct to two significant figures.

(*MEG**)

87 $\frac{1}{f} = \frac{1}{u} + \frac{1}{v}$

Find f, correct to three significant figures, when $u = 2.50$ and $v = 1.25$. (*LEAG*, 1988)

Units 2.27 and 2.30

88 Lilian asked her uncle how old he was. 'In 13 years, I'll be twice as old as I was 7 years ago,' he replied.

(a) Taking his age now to be x years, write down

(i) his age in 13 years, in terms of x,

(ii) an equation in x.

(b) Solve your equation and find Lilian's uncle's age. (*MEG*, 1988)

89

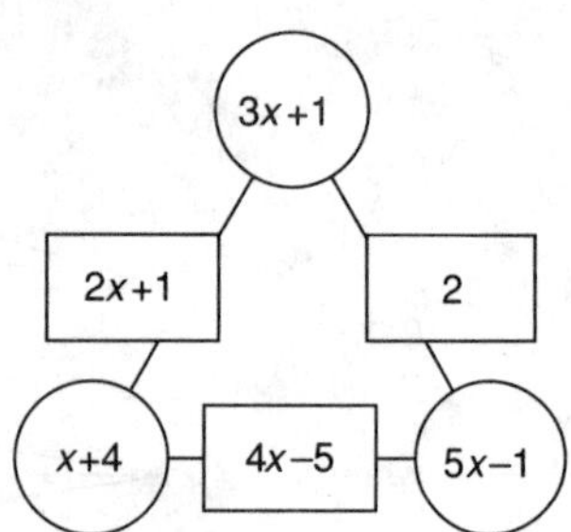

(a) The expression in each rectangle is added to the expressions in the two adjoining circles. One of these totals is given as *Answer* (i).

Find the other totals, in their simplest form: *Answer* (i) $6x + 6$

(b) If any two of these totals are equal, find the value of x and hence the value of each total.

(c) Find an expression, in its simplest form, for the difference between the expression in the top circle and the total of the expressions in the other two circles.

(d) If the sum of the expressions in the three circles is 49, find the value of x.

(e) If four times the expression in the bottom rectangle equals three times the sum of the expressions in the other two rectangles, find the value of x.

(*NISEC*, 1988)

90 In 1978 it cost x pence to send a letter by first class post and 2 pence less to send the same letter by second class post.

(a) Write down, in terms of x, the cost of sending a letter by second class post.

(b) 'I posted 19 similar letters, 12 by first class post, the rest by second class post, and I spent £1.57.' Express this statement as an equation in x and solve it.

(c) Joanne posted 23 similar letters, 8 by first class post and 15 by second class post. How much change did she get from £2? (*NEA*, 1988)

Unit 2.28

91 (i) Express $\frac{3^2 \times 3^4}{3^8}$ as a single power of 3.

(ii) State your answer as a fraction. (*NEA**)

92 (a) Evaluate

(i) $2^4 - 4^2$, (ii) $3^4 - 4^3$.

(b) Place these three numbers in order of size, smallest first:

9.12×10^5 1.92×10^6 2.19×10^5

(*SEG*, 1988)

93 Which is greater, and by how much: 2^{-3} or 3^{-2}? Express the difference as a single fraction.

(*NEA*, 1988)

94 (a) Calculate

$3^4 + 2^{-3} - 5^0$

(b) Find the value of x if $5^x = 125$,

(c) Find the value of y if $2^y = \frac{1}{16}$.

(*NISEC*, 1988)

Unit 2.29

95 Multiply out the brackets and collect together like terms.

$3(x + 2y) + 4(3x - 2y)$ (*SEG*, 1988)

96 Simplify $3(2x - 1) - 2(3x - 4)$ (*NEA*, 1988)

97 Factorize $14x + 49y$. (*SEG*, 1988)

98 Factorize completely $2\pi rh + \pi r^2$. (*MEG*, 1988)

99 Factorize completely $6xy^2 - 12x^2y$. (*NEA*, 1988)

100 n is a positive whole number.

(a) Explain why the number $2n + 1$ must be odd.

(b) Write down, in terms of n, the next odd number after $2n + 1$.

(c) Add together these two odd numbers. Simplify and factorize the total.

(d) Explain why the sum of two consecutive odd numbers must be a multiple of 4.

(*MEG**)

Unit 2.30

101 Solve the equations

(a) $5z = 18$, (b) $8 + 3w = 14$. (*MEG*, 1988)

102 Solve

(a) $3x - 4 = 11$ (b) $4p^2 = 9$ (*LEAG*, 1988)

103 Solve $2(3x + 5) = 22$. (*NEA**)

104 Solve $\frac{2x - 1}{4} = 5$. (*NEA**)

105 Solve the equation $\frac{1 - 3x}{5} = 2$. (*NEA**)

Unit 2.31

106 Chris is ironing one evening and listening to the radio. The power used by each appliance is given in the following table.

Appliance	Power
Iron	1.2 kilowatts (kW)
Radio	40 watts
Light bulb	100 watts
Fire	2 kilowatts (kW)

The number of units of electricity used is given by the formula

POWER IN kW × TIME IN HOURS = UNITS USED.

(One kilowatt = 1000 watts.)

(a) Chris starts ironing at 8 p.m. with both the radio and light on. At 8.45 p.m. he feels cold and switches on a 2kW electric fire. He finishes ironing at 9.30 p.m. and switches everything off. How many units of electricity does Chris use between 8 p.m. and 9.30 p.m.?

(b) One unit of electricity costs 5.67p. Find the cost of the electricity Chris has used, correct to the nearest penny. (*NEA*, 1988)

107 Coats of two lengths are made from a roll of material. T is the total number of coats made and S the number of shorter length. The formula for N, the number of metres left on the roll is

$$N = 40 - (\tfrac{3}{4}T - \tfrac{1}{8}S).$$

If fifty coats are made, seventeen being of shorter length, find the number of metres left on the roll. (*NISEC*, 1988)

108 The amount of sleep a child needs (S hours) depends upon its age (A years) and is given approximately by the formula

$$S = 17 - \tfrac{1}{2}A.$$

(a) How many hours sleep should a child of 7 years have each night?

(b) If you were told a boy should be sleeping approximately 12 hours per night, what age would he be?

(c) If a girl's age is equal to the number of hours that she should be sleeping, what is her age? (*NISEC*, 1988)

109 v, u, a and t are related by the formula $v = u + at$.

(a) Find v when $u = 60$, $a = -10$ and $t = 4$.

(b) Find u when $v = 55$, $a = 4$ and $t = 12$.

(c) Express a in terms of v, u and t. (*MEG**)

110 Given that $T = 2\pi\sqrt{\dfrac{l}{g}}$,

(a) estimate the value of T, correct to 1 significant figure, when $l = 243$, and $g = 981$,

(b) express g in terms of T, π and l. (*MEG**)

Unit 2.32

111 What is the gradient of the line segment AB?

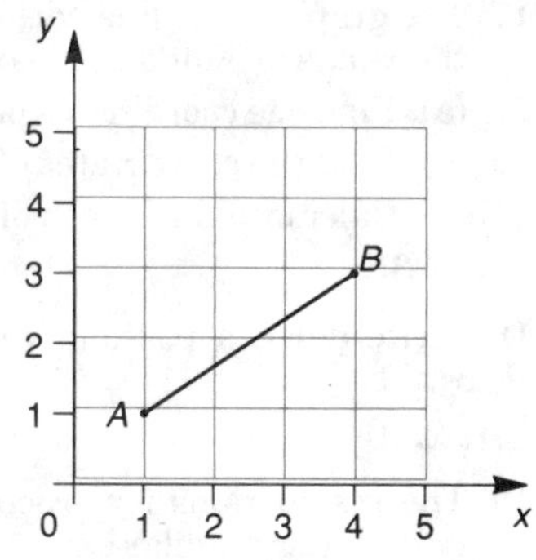

(*NEA**)

112 The diagram shows the point A with coordinates (2, 3).

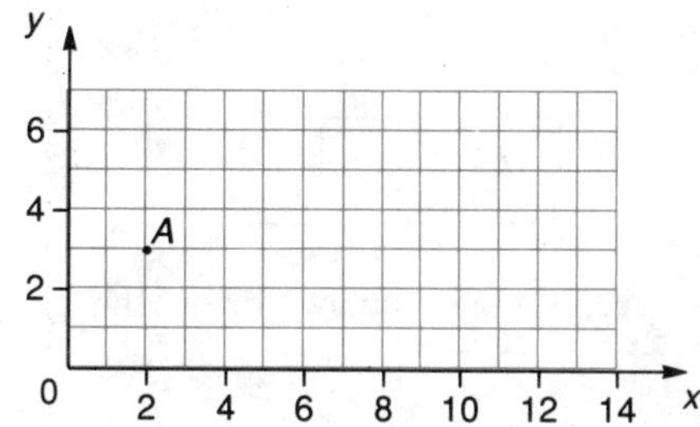

(a) Draw in the straight line passing through A with gradient $-\frac{1}{2}$.

(b) Write down the coordinates of the point where your line crosses the y-axis. (*MEG*, 1988)

Unit 2.33

113 A manufacturer has to make small rectangular tiles of different areas to cover various surfaces exactly. In each case, the length of the tile has to be three times the breadth.

(a) If the breadth of the tile is x cm, show that the area of the tile, A cm^2, is given by the expression $A = 3x^2$.

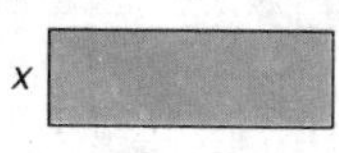

The manufacturer makes out a table and draws a graph, to read off various sizes of tile.

x	0	0.5	1	1.5	2	2.5	3
$A = 3x^2$				6.75		18.75	

(b) Complete the table above.

(c) Plot these values of x and A and complete the graph below.

(d) From the graph, find
 (i) the area of a tile of breadth 2.8 cm.
 (ii) the breadth of a tile of area 11 cm^2.

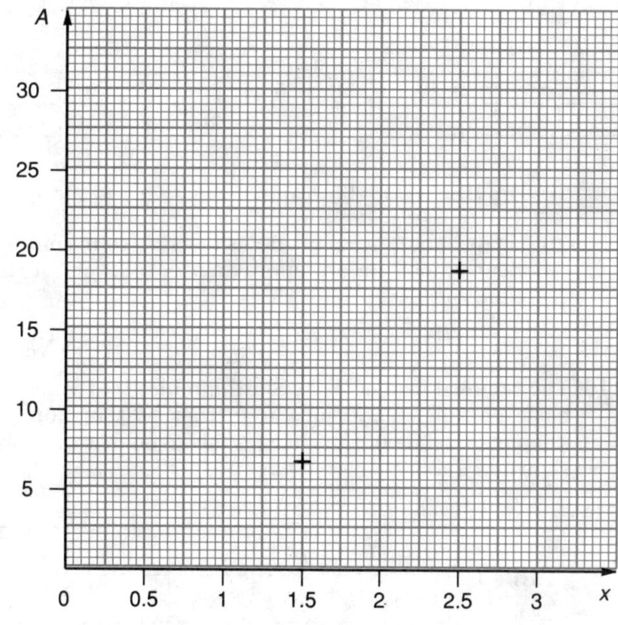

(*NISEC*, 1988)

Units 2.33 and 2.34

114 (a) Complete the table below for the equation $y = 5 - 2x$.

x	−2	0	2	4
y				

(b) On the graph paper below, draw the graph of $y = 5 - 2x$.

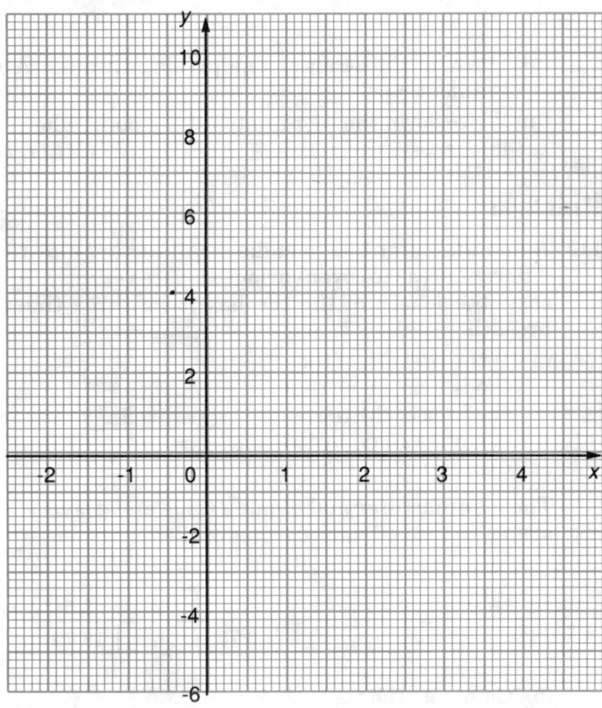

(c) What is the gradient of this graph?
(d) For what range of values of x is $5 - 2x$ less than 0?
(e) Solve the equation $5 - 2x = 6$. *(MEG, 1988)*

115 Given that $y = \frac{9}{x}$, complete the following table of values, stating the values, where appropriate, to two decimal places.

x	1	2	3	4	5	6	7	8	9
y	9		3				1.29	1.13	

(i) Draw on a grid the graph of $y = \frac{9}{x}$ for $1 \leqslant x \leqslant 9$.
(ii) Using your graph and showing your method clearly, obtain an approximate solution of the equation

$$\frac{9}{x} = 2.4$$

(NEA)*

116 The removal firm of W. E. Shiftham hires out vans at a basic charge of £20 plus a further cost of 30p per kilometre. Some of the charges for given distances are shown in Table 1.

Table 1

Distance (x km)	0	100	200	300
Charge (£C)	20			110

(a) Complete Table 1.
(b) Use the values from Table 1 to draw a graph to show the charges up to a distance of 300 km.

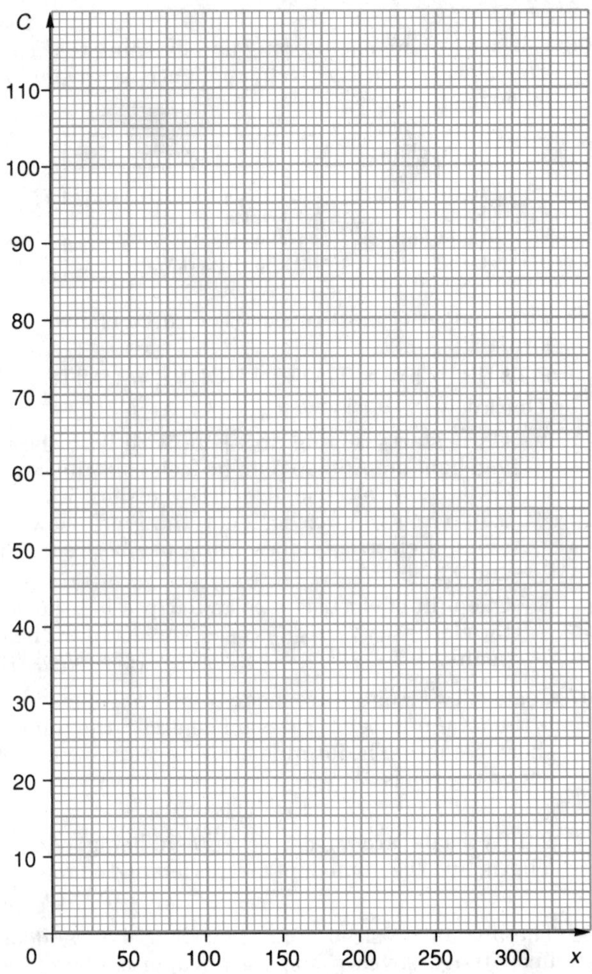

Another firm, D.I.Y. Transport, hires out vans at a basic charge of £35 plus a further cost of 20p per kilometre.

Table 2

Distance (x km)		0 100	200	300
Charge (£C)				

(c) Complete Table 2 for D.I.Y. Transport charges.
(d) Using the same axes as in part (b), draw a graph to show the charges of D.I.Y. Transport up to a distance of 300 km.
(e) For what distance do both firms charge the same amount?
(f) (i) Which firm is the cheaper for a journey of 180 km?
(ii) What is the difference in charges between the firms for a journey of 180 km?
(g) For D.I.Y. Transport, write down a formula giving the value of C in terms of x.

(LEAG, 1988)

Units 2.34 and 2.36

117 The graph of the line with equation $5x + 12y = 60$ cuts the x-axis at A and the y-axis at B.
(a) Find the coordinates of A.
(b) Find the coordinates of B.
(c) Calculate the length of AB. *(MEG*)*

Unit 2.35

118 Write down a possible value of x so that $2x < 4$ and $x > 1$. *(SEG*)*

Unit 2.36

119 The instructions for erecting a greenhouse say: 'First make a rectangular base 2 m by 3.5 m. To check that it is rectangular measure the diagonal. It should be about 4 m.'

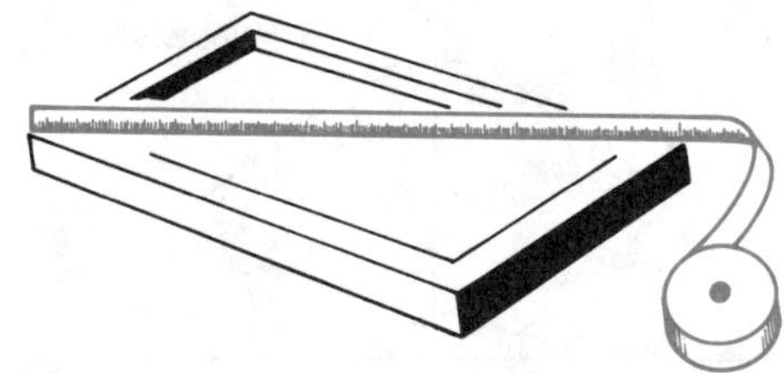

Using Pythagoras' theorem, explain why the diagonal should be about 4 m. (*SEG**)

120 (a) State two facts about the diagonals of a rhombus.

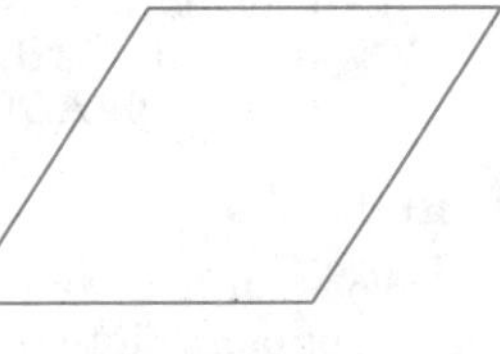

(b) A rhombus has diagonals of lengths 40 cm and 42 cm. Calculate the length of one side. (*MEG*, 1988)

121

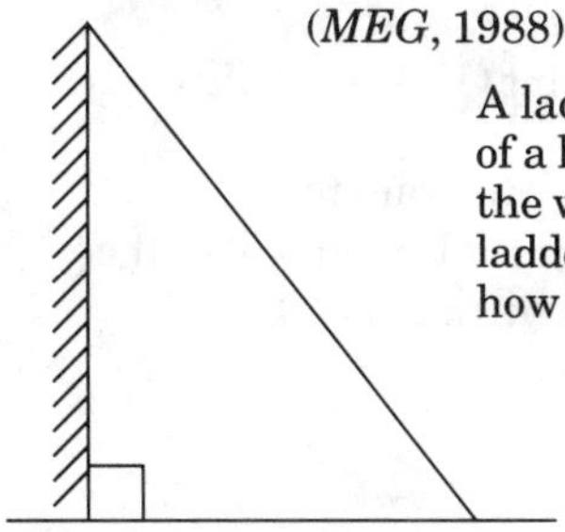

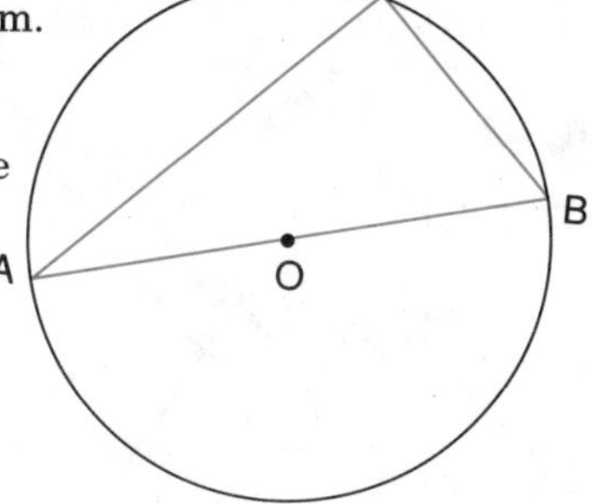

A ladder is set against the side of a house with its foot 5 m from the wall. If the length of the ladder is 10 metres, estimate how far up the wall it reaches. (*NISEC*, 1988)

122 The circle shown has centre O and radius 5 cm. PB has length 6 cm. Calculate

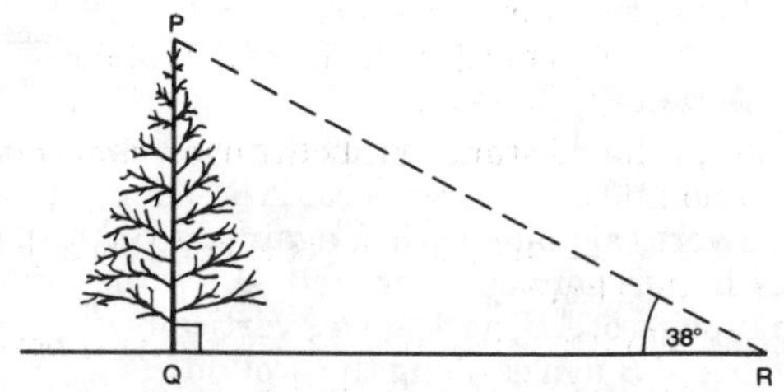

(a) the size of the angle APB;

(b) the length of AP. (*NISEC**)

Unit 2.37

123

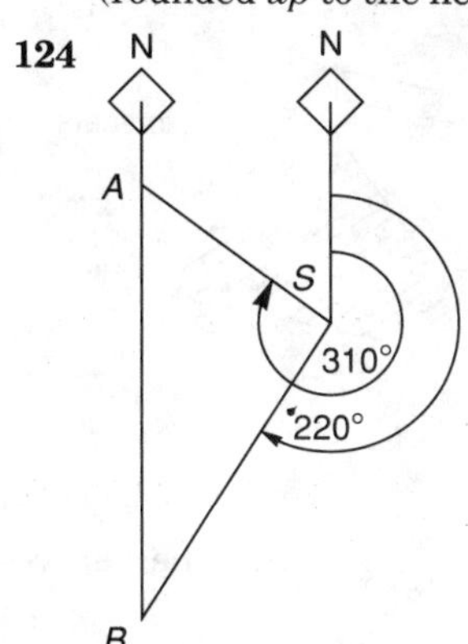

A tree is said to be dangerous and is to be cut down. For reasons of safety when it falls, it is necessary to know its height. A point R is 19.8 m from the foot of the tree and the angle of elevation of the top of the tree from R is 38°. Use trigonometry to estimate the height of the tree (rounded *up* to the nearest metre). (*NISEC**)

124

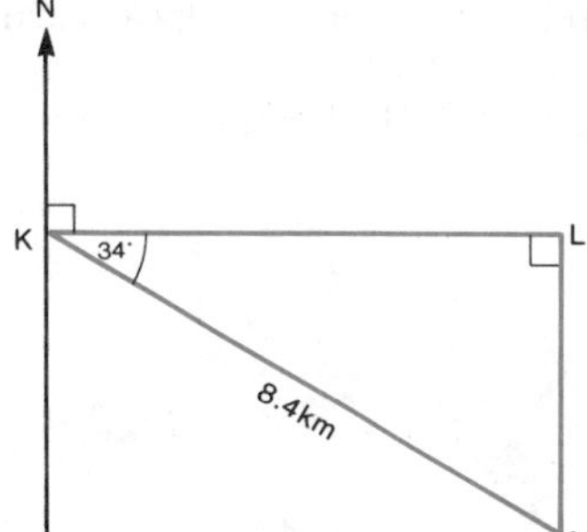

The diagram shows two navigation lights *A* and *B* with *A* due north of *B*. From a ship, *S*, the bearing of *A* is 310° and the bearing of *B* is 220°.

(a) Calculate

(i) angle *ASB*,

(ii) angle *ABS*.

(b) The distance *AB* is 2000 m; calculate the distances *SA* and *SB*. (*SEG*, 1988)

125

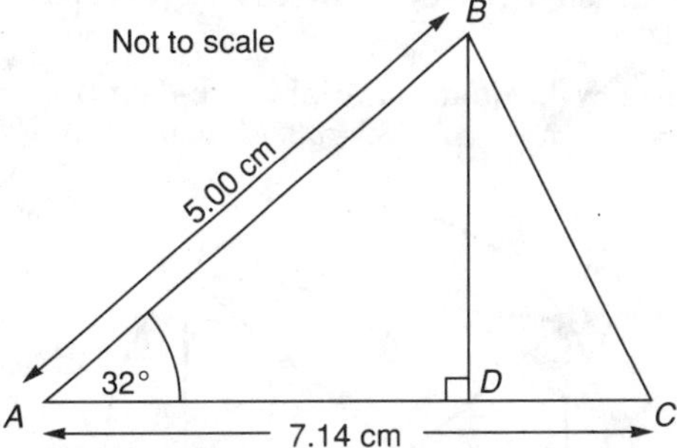

(a) In the above figure, not drawn to scale, L is due east of K, M is due south of L, distance KM = 8.4 km and ∠LKM = 34°. Calculate:

(i) the bearing of M from K;

(ii) the distance LM, correct to two decimal places.

(b) A boat is 80 m from the foot of the cliff which is 25 m high. Calculate the angle of elevation from the boat to the top of the cliff. (*WJEC**)

126 A man lying down on top of a cliff 40 m above sea level was in line with a ship and some dangerous rocks whose angles of depression were 25° and 36° respectively. Calculate the distance between the ship and the dangerous rocks, correct to one decimal place. (*NISEC*, 1988)

Units 2.36 and 2.37

127

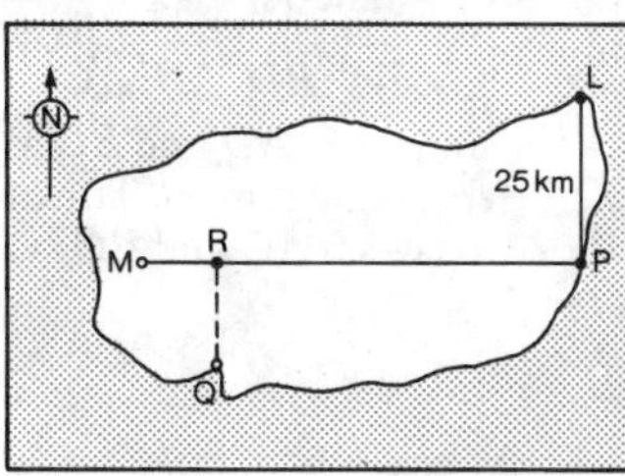

In the figure, *ADC* is a straight line, *AB* = 5.00 cm, *AC* = 7.14 cm, angle *BAC* = 32° and angle *BDA* = 90°.

(a) Calculate the length of

(i) *AD*, (ii) *CD*.

(b) (i) Work out 5 sin 32°.

(ii) Which length in the diagram corresponds to this?

(c) Calculate the length of *BC*. Give your answer correct to 2 significant figures. (*MEG*, 1988)

128 The diagram shows a sketch map of an island. The lighthouse L is 25 km due north of Portpearl (P) and the Mount (M) is 96 km due west of Portpearl.

(a) Calculate, to the nearest kilometre, the distance of the lighthouse from the Mount.

(b) Calculate to the nearest degree, the size of angle LMP, and hence find the bearing of L from M.

The Quay (Q) is 20 km from the Mount on a bearing of 125°. The Rooftop Hotel (R) is due north of the Quay and due east of the Mount.

(c) Draw a *rough sketch* of △MRQ and mark on it the length of MQ and the size of each of its three angles.

(d) Calculate, in km, to 1 decimal place, the distance of the Rooftop Hotel from
(i) the Mount, (ii) the Port. (*LEAG**)

List 3

Unit 3.1

1 AB and AC are chords of a circle and AB = AC. The diameter AD meets the chord BC at M and angle ACM = 62°.

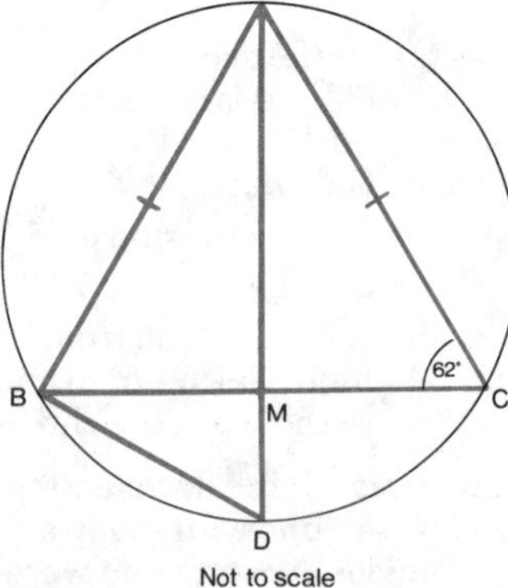

(a) (i) Write down the size of angle ABD.
(ii) Calculate the size of angle DBM.

(b) Given that BM = MC = 5 cm, calculate correct to one decimal place,
(i) the length of AM, (ii) the length of AB. (*MEG**)

2 ABCD is a cyclic quadrilaterial in which ∠DAC = 48°, ∠ACD = 32°, and ∠ADB = 53°. Calculate the size of ∠BAC.

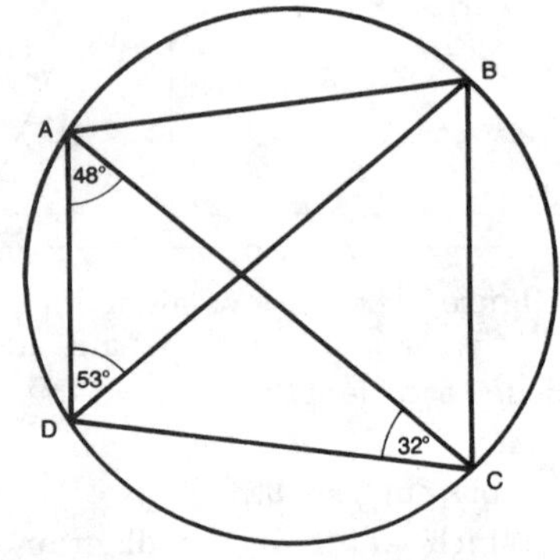

(*NEA**)

3 In this question you must give valid reasons for your answers. Numbers on their own will not be sufficient.

The diagram shows the cross-section of a tunnel. The tunnel is circular with a platform *DC* in it. The platform is held by five rods *AB*, *BC*, *BD*, *AD*, *AC*. Rods *AB*, *AD* and *BC* are all the same length. The angle between *AC* and *BC* is 30°.

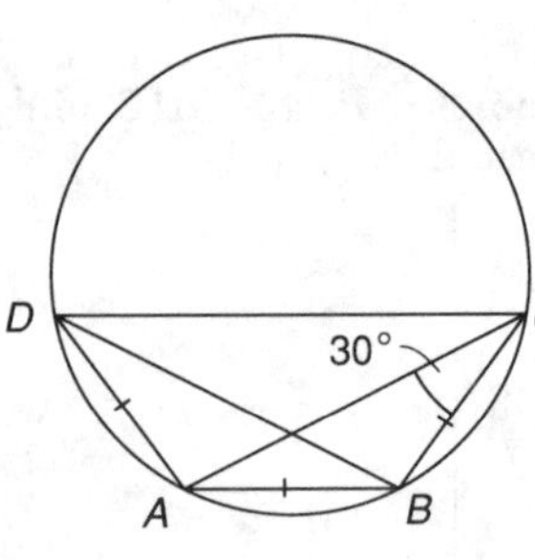

(a) Find
(i) ∠*ADB*,
(ii) ∠*ABD*,
(iii) ∠*DBC*,
(iv) ∠*BDC*.

(b) (i) Explain how you know that platform *DC* must be parallel to rod *AB*.
(ii) What does the answer to (a)(iii) tell you about *DC*?

(*WJEC*, 1989)

4

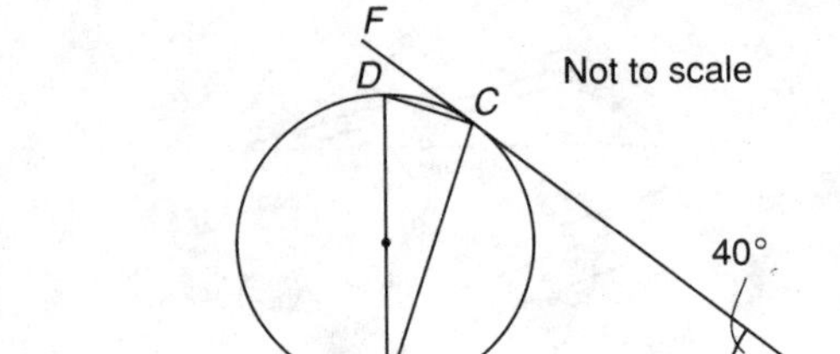

In the diagram, *BCF* and *BAE* are tangents to the circle, of which *AD* is a diameter. Angle *ABC* = 40°.

(a) Explain why triangle *ABC* is isosceles.

(b) Calculate the size of
(i) angle *CAB*, (ii) angle *DAC*,
(iii) angle *ADC*. (*MEG*, 1988)

Unit 3.2

5 The points A and B are fixed and are 8 cm apart. The locus of a point P is the set X, where
$X = \{P{:}AP = 2 \text{ cm or } BP = 5 \text{ cm}\}$.
The locus of another point Q is the set Y, where
$Y = \{Q{:}BQ = k \text{ cm}\}$

(a) Indicate clearly on a diagram the set X.

(b) State the range of possible values of k when
(i) $X \cap Y = \varnothing$, (ii) $n(X \cap Y) = 2$

(*NEA**)

6

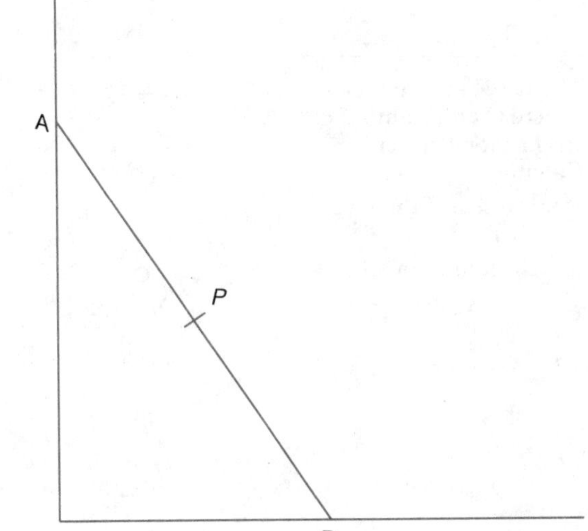

The diagram, which is drawn to a scale of 1 cm to represent 0.5 m, shows a rod *AB*, of length 3 m, resting in a vertical plane with *A* against a vertical wall and *B* resting on horizontal ground. Draw the locus of *P*, the mid-point of *AB*, as *A* moves vertically up and down the wall and *B* moves along the ground.

Unit 3.3

7 In the diagram, triangle *ABC* is an enlargement of triangle *PQR* with *O* as centre of enlargement. The area of triangle *PQR* is 2 cm². Calculate the area of triangle *ABC*.

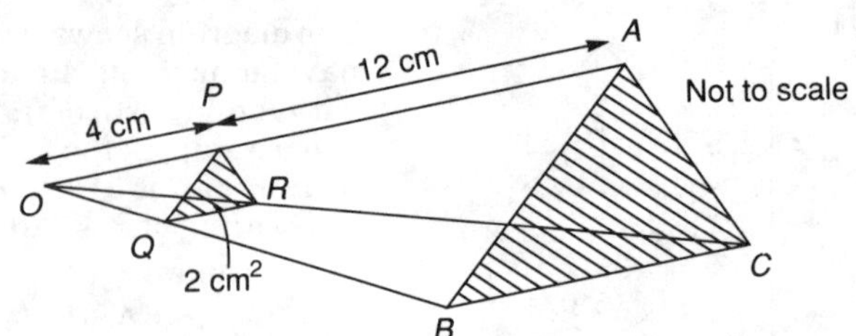

(*MEG*, 1988)

8 On graph paper, draw the triangle with the vertices A (−2, −2), B (1, 1) and C (4, −3).

(a) Draw the image of ABC under a reflection in $x = 3$ and label it $A_1B_1C_1$.

(b) Draw the image of ABC under a reflection in $y = 0$ and label it $A_2B_2C_2$.

(c) Draw the image of $A_2B_2C_2$ under an enlargement, centre (0, 0) and scale factor $\frac{3}{2}$, and label it $A_3B_3C_3$.

(d) If the area of $A_2B_2C_2$ is t cm^2, find the area of $A_3B_3C_3$ in terms of t.

(*NISEC*, 1988)

9 A plastic cup has base diameter 5.0 cm, top diameter 7.5 cm and depth 7.0 cm. Consider this as being formed by removing a cone *OXY* from a cone *OAB* as shown in the figure.

(a) State the scale factor of the enlargement mapping *XY* onto *AB*.

(b) Explain why the volume of cone *OXY* is $\frac{8}{27}$ that of cone *OAB*.

(c) State the height, h centimetres, of cone *OAB*.

(d) Calculate the volume of liquid which the cup will hold. (*MEG*, 1988)

Unit 3.4

10 The scale of a map is 1:25 000. A forest is represented on the map as a shape whose perimeter is 12 cm and whose area is 10 cm^2.

(a) Find the perimeter of the forest in kilometres.

(b) Find the area of the forest in square metres.

(*MEG**)

11 A photocopier can print copies smaller or larger than the original. The ratio of lengths in the original to lengths in the copies must be one of the following:

1:0.5 1:0.7 1:1 1:1.4 1:2

A firm has always used the ratio 1:1, but now wishes to reduce the area of paper used for each copy by about one half. Which ratio should the firm choose? Explain your answer. (*SEG*, 1988)

12 Two ball bearings have diameters of 1 cm and 2 cm respectively. What is the ratio of their volumes in its simplest form? (*SEG*, 1988)

13 The diagram, which is not drawn to scale, represents a symmetrical white sign fused on to a road with hot molten material.

Angle *BAC* = 2 × angle *DAE*.

In the following calculations, work to four significant figures and give answers to two significant figures.

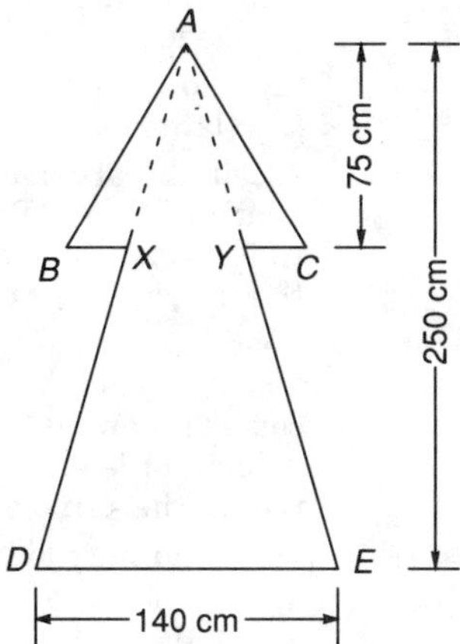

(a) (i) Use similar triangles to calculate the length *XY*.

(ii) Calculate the size of angle *DAE*.

(iii) Calculate the length *BC*.

(iv) Calculate the surface area of the sign.

(b) Each sign is 3 mm in depth and the material for 30 such signs can be poured from a full cylindrical boiler, 40 cm in depth.

(i) Calculate the volume of material used for each sign.

(ii) Calculate the internal radius of the boiler.

(*NEA*, 1988)

Unit 3.5

14

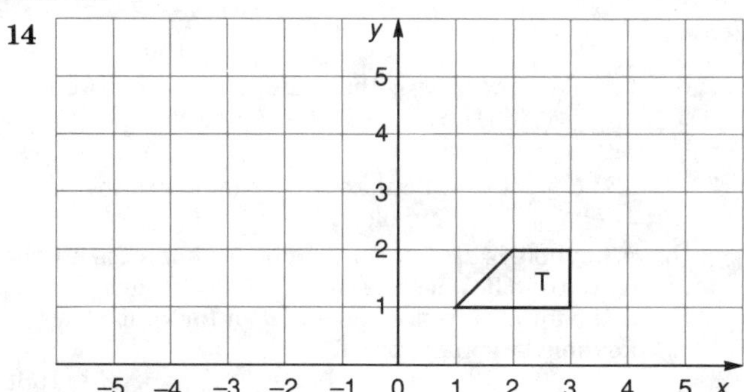

Trapezium T is reflected in the line $y = 3$ to give trapezium T_1.

Trapezium T_1 is then rotated 90° anticlockwise about (0, 0) to give trapezium T_2.

Trapezium T_2 is then translated $\begin{pmatrix}6\\0\end{pmatrix}$ to give trapezium T_3.

(a) Show the positions of T_1, T_2 and T_3 on the diagram.

(b) Describe the single transformation that would take T to T_3. (*NEA*, 1988)

15 Transformation **A** is 'reflect in the line $y = x$, followed by the translation $\begin{pmatrix}-1\\1\end{pmatrix}$'.

Transformation **B** is 'reflect in the line $x + y = 0$'.

(a) On graph paper, using a scale of 2 cm to 1 unit on each axis,

(i) draw the triangle, T, with corners at (0,0), (2,0) and (2,1),

(ii) draw the image of T under **A**. Label it T′.

(b) Draw the image of T′ under **B**. Label it T″.

(c) T may be mapped directly onto T″ by the transformation **C**: 'half-turn about a point W, followed by a translation $\begin{pmatrix}p\\q\end{pmatrix}$'.

Find the coordinates of W and the vector $\begin{pmatrix}p\\q\end{pmatrix}$.

(*LEAG*, 1988)

16 On graph paper draw the triangle ABC, where A, B, C are the points (1, 3), (2, 3), (2, 5) respectively.

The transformation **M** is a reflection in the line $x = -1$.
The transformation **N** is a reflection in the line $y = 1$.

T is the translation $\begin{pmatrix}2\\-2\end{pmatrix}$.

(a) Triangle ABC is mapped onto triangle $A_1B_1C_1$ by **M**. Triangle $A_1B_1C_1$ is mapped onto triangle $A_2B_2C_2$ by **N**.
Triangle $A_2B_2C_2$ is mapped onto triangle $A_3B_3C_3$ by **T**.
Draw these triangles on your diagram and label them clearly.

(b) Describe the single transformation which maps triangle ABC onto triangle $A_3B_3C_3$.

(c) A further transformation **R** is an enlargement, centre the origin, scale factor $\frac{1}{2}$. Draw the image of triangle ABC under **R**.

(d) If the area of triangle ABC is x square units, state the area of the image of triangle ABC under **R**.

(*NISEC**)

Unit 3.6

17 The diagram represents a keyhole. The perimeter of the keyhole consists of two straight lines and two arcs of circles, one of radius 7 cm and the other of radius 2 cm. Both circles have centre O.

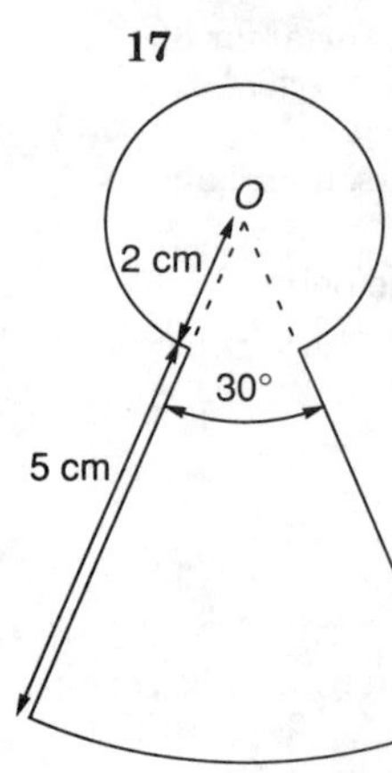

A formula for the length of an arc of a circle is given by

$$\text{arc length} = \frac{\theta \times \pi \times r}{180}$$

where r is the radius of the circle and $\theta°$ is the angle at the centre of the circle.

(a) Calculate the perimeter of the keyhole.

(b) A keyhole is draughtproof if its perimeter is no more than 3 times the thickness of the door. What is the minimum thickness of door for which this keyhole is draughtproof?

(*NEA*, 1988)

18 The shape of the top of a table in a cafe is shown by the part of the circle, centre O, in the diagram. The angle BOD = 90° and BO = OD = 50 cm. The top of the table is made of formica and a thin metal strip is fixed to its perimeter.

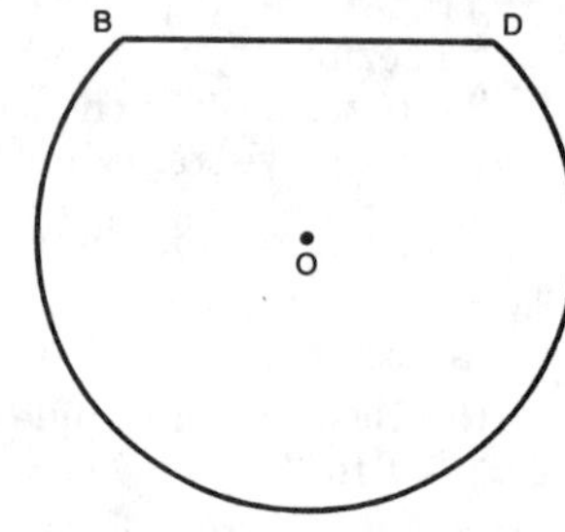

(a) Calculate
  (i) the length of the metal strip,
  (ii) the area of the formica surface.

(b) If the table top is to be cut from a square of formica of area 1 m^2, what percentage of formica is wasted?

(*SEG**)

19 Fred has to make a cone of base radius 3.5 cm and vertical height 12 cm. To do this he uses a sector of a circle as shown in the diagram below.

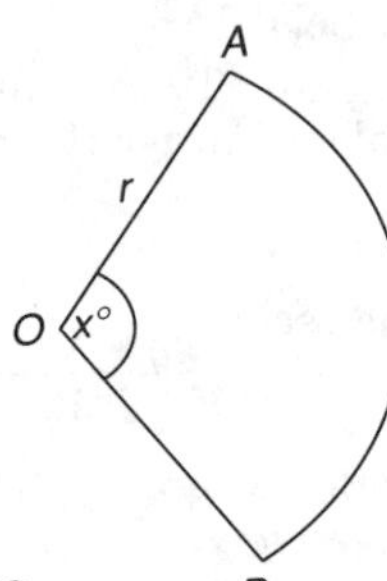

(a) Draw a diagram of the cone, indicating clearly the positions of O, A and B.

(b) Calculate
  (i) the radius, r cm, of the sector,
  (ii) the angle, $x°$, at the centre of the sector.

(*MEG*, 1988)

20

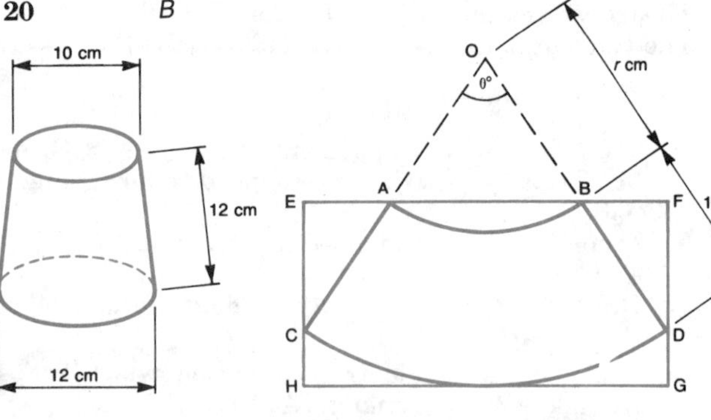

Fig. 1 Fig. 2

A mathematical DIY enthusiast plans to re-cover a lampshade of circular cross-section. The dimensions of the lampshade are shown in Fig. 1. The fabric is to be cut from a rectangular piece of material, EFGH, to the pattern shown in Fig. 2. The arcs AB and CD are from separate circles with the same centre O and each arc subtends the same angle $\theta°$ at O.

(a) Using the measurements given in Fig. 1 write down, as a multiple of π, the lengths of:
  (i) arc AB, (ii) arc CD.

(b) Using the measurements given in Fig. 2 write down, in terms of r, θ and π, the lengths of:
  (i) arc AB, (ii) arc CD.

(c) Use the results of (a) and (b) to find:
  (i) r, (ii) θ.

(*LEAG**)

Unit 3.7

21 A silo used for storing grain is made from a cylinder and a cone as shown in the diagram below. The cylinder is closed at the top.

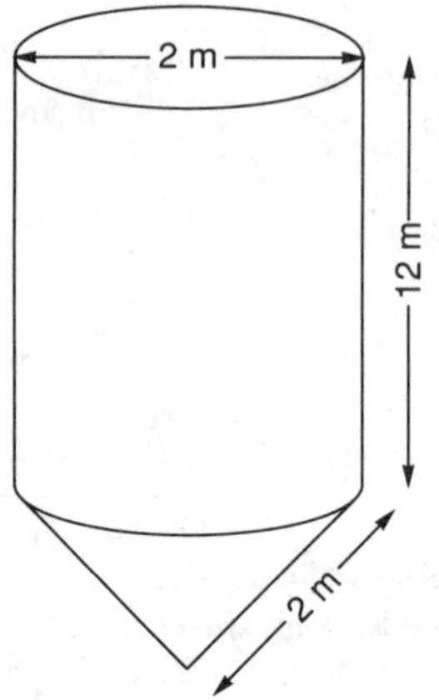

Formulae for cone:
$V = \frac{1}{3}\pi r^2 h$
$A = \pi r l$
r = radius, h = height,
l = slant height
You may take $\pi = 3.14$

(a) Calculate the cost of painting the complete external surface, correct to the nearest £, at £1.20 per square metre.

(b) Calculate the volume of grain, correct to the nearest m^3, that the silo will hold when 70 per cent full.

(*NISEC*, 1988)

22

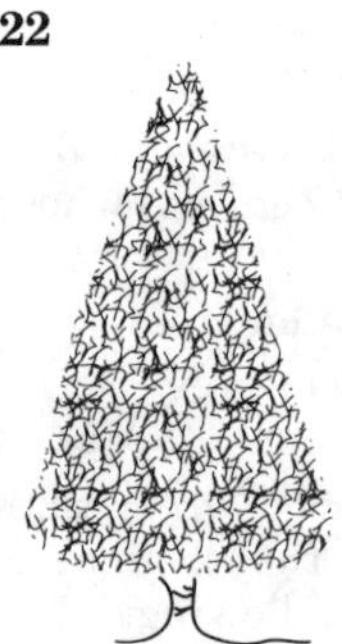

To estimate the volume of timber in the trunk of a conifer, a pupil considered the trunk to be a cone and measured the circumference of the base to be 68 cm. To find the height she walked back 30 m from the base of the tree and took a sighting of the top of the tree.

From her eye level (1.2 m above the ground), the angle of elevation to the top of the tree was 26°.

(a) Calculate the height of the tree.

(b) Calculate the volume of timber (in m^3) in the trunk of the tree.

(*NEA*, 1988)

23 (In this question give all your answers correct to 3 significant figures.)

(a) A lead ball of radius 4 cm is melted and cast into small balls each of radius 0.25 cm.
  (i) Calculate the volume, in cm^3, of the large lead ball.
  (ii) Calculate the volume, in cm^3, of a single small lead ball.
  (iii) How many small lead balls can be cast from the large ball?

(b) A cylindrical can of radius 5 cm contains water to a depth of 6 cm. Four thousand lead balls each of radius 0.25 cm are dropped into the can. Calculate the rise, in cm, of the water level.

(c) Lead in water is believed to poison water birds. A fisherman has 8 small lead balls on his line. He considers an alternative arrangement of the same volume of lead using a single lead ball in order to reduce the surface area.
  (i) Find the radius of this alternative lead ball.
  (ii) Find the surface area of this alternative lead ball.
  (iii) Calculate the surface area of a small lead ball of radius 0.25 cm.

(iv) Complete the following table to display all the evidence about the alternative balls.

	One small lead ball	8 small lead balls	One alternative lead ball
Radius	0.25 cm	0.25 cm	
Surface area			
Volume			

(*LEAG*, 1988)

24 (In this question take π to be 3.142 and give each answer correct to three significant figures.)
A solid silver sphere has a radius of 0.7 cm.

(a) Calculate:

(i) the surface area of the sphere;

(ii) the volume of the sphere.

(b) A silversmith is asked to make a solid pyramid with a vertical height of 25 cm and a square base. To make the pyramid, the silversmith has to melt down 1000 of the silver spheres.
Assuming that none of the silver is wasted, calculate the total surface area of the pyramid.
(*MEG**)

Unit 3.8

25 Nineteen girls are employed in an office. The Venn diagram shows some details about the number who can do audio-typing (A), shorthand-typing (S) and use the word processor (W). They all have at least one of these skills.

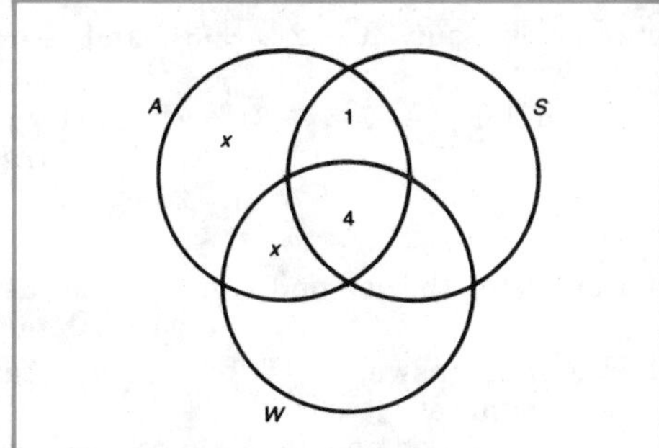

(a) 11 girls can do audio-typing. Find x.

(b) If 6 girls cannot do either method of typing, how many can do shorthand-typing?

(c) Nobody does only shorthand-typing. Find:

(i) how many can use the word processor,

(ii) how many can both use the word processor and do shorthand-typing.

(d) Copy the Venn diagram and shade the region $W \cap A' \cap S'$.
Give a brief description of this set. (*SEG**)

26

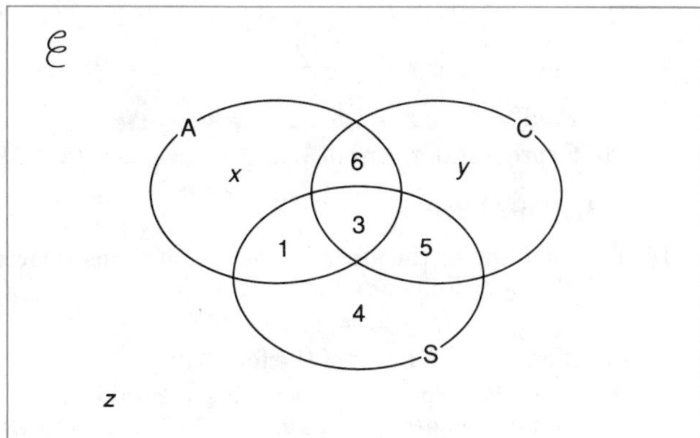

The Venn diagram represents a class of 30 children.
A = {children who are proficient in athletics},
C = {children who are proficient in cycling},
S = {children who are proficient in swimming}.
There are 2 children who are proficient only in athletics and 21 who are proficient in cycling.

(a) Find the values of x, y and z.

(b) Calculate the number of children who are proficient in swimming.

(c) Calculate $n(S \cap C)$.

(d) Calculate $n((S \cup C \cup A)')$. (*LEAG*, 1988)

27 A Road Safety Officer reported to the Head of a certain school as follows:
'I examined 100 bicycles of your pupils, looking for faults in brakes, steering and saddle heights. I found 9 cases of defective brakes, 4 of bad steering and 22 bicycles with saddles at the wrong height.
'It is sad to reflect that although three-quarters of the bicycles had none of these faults, 4 had two faults and 3 failed on three counts. The 16 bicycles which had only saddle height faults, I have corrected straight away.'

(i) Present this information in a Venn diagram, using
B = {bicycles with faulty brakes},
S = {bicycles with bad steering}, and
H = {bicycles with saddles at the wrong height}.

(ii) Evaluate $n\{B \cup S' \cup H'\}$.
Interpret this result. (*NEA**)

Unit 3.9

28 The total rainfall each year is recorded for 80 years at a weather station. The graph shows this information as a cumulative frequency curve.

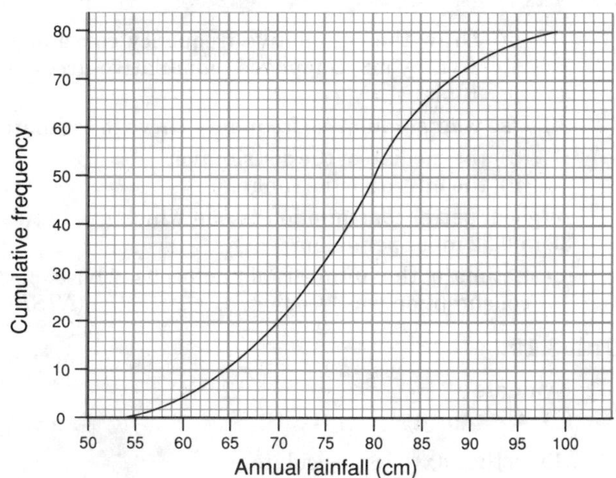

(a) How many of these years had less than 80 cm of rainfall each?

(b) How many years had more than 90 cm of rainfall each?

(c) What was the median annual rainfall?
(*MEG*, 1988)

29 In an examination there were 5000 candidates and the marks they obtained are summarized in the table below.

Mark obtained	Number of Candidates	Mark obtained	Number of Candidates
20 or less	250	60 or less	3200
30 or less	500	70 or less	4000
40 or less	1000	80 or less	4500
50 or less	2000	100 or less	5000

(a) Draw a cumulative frequency diagram to represent these results.
(Use a scale of 2 cm to represent 20 marks on the x-axis and 2 cm to represent 500 candidates on the cumulative frequency axis.)

(b) Using the cumulative frequency diagram, or otherwise, find:

(i) the number of candidates who scored 82 marks or less;

(ii) the median mark:

(iii) the interquartile range;

(iv) the percentage of candidates who scored more than 70 marks;

(v) the minimum mark required for a pass if 80 per cent of the candidates passed the examination. *(MEG*)*

30 In a survey 100 motorists were asked to record the petrol consumption of their cars in miles per gallon. Each figure was rounded to the nearest mile per gallon and the following frequency distribution was obtained.

Miles per gallon	26–30	31–35	36–40	41–45	46–50	51–55	56–60
Frequency	4	6	18	34	20	12	6

(a) (i) State the limits of the modal class of this distribution.

(ii) Complete the following 'less than' cumulative frequency table.

Miles per gallon (less than)	30.5	35.5	40.5	45.5	50.5	55.5	60.5
Number of motorists	4	10					

(iii) Draw the cumulative frequency curve (ogive) from your completed cumulative frequency table.

(b) Use your cumulative frequency curve to estimate:

(i) the median of the distribution

(ii) the interquartile range.

A 'good' petrol consumption is one which lies between 38 and 52 miles per gallon.

(c) Estimate the number of motorists whose petrol consumption was 'good'. *(NISEC*)*

Unit 3.10

31 Evaluate

(a) $4^{1/2}$ (b) 4^{-1} (c) 4^0 *(SEG*)*

32 Given that $f(x) = 8^x$, calculate

(i) $f(\frac{2}{3})$ (ii) $f(-\frac{1}{3})$. *(NEA*)*

33 Simplify the following leaving your answer in index form:

(a) $3^3 \times 3^4$ (b) $(2^{1/3})^6$ (c) $10^{1/2} \times 10^{1/2}$ *(SEG, 1988)*

34 (a) Calculate $64^{2/3} \times 2^{-4}$.

(b) Find the value of n if $2^n = \frac{1}{\sqrt{8}}$ *(NISEC, 1988)*

35 A population of bacteria is known to double in number every hour. At 2.00 p.m. on a certain day the population is estimated to be 1000.

(a) What will the population be at 6.00 p.m. on the same day?

(b) At what time will the population number 1000×2^{10}?

(c) At what time will the population number $1000 \times 2^{1/2}$?

(d) Evaluate this population, correct to 3 significant figures. *(MEG*)*

Unit 3.11

36 Nelson decides to plant vegetables in a piece of garden which is rectangular in shape. He uses a long cane to measure the land and finds that it is 5 cane lengths plus one stride by 3 cane lengths plus one stride. The plan of the land and the proposed vegetable plots is shown below. The unshaded area represents a path.

C = cane length; S = stride.

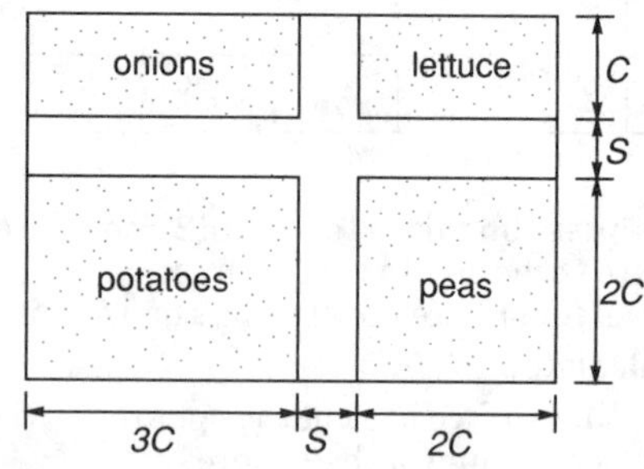

(a) Find, in terms of C, the total area of land used for growing vegetables.

(b) Find, in terms of C and S, the area of the path.

(c) The area of the potato plot is 216 square feet. Find C. *(SEG, 1988)*

Units 3.11 and 3.12

37 (a) Expand $(3x + 2)(2x - 5)$, writing your answer in its simplest form.

(b) Factorize $16x^2 - 49$. *(NISEC, 1988)*

Units 3.11 and 3.16

38 (a) Multiply out $(x - 2)(x + 3)$ and simplify your answer.

(b) Given that $(x - 2)(x + 3) = 6$, solve for x. *(LEAG, 1988)*

Unit 3.12

39 (a) Complete the second bracket so as to make $p^2 - q^2 = (p - q)(\quad)$ a true statement.

(b) Use your answer to (a) to help you calculate the exact value of

$$10\,000\,000\,001^2 - 9\,999\,999\,999^2$$

(MEG, 1988)

40 Factorize completely $3x^2 - 48$. *(NEA*)*

41 Factorize $6x^2 + 7x - 20$. *(NEA*)*

Units 3.12 and 3.16

42 (a) Factorize $x^2 + 11x + 24$.

(b) Solve $y^2 + y - 6 = 0$. *(LEAG, 1988)*

Unit 3.13

43 The voltage, V volts, available from a 12 volt battery of internal resistance r ohms when connected to apparatus of resistance R ohms, is given by

$$V = \frac{12R}{(r + R)}.$$

(a) Find V when $r = 1.5$ and $R = 6$.

(b) Express R in terms of V and r. *(MEG, 1988)*

Units 3.13 and 3.16

44 The formula for the surface area, A, of a closed circular cylinder of radius r and height h is

$$A = 2\pi r(r + h).$$

(a) Make h the subject of the formula.

(b) Find the radius, in cm to one decimal place, of a cylinder whose surface area is 120π cm^2 and whose height is 12 cm. *(LEAG, 1988)*

Unit 3.14

45 A group of students on a Business Studies course are making 'Solitaire' games which they are selling for £1 each. Apart from a loan of £20 which has to be repaid, all the income is profit.

(a) Write down an expression for the total profit after n games have been sold.

(b) How many games have to be sold to give an average profit of 75p on each game? (*NEA*, 1988)

46 A metal rod of length 65 cm is cut into 10 pieces, each piece being 1 cm longer than its predecessor. Find the length of the shortest piece. (*NEA*, 1988)

47 A field 100 metres square is divided into two trapeziums and a triangle, as shown in the diagram. BD is x metres long.

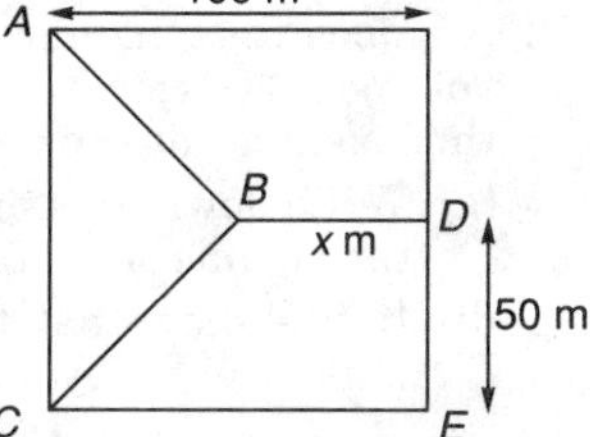

(a) What is the perpendicular distance from B to AC in terms of x?

(b) What is the area of triangle ABC in terms of x?

(c) What is the area of trapezium $CBDE$ in terms of x?

(d) Each of the three parts of the field has the same area. What is the length of BD? (*WJEC*, 1988)

Units 3.14 and 3.16

48 (a) At the moment, Paul is six times as old as his daughter Jane.

(i) If Jane's present age is x years, write down, in terms of x, the age Paul will be in 12 years' time.

(ii) In 12 years' time Paul will be three times as old as Jane. Write down an equation for x and hence find Jane's present age.

(b) Solve the equation $(x - 1)^2 = 3$, giving your answers correct to two decimal places. (*MEG**)

Unit 3.15

49 The cost, £C, of making n articles is given by the formula

$$C = a + bn$$

where a and b are constants.

The cost of making 4 articles is £20 and the cost of making 7 articles is £29.

Write down two equations in a and b. Solve these equations to find the values of a and b. (*LEAG*, 1988)

50 (a) When $x + y = 5$ and $3x + 2y = 4$ find the values of x and y.

(b) The organizers for a charity concert sold 500 tickets. There were two prices; £3 for adults and £2 for children. The money received from the sale of adult tickets was £400 more than the money received from the sale of children's tickets. How many adult tickets were sold? (*SEG*, 1988)

51

Day	PAS	UHT	Pints	Money
Monday	296	41	337	£81.70
Tuesday	320	56	[illegible]	[illegible]
Wednesd[illegible]	[illegible]	[illegible]	349	£84.74

Pasteurized milk (*PAS*) costs 24p per pint and *UHT* milk costs 26p per pint. A milkman keeps a record of his sales, but spills coffee on his record book.

(a) How many pints of milk did he sell on Tuesday?

(b) How much money did he take on Tuesday?

(c) How many pints of each type did he sell on Wednesday? (*WJEC*, 1988)

52 Given that

8 bolts and 6 nuts weigh 138 grams
and 3 bolts and 5 nuts weigh 71 grams,

work out the weight of each of the following:

(a) 4 bolts and 3 nuts, (b) 11 bolts and 11 nuts,
(c) 3 bolts and 3 nuts, (d) 1 bolt (e) 1 nut. (*NEA*, 1988)

Unit 3.16

53 Solve the equation $3x^2 + 12x = 0$. (*NEA*, 1988)

54 Sid decides to invest £240 in British Gas Shares.

(a) If each share costs x pence write down an expression for the number of shares received.

(b) If each share had been 10p less, Sid could have bought another 80 shares. Form an equation for x and show that it reduces to

$$x^2 - 10x - 3000 = 0.$$

(c) Calculate the price which Sid paid for each share. (*SEG*, 1988)

55 Derrick has to mark out a triangular flower bed ABC, as shown in the diagram. The distance AB must be 10 m and the angle APB must be 90°.

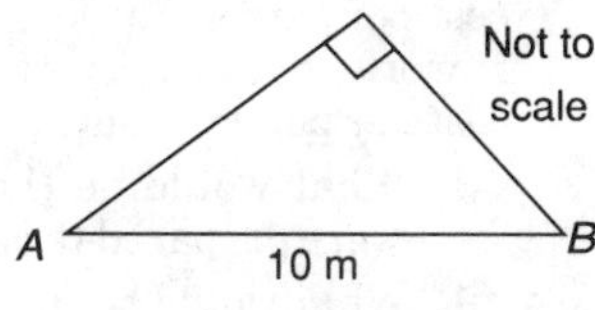

The lengths of the other two sides, AP and BP, must total 13 m.

(a) Taking the length of AP as x metres, form an equation in x, and show that it simplifies to $2x^2 - 26x + 69 = 0$.

(b) Solve this equation to find the two possible values of x, correct to 2 decimal places. (*MEG*, 1988)

56 A plastics firm is asked to make a small open rectangular container with a square base. The side of the base is x mm and the height of the container is h mm.

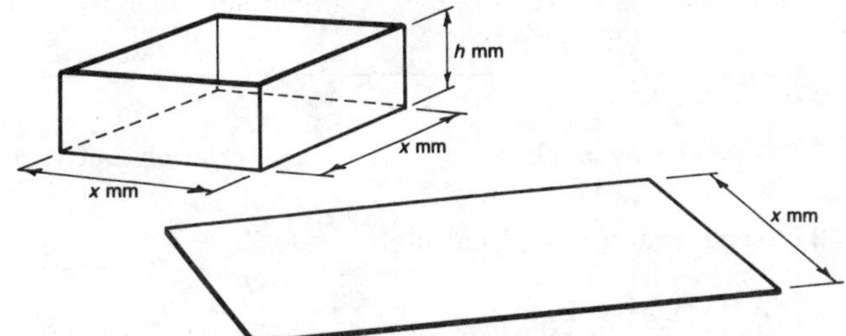

The pieces making up the faces of the container are cut from a single rectangular strip of plastic of width x mm.

(a) Write down, in terms of x and h:

(i) the length of the piece of plastic;

(ii) the area of the piece of plastic.

The area of plastic used for one container is 2500 mm^2.

(b) Use your answer in (a)(ii) to find an expression for h in terms of x.

(c) Find the value of x when the height is 20 mm.

(d) Write down, to the nearest millimetre, the dimensions of the strip of plastic. (*LEAG**)

Units 3.16 and 3.18

57 (a) Solve the equation $x^2 - 4x - 5 = 0$.

(b) Using the axes below, sketch the graph of

$y = x^2 - 4x - 5$, showing clearly its axis of symmetry.

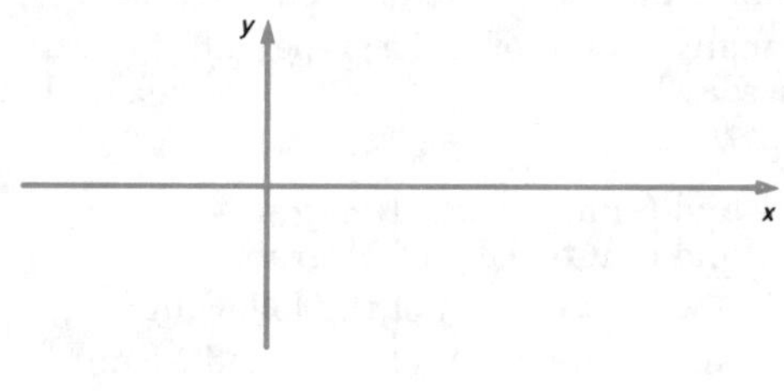

(*MEG**)

Unit 3.17

58 Solve the equation $\dfrac{2x-1}{3} - \dfrac{x-2}{5} = \dfrac{x}{2}$.

(*MEG*, 1988)

59 Solve the equation $\dfrac{3}{x-7} = 2$.

(*MEG**)

Unit 3.18

60 A group of students went to play a game of rounders in the park. During play, one of the windows of a nearby building was broken. The students, agreeing that they should admit to the breakage, discussed who should pay for the new window. They realized that the more of them who were prepared to contribute, the less it would cost per person.
It worked out that if 10 of them were to contribute, the cost per person would be £6.

(i) What would be the cost per person if 15 of them were prepared to contribute?

(ii) What would be the cost per person if 8 of them were to contribute?

(iii) Find the formula relating c, the cost in pounds per person, and n the number of students.

(iv) Which one of the following sketch graphs labelled A, B, C, represents this relation?

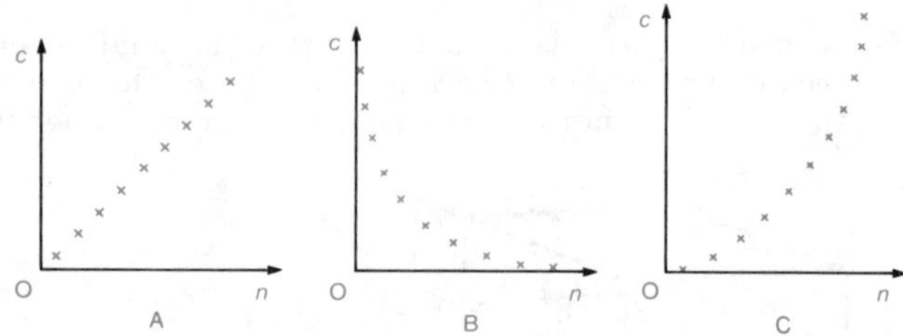

(v) Draw a sketch graph of the relation between c and $\dfrac{1}{n}$.

(*WJEC**)

61 A farmer has 16 m of fencing which he is going to use to make a rectangular pen $PQRS$ in which to keep chickens.
He has been advised that he should allow 1 m^2 for each chicken. The pen is to be built using a barn wall as one side, as shown in the diagram. He wants to design the pen in such a way that he can keep the maximum number of chickens in it.
Let the length of PS be x metres.

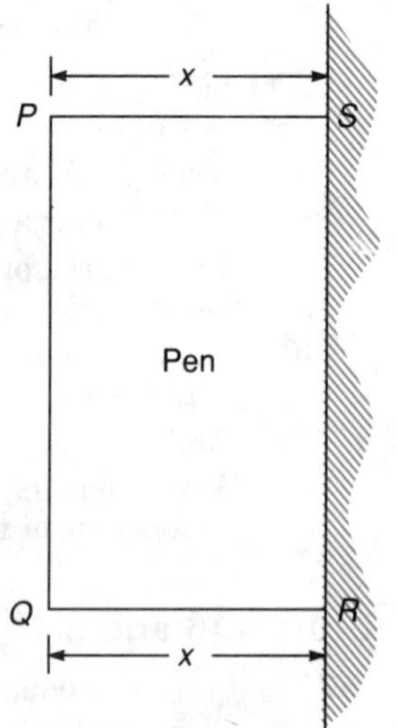

(a) Write down, in terms of x, an expression for the length of the side PQ.

(b) Show that the area, A square metres, of the pen is given by $A = 2x(8 - x)$.

(c) Complete the table below, which gives the value of A for different possible values of x.

x	0	1	2	3	3.5	4	4.5	5	6	7	8
A		14	24	30	31.5			30	24	14	0

(d) Draw the graph of A against x. Use your graph to find the maximum number of chickens that the farmer may keep in the pen and write down the dimensions of the pen that he should use.

(*NEA*, 1988)

62 An open rectangular tank with square base has a volume of 200 cm^3. The base has sides of length x cm and the height of the tank is h cm.

(a) Write down an expression, in terms of x and h, for the volume of the tank.

(b) Hence show that the surface area, S cm^2, of the tank, is given by

$$S = x^2 + \frac{800}{x}.$$

(c)

x	2	3	4	6	8	10	12
x^2	4						
$\dfrac{800}{x}$	400	267					
S	404	276					

Copy and complete the table above giving all figures to the nearest whole number.

(d) Using a scale of 1 cm for 1 unit on the x-axis and 1 cm for 25 units on the S-axis, draw the graph of

$$S = x^2 + \frac{800}{x}.$$

(e) From your graph find the least value of the surface area of the tank and the length of the side of the tank, in this case.

(*LEAG*, 1988)

Unit 3.19

63 (i) Factorize $x^2 - 5x + 6$.

(ii) Solve the equation $x^2 - 5x + 6 = 0$.

(iii) The diagram shows the graph of $y = x^2 - 5x + 6$. Write down the coordinates of the points marked A, B and C.

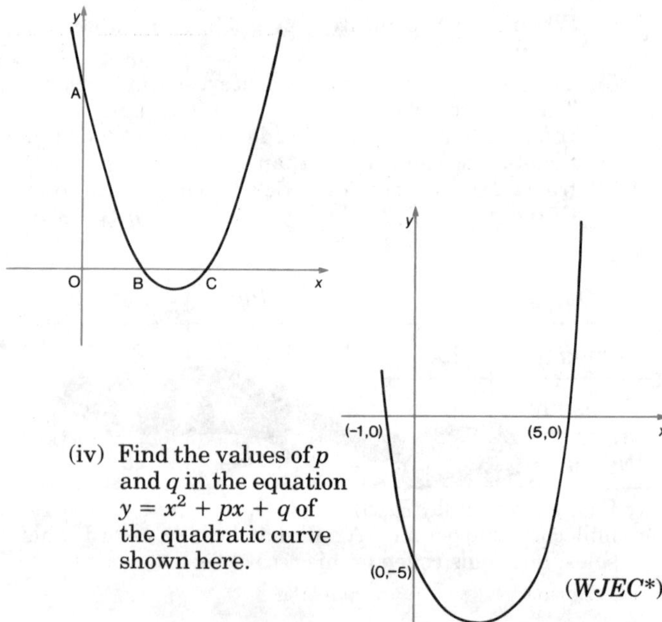

(iv) Find the values of p and q in the equation $y = x^2 + px + q$ of the quadratic curve shown here.

(*WJEC**)

64 (a) Complete this table for values of $x^2 + 3x + 1$.

x	-5	-4	-3	-2	-1	0	1	2
$x^2 + 3x + 1$	11		1		-1		5	

(b) Draw the graph of $y = x^2 + 3x + 1$ for values of x from -5 to 2.

(c) Use your graph to find approximate solutions to $x^2 + 3x + 1 = 4$. *(NEA, 1988)*

65 (a) Copy and complete the table given below for $y = \dfrac{x^2}{4} + \dfrac{4}{x} - 2$.

x	1	1.5	2	2.5	3	3.5	4
$x^2/4$		0.56				3.06	
$4/x$		2.67				1.14	
-2		-2				-2	
y		1.23				2.20	

(b) Using a scale of 4 cm to 1 unit on the y-axis and 2 cm to 1 unit on the x-axis, draw the graph of $y = \dfrac{x^2}{4} + \dfrac{4}{x} - 2$ for $1 \leqslant x \leqslant 4$.

(c) Using the same axes and scales, draw the graph of $y = \dfrac{x}{4} + 1$.

(d) Write down the values of x where the two graphs intersect.

(e) Show that these graphs enable you to find approximate solutions to the equation $x^3 - x^2 - 12x + 16 = 0$. *(LEAG*)*

Unit 3.20

66 Find the smallest integer which satisfies the inequality $5x - 7 > 2x + 13$. *(NEA*)*

67 (a) Solve the equation $x^2 - 4x - 21 = 0$.

(b) Solve the inequality $2 - 3x < 3 + 2x$. *(MEG, 1988)*

68 Give the three inequalities satisfied by all points in the shaded region (including its boundaries) and by no other points. *(MEG, 1988)*

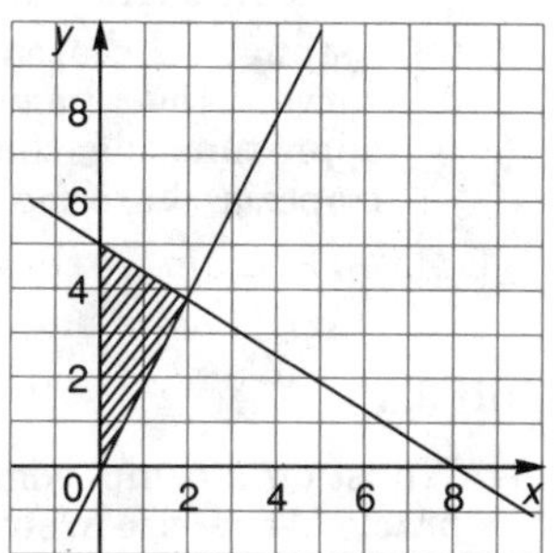

69 On the same piece of graph paper, draw the graphs of $y = \dfrac{6}{x}$ and $x + y = 9$ for $1 \leqslant x \leqslant 7$.

Hence find all the pairs of positive integers whose product is greater than 6 and whose sum is less than 9. *(NEA, 1988)*

Unit 3.21

70 $f(x) = 3 - 2x$.

(a) Calculate f(4).

(b) Calculate ff(4).

(c) Obtain and simplify an expression for ff(x).

(d) Calculate $f^{-1}(2)$.

(e) Obtain an expression for $f^{-1}(x)$. *(MEG, 1988)*

71 A function f(x) is defined as $f(x) = x^2 + 5x - 24$.

(a) Evaluate

(i) f(-2), (ii) f(-3).

(b) Find the values of x for which

(i) $f(x) = 0$, (ii) $f(x) = -24$. *(SEG*)*

72 The functions f and g are defined by

$f{:}x \longrightarrow 2x - 1$

$g{:}x \longrightarrow x^2$.

(a) Find

(i) f(2),

(ii) the value of x such that $f(x) = 7$.

(b) Express

(i) gf in the form $gf{:}x \rightarrow \ldots$,

(ii) the inverse of f in the form $f^{-1}{:}x \rightarrow \ldots$. *(LEAG, 1988)*

73 Two functions f and g are defined as follows:

$f(x) = \dfrac{1}{2x - 1}$ $(x \neq 0.5)$,

$g(x) = x^2$.

(a) Find the value of

(i) f(2) (ii) gf(2)

(b) Find an expression for

(i) gf(x) (ii) fg(x)

(c) Show that there is only one value of a for which fg(a) = gf(a). *(NEA, 1988)*

Unit 3.22

74 The surface area of a sphere is proportional to the square of its radius.

A sphere of radius 2.0 cm has a surface area of 50.3 cm^2.

(a) Find the surface area of a sphere of radius 3.0 cm.

(b) Find the radius of a sphere of surface area 201 cm^2. *(MEG, 1988)*

75 For a given mass of gas at constant temperature, James has been told that the pressure of the gas is inversely proportional to the volume of the gas.

He has already measured the pressure of 800 cm^3 of the gas. It is 1.5 pascals.

He allows this gas to expand to 1050 cm^3, keeping the temperature constant.

What pressure should James expect when he reads the measuring gauge? Give your answer in pascals to a reasonable degree of accuracy. *(LEAG, 1988)*

76 For extractor fans, revolving at the same rate, the volume of air, V m^3, extracted per minute varies as the cube of the diameter, d metres, of the fan.

(a) From the table below, find the formula expressing V in terms of d.

d	0.25	0.6	
V		129.6	75

(b) Use this formula to complete the above table.

(c) Rearrange the formula to express d in terms of V. *(NISEC, 1988)*

Unit 3.23

77 Given that $3x + 4y + 7 = 0$,

(a) write the equation in the form $y = mx + c$,

(b) what is the gradient of the straight line represented by this equation? *(NEA, 1988)*

78 Huw observes a bird flying directly away from a bird box. He starts his watch and finds out how far the bird is from the box at different times.

This graph is drawn from his results.

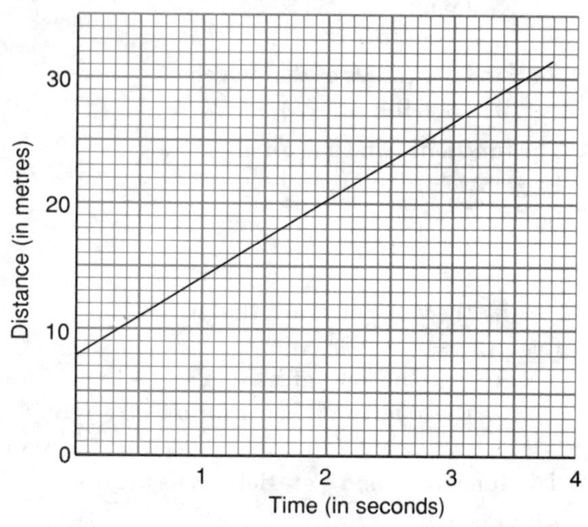

(a) How far is the bird from the box when Huw starts his watch?

(b) How fast is the bird flying?

(c) Write down a formula for the distance, d, the bird is from the box in terms of time, t.

(*WJEC*, 1988)

79 (*NOTE: Answers to this question using measurements from a scale drawing will receive no credit. You may make a sketch on graph paper.*)

A is the point $(-1, -3)$.

(a) Find the equation of the line ℓ, with gradient 2, which passes through A.

P is the point (6, 1). The line through P perpendicular to ℓ, meets ℓ at B.

(b) (i) Find the equation of the line PB.

(ii) Hence find the coordinates of B.

The line through P, parallel to BA, meets the line through A, parallel to the x-axis, at Q.

(c) (i) Find the coordinates of Q.

(ii) Find the lengths of BA and PQ in surd form and show that they are in the ratio 3:2.

(iii) Find the area of ABPQ.

(*NISEC*, 1988)

Unit 3.24

80 A player hits a ball vertically upwards. At a time t seconds later the height of the ball above the ground is y metres, where $y = 1 + 15t - 5t^2$.

Corresponding values of t and y are given in the table:

t	0	0.5	1	2	2.5	3
y	1	7.25	11		7.25	1

(a) Calculate the height, y, of the ball above the ground 2 seconds after it was hit.

(b) Using a scale of 2 cm per unit on both axes, draw the graph of $y = 1 + 15t - 5t^2$ for values of t from 0 to 3.

(c) Use your graph to estimate

(i) the length of time for which the ball is at least 6 m above the ground,

(ii) the maximum height of the ball above the ground.

(d) By drawing a straight line on your graph, estimate the speed of the ball 0.5 seconds after it was hit.

(*SEG*, 1988)

81 The velocity v m/s of a ball rolling down a slope is given by $v = 3t$ where t seconds is the time after the ball is released.

(a) Complete this table for values of v.

t	0	1	2	3	4	5
v						

(b) Draw the graph of v against t for values of t from 0 to 5.

(c) Find the gradient of this graph.

(d) What does the gradient of this graph represent?

(*NEA*, 1988)

82

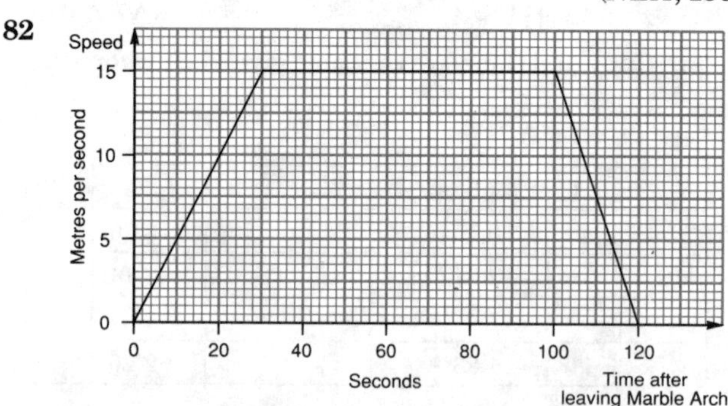

A train runs between two stations, Marble Arch and Bond Street. The journey takes 2 minutes. The graph above is the speed–time graph for the train during the journey. Use the graph to find

(i) the greatest speed of the train,

(ii) the acceleration during the first 30 seconds,

(iii) the length of time for which the train is slowing down,

(iv) the distance the train moved at its greatest speed,

(v) the distance between the two stations.

(*LEAG*, 1988)

83 The following table is based on the performance figures for a car as it accelerates from rest.

Time (seconds), t	0	2	4	6	8	10
Velocity (metres per second), v	0	10	18	23.5	27.5	31

(a) Draw the graph of v against t.

(b) By drawing the tangent to the curve at (4, 18), estimate the gradient of the curve at this point. State the significance of this value.

(c) Estimate the area of the region bounded by the curve, the t-axis and the line $t = 10$ by approximating this area to a triangle and four trapezia. State the significance of this value.

(*NEA*, 1988)

Unit 3.25

84 Whilst on a camp, some Venture Scouts were doing a practical exercise in surveying on level ground.

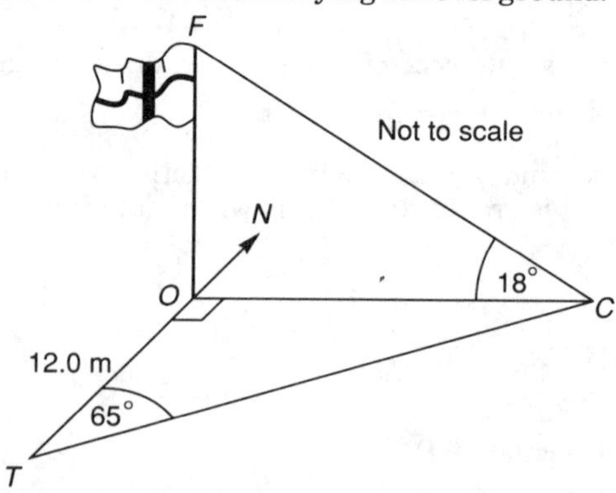

Colin, at point C, due East of the vertical camp flag pole, OF, records the angle of elevation of its top, F as 18°. Trudy, at point T, notes that she is 12.0 metres due South of the flag pole and that angle OTC is 65°.

(a) Calculate the bearing of T from C.

(b) Calculate, to the nearest tenth of a metre,
   (i) the distances OC and CT,
   (ii) the height of the flag pole.

(c) It is decided to fix a taut rope from a point half way up the pole to the point on TC which is nearest to the foot of the pole, O. Calculate the angle which this rope will make with the ground. (*MEG*, 1988)

85 (In this question, give all distances to the nearest 0.01 km and all angles to the nearest one-tenth of a degree.)

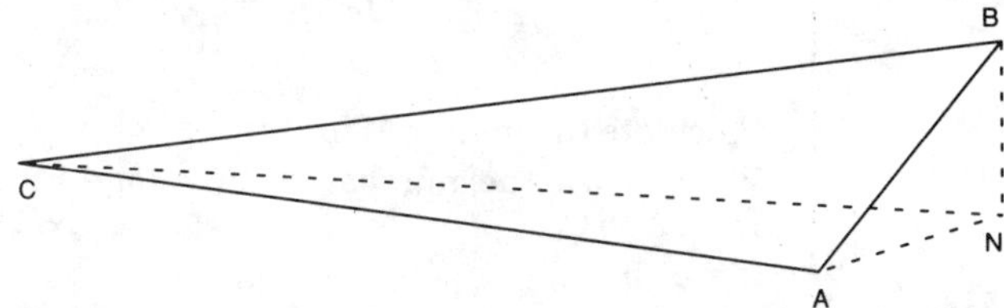

The figure represents three villages A, B and C on a hillside. A C and N are at the same height above sea level and N is vertically below B. Angle CAB is 90° and angle BAN is 2.5°. The villages are linked by three straight roads AB, AC and CB, where AB = 8 km and AC = 12 km.

Calculate
(a) the height of B above N,
(b) the horizontal distance AN,
(c) the horizontal distance CN,
(d) the angle of elevation of B from C. (*LEAG*, 1988)

86 The diagram shows an Egyptian pyramid of height 150 m and square base ABCD of side length 240 m. V is the vertex of the right pyramid, E and F are the midpoints of AB and DC respectively and X is the point of intersection of the diagonals of the square base.

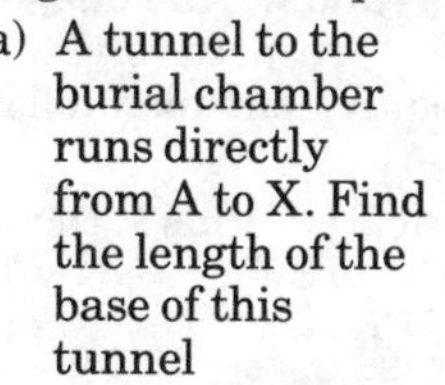

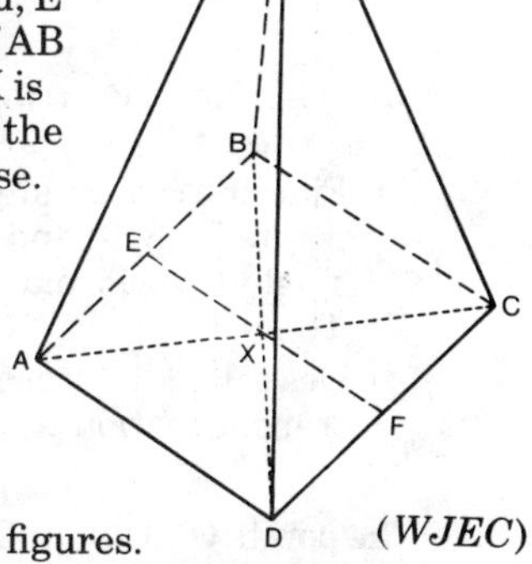

(a) A tunnel to the burial chamber runs directly from A to X. Find the length of the base of this tunnel correct to 3 significant figures. (*WJEC*)

(b) As a tourist attraction, young Egyptians run from the base to the top V of the pyramid. If Abdi runs from F directly to V and Abda runs from A directly to V, what angles to the horizontal do each of their paths make? (*WJEC**)

Unit 3.26

87 Find the value of x such that $90 < x < 180$ and $\sin x° = 0.4567$. (*NEA*, 1988)

88

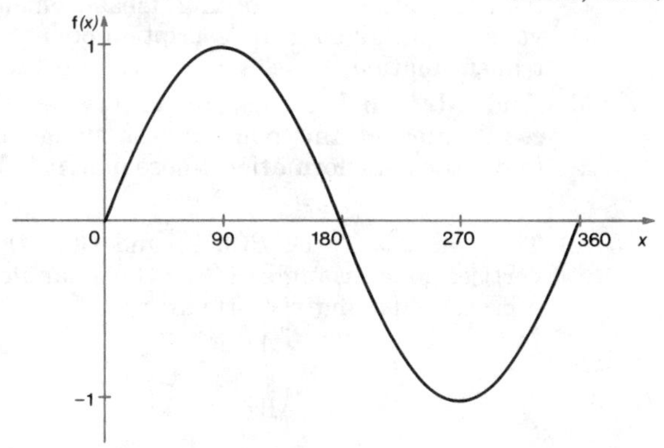

The diagram is a sketch of the graph of $f(x) = \sin x°$ for $0 \leqslant x \leqslant 360$.
   (i) On the same axes, draw a line to show how you would find the set of solutions of the equation $f(x) = 0.6$.
   (ii) On another set of axes, sketch the graph of $g(x) = 1 - \sin x°$ for $0 \leqslant x \leqslant 360$.
   (iii) Given that $h(x) = \dfrac{2}{x}$, express $hf(x)$ in terms of x and evaluate $hf(40)$. (*NEA**)

Unit 3.27

89 A ship leaves a port P on the bearing of N50°E and steams to a point Q which is 7 miles from P. At Q the ship changes course to the bearing N35°W and steams a further distance of 5 miles to arrive at a port R.
Calculate
   (i) the distance PR, in miles, correct to 3 significant figures;
   (ii) $\angle$PRQ;
   (iii) the bearing of R and P. (*WJEC**)

90 The diagram represents two fields ABD and BCD in a horizontal plane ABCD.

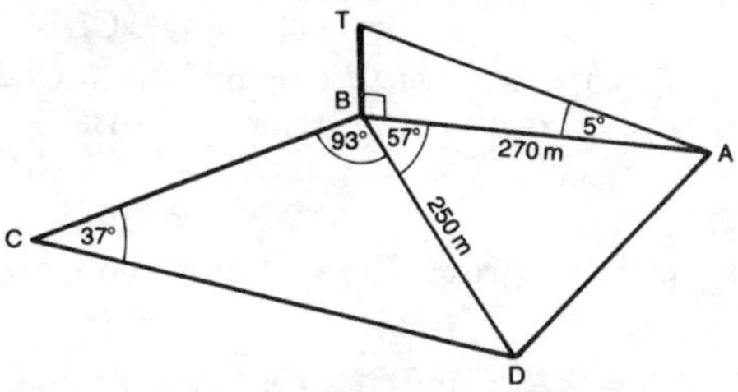

AB = 270 m, BD = 250 m, angle ABD = 57°, angle BCD = 37° and angle CBD = 93°.
A vertical radio mast BT stands at the corner B of the fields and the angle of elevation of T from A is 5°.
Calculate, correct to three significant figures,
(a) the height of the radio mast,
(b) the length of AD,
(c) the length of BC,
(d) the area, in hectares, of the triangular field ABD (1 hectare = 10^4 square metres). (*MEG**)

Unit 3.28

91

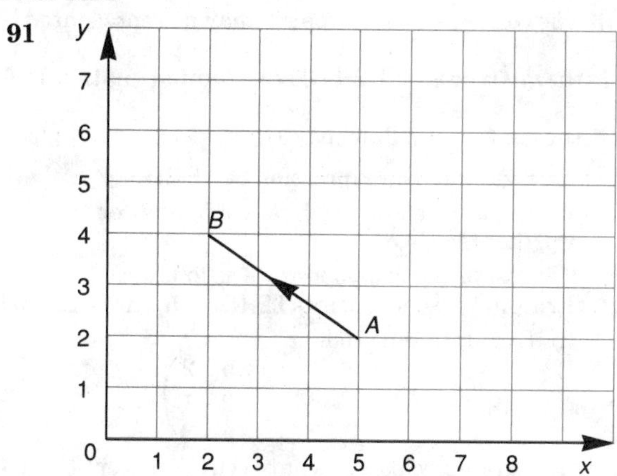

In the diagram A is the point (5, 2) and B is the point (2, 4).
(a) Write $\overrightarrow{AB}$ as a column vector.
(b) Calculate, correct to one decimal place, the magnitude of $\overrightarrow{AB}$.
(c) $\overrightarrow{BC} = \begin{pmatrix} 5 \\ 2 \end{pmatrix}$. Calculate $\overrightarrow{AB} + \overrightarrow{BC}$ as a single column vector, and show this vector on the diagram.
(d) Write down (as a column vector) the position vector of the point A. (*NEA*, 1988)

92 Given that $\mathbf{a} = \begin{pmatrix} 4 \\ -5 \end{pmatrix}$ and $\mathbf{b} = \begin{pmatrix} -3 \\ 2 \end{pmatrix}$, find $\mathbf{a} - 2\mathbf{b}$. *(LEAG, 1988)*

93 In the triangle OAB shown in the figure, $OC = \frac{2}{3}OB$, $\overrightarrow{OA} = \mathbf{a}$, $\overrightarrow{OB} = \mathbf{b}$.

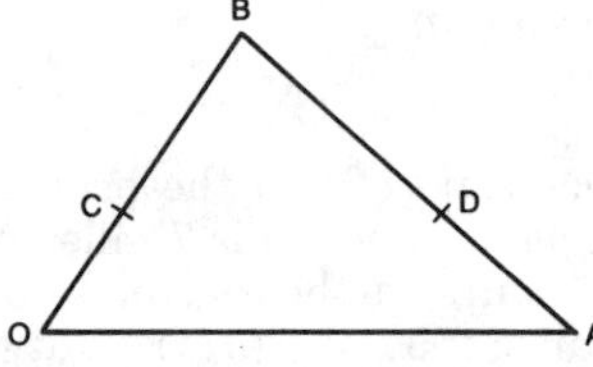

(a) Express the vectors $\overrightarrow{OC}$, $\overrightarrow{CB}$ and $\overrightarrow{BA}$ in terms of **a**, or **b**, or **a** and **b**.
The point D divides BA in the ratio 3:2.
(b) Find $\overrightarrow{BD}$ and $\overrightarrow{CD}$ in terms of **a**, or **b**, or **a** and **b**.
(c) Give the special name of the quadrilateral OCDA.
(d) Calculate the value of $\dfrac{\text{area of triangle OAB}}{\text{area of triangle CDB}}$.
(e) Given that the area of the quadrilateral OCDA is 48 cm^2, find the area of the triangle CBD. *(LEAG*)*

94 *OPQR* is a parallelogram. The vectors **x** and **y** are such that

$$\overrightarrow{OP} = \mathbf{x} + \mathbf{y} \text{ and } \overrightarrow{OR} = \mathbf{x} - \mathbf{y}.$$

(a) Express as simply as possible in terms of **x** and/or **y**
(i) $\overrightarrow{OQ}$, (ii) $\overrightarrow{RP}$.
(b) What special type of parallelogram is *OPQR*
(i) when $|\mathbf{x} + \mathbf{y}| = |\mathbf{x} - \mathbf{y}|$?
(ii) when $|\mathbf{x}| = |\mathbf{y}|$? *(MEG, 1988)*

Unit 3.29

95 Trackpaks of various sorts are sold for model railways. Trackpak *C* contains 5 straights, 2 points and 4 curves. Trackpak *D* contains 2 straights, 1 points and 8 curves.
(a) The contents of Trackpak *C* may be represented by the matrix $\mathbf{C} = \begin{pmatrix} 5 \\ 2 \\ 4 \end{pmatrix}$. Give a similar matrix **D** for the contents of Trackpak *D*.
(b) (i) Evaluate the expression $3\mathbf{C} + 2\mathbf{D}$.
(ii) Explain clearly what your answer to (b)(i) represents.
(c) The cost of the components is as follows:
Straight 95p each, points £2.15 each, curve £1 each.
(i) Evaluate the product

$$(0.95 \quad 2.15 \quad 1.00) \times \begin{pmatrix} 5 & 2 \\ 2 & 1 \\ 4 & 8 \end{pmatrix}$$

(ii) Explain clearly what your answer to (c)(i) represents. *(MEG, 1988)*

96 It is given that

$$\mathbf{M} = \begin{pmatrix} 3 & 1 \\ 1 & 2 \end{pmatrix} \text{ and } \mathbf{N} = \begin{pmatrix} 1 & 4 \\ -3 & 2 \end{pmatrix}.$$

(a) Express $\mathbf{M} + 3\mathbf{N}$ as a single matrix.
(b) Express $\mathbf{M}^2$ as a single matrix. *(MEG*)*

97 (i) Write down the matrix **M** which is the route matrix for the network shown.

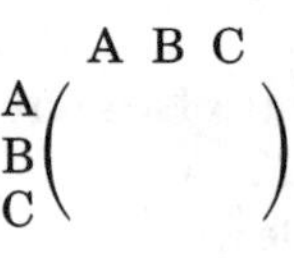

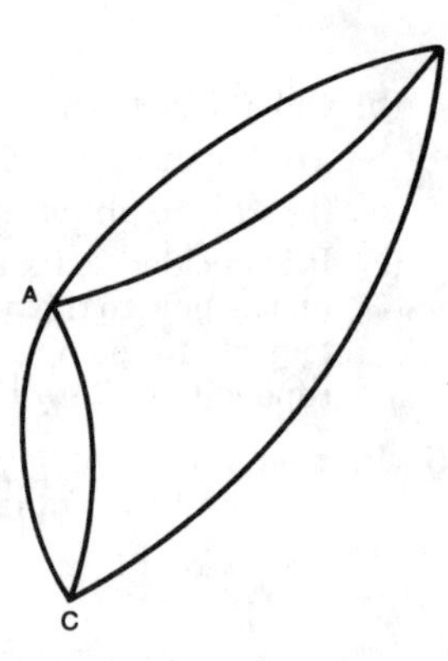

(ii) Calculate the matrix $\mathbf{M}^2$.
(iii) Write down the number of two-stage routes from A to C. *(NEA*)*

Unit 3.30

98 A transformation **S** is described by the matrix

$$\begin{pmatrix} 0 & -1 \\ -1 & 0 \end{pmatrix}.$$

T is the translation with vector $\begin{pmatrix} 3 \\ 3 \end{pmatrix}$.

(a) In the diagram, show the image of the triangle ABC under the transformation **S**.

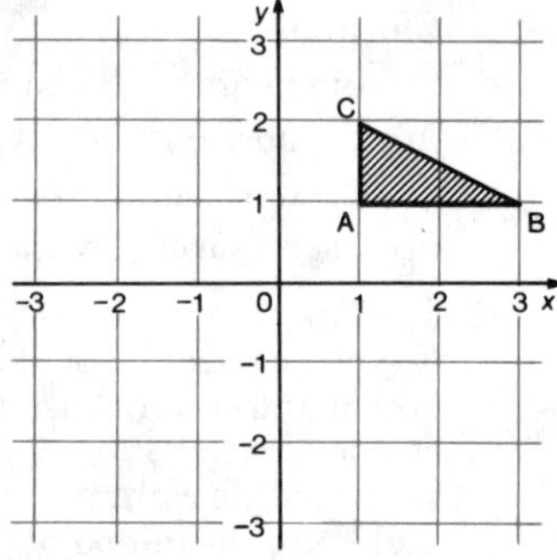

(b) Describe the transformation **S** in geometrical terms.
(c) Find the coordinates of P′ and Q′, the images of the points P, (3, 0) and Q, (2, 1) respectively, under the single transformation equivalent to **S** followed by **T**.
(d) Describe in geometrical terms the single transformation equivalent to **S** followed by **T**. *(MEG)**

99 The points O (0, 0), A (2, 0) and B (2, 1) are transformed by the matrix **M** where

$$\mathbf{M} = \begin{pmatrix} 1 & -1 \\ 1 & 1 \end{pmatrix}$$

into O, A′ and B′ respectively.
(a) Find the coordinates of A′ and B′.
(b) Using graph paper and taking a scale of 2 cm to 1 unit on each axis, draw and label triangle OAB and its image triangle OA′B′.
(c) The transformation whose matrix is **M** can be obtained by a combination of two separate transformations. By taking measurements from your graph, give a full description of each of these transformations.
(d) Find $\mathbf{M}^{-1}$ and hence, or otherwise, find the coordinates of the point whose image is (6, 2) under the transformation whose matrix is **M**. *(LEAG*)*

100 (a) The points *A*(1, 1), *B*(3, 2) and *C*(2, 4) are the vertices of a triangle *ABC*. The triangle can be represented in matrix form as:

$$\begin{matrix} A & B & C \end{matrix}$$
$$\begin{pmatrix} 1 & 3 & 2 \\ 1 & 2 & 4 \end{pmatrix}$$

Triangle ABC is transformed into $A'B'C'$ by the matrix $\begin{pmatrix} 2 & 0 \\ 1 & 1 \end{pmatrix}$.

Triangle $A'B'C'$ is then transformed into A″B″C″ by the matrix $\begin{pmatrix} 1 & 0 \\ -1 & 2 \end{pmatrix}$.

Find the coordinates of the points A″B″C″.

(b) What single matrix would perform the combined transformation in part (a)?

(c) Describe fully the combined transformation in part (a).

(*SEG*, 1988)

SCE QUESTIONS

Foundation level

Unit 1.3

1 In an inter-schools competition, a win gains 4 points, a draw gains 2 points and a loss gains 0 points.

	Played	*Won*	*Drawn*	*Lost*
Northfield H.S.	15	10	2	3
Inverbeg Academy	15	8	5	2
Eskview H.S.	14	7	4	3

How many points does Inverbeg Academy have?

Unit 1.12

2*

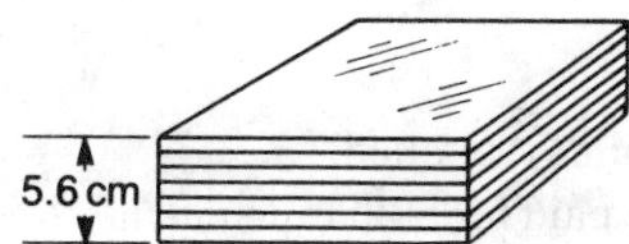

A pile of 7 similar panes of glass is 5.6 cm thick. What is the thickness (in centimetres) of each pane?

Unit 1.22

3 What is the total cost of the television set?

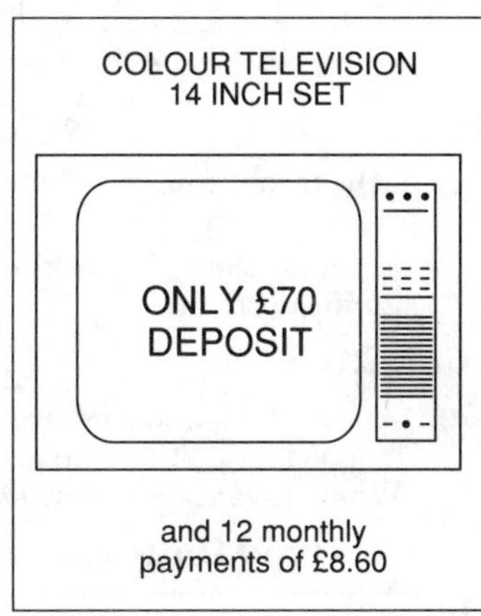

Unit 1.32

4 This map shows some roads leading from a roundabout.

(a) Where does the road to the east of the roundabout lead to?

(b) In which direction should you leave the roundabout to go to the Sports Centre?

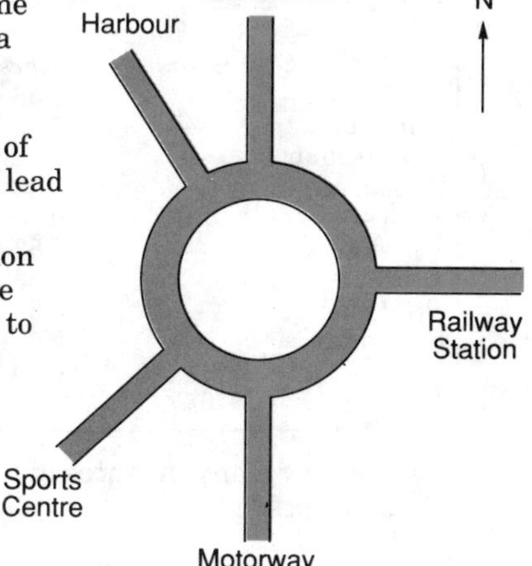

Unit 1.62

5 When you hire a tent from the Western Tent Company, they work out the cost of the hire by using the formula:

cost = (number of days × £15) + £30

Find the cost of hiring a tent for 14 days.

Unit 1.64

6 Rosehall Youth Club buys badges from a mail order company. The badges cost 10p each but on some orders there is a charge to pay for postage.

The flowchart shows how to work out the cost of buying the badges by mail order.

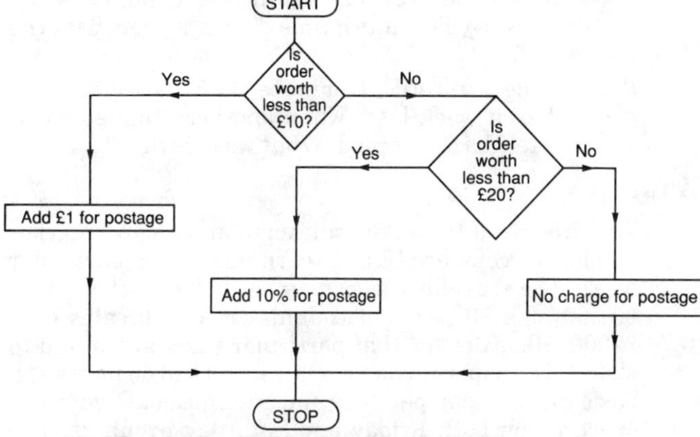

(a) The club orders badges worth £4.50. How much will they cost altogether?

(b) (i) Find the cost of ordering 195 badges.

(ii) Find the cost of ordering 205 badges.

(iii) What do you notice about the answer to (b)(ii) compared to the answer to (b)(i)?

(c) What is the greatest number of badges that can be bought for £19? (Remember this includes the cost of postage.)

Unit 1.67

7 George counted the vehicles he saw during a car journey. The diagram below shows his results.

Represents 4 vehicles

Bus

Car

Lorry

Taxi

(a) How many buses did he see?

(b) How many more cars than lorries did he see?

Unit 1.68

8 Staines Farm Dairy delivers milk to the villages round about. The table overleaf shows the daily milk deliveries for one week.

Day	*Total number of pints delivered*
Monday	1400
Tuesday	1350
Wednesday	1380
Thursday	1420
Friday	1450
Saturday	1490
Sunday	1520

What is the average number of pints deliverd daily?

Unit 2.27

9 Simplify $3x + 6y - 7x$.

General level

Unit 1.12

1* (a) An athlete broke the world indoor record for the 800 metres race, by running it in 1 minute 44.67 seconds. The previous record was 1 minute 46.53 seconds. By how much time did the athlete beat the record?

(b) The new record, 1 minute 44.67 seconds, was broken a week later when another athlete beat it by 4 tenths of a second. What was his time?

Unit 1.18

2* Two friends, a travelling salesman and a supermarket employee, compared their earnings for a particular week. The travelling salesman earned a basic wage of £62.60 plus 10 per cent commission on all sales over £2000. His sales for that particular week amounted to £2488. The supermarket employee worked 40 hours at a basic rate of £2.40 per hour and an additional two hours overtime on both Friday and Saturday evenings. The overtime rate on a Friday is time and a half and on Saturday it is double time.

(a) Calculate how much the travelling salesman earned in the week.

(b) Calculate how much the supermarket employee earned in the week.

(c) Who earned more and by how much?

Unit 1.50

3* The playing times for the five tracks on one side of a record album are 4 min 27 sec, 3 min 19 sec, 5 min 4 sec, 4 min 52 sec and 6 min 18 sec. What is the total playing time for this side of the album?

4 The village bus runs from Abington to Dalmuir twice a day. The bus always takes the same time for each journey. The timetable at the bus stop has been partly destroyed.

Use the information left to fill in the times which should be written in boxes, A, B and C.

VILLAGE BUS		
d. Abington	09 40	A
a. Ballaig	10 00	12 55
a. Carbeth	B	13 50
a. Dalmuir	11 45	C
d. depart; a. arrive		

Unit 1.54

5 Plum Stores provide radiators for central heating. They sell three different models of radiator:

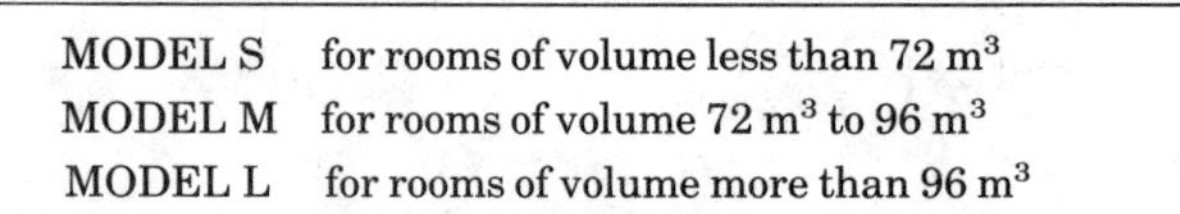

MODEL S	for rooms of volume less than 72 m^3
MODEL M	for rooms of volume 72 m^3 to 96 m^3
MODEL L	for rooms of volume more than 96 m^3

Sally wants to fit a radiator in her living room which measures 4.8 m by 6.4 m. The room is 2.8 m high.

Which model of radiator should she buy for her living room?

Unit 1.60

6* The diagram shows the reading on a scale when a parcel is weighed.

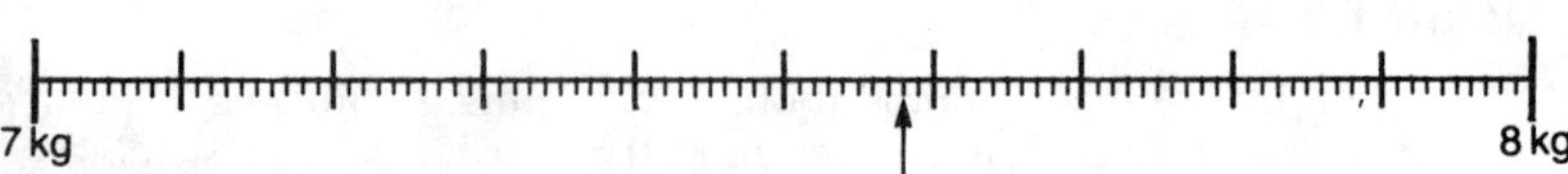

What is the weight of the parcel?

Unit 1.62

7 A doctor's travelling expenses £C are worked out as follows:

For journeys of 150 miles or less $C = \dfrac{18N}{100}$.

For journeys of more than 150 miles

$C = 27 + \dfrac{(N - 150)11}{100}$.

N is the number of miles travelled.

(a) How much is she paid for a 90 mile journey?

(b) How much is she paid for a journey of 216 miles?

Units 2.4 and 2.8

8 Approximations to $\sqrt{2}$ can be found be evaluating terms of the sequence

$$1,\quad 1 + \frac{1}{2},\quad 1 + \cfrac{1}{2 + \cfrac{1}{2}},\quad 1 + \cfrac{1}{2 + \cfrac{1}{2 + \cfrac{1}{2}}},\ \ldots$$

each term being a better approximation than the previous terms.

Calculate the value of the fourth term correct to three significant figures.

Unit 2.7

9* A recent road survey reported that 26 out of 325 cars stopped for testing had brakes in a dangerous condition. What percentage of cars stopped had dangerous brakes?

Unit 2.8 (and Units 1.50, 1.68)

10

2nd APRIL
READINGS IN SCOTLAND

	Sunshine Hours	*Rainfall Inches*	*Temperatures Min. °C*	*Max. °C*
Dyce	—	0.38	8	14
Turnhouse	—	0.10	10	15
Eskdalemuir	—	1.22	9	13
Abbotsinch	—	0.78	7	14
Kinloss	1.8	0.00	9	17
Lerwick	—	0.83	7	11
Leuchars	—	0.09	9	15
Prestwick	—	0.54	9	14
Stornoway	—	0.66	10	13
Tiree	—	0.30	8	13
Wick	0.7	0.10	9	15

(a) For how many **minutes** did the sun shine in Wick on 2nd April?

(b) Find the average of the rainfall readings shown in the table.
Answer in inches to two decimal places.

Unit 2.11

11 A mortar mix is made of cement, sand and water mixed in the ratio 1:3:5. What percentage of the mixture is sand?

Units 2.21 and 2.22

12* Calculate the area of the following shape.

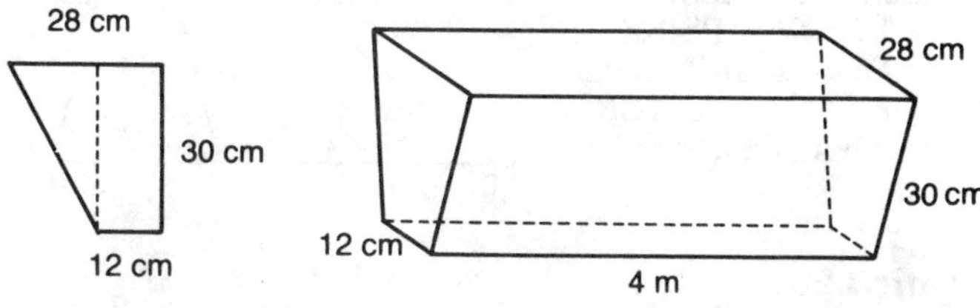

A concrete beam of length 4 metres is made with this shape as cross-section. Calculate, in cubic metres, the volume of concrete in the finished beam.

Unit 2.29

13 Simplify $3(x + 2y) - 7x$.

Unit 2.30

14* Solve $2(y + 3) = 5$.

15 Solve the equation $5n = 3n + 15$ to find the value of the number n.

Unit 2.34

16* Solve the equations
$x - 2y + 6 = 0$ and
$x + y - 6 = 0$
The first line has been drawn on the graph paper.

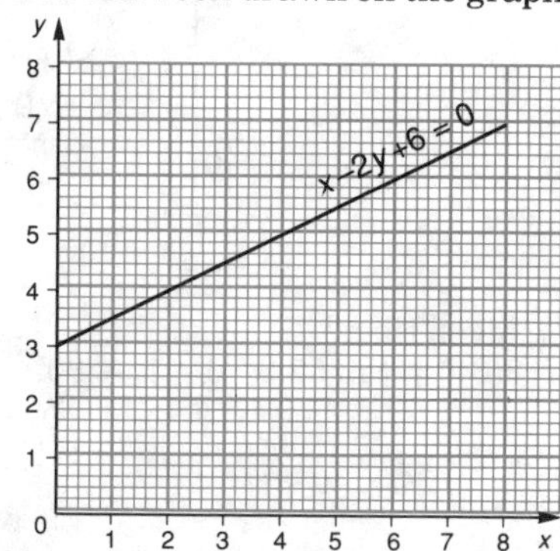

Unit 2.37 (and Unit 2.18)

17* (a) A tall rotting tree is to be cut down and it is necessary to know its height. At a distance of 19.8 metres from the foot of the tree, the top is at an angle of 57° measured with level ground. What is the height of the tree?

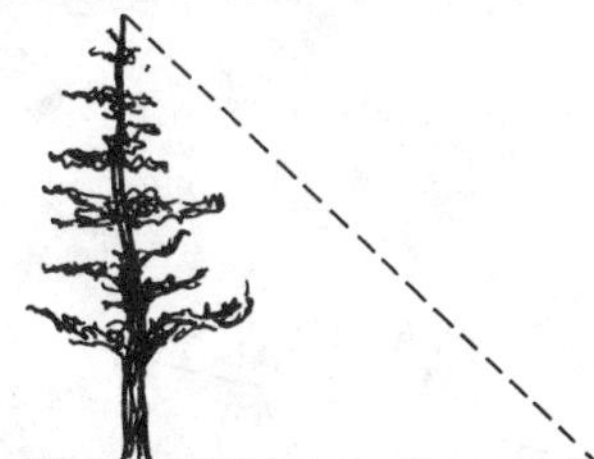

(b) Another unclimbable tree is also to be measured before it is cut down, but the instrument for measuring angles is not available. It is a bright sunny day and you have a metre stick as well as a measuring tape. Using the shadows cast by the tree and the stick, explain how you could find the height of the tree, showing clearly what measurements you would have to make.

Unit 3.4

18 The small box of Le Chic chocolates is **similar** in shape to the large box but its edges are **half as long**.

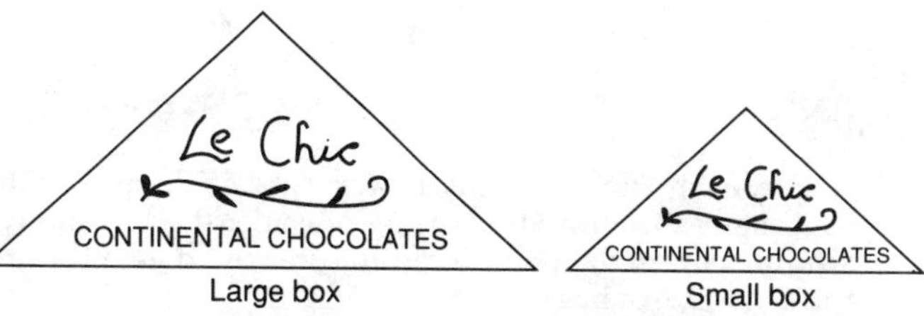

The area of the face shown of the large box is 320 cm^2. What is the area of the corresponding face of the small box?

Credit level

Unit 1.44

1 A TV detector van picks up signals from a TV transmitter on a bearing of 055°. The van is driven 1500 yards in an easterly direction and another reading is taken. The signals are now picked up on a bearing of 320°.

Make a scale drawing of this information and use it to find the distance between the transmitter and the second position of the van.

Unit 1.55

2* Find how many hours a colour television can be run for the price of a packet of cigarettes given that the following are true:

(i) A packet of cigarettes costs 85p
(ii) A unit of electricity costs 4.25p.
(iii) A 1000 watt appliance run for one hour uses one unit of electricity.
(iv) A colour television uses 160 watts.

Unit 2.23

3* The formula for the volume, V, of a cylinder of radius r and height h, is
$$V = \pi r^2 h$$
Describe the effect on the volume of doubling the radius and halving the height.

Unit 2.36

4 A beam with a square cross-section of side x centimetres is to be cut from a cylindrical log of diameter 50 centimetres. What is the length of the side of the largest square beam which can be cut from this log? Give your answer correct to the nearest centimetre.

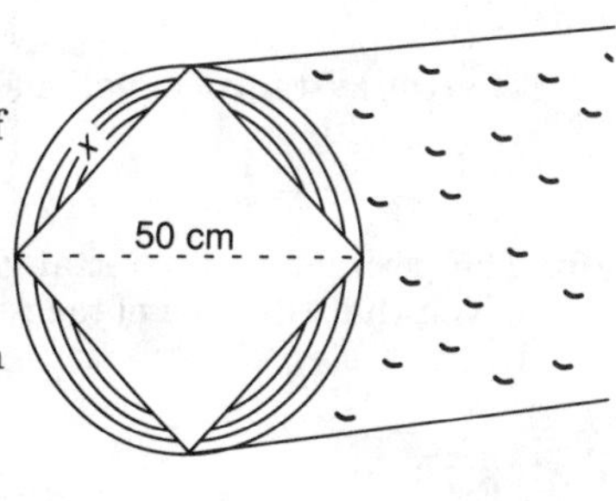

Unit 3.1

5 A circular bar has a diameter of 34 millimetres. The whole length of the bar is machined to give a flat surface of width 16 millimetres.

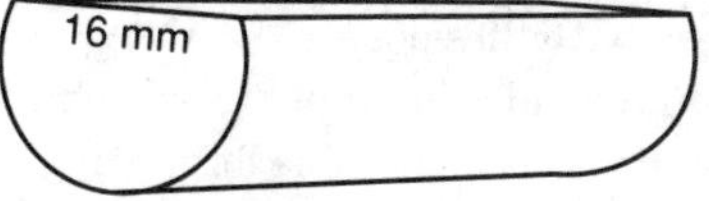

Calculate the depth of the cut, x millimetres, which must be made to give this surface width.

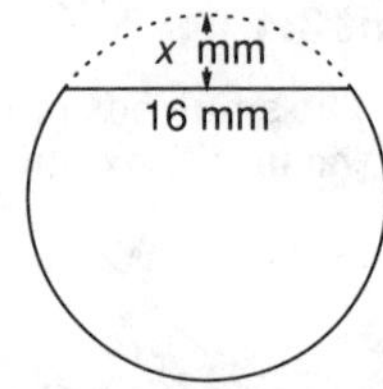

Unit 3.4

6 A gardener can fill eight flower pots of diameter 15 centimetres from a 50 litre bag of compost. How many **similar** pots of diameter 5 centimetres could he fill from the same size of bag?

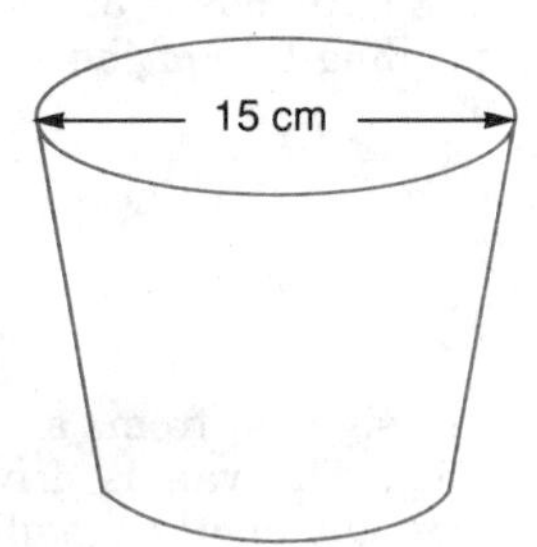

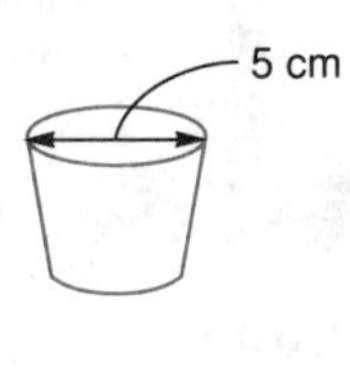

Unit 3.10

7* Simplify $a^{3/2}(a^{1/2} - a^{-1/2})$.

Unit 3.13

8* The diagram shows an equilateral triangle and two regular polygons meeting at a point P. It can be shown that

$$\frac{1}{m} + \frac{1}{n} = \frac{1}{6}$$

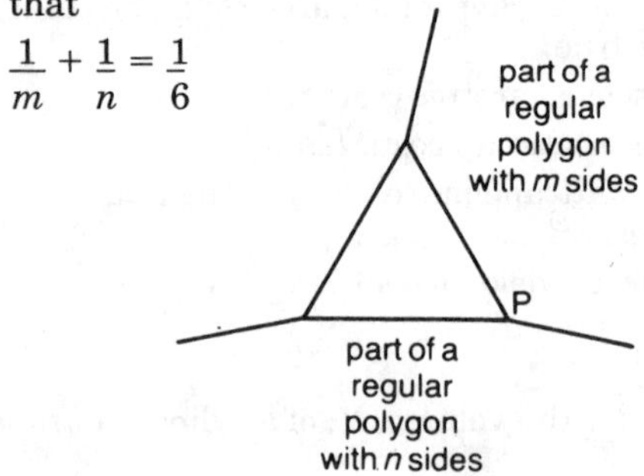

(a) If one polygon has 7 sides, how many sides has the other?

(b) Express m in terms of n.

(c) Give one other pair of unequal values of m and n.

Unit 3.15

9 Solve the system of equations

$$xy = -2$$
$$x + y = 1.$$

10* The perimeter of a rectangle is 10 times its breadth. Given that the area of the rectangle is 100 cm^2, what is its perimeter?

Unit 3.16

11* The number, d, of diagonals of a polygon with n sides is given by

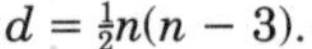

$d = \frac{1}{2}n(n - 3)$.

(a) How many diagonals has a polygon with 20 sides?

(b) How many sides has a polygon with 20 diagonals?

(c) Show that it is impossible for a polygon to have 30 diagonals.

12* Find the value of the positive root of $2x^2 - 7x - 3 = 0$ correct to 3 significant figures.

Unit 3.17

13* Express $\frac{5}{x} - \frac{2}{(x - 3)}$ as a single fraction.

14* In triangle PQR, QS bisects angle PQR. It can be shown that PQ:QR = PS:SR. Given that PS is 0.5 cm longer than SR, what is the length of PR?

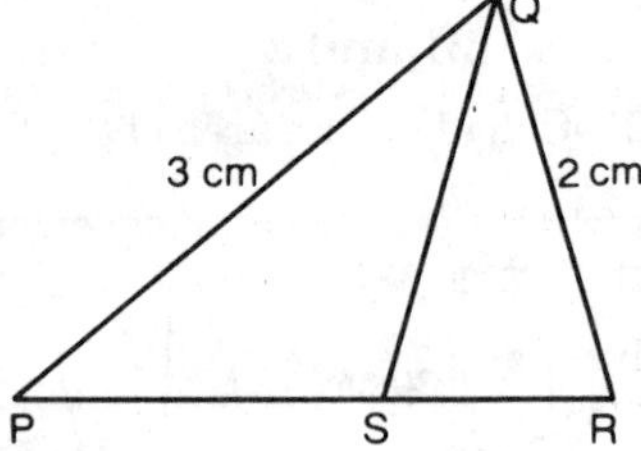

Unit 3.22

15* The variables x, y and z are connected by the relation $x = \frac{ky}{z^2}$ where k is a constant.

(a) Express this relation in words by completing the following variation statement connecting x, y and z.

'x varies ... and ...'

(b) If $x = 9$ when $y = 6$ and $z = 4$, find the value of the constant of variation k.

(c) Hence, or otherwise, find z when $x = 10$ and $y = 15$.

Unit 3.23

16 Write down the equation of the straight line joining A and B.

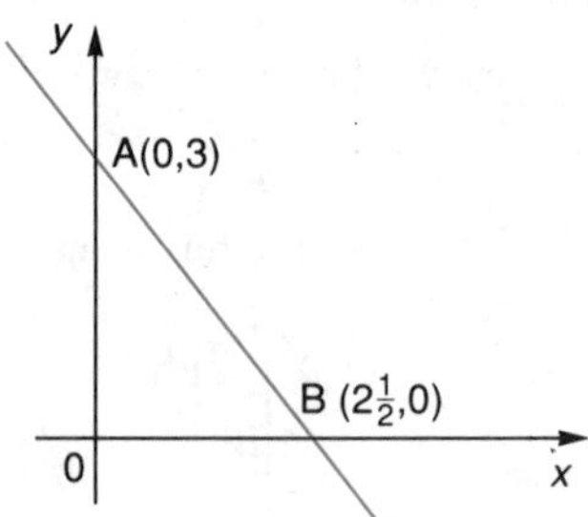

Unit 3.26

17 Calculate x, given that $\sin x° + \cos 35.4° = \tan 52.9°, 0 < x < 90$.

Unit 3.27

18

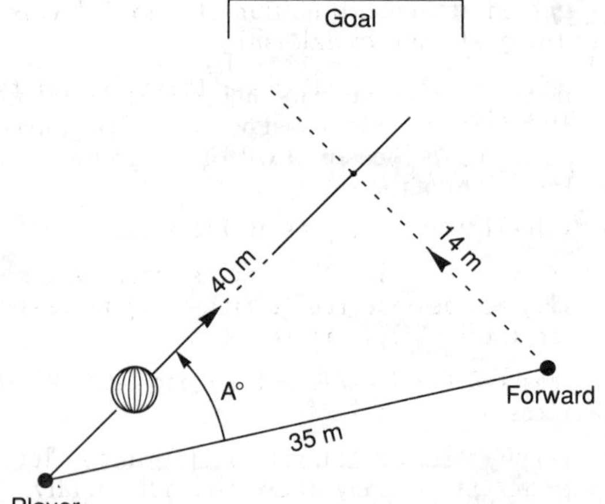

The above diagram shows the direction in which a player passed the ball to a forward who was running towards goal.

Calculate the size of the angle marked A° in the diagram.

AURAL TESTS

Level 2

1 What is the cost of six loaves at 45 pence each?

2 In a game of darts, a player scores 99 with his first three darts. If his score starts at 501 what will his new total be when 99 has been subtracted?

3 Jennifer bought five ribbons each one and a half metres long. How much ribbon did Jennifer buy altogether?

4 I bought four boxes of chocolates for £9.60. Each box cost the same. What was the price of each box?

5 Bus fares are increased by 10 per cent. If the old fare was 50 pence, what is the new fare?

6 The diameter of a circular pipe is about eight centimetres. Approximately what is the circumference of the pipe?

7 Rob is paid time and a half for working Saturday morning. If Rob is normally paid £2.50 an hour, how much is he paid for working four hours on a Saturday morning?

8 Julia arrived at the cinema 22 minutes before the picture started. Her friend Alex arrived nine minutes before it started. How long had Julia been at the cinema before Alex arrived?

9 A journey takes one hour by bike. The same journey by car is three times as quick. How long does the journey take by car?

10 Write down an approximate value for the area of a rectangle which measures 39 centimetres by 21 centimetres.

11 Estimate in degrees the size of this angle.

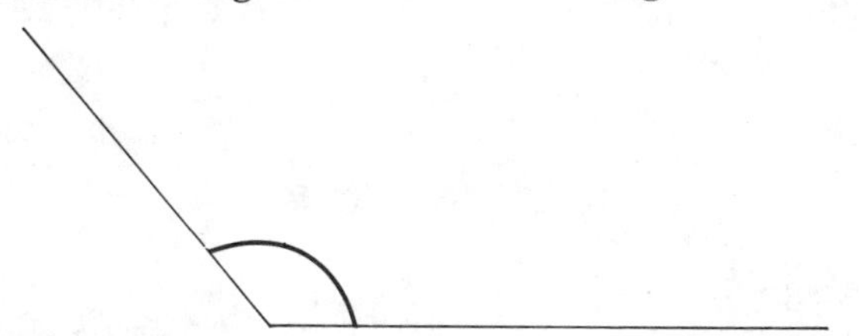

For the rest of the test, you need to use the information given at the end of this section.

12 What is the cost of having a skirt and a blouse cleaned?

13 What is the sale price of a television set which was previously marked at £360?

14 Tracy arrived at Redruth station at 8.45. What is the time of the next train to Saltash?

15 How much will it cost a mother and three children to sit in the front stalls?

Level 3

1 What is the cost of eight pens at 99p each?

2 A paper boy delivers 230 papers each week. By Wednesday he has delivered 92. How many more should he deliver in the rest of the week?

3 A tyre costs £20 plus VAT at 15 per cent. What is the total cost of the tyre?

4 Four people visit a Chinese restaurant. The bill comes to £29.60. If they share the bill equally, how much does each pay?

5 Train fares rise by 20 per cent. If the old fare is £1.40, what is the new fare?

6 The circumference of a cylindrical tank is 27 metres. Approximately what is its radius?

7 Eight rods, each one and three-quarter metres long, are placed end to end in a straight line. What is the total length of the line of rods?

8 At midday the temperature was four degrees Celsius. At midnight the temperature was minus nine degrees Celsius. How much did the temperature fall between midday and midnight?

9 The average age of three girls is 16 years. If two girls are aged 18 and 13 years what is the age of the third girl?

10 How many 18 pence stamps can be bought for £2?

11 Estimate in degrees, the size of the smallest angle in this triangle.

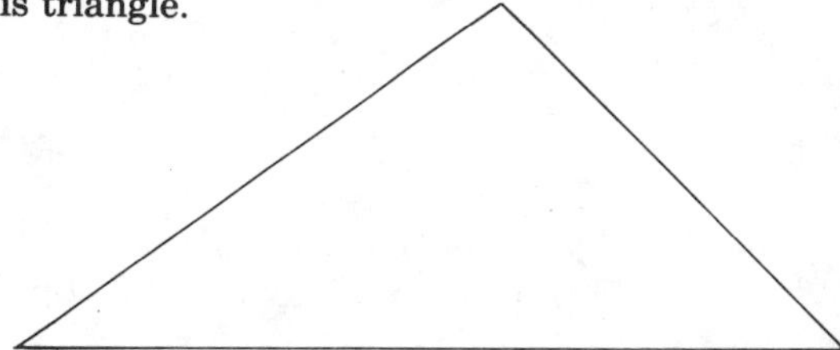

For the rest of the test, you need to use the information given at the end of this section.

12 What is the cost of having a ladies suit, a gents suit and a coat cleaned?

13 The price of a portable radio in the sale is £25.20. What was the price of the radio before the sale started?

14 Tony arrives at Redruth station at 10.17 and catches the first available train to Plymouth. How long is the journey?

15 How much will it cost three adults and five children to sit in the front stalls?

Information for aural tests (all levels)

Question 12

Dry Cleaners

Ladies 2-piece suit	£3.80
Dress	£2.30
Skirt	£1.65
Blouse	£1.55
Gents 2-piece suit	£3.90
Jacket	£2.20
Trousers	£1.70
Coat	£3.75

Question 13

SALE
25% off all
electrical goods.
Limited period only.

Question 14

Penzance	d	06 18	07 30	08 30	09 33	10 00
Camborne	d	06 37	07 53	08 47	09 56	10 24
Redruth	d	06 44	08 00	08 54	10 03	10 31
Truro	d	06 56	08 12	09 06	10 15	10 43
St Austell	d	07 14	08 31	09 24	10 34	11 03
Bodmin Parkway	a	07 31	08 51	09 39	10 54	11 20
Menheniot	a	07 49	—	—	—	—
Saltash	a	08 04	—	—	11 27	—
Plymouth	a	08 20	09 33	10 20	11 38	12 03

Question 15

Cumfy Cinema
Admission Prices

Front Circle	£3.50
Rear Circle	£3.00
Front Stalls	£2.80
Rear Stalls	£2.20

Children half price

OTHER FORMS OF ASSESSMENT

All GCSE mathematics syllabuses include several different forms of assessment for full-time students. In addition to the usual timed written examinations, you may have to do an aural test, oral test, mental arithmetic test, coursework, etc. Look at Table 2 on pp. xiv - xv for details of how you will be assessed on your syllabus.

This section looks at some of these other forms of assessment. It will help to explain some of the work which may contribute to your final grade.

Aural tests

An aural test may be part of your GCSE assessment. Look in Table 2 on pp. xiv – xv to find out if your syllabus is tested in this way.

In an aural test you have to *listen* to the questions. You do *not* have a written copy of the questions to look at and read.

The way your aural test is presented to you will depend on your Examining Group. Here are some details to find out about your aural test. (Your teacher should know the answers to these questions.)

- How many questions will there be?
- How many times will each question be read?
- Will a question be repeated if you ask?
- How long will you have to answer each question?
- Could the questions be about any work in your syllabus or could they be about some coursework you have done?

You will probably have some mock aural tests at school or college before your final test. An aural test may sound easy but there will be a lot to do in a short time. You have to:

- listen to the question and information,
- decide what to do and how to do it,
- work out the answer,
- write the answer clearly on your answer sheet,
- check that you have given any units correctly.

Unlike a 'written examination' you cannot reread the question or go back to check some information read to you. You may find it useful to jot down some information as the question is read to you. Do not be tempted to write down the whole question. Doing this will just waste valuable time.

Any aural test you take will be matched to your 'target grade' in difficulty. So a different aural test will be set at each level. Two sample aural tests, at different levels, are given on p. 209. Ask someone you know to give you a mock aural test by reading out the test for your level. Organize this mock test like the 'real thing'. You will need a pen or pencil and an answer sheet. These are likely to be the only items you will be allowed in the actual test. You will not be allowed to use a calculator or other calculating device (apart from your brain!) in this type of test. Your 'tester' should read each question twice. After the second reading of a question you should have a reasonable time (about 15–30 seconds) to work out your answer and write it down. If you need to do any rough work or jot anything down, then do this on your answer sheet.

To give yourself more practice, you can make up some aural tests yourself. Work with some friends and test each other. Make the questions 'real life questions', not just 'sums'. For example, use 'How much do five twelve pence stamps cost?' not 'What is 5×12?' Write some questions using tables, e.g. timetables, and estimating, e.g. angles and lengths.

Coursework

Being assessed on your 'coursework' does not mean that you are simply assessed on your day-to-day work in mathematics. For coursework you will be set, or have to choose, specific tasks to do and report on during the final year(s) of your GCSE course. Coursework tasks may be: mathematical investigations, problem-solving, practical work, extended project work. You will find details of the coursework tasks for your syllabus in Table 3 on pp. xvi–xvii.

Whatever form of coursework you may do, the examiners will want to know how you approached the task and whether you can communicate your findings to other people. You will be expected to present a written report on your work and you may be asked questions about it by your examiner. Basically, they could ask you the following questions.

Did you . . .

- understand the task?
- plan the work carefully?
- use a suitable method?
- use the right information?
- choose suitable equipment?
- do the work accurately?
- need to change your strategy after you obtained some early results?
- look for and find any patterns?
- manage to find a general result?
- test any results you found?
- carry the task through to a suitable point?
- explain your findings clearly using appropriate mathematical language, symbols, tables, graphs, etc. as necessary?
- evaluate your results?
- suggests any other possibilities for further study?

So make sure that you can answer questions like these about your coursework. Try explaining your work to someone else to see if they and you understand it.

These are also some of the main questions your examiner will be considering when marking your coursework. So check that your report(s) cover these points.

INVESTIGATIONS

Investigating is 'finding out'. In a mathematical investigation you explore an idea mathematically. You try to find out more about the idea by asking your own questions about it and trying to answer some of them. You may be given a 'starting point' which gives you clues about questions to think about. Different students may have the same starting point but by asking different questions they will explore different ideas and report many different findings. Some questions may lead to even more questions and further investigations but others may lead to dead-ends.

There is usually not a definite finishing point or a final right or wrong answer to an investigation. How much you can find out often depends on how much time you have to spend on the investigation.

When working on an investigation, as well as finding out that something happens, try to find out why and how it happens. Use squared paper, drawing instruments, a calculator, models, or anything that makes the work easier to do and explain.

Here is an example of an investigation:

Investigation 1
A school uses square-topped tables in the hall for school dinners. No more than four children can sit at one table. Sometimes the tables are put together to make bigger surfaces. Investigate the number of children who can sit around different table arrangements.

The following is an outline of the work on this investigation 'in progress'. Some of the points that the student considered when doing it are given too.

Try some simple cases

Start with tables in a single row.
Eight can sit at this arrangement.

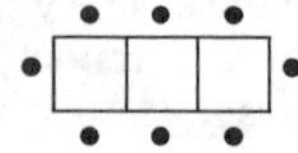

Try another.
Fourteen can dine at this one.

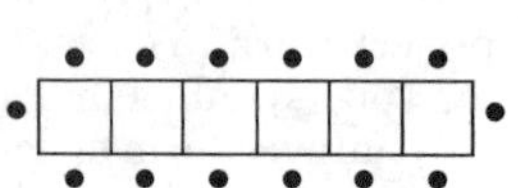

Working like this isn't getting me anywhere! Squared paper would help.

Be logical

Start at the beginning and build up logically.

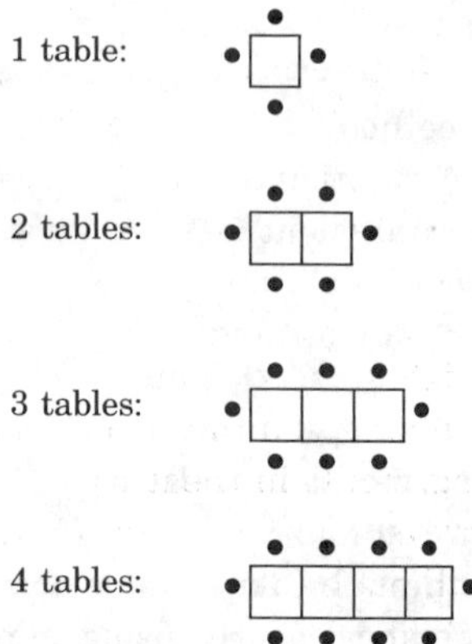

This looks like a good start, but I still can't see any pattern.

Make a table of results

Number of tables	1	2	3	4
Number of diners	4	6	8	10

This looks more promising.

Look for patterns

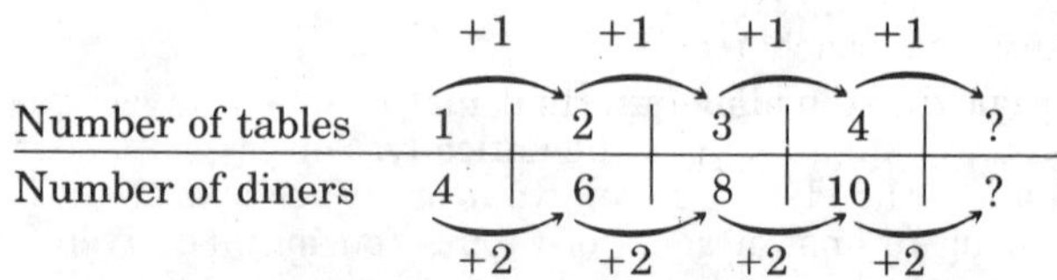

I predict that the next one should be:
5 tables seat 12 children.

Let's try it.

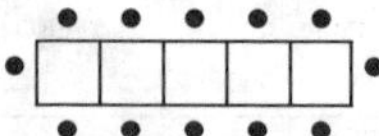

That works! Perhaps there is a rule?

Try to find a rule

The number of diners seems to be:
double the number of tables and add 2.
In symbols this would be:

$$d = 2t + 2$$

Where d = number of diners,
t = number of tables.

Now I need to check if it always works!

Test the rule

Test the rule for another single row arrangement.

Predict: for 8 tables

$$\text{number of diners} = (2 \times 8) + 2 = 18$$

Check:

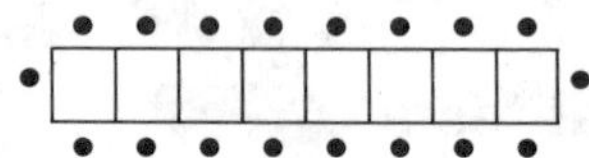

So the rule seems to work for '1 row' arrangements. Test it with some more to be sure.

I wonder if the rule works for all rectangular arrangements?

Try the rule for new situations

Let's try the rule for a double row.

Predict: for 2×5 table arrangement

$$\text{diners} = (2 \times \text{tables}) + 2 = (2 \times 10) + 2 = 20 + 2 = 22$$

Check:

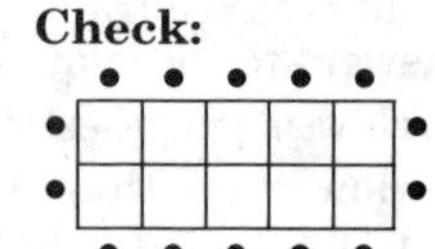

But only 14 can sit down! Oh! I see what's happened! Children can sit around the outside but not down the middle!

So, the rule needs to be changed.

Try to find a rule for all cases

Try a rectangular arrangement of $m \times n$ tables.

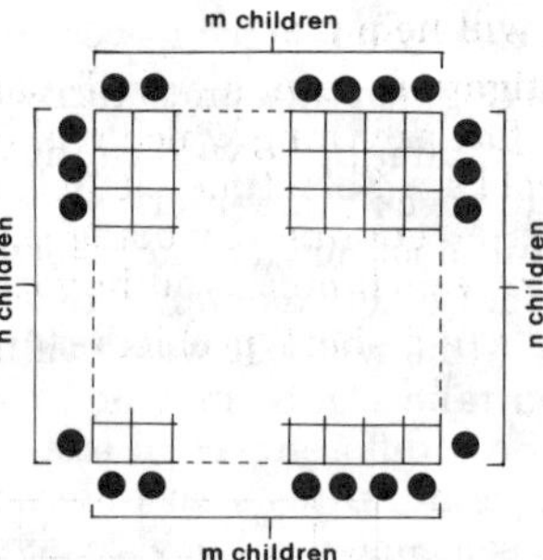

m children can sit along each length of the rectangle.
Total: $2m$ children.

n children can sit along each 'width' of the rectangle.
Total: $2n$ children.

So the total number of diners d is:

$$d = 2m + 2n = 2(m + n)$$

This is a general rule for all rectangular arrangements.

Are there any other arrangements?

What happens if . . . ?

What happens if the arrangements are not rectangular? The tables could be put into:

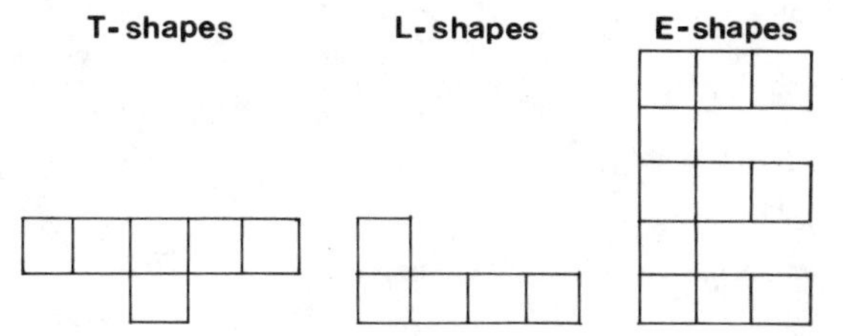

and so on.

What happens if the tables are not square topped? The tables might be other shapes like:

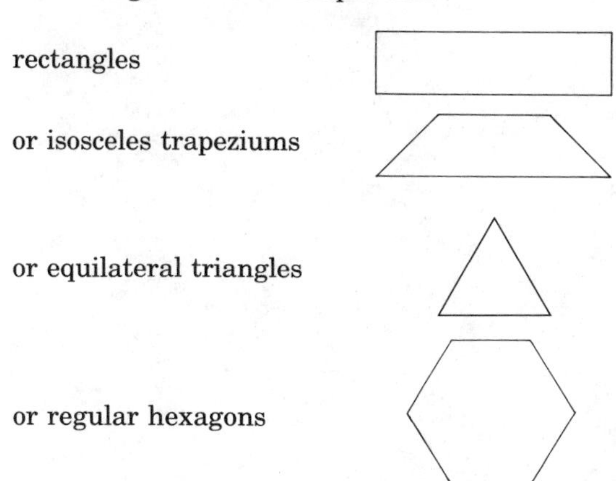

rectangles

or isosceles trapeziums

or equilateral triangles

or regular hexagons

and so on.

Investigate some of these if you have time.

PROBLEM-SOLVING

As a coursework task you may be given a problem to solve using your mathematical knowledge. The problem will basically be a question or questions to be answered. The information which you need in order to solve the problem may be given or you may have to find the information yourself. There may be many different ways to solve a problem, but they should all lead to the same answer(s).

Always start by asking yourself:

What does the problem ask me?

What does the problem tell me?

What do I need to find out?

What equipment will help me?

As with an investigation, use squared paper, drawing instruments, etc, in fact anything which makes it easier for you to solve the problem. Sometimes it helps to look at a simpler form of the problem first. By doing this you may be able to spot a pattern which helps you in your solution.

Here is an example of a short 'problem-solving task'.

Problem 1

A chessboard contains 64 small squares. How many squares altogether can you see drawn on a chessboard?

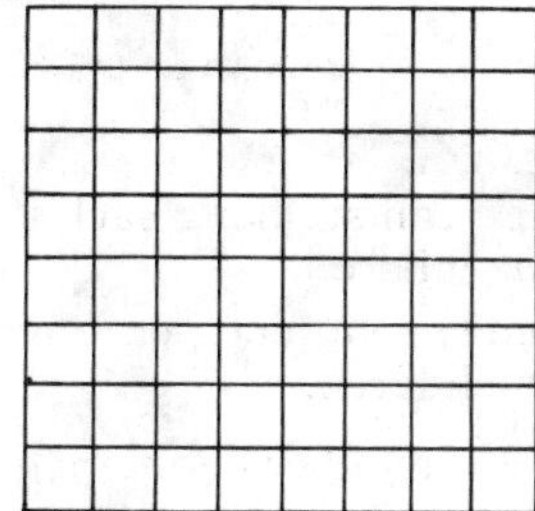

You can start with a 1×1 board 1 square

Then a 2×2 board

4 this size 1 this size so, $4 + 1 = 5$ altogether

Next a 3×3 board

9 this size

4 this size

1 this size

So, $9 + 4 + 1 = 14$ altogether

And so on.

Now try to solve the problem yourself.

The answer is 204 squares.

Explain to a friend how you worked it out.

PRACTICAL WORK

A practical coursework task may be designed to assess:

- 1 your practical skills in mathematics and drawing, for example, your ability to use measuring instruments.
- your ability to use the mathematics you know in the real world, for example, in planning a kitchen.

Your teacher or Examining Group will suggest topics suitable for practical tasks. Here are some examples:

1 Model making.
2 Packaging.
3 Measuring heights and weights.
4 Costing the running of a car or motorbike.
5 Seating arrangements in theatres.
6 Shopping surveys.
7 Traffic light siting.
8 Design of gear wheels.
9 Tessellations and patterns.
10 Navigation.

EXTENDED PIECES OF WORK

Some coursework tasks are intended to be extended pieces of work or projects which you will do over a longer period of time. The tasks will usually be investigations or practical work. Topics for these tasks will usually be chosen after discussions with your teacher. Here are a few ideas:

1 Planning a holiday.
2 Redecorating a room.
3 Surveying school meals.
4 Organizing the school sports day.
5 Designing a car park.

HINTS ON TAKING EXAMINATIONS

Examination nerves are common and understandable. If you have prepared yourself for the examination by doing a sensible course of revision, then they should not be too serious. However, you may not do yourself justice if you have a poor examination technique. The following hints should help you to tackle your written examinations with greater confidence.

Before the day

Before the actual day of your examination make sure you know:

- the date, day, time and place of each paper of your examination,
- how to get to your examination centre if it is not well known to you,
- your candidate number,
- your examination centre number,
- the telephone number of your examination centre.

Prepare any equipment you will need for your examination:

- pens, which are comfortable to use, and ink,
- sharp pencils, a pencil sharpener and a rubber,
- drawing instruments such as a ruler, compasses, protractor, set squares,
- a calculator you know how to use, and spare batteries (check that you know how to replace them quickly),
- an accurate watch or small clock.

On the day

BEFORE THE EXAMINATION

Check that you have all the equipment you will need before setting off for your examination centre. Allow yourself plenty of time to get there. If you are delayed, contact your examination centre (have the telephone number with you) to explain what has happened. Arrive at the examination room early, a late start cannot be a good start.

JUST BEFORE THE START

Listen carefully to the invigilator. There may be some changes or special instructions which you were not expecting or some errors in the paper. Fill in any details such as your candidate number and examination centre number when the invigilator tells you to do so.

READING THE INSTRUCTIONS

Read the instructions on your examination paper very carefully. Make sure that it is the correct examination paper! Although you will be familiar with the papers, the way they are presented can change without notice.

Make sure that you note from the actual paper in front of you:

- the number of sections and questions you have to do,
- how much time you have to do them in (the paper may suggest the time you should allow for each section),
- which questions, if any, are compulsory,
- what choice of questions if any, you have,
- how to present your answers (on the question paper or in an answer booklet; in one booklet or each section separately; each answer on a new page or immediately following the previous one; and so on . . .).

PLANNING YOUR TIME

Quickly calculate the length of time you should spend on each question. You will have practised doing this for 'past or specimen papers' but make sure that you use the instructions on your *actual* examination paper, not the one you are expecting. Try to allow about 10 minutes at the end for checking your paper.

CHOOSING THE QUESTIONS

Read the *whole* paper carefully. If the paper gives you a choice of questions, tick those you are going to answer. Always do your 'best' questions first. Questions at the beginning of the paper may be the easiest and are worth attempting first. Try to answer full questions if you can, but do not spend too long doing so. You can sometimes pass an examination by answering a lot of part questions. Indeed, questions are often structured – the first part being easier to answer than later parts. Some Examining Groups list the marks to be awarded for each question or part question. This information will help you to decide which questions or part questions to do. The harder questions usually carry the most marks.

ANSWERING THE QUESTIONS

Hints on answering questions are given on p. 162. Allow a sensible proportion of time for each section you have to answer. You should have practised doing this during your revision. If you find you are spending too long on a question, it is wise to leave it and move on to the next. Return to it later if you have time. A fresh look at a question often helps.

DOING THE CORRECT NUMBER OF QUESTIONS

Make sure you answer the correct number of questions. If you answer less than the number required, you are limiting the number of marks available to you. Remember the first part of many questions are easier that the later parts. Different Examining Groups have different policies regarding candidates who have answered too many questions, so try to find out your Examining Group's policy.

If you answer too many questions and your Examining Group:

- marks all your questions and ignores your worst marks – hand in all your answers,
- ignores your last questions, – cross out the questions you feel you have done badly, leaving only the correct number to be marked.

AT THE END

Before handing in your examination paper check that:

- any 'front sheet' is completed according to the instructions,
- every loose page is clearly marked with your examination number, etc,
- every answer is numbered correctly,
- pages are numbered clearly and in order.

ANSWERS

GCSE QUESTIONS

List 1

1 (i) 5 (ii) 4.607 (iii) 10

2 (a) $3.12 \approx 3, 4.36 \approx 4, 3 \times 4 = 12$ (b) 13.6032

3 40 804

4 3100

5 5511

6 (a) 1 400 000, 600 000 (b) 1 million hectares

7 (a) 31 (b) D (c) A, E or B, D (d) 34 (e) N, R, T, U

8 270

9 (a) 1440 (b) 160

10 80 seconds

11 (a) 3500 (b) gram

12 (a) 13 218 (b) 13 000

13 (a) 2, 4, 6, 8, 10, 12 (b) 3, 5, 9 (c) 6, 12
(d) 2, 3, 5, 7, 11 (e) 4, 9

14 (a) (i) 9, 36 (ii) 1, 4, 16, 64
(b) 16, 25 (c) 81 (d) 7

15 (a) 16, 19 (b) 96, 192 (c) 36, 49 (d) 5, 2.5

16 (a)

(b)

Number of levels	*Number of bricks*
1	1
2	4
3	9
4	16

(c) 100

17 (a) (i) 8p (ii) 16p (b) (i) 32p (ii) 64p
(c) (i) 88p (ii) 152p or £1.52 (d) 14 years
(e) No. Each year the increase is double the increase for the previous year, i.e. an even number of pence; this increase is added to an even number of pence.
Even number + even number = even number.
(f)

Age (years)	5	6	7	8	9	10	11
Pocket money (p)	23	24	27	36	63	144	387

18 (a) 169 (b) 289

19 (a) 5 cm (b) 20 cm

20 (a) 5 (b) Status Quo
(c) 1 Nick Berry
2 Five Star
3 Paul Young
4 Madonna
5 Status Quo

21 (a) 22 00 (b) 08 00 (c) 15 00

22 (a) Cairo (b) Moscow (c) 31 degrees

23 $^+5, ^-2, ^-9, ^+3$

24 (a) (i) $\frac{3}{8}$ (ii) $\frac{1}{8}, \frac{1}{4}, \frac{3}{8}, \frac{1}{2}$ (b) $\frac{3}{16}, \frac{1}{4}, \frac{5}{16}, \frac{3}{8}, \frac{7}{16}, \frac{1}{2}$

25 (a) $1\frac{3}{4}$ (b) 1.75

26 (a) $\frac{1}{20}$ (b) (i) $\frac{2}{5}$ (ii) 8.6 grams

27 240

28 (a) $\frac{7}{8}$ (b) 0.875 (c) 179 (d) $\frac{5}{8}$ (e) 45 mph

29 (a) $\frac{5}{8}$ (b) $\frac{3}{8}$ (c) 6

30 $3\frac{1}{4}$

31 5.47

32 0.088 0.625 0.66 0.667

33 (a) 230.9, 231.1, 232.7, 231.4, 230.7
(b) James Logan
(c) Logan, Bingham, Jones, Stewart, Adams
(d) 46.14 seconds

34 8.35 m

35 4 hours 10 minutes

36 Barnly

37 (a) (i) 0.9 (ii) 0.875
(iii) The first test, because 0.9 is greater than 0.875
(b) 85%

38 25%

39 (a) 157.5 g (b) 173.64375 , 173.6g (1 dp)

40 (a) £276 (b) 26 (c) £6.91

41 (a) £16.14 (b) £20.33
(c) gloves, tie, tights, hankies
gloves, tie, record, hankies
gloves, tie, tights, scarf

42 £2.80

43 £1.54, 45p, £1.44, $1\frac{1}{2}$ lb, £5.68

44 (a) £36.80
(b) No. 13 days lost in a 13 week period leaves 52 days to travel: $52 \times £2.80 = £145.60$. So the season ticket was still 40p cheaper.

45 (a) 1600 (b) £7600
(c) (i) 1200 (ii) $\frac{1}{4}$ (d) £157.50

46 (a) £300.96 (b) £1831.68 (c) £1872
(d) £145.80 (e) £3544.56

47 £6000

48 £55 935·

49 (a) (i) £144 (ii) £4.50 (iii) £7.20 (iv) £226.80
(b) £17.01

50 (i) £4200 (ii) £4420 (iii) £374.50

51 (a) 38 hours, 1215 boards, £141.30

(b) 31.973684 32

52 £21

53 (i) £7260 (ii) £2105.40

54 (a) 30p (b) £4

55 (a) 479 (b) 3261 (c) £22.62, £30.77

56 £69.69

57 (a) £270 (b) £296.33

58 (a) £360 (b) £1860

59 £2.17

60 (a) £1106 (b) £5972.40 (c) £7078.40

61 (a) £60 (b) £180 (c) £30

62 £6.60

63 (a) £100 (b) 500 (c) £44 profit

64 (a) £12.50 (b) 62.5%

65 (i) £20.52 (ii) £36.90

66 (i) £291 (ii) £27.75 (iii) £21 (iv) £1359

67 (i) 07 50 (ii) 07 42

68 (a) 2 hours (b) 720 degrees

69 $x = 52°, y = 57°$

70 $x = 50°, y = 25°, z = 80°$

71 (a) 15° (b) 120° (c) 240°

72 $x = 90°, y = 170°, z = 100°$

73 (a) (i) 13° (ii) 116° (b) 347°

74

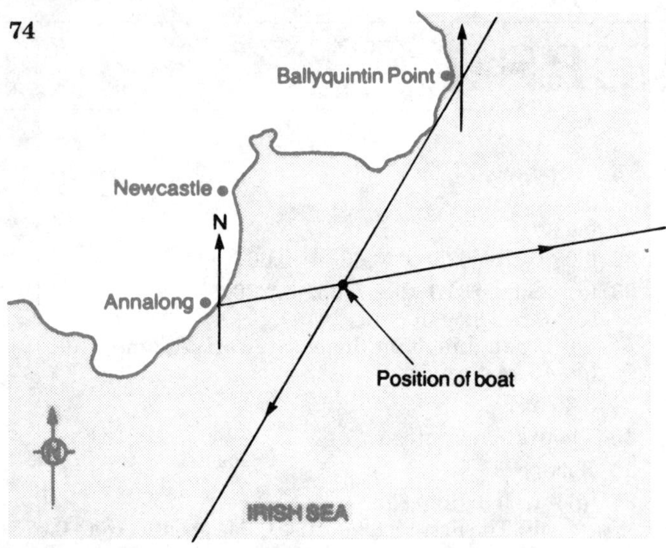

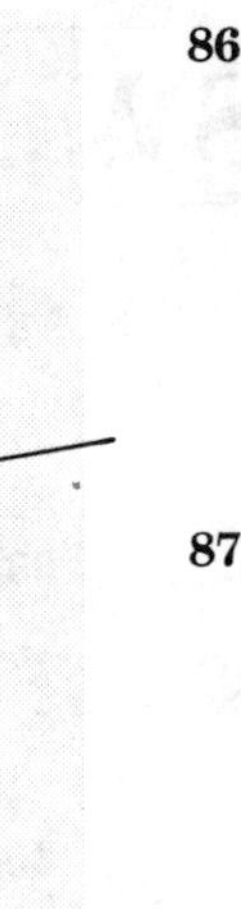

75 (a) octagon (b) (i) quadrilateral (ii) hexagon

76 $p = 45°, q = 67.5°, r = 135°$

77 $x = 60°, y = 120°, z = 60°$

78 (a) rhombus (d)
(b) kite
(c) square

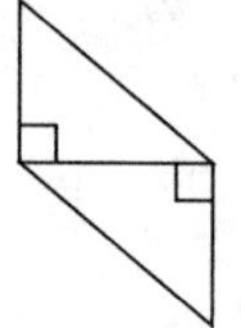

79 (a) A or C (b) C (c) parallelogram

80 63°

81 40 003.6 km

82 (a) 6.28 ft (b) (i) 439.6 ft (ii) 400 ft

83 (a) 7.85 cm (b) 10

84 90.044257 ≈ 90 m

85 (a)

(b) (i)

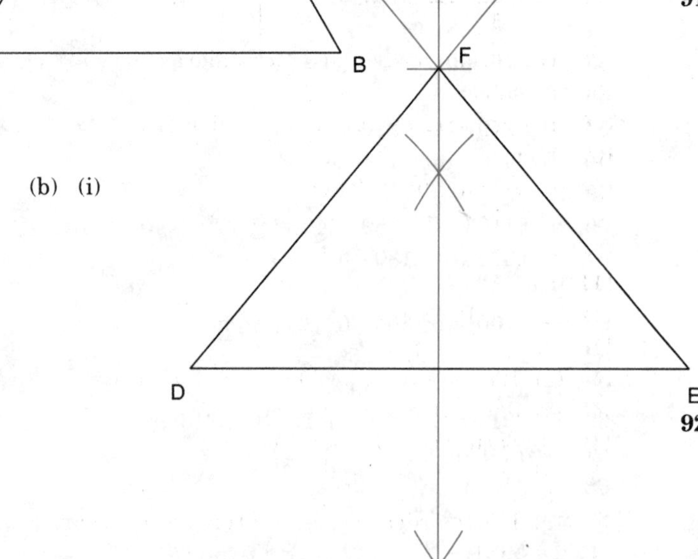

(ii) 83°

86

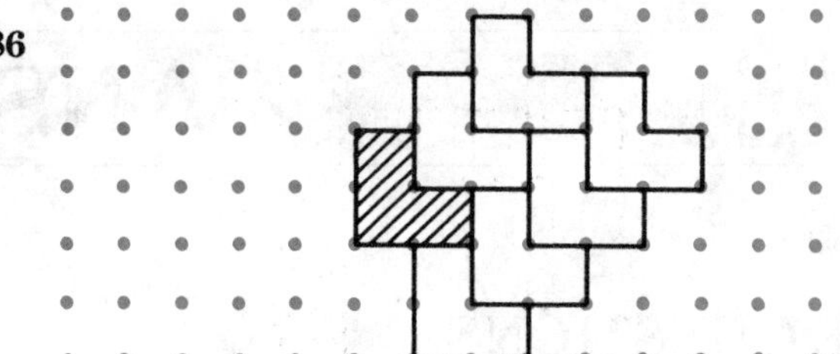

87 Some possibilities:

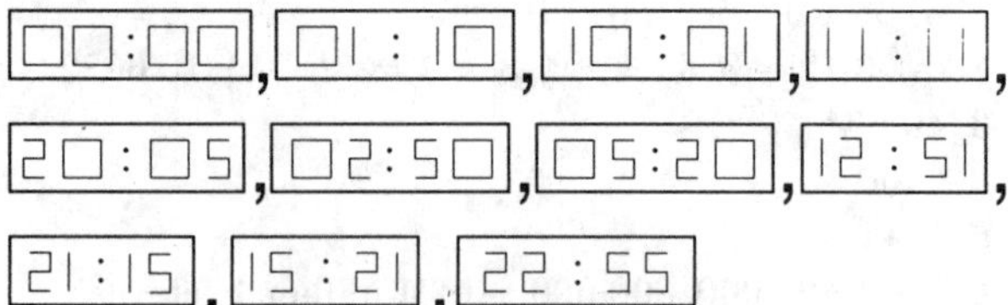

88

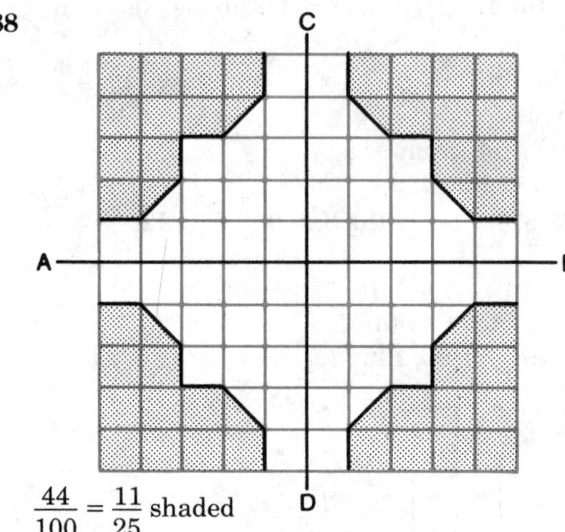

$\frac{44}{100} = \frac{11}{25}$ shaded

89 (a) order 3 (b) order 2 (c) order 1

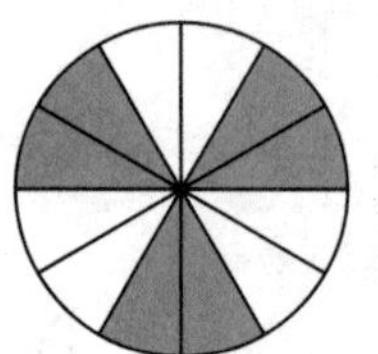

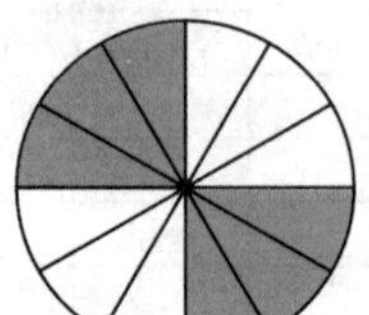

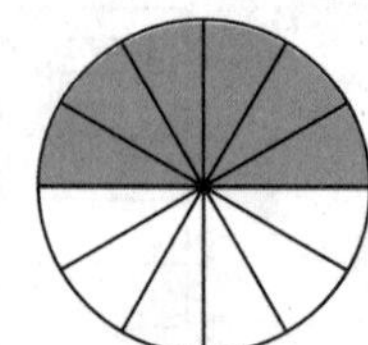

90 (a) A translation of 5 units to the right and 3 units up *or* a translation $\begin{pmatrix}5\\3\end{pmatrix}$.

(b) A reflection with the y-axis as mirror line.

91

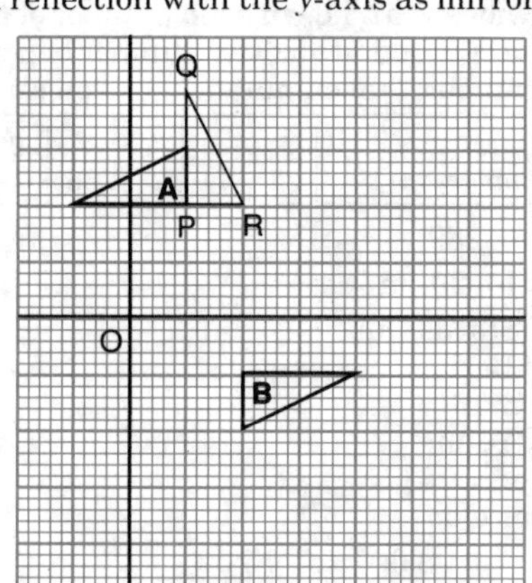

92

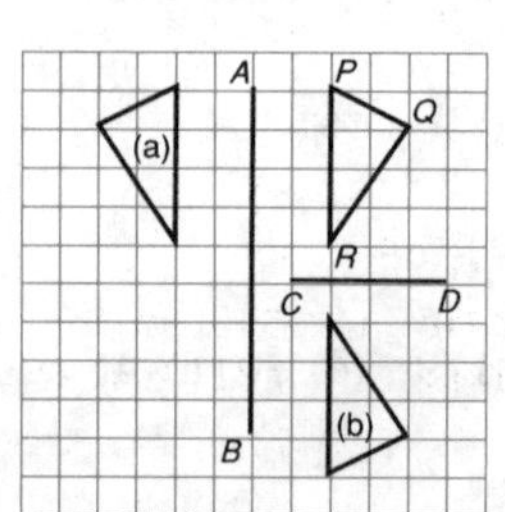

93

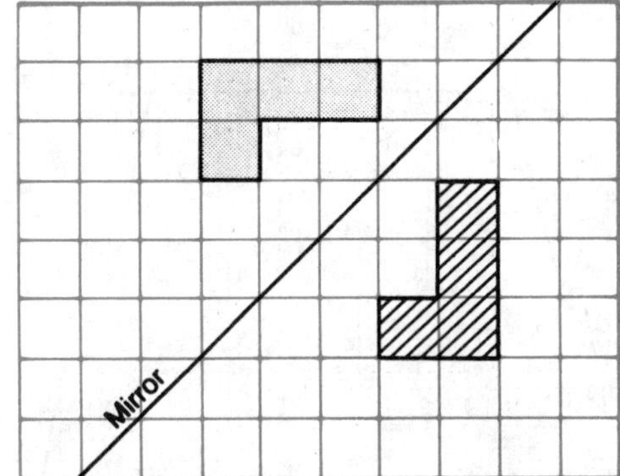

94

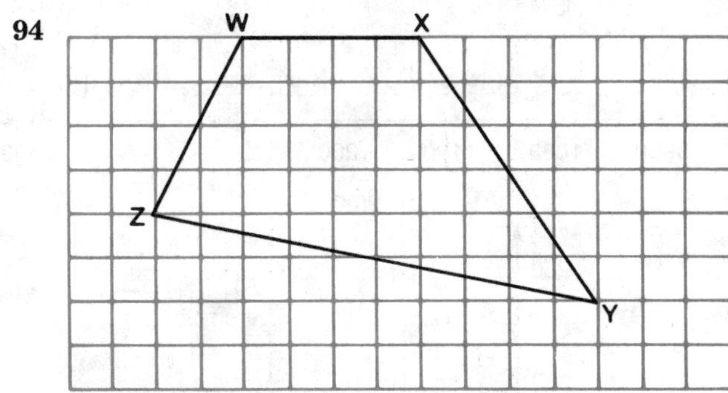

95 (a) 12 in^2 (b) 9 in by 12 in (c) 42 in (d) 108 in^2 (e) 9 times

96 4.68 m

97 (a) 2 cm (b) 8 m

98 (a) Clacton (b) approx. 340 km (c) Norwich (d) approx. 067°

99 (a) (i) 2 cm (ii) approx. 1 cm to 28 km
(b) (i) 2.9 cm (ii) 81.2 km

100 (a)

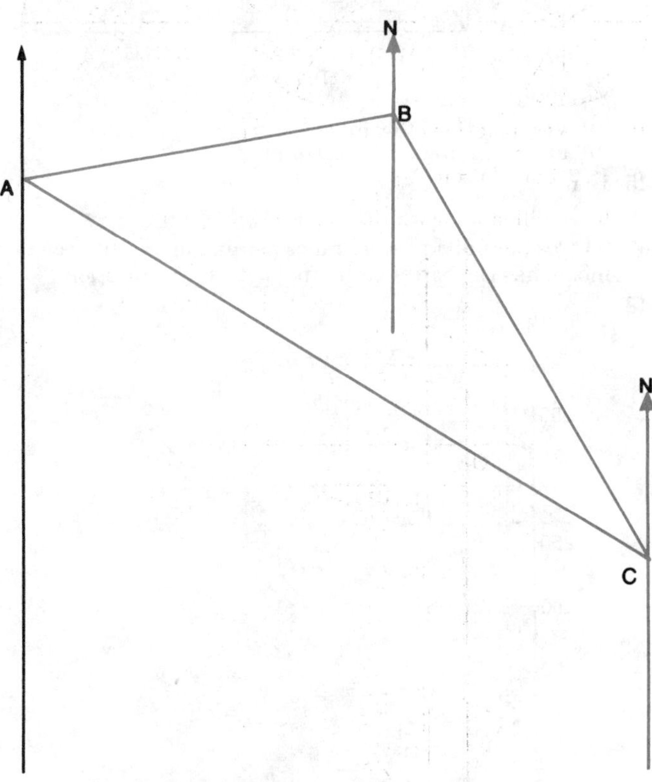

(b) (i) approx. 97 mm or 9.7 cm
(ii) approx. 485 m (from 9.7×50 m)
(c) (i) approx. 41° (ii) approx. 121° (iii) approx. 301°
(d) approx. 415 m

101

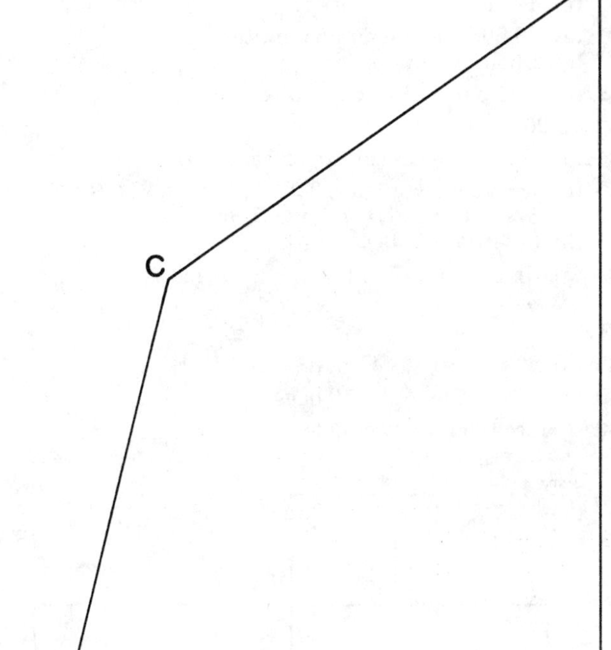

102 (i) 5 (ii) 8 (iii) 12 (iv) 6 (v) 9 (vi) 16 (vii) 9
(viii) When the two solids are fastened together, two faces join, so one face of each solid is 'lost' inside the combined shape.

103 (a) 14
(b) 30 (assuming all top faces which can be seen in the picture are visible in the window)
(c) 5 m^2

104

(Other solutions are possible. Make a cube and check!)

105 (a) cuboid (b) A and E

106 (i) regular tetrahedron (ii) 4 (iii) 6

107 20 cm

108 (a) 24 cm (b) 0.12 mm

109 19.58 km

110 1.24 kg

111 (a) 1.7 kg (b) 1700 g (c) 3.74 lb

112 approx. 10 apples

113 12

114 (a) 12.5 cm (b) 2 kg 200 g (c) 0.75 litres

115 (a) km (b) m^2 (c) ml (d) cm^2

116 (a) Saturday (b) 31st (c) 4
(d) Monday (e) Wednesday
(f) yes
(g) If it was a leap year, i.e. 29 days in February.

117 13 April

118 95 million

119 13.40 or 1.40 p.m.

120 (i) $1\frac{3}{4}$ hours (ii) Blackpool Holiday Show (iii) 12 June (iv) 5 hours

121 (a) 19 50 (b) 1 hour 55 minutes (c) 1 hour 5 minutes

122 (a) 5.45 p.m. (b) 20 minutes

123 13.20

124 (a) 20 cm (b) 15 cm (c) 20 cm (d) 3 cm

125 (a) Possible rectangles: $3 \times 11, 1 \times 13, 2 \times 12, 4 \times 10, 5 \times 9, 6 \times 8, 7 \times 7$
(b) (i) 7×7 (ii) 49 square units

126 (a) (i) 9.22 m (ii) 4.9824 4.98 m^2
(b) (i) 9 m (ii) 5 m^2

127 approx. 12 cm^2

128 (a) 22 m^2 (b) (i) 4 (ii) 88

129 (a) 435.615 m^2 (b) 10 bags

130 Reduced copy of a possible net:

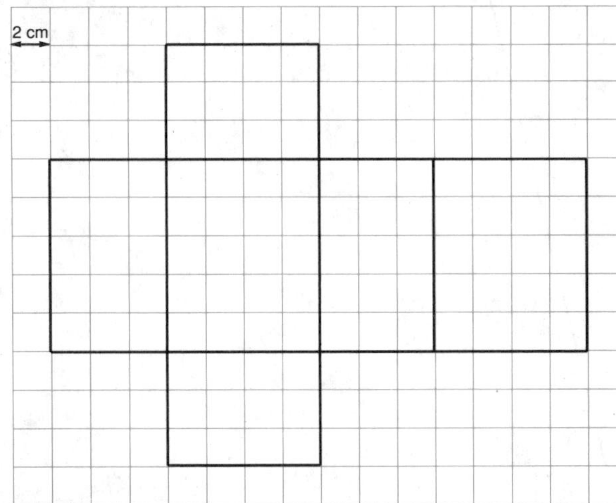

(b) (i) 94 cm^2 (ii) 376 cm^2
(c)

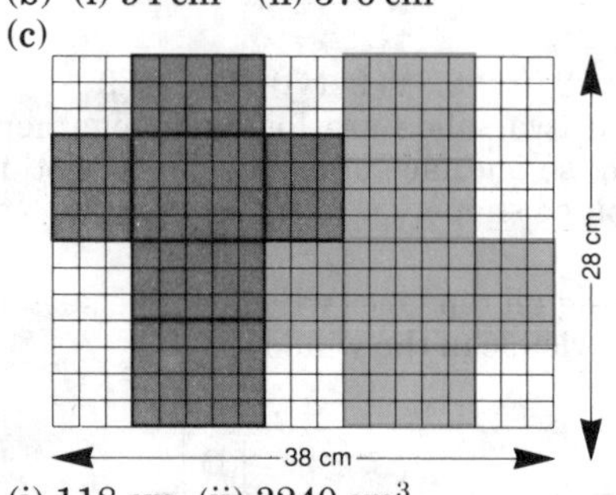

By fitting nets together you can use a card 28 cm by 38 cm, i.e. 1064 cm^2. (Answer will depend on *your* net.)

131 (i) 118 cm (ii) 3240 cm^3

132 8 litres

133 (a) 40 cm^3 (b) 480 cm^3 (c) 6 cm (d) 576 matches

134 (a) Method 1: Stacking upright, $6 \times 4 \times 3 = 72$ cans.
Method 2: Stacking horizontally, $4 \times 4 \times 5 = 80$ cans.
(b) 47 250 cm^3.
(c) Method 1: empty space 17 010 cm^3.
Method 2: empty space 13 650 cm^3.

135 £27.50

136 $12\frac{1}{2}$ minutes

137 35 miles per gallon

138 (a) 250 min = 4 h 10 min (b) 9.10 a.m.
(c) 396 min = 6 h 36 min

139 (a) (i) 5.0769231 [C] ≈ 5.1 g
(ii) 5.5555556 [C] ≈ 5.6 g
(b) 'Big value' because it gives more grams per penny.

140 7.5 mph

141 5 hours

142 (a) 48 minutes (b) 7.47 a.m.

143 (a) 09 40 (b) 10 minutes
(c) (i) 25 minutes (ii) 48 km/h
(d) (i) 13 15 (e) (ii) 14 30
(d) (ii) (e) (i)

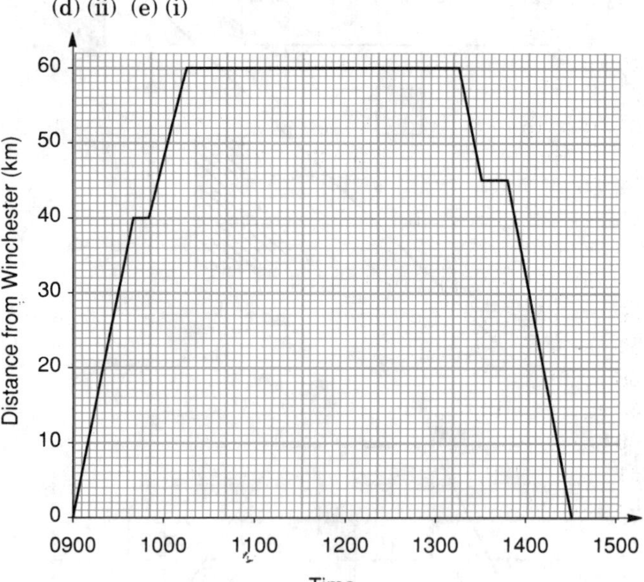

144

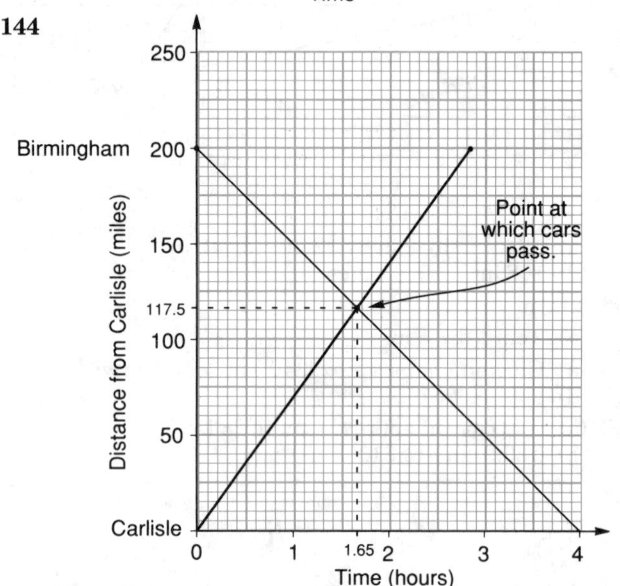

From the graph:
(a) approx. 117.5 miles
(b) approx. 1.65 h = 1 h 39 min

145 15 p

146 54 km/h

147 6 litres per 100 km ≈ 47 miles per gallon. So the second model has the better estimated petrol consumption.

148

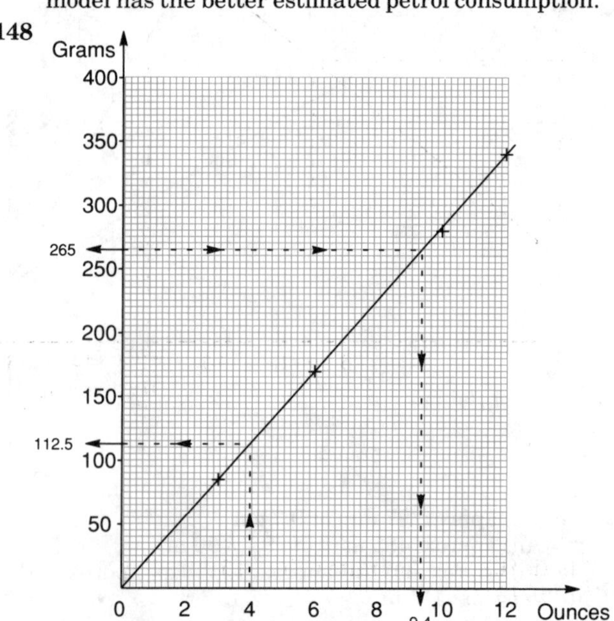

From the graph:
(a) approx. 112.5 g (b) approx. 9.4 ounces

149 (a) 60 mph (b) approx. 96 km/h (c) approx. $\frac{5}{8}$

150 4175

151 10 oz plain chocolate, 5 tablespoons rum, 10 egg yolks, 15 egg whites, $1\frac{1}{4}$ pints double cream

152 80 girls

153 (a) 1.25 litres (b) 1 litre (c) 8 litres

154 (i) £6 (ii) £5.21

155 (a) 95 minutes (b) 11 45

156 (a) 23.65 (b) 48

157 (a) 720° (b) 120°

158 44.48

159 (a) 11 (b) 17, 19

160 (a) 4 (b) 5, 6

161 (a) (1, 2)(2, 3)(3, 1)(3, 4) (b) NIGHT (c) (0, 0)

162 (a) and (c)(i)

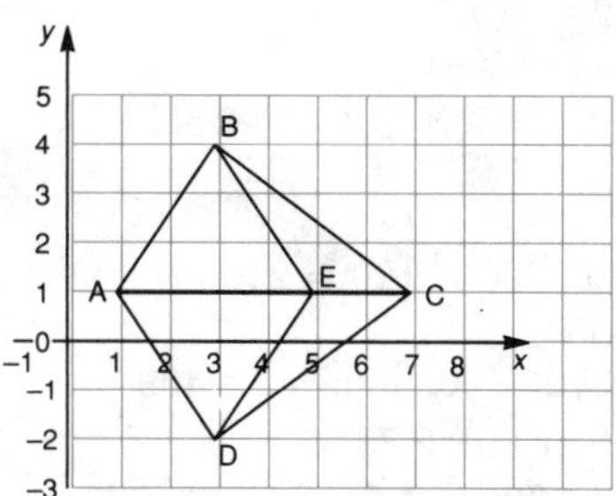

(b) D(3, $^-2$) (c)(ii) E(5, 1) (d) 6 square units

163 (i) 8.12 a.m. (ii) 40.5°C (iii) 10.24 a.m. (iv) 7 hours 36 minutes (v) 8 p.m.

164 (a), (b) and (c)

From this graph:

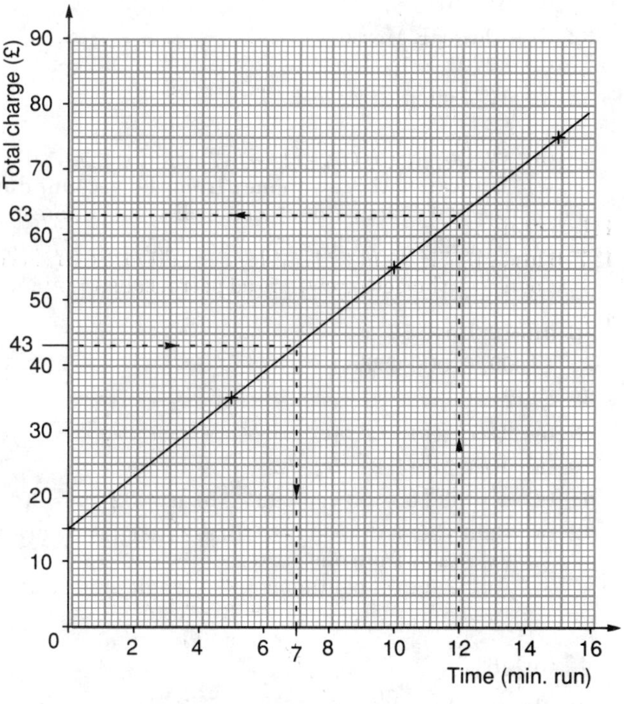

(d) (i) £63 (ii) 7 minutes (iii) £15
(e) £115

165 (a) and (b)

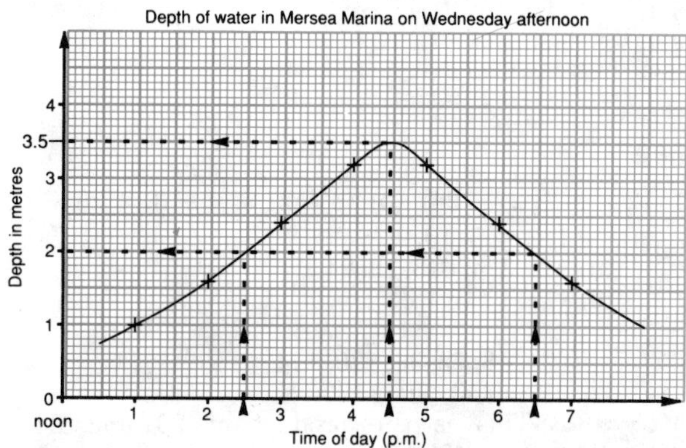

From the graph:
(c) 2 m (d) 2.30 p.m. (e)(i) 3.5 m (ii) 4.30 p.m.

166 (a) £3 500 000 (b) £13.5 million (c) 3:2
(d) Pictogram showing the income received by a charity fund in 1985.

Key ☐ represents £2 million

Donations ☐ ☐ ☐ ☐

Interest ☐ ☐ [

Legacies ☐

167 (a)

Egg size	*Number of eggs*
1	1
2	2
3	5
4	11
5	7
6	4

(b) Size 4
(c)

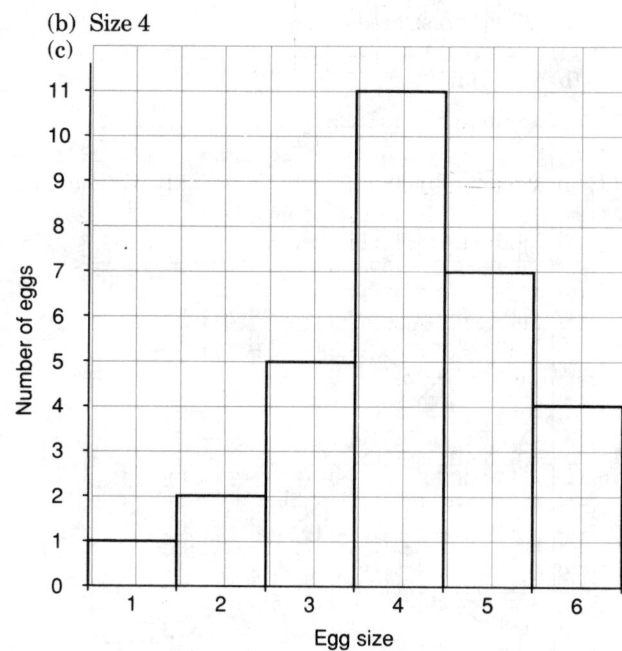

168 (a) yellow and violet (b) 16 (c) 2 (d) 10 per cent

169 (a) 75 264 (b) 12 544

170 6 (b) 2 (c) 3

171 (a) 6°F (b) 52.5°F

172 (a) $\frac{1}{3}$ (b) $\frac{2}{3}$ (c) 10
173 (i) $\frac{2}{8} = \frac{1}{4}$ (ii) $\frac{3}{8}$
174 (a) $\frac{8}{13}$ (b) $\frac{5}{12}$

List 2

1 $12 \times (4 - 2) = 24$ (b) $(6 - 2) \times (4 + 3) = 28$
2 (a) (i) 1, 2, 4, 5, 10, 20
(ii) 1, 2, 3, 4, 6, 8, 12, 24
(iii) 1, 2, 4 (iv) 4
(b)
(ii) 24, 48, 72, 96, 120, 144
(iii) 120, 240 (iv) 120
(c) 480: This is the product of 20 and 24, i.e. $20 \times 24 = 480$
3 (a) (i) 1, 2, 3, 4, 6, 8, 12, 16, 24, 48
(ii) 1, 2, 3, 4, 6, 8, 9, 12, 18, 24, 36, 72
(b) 1, 2, 3, 4, 6, 8, 12, 24
(c)(i) 2, 3 (ii) $2 \times 2 \times 2 \times 2 \times 3$ *or* $2^4 \times 3$
4 (a) (i) $2 \times 3 \times 3 \times 7$ or $2 \times 3^2 \times 7$
(ii) $2 \times 2 \times 3 \times 5 \times 7$ or $2^2 \times 3 \times 5 \times 7$
(b) $2^2 \times 3^2 \times 5 \times 7 = 1260$
5 (a) −10°C (b) Thursday (c) 8°C
(d) 1°C (from Friday midnight to Saturday noon)
(e) 3°C
6 (a) 27.2°C (b) 0.2266667 [C] ≈ 0.2°C/sec (1 d.p.)
7 (a) 91, 140
(b) by adding on consecutive square numbers (36, 49)
8 (a)
(b) 0, 3, 9, 18
(c) 0, 1, 3, 6
(d) 10, 15
(e) 63 (21 × 3)
(f) 6th row, 9th column
9 (a) (i) 16 (ii) 19 (iii) 46
(b) $r = 4 + 3(s - 1)$ *or* $r = 3s +$ £
(c) 23 (d) $s = \frac{1}{3}(r - 1)$
(e) 39 squares; 2 rods left over
10 (a) $p =$, $q = 1.5$
(b) and (d)(ii)

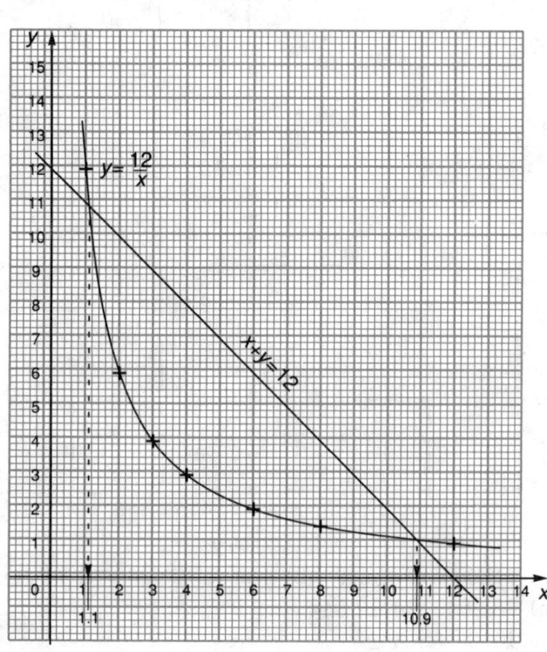

(c) $y = \dfrac{12}{x}$
(d) (i) three 'simple' points are (0, 12), (12, 0), (6, 6).
(e) $x \approx 10.9$ and 1.1 (f) −1
11 (a) $\frac{2}{30}$ or $\frac{1}{15}$ (b) $\frac{1}{5}$
12 (a) $\frac{1}{20}$ (b) 5
13 $1\frac{1}{2}$ metres
14 1200 litres
15 (a) (i) 2.4242324 (ii) 0.2402402 (ii) 0.0240024
(b) They are recurring decimals with the digits 2 and 4 repeated.
16 $\frac{127}{48}$
17 $\frac{7}{20}$
18 14%
19 (a) £7.99 (b) 20%
20 £7500
21 7.5144509 [C] ≈ 7.5 mg (1 d.p.)
22 (a) −10°C (b) −40°C
(c) $F = 2(C + 15)$
(d) 2.94 % (to 3 s.f.)
23 (a) Using $r \approx 7$, $h \approx 3$, $\pi \approx 3$ gives
$V \approx 3 \times 3^2(7 - \frac{3}{3}) = 162$.
(b) 161.9 (to 1 d.p.)
24 $17\frac{3}{4} \times 120 \approx 20 \times 120 = 2400 \approx 2000$ (to 1 s.f.)
25 (a) 15 400
(b) lowest 23 500; highest 24 499
26 (a) (i) 9.8 m² (ii) 9.79 m²
(b) upper limit: $5.5 \times 2.5 = 13.75$ m²;
lower limit: $4.5 \times 1.5 = 6.75$ m²
27 9.3×10^7 miles
28 2.8846×10^{-2} [C] 3×10^{-2} cm (to 1 s.f.)
29 (a) 1.5117×10^5 km² (b) 6.3:1
30 1.4×10^{23}
31 (a) (i) 6 ten thousands or 60 000
(ii) 6 tenthousandths or 0.0006
(b) 6×10^8
32 (i) A Pluto, B Mercury
(ii) 4.2701×10^9 km
33 (a) 11 % simple interest
(b) £209.83
34 (a) £2500 (b) (i) £2100 (ii) £2205 (iii) £2431.01
(c) You can withdraw money from the account during the two years without losing all of the 'interest'.
35 (a) 61.4125, 52.200625, 44.370531, 37.714951, 32.057709
(b) 1.8 m
36 Jill 12; Dave 18
37 £1200, £2000, £2800
38 £112.50
39 (a) 120° (b) 60° (c) 50°
40 (a) 108° (b) 72° (c) 72°
41 (a) $a = 53°$, $b = 53°$, $c = 90°$ (b) $a = 32°$, $b = 90°$
42 (a) Split the pentagon into three triangles by drawing diagonals from one vertex.
Angle sum of pentagon = 3 × angle sum of triangle
= 3 × 180°
= 540°
(b) 36°
43 (a) 90° (b) 100°
44 18°
45 ∠ACB = 90° (angle in a semicircle),
∠ABC + 90° + 32° = 180° (angle sum of triangle),
therefore ∠ABC = 58°.
46 (a) 35° (b) 70° (c) 55°
47 (a) 90° (b) 39° (c) 25°

48 (i) AD = 112 m (iii) BT = 48 m

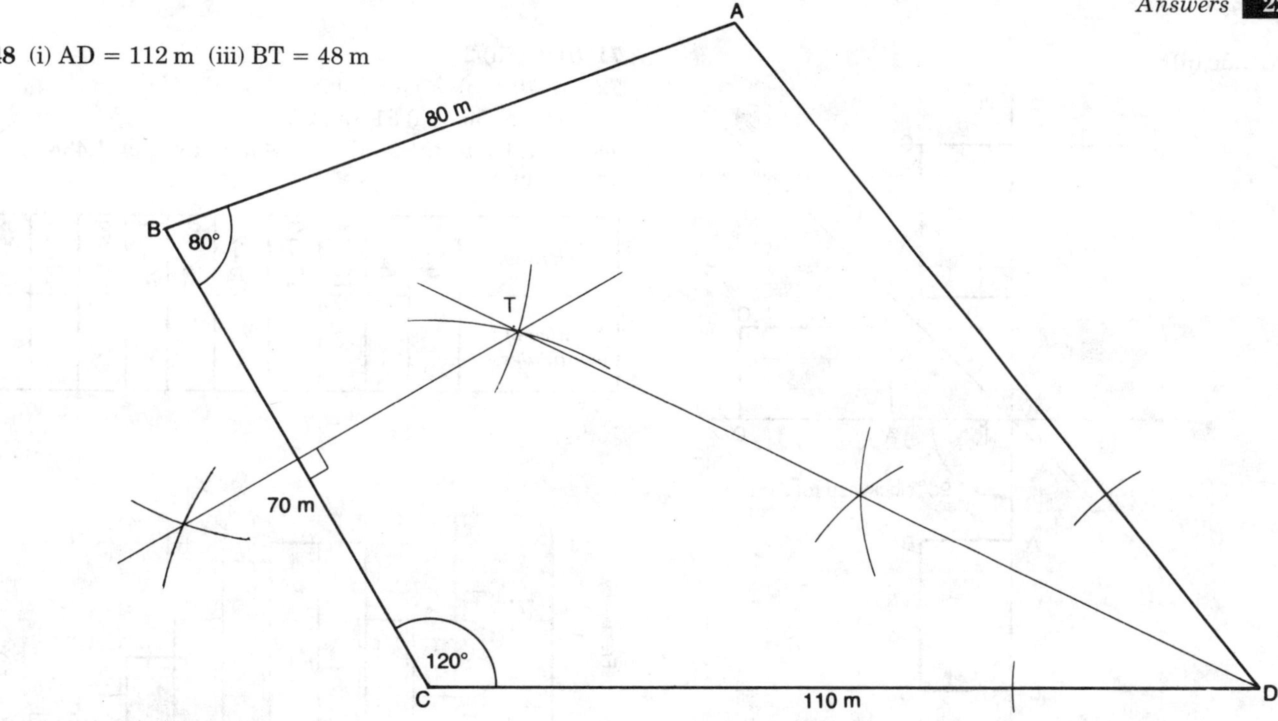

49 The diagram should be an equilateral triangle with sides 6 cm long.

50

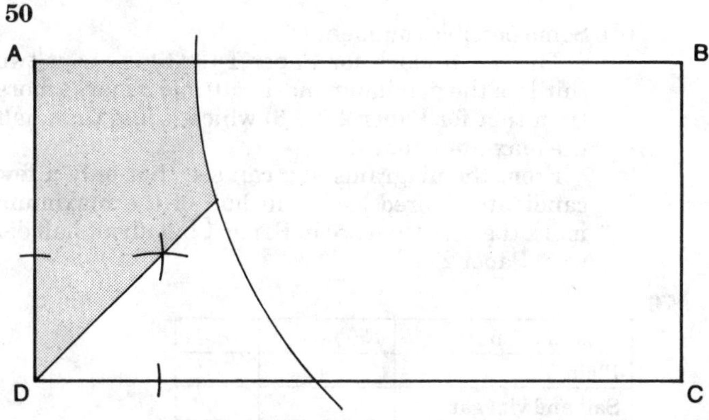

Submarine must be in shaded region

The diagram shows an arc, radius 6 cm, centre B, the bisector of angle ADC and the required shaded region.

51

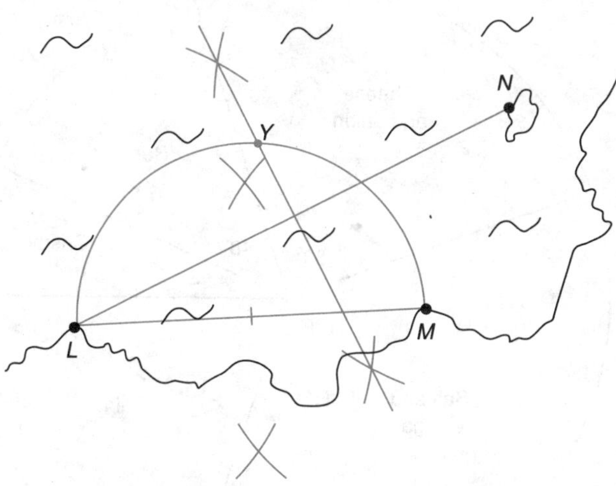

Y is the point of intersection of the semicircle with LM as diameter and the perpendicular bisector of LN.

52 (a)

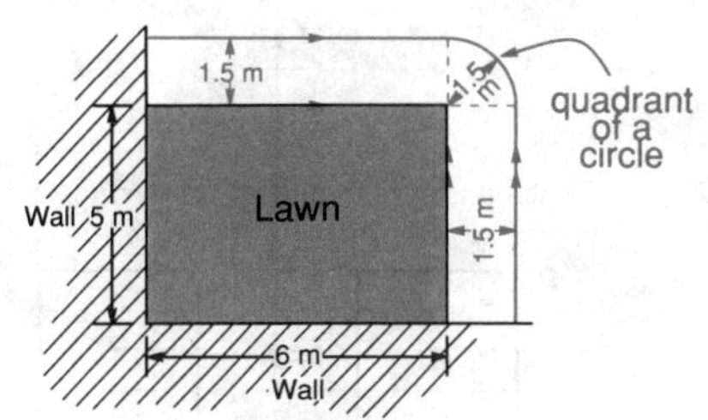

(b) 18.27 m^2 (to 2 d.p.)

53 (a) B (b) E and F

54 (a) enlargement, scale factor 2, centre (4, 1)
(b) B, C and E

55 (a) $\frac{2}{5}$ or 0.4
(b) and (c)

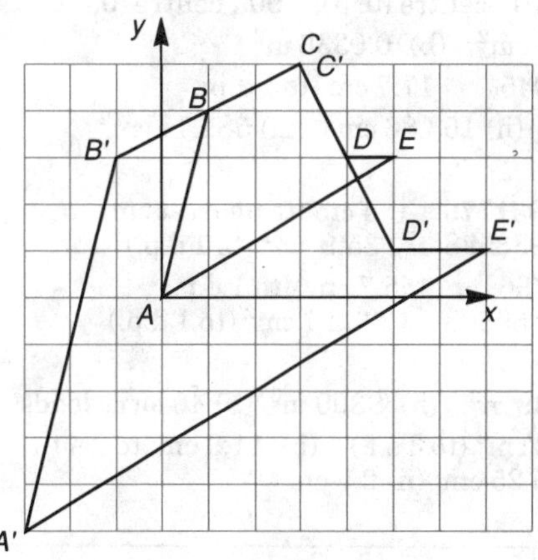

56 (a) 1.5 (b) 9 cm

57 $x = 7$ cm, $y = 10$ cm

58 (a) a translation of 3 cm parallel to AB
(b) a reflection in CN
(c) a rotation of 180° about the midpoint of CM

59 (i) and (ii)

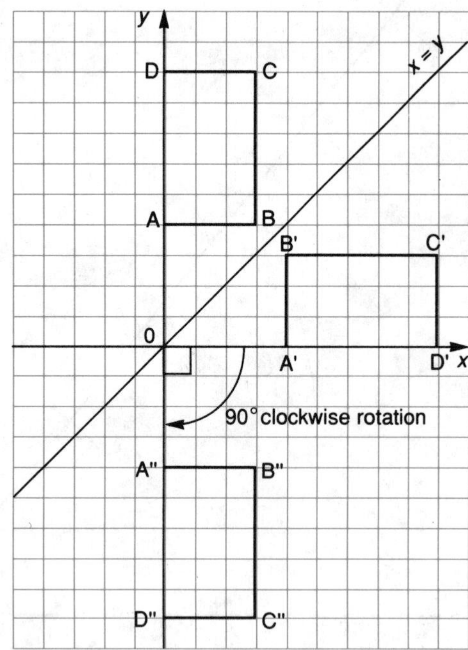

(iii) reflection in the x-axis

60 (a) (b) (c)

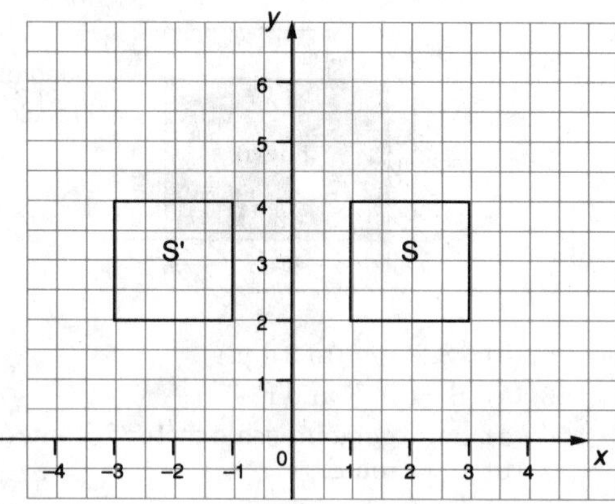

(d) a translation 4 units to the left, parallel to the x-axis

(e) (0,1)

(f) Some possible rotations are:
$-270°$, centre (0, 1); 180°, centre (0, 3);
$+270°$, centre (0, 5); $-90°$, centre (0, 5).

61 (a) 336 cm^2 (b) 0.0336 m^2

62 17.720045 17.7 cm (to 1 d.p.)

63 (i) 7 cm (ii) 153.86 cm^2 (iii) 581.14 cm^2

64 81 m^2

65 (a) 3.9931776 C 4 cm (to nearest cm)
(b) 35.938598 C 35.9 cm^2 (to 1 d.p.)

66 455.65796 C 455.7 cm^3 (to 1 d.p.)
(b) 332.69808 C 332.7 cm^2 (to 1 d.p.)

67 28.75 m^3

68 (a) (i) 49 m^2 (ii) 9800 m^3 (b) 40 lorry loads

69 (a) 502 cm^3 (to 3 s.f.) (b) 11.9 cm (to 3 s.f.)
(c) (i) 5.25 cm (ii) 2.8 cm

70 (a)
(b) 21

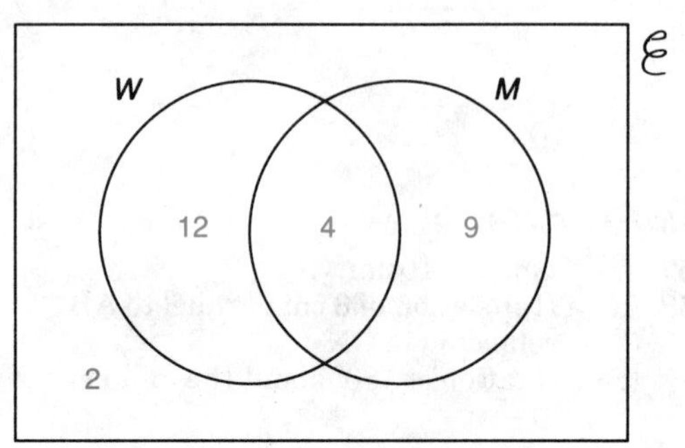

71 (i) 22 (ii) 2

72 (a) 10 (b) 9 (c) 7.968

73 (i) 8 (ii) 30 (iii) 81 (iv) 2.7

74 (a) $1.6 \leqslant w < 1.8$ (b) $1.2 \leqslant w < 1.4$ (c) 1.438 kg

75 (a) 32.6

Mark range	0–4	5–9	10–14	15–19	20–24	25–29	30–34	35–39	40–44	45–49
Number of candidates	1	2	6	10	10	9	6	3	2	1

(c)

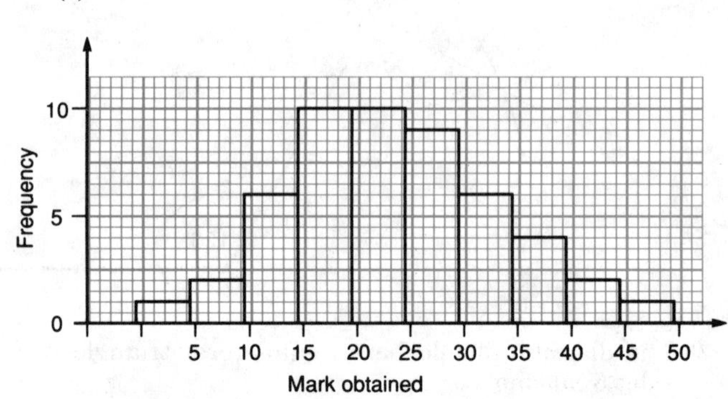

(d) Some possible comments:
The mean mark for Paper 1 (32.6) is about two thirds of the maximum mark (50) and 9 marks more than that for Paper 2 (23.6) which is less than half the maximum mark.
From the diagrams you can see that only a few candidates scored less than half of the maximum mark (i.e. less than 25) in Paper 1 but about half did so in Paper 2.

76

Type of crisp	*Frequency*	*Angle*
Plain	9	72°
Salt and vinegar	16	128°
Cheese and onion	11	88°
Beef	6	48°
Crispy bacon	3	24°
Total	45	360°

(c)

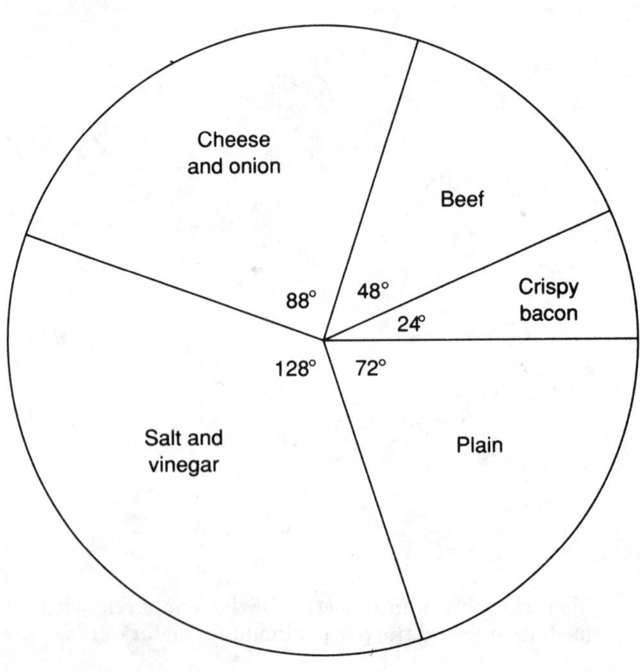

77 

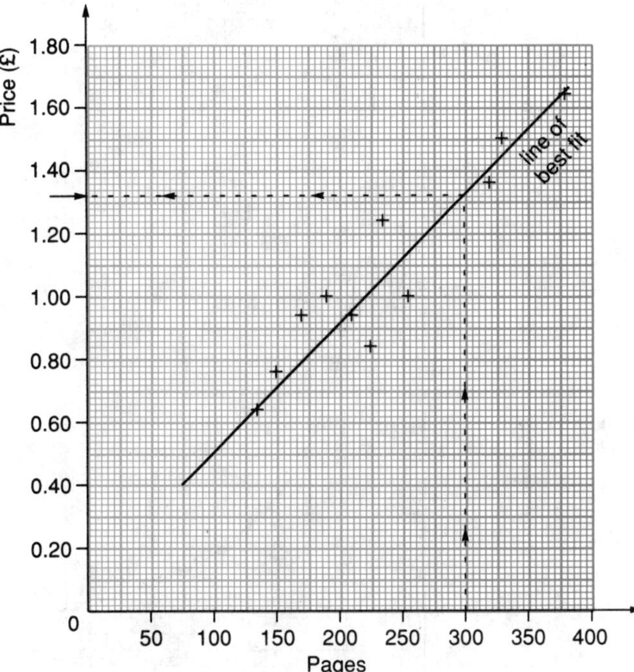

(ii) Use your line of best fit to find your estimate. From this line: £1.32.

78 (a) 200 (b) $\frac{4}{25}$

79 (a)

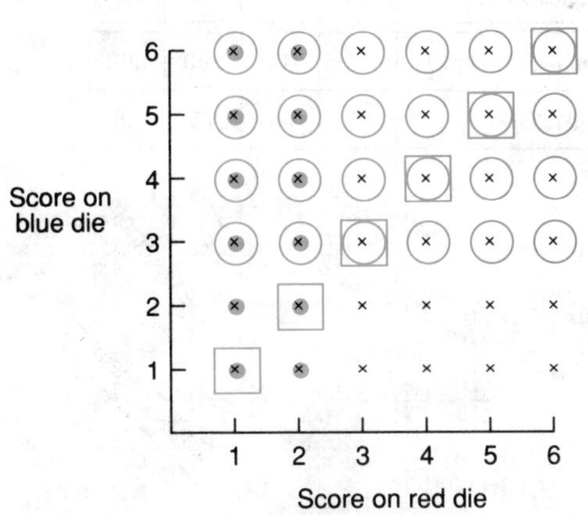

(b) (i) $\frac{12}{36} = \frac{1}{3}$ (ii) $\frac{24}{36} = \frac{2}{3}$ (iii) $\frac{6}{36} = \frac{1}{6}$

80 (a) $\frac{6}{25}$ (b) $\frac{13}{25}$

81 (a) $\frac{1}{10}$ (b) $\frac{4}{10} = \frac{2}{5}$ (c) $\frac{6}{10} = \frac{3}{5}$

82 (a)

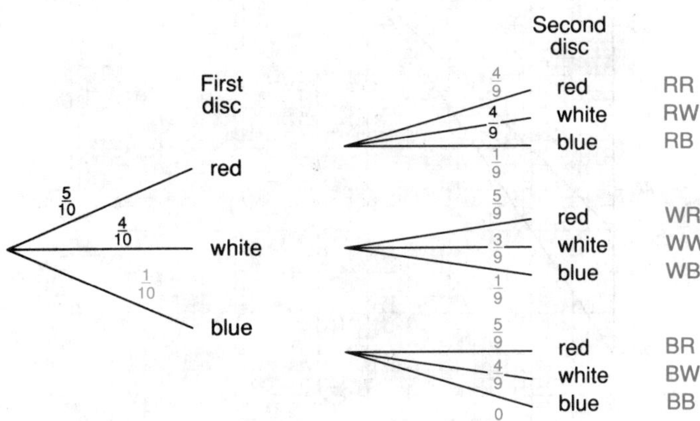

(b) (i) $\frac{2}{9}$ (ii) 0 (iii) $\frac{32}{90} = \frac{16}{45}$ (iv) $\frac{58}{90} = \frac{29}{45}$

83 (i) £$(C + 3A)$ (ii) $T = C + nA$

84 (a) 13 (b) 9
(c) $n + (n - 1) = 2n - 1$
(d) $16 - n$

85 (a) 4 (b) -4.6864

86 5.7

87 0.833

88 (a) (i) $x + 13$
(ii) $x + 13 = 2(x - 7)$
(b) 27

89 (a) (i) $8x + 2$ (ii) $10x - 2$
(b) $x = 2$, total 18
(c) $(-3x - 2)$ or $3x + 2$
(d) 5 (e) 2.9

90 (a) $(x - 2)$ pence
(b) $12x + 7(x - 2) = 157 \Rightarrow x = 9$
(c) 23p

91 (i) 3^{-2} (ii) $\frac{1}{9}$

92 (a) (i) 0 (ii) 17
(b) $2.19 \times 10^5, 9.12 \times 10^5, 1.92 \times 10^6$

93 2^{-3} ($\frac{1}{8}$) is greater than 3^{-2} ($\frac{1}{9}$), by $\frac{1}{72}$

94 (a) $80\frac{1}{8}$ (b) $x = 3$ (c) $y = -4$

95 $15x - 2y$

96 5

97 $7(2x + 7y)$

98 $\pi r(2h + r)$

99 $6xy(y - 2x)$

100 (a) Doubling any positive whole number gives an even number, so $2n$ is even. Adding 1 to an even number gives an odd number, so $2n + 1$ is odd.
(b) $2n + 3$ (c) $4(n + 1)$
(d) The sum of any two consecutive odd numbers can be written as $4(n + 1)$. This is a multiple of 4 since $(n + 1)$ is a positive whole number.

101 (a) $z = 5\frac{3}{5}$ or 5.6 (b) $w = 2$

102 (a) $x = 5$ (b) $p = \frac{3}{2}$ or 1.5

103 $x = 2$

104 $x = 10\frac{1}{2}$ or 10.5

105 $x = -3$

106 (a) 3.51 units (b) 20p

107 $4\frac{5}{8}$ m or 4.625 m

108 (a) $13\frac{1}{2}$ hours (b) 10 years old (c) $11\frac{1}{3}$ years old

109 (a) $v = 20$ (b) $u = 7$ (c) $a = \dfrac{v - u}{t}$

110 (a) 3 (b) $g = \dfrac{2\pi^2 l}{T^2}$

111 $\frac{2}{3}$

112 (a)

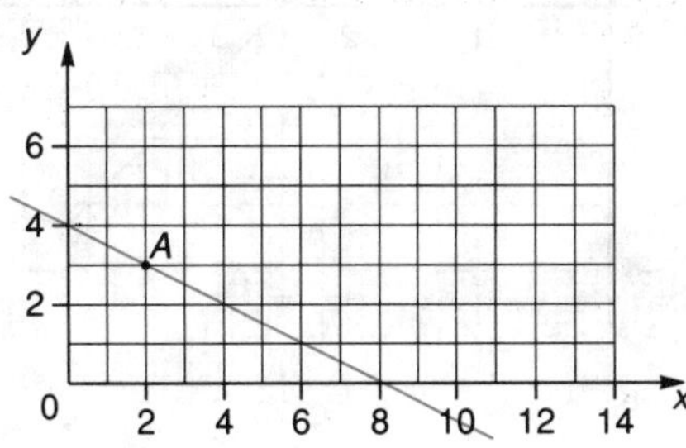

(b) (0, 4)

113 (a) breadth = x; length = $3x$;
area of tile (A) = length × breadth
$= 3x \times x = 3x^2$

(b)

x	0	0.5	1	1.5	2	2.5	3
$A = 3x^2$	0	0.75	3	6.75	12	18.75	27

(c)

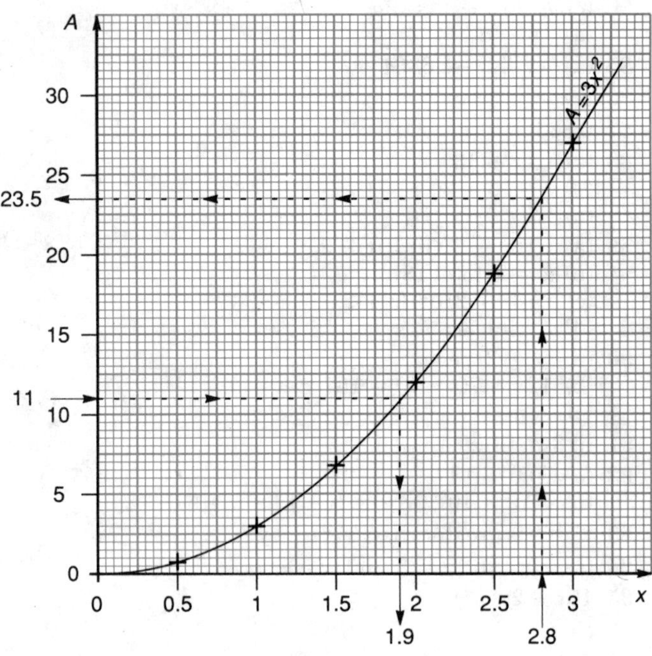

(d) From the graph:
(i) approx. 23.5 cm^2 (ii) approx. 1.9 cm

114 (a)

x	−2	0	2	4
y	9	5	1	−3

(b)

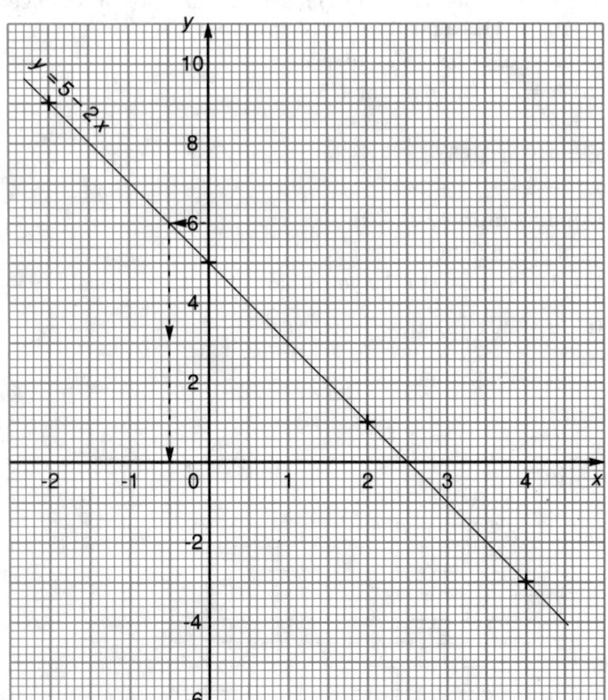

(c) −2 (d) $x > 2.5$ (e) $x = -0.5$

115

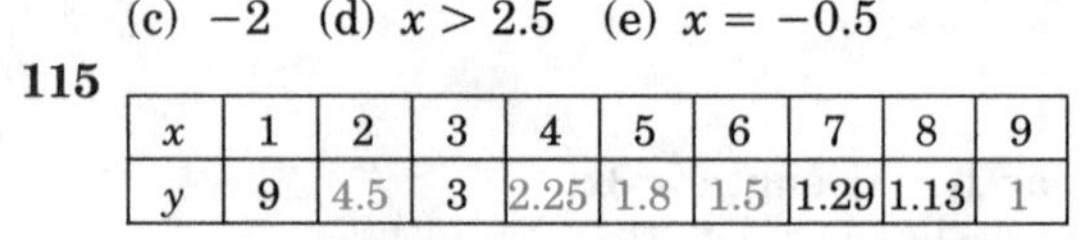

x	1	2	3	4	5	6	7	8	9
y	9	4.5	3	2.25	1.8	1.5	1.29	1.13	1

(i)

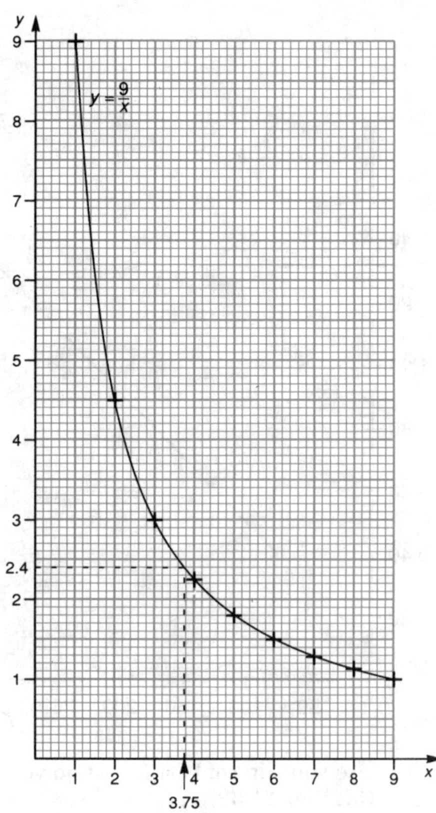

(ii) From the graph: $x \approx 3.75$

116 (a)

Distance (x km)	0	100	200	300
Charge (£C)	20	50	80	110

(c)

Distance (x km)	0	100	200	300
Charge (£C)	35	55	75	95

(b) and (d)

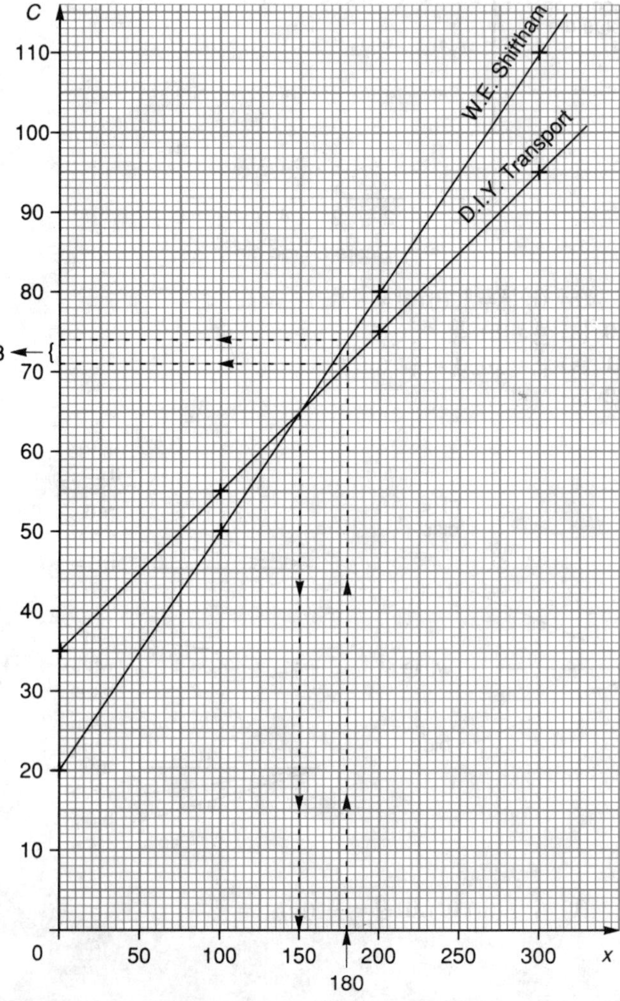

(e) 150 km (f) (i) D.I.Y. Transport (ii) £3
(g) $C = 35 + 0.2x$

117 (a) (12, 0) (b) (0, 5) (c) 13

118 Any number between 1 and 2 (but *not* 1 or 2) is a possible value of x.

119 By Pythagoras' theorem, the length of the diagonal is $\sqrt{[2^2 + (3.5)^2]}$ m $= \sqrt{16.25}$ m ≈ 4 m

120 (a) The diagonals of a rhombus bisect each other at right angles.
(b) 29 cm

121 8.660254 [C] 8.7 m (to 1 d.p.)

122 (a) 90° (b) 8 cm

123 16 m

124 (a) (i) 90° (ii) 40°
(b) SA ≈1286 m, SB ≈1532 m (to the nearest metre)

125 (a) (i) 124° (ii) 4.7 km (b) 17.4° (to 1 d.p.)

126 30.7 m

127 (a) (i) 4.24 cm (to 2 d.p.) (ii) 2.90 cm (to 2 d.p.)
(b) (i) 2.65 (to 2 d.p.) (ii) *BD*
(c) 3.9 cm

128 (a) 99 km (b) angle LMP = 15°, bearing 075°
(c)

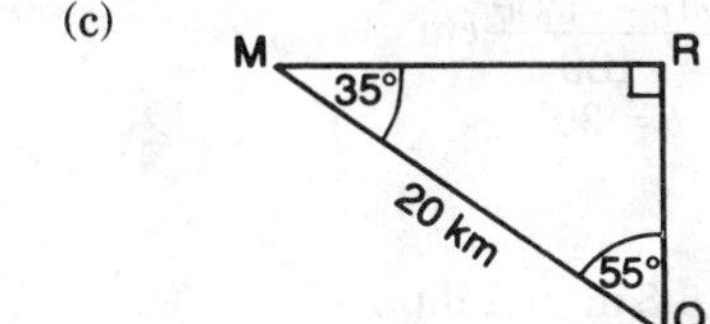

(d) (i) 16.4 km
(ii) 79.6 km

List 3

1 (a) (i) 90° (ii) 28° (b) (i) 9.4 cm (ii) 10.7 cm

2 47°

3 (a) (i) 30° (angles in the same segment)
(ii) 30° (base angles of isosceles triangle DAB)
(iii) ∠ABC = 180° − 60° = 120° (angle sum of a triangle)
∠DBC = ∠ABC − ∠ABD = 90°
(iv) ∠BAC = 30° (base angles of isosceles triangle ABC)
∠BDC = ∠BAC = 30° (angles in the same segment)
(b) (i) ∠BDC = ∠ABD = 30° are in the position of equal alternate angles for lines DC and AB. So DC‖AB.
(ii) DC is the diameter of the circle. (angle in a semicircle)

4 (a) AB and BC are equal tangents from the point B to the points of contact A and C.
(b) (i) 70° (ii) 20° (iii) 70°

5 (a)

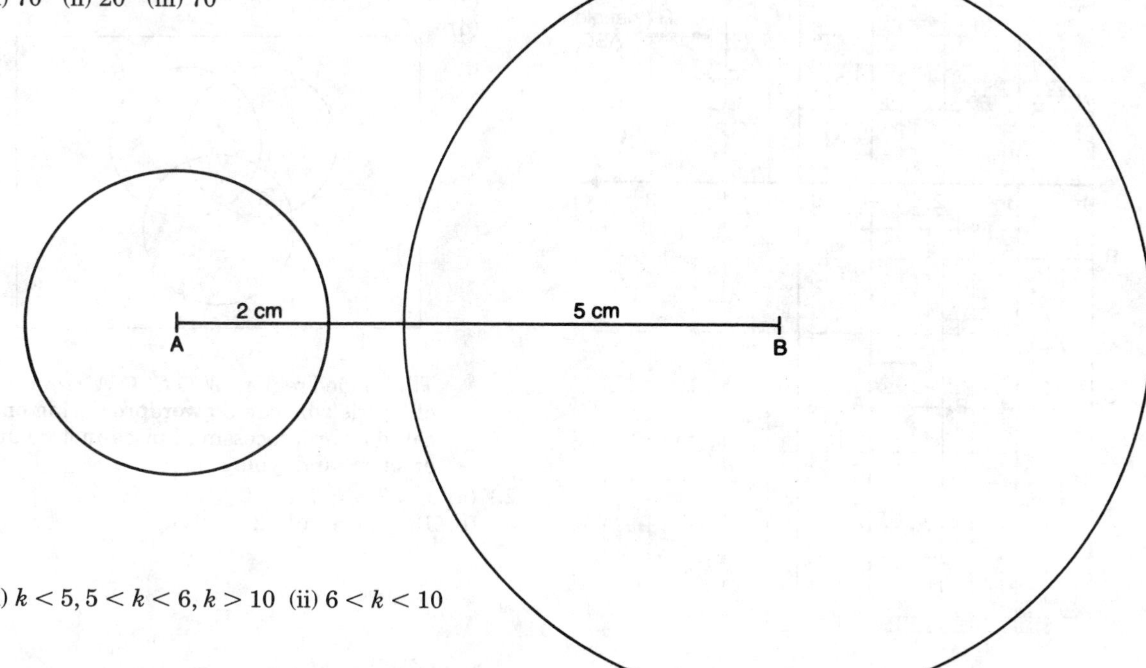

(b) (i) $k < 5, 5 < k < 6, k > 10$ (ii) $6 < k < 10$

6

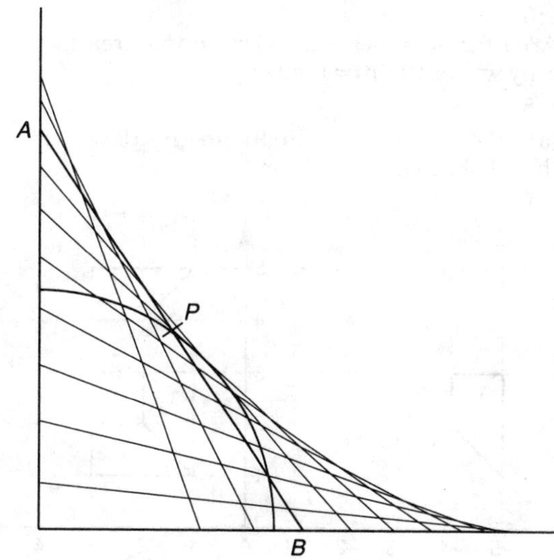

7 32 cm^2

8 (a) (b) (c)

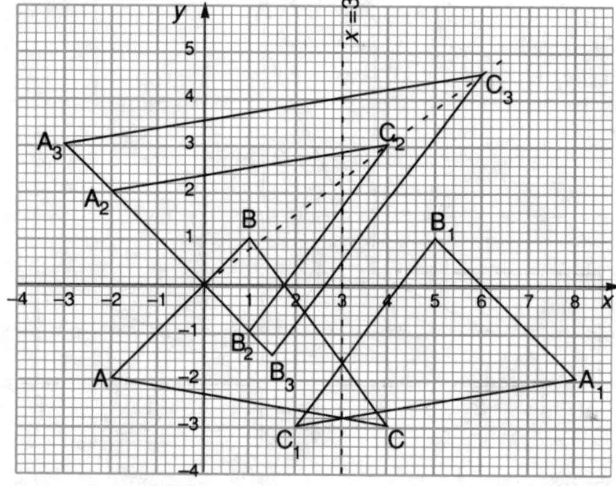

(d) $(\frac{9}{4})t$ cm^2

9 (a) $\frac{3}{2}$ or 1.5
(b) volume factor of enlargement = (scale factor)^3
$= (\frac{3}{2})^3 = \frac{27}{8}$
volume of cone $OAB = \frac{27}{8} \times$ volume of cone OXY
i.e. volume of cone $OXY = \frac{8}{27} \times$ volume of cone OAB
(c) 21 cm (d) 217.62074 [C] 217.6 cm^3 (to 1 d.p.)

10 (a) 3 km (b) 6.25×10^5 m^2 or 625 000 m^2

11 1:0.7
Area factor = (scale factor)^2, so the area factor of the copy will be $(0.7)^2 = 0.49 \approx \frac{1}{2}$.

12 1:8

13 (a) (i) 42 cm (ii) 31° (iii) 91 cm (iv) 19 000 cm^2
(b) (i) 5800 cm^3 (ii) 37 cm

14 (a)

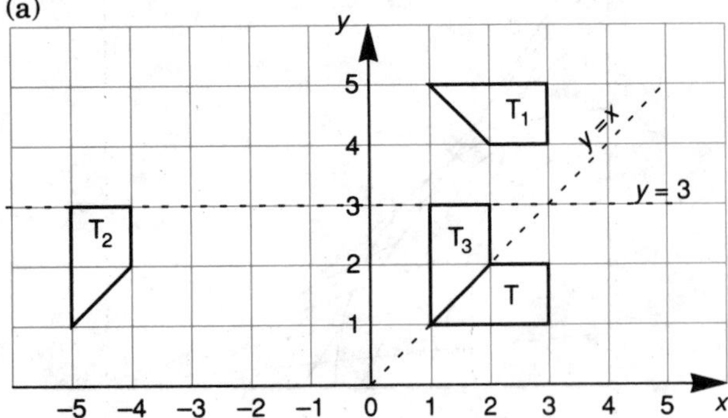

(b) reflection in $y = x$

15 (a)(b)

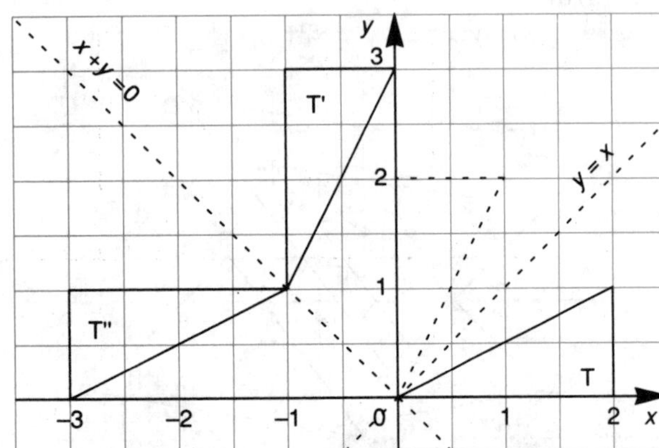

(c) $W\,(0, 0), \begin{pmatrix} 1 \\ -1 \end{pmatrix}$

16 (a), (c)

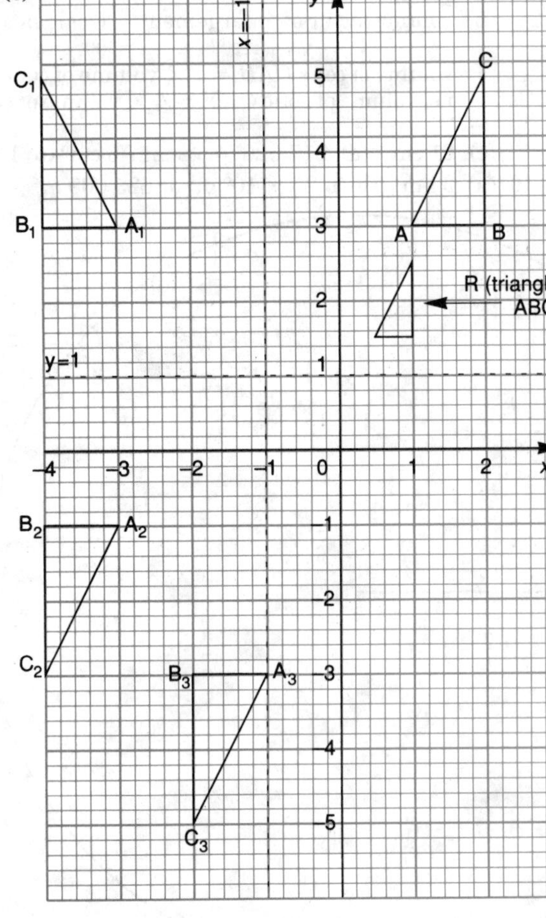

(b) rotation of 180° about the origin (0, 0) as centre
(d) $\frac{1}{4}x$ square units

17 (a) 25.184364 [C] 25.2 cm (to 1 d.p.)
(b) 8.394788 [C] 8.4 cm (to 1 d.p.)

18 (a) (i) 306.33013 [C] 306 cm (to 3 s.f.)
(ii) 7140.4862 [C] 7140 cm^2 (to 3 s.f.)
(b) 28.6% (to 3 s.f.)

19 (a)

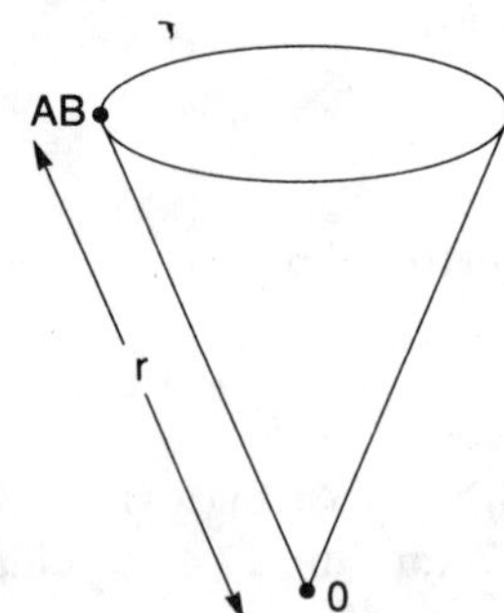

(b) (i) 12.5 cm
(ii) 100.8°

20 (a) (i) 10π cm (ii) 12π cm
(b) (i) $\dfrac{\pi r\theta}{180}$ cm (ii) $\dfrac{\pi(r + 12)\theta}{180}$ cm
(c) (i) $r = 60$ cm (ii) $\theta = 30°$

21 (a) £102 (b) 28 m^3

22 (a) 15.831978 [C] 15.8 m (to 1 d.p.)
(b) 0.19418777 [C] 0.2 m^3 (to 1 d.p.)

23 (a) (i) 268 cm^3 (ii) 0.0654 cm^3 (iii) 4096
(b) 3.33 cm
(c) (i) 0.500 cm (ii) 3.14 cm^2 (iii) 0.785 cm^2
(iv)

	One small lead ball	8 small lead balls	One alternative lead ball
Radius	0.25 cm	0.25 cm	0.500 cm
Surface area	0.785 cm^2	6.28 cm^2	3.14 cm^2
Volume	0.0654 cm^3	0.524 cm^3	0.524 cm^3

24 (a) (i) 6.16 cm^2 (ii) 1.44 cm^3
(b) 851 cm^2

25 (a) 3 (b) 7
(c) (i) 15 (ii) 6
(d)

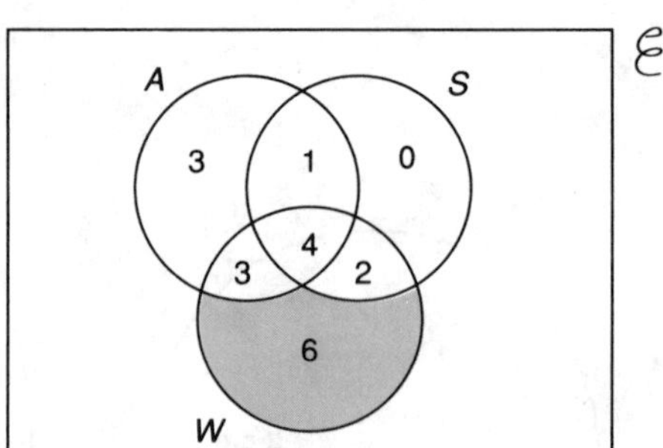

The shaded region $(W \cap S' \cap A')$ represents the set of 6 girls who can do wordprocessing only (i.e. who can do wordprocessing but cannot do audio-typing or shorthand typing).

26 (a) $x = 2, y = 7, z = 2$
(b) 13 (c) 8 (d) 2

27 (i)

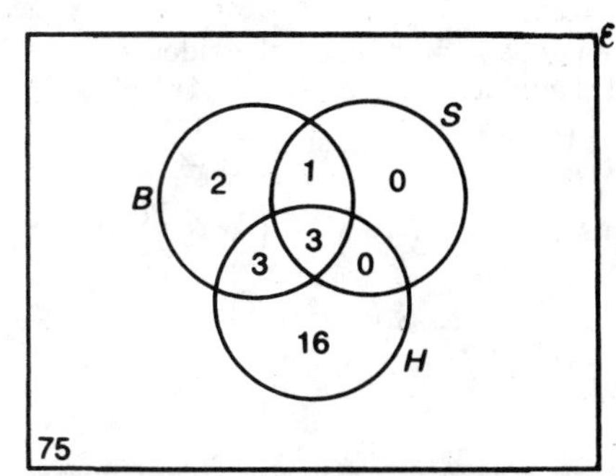

(ii) 100 Those bikes with incorrect saddle heights and bad steering also had faulty brakes.

28 (a) approx. 49 (b) approx. 8 (c) approx. 78 cm

29 (a)

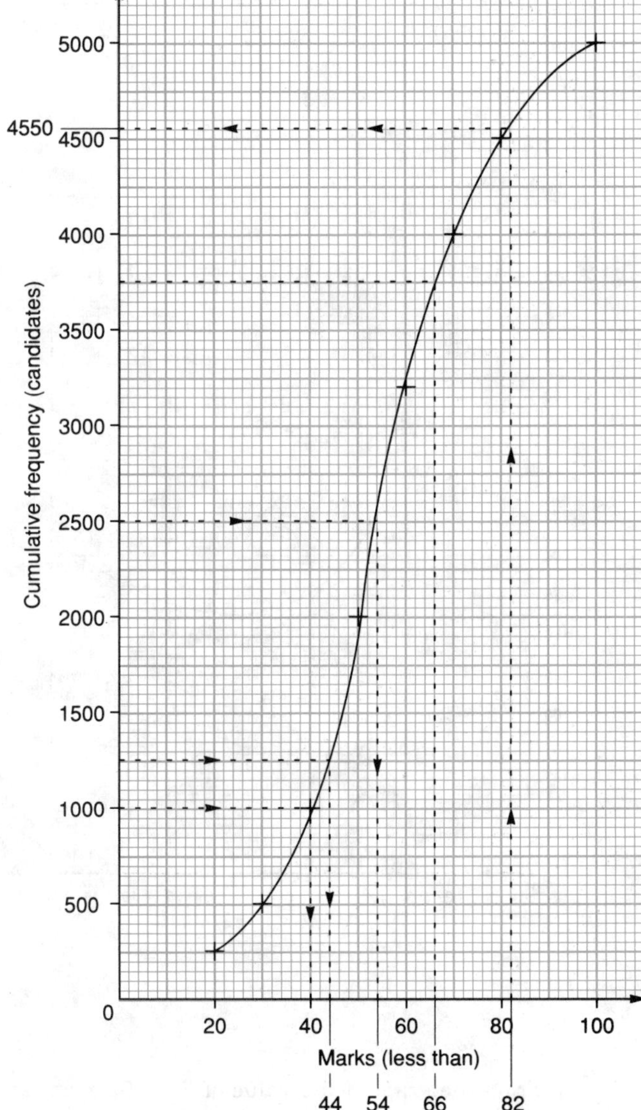

(b) (i) 4550 (ii) 54 (iii) 22 (iv) 20% (v) 40

30 (a) (i) 41–45

(ii)

Miles per gallon (less than)	30.5	35.5	40.5	45.5	50.5	55.5	60.5
Number of motorists	4	10	28	62	82	94	100

(iii)

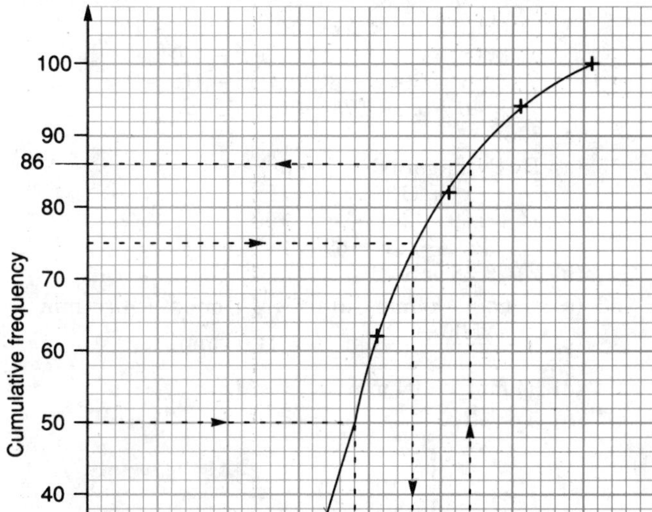

From the graph:
(b) (i) 44 miles per gallon (ii) 8.5 miles per gallon

31 (a) 2 (b) $\frac{1}{4} = 0.25$ (c) 1

32 (i) 4 (ii) $\frac{1}{2} = 0.5$

33 (a) 3^7 (b) 2^2 (c) $10^1 = 10$

34 (a) 1 (b) $-\frac{3}{2}$

35 (a) 16 000 (b) midnight
(c) 2.30 p.m. (d) 1410

36 (a) $15C^2$ (b) $S^2 + 8CS$ (c) 6 feet

37 (a) $6x^2 - 11x - 10$ (b) $(4x - 7)(4x + 7)$

38 (a) $x^2 + x - 6$ (b) $x = -4$ or $+3$

39 (a) $p^2 - q^2 = (p - q)(p + q)$ (b) 40 000 000 000

40 $3(x + 4)(x - 4)$

41 $(3x - 4)(2x + 5)$

42 (a) $(x + 8)(x + 3)$ (b) $y = -3$ or $+2$

43 (a) 9.6 volts (b) $R = \dfrac{Vr}{(12 - V)}$

44 (a) $h = \dfrac{A}{2\pi r} - r$ or $h = \dfrac{A - 2\pi r^2}{2\pi r}$ (b) 3.8 cm

45 (a) £$(n - 20)$ (b) 80

46 2 cm

47 (a) $(100 - x)$ m (b) $50(100 - x)\ \text{m}^2$
(c) $25(x + 100)\ \text{m}^2$ (d) $33\frac{1}{3}$ m

48 (a) (i) $6x + 12$ (ii) $6x + 12 = 3(x + 12)$; 8 years old
(b) $x = 2.73$ or -0.73

49 $20 = a + 4b$, $29 = a + 7b$
$a = 8$, $b = 3$

50 (a) $x = -6$; $y = 11$ (b) 280

51 (a) 376 (b) £91.36 (c) 300 *PAS*, 49 *UHT*

52 (a) 69 g (b) 209 g (c) 57 g (d) 12 g (e) 7 g

53 $x = 0$ or -4

54 (a) $\dfrac{24\,000}{x}$

(b) $\frac{24\,000}{(x-10)} = \frac{24\,000}{x} + 80$

$24\,000x = 24\,000(x-10) + 80x(x-10)$

$300x = 300(x-10) + x(x-10)$

$300x = 300x - 3000 + x^2 - 10x$

$0 = x^2 - 10x - 3000$

(c) 60p

55 (a) By Pythagoras' theorem:

$x^2 + (13-x)^2 = 10^2$

$x^2 + 169 - 26x + x^2 = 100$

$2x^2 - 26x + 69 = 0$

(b) $x = 9.28$ or 3.72

56 (a) (i) $(x + 4h)$ mm (ii) $x(x + 4h)$ or $(x^2 + 4hx)$ mm^2

(b) $h = \frac{2500 - x^2}{4x}$ mm (c) 24.03 mm

(d) 24 mm × 104 mm

57 (a) 5 or −1

(b)

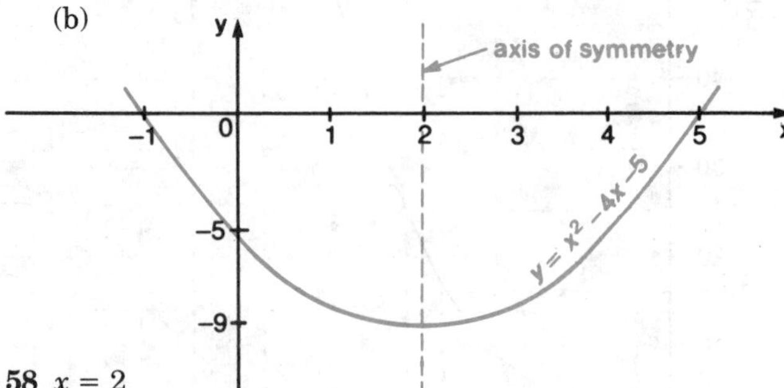

58 $x = 2$

59 $x = 8.5$ or $8\frac{1}{2}$

60 (i) £4

(ii) £7.50

(iii) $C = \frac{60}{n}$

(iv) B

(v)

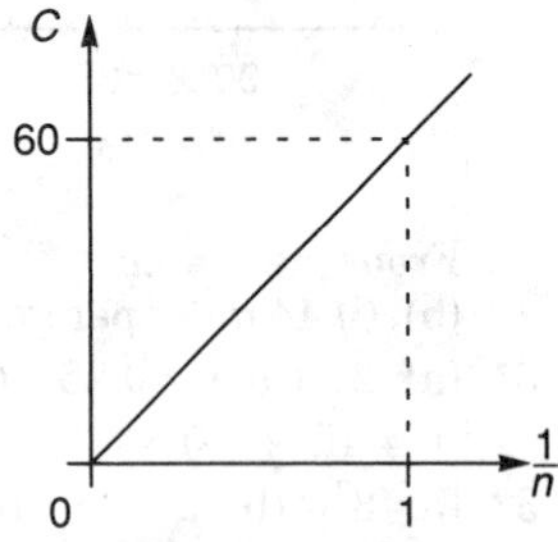

61 (a) $16 - 2x = 2(8 - x)$

(b) $A = \text{length} \times \text{breadth} = 2(8-x) \times x = 2x(8-x)$

(c)

x	0	1	2	3	3.5	4	4.5	5	6	7	8
A	0	14	24	30	31.5	32	31.5	30	24	14	0

(d)

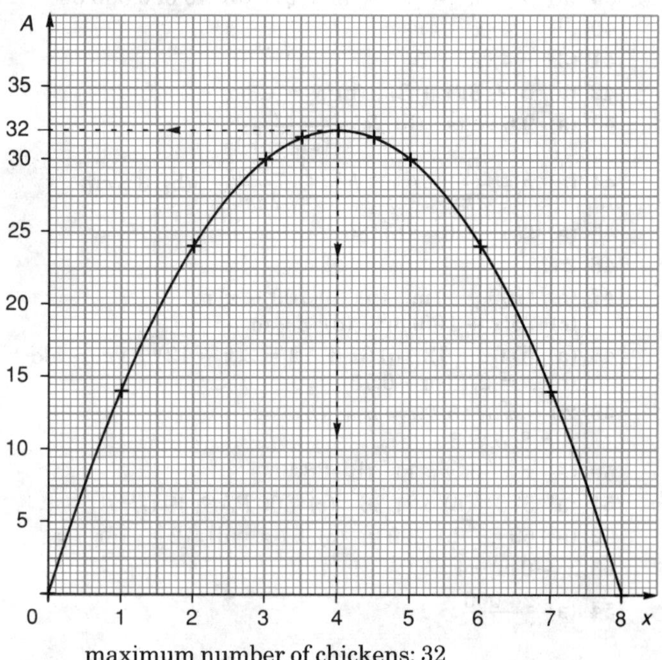

maximum number of chickens: 32

dimensions of pen: 8 m × 4 m

62 (a) $V = x^2h$

(b) area of base $= x^2$; area of 4 sides $= 4xh$

total surface area: $S = x^2 + 4xh$

But $V = 200 = x^2h$, so $h = \frac{200}{x^2}$

This gives $S = x^2 + \left(4x \times \frac{200}{x^2}\right)$

i.e. $S = x^2 + \frac{800}{x}$

(c)

x	2	3	4	6	8	10	12
x^2	4	9	16	36	64	100	144
$\frac{800}{x}$	400	267	200	133	100	80	67
S	404	276	216	169	164	180	211

(d)

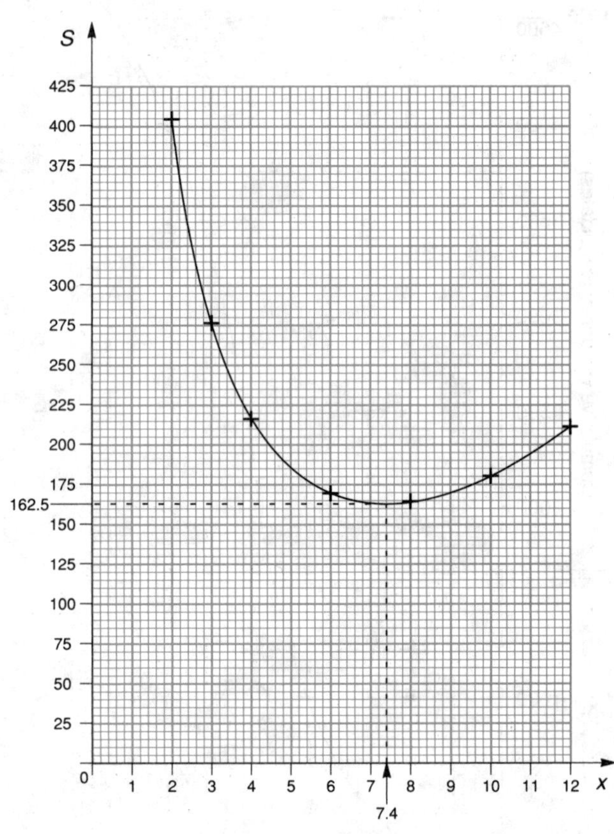

(e) From the graph: least value of $S \approx 162.5$ cm^2 and $x \approx 7.4$ cm

63 (i) $(x-3)(x-2)$

(ii) $x = 3$ or 2

(iii) A(0, 6), B(2, 0), C(3, 0)

(iv) $p = -4$, $q = -5$

64 (a)

x	−5	−4	−3	−2	−1	0	1	2
$x^2 + 3x + 1$	11	5	1	−1	−1	1	5	11

(b)

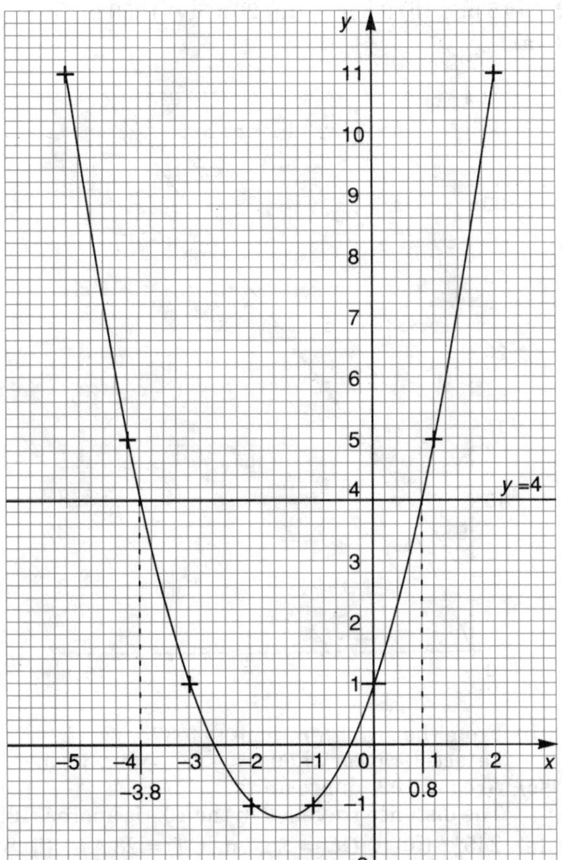

(c) From the graph: $x \approx 0.8$ or -3.8

65 (b) and (c)

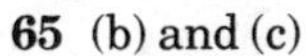

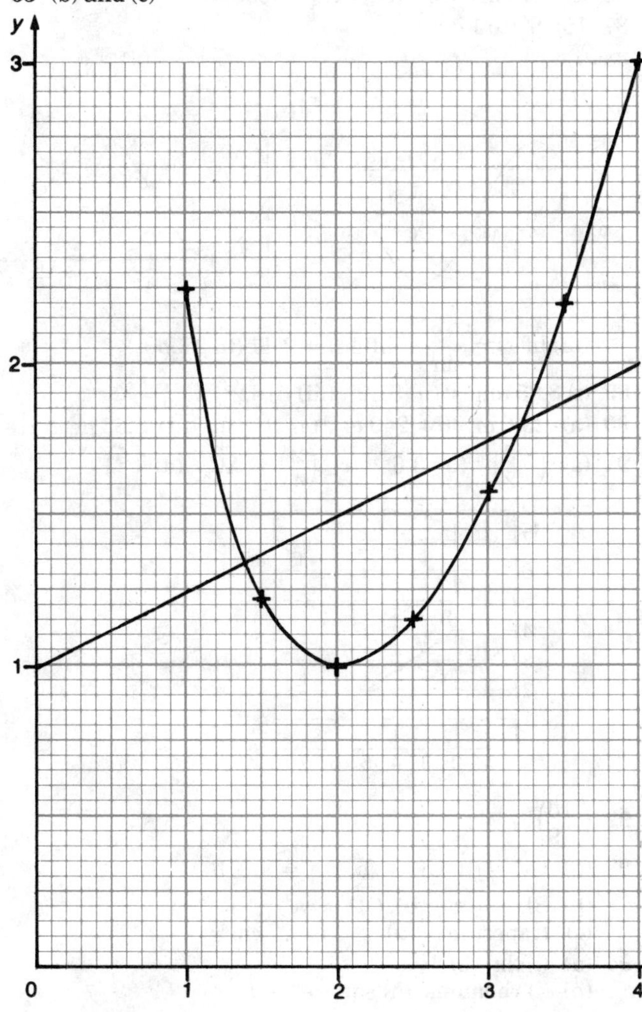

65 (a)

x	1	1.5	2	2.5	3	3.5	4
$x^2/4$	0.25	0.56	1	1.56	2.25	3.06	4
$4/x$	4	2.67	2	1.6	1.33	1.14	1
-2	-2	-2	-2	-2	-2	-2	-2
y	2.25	1.23	1	1.16	1.58	2.20	3

(d) $x \approx 1.4, 3.2$

(e) The equation $x^3 - x^2 - 12x + 16 = 0$

can be rewritten: $\dfrac{x^3}{4x} - \dfrac{x^2}{4x} - \dfrac{12x}{4x} + \dfrac{16}{4x} = 0$

i.e. $\dfrac{x^2}{4} - \dfrac{x}{4} - 3 + \dfrac{4}{x} = 0$

$\dfrac{x^2}{4} + \dfrac{4}{x} - 2 = \dfrac{x}{4} + 1$

66 7

67 (a) $x = -3$ or 7 (b) $x > -\frac{1}{5}$

68 $x \geqslant 0, y \geqslant 2x, 8y + 5x \leqslant 40$

69

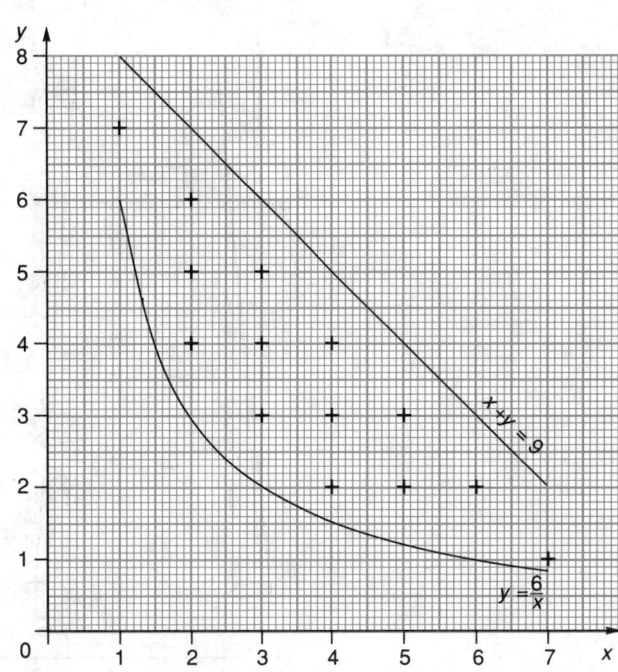

The pairs of positive integers are: (1, 7), (2, 4), (2, 5), (2, 6), (3, 3), (3, 4), (3, 5), (4, 2), (4, 3), (4, 4), (5, 2), (5, 3), (6, 2).

70 (a) -5 (b) 13 (c) $4x - 3$ (d) $\frac{1}{2}$ (e) $\frac{1}{2}(3 - x)$

71 (a) (i) -30 (ii) -30 (b) (i) $-8, 3$ (ii) $-5, 0$

72 (a) (i) 3 (ii) 4

(b) (i) $\mathrm{gf}: x \to (2x - 1)^2$ (ii) $\mathrm{f}^{-1}: x \to \frac{1}{2}(x + 1)$

73 (a) (i) $\frac{1}{3}$ (ii) $\frac{1}{9}$ (b) (i) $\dfrac{1}{(2x-1)^2}$ (ii) $\dfrac{1}{2x^2 - 1}$

(c) $\dfrac{1}{(2a-1)^2} = \dfrac{1}{2a^2 - 1} \Rightarrow 2a^2 - 1 = (2a - 1)^2$

$\Rightarrow a^2 - 2a + 1 = 0$

$\Rightarrow (a - 1)^2 = 0$

$\Rightarrow a = 1$

i.e. only one value of a

74 (a) 113.75 cm^2

(b) 4.0 cm (to 1 d.p.)

75 1.142857 [C] 1.1 pascals (to 1 d.p.)

76 (a) $V = 600d^3$ (b)

d	0.25	0.6	0.5
V	9.375	129.6	75

(c) $d = \sqrt[3]{\dfrac{V}{600}}$

77 (a) $y = -\frac{3}{4}x - 7$ (b) $-\frac{3}{4}$

78 (a) 8 m (b) $6\ \text{ms}^{-1}$ (c) $d = 6t + 8$

79 (a) $y = 2x - 1$ (b) (i) $y = -\frac{1}{2}x + 4$ (ii) (2, 3)
(c) (i) (4, 3)
(ii) $BA = 3\sqrt{5}, PQ = 2\sqrt{5}$;
$BA:PQ = 3\sqrt{5}:2\sqrt{5} = 3:2$
(iii) 25 square units

80 (a) 11 m (b)
(c) (i) 2.2 seconds
(ii) 12.25 m
(d) The gradient of the tangent at $t = 0.5$ is 10 m/s, an estimate of the speed of the ball after 0.5 seconds.

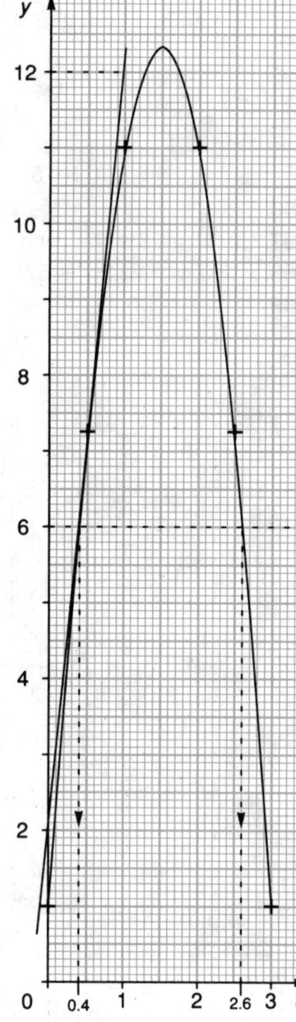

81 (a)

t	0	1	2	3	4	5
v	0	3	6	9	12	15

(b)

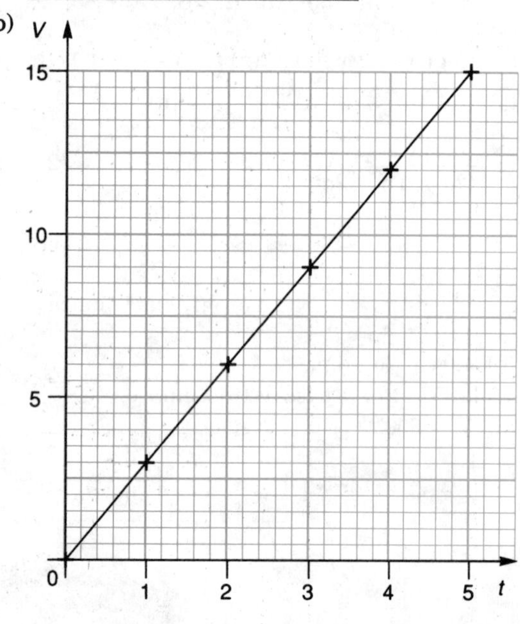

(c) 3 (d) the acceleration of the ball ($3\ \text{m/s}^2$)

82 (i) 15 m/s (ii) 0.5 m/s (iii) 20 s (iv) 1050 m (v) 1575 m

83 (a)

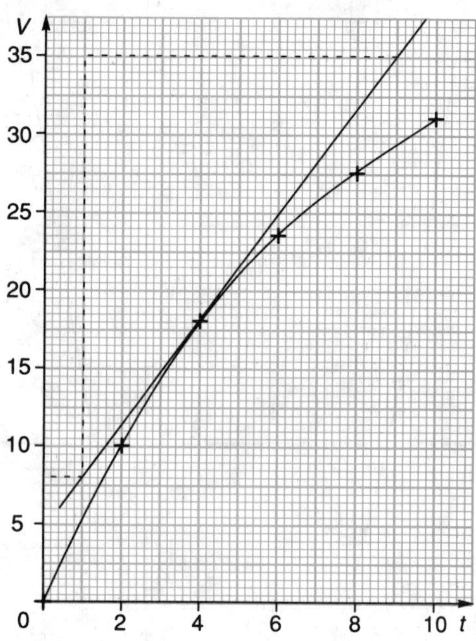

(b) From the graph: gradient ≈ 3.375.
i.e. acceleration when $t = 4$ is approx. $3.4\ \text{m/s}^2$.
(c) Area ≈ 199 square units
The distance travelled in the 10 s is approx. 199 m.

84 (a) 245° (b) (i) $OC = 25.7$ m, $CT = 28.4$ m (ii) 8.4 m
(c) 21.0°

85 (a) 0.348 km (b) 7.99 km (c) 14.43 km (d) 2.1°

86 (a) 170 m (b) Abdi 51.3°, Abda 41.5°

87 152.8° (to 1 d.p.)

88 (i) (ii)

f(x); 1; f(x) = 0.6; 0; 90; 180; 270; 360; x; −1

g(x); 2; 1; 0; 90; 180; 270; 360; x

(iii) $hf(x) = \dfrac{2}{\sin x}$; $hf(40) = 3.11$ (to 2 d.p.)

89 (i) 8.95 miles (ii) 51.2° (iii) 016.2°

90 (a) 23.6 m (b) 249 m (c) 318 m (d) 2.83 hectares

91 (a) $\begin{pmatrix}-3\\2\end{pmatrix}$ (b) 3.6 (c) $\begin{pmatrix}2\\4\end{pmatrix} = \overrightarrow{AC}$ (d) $\begin{pmatrix}5\\2\end{pmatrix}$

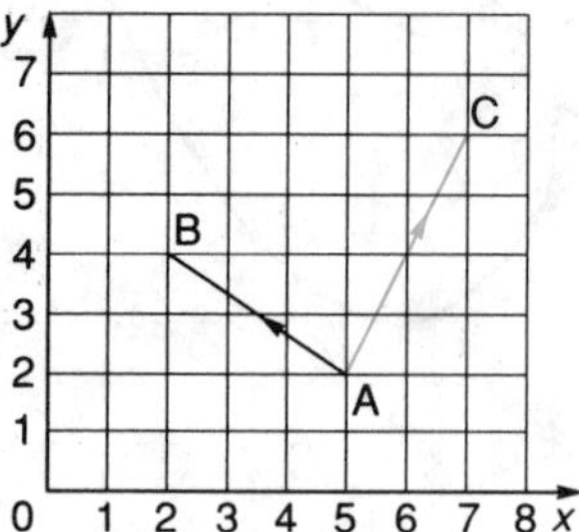

92 $\begin{pmatrix}10\\-9\end{pmatrix}$

93 (a) $\overrightarrow{OC} = \frac{2}{5}\mathbf{b}$, $\overrightarrow{CB} = \frac{3}{5}\mathbf{b}$, $\overrightarrow{BA} = \mathbf{a} - \mathbf{b}$
(b) $\overrightarrow{BD} = \frac{3}{5}(\mathbf{a} - \mathbf{b})$, $\overrightarrow{CD} = \frac{3}{5}\mathbf{a}$
(c) trapezium (d) $\frac{25}{9}$ (e) $27\ \text{cm}^2$

94 (a) (i) $2\mathbf{x}$ (ii) $2\mathbf{y}$
(b) (i) rhombus (ii) square

95 (a) $\begin{pmatrix}2\\1\\8\end{pmatrix}$ (b) (i) $\begin{pmatrix}19\\8\\28\end{pmatrix}$ (ii) the total content of three Trackpaks *C* and two Trackpacks *D*.

(c) (i) (13.05 12.05)

(ii) The cost of the components in *C* and *D*.

96 (a) $\begin{pmatrix}6 & 13\\-8 & 8\end{pmatrix}$ (b) $\begin{pmatrix}10 & 5\\5 & 5\end{pmatrix}$

97 (i) $\begin{pmatrix}0 & 2 & 2\\2 & 0 & 1\\2 & 1 & 0\end{pmatrix}$ (ii) $\begin{pmatrix}8 & 2 & 2\\2 & 5 & 4\\2 & 4 & 5\end{pmatrix}$ (iii) 2

98 (a)

(b) reflection in the line $y = -x$

(c) P′(3, 0), Q′(2, 1)

(d) reflection in the line $x + y = 3$

99 (a) A′(2, 2), B′(1, 3)

(b)

(c) enlargement, centre O, scale factor $\sqrt{2}$

anticlockwise rotation of 45° about the origin O

(d) $\frac{1}{2}\begin{pmatrix}1 & 1\\-1 & 1\end{pmatrix}$, (4, −2)

100 (a) A″(2, 2), B″(6, 4), C″(4, 8)

(b) $\begin{pmatrix}2 & 0\\0 & 2\end{pmatrix}$

(c) enlargement, scale factor 2, centre the origin O

SCE QUESTIONS

Foundation level

1 42

2 0.8 cm

3 £173.20

4 (a) railway station (b) Southwest

5 £240

6 (a) £5.50 (b) (i) £19.50 (ii) £20.50

(iii) Ordering 205 badges costs less than ordering 195 badges.

(c) 17

7 (a) 12 (b) 9

8 mean 1430; median 1420; no mode

9 $-4x + 6y$

General level

1 (a) 1.86 s (b) 1 min 44.27 s

2 (a) £111.40 (b) £112.80

(c) supermarket employee, £1.40 more

3 24 minutes

4 A 12 35, B 10 55, C 14 40

5 Model M

6 7.58 kg

7 (a) £16.20 (b) £34.26

8 1.42

9 8 per cent

10 (a) 42 minutes (b) 5.45 inches

11 $33\frac{1}{3}$ per cent

12 600 cm^2; 0.24 m^3

13 $-4x + 6y$ or $6y - 4x$

14 $y = -\frac{1}{2}$ or -0.5

15 $n = 7\frac{1}{2}$ or 7.5

16 $x = 2, y = 4$

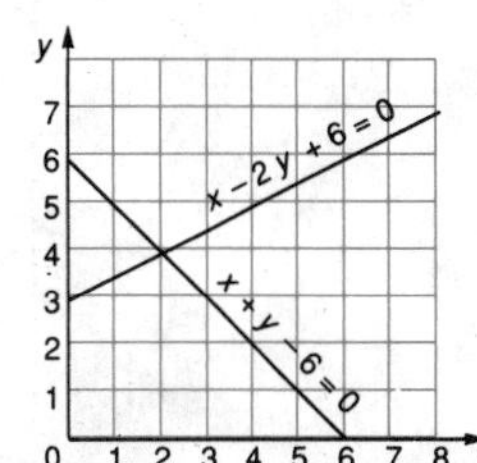

17 (a) 30.489326 C 30.5 m (to 1 d.p.)

(b) Measure shadows AD, AB.

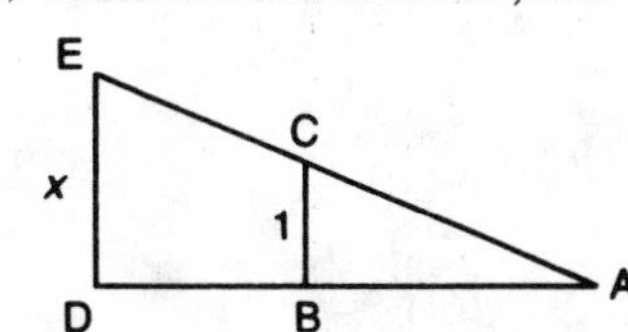

$$\frac{x}{1} = \frac{AD}{AB} = \frac{\text{length of shadow of tree}}{\text{length of shadow of stick}}$$

18 80 cm^2

Credit Level

1

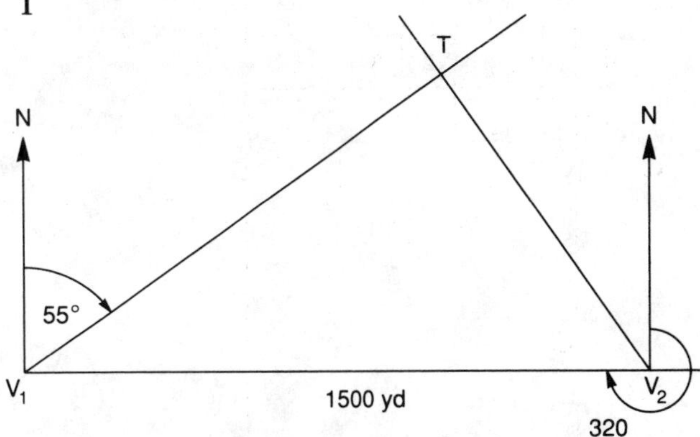

Scale: 1 cm represents 200 yards

Distance between transmitter and second position of the van: $TV_2 \approx 860$ yards.

2 125 hours

3 the volume is doubled

4 35 cm

5 2 mm

6 216

7 $a^2 - a = a(a - 1)$

8 (a) 42 (b) $m = 6n/(n - 6)$
(c) possible answers: 8 and 24; 9 and 18; 10 and 15

9 $x = 2, y = -1$ or $x = -1, y = 2$

10 50 cm

11 (a) 170 (b) 8
(c) $30 = \frac{1}{2}n(n - 3) \Rightarrow n^2 - 3n - 60 = 0$
$n^2 - 3n - 60$ has non-integral roots so a polygon cannot have 30 diagonals.

12 3.89

13 $\dfrac{3(x - 5)}{x(x - 3)}$

14 2.5 cm

15 (a) x varies directly as y increases/decreases and inversely as the square of z (z^2) increases/decreases.
(b) $k = 24$ (c) 6 or -6

16 $5y = -6x + 15$ or $y = -1.2x + 3$

17 30.471467 [C] $x \approx 30.5°$ (to 1 d.p.)

18 20.127605 [C] A $\approx 20.1°$ (to 1 d.p.)

AURAL TESTS

Question	Level 2	Level 3
1	£2.70	£7.92
2	402	138
3	$7\frac{1}{2}$ m	£23
4	£2.40	£7.40
5	55p	£1.68
6	about 24 cm	4.5 m
7	£15	14 m
8	13 minutes	13 degrees Celsius
9	20 minutes	17 years
10	800 cm^2	11
11	about 130°	about 35°
12	£3.20	£11.45
13	£270	£33.60
14	10 03	92 minutes
15	£7.00	£15.40

INDEX

GCSE REVISE MATHEMATICS
Review Form

We'd really appreciate your comments, criticisms and suggestions as a user of this study aid - so that we can make the next edition even better and more helpful to you and your fellow students. So please answer the following questions as honestly and specifically as you can. As an added incentive, you'll also be eligible for our FREE KEYFACTS offer, when you send this form in to us together with two cut-off coupons from featured GCSE titles. See the inside back cover for details.

I Please rate this book on the following factors:

(a) on a scale of A (excellent) to E (very bad); and

(b) on a scale of 1 (very important to you) to 5 (of no interest to you).

Add your own comments and suggestions on each point, if you'd like to.

1. Coverage of the topics you need for your assignments/exams

   A B C D E **1 2 3 4 5**

2. Up-to-dateness of topic coverage and exam questions

   A B C D E **1 2 3 4 5**

3. Presentation of material in general: attractiveness and distinctiveness of cover, use of space, colour, diagrams, illustration etc.

   A B C D E **1 2 3 4 5**

4. Presentation of material for ease of reference: locating specific areas/points, headings, index, contents pages etc.

   A B C D E **1 2 3 4 5**

5. Extent and type of illustrative questions and exam question practice

   A B C D E **1 2 3 4 5**

6. Provision of advice on studying and revision techniques

   A B C D E **1 2 3 4 5**

7. 'Tone of voice' of the text - for ease of reading and personal preference

   A B C D E **1 2 3 4 5**

GCSE REVISE MATHEMATICS
Review Form

II How do you know about Letts Study Aids?

☐ Teacher ☐ Letts advertisement in ____________ ☐ Bookshop

☐ Friends ☐ Other ____________

III What time of year did you buy your Letts Study Aid?

☐ Start of school year ☐ Beginning of exam term ☐ Just before exams

☐ Other ____________

IV How have you mainly used your Letts Study Aid?

☐ Backup to school work ☐ Long term revision ☐ Last minute revision

☐ Other ____________

V Do you find the term 'Study Aid' helpful as a description of a book like this one?

What term do you think would describe it best?

☐ Study Aid ☐ Study Guide ☐ Course Companion ☐ Revise Guide

☐ Revision Aid ☐ Other ____________

Name: ____________ Exam being taken: ____________

Address: ____________ Examining board: ____________

____

____________ Date of exam: ____________

____________ Signed: ____________

Thank you for your help.

Don't forget to enclose your coupons for a *free*
KEYFACTS PASSBOOK and **PASSCARDS** of your choice!